D HIGH CHANCELLOR OF IRELAND.

, 1900.

KING'S INNS BARRISTERS

1868-2004

a companion volume for
KING'S INNS ADMISSION PAPERS 1607-1867

TIMOTHY SULLIVAN (1874-1949)

Called to the Bar in Michaelmas Term 1895; K.C. 1918;
appointed first President of the High Court, 5 June 1924, and
Chief Justice of the Irish Free State, 12 Dec. 1936; retired 1946.

PORTRAIT BY HIS WIFE MAEV (*née* HEALY)

Oil on canvas, approx. 20" x 16",
hung in the Benchers' Room at King's Inns.

A label on the back reads:
'Painted at the Viceregal Lodge about 1924 by Maev Sullivan'

KING'S INNS

BARRISTERS

1868-2004

Edited by
KENNETH FERGUSON
LL. B., Ph. D., Barrister-at-Law

DUBLIN
THE HONORABLE SOCIETY OF KING'S INNS
in association with
THE IRISH LEGAL HISTORY SOCIETY
2005

PUBLISHED   IN   2005   BY
THE   HONORABLE   SOCIETY   OF   KING'S   INNS

AND   AVAILABLE   FROM
THE   UNDER-TREASURER,   HENRIETTA   STREET,   DUBLIN   1
Tel: + 353 1 874 4840.   Fax + 353 1 872 6048
http://www.kingsinns.ie
e-mail: publications@kingsinns.ie

ISBN 0-9512443-2-9

TYPESET BY KENNETH FERGUSON
PRINTED IN IRELAND BY COLOURBOOKS LTD.,
105 BALDOYLE INDUSTRIAL ESTATE, BALDOYLE, DUBLIN 13

"For inquire, I pray thee, of the former age, and prepare thyself to the search of their fathers:"

Job 8, 8.

CONTENTS

THE INDEX, 1868-1968

THE ROLLS, 1868-2004

ABBREVIATIONS

The following abbreviations have been used in this volume:

A.G.	Attorney-General
appt.	appointed
Austr. Barr.	Australian Barrister
b.	born
B.A.	Bachelor of Arts
B.L.	Barrister-at-Law
C.J.	Chief Justice
d.	daughter; *or* died
decd	deceased
D.N.B.	*Dictionary of National Biography*
E	Easter Term
E.C.	European Community [1]
eld.	eldest
Engl. Barr.	English Barrister
G.I.	Gray's Inn
H	Hilary Term
H.C.	High Court
I.L.T. & S.J.	*The Irish Law Times and Solicitors' Journal*
I.T.	Inner Temple
K.C.	King's Counsel
K.I.	King's Inns
L.C.J.	Lord Chief Justice
L.I.	Lincoln's Inn
M	Michaelmas Term
M.P.	Member of Parliament
M.T.	Middle Temple
N.I. Barr.	Northern Ireland Barrister
N.U.I.	National University of Ireland
prom.	promoted
Q.C.B.	Queen's College, Belfast
Q.C.C.	Queen's College, Cork
Q.C.G.	Queen's College, Galway
Q.U.B.	Queen's University, Belfast
res.	resigned
ret.	retired
s.	son
S.C.	Senior Counsel
SC	Supreme Court
surv.	surviving
T	Trinity Term
T.C.D.	Trinity College, Dublin
U.C.C.	University College Cork
U.C.D.	University College Dublin
Q.C.	Queen's Counsel
R.U.I.	Royal University of Ireland
young	youngest

---

[1]   The reference is to barristers called pursuant to Council Directive No. 89/48/EEC of 21 December 1988, which introduced, for regulated professions, a general system for the recognition of higher education diplomas awarded on completion of professional education and training of at least three years' duration. The Directive was applied by S.I. No. 1 of 1991, in which the Council of King's Inns is named.

A NOTE ON DISCREPANCIES IN THE NUMBERING OF THE KING'S INNS MANUSCRIPTS

The Admission Papers, along with other manuscripts of the Honorable Society of King's Inns, are held, tied in bundles, in boxes shelved in the basement of the Library in Henrietta Street.

The barristers' files for the years covered by this volume are arranged by year and term of call. Thus, for 1868, the files are regularly numbered H/01-H/07, E/01-E/07, T/01-T/06 and M/01-M/06. The system, alas, is subject to numerous minor discrepancies, represented by unused file numbers and interpolated numbers (the latter indicated in the following list by an asterisk). These curiosities, which generally appear to be attributable to circumstances contemporaneous with the Call that required an adjustment of the sequence, are found as follows:

1870 M/01-M/02, M/02*, M/03-07, M/09 [interpolated M/02*; no M/08] [9 called]
1871 H/01; H/03-05 [no H/02] [4 called]
1871 T/01, T/01a, T/02-06 [7 called]
1872 H/01-04, H/06-11 [no H/05] [10 called]
1872 T/01-02, T/02x, T/03-07, T/07a, T/08-10, T/12-13 [two interpolations; no T/11] [14 called]
1872 M/01, M/03-09 [no M/02] [8 called]
1873 H/01-05, H/05x, H/06-13 [14 called]
1874 H/01-02, H/02x, H/04-10 [H/02x interpolated; no H/03] [10 called]
1875 E/01, E/01x, E/02-07 [8 called]
1877 E/01-E/06, E/06a, E/07-09 [10 called]
1878 M/01-03, M/03x, M/04-09, M/11 [M/03x interpolated; no M/10] [11 called]
1883 H/01, H/02*, H/03, H/04* [irregularity of citation] [4 called]
1884 T/02-02, T/02x, T/03-05 [6 called]
1887 H/01-07, H/07x, H/08-10, H/12 [H/07x interpolated; no H/11] [12 called]
1894 T/01-02, T/02x, T/03-09 [10 called]
1895 H/01-03, H/03x, H/04-09 [10 called]
1896 H/01-02, H/04-5 [no H/03] [4 called]
1897 M/01-5, M/05a, M/06-15 [16 called]
1900 H/01-02, H/02x, H/03-06 [7 called]
1901 H/01, H/02x, H/03-05 [irregularity of citation] [5 called]
1905 E/01, E/01*, E/02-03 [4 called]
1905 T/02-T/12 [no T/01] [11 called]
1908 H/01, H/01x, H/02-03 [4 called]
1908 M/01-03, M/05-08 [no M/04] [7 called]

1912 T/01, T/03-T10, T/10a, T/11-15 [no T/02; T/10a interpolated] [15 called]
1917 H/01, H/01x, H/02 [3 called]
1917 T/01-19, T/21-30 [no T/20] [29 called]
1918 H/01-03, H/04x [irregularity of citation] [4 called
1918 E/01x [irregularity of citation] [1 called]
1918 T/01-19; T/20x, T/21x [irregularity of citation] [21 called]
1918 M/01-06, M/07? [question mark affixed to M/07] [7 called]
1919 E/01, E/01x, [no E/03], -E/04x? [3 called]
1919 T/02-04, T/04x, T05-6 [no T/01] * [8? called]
1920 M/02-12 [no M/01] [11 called]
1921 T/03? [4 called]
1922 M[?], M/01-8 [9 called]
1923 M/03, as result of misfiling, used twice [14 called] See: Crawford, William Ernest; Dixon, Martin Joseph.
1924 T/01-3, T/05-6 [no T/04] [5 called]
1924 M/01-4, M/04x, M/05-11 [12 called]
1926 E/02 [no E/01 or E/03] [3 called]
1926 T/01-05] [3 called; confusion with Easter]
1927 M/01-06, M/08-27 [no M/07] [27 called]
1930 M/01-03, M/03x, M/04-11 [11 called]
1931 M/01, M/01x, M/02-18 [19 called]
1961 T/03-09 [no T/01 or T/02] [7 called]
1962 T/01-03, T/05 [no T/04] [4 called]
1966 T/01-09, T/11-13 [no T/10] [12 called]
1967 M/01, M/01-14 [M/01 used twice] [15 called]

Papers for Robert Henry S. Tuite (H 1946) are missing, and his name was overlooked when the index was first compiled. There were indications from which Mrs. Clancy was able to discern as missing the Memorials of four other barristers: Charles Frederick Garfield Doran (1913/T/14) [Memorial and papers missing]; Captain Joseph Kavanagh (M 1922), Maurice Danaher (1925/M/03), and James Peter Murnane (1925/M/14) [Memorials missing; receipts only].

PRINCIPAL WORKS OF BIOGRAPHICAL REFERENCE

Francis Elrington Ball, *The Judges in Ireland 1221-1921* (2 vols., London, 1926; reprinted, Dublin, 1993).

Henry Boylan, *A Dictionary of Irish Biography* (Dublin, 1978; 2nd edition, 1988; 3rd edition, 1999).[1]

Maureen Cairnduff, *Who's Who in Ireland 'the influential 1,000'* ([1st edition] Dún Laoghaire, 1984). [2]
-- *ibid.*, 'Updated 2nd edition' (Dún Laoghaire, 1991)
-- [3rd edition] *The Influential 1000; Who's Who in Ireland plus 200 rising stars* (Dún Laoghaire, 1999).[3]

The Dictionary of National Biography [Leslie Stephen and Sidney Lee (eds.)], 66 vols. (in 22) [to 1900] (1908-9); 6 decennial vols. [1901-1960]; *Missing Persons* (1993); *Oxford D.N.B.* (60 vols., 2004).[1]

The Irish Law Times and Solicitors' Journal (114 vols., Dublin, 1867/8-1980).

James Meenan (ed.), *Centenary History of the Literary and Historical Society of University College Dublin 1855-1955* (Tralee: [1956]; reprinted, with a memoir of James Meenan, Dublin: 2005).

Kate Newman (ed.), *Dictionary of Ulster Biography* (Belfast, 1993).[1]

Louis McRedmond (ed.), *Modern Irish Lives: Dictionary of 20th-century Irish Biography* (Dublin, 1996).[1]

Register of the Alumni of Trinity College Dublin (9 vols., Dublin: 1928-1970).[4]

Thom's Directory [Until 1958 the volumes contain lists of judges and barristers, with addresses, and in some instances a note of the appointment held].

Brian M. Walker (ed.), *Parliamentary Election Results in Ireland, 1801-1922* (Dublin, 1978) and *Parliamentary Election Results in Ireland, 1918-92* (Dublin and Belfast, 1992).

Who's Who [first published by A & C. Black in 1849]. Conveniently to be consulted in the version *Who was Who* (10 vols; London, 1920-2001), with volumes for 1897-1915; 1916-1928; 1929-1940; 1941-1950; 1951-1960; 1961-1970; 1971-1980; 1981-1990; 1991-1995; and 1996-2000. Also: *Who was Who: A cumulated Index 1897-1990* (London, 1991).

---

[1]   See below, pages 65-6, for the persons noticed in the *D.N.B.* and similar works.

[2]   The 1st edition of Maureen Cairnduff's *Who's Who in Ireland* has entries for the following post-1968 barristers: Kader Asmal [M 1975], George Birmingham [M 1976], John Bruton [M 1972], Michael Fingleton [T 1974], Mary McAleese [T 1978], Seán O'Leary [T 1980] and Dick Spring [M 1974]. Seán Doherty and David Leahy are mentioned as having been educated at the King's Inns.

[3]   Maureen Cairnduff's 2nd or 3rd editions have entries for the following post-1968 barristers: Colm Allen [T 1973], John Bruton [M 1972], David Byrne [M 1970], Frank Clarke [T 1973], Susan Denham [T 1971], Emily Egan [T 1994; listed in 1999 as a 'Rising Star'], Michael Fingleton [T 1974], Mary Finlay [H 1980], John Gordon [M 1973], Adrian Hardiman [M 1974], Peter Kelly [T 1978], Maura King [T 1991, listed in 1991 among 'People of tomorrow'], Vivian Lavan [T 1969], Conor Maguire [M 1971], Mary McAleese [T 1978], John Gerard McKenna [T 1982], Patricia O'Donovan [T 1975], Philip O'Sullivan [T 1969], John Quirke [T 1974], Dick Spring [M 1974], Ercus Stewart [M 1970], and David Went [T 1970].

[4]   The 2nd (1930), 3rd (1933), 4th (1937), 5th (1950), 6th (1955), 7th (1962), 8th (1965) and 9th (1970) editions of the Trinity College *Register* offer an appendix of obituaries noting the dates of death of deceased graduates. The 10th (1983) and subsequent editions have abandoned the practice. Two of the volumes were brought out by barristers. The 1st edition was edited by T.U. Sadleir [H 1906]; the 9th by J.S.R. Cole [T 1935].

INTRODUCTION

This work represents the continuation of (and is envisaged as a companion to) the book entitled *King's Inns Admission Papers 1607-1867*, edited by Edward Keane, P. Beryl Phair and Thomas U. Sadleir, and published in 1982 by the Stationery Office, Dublin, for the Irish Manuscripts Commission. The attempt has been made to match this book in size and appearance with the attributes of its predecessor; but there are inevitably a few differences which arise from changed circumstances and the nature and opportunities of the materials.

The book *King's Inns Admission Papers 1607-1868* and this work

The volume published by the Irish Manuscripts Commission in 1982 listed in alphabetical order the names of those recorded as having sought admission to the Honorable Society of King's Inns from the time of the revival of the Society in 1607 to the year 1867. Because in these years the King's Inns catered for all branches of the profession, that list embraced not only barristers but attorneys and solicitors.[1] It also included law students who did not proceed to be called to the Bar,[2] and the apprentices of attorneys and solicitors who did not secure admission to the rolls. The most important respect in which this volume differs from its predecessor is that it is confined to the branch of the profession with which the Honorable Society of King's Inns is now exclusively associated: the barristers.

A second, but related, difference is that attainment of the degree of barrister, rather than entry to the Inns as a law student, has been made the criterion for inclusion. A decision to confine the volume to graduate barristers would have been rational in itself, but candour requires that it be confessed that the records of the King's Inns have not been fully explored. The papers so far indexed are those which came into being on the occasion of the graduating student's application to be called to the Bar. Papers of similar character submitted (typically three years earlier) by the aspirant student on

---

[1] By section 78 of the Supreme Court of Judicature Act (Ireland), 1877 [40 & 41 Vict., cap. 57] attorneys and solicitors were assimilated under the common title of 'Solicitors of the Court of Judicature'.
[2] Thus, the names of the barristers called in 1868 and 1869, and most of those called in 1870, are to be found, as law students, in the earlier volume.

first seeking admission to the Inns have not yet been indexed. The result is that students of the King's Inns who did not pursue their studies to a conclusion are not included. Languishing among the unpublished records of the Society are likely to be the names of some persons of distinction who made their mark in a career other than law. This point may be illustrated by reference to Lord MacDermott's memoirs. J.C. MacDermott was one of a group of twenty called to the Bar in November 1921, but he belonged to a class of twice that number, not all of whom pursued their studies to conclusion.[3] Lord MacDermott mentions a couple of contemporaries who were never called to the Bar: one of these, destined to be associated not with lawyers but with gypsy musicians, was Walter Starkie (1894-1976), the author of *Raggle-Taggle*, precisely the sort of person who would have been noticed in this volume had his name been included among the barristers.[4]

Among the same untouched papers, which possess a bulk greater than that of what has been indexed, may possibly repose the names of a few post-1867 solicitors, whose continued right to be admitted to King's Inns is a subject considered further below.

While continuity was desired, and should be discernible, in the scheme of the work, the publication of the chronological Rolls of the Outer and Inner Bars represents an innovation, as does the inclusion of two introductory historical essays.

The Aphabetical Index, 1868-1968

The reader is offered, for the 101 years which separate 1868 from 1968, a continuation of the alphabetical listing which made the earlier list a valuable genealogical tool. As heretofore, an entry typically gives the full name of the applicant (who in this volume is always a graduating barrister); the names, and place of residence, of the applicant's parents; and the applicant's rank among the sons or daughters of the family. The entries also supply details of the applicant's age and education — species of information that were not always available for the years covered in the previous volume. The term and year of a person's admission to the Inns are, as before,

---

[3]   J.C. MacDermott, *An Enriching Life* (Belfast, 1980), p. 138. Lord MacDermott wrote: 'The men included quite a number of ex-service students like myself; some who had already succeeded in one career and wanted to add, as garnishing or else with a view to practise, the degree of barrister-at-law; and some a good deal younger for whom the Bar was their first choice'.

[4]   Ibid., p. 143. The other was the rugby-player Bob Scott, then a teacher at the Masonic Boys' School and afterwards Headmaster of St. Andrew's College.

Another contemporary student not called was the U.C.C. historian James Hogan (1898-1963): see Donnchadh Ó Corráin (ed.), *James Hogan: Revolutionary, Historian and Political Scientist* (Dublin, 2001), p. 6.

invariably recorded; as likewise are the term and year of his call to the Bar.

A new feature of the present listing is that an archival reference is supplied which identifies not only the location of the record but the number of items of which it is composed. Two items — a receipt for £50, and the applicant's own statement of his parentage and education and desire to be called to the Bar [a printed form styled 'Memorial', generally incorporating a practising barrister's certificate of the applicant's fitness] — are a minimum expectation: but the file may include a Bencher's statement of his intention to propose the applicant for Call, a certificate from one of the London Inns testifying to the applicant's having satisfied the dining requirements of that Inn, certificates from King's Inns lecturers (styled 'Professors') as to the candidate's attendance at lectures or performance in examinations, as well as items of correspondence.

The nature of the material may be illustrated by reference to the record for Lord Carson (called at Easter 1877), which contains five items. The most important is the Memorial, here a form printed by Alexander Thom to look like a scribe's copper-plate. The form used by Carson embodied the certificate of the practising barrister [W. Bennett Campion, Q.C.] and the statement of intention of the Bencher [Richard Armstrong]. The other documents in Carson's file are a certificate from the Middle Temple, and three certificates from as many Professors of Legal Education at the King's Inns.

No. 1.—LAW STUDENT'S MEMORIAL

FOR ADMISSION AS A BARRISTER.

TO THE RIGHT HONORABLE AND HONORABLE

THE BENCHERS

OF THE HONORABLE SOCIETY OF THE KING'S INNS.

The Memorial of

Name in full. _Edwd Henry Carson B.A. T.C.D._

Sheweth

That he is the Second _son of_ Edwd Henry Carson C.E. _of_ 25 Harcourt St _in the County of_ the city of Dublin _and of_ Isabella _otherwise_ Lambert _his wife._

Detail from the Memorial of Edward Henry Carson, dated 10th April 1877

The biographical detail abstracted from the Memorials forms the basis of the Alphabetical Index, and is the first (and often only) component of every entry. The transcription of this material was the work of Mrs. Julitta Clancy, M.B.E., an archivist and indexer by profession, who has edited recent volumes of *The Irish Digest*. Mrs. Clancy was assisted in the later stages of the project by Mrs. Margaret Connolly, and completed her work in June 1998.

The volume published in 1982 reposed on the work of T.U. Sadleir, a King's Inns barrister whose name is to be found in the body of this work, and about whom it is proper to say a few words.[5] Tom Sadleir was a distinguished genealogist, most of whose career was spent in the Office of Arms in Dublin Castle. After his retirement, in 1943, from that Office, he accepted employment as assistant librarian in King's Inns, where he is remembered, typically seated at his desk at one end of the Library, labouring in solitude on the slips that were the foundation of the 1982 book.[6] Sadleir added a few references to the *D.N.B.*, Ball's *Judges,* and his own *Alumni Dublinenses*: but in the earlier volume the scale of biographical annotation based on extraneous sources was constrained by the difficulty of the endeavour.

In this respect the present editor's task has been easier, and he has been active to the extent that the opportunities and rewards beckoned. The century that began in 1868 coincided with the best years of *The Irish Law Times and Solicitors' Journal*, a publication which faithfully served practitioners at a time when numbers in both branches of the profession were much smaller. The practising Bar was still close-knit, and its 300-odd members knew each other and were known to the barrister-editors of *The Irish Law Times*.[7] That admirable weekly publication sought, like *The Times* of London, to be a newspaper of record. Orderly perusal of its volumes has brought to light the obituaries of many of those whose names are included in this work, and such obituaries have been an easy and fruitful quarry of biographical information. In respect of those who have died since the demise (in 1980) of the *Irish Law Times*, the task of biographical annotation has been markedly more burdensome, and is manifestly incomplete.

---

[5] The photograph of him on his call to the Bar in 1906 was published in Susan Hood, *Royal Roots — Republican Inheritance: The Survival of the Office of Arms* (Dublin, 2002), p. 91.

[6] Sadleir died in 1957, with the work incomplete. Twenty-five years later the materials which he had assembled on slips were published by Edward Keane and Beryl Phair. Mrs. Phair (*née* Eustace), a T.C.D. history graduate of 1930, had been Sadleir's secretary in the Office of Arms. Both she and Mr. Keane have since died.

[7] Editors of the *Irish Law Times*: E.N. Blake, -1892; H. M. FitzGibbon, 1892-1906; W.J. Johnston, 1906-11; James Henry, 1911-1929; R. St. J. Chadwick, 1930-1; Herbert Hare, 1931-49; Lionel Winder, 1950-80.

THOMAS ULICK SADLEIR (1882-1957)
Photographed on his call to the Bar in Hilary Term 1906.

The original compiler of *King's Inns Admission Papers 1607-1867* (Dublin, 1982) had been a principal contributor to the *Georgian Society Records* and joint author (with G.D. Burtchaell) of *Alumni Dublinenses*. From 1913 to 1943 he was a member of the staff of the Office of Arms, where he became Deputy to the Ulster King of Arms and the last administrator of the Office. He was Assistant Librarian of King's Inns from 1945 to 1957.

THE

IRISH LAW TIMES,

AND

SOLICITORS' JOURNAL.

 A WEEKLY NEWSPAPER,

AND

GAZETTE OF LEGAL POSTINGS.

Pro Rege, Grege, Lege.

VOLUME I.—1867-8.

DUBLIN:
PRINTED AND PUBLISHED BY
JOHN FALCONER, 53, UPPER SACKVILLE-STREET.

1868.

TITLE PAGE OF THE FIRST VOLUME OF THE
IRISH LAW TIMES AND SOLICITORS' JOURNAL.

This weekly publication was the source of much biographical information.

The stamp 'Law Library * Dublin Castle' indicates that the volume was acquired when the Law Library was re-established, after the destruction of the Four Courts, in St. Patrick's Hall at Dublin Castle. Many of the Law Library's older volumes bear this stamp.

1867: the departure of the solicitors

A few words may be directed to an aspect of the work apt to seem mysterious: its temporal limits. The watershed between 1867, the terminal year of the earlier volume, and 1868, the year from which the present lists commence, has to do with the removal from the Benchers of King's Inns of their tutelage over the education of attorneys and solicitors. The change flowed from the enactment of the *Attorneys and Solicitors (Ireland) Act,* of 1866,[8] a subtle statute in which the parliamentary draughtsman achieved his purpose with no mention of the Honorable Society of King's Inns and without revealing that the Benchers had hitherto supervised the education of attorneys. A casual reader of the statute book would have been hard put to appreciate the change that had been effected.

Prior to 1866 the attorneys and solicitors had striven for many years to establish a professional association independent of King's Inns. Early steps in this direction had been taken in 1774, when a 'Society of Attornies' was established, and in 1791 when the 'Law Club of Ireland' appeared, a body which survived, as a club, until 1899. Such groupings were precursors of the modern Law Society, formed in 1830 as the 'Law Society of Ireland', and reconstituted in 1841 as 'The Society of the Attorneys and Solicitors of Ireland'. This was the name by which the Society received its royal charter in 1852 and by which it was known to the legislature in 1866.[9]

By 1866 the control of solicitors' education by the King's Inns had become anomalous. The London Inns had no such function, and English precedent pointed towards the transfer of the duty to the Law Society. Proposals to end the Benchers' control of the

---

[8] 29 & 30 Vict., cap. 84. See especially ss 28, 30, 49. The oblique way in which the parliamentary draughtsman achieved his aim in 1866 demonstrated skill and tact. A new office, that of the Registrar of Attorneys and Solicitors, was established, and that office was 'vested' in the Incorporated Society of the Attorneys and Solicitors of Ireland. Two clauses in the 1866 Act were effective to deprive the Benchers of their former jurisdiction. One was section 30, which provided that from the 1st day of January 1867 it should not be lawful for the Commissioners of Inland Revenue to issue a stamp on an attorney's licence to practise save upon the production of a certificate from the new Registrar of Attorneys and Solicitors. The Registrar's document was to have 'the same Force and Effect as the stamped Certificate heretofore issued authorising Persons to practise as such Attorneys and Solicitors'. The other was section 49 which provided that henceforth no fees (other than examination fees payable to the Law Society) were to be paid by any person seeking to be bound as an apprentice or to be admitted and enrolled as a solicitor. This removed the aspirant solicitor's obligation to become a member of King's Inns. The fees accustomed to be charged by King's Inns sufficed to deter voluntary membership.

[9] In 1888 'The Society of the Attorneys and Solicitors of Ireland' became the Incorporated Law Society of Ireland, a title which it retained until 1994, when it resumed the name with which it began in 1830, the Law Society of Ireland.

education of attorneys and solicitors had been canvassed in Ireland for thirty years. In the parliamentary sessions of 1838 and 1839 Daniel O'Connell had introduced Bills, which, if enacted, would have incorporated both the King's Inns and the Law Society, envisaging that solicitors should not thereafter be members of King's Inns. By 1866 the inevitability of reform was accepted, and the Benchers did not oppose the Bill. A Committee of the Benchers considered the draft Bill with care, and made some suggestions for its improvement, recommendations which were submitted to the Attorney-General. An extract from the Benchers' Minute Book containing a portion of the Committee's report is printed opposite.

In 1866 the parliamentary draughtsman avoided any intrusion into the liberty of professional association. There was neither a requirement that attorneys and solicitors should become members of the Law Society, nor that they should cease to be members of King's Inns. A curious result of the draughtsman's restraint was that professional affiliation to these bodies remained optional for the solicitor. Even in the mid-twentieth century *Thom's Directory* was accustomed to indicate by an asterisk those solicitors who were members of the Incorporated Law Society; and many names were not so designated. Likewise there was no restriction on the attorneys' continuing to be members of King's Inns. Solicitors and apprentices who had joined the Society before the legislative change (having paid good money to do so) remained members, and some continued to exercise their right to dine in the Hall of the Inns. In practice the legislation of 1866 made the Inns a barristers' body, but King's Inns placed no bar on solicitors joining the Society after 1866. A solicitor, Horace Wilson, enquired about membership of the Inns as late as 1893. His enquiry prompted the Benchers to examine their regulations, and an illuminating report made by the Standing Committee on this occasion is appended.[10]

By law, with effect from 1st January 1867, the duty of maintaining 'an alphabetical Roll or Book or Rolls or Books of all Attorneys and Solicitors' was imposed on the Incorporated Society of the Attorneys and Solicitors of Ireland; and with this body, now the Law Society, the duty has since remained through successive re-enactments. On the occasion of the appearance of this volume the King's Inns may fairly plead that the onus of publishing the post-1867 records of solicitors has passed to the Law Society.[11]

---

[10] *Infra*, pp 16-7. Grateful acknowledgment is due to a footnote in Daire Hogan, *The Legal Profession in Ireland 1789-1922*, p. 123.
[11] The Law Society has recently published the roll of solicitors admitted during each of the fifty years 1952-2001: see Eamonn G. Hall and Daire Hogan, *The Law Society of Ireland, 1852-2002: Portrait of a Profession* (Dublin, 2002), pp 230-83.

EXTRACT FROM THE REPORT OF THE BENCHERS'
COMMITTEE ON THE ATTORNEYS BILL OF 1866

Tuesday 5th June 1866
[245-9] Report [dated 2nd June 1866] of the Committee on the
Attorneys Bill, a copy of which was sent to the Attorney General

'In effect it is proposed by the Bill that subject to the supervision
of the Lord Chancellor, the Master of the Rolls, and the Chief
Judges [247] the Incorporated Society shall for the future have
the control and direction of the profession of Attorneys and
Solicitors and the receipt and application of the fees payable by
their Apprentices. The practising Attorneys of Ireland on the
Roll of last year were 1246 in number. There are several Law
Societies or clubs connected with their profession, all voluntary
institutions and self-regulating in respect of the admission of
members, viz. The Law Club established in 1791, The
Incorporated Society established in 1841, The Cork Law Society
and The Belfast Law Club. The Incorporated Society consists of
430 members, being about one third of the entire profession; and
the other Law Societies or Clubs have each a smaller number of
members. But we have reason to believe that there are some
hundreds of Attorneys who are not members of any of these
Societies or Clubs. We therefore think that all these Societies or
Clubs even if taken together, and of course each taken by itself
cannot be said to represent the profession. In 1838 Mr O'Connell
introduced into the House of Commons a Bill to incorporate into
a Law Society certain practising attorneys, whose names to the
number of 331 are set out in a Schedule to the Bill. But the Bill
contained a provision which enabled every Attorney or Solicitor
to become a member of that Society by the payment of a fee, and
we are of opinion that the Bill now under consideration should
contain a similar provision. We are of opinion [248] that the
Incorporated Law Society should be made to embrace the entire
profession, each member of the profession having a voice in the
election of the governing body of the Society. We are also of the
opinion that all Attorneys and Solicitors hereafter to be admitted
shall by virtue of such admission and in consideration of the fees
paid by them to the Registrar thereupon become members of the
Incorporated Society.'

The changes made by the 1866 Act coincide with a change in the way in which the King's Inns records have been organised. The papers up to and including 1867 are now arranged in one series in alphabetical order, without reference to date of admission to the Inns or of call to the Bar. These papers were the subject of the previous volume, and their re-arrangement by surname aided the preparation of that volume.[12] The papers since 1868 are arranged in two annual series, one for students, the other (the portion which has been indexed) for barristers. It is thought that this represented the original arrangement of the pre-1867 records.

1968: the terminal date of the alphabetical index now offered

Now that it has been shown why the present list commences in 1868 and why it is confined to barristers, an explanation is due as to why the main alphabetical index concludes in 1968. The choice of 1968 was not intended to reflect a watershed in professional life, nor even to be an echo of the starting date 101 years earlier. The year emerged by accident in response to the progress of work on the archives. The index was compiled for King's Inns in 1998, thirty years after the latest of the recorded entries. The selection of 1968 represented the observance, in accordance with prevailing archival standards, of a 30-year interval in according access to records.

---

[12] The *Attorneys and Solicitors (Ireland) Act* came into force on 1st January 1867. It might have been more rational if the change in the King's Inns filing arrangements had been made to coincide with that date, but the delay of a year is explicable if the intent were to examine the effect produced by the Act.

It is probable that T.U. Sadleir was responsible for choosing the 1867 date, and for the decision to include all the papers of that year in his rearrangement of the records. It may well be that his motives were not clearly understood by his successors, for it is noteworthy that Mr. Keane and Mrs. Phair do not, in their introduction to the 1982 volume, explain why 1867 was chosen as the terminal year for the papers included in that volume. On page xii of their introduction, where the 1867 date is mentioned, they allude only to the introduction of civil registration of births, marriages and deaths. As the system of civil registration came into force on 1st January 1864, that allusion is unconvincing as an explanation.

It is probable that Mr. Keane and Mrs. Phair found the records in their present form as arranged by the late T.U. Sadleir, and acquiesced in that rearrangement gratefully and without qualms. Indeed, they complain that the post-1868 records 'are tedious to consult being tied in bundles in chronological order'.

The Roll of the Outer Bar, 1868-2004; the Roll of the Inner Bar 1880-2004; and the list of Judges and Law Officers

The project of producing this book originated as one to publish the alphabetical index compiled by Mrs. Clancy: but reflection suggested that the opportunity should not be missed to compile a work that would render the listing of barristers complete. The case for publishing an up-to-date compilation may be adjudged unanswerable when it is realised that since 1960 it has not been possible to find, as previously, a full list of barristers qualified to practise. The last lists of this character appeared in the 1958 and

---

BARRISTERS AND *THOM'S DIRECTORY*

The custom of publishing a list of barristers in the Dublin street directories commenced in Wilson's *Dublin Directory* in 1762 and continued, under Thom, annually until 1958, the last year of *Thom's Directory* in its old format. Thom's list was never confined to the practising bar, and always included those who, having acquired the qualification, either retreated into obscurity, or made their mark elsewhere. The first list, as well as the last, embraced men eminent in public life who did not practise. The 1958 list, for example, includes the names of Garret FitzGerald and Charles Haughey, non-practising barristers who, like many of their predecessors in earlier lists, were waiting to make their mark in a local legislature.

Thom was not published in 1959. A list of barristers was printed in the second volume of the 1960 edition, but has not appeared subsequently.

1960 editions of *Thom's Directory*. It is true that lists of subscribers to the Law Library have continued to be published annually in the *Law Directory*,[13] and in recent years, in the diaries of the Bar Council;[14] but the subscribers to the Law Library constitute fewer

---

[13] The *Law Directory*, an annual solicitors' publication, first appeared in 1886. Here publication of a full list of barristers in the form familiar from *Thom*, with members of the Law Library distinguished by an asterisk, continued until 1963. In 1964 this format was replaced by a list of subscribers to the Law Library.
[14] The Bar Council publications have an ephemeral character, and it may be of bibliographical utility to specify works that contain lists of subscribers to the Law Library: *General Council of the Bar of Ireland Member's Handbook*. List of Subscribers 1987 [28 pages]; 1988 [32 pages]; 1990 [37 pages]; 1991 [38 pages]; 1992/93 [40 pages]. *Bar Council of Ireland Year Book and Diary,* Oct. 1995 to Dec. 1996; Oct. 1996 to Dec. 1997; Oct. 1997 to Dec. 1998; Oct. 1998 to Dec.

than a third of those who have been called to the Irish Bar. Short of going to the archives, even the King's Inns possessed no ready means of identifying its numerous recent graduates.

The Roll of the Outer Bar here printed has been compiled, with greater difficulty than was anticipated, from the following sources.

(i) Julitta Clancy's chronological list

For the years 1868-1968 a chronological list compiled by Mrs. Clancy was available based on her work in indexing the Memorials.

(ii) The Under-Treasurer's Call Lists

It has always been one of the Under-Treasurer's duties to produce lists of the graduating barristers seeking Call. These lists were printed until 1941, since when they have been typewritten. Various versions exist of the typewritten lists of recent decades. Sometimes discrepancies appear in the typescript, suggesting that the Under-Treasurer had issued an amended version: but a more common feature is that the lists bear manuscript amendments, indicating last-minute changes. Copies of Call Lists have been found as follows:-

The King's Inns Library possesses two bound volumes entitled *"Call" lists*, which cover the periods Easter 1861 to Trinity 1900, and Michaelmas 1900 to Trinity (*recte* Michaelmas) 1926 respectively. The Library also has folders which contain, loose, the Call Lists for the following periods: M 1927 to M 1936; M 1937 to M 1946 (printed until 1941); T 1947 to M 1959; M 1960 to M 1978; M 1979 to T 1984; T 1985 to 1993; and 1994 to 2003.

The King's Inns General Office holds somewhat fuller sets of the recent typewritten lists. These are kept in two green binders entitled respectively 'Call Lists 1942/79' and 'Call Lists 1980/-'.

The Office of the Supreme Court has yielded Call Lists for the years since 1958. As these were used by the Registrar of the Supreme Court on the day of call, and bear his annotations, they are undoubtedly the most authentic.

The Irish Law Times. Copies of the Call Lists have traditionally been offered to newspapers, and reports of Calls (at one time with photographs) used to appear in *The Irish Times* and other newspapers. *The Irish Law Times* also received copies of Call Lists, and could be relied on to publish the details. The last Call to be thus noted in the *Irish Law Times* was that for Trinity 1979.

1999; Oct. 1999 to Dec. 2000; Oct. 2000 to Dec. 2001; Oct. 2001 to Feb. 2003; Oct. 2002 to Feb. 2004; Oct. 2003 to Feb. 2005; Oct. 2004 to Feb. 2006.

(iii) The Benchers' Minute Books

The most authentic of the King's Inns records is the series of Benchers' Minute Books. It was the custom, using the formula 'Be it remembered that on this day the following gentlemen were admitted to the degree of barrister-at-law and subsequently called to the Bar in the Supreme Court ...', to transcribe into the Minutes, in the writing of the Under-Treasurer, the names of those called. These entries are intermixed with minutes of the general administrative business of the Benchers.

(iv) The Roll of the Outer Bar

It is arguable that the best modern evidence of call to the Bar is found not at the King's Inns but in the Office of the Supreme Court, which holds four volumes that together constitute, for the years since 1927, the 'Roll of the Outer Bar'. These volumes consist of pages of signatures punctuated by headings (in calligraphy) of the year and term of call. They are entitled as follows:

> Saorstát Éireaann — Roll of Outer Bar. Hilary Term 1927 to Michaelmas Term 1951.
> Rolla an Bharra. Hilary Term 1952 to Michaelmas Term 1982.
> Roll of the Outer Bar. Trinity Term 1983 to Easter Term 1993.
> Roll of the Outer Bar. Trinity Term 1993 -.

The editor and the Honorable Society of King's Inns wish to express their gratitude to Mrs. Mary Hennessy and Miss Catherine Higgins, Barrister-at-Law, of the Supreme Court Office for facilitating access to the records in their care.

It is not clear why the Roll kept in the Supreme Court commences only in 1927; nor is it known whether the keeping of this Roll had any precedent:[15] but it is possible that the establishment of a Roll of the Outer Bar constituted an innovation. Since 1921 King's Inns graduates had enjoyed the right to be called

---

[15] No pre-1927 roll of signatures is known to survive, nor is any known to have existed, and it may be speculated that no independent record of call to the Outer Bar was kept at the Four Courts prior to 1922. While in Ireland the Lord Chancellor called men to the Bar in open Court, a practice which differed from the arrangement in London, where barristers were called by the Treasurers of their respective Inns, it does not follow that the Irish court would necessarily have kept its own record of the event. In both jurisdictions call to the Bar was essentially a function delegated by the judges to the Inns, and it is not hard to suppose that the Irish Lord Chancellor (who was generally the Treasurer of King's Inns) was content to delegate the keeping of records to the Under-Treasurer. For the practice in London, see J.H. Baker, 'The Degree of Barrister', in his book, *The Common Law Tradition: Lawyers, Books and the Law* (London, 2000), pp 69-76.

It is more likely that a record was kept prior to 1922 of men called to the Inner Bar, for this ceremony was associated with the taking of the oath of allegiance. This would explain why the Roll of the Inner Bar duly commences in 1924 when the Irish Free State created its first Senior Counsel.

to the Bar in Belfast as well as in Dublin, and it may be conjectured that a need was felt for the Courts in Dublin Castle to keep a distinct record now that graduation from King's Inns was no longer synonymous with membership of the Dublin Bar. This conjecture is probably correct, but it does not explain why the listing does not commence in November 1921, on the occasion of the first Call after the coming into force of the Government of Ireland Act, or in July 1924, when the new courts of the Irish Free State were inaugurated and when the Roll of the Inner Bar was instituted, or in 1925 or 1926 when the Benchers of King's Inns were concerned with the consequences of the breach with the Belfast Benchers. The best explanation is perhaps that the 1927 start was a dilatory response to the foregoing considerations.

The Roll of the Inner Bar

Call to the Inner Bar is the prerogative of the Government, and no function of the King's Inns. It nevertheless seemed convenient that this book should seek, for the sake of completeness, to provide a list of those barristers on whom the honour of a silk gown had been conferred. For the early years, the list here offered is a reconstruction, based on materials in *Thom's Directory* and the *Irish Law Times*. For the years since 1924, however, it is based on the best evidence.[16] The Supreme Court holds two volumes that constitute the 'Roll of the Inner Bar'. The earlier of these commences with the words 'Roll of Barristers who have been granted Patents of precedence', and is a record of calls between Monday 14th July 1924 and 3rd October 1983. The later is a book that begins with the call of 16th March 1984. Like the volumes that constitute the Roll of the Outer Bar, these are books of signatures. Signatures are excellent evidence, provided that they can be deciphered. In the light of the proviso it is well that the Supreme Court has preserved files, dating from 1939, of papers relating to the grant of Patents of Precedence and call to the Inner Bar.[17]

---

[16] The only name missing from the Roll of the Inner Bar (and this because his call within the Bar predated the keeping of the List) is that of John O'Byrne who was called within the Bar on 11th June 1924, the day the new Courts of the Irish Free State were inaugurated. It is a curiosity that the Free State made him a *King's Counsel*. Those called subsequently were designated *Senior Counsel*.

[17] The presence of his signature on the Roll is undoubtedly the best evidence of a person's admission; but there are instances in which sense can be made of the Court Roll only by reference to extrinsic evidence. It is worthy of admonitory remark that the names of some colleagues have found their way into this volume solely because their signatures could be interpreted by reference to a typewritten Call List and to the relative position of their scrawled signatures to the legible names of others.

Judges and Law Officers

The lists of judges and law officers, likewise offered in the cause of completeness, have been compiled exclusively from secondary sources. Such include, for the earlier years, *Thom's Directory*, the *Northern Ireland Reports*, and the Succession Lists compiled by V.T.H. Delany which appear as appendices to his biography of *Christopher Palles* (Dublin, 1960), pp 177-87. For recent years the information published in the initial pages of the volumes of *The Irish Reports* has been followed.

Accuracy of the Lists

Some six thousand names are included in the lists now published. Considerable care has been taken to ensure that the information published is accurate, but it is inevitable in a work of this scale that error can occur. The materials from which the information has been transcribed present difficulties not only of legibility but of interpretation. The principal problems have arisen with overseas students on whom the degree of barrister-of-law was conferred, but who were not called to the Irish Bar; with some of the Australian barristers who communicated an intention to be called, but did not present themselves; and with individuals who, by reason of illness or other eventuality, did not attend for call. The Roll and the Call Lists are on occasion discrepant. The available information has been interpreted as best it allowed, and assumptions have been made, silently. The lists here published are not to be construed as conferring the degree of barrister on anyone who was not previously entitled to it, nor is the omission of a name to be construed as disentitling a person who had previously obtained the qualification. Should a question or doubt arise, recourse should be had to the Roll in the custody of the Registrar of the Supreme Court and to the records of King's Inns in the custody of the Under-Treasurer.

Modern constraints on the disclosure of personal information

The personal information in this book is available because the Honorable Society of King's Inns required its students to supply details of their age and parentage. The concern with age arose because of the need to ensure that persons were not inadvertently called to the Bar while still minors. The interest in parentage was directed to ensuring the probity of an honourable profession. The Benchers will not have been displeased if those who applied to them could adduce a pedigree of social or legal distinction; but the explanation for the collection of what is now valuable genealogical information lay in the assumption, general in society, that family antecedents were relevant to character and aptitude.

Since the enactment of the Data Protection Act, 1988, the disclosure of personal information about living persons has become a matter for circumspection. It is here relevant to observe that the personal information contained in this volume is confined to persons called to the Bar in or before 1968, the youngest of whom was born in 1947. It may likewise be added that much of this information was previously made available to the Press, having been furnished, at the time of the person's Call, in the Call Lists distributed by the Under-Treasurer to the *Irish Law Times* and the daily newspapers.

To most aspirant barristers and their parents the opportunity of publicity at Call will not have been unwelcome, but one instance is recorded of a barrister who requested that details of his Call should not be given to the Press. At the Benchers' meeting on 27 May 1964:[18]

> The Under-Treasurer informed the meeting that [a named candidate] had requested that the report of his admission to Degree & Call to the Bar be not given to the Press for publication. This request was rejected as contrary to established custom.

The succinct form of the Minute of 1964 suggests that the Benchers had little difficulty in adjudicating on a question that would be apt to be more troublesome to their successors today.

The Council of the Irish Legal History Society and the Library Committee of King's Inns

The publication of this volume has been undertaken in association with the Irish Legal History Society, which has assisted the project by ordering copies for distribution to its members. Professor W.N. Osborough, long the guiding spirit of that Society, and lately its President, graciously agreed to write the essay that appears below under his name, and read the text with a close attention for which the editor is most grateful.

From the side of King's Inns Mr. Charles Lysaght, Barrister-at-Law, read the text with similar care, and helped generously with the work of biographical annotation. The editor is grateful too to the Under-Treasurer, Mrs. Camilla McAleese, and to his colleagues on the Library Committee, in particular its chairman, Mr. James O'Reilly, Senior Counsel, and Mr. Jonathan Armstrong, the Librarian of King's Inns. Mr. Justice Hugh Geoghegan, a former chairman of the Library Committee, and a current member of the Council of the Irish Legal History Society, has bestowed a benevolent interest in the project in both such capacities.

Kenneth Ferguson
July 2005

---

[18]   Benchers' Minute Book 1957 to 1964, pp 338-9.

APPENDIX

SOLICITORS AND THE KING'S INNS
AFTER THE ACT OF 1866

from
Report of the Standing Committee on the admission of Solicitors
Benchers' Minute Book 1885-1901, pp 262-6.

Hilary Term Wednesday 18th January 1893.

Read the Report of the Standing Committee as follows:
   In pursuance of the Resolution of the Bench of 11th January 1893
we have considered Mr Horace Wilson's letter dated 5th December
last and we make the following report.
   [263] The Society of King's Inns from its foundation received
Attorneys and Solicitors as Members, and for more than a hundred
and fifty years such membership was a necessary condition to their
being admitted to practise in courts of Law and Equity. They were
relieved from this condition by the Attorneys and Solicitors Act
(Ireland) 1866; and since its passing there has been no instance of a
Solicitor seeking to enter the Society. Its constitution however
remains unchanged, and if there are new Solicitors who wish to
become Members, we are of opinion that there is nothing in the
recent legislation to prevent or render inexpedient their admission,
but that in consequence of the actual circumstances, some
modifications must be made in the rules regulating their reception
into the Society. From the beginning of the present century down to
the year 1866 a person proposing to qualify himself for the
profession of Attorney or Solicitor paid a fee to the Society of
King's Inns and applied by Memorial to the Benchers for
permission to enter on his apprenticeship. The granting of such
permission did not enable him to join the Society at once, but it
amounted to a recognition of his right to be made a member upon
his being enrolled as an Attorney or Solicitor and upon his paying a
further fee. The fees then payable were for [264] many years the
sums of £4. 8. 11½ and £13. 11. 3, respectively. When the Bench in
the year 1860 required Apprentices to attend law lectures and to
pass examinations in certain branches of general and legal
knowledge each fee was increased by the sum of three guineas for

the purpose of meeting the expenses incurred by the Society in carrying out the educational programme. Thus the entire amount contributed by a Solicitor to the funds of the King's Inns at the time of the passing of the Act of 1866 was £24. 6. 2½. As that statute has made independent provision for the supervision of the indentures of apprenticeship and for the instruction and examination of Apprentices we are of opinion that the two fees of three guineas ought not now to be charged. We have carefully considered whether any change ought to be made in the sum of £13. 11. 3 which may be regarded as the fee heretofore paid by Solicitors for actual admission into the Society: unless alteration of circumstances has rendered this amount substantially inequitable it is manifestly desirable to maintain it. The retention tends to keep up the continuity of the connection of Solicitors with the Inns of Court and to show that what is now done is not a new point of departure. Barristers pay (in addition to educational fees) the sum of £18. 6. 0 upon their admission as Students and £40. 0. 0 upon their call to the Bar. Receiving as they do their right to practise [265] their profession from the Society of King's Inns it is just that their contribution to its funds should largely exceed that of men who are not dependent upon it for their professional status. Apart however from this consideration, every member of the Society enjoys valuable privileges. He is entitled for life to the use of one of the best libraries in the United Kingdom; an excellent dinner is supplied in the Hall on 92 days in the year at an exceptionally moderate price and there is no annual or other payment in addition to the sum contributed on admission. We therefore recommend the retention of the fee of £13. 11. 3. We further recommend that the mode of admission of a Solicitor be made analogous to that of a Barrister and that having obtained from a member of the Society (not being a Bencher or Law Student) a certificate that he is a fit and proper person to be admitted and a Bencher having signified his intention of proposing him, he be submitted to the Bench for election.

(Signed) C. Palles, A.M. Porter M R
Hugh Holmes, M. Harrison
Robert R Warren, D. P. Barton

The Vice Chancellor moved
The Lord Chief Justice seconded
Resolved
That the above Report be received and adopted and that a letter be written to [266] Mr Wilson in accordance therewith.

Landmarks in the history of King's Inns:
1872, 1885, 1921, 1925

by W.N. OSBOROUGH

Compulsory lectures (1872)

The King's Inns to which students reading for the Irish Bar were admitted in the late 1860s was very different from the Inns of twenty years before. By virtue of the *Attorneys and Solicitors (Ireland) Act* of 1866[1] solicitors ceased to be obliged to be members of the Inns. It was to cater exclusively thereafter for Bar students. Perhaps more significantly, in 1850 the Inns for the first time in its history had put in place a system of formal educational training, a system involving in the early years a shared responsibility for lectures with Trinity College.[2] This major departure, a legacy of pressure that had built up following the closure of the short-lived Dublin Law Institute, presented a challenge to the Benchers as the Inns governing authority over the formulation of the consequential student regulations. What would now be regarded as an extremely curious, if not perverse, stance was soon to be adopted. Apart from the obligation to keep a prescribed number of terms' commons at one of the inns of court in London, regulations stipulated either attendance at lectures or the passing of an examination. This dual system lasted from 1864 to 1872. In the latter year, as Daire Hogan has it,[3]

> the Benchers, considering that legal education was not being properly served by a system in which the majority of students preferred to take their chance with an examination rather than to spend a year attending lectures, made both lectures and examinations compulsory.

This decision of the Benchers in 1872 proved final, but it is plain that it did not bring controversy to an end, for a few years later the

---

[1]   29 & 30 Vict., c. 84. The change was arranged inferentially.
[2]   Daire Hogan, *The Legal Profession in Ireland, 1789-1922* (Dublin, 1986), ch. 8; Colum Kenny, *Tristram Kennedy and the Revival of Irish Legal Training, 1835-1885* (Dublin, 1996), ch. 8.
[3]   Hogan, *The Legal Profession in Ireland*, p. 110.

Inns Education Committee was asked to review the situation. Objections had been raised against compulsory lectures on the ground that, in view of other avocations of students, attendance at lectures would be inconvenient. The Education Committee retorted that 'if once excuses of that kind are allowed, they will not be wanting, and it would at once subvert the entire system'. They had in mind the larger picture as well. 'No College or Educational Institute', they argued,[4]

> can be carried on if the convenience of the student were to be a ground for dispensing with the attendances at lectures, examinations, or other collegiate requirements.

The committee threw their whole support behind the rule change that had been introduced in 1872. The Benchers were advised to stand firm; they did; and the system of both compulsory lectures and the passing of examinations was set to endure. 'Regular attendance upon lectures', the committee maintained,[5]

> followed by an examination of the student shortly after the lectures on the subject of them, affords a much better guarantee for the competency of the student than any examination. Proficiency at an examination may be the result of hurried preparation, and of information hastily derived from a professional instructor, whose experience enables him to forecast the subjects of examination. Under such circumstances, the student will forget the information nearly as rapidly as he acquired it.

There was a further dimension to insistence on attendance at lectures on which the committee chose to lay stress. 'The value', they said,[6]

> of having a number of students collected at lectures is very great; it begets emulation, and, in this manner, proves the best incentive to study. Students thus thrown together naturally confer upon the subject of the lecture.

In the years that have elapsed since 1876, the date of this report from the Education Committee, many changes have been made to the regulations setting out the actual obligations cast on successive generations of Bar students. Curriculum changes and relations with the university law schools have been to the fore in these various alterations. It would be otiose to itemise them here, a task best left to the historian of the King's Inns for the twentieth century.

One major change in the educational arrangements introduced in 1885 deserves separate consideration, however. And this, together with two other historical episodes which impacted on the Inns and its practice in relation to the admission of Bar students — the entry

4   Id., p. 7.
5   Id., p. 5.
6   Ibid.

of women students and one consequence of Partition in Ireland —
will constitute the focus for the rest of this introduction to the
modern admission lists.

Abolition of the requirement to keep terms in London (1885)

From the reign of Henry VIII down to 1885 students reading for
the Irish Bar were obliged to 'reside' for a specified number of years
at one or other of the inns of court in London — Gray's Inn,
Lincoln's Inn, the Inner Temple or the Middle Temple. The
requirement was sanctioned by the Irish Statute of Jeofailles of
1542,[7] and was to be rigorously enforced: proof of such residency is
regularly included in the documentation for each student seeking his
call prior to the legal change of 1885. A curiosity of the 1542
statutory provision is that the statute roll itself (no longer extant)
and the printed text were to reveal a blank where the stipulated
number of years of residence should have been indicated. As Colum
Kenny has shown in his extended discussion of this historical
conundrum, however, the legislative *lacuna* was eventually rectified
in 1628 by administrative *fiat*, the authorship of which remains
undetermined.[8] Thus, finally, was born the obligation to 'reside' at
one of the London inns for a plainly designated period, in effect to
eat dinners there over a set number of days for a set number of terms
— the obligation notoriously castigated by Sir Edward Carson as
'one of the badges of servitude on the Irish nation'.[9]

Unsuccessful attempts were made to abolish the requirement at
the Westminster parliament in the years 1842, 1856 and 1859.[10]
More sustained pressure to achieve the same result built up in the
1870s. In rapid succession, in 1872, 1874, 1878 and 1881, bills were
introduced, again aimed at ending the requirement. None made it to
the statute book. Throughout this prolonged agitation to effectuate
what would have constituted a major change in the rules on
admission to the Irish Bar, the Benchers of King's Inns, who were
most immediately concerned (apart from the students themselves),
showed themselves generally hostile. Yet there was not total
unanimity. At a Benchers' meeting held on 22 April 1872, when the
bill lately introduced by Sir Colman O'Loghlen and others came
under review, Vice-chancellor Chatterton and Chief Baron Pigot
sought support from their fellow Benchers for a motion expressing

[7]   33 Henry VIII, sess. 2, c. 3.
[8]   Colum Kenny, *King's Inns and the Kingdom of Ireland: the Irish 'Inn of
Court'*, *1541-1800* (Dublin, 1992), pp 97-8.
[9]   Edward Marjoribanks, *The Life of Lord Carson*, vol. 1 (London, 1932), p. 17.
[10] Colum Kenny, *Tristram Kennedy and the Revival of Irish Legal Training*, ch. 9.

strong disapproval. Mr. Justice Fitzgerald and Baron Deasy, for their part, however, attempted to garner support for an amendment, the consequence of which, had it been adopted, being that the Benchers would not have straightaway publicly articulated their opposition to the bill's second reading, but would rather have referred the measure to the Benchers' own Education Committee 'to suggest such amendments as may be considered advisable'. The amendment was negatived, the substantive motion accepted, and the rider attached that the Irish government was to be immediately apprised of the Benchers' opposition.[11]

The identical question came before the Benchers again on 29 April 1874, following the receipt by them of a letter from the then Irish chief secretary, Sir Michael Hicks-Beach, enclosing the text of another bill and seeking their views. On this occasion, Vice-chancellor Chatterton and the master of the rolls, Edward Sullivan, found unanimous support for their motion expressing strong disapproval.[12] A bill to the same effect, but the first to have secured government backing, came under the consideration of the Benchers four years later, in 1878. The Benchers remained unmoved, and a motion proposed on 24 April by Sullivan and seconded by the chief justice of common pleas, Michael Morris, was carried without a dissent. The motion itself read that the Benchers[13]

> unanimously and emphatically adhere to the resolution adopted by the Benchers on 22 April 1872 and on 29 April 1874 and hereby express our opinion that the rule now in force requiring the attendance of the Irish students for four terms at one of the inns of court in England ought to be maintained.

Nothing new was added to the continuing controversy when, on 4 June 1879 and 20 April 1881, in response to further parliamentary initiatives, the Benchers reiterated their opposition.[14]

With the publication early in 1885 of the Barristers Admission (Ireland) Bill, the last instalment in this long-running drama was fated to be played to a finish. Or so at least things must have appeared to the Irish Bar students of the times who, persuaded that a critical parliamentary vote was in the offing, now split into two camps. On 20 February, a group of 52 of them petitioned the Benchers to seek the suspension of the custom obliging students to attend at a London inn of court; they went on to urge that the four terms thus saved might by preference be devoted to further lectures or further terms' commons or both in Dublin. On 19 March,

---

[11]   King's Inns MSS: Benchers' Minute Book, 1870-1885, pp 115-6.
[12]   Id., pp 190-1.
[13]   Id., pp 297-8.
[14]   Id., pp 334, 373-4.

however, a fractionally larger segment of the student body, numbering 59, presented a 'declaration' to the Benchers which espoused a diametrically different viewpoint. In this declaration the 59 recited that they were

> entirely without sympathy with the prayer of the petition [of the 52 students], and trusting that the ancient and useful regulation of keeping terms commons in London may always be retained and enforced.

Faced with this clear division within the body of Bar students, the Benchers for the first time since 1872 now seem to have hesitated over their choice of action. At their meeting held on 22 April, majority support was eventually secured for a compromise. The petition of the 52 and the declaration of the 59, together with a copy of the Barristers Admission (Ireland) Bill itself were to be transmitted to the Education Committee, who would be asked to report on the entire question at the Benchers' next scheduled meeting. At this meeting support for the Benchers' traditional hostile stance had been sought by Mr. Justice Harrison and Mr. Justice Lawson. The compromise proposed by Serjeant Hemphill and seconded by Mr. Justice Murphy was, however, carried on a division. The votes for and those against are not recorded.[15]

Time was now running out. The very day that saw the Benchers of King's Inns in Dublin convey these instructions to their Education Committee — 22 April 1885 — the House of Commons in London gave the contentious Barristers Admission (Ireland) Bill its second reading. The proposer of the bill, long prominent in the campaign to have the requirement abolished, was the colourful and controversial M.P. for Co. Louth, Philip Callan.[16] Callan, in presenting his case, relied on a fistful of arguments. Most reliance was placed on the changes that had recently been made in provision for educating Bar students in Dublin — an allusion to the lecture programme established in 1850 by King's Inns acting in tandem with the law school of Trinity College. The requirement that the Irish Bar student attend at an inn of court in London, Callan insisted, brought about an interruption of studies, and invited condemnation as a useless expenditure of time and money. To eat, and to have to pay for, six dinners at four different periods each year, the Louth M.P. declared, was both absurd and inconvenient.

---

[15] Id., pp 474-5. The meeting held on 22 April 1885 should have taken place a week earlier but that meeting, fixed for 15 April, had been adjourned owing to the death of Lord Chancellor Sullivan, the former Master of the Rolls.
[16] On Callan, see further Kenny, *Tristram Kennedy and the Revival of Irish Legal Training*, pp 209-15.

Callan's next point furnishes an excellent example of the inability of the Irish M.P., presented with a captive audience, to resist the temptation to play to the gallery. The dinner Irish Bar students were obliged to consume was eaten, Callan would have had his parliamentary audience believe, just when the music halls and theatres were open; the students were thus prevented from attending the music hall, although probably they would prefer the higher class of entertainment which was found at the theatre. Turning to register a more serious point, Callan was to observe that if it was deemed essential that the Irish barrister should know England, it was surely as essential that the English barrister should have some acquaintance with Ireland. There was to be an attack on a fellow M.P., David Plunket, one of the M.P.s for Trinity College and a King's Inns bencher. Plunket, who opposed any change, was a director of the London and North Western Railway Co. and was to be suspected, accordingly, of harbouring a vested interest in the maintenance of the *status quo*. Callan concluded by mentioning the circumstance that Irish Bar students had 'numerously' petitioned in favour of a change.[17] He did not mention the declaration of the 59 supporting no change, an omission for which Callan was immediately reprimanded by the other M.P. for Trinity, Edward Gibson, later elevated to the Irish lord chancellorship as Lord Ashbourne.[18] C.N. Warton, M.P. for the English constituency of Bridport, expressed support for what was increasingly shown to be the minority view — that there should be no change. A practice, he averred, founded on an act of parliament passed in the reign of Henry VIII should not be lightly set aside. Besides, Warton insisted, dinners at the London inns of court, without the Irish students, would 'lose all their salt'.[19]

In the course of the debate, the suggestion was aired that before any decisive step was taken, the views of the King's Inns Benchers should once more be sought. (At this very moment, it will be recalled, these self-same Benchers were pondering their own next move.) Campbell-Bannerman, the Irish chief secretary, was broadly favourable to such a proposal, but other M.P.s had very different ideas, T.M. Healy, M.P. for Monaghan at the time, among them. Healy insisted that the people of Ireland were prevented 'by the present medieval arrangements' from flocking into the profession in large numbers. The question itself, he added, was not a matter for Benchers, barristers or students to pronounce on.[20] R.T. Reid, M.P.

---

[17] *Hansard*, 3, vol. 297, cols. 418-9.
[18] Id., col. 420.
[19] Id., cols. 420-1.
[20] *Hansard*, 3, vol. 297, cols. 421-2.

for the English constituency of Hereford, agreed. 'If they had to wait', he asserted, 'until they had the opinion of judges and benchers for legal reform, they would have very little reform indeed'.[21] For Plunket, the bencher, the M.P. for Trinity (and also the director in the L. & N.W. Ry. Co.), this was going much too far. 'The statement', Plunket declared,[22]

> that the Benchers were not a good authority to pronounce an opinion and give advice on this subject seemed to him to be one of the most extravagantly Radical propositions he had ever heard.

The House of Commons finally voted on the proposal to adjourn the debate on the bill in order to secure the views of the King's Inns Benchers. The proposal was defeated on a vote of 122 to 30. The measure itself was then accorded its second reading.[23]

The bill was scheduled to be debated in the House of Lords on 8 May. Before then, however, the Education Committee, as instructed on 22 April, had met and reported to the full body of Benchers. The report, considered by the Benchers on 29 April, contained the unanimous recommendation that the Benchers should abandon the fight and accept the principle contained in the bill; attendance at one of the London inns of court could be optional in future. Baron Dowse and Serjeant Hemphill then proposed that this report be accepted (which it was), and its terms communicated to the Irish government. And not only to them, but also to the two M.P.s for Trinity, Messrs. Plunket and Gibson (who had batted on behalf of the Benchers in the Commons debate), and to Lord Fitzgerald, the Irish lord of appeal in ordinary, who would now be moving the second reading of the Barristers Admission (Ireland) Bill in the Lords.[24]

The Benchers having withdrawn their opposition and having signalled their support (however grudgingly this may have been given), the second reading debate in the House of Lords constituted something of an anti-climax. Lord Fitzgerald, however, profited from the occasion extended to him to offer a useful historical perspective on a controversy that had engaged the attentions of the parliament at Westminster from 1842 on.[25] The lack of educational provision for potential barristers in the Ireland of the Tudors, he was convinced, had furnished a justification for the requirement

---

[21] Id., col. 422.
[22] Id., col. 425.
[23] Id., col. 426.
[24] Benchers' Minute Book, 1885-1901, p. 3.
[25] On Fitzgerald see Lord Lowry, 'The Irish lords of appeal in ordinary', in D.S. Greer and Norma Dawson (eds.), *Mysteries and Solutions in Irish Legal History* (Dublin, 2000), pp 193-5.

introduced by the Statute of Jeofailles. The relevant section in the statute Fitzgerald dubbed 'a very wise provision' because, he went on, the acts passed in Ireland in the reign of Henry VIII 'and that of his predecessor, especially the statute of Henry VII, familiarly known as Poynings' Law, introduced large changes into the law of Ireland' — a historical pronouncement which certainly rings true. 'Besides, at that time,' Fitzgerald continued,[26]

> there was no other school of law, so far as these countries were concerned, except that which existed here [i.e. in England]; and there were advantages in the arrangement, in as much as it enabled Irish students to become familiar with the law of England, and the manner and justice of its administration.

Contributors to the second reading debate in the Commons had expressed a measure of regret at what was perceived as the passing of the old order. In following suit, Fitzgerald emphasised one point to which no previous allusion had been made. He was saddened, he remarked, at one possible consequence of the change that was now inevitable. 'To some extent', Fitzgerald opined,[27]

> the existing practice promotes a homogeneous administration of the law, and gives Irish students an opportunity of seeing the administration of the law in this country, and I am happy to say of sometimes inducing them to remain here for life. They, in the past, have often become the great prize-holders, and the English Bar has been strengthened by the introduction of men who have shed lustre on both the Bar and the Bench of England.

At which juncture in his remarks, Fitzgerald alluded to the case of Earl Cairns, although there were, naturally, others he might have named, who like Cairns had made their careers in England.[28] 'I should be sorry,' Fitzgerald concluded, 'if this chance should be taken away'.[29]

No objection was taken to the Barristers Admission (Ireland) Bill in the Lords, and the rest of its passage through parliament was remarkably smooth. The measure received the royal assent on 21 May. A few days later, at their meeting in Dublin on 1 June, the Benchers adopted concessionary arrangements in aid of three Bar students. The circumstances are unclear, but it is likely, now that the Barristers Admission (Ireland) Act was in force, that these

---

[26] *Hansard*, 3, vol. 298, col. 3.
[27] Id., col. 4.
[28] R.F.V. Heuston, 'Hugh McCalmont Cairns', (1975) 26 *N.I.L.Q.* 269. See, too, R.F.V. Heuston, 'James Shaw Willes', (1965) 16 *N.I.L.Q.* 193.
[29] *Hansard*, 3, vol. 298, col. 4. The legislation as finally enacted gave the Irish Bar student the option of keeping four of the obligatory twelve terms' commons at one of the London inns (Barristers Admission (Ireland) Act 1885, s. 3), so both Fitzgerald's anxieties and Mr. Warton's concerns over a deterioration in the ambience of dinners at the London Inns, it can be seen, were taken into account.

arrangements acknowledged an entitlement on the part of existing students to an exemption from keeping further terms' commons in London, as indeed had been spelt out by the measure itself.[30]

Women (1921)

On 1 November 1921, Frances Christian Kyle became the first woman to be called to the Irish Bar. She was immediately followed by Averil Kathleen Slatter Deverell.[31] Both were graduates of the law school of Trinity College. Part of the pressure behind the campaign that led to the passing of the Barristers Admission (Ireland) Act in 1885 was to remove a perceived financial disincentive to embarking on a career at the Irish Bar. The adoption of the Sex Disqualification (Removal) Act in 1919,[32] which applied generally throughout the United Kingdom, had the effect of removing an actual legal barrier in the way of women seeking to enter any profession, including that of the law. In Ireland, the Misses Kyle and Deverell were among the earliest beneficiaries of this radical social change.

That there existed this gender barrier in the case of the legal profession had been recently confirmed in England. In 1913, in the case of a Miss Bebb, an Oxford graduate, a unanimous Court of Appeal affirmed the decision of Mr. Justice Joyce to refuse Miss Bebb redress.[33] She had sought a declaration that she was a 'person' within the intendment of the English Solicitors Act 1843;[34] and a mandamus directing the Law Society to admit her to the preliminary examination, or, alternatively, an injunction restraining them from refusing to admit her: *Bebb* v. *Law Society*.[35] Earlier still, in 1872, the Supreme Court of the United States, in ruling on an appeal brought by a Mrs. Myra Bradwell from the state of Illinois, held that the identical barrier, which in her case took the form of the refusal of a licence to practise as an attorney, represented no violation of the federal constitution. The supposed entitlement of a woman to practise law failed to count as a privilege protected under the Fourteenth Amendment: *Bradwell* v. *Illinois*.[36]

---

[30] Barristers Admission (Ireland) Act 1885, s. 2; Benchers' Minute Book, 1885-1901, p. 7.
[31] King's Inns MSS: Benchers' Minute Book, 1917-1928, p. 150.
[32] 9 & 10 Geo. V, c. 71.
[33] [1913] W.N. 209.
[34] 6 & 7 Vict., c. 73: s. 48.
[35] [1914] 1 Ch. 286. The English Bar had been similarly resistant. See the opinion of the judges in 1903, discussed by the Earl of Desart in his contribution to the debate on the Barristers and Solicitors (Qualification of Women) Bill in the House of Lords on 11 March 1919: *Hansard*, 5, *House of Lords*, vol. 33, cols. 596-9.
[36] 16 Wall. 130, 83 U.S. 442, 21 L. Ed. 644.

The attitudes which prevailed in the half century or so prior to the change wrought in Britain and Ireland by the legislation of 1919 are reflected in dicta to be found in both of these cases. In *Bradwell* v. *Illinois* Mr. Justice Bradley's concurring judgement repeated the truism that the admission of women to practice as attorneys was indeed, as the supreme court of Illinois had held, 'contrary to the rules of the common law and the usages of Westminster Hall from time immemorial'.[37] In an addendum to the court's opinion delivered by Mr. Justice Miller, an addendum in which Mr. Justice Field and Mr. Justice Swayne joined, Mr. Justice Bradley ranged very much wider. These additional thoughts of the judge, it is clear in retrospect, espoused no feminist programme. 'The natural and proper timidity and delicacy which belongs to the female sex', Bradley wrote,[38]

> evidently unfits it for many of the occupations of civil life. The constitution of the family organization, which is founded in the divine ordinance, as well as in the nature of things, indicates the domestic sphere as that which properly belongs to the domain and functions of womanhood. The harmony, not to say, identity of interests and views which belong or should belong to the family institution, is repugnant to the idea of a woman adopting a distinct and independent career from that of her husband ...
>
> The paramount destiny and mission of women are to fulfil the noble and benign offices of wife and mother. This is the law of the Creator.

Paradoxically, it might be thought, in the light of Mr. Justice Bradley's remarks, the judge took some pains to assert that, from a woman's point of view, the prospects were not entirely bleak. Whilst maintaining his stance that in the future women should not count on being admitted to every office or position, the judge did add this:[39]

> The humane movements of modern society, which have for their object the multiplication of avenues for women's advancement, and of occupations adapted to her condition and sex, have my heartiest concurrence.

In 1913, in England, in Miss Bebb's case, the Court of Appeal eschewed resort to language that might have been reckoned in the slightest degree emotive. In affirming the decision of Mr. Justice Joyce, Sir Herbert Cozens-Hardy, the master of the rolls, asserted the lack of any historical precedent for women to be admitted into practice. Sir Edward Coke, relying on the blunt declaration in the *Mirror of Justices* 'Fems ne poient estre attorneyes', had maintained

---

[37]   16 Wall. at 140.
[38]   16 Wall. at 141.
[39]   16 Wall. at 142.

quite the reverse.[40] At the same time, the master of the rolls went out of his way to heap scorn on one of the arguments which in the past had been brought forward in defence of the gender bar — woman's supposed intellectual inferiority:[41]

> We have been asked to hold, what I for one quite assent to, that, in point of intelligence and education and competency women — and in particular the appellant here, who is a distinguished Oxford student — are at least equal to a great many, and probably, far better than many, of the candidates who will come up for examination, but that is really not for us to consider.

The Sex Disqualification (Removal) Act of 1919[42] received the royal assent on 23 December 1919. It brought all debate to an end, with its blunt declaration in section 1 that

> A person shall not be disqualified by sex or marriage from the exercise of any public function, or from being appointed to or holding any civil or judicial office or post, or from entering or assuming or carrying on any civil profession or vocation, or for admission to any incorporated society (whether incorporated by Royal Charter or otherwise), and a person shall not be exempted by sex or marriage from the liability to serve as a juror.

Proposing the second reading of the measure in the House of Lords the previous July, the Lord Chancellor, Lord Birkenhead, acknowledged that the changes contained in it were likely to prove 'surprising' and 'to many extremely disagreeable', but went on swiftly to assert his conviction that there was now to be no going back. 'The only observation which one may, perhaps, venture to make', the Lord Chancellor continued,[43]

> is that the current and development of events have plainly so proceeded as to produce, whether we wish it or whether we do not wish it, a complete revolution in the position of women ... The time has gone — in the judgment of the Government, gone for ever — in which it is possible to justify the exclusion of women from the various fields of activity which are opened out to them in this bill.

In April 1920, barely four months after the act of 1919 came into force, Lord Birkenhead in his judicial capacity presided at a hearing in the House of Lords where Georgina Frost continued her battle to win appointment as petty sessions clerk for the districts of Sixmilebridge and Newmarket-on-Fergus in Co. Clare. Miss Frost had been unanimously chosen by the magistrates for these districts in succession to her father, but the Irish lord lieutenant of the day had refused to ratify the appointment, citing the gender bar. Miss

40 [1914] 1 Ch. at 293-4.
41 [1914] 1 Ch. at 294.
42 9 & 10 Geo. V, c. 71.
43 *Hansard*, 5, *House of Lords*, vol. 35, col. 896: 22 July 1919.

Frost sought redress in a petition of right but suffered defeat in the Irish High Court (Mr. Justice Barton), a decision affirmed by a majority in the Irish Court of Appeal (Lord Chief Justice Molony and Lord Justice Ronan; Lord Shandon dissenting).[44]

Miss Frost lost her appeal in the Court of Appeal on 20 December 1918. By the time her further appeal came to be heard by the House of Lords in April 1920, the new law had entered into force. This, in Lord Birkenhead's opinion, altered the situation altogether. In view of the provisions of the Sex Disqualification (Removal) Act, their lordships, he is reported to have observed, were of opinion that, without further ado, Miss Frost should now be appointed to the post she had sought, such appointment being dated as from the time of her election by the magistrates of the two districts in Co. Clare. A communication to this effect would now be made to the lord lieutenant in Dublin.[45]

The measure that became the act of 1919 superseded a more restricted bill which had been introduced into parliament by Lord Buckmaster under the designation of the Barristers and Solicitors (Qualification of Women) Bill. Whether this latter bill should or should not have encompassed Ireland had been considered by the Benchers of the King's Inns on 3 April 1919. 'While expressing no opinion upon the merits of the proposal', the pertinent minute records, 'we are of opinion that if the principle is applied and adopted in England and Scotland, no reason exists why Ireland should be excepted'. [46]

Within weeks of the act of 1919 coming into force, on 12 January 1920, the Benchers had placed before them memorials seeking admission as students of the Inns from Miss Kyle and Miss Deverell, both already graduates of Trinity College. Action was postponed to seek clarification from the inns of court in London as to whether the latter made any special arrangements.[47] They did not, Gerald FitzGibbon, the future Supreme Court judge, later reported, and he advised the Benchers to follow suit.[48] At the same time as the Benchers then approved the admission as Bar students of the two women, they granted a concession. Theoretically, under the educational arrangements then obtaining, both women should have

---

[44] *Frost* v. *The King* [1919] 1 I.R. 81, (1917) 51 I.L.T.R. 146 (Barton J.); [1919] 1 I.R. 84 (Court of Appeal).
[45] For an account of the proceedings in the House of Lords, see both (1920) 54 *I.L.T.& S.J.* 104 and [2000] 1 I.L.R.M. 479.
[46] Benchers' Minute Book, 1917-1928, p. 51. For discussion on the Barristers and Solicitors (Qualification of Women) Bill, see *Hansard*, 5, *House of Lords,* vol. 33, cols. 589-600: 11 Mar. 1919.
[47] Benchers' Minute Book, 1917-1928, p. 94.
[48] Id., p. 96.

been obliged to return to Trinity to attend lectures and pass examinations which they had already done some time before. That obligation was now waived.[49]

On 25 October 1921, Miss Kyle and Miss Deverell sought and were given further concessions.[50] By this stage both women had passed their final examinations but fell short of the number of terms' commons it was obligatory upon them to keep at the Inns. In Miss Deverell's case, exemption from the ordinary requirement was granted 'in consideration of her war service',[51] the basis for King's Inns concessions of the period, about which much more will shortly be heard. In Miss Kyle's case, exemption from the strict regulation was based on academic grounds. Her success in Bar examinations had indeed been outstanding, confirming in an exemplary fashion the master of the rolls Sir Herbert Cozen-Hardy's assessment of female intelligence that fell from his lips at the hearing of Miss Bebb's case in 1913. In May 1921, she had come top of the class of 26 students, beating the future Lord Chief Justice of Northern Ireland, J.C. MacDermott, into second place and Patrick McGilligan, the future law professor at University College Dublin and Irish government minister, into third, and capturing the 1st Victoria Prize of £25. And in October she again beat MacDermott to secure the prestigious John Brooke scholarship of £50 per annum for three years.[52]

The Benchers voted 17-11 in favour of granting the concessions sought by the Misses Kyle and Deverell on 25 October.[53] The outcome entailed that the way now lay open for both women to receive their call on 1 November, which duly took place.

Partition (1925)

Miss Kyle was later to pursue her professional career in Northern Ireland.[54] The first woman to be called to the Irish Bar, she was also one of the last students from what became Northern Ireland who planned to concentrate their energies there to seek admission as a student of King's Inns. From 1 August 1925, students falling into that category ceased to be governed by earlier regulations that had made membership of King's Inns in Dublin mandatory. As from this crucial date fresh educational arrangements were put in place for

[49] Id., pp 97-8.
[50] Id., p. 150
[51] Ibid.
[52] Benchers' Minute Book, 1917-1928, pp 139, 148, 150.
[53] Id., p. 150
[54] I am grateful for this information to Mr. Jonathan Armstrong, the Librarian at King's Inns.

putative Northern barristers, arrangements that included revival of the obligation to keep terms' commons at one of the London inns of court. A new Inn of Court of Northern Ireland was established at the Belfast law courts on 11 January 1926,[55] and to help meet the costs likely to be incurred in connection with the new Inn's educational provision, statutory authority was sought and obtained for the transfer to the Inn of stamp duties payable on admission as a Northern Bar student and on call to the Northern Bar.[56] Clearly, these arrangements were thus intended to be other than temporary. Unsurprisingly, the changes provoked a sizeable reduction in the Northern intake of students at King's Inns, as the latter adjusted to what became for it the novel task of preparing students, virtually exclusively, if not quite totally, for practice as barristers before the courts of the Irish Free State.[57]

The creation of Northern Ireland under the provisions of the Government of Ireland Act 1920[58] entailed the establishment of a separate judicature with headquarters in Belfast. What the change was likely ultimately to mean for Bench and Bar throughout the island was not immediately apparent. The act of 1920 included in the transitional arrangements the guarantee that all existing Irish barristers would enjoy rights of audience in both the courts of Northern Ireland and those of Southern Ireland;[59] but no attempt was made to go further than that. Within the judiciary and among members of the Bar the view was clearly prevalent that Bench and Bar would somehow remain united and prove resilient enough to counter any political buffeting to which either might in the future be exposed. The Government of Ireland Act received the royal assent on 23 December 1920, but many of its central provisions did not come into effect until later the following year. Ample time was thus afforded for Bench and Bar to take stock of the new situation. In the spring of 1921 Mr. Justice Gibson retired; in accordance with custom, he was elected an honorary bencher of King's Inns. In a letter expressing his thanks at the honour, Gibson touched on the contemporary political situation. 'May I add to my farewell', he wrote,[60]

---

[55] (1926) 60 *I. L. T. & S. J.* 21; J. Ritchie, 'The Inn of Court of Northern Ireland' (1964) 15 *N.I.L.Q.* 463; J.A.L. McLean, 'The Honorable Society of the Inn of Court of Northern Ireland' (1972) 23 *N.I.L.Q.* 90.
[56] Finance (Stamp Duty) Act (N. I.) 1926 (16 & 17 Geo. V, c. 24 (N. I.)).
[57] King's Inns would continue to train for the profession of barrister many students from overseas; these would commonly return there on qualifying.
[58] 10 & 11 Geo. V, c. 67.
[59] 7th. sch., pt. III, cl. 4.
[60] Benchers' Minute Book, 1917-1928, p. 135: 13 Apr. 1921.

my hope and prayer that the Bar of Ireland whatever may befall, hitherto united as one body, inspired with fraternal loyalty to their fellows will continue to transmit their fine traditions, and that Bench and Bar together will never fail to preserve and uphold the lofty standard of their predecessors, so honoured by us all for learning, independence and courage.

At the inaugural meeting of the Law Students' Debating Society held at King's Inns the following October, Sir John Ross, the Lord Chancellor, took up the refrain. 'They were at a time', he is reported to have remarked,[61]

when many things were being split, when the word partition was continually in print before their eyes, when the judiciary of the country was separated and partitioned between Northern Ireland and Southern Ireland, when the great profession of the Bar was divided and split up, and when education, primary and secondary, was split up.

There was one unequivocal guarantee he was prepared to give the Bar students on the occasion:[62]

There was one thing that would never be split up, and that was the Honourable Society of the Benchers of King's Inns.

The inaugural meeting of the Debating Society was held on 20 October. Five days later, on the 25th, the Benchers of the Inns sought to make good on the promise Ross had given, when they asked the Standing Committee to bring forward proposals for changes to their rules necessitated by the inauguration of the new court structure in the North.[63] Despite initial objections from Lord Justice O'Connor,[64] objections which were to be repeated at a later stage by the recorder of Dublin, Sir Thomas O'Shaughnessy,[65] the resultant proposals, later enshrined in a new set of rules, formed the basis of an agreement between Dublin and Belfast which lasted down to 1925.

There were several aspects to the final agreement. It was arranged, in the first place, that all judges of either Supreme Court of Judicature (whether of Southern Ireland or Northern Ireland) would *ex officio* become Benchers. A Northern Committee of Benchers was to be established to deal primarily with questions of the education of students in Northern Ireland and of the disciplining of barristers there. It was arranged too — and this proved a critical stipulation — that any student admitted to the degree of barrister-at-law by King's Inns was to be granted rights of audience in the courts of both Southern Ireland and Northern Ireland. Final

---

[61] (1921) 55 *I.L.T.& S.J.* 269.
[62] Ibid.
[63] Benchers' Minute Book, 1917-1928, p. 148.
[64] Ibid.
[65] Id., p. 179: 7 June 1922.

examinations for Bar students would continue, as before, to be held at King's Inns in Dublin, but lectures and examinations, other than the final examination, could be offered concurrently in Belfast by a newly appointed King's Inns professor. Special concessions were also accorded Northern students as regards the number of terms' commons they would be obliged to keep at King's Inns in the future.[66]

Although problems arose immediately over the method of election of Benchers to serve on the Northern Committee of Benchers (problems which, however, seem to have been overcome),[67] the new arrangements gave every appearance of working well enough. Books from the King's Inns library were forwarded to Belfast to form the nucleus of a Bar Library there. The Benchers resident in the North arranged the time of their regular meetings in Belfast so that there would materialise no clash with the time of the meetings of the full body of Benchers in Dublin. A plan to schedule important business at a specified regular meeting of Benchers in Dublin also seems to have been endorsed.[68]

The auguries for the survival of the arrangement, the outlines of which had been discussed in October 1921, were not, however, the best. In July 1922, a split in the solicitors' profession came about when the Incorporated Law Society of Northern Ireland obtained its royal charter, and the Northern Ireland parliament enacted legislation that recognised this state of affairs.[69] So far as King's Inns was concerned, the first real sign of trouble was delayed until November 1923. That month the Benchers in Dublin contemplated admitting as a student of the Inns one John Walker, a student from Northern Ireland. On 8 November the Northern Benchers wrote to Dublin protesting over any such decision, adding, in what clearly threatened a breach of the spirit of the agreement of 31 October 1921, that any decision to admit Walker would not be recognised in Belfast. In consequence, the Walker case was the focus of prolonged discussion by all the Benchers in Dublin the following month. A majority, doubtless influenced by what Belfast had told them, voted not to admit Walker. Walker petitioned unsuccessfully in the course of the next year and a half to have that decision reversed.[70]

[66]   Benchers' Minute Book, 1917-1928, pp 153-4 (31 Oct. 1921), 176 (17 May 1922), 185-8 (14 June 1922).
[67]   Benchers' Minute Book, 1917-1928, pp 154-5 (31 Oct. 1921), 160-1 (11 Jan. 1922), 185 (14 June 1922), 216-7 (11 Jan. 1923).
[68]   Benchers' Minute Book, 1917-1928, pp 165-6 (18 Jan. 1922), 168 (20 Apr. 1922).
[69]   Solicitors Act (N.I.) 1922: 12 & 13 Geo. V, c. 19 (N. I.).
[70]   Benchers' Minute Book, 1917-1928, pp 247, 250-1, 262, 284, 317 (10 Nov. 1923-16 Apr. 1925).

Walker's memorial seeking admission was turned down by the Benchers, but in 1924 and again early in 1925 the main body of the Benchers in Dublin granted concessions to a number of students, concessions which plainly infuriated the Northern Committee in Belfast, leading them to protest that they were 'not to be allowed to scrutinize or object to the credentials of any ... student when applying for admission to the Bar of Northern Ireland'.[71]

Three individual cases are mentioned in the exchange of letters between A. Newton Anderson, for the Benchers in Belfast, and Richard Armstrong, the Under-Treasurer at King's Inns for the Benchers in Dublin. Derogation from the rules had been allowed in the case of Major Michael Joseph O'Brien Twohig in the spring of 1924 and again in the case of Leon Ó Broin in the autumn of the same year.[72] The derogation which had the effect of permitting call to the Bar in the case of both students earlier than would otherwise have been allowed was grounded on 'military service', precisely the argument, it may be recalled, of which Miss Averil Deverell had also availed back in 1921. As it happens, on 1 November 1924 — the date when the derogation in favour of Ó Broin was voted through on a show of hands — the Benchers had before them a motion in the name of one of their number, Alexander Blood K.C., which by implication tackled this very issue. 'As and from this date', the wording of Blood's motion ran, that

> no student's memorial praying for concessions or exceptions in consideration of any description be received by the Under-Treasurer unless previously certified in writing by two Benchers, to be [of] a special and exceptional nature and deserving the consideration of the Bench.

Blood's initiative attracted no support, and no action along the lines he had suggested was taken.[73] The Under-Treasurer, Mr. Armstrong, in his letter to Mr. Newton Anderson of 11 May 1925, pointed out that three members of the Northern Committee of Benchers had been present at the meetings of the full body of Benchers in Dublin at which the memorials of the two students in question had been considered and that no objection had then been raised. In the letter, he set out in stark fashion the views of the Standing Committee in Dublin. 'Mr. Leon O'Brien and Mr. O'Brien Twohig', Armstrong wrote, 'were not granted any concessions which had not previously

---

[71] Letter from the Northern Committee to the Under-Treasurer, King's Inns, quoted, Richard Armstrong, Under-Treasurer, to A. Newton Anderson, Permanent Secretary, Law Courts, Belfast, 20 June 1925: Benchers' Minute Book, 1917-1928, between pp 330 and 331.
[72] Benchers' Minute Book, 1917-1928, pp 257-8, 299-300.
[73] Id., pp 303-4.

been granted to many candidates who had War Service'. The Committee of Benchers, he continued,[74]

> does not seem to realise that War conditions continued in Ireland for a considerable period after they had terminated elsewhere. The Benchers consider that gentlemen who were actively engaged, as Messrs. O'Brien Twohig and O'Brien were, in establishing the Government of the Irish Free State against domestic foes, are entitled to no less consideration than those who were engaged in the European War.

The case of the expedited call to the Bar of Kevin O'Higgins, the Free State Minister for Justice, proved no less contentious. On 19 January 1925, at the start of Hilary term, the Benchers in Dublin admitted him as a student and sanctioned his call to the Bar that very term. Alexander Blood, K.C., who had earlier moved the abortive motion to impose restrictions on students seeking concessions, took the initiative. With Mr. Justice Wylie seconding, he now proposed

> that in consideration of the position of Mr. Kevin O'Higgins as Minister of [sic] Justice, his educational attainment and the experience of legal matters acquired by him therein and elsewhere,

the memorial O'Higgins had presented should be granted. It was, unanimously.[75] Call followed immediately.[76] The Benchers in their Belfast redoubt were not impressed. O'Higgins, they declared, had 'never attended a lecture or passed an examination of the Society'. Mr. Armstrong, in his letter of 11 May 1925, agreed, but was able to cite three precedents where exactly the same thing had occurred: from June 1919, the case of a Mr. A.H. Burne, and from October 1920, the cases of Messrs. O'Grady and Blood. Benchers who now served on the Committee of Benchers in the North had been present on both occasions and had voiced no objections. Messrs. O'Grady and Blood, Armstrong wrote, were demonstrated to possess other legal qualifications which entitled them to their expedited calls. So, too, in his estimation (conveying the plain thoughts of the Standing Committee), did Kevin O'Higgins. The latter, he explained,[77]

> in addition to his training in the Incorporated Law Society and as an apprentice to the late Mr. Maurice Healy, had obtained the degree of LL.B. and had acquired considerable experience in legal affairs as Minister for Home Affairs and subsequently for Justice and he is a Member of the Rule making authority of the Courts of Justice.

None of this won over the Northern Committee of Benchers, however much particular individuals may have felt embarrassment

---

[74]   Benchers' Minute Book, 1917-1928, between pp 320 and 321.
[75]   Id., p. 311.
[76]   Id., p. 312.
[77]   Richard Armstrong to A. Newton Anderson, 11 May 1925: Benchers' Minute Book, 1917-1928, between pp 320 and 321.

over their previous support for an admissions policy to which they now took exception. It became clear, as the months rolled by, that in the North the Benchers resident there sought to exercise an authority which the full body of Benchers in Dublin was convinced it was not theirs to wield. The claim, apparently advanced by Belfast, that mere judicial refusal to confer a right of audience on persons called in Dublin somehow constituted no breach of the agreement of October 1921 provoked further disagreement between the two sides.[78] Dublin, for its part, would have none of this: authority lay technically not with the judiciary but with the Benchers. Further letters were to be exchanged, with neither side indicating any inclination to climb down. Time was now running out since early in the summer of 1925 the Northern Benchers had announced that new arrangements for Northern Bar students would operate as from 1 August. On 29 June, talk of a last-minute compromise was still in the air when Belfast proposed a conference to settle outstanding differences.[79] But with the agenda focusing on the fate of Northern Bar students who had already entered King's Inns, it would be wrong to regard the suggested conference as in any way seen by anyone as a means to restore the *status quo*. In the event, it was never convened. On 14 July, with just a fortnight to go, Dublin countered the proposal from Belfast with its own suggestion that a special meeting might be held at King's Inns in Dublin four days later, on the 18th.[80] This last initiative was rebuffed. Stalemate had been reached. The split that Sir John Ross had assured his audience of Bar students back in October 1921 would never take place was now about to occur.

The following Michaelmas term Mr. Newton Anderson, who had previously handled all correspondence on behalf of the Northern Benchers, wrote to the Under-Treasurer at King's Inns, Mr. Armstrong, to remove any possible doubt that the split itself was now a *fait accompli*. 'To prevent any possibility of misunderstanding', Anderson pointed out,[81]

> I am requested to repeat that as and from the 1st August the agreement which existed between the Benchers of King's Inns and the Committee of Benchers of Northern Ireland, was determined, and the Committee as such ceased to exist.

---

[78] Richard Armstrong to A. Newton Anderson, 20 June 1925 (above, n. 72).
[79] Newton Anderson to Richard Armstrong, 29 June 1925: Benchers' Minute Book, 1917-1928, pp 332-3.
[80] Benchers' Minute Book, 1917-1928, pp 333-4.
[81] Id., p. 346.

On 11 January 1926, as we have already seen, a separate inn of court for Northern Ireland was formally inaugurated at the law courts in Belfast.[82]

The last word, even so, may be left with the King's Inns Under-Treasurer, who in his letter of 20 June 1925 (drafted in all likelihood by Mr. Justice FitzGibbon) could not resist the temptation to rub a little salt into the wounds. 'The refusal of the Judges of Northern Ireland', Mr. Armstrong wrote,[83]

> to recognise the degree of the Society [of King's Inns] will not impair its value in those more important portions of the British Dominions from which students in considerable numbers are accustomed to resort to King's Inns.

---

[82] For Sir William Moore's speech on the occasion (which omitted any reference to the bitterness evinced in the exchanges between Belfast and Dublin), see (1926) 60 *I.L.T.& S.J.* 21.
[83] Richard Armstrong to A. Newton Anderson, 20 June 1925 (above, n. 72).

A portrait of the Irish Bar, 1868-1968

by KENNETH FERGUSON

I: The Age of Loyalty and of the FitzGibbons

In January 1868 the Benchers of the Honorable Society of King's Inns entertained the Lord Lieutenant to dinner. Nearly all the Benchers were present, together with some forty other barristers and more than thirty solicitors (the presence of the latter testifying to the circumstance that all but the most recently qualified solicitors had been required to be members of the Society, and were accustomed to avail of its facilities). The *Irish Law Times* reported that there was 'not a single vacant seat throughout the length and breadth of the spacious hall'. After dinner, when grace had been said, the Lord Chancellor [Abraham Brewster] rose, and said: 'May it please your Excellency, my Lords, and Gentlemen, I have the honour to propose the only toast which, according to ancient usage, is proposed in this hall, "The health of her gracious Majesty the Queen"'. *The Irish Law Times* reported that the toast was 'received with an amount of enthusiasm seldom, if ever before, exhibited, and which was, no doubt, intended to convey to the Marquis of Abercorn an emphatic expression of respect for him as an individual, as well as a trusty representative of Royalty, at a period the most critical in the chequered history of this country'. 'Such assurances of confidence', it added, 'emanating from a body of men such as were there assembled — the most enlightened in the community — must have a salutary effect, more especially when it has been found necessary to suspend the Constitution throughout the land'.[1] The cheers are reported to have rung through the hall for several minutes; and the *Irish Law Times* thought the event 'deserving of something more than passing notice'. Those attracted to psychological analysis might ponder whether the length and exuberance of the cheering did not betray an underlying insecurity: but it can hardly have seemed so at the time.

---

[1] The reference was to the continued suspension of *Habeas Corpus*: The Habeas Corpus, Ireland, Act, 31 & 32 Vict. cap. 7, was the first legislative measure of 1868.

II: Gerald Fitzgibbon's *Ireland in 1868*.

One of those reported to have been present at the banquet was 'Master Fitzgibbon',[2] a serving officer of the court, and a man of considerable literary ability. Born on the last day of 1793, and in his 75th year when he sat down to the viceregal dinner, he had been Receiver-Master in Chancery since 1860: he would continue to labour in that office for another seven years, and survive until his ninetieth year. In the weeks

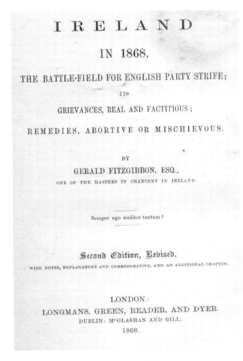

I R E L A N D

IN 1868,

THE BATTLE-FIELD FOR ENGLISH PARTY STRIFE;

ITS

GRIEVANCES, REAL AND FACTITIOUS;

REMEDIES, ABORTIVE OR MISCHIEVOUS.

BY

GERALD FITZGIBBON, ESQ.,

ONE OF THE MASTERS IN CHANCERY IN IRELAND.

Semper ego auditor tantum?

Second Edition, Revised,

WITH NOTES, EXPLANATORY AND CORROBORATIVE, AND AN ADDITIONAL CHAPTER.

LONDON:
LONGMANS, GREEN, READER, AND DYER.
DUBLIN: McGLASHAN AND GILL.
1868.

following the dinner this elderly barrister wrote *Ireland in 1868*, a book with a title that could not be more apposite to our theme.[3] The preface is dated, from a house that would remain the residence of his son and grandson, '10, Merrion Square, N., Dublin, 25th May 1868'. It is a work which offers a notable insight into the state of Ireland and its Bar at the outset of our period.

Gerald Fitzgibbon (1793-1882) duly described himself on the title page of *Ireland in 1868* as 'one of the Masters in Chancery in Ireland'. It was a necessary form of identification, for he was the father of a like-named son (1838-1909), who was already a Q.C., and set (in 1878) to become a Lord Justice of Appeal. He was also the grandfather of a like-named grandson (1866-1942), called to the Bar in 1891 (thus a person whose name appears in these lists) and destined to be one of the judges of the first Supreme Court of the Irish Free State. The progenitor of this dynasty of

---

[2]   The orthography of the family name varies. The *D.N.B.* used Fitzgibbon for the Master in Chancery, and FitzGibbon for his son, the Lord Justice. That convention has been followed here, save in quotations.
[3]   Gerald Fitzgibbon, *Ireland in 1868, the battle-field for English party strife; its grievances, real and factitious; remedies, abortive or mischievous*, 2nd edition (London, 1868). Fitzgibbon is noticed in the *D.N.B.* by J.M. Round. Some circumstances of his youth are preserved in J.G. Swift MacNeill, *What I have seen and heard* (London, 1925), pp 132-3.

barristers was himself a *novus homo*, the son of a tenant farmer from Glin in County Limerick. Some distant kinship perhaps existed between his family and the ancestors of the Earl of Clare, whose family roots were also in County Limerick; but the connection is too remote to be established. The coincidence of name nevertheless makes it tempting to draw parallels between the two families, each of which provided a member who stood at or near the pinnacle of his profession and exercised considerable political influence.

Born in the era of Grattan's Parliament, Master Fitzgibbon retained in old age the self-confidence that came from belonging to a community that enjoyed an ascendancy in the affairs of the state, and to a profession that in his formative years led — and, at the time of the Act of Union, almost monopolised — the articulation of Irish public opinion. Fitzgibbon's book is one of the last examples of a *genre* — a work by a barrister speaking with confidence on behalf of Ireland, Protestant Ireland. Fitzgibbon, as his book makes clear, was a member of the Established Church, one of the 700,000 'Protestants of Ireland', whom he saw as constituting 'a perfectly distinct and definite body'.

III: Fitzgibbon's views on Ireland

Fitzgibbon's book was prompted by a *frisson* of alarm about the course of events, but not by panic or despair: he anticipated the currents that were flowing in the history of Ireland in the succeeding half century, but not the deluge. Fitzgibbon believed that if Ireland were governed firmly, with unity of purpose in England, the threat posed by Irish agitation could be contained. The confident qualities of Gerald Fitzgibbon and his book are those of an era that was on the point of ending, and may be contrasted with the increasingly beleaguered tone that characterised the ages of his son and grandson.

The Fenian rebellion of 1867 was uppermost in public memory. Of the Fenian threat itself the author was dismissive:[4]

> This Fenian conspiracy has alarmed the public mind of England; and this fact is obvious, and known to every one. The alarm, in Ireland, is trifling, and local, and nothing is apprehended from the Fenian conspiracy, beyond a repetition of stealthy acts of outrage upon undefended property or life.

The problem that Fitzgibbon identified was that 'the public mind of England has been wrought into anxiety to do some act of justice towards Ireland, by which to stop the agitation':[5]

---

[4]   *Ireland in 1868*, p. 258.
[5]   Ibid., p. 259; pp 266-7.

The English people are annoyed, and irritated by Irish agitation and discontent. They are alarmed by Fenian atrocities, committed even in England, and by bold, and constantly repeated assertions they have been persuaded that the severance, and disendowment of the Irish Church will produce the peace and quiet which they are desirous to have. Are peace and quiet, more than any other benefits, to be purchased at the expense of national faith, and by a dishonourable violation of contract? If it be right, and lawful, and honest, for the English people, to purchase peace and quiet by abolishing the religion, by confiscating the property, and by trampling upon the vested rights of 700,000 Irish Protestants, no one can see why the same reasoning may not make it right, and lawful, and honest to kill these Protestants, that England may be no longer troubled by the controversies between them and the Roman Catholics.

'Irish discontent,' he wrote, 'both real and pretended, and even the treasonable conspiracy of the Fenians, are falsely attributed to the existence of this Establishment'. The threatened disestablishment of the Irish Church, the continuance and preservation of which was deemed by the fifth article of the Act of Union to be 'an essential and fundamental part of the Union', was the spark that set Fitzgibbon to write. Like his younger contemporary and colleague Isaac Butt, he regarded disestablishment as a breach of national faith:[6]

The Protestants of Ireland were one of the high contracting parties to this national compact. Their consent was absolutely necessary, and there could have been no such compact without their consent. They still exist, as a perfectly distinct and definite body, enjoying the benefits of the united Church, with which their own previously separate and distinct Church was then united, upon the terms, that it should so remain united for ever ...

Fitzgibbon was deeply suspicious of clerical Roman Catholicism; and dismayed by the demand for denominational education.

A great part of the book was devoted to agrarian conditions, and to the relationship of landlord and tenant, a subject on which Master Fitzgibbon wrote with the benefit of his eight years' experience of dealing with the 'circumstances of nearly 19,000 tenants holding under the Court of Chancery' on 450 estates.[7] Fitzgibbon's remedy for the troubles of the Irish countryside was to apply the existing laws. He reposed confidence in the ability of landlords, given conditions of quiet, to take the lead in making the improvements that enlightened self-interest dictated. Fitzgibbon had no inkling that parliament would within a very few years effect a wholesale transfer of the ownership of the soil from the landlords to the tenants. This

[6]   Ibid., p. 262.
[7]   Ibid., p. 311-2.

transfer was well-nigh complete by the time the Irish Free State came into existence. The measure of the revolution it produced is well illustrated in a passage from the judgment of Fitzgibbon's grandson in *Re Westby, Minors*, a case of 1934 about whether a landowner's children should be sent to school in England:[8]

> Of the vast possessions in the County Clare which made Francis Valentine Westby the third largest landowner in that county, and one of the limited number in all Ireland which owned over 25,000 acres, I understand that not a rood remains in the possession of his grandson. The duties imposed upon the owner of such an estate no longer remain to be performed, and where the minor's ancestors filled the offices of Deputy Lieutenant, High Sheriff, Grand Juror or Justice of the Peace, the policy of successive Governments which has transferred the land to its occupiers, has left people in the position of the Westbys without employment for their energies.

IV: Fitzgibbon and the law

For the law Fitzgibbon entertained a regard that may be characterised as reverential. In contrast to the spirit that was abroad a century later, when the young voices of 1968 were calling for laws to be changed, Fitzgibbon's legal instincts were conservative: 'I am reasoning against the demolition of ancient and useful Institutions, and against exceptional legislation for Ireland ...'[9] Laws were to be applied and interpreted, not made by judicial innovation:[10]

> In a free country individual rights must be respected ... It is of the highest importance to the community that these questions, when brought before legal tribunals, shall be decided according to justice, and according to established law. Every unjust and illegal decision is a demoralizing lesson ... When the laws have grown to gigantic dimensions — when, by inevitable complications, the administration of justice according to them has become a work of great difficulty ... the interests of society are deeply concerned in the selection of the men to whom this arduous duty is assigned.

Fitzgibbon, with some sharpness, regarded as a grievance, and characterised as a 'system of misrule', the practice whereby judicial appointment was usually a reward for political services:[11]

> Occasions arise, but they are rare, in which the party in power may think it expedient to promote a man recommended only by his position in the profession; but such exceptions are no more than sufficient to prove the rule of which the country has just reason to complain ...

He wanted to raise judges on merit from the Bar. 'To shut up every road to the Bench, except that which passes through the House of

---

8   [1934] I.R. 311.
9   *Ireland in 1868*, p. 303.
10   Ibid., p. 300.
11   Ibid., p. 303.

Commons' was injurious. It bestowed 'the judicial office on men who never had, or on men who have lost their practice'. It constrained movement at the practising Bar. The effect was[12]

> to deprive laborious aspirants of the accession of business descending on them, when a lawyer gives up a large professional income for a seat on the Bench. It keeps old men at labour disproportioned to failing strength, and continues them an obstacle in the way of rising talent, while it deprives the country of their services in an office that cannot be worthily filled.

On the branch of the profession that he himself had embraced, and in which by dint of his intellect and application he had risen to be a serjeant, he set a high value:[13]

> Next to the importance of learning, ability, and integrity, on the bench of justice, is the importance of learning, ability and a high tone of moral sentiment in those who are permitted to exercise highly cultivated skill and talents, in advocating the rights of litigant parties, and in swaying the judgments of those whose duty it is to decide according to law and justice. From this necessarily tolerated profession the judges must ever be selected; and this is but one of the many social reasons for raising, and keeping up the standard of forensic dignity and morality.
>
> If you believe, that the prosperity, and the morals of a civilized nation must mainly depend, as they clearly must, upon an able and upright administration of law and justice, tamper not, for party purposes, with the members of an honourable profession, from which the ministers and functionaries must be selected from whose ability, learning, and integrity that greatest of all national blessings must flow, or not exist at all.

In the succeeding century Fitzgibbon's wish that judges should be appointed on merit and not primarily as a reward for political services came nowhere close to being realised. With the odd exception that proves the rule, judicial appointments were in the first instance political, regardless of whether the choice was made at Westminster or in Dublin. The redeeming factor, as Serjeant Sullivan discerned, was that 'political patronage was tempered by the tradition, that of party claimants, the best should have the preference'.[14] Fitzgibbon's own descendants were to be beneficiaries of this system of patronage among the worthy. His son came on the bench in 1878 having served as Disraeli's Solicitor-General; and in 1924 that son's son was appointed to the Supreme

12 Ibid., p. 302.
13 Ibid., p. 300; pp 315-6.
14 A.M. Sullivan, *Old Ireland: Reminiscences of an Irish K.C.* (London, 1927), p. 152. The passage continues: 'It put upon the judicial bench Palles, Fitzgibbon, Porter, and Andrews, men whose superiors I have yet to meet. After 1886 the preference of the best began to disappear, then even decency was discarded, and in recent years some transactions were as flagrant as cash sales'.

Court of the Irish Free State. The latter, the senior of two barrister-grandsons of Master Fitzgibbon,[15] had come to notice as one of the members in the Dáil for the University of Dublin. He was chosen to occupy the seat in the Supreme Court reserved for a Protestant. Under a convention which emerged at this time, and that can be seen to have been observed until the 1970s, a place at each level of the court system was so reserved.[16]

While there was no reform of the method of judicial appointments, the ideals that Fitzgibbon set for his profession were generally maintained. Ability, learning and integrity were not lacking. 'When the Judicature Act came into operation', wrote V.T.H. Delany, 'the Bench in Ireland was occupied by some of the most illustrious personages in its long history'.[17] 'When I first began my acquaintance with it', remarked Maurice Healy, the genial raconteur, 'the Irish Bench could compare with any college of justice in any age'. The tone of the Irish Bar was honourable. Of the Bar at the Four Courts, Healy wrote:[18]

> The Irish Bar was a corporate body; if the soul of that body must, even in Ireland, be considered incorporate, it nevertheless had the gift of showing itself, not as a ghost, but as a conscience. Like all bodies, it had its diseases and infirmities; but it had no need to wait for another life in which to put on incorruption.

The profession that Master Fitzgibbon loved fared better over the succeeding century than the arrangements he cherished in church and state. The pace of change in public affairs was rapid, and for a man of Fitzgibbon's time, the reverses (had he been able to foresee them) would have ranked as catastrophic. His son still prospered, as did his grandsons — Gerald adapting himself gracefully to changed circumstances by accepting the reduced judicial salary offered by the Free State — but profound change had occurred; and, after three generations, this legal dynasty was not continued.

---

[15] The other was the third Gerald's cousin Frank (1881-1970), who specialised in Income Tax. The youngest Gerald was a man of modest character, noted for his carefully reasoned judgments, and for his family's long legal memory. See: Patrick Lynch, *Some Members of the Munster Circuit* (Cork: Woodlands Press, 1946), pp 42-4, 'Gerald Fitzgibbon'. John Ross, in *The Years of My Pilgrimage*, p. 213, tells us that Gerald Fitzgibbon acted as the 'Grand Secretary' of 'The Irish Lights', Lord Rathmore's country-house party that gathered at the Greenore Hotel.

[16] Weldon Parke (who had filled the place of Gardner Budd in the Supreme Court in 1976) was not succeeded by a Protestant in that Court when he died in 1981, nor was Herbert McWilliam (who had taken Parke's place in the High Court in 1976) when he retired from the latter Court in 1985.

[17] V.T.H. Delany, 'The Bench and Bar in Ireland', in L.G. Pine (ed.), *Burke's Genealogical and Heraldic History of the Landed Gentry of Ireland* (4th edition, 1958), pp xxx-xxxiv, at p. xxx.

[18] *The Old Munster Circuit*, p. 27; p. 272.

The FitzGibbons, son and grandson of the author of *Ireland in 1868*. (left) Lord Justice Gerald FitzGibbon (1838-1909); (right) Mr Justice Gerald FitzGibbon (1866-1942), Judge of the Supreme Court of the Irish Free State. The portrait of the latter, which hangs in King's Inns, was painted in 1922 by Dermot O'Brien, grandson of William Smith O'Brien.

King's Inns Barristers, 1868-2004, page 46.

V: Lord Justice FitzGibbon

Fitzgibbon's son, who sat as a Lord Justice from 1878 until his death in 1909, had been bred to the law from earliest youth. His father had taken him to the Four Courts, as a boy of six, to witness the O'Connell State Trial; and in later life the Lord Justice claimed to be one of the few then living who had heard O'Connell speak.[19] The judge was a tall man who cut a large figure in public life. A stalwart Churchman, and a leading member of the Masonic Order and contributor to its charities, FitzGibbon was the pre-eminent layman of his generation. As a member of the General Synod, he immersed himself in the affairs of the disestablished Church, and could still radiate a feeling of confidence in the latter's future: 'We are here for the purpose of manifesting the earnestness and the unanimity of our love for the Church to which we belong ...', he told a public meeting on 1 June 1904. 'You who are in the beauty of womanhood and the strength of manhood know for whom you are working — for your children that are to be the next generation'.[20] According to a church historian, 'No judge took so large a part in public life'. 'The strength of his personality, his unsurpassed eloquence, his magnificent lucidity in argument, his alertness and energy, all made him incomparably the most influential layman in the Church of Ireland'.[21]

The Lord Justice built himself a house, *Kilrock*, on the Hill of Howth. Here in 1899 he was at home to a journalist from a periodical called *The World*, who wrote a revealing description of his visit:[22]

> Your host works at a writing-table from which, as he sits, he has a full view of Ireland's Eye and the Island of Lambay set in aquamarine, the horizon terminating to the north in the misty blue Mourne Mountains. The bookshelves are full of the most varied assortment of literature. There are several presentation copies, the authors of which have been at one time or another your host's guests in Howth, including Lord Wolseley's *Wellington*, Lord Roberts's *Forty-one Years in India*, Mr. John Morley's *Voltaire*, and Professor Webb's *Faust*. That there are plenty of classical

[19]   J.G. Swift MacNeill, *What I have seen and heard*, pp 133-4.
[20]   Henry E. Patton, *Fifty Years of Disestablishment: A Sketch* (Dublin, 1922), p. 219. There is a photograph of Lord Justice FitzGibbon on p. 218.
[21]   Ibid., p. 242.
[22]   Reprinted in *I.L.T. & S.J.*, 6 May 1899, pp 186-8. The piece continues: 'He [FitzGibbon] also will probably show you the sketch book of the late Mr. Irwin, the artist who represented the *Illustrated London News* at the famous O'Connell State trial in 1844. The book contains scores of drawings of the *dramatis personae* of that *cause célèbre*, including the Liberator, the late Mr. Francis Macdonogh, Tom Steele, and others. A few years later the Lord Justice's father figured in the State trials arising out of the Young Ireland movement, in which he defended the late John Gray and Richard Lalor Shiel.'

works goes without saying for the Lord Justice is a well-known scholar, and well-nigh 'swept the board' during his undergraduate course at Trinity College, Dublin. If you ask him, he will show you his case of medals, among which are the Berkeley gold medal for Greek, the gold medal in classics, the silver medal in history, law, and literature, the last two of which he won at his degree examination in 1859. On that occasion your host was beaten by Professor Mahaffy, to whom was awarded the classical studentship, the most valuable prize in the gift of the College. He has also two of the medals awarded to him by the Trinity College Historical Society — one for essay writing, and the other for oratory ...

To the left hand, over a bureau, are two large and most interesting photographs. One is a group of four very young barristers — namely, Edward Gibson, Sam Walker, Gerald FitzGibbon, and R.P. Carton. The other group, which was taken twenty years later, only includes the first three, who had meantime become Lord Chancellor Ashbourne, Lord Chancellor Walker, and Lord Justice FitzGibbon; and it was only by an accident that the fourth, Judge Carton, was not of the party. For many years past it has been his custom to open his residence at Howth during the week after Christmas and entertain a house party. At these reunions Lord Justice FitzGibbon gathers together a great many old friends, and among the guests he has entertained to meet them have been Mr. John Morley, Lord Roberts, Mr. Arthur Balfour, Lord Wolseley, Lord Ashbourne, and the late Lord Randolph Churchill, all of whom he has himself photographed, either singly or in groups ....

The friendship between FitzGibbon and Lord Randolph Churchill mentioned in this passage was politically very significant. The two corresponded assiduously, and it is worthy of recall that Lord Randolph's well-known reference to playing the Orange card is found in a letter to FitzGibbon.[23] The family's unimpeachable Tory connections did not, however, prevent FitzGibbon from having broad friendships (which extended, for example, to Father Healy of Little Bray); nor did they stand in the way of the marriage of his daughter to a near-relative of Gladstone, as readers of the *Irish Law Times* were informed on 6 May 1899:[24]

MARRIAGE OF MR. JOHN STEUART GLADSTONE AND
MISS FITZGIBBON.

On Saturday morning last the marriage of Mr. John Steuart Gladstone, grand-nephew of the late Right Hon. Wm. Ewart Gladstone, and Miss Anne FitzGibbon, third daughter of the Right Hon. Gerald FitzGibbon, Lord Justice of the Supreme Court of

---

[23] Letter dated 16 February 1886, quoted in W.S. Churchill, *Lord Randolph Churchill* (2 vols., 1906), ii, 59 [or 2nd edition (1951), 446]. The friendship between Lord Randolph Churchill and the Lord Justice is mentioned by R.F. Foster, 'To the Northern Counties Station: Lord Randolph Churchill and the prelude to the orange card', in F.S.L. Lyons and R.A.J. Hawkins (eds.), *Ireland under the Union* (Oxford, 1980), pp 237-87, at pp 241-2.

[24] *I.L.T. & S.J.*, xxxiii, 6 May 1899, p. 188.

Appeal in Ireland, was celebrated in St. Stephen's Church, Lower Mount-street, Dublin. The ceremony was performed by the Rev. Canon Walsh, D.D., rector of the church, and uncle of the bride, assisted by the Rev. Wm. FitzGerald, M.A., cousin of the bride. The function was a purely private one, members of the respective families alone being present. The reception was held on the previous Thursday.

Although he came from a different religious and political background, Maurice Healy sensed FitzGibbon's Olympian stature, and was one of his courtroom admirers.[25]

When I was a law student, Gerald Fitzgibbon was President of the Law Students' Debating Society, and the only time I ever met him personally was at one of our meetings when he asked me to squire some ladies for him. But I knew him well in court; I never missed an opportunity of hearing him, for never was there a man endowed with so beautiful a speaking voice and so well able to make use of it. He was so tall a man that he had a lean-forward attitude that was almost a stoop. He had an enormous head; and he had one of the most mobile faces that I have ever seen ...

An argument in the Court of Appeal when he was a member was an intellectual treat. For Fitzgibbon always argued the case with counsel; and, whereas nothing is more irritating to counsel than to be constantly interrupted by the Judge, this never applied to Fitzgibbon's interventions, for the reason that he always listened to the answers to his questions. And one could argue with him "in shorthand" as it were: an allusion to "Smith v. Jones and that line of cases" was always sufficient to direct his mind along the path you wished it to go, although, when it became necessary to demonstrate the hair's-breadth that made all the difference between Smith v. Jones and the case under consideration, nobody could split the hair with greater precision or accuracy.

FitzGibbon died in office in 1909, greatly mourned, and deemed worthy of a grand memorial. A statue of the Lord Justice was commissioned from Albert Bruce Joy, R.H.A. This statue, which was accounted a good likeness, was unveiled on 27 May 1914, and is still to be seen in the north aisle of St. Patrick's Cathedral.[26]

---

[25]   *The Old Munster Circuit*, pp 259-60.
[26]   *I.L.T. & S.J.*, xlviii, 30 May 1914, p. 150.

VI: The Four Courts

Had the FitzGibbon statue been placed, not in St. Patrick's Cathedral, but in the Four Courts, it would have shared the fate of the six statues that formerly occupied that number of the eight niches in the Round Hall that are now empty. Men called to the Bar in 1868 would already have known two of these sculptures — those of Sir Michael O'Loghlen, Master of the Rolls (1789-1842), and Chief Baron Joy (1763-1835). In 1884 they would have become acquainted with the statues, both of which were unveiled that year, of Plunket and Sheil. These also honoured men of an earlier era; but

---

LEGAL STATUARY

It may be that Lord Justice FitzGibbon will prove to be the last Irish judge to be commemorated by a life-sized statue in stone. Judicial eminence still leaves its mark in portraiture, but few of the barristers in this book have been honoured in public statuary. A recent exception is Niall McCarthy, who is commemorated by a bronze in the Reading Room of the National Archives (a work of which King's Inns has a copy). Lord Carson's statue outside the Parliament Buildings at Stormont prevails in grandeur, but this monument was earned for political, rather than legal, service. Similarly Patrick Pearse, to whom there are busts in Leinster House (by Oliver Sheppard) and in Tralee (by Yann Renard Goulet), was not honoured for his couple of court appearances in cases related to the Irish language. The King's Inns possesses busts of Tim Healy, Cearbhall Ó Dálaigh and Brian Walsh. There are busts of Tom Kettle (by Albert G. Power) and of Willie Redmond (by Oliver Sheppard) in St. Stephen's Green and at Wexford respectively; and one of John Patrick Joseph O'Reilly (father of Sir Anthony O'Reilly) in Trinity College, a piece which the College commissioned in recognition of a benefaction by Sir Anthony.

---

the two remaining figures were of men they would have known in the flesh, judges who had graced the bench in 1868. Whiteside and O'Hagan, whose statues were unveiled in 1880 and 1887 respectively, had sat in what are now Courts 1 and 4, Whiteside (1804-76) as Chief Justice of the Queen's Bench (1866), and O'Hagan (1812-1885) as Lord Chancellor (1868). All the statues succumbed in 1922 in the greater ruin of the Four Courts. Constantine Curran, the intellectually-able Registrar of the Supreme Court who wrote knowledgeably about the history of the Four Courts and generally on the architecture of Georgian Dublin, beheld the destroyed statues:[27]

---

[27] C.P. Curran, 'Figures in the Hall', in *Record of the Centenary of the Charter of the Incorporated Law Society of Ireland 1852-1952* (Dublin, 1953), pp 75-82; reprinted in *Gazette of the Incorporated Law Society of Ireland*, vol. lxvi (1972), pp

On the 3rd July 1922 I saw them prostrate under the open sky ...
Lord Chancellor, judges, and advocates broken and calcined. I stuck
my thumb into Joy — he had the consistency of cream cheese.

The Irish Bar has been at home in its Pantheon on the banks of
the Liffey since the Courts opened there on Friday 3 November
1796.[28] Were the building to be located in a continental city, the
Four Courts would probably be known as the palace of justice.
Whiteside called it such, when he referred to the Four Courts as a
'Palace of Justice surmounted by a dome flying into the air'.[29] An
early English admirer — a barrister of the Middle Temple — had a
kindred insight when he described the edifice as a 'temple of
justice'. 'I will venture to affirm,' wrote John Carr in 1805, 'that
Justice has not such a temple in any other country'. Lord Chief
Justice Molony used the same phrase in 1924, when he lamented
that the 'hand of fate' had 'left Ireland without its great Temple of
Justice'.[30] The favoured appellation of 'Pantheon' has architectural
authority, for Dr. Edward McParland has observed that the ultimate
model for the drum and dome of Gandon's design was the temple
dedicated to all the gods of ancient Rome.[31] Earlier in the eighteenth
century that great building had been imitated in Paris, and a visitor
to the *Panthéon* who knows the Four Courts will find points of
resemblance.[32]

45-7; and in Caroline Costello (ed.), *The Four Courts: 200 Years* (Dublin, 1996),
pp 105-112.
    One piece of statuary from the Round Hall was evacuated before the disaster,
and survives, in a much weathered form, facing the façade of the King's Inns.
'There used to be a colossal figure of Justice in the centre of the hall. But her scales
got broken and ... the Benchers had the poor maimed Justice removed to the quiet
garden of the Inns of Court': Matthias Bodkin, *Recollections of an Irish Judge*
(1914), p. 88. C.P. Curran says ('Figures in the Hall') that this statue, which may
have held aloft a gas-lit torch, was erected about 1840, and removed in April 1880.
[28]   In 1996 the bicentenary of the opening of the Four Courts was celebrated on the
wrong day. Friday 3 November 1796 was 'the essoign day for the Judges' when
they sat in advance of the term that commenced on Monday 6 November.
[29]   The phrase, found in W.D. Ferguson's edition of Whiteside's *Early Sketches*
(1870), is quoted in *I.L.T. & S.J.,* lvi (1922), pp 115-6.
[30]   John Carr, *The Stranger in Ireland: or, A tour in the southern and western
parts of that country in the year 1805* (1805), Chapter XXI; *I.L.T. & S.J.,* lviii, 31
May 1924, pp 138-9. Bodkin, *Recollections of an Irish judge,* p. 85, used 'Palace of
Justice'.
[31]   Edward McParland, *James Gandon, Vitruvius Hibernicus* (1985), pp 157-9,
163; and ibid., *Public Architecture in Ireland 1680-1760* (2001), p. 117.
[32]   The *Panthéon,* built as the church of Sainte Geneviève, was designed in 1764 by
Jacques-Germain Soufflot (1713-80), who, like Gandon, was also influenced by the
double dome of Wren's St. Paul's Cathedral. Another Gandon design, the portico
of the House of Lords, has been linked with Sainte Geneviève [McParland,
Gandon, p. 80], but Gandon knew the buildings of Paris only from their plans.

The destruction of the Dublin imitation, which it was the lot of Constantine Curran to describe,[33] occurred close to the mid-point of the period we are surveying. The event coincided with historic changes in the government of Ireland, and was a watershed in professional life. For nine years after the destruction the courts were in exile, a period during which they were accommodated first at the King's Inns, and then, not uncomfortably, in Dublin Castle.[34]

The exile at Dublin Castle, which might easily have proved permanent, happily came to an end in October 1931, when the Bar was able to return to its Pantheon. Inevitably the intervening work of reconstruction had wrought changes to the fabric. The architecture of the re-built Four Courts offers many clues to what had previously existed, but there are also nuances of which observation alone gives no hint.[35] The Wings, for example, were entirely remodelled, their corridors relocated from the south to the north side. The internal design of the Round Hall courts, offices and staircases was altered, as, notably, was the location of the Law Library.

The work of the 1920s was not the first to have been carried out on Gandon's creation. The building had been the subject of previous adaptations, the earliest of which had produced an extension on its northern side.[36] In 1835 two courts additional to the original design, the Rolls Court and the Nisi Prius Court [the latter later distinguished as 'Nisi Prius No. 1'], had been constructed. These occupied sites which correspond roughly with the locations of the later Courts No. 5 and 6 (the latter, since 1996, designated the Hugh

[33] Gerard Hogan has published Curran's contemporary notes on the destruction. See Gerard Hogan, 'Hugh Kennedy, the Childers Habeas Corpus application and the Return to the Four Courts', in Caroline Costello (ed.), *The Four Courts: 200 Years* (Dublin, 1996), pp 177-219, at 181-3.

[34] The Courts in Dublin Castle are described in *I.L.T. & S.J.*, lvii, 7 April 1923, p. 88, and 14 April 1923, pp 92-3.

[35] Two articles by T.J. Byrne, the Board of Works architect who supervised the restoration, are found as follows: 'Reconstruction work at the Four Courts, Dublin', in *The Irish Builder and Engineer*, vol. lxx, no. 2 (21 January 1928), pp 54-60; and 'Some reconstruction work at the Four Courts, Dublin', in *Transactions of the Institution of Civil Engineers of Ireland,* vol. liv (1929), pp 86-122. Other articles, by anonymous contributors, touching the Four Courts and its rebuilding are found in *The Irish Builder and Engineer* as follows: vol. lviii, no. 15 (22 July 1916), 'The Four Courts, Dublin'; vol. lxiv, no. 14 (15 July 1922), p 489 'The architecture of the Four Courts, Dublin'; and pp 494-7, 'The Four Courts: its rise and fall'; vol. lxvii, no. 5 (7 March 1925), p. 169 'Reconstruction No. 1 - the Four Courts'; vol. lxvii, no. 15 (25 July 1925), p. 617,'Reconstruction of the Four Courts, Dublin'.

[36] Space was also set aside in the main building for Admiralty, Bankruptcy, and Lunacy Courts, and for a Court of Appeal.

Kennedy Court). We shall see that the first purpose-built Law Library was above these courts.[37]

Since 1931 the Round Hall courts have been identified, under a system reckoned clockwise from the north-east, merely by number.[38] Under the arrangement that Gandon devised, these courts had accommodated the King's Bench (No. 1), the Common Pleas (No. 2), the Exchequer (No. 3) and the Chancery (No. 4). After the Judicature Act, and the consequent merger of the Common Law courts, the name of the Court of King's Bench was adjusted to 'King's Bench No. 1', the Court of Common Pleas became 'Nisi Prius No. 2', and the Court of Exchequer 'King's Bench No. 2'. These names are to be found on the plan on page 59.

When rebuilt, the Round Hall courts differed somewhat in their internal arrangement. The original layout of these four courts, all similar, and of equal dimensions, was described by Malton as follows:-

> On rising five steps, and removing a curtain immediately at the back of the columns, the court is entered; a wainscot screen crosses it, having a door at each extreme for admission of the lawyers, counsel, and witnesses. On each side is a gallery, one for the jury, the other for the Sheriff and other Officers. The Judges sit in a cove formed by a niche in the end of the court, with semi-eliptical sounding-boards over their heads. Each court is lighted by six windows, three on each side, above the cornice, which is on a level with the cornice over the columns of the hall. Level with the galleries are apartments for the jurors to retire.

The courts are now top-lit; but their predecessors had windows at the front and back, those at the front admitting light from a triangular shaft (of the existence of which the regular elegance of the classical facade gave no hint), those at the back affording a glimpse of the dome. From another source we have confirmation that the courts originally had no doors: 'instead of noisy doors, double green curtains are used'.[39] From the same source we learn that the galleries were 'ascended to by stairs from [within] the courts'. The stairs led to the jury-rooms, 'by which the juries are prevented from having any communication with the public; a very

---

[37] As designed by Gandon, the space between the Round Hall and the Supreme Court constituted (and was described by Malton as) 'a spacious apartment called the Chancery-Chamber', under which there was 'an extensive coffee-room, with other conveniences'. By 1813 the Chancery Chamber had become the Rolls Court.
[38] The numerical system originated in 1923 when the courts were accommodated in Dublin Castle.
[39] John Carr (1805). Glass doors, and panelling from floor to ceiling between the columns, replaced the curtains: see a photograph in Albert E. Richardson, *Monumental Classic Architecture in Great Britain and Ireland* (1914), p. 27.

necessary caution, which is not practised in England'. The man who left this description added:

> Perhaps the jury-boxes are too much elevated for the counsel to address the jury with ease ...

The same writer referred to the custom in Ireland whereby a witness did not go 'into the box', or (as in America) 'take the stand', but rather was put 'on the table':

> I was surprised to find, considering how infinitely superior the arrangements of their courts were, that they had no witness-box. The witness is hoisted upon the table, where the counsel within the bar sit, with all the mud and filth adhering to his shoes, where he is seated upon a chair; and a lady is exposed in the same manner.

It is thought that the Round Hall courts had been equipped with witness boxes before 1922, but the old arrangement for seating the witness on a chair on the platform or table between bench and bar survived in country courthouses.[40]

The spirit of the Round Hall in the time before the Judicature Act was wittily evoked by Serjeant Sullivan in a lecture delivered at Cambridge in 1928.[41] In the extract below Sullivan recalled the character of the old Common Law courts using a well-found formula that belonged to the lore of the profession:[42]

> Forty years ago in my old country the legal world was in a state of transition. The old order was changing in a great number of ways.

---

[40]   Cf. A.M. Sullivan, *The last Serjeant*, p. 64; and the photograph of Clifden Courthouse in Mildred Dunne and Brian Phillips (compilers), *The Courthouses of Ireland* (Kilkenny, 1999), p. 107, photo. no. 5.

[41]   A. M. Sullivan, 'The last forty years of the Irish Bar', printed in the *Cambridge Law Journal*, iii (1929), pp 365-75. This characterisation of the common law courts was not original. The same theme can be found in M. Bodkin, *Recollections of an Irish Judge*, p. 124, and in Marjoribanks, *The Life of Lord Carson*, i, p. 23, where the judgment on the competing merits of the three courts is attributed to Lord Killanin.

[42]   The judges whose qualities are contrasted were Michael Morris [Lord Killanin], Christopher Palles, and George Augustus Chichester May:-

Michael Morris, Lord Killanin (1826-1901), a Roman Catholic and Unionist, was appointed a justice of the Common Pleas in 1867 and Chief Justice of that Court in 1876. He became Chief Justice of the (post-Judicature Act) Queen's Bench Division in 1887, and went to the House of Lords in 1889. See Maud Wynne, *An Irishman and his family: Lord Morris and Killanin* (London, 1937).

Christopher Palles (1831-1920), a Roman Catholic and Liberal, was the celebrated last Chief Baron of the Exchequer, an office he held from 1874 until his retirement in 1916. He had allowed his court to be merged in the Queen's Bench Division in 1898. See V.T.H. Delany, *Christopher Palles* (Dublin, 1960).

George Augustus Chichester May (1815-1892) was appointed Chief Justice of the Queen's Bench in 1877. Following the coming into force of the Judicature Act in January 1878, he became Chief Justice of the new Queen's Bench Division, a post he held until 1887, when he resigned. Because of the date of his resignation it is unlikely that Sullivan had known May, a circumstance that confirms the impression that Sullivan was relating not his own story but a Law Library yarn.

The Judicature Act had just got into swing and although four Courts still opened in the hall beside the Liffey they were soon to be fused into one. These were at that time the Court of Chancery, the Court of Queen's Bench, the Court of Exchequer, and the Court of Common Pleas, and the doors of these four opened on the Central Hall and their names stood over them. The Court of Chancery stood by itself, but it was thought in those days that you had your choice of three Common Law Courts in which to have your case tried. If you had some merit on your side but thought that the law was against you, you issued your writ in the Queen's Bench, which was presided over by Mickey Morris, as he was invariably called although he was a lord, because Mickey had a good deal of common sense, a great deal of humanity, but his ideas of jurisprudence were peculiarly his own. On the other hand, if you were strongly of opinion that however iniquitous your client was, he had the law on his side, you issued your writ in the Court of Exchequer, presided over by Christopher Palles, the greatest judge before whom I have ever appeared. Christopher Palles decided according to what he believed to be the law, and would pay no attention to any other consideration that might be advanced before him. On the other hand there was a third course: if you had neither law nor merits you went to the Court of Common Pleas, which in that day was presided over by Chief Justice May, before whom no case was certain and no case was hopeless.

VII: The Law Library

The Law Library, the institution that became central to the life of the Irish Bar, has occupied three distinct locations at the Four Courts; and had its origins in a fourth.[43] During the years of exile, it inhabited two borrowed homes: the King's Inns Library (April 1922-April 1923), and St. Patrick's Hall at Dublin Castle (11 April 1923-31 July 1931).

The Law Library had informal origins, not to be dated precisely, in the decade before 1818, the year in which the Benchers first paid a salary of £30 to its librarian. Serjeant Sullivan set out what were believed to have been the origins of the institution:[44]

> An enterprising merchant bought a law library, put it on movable stalls, and set it up daily on the quay opposite the courts. Hence books could be hired when wanted for a shilling or sixpence. This was such a convenience that a committee of the bar fitted up a small

---

[43] It never occupied the space in the dome identified on the 1813 plans with the words 'originally intended for a Library': See *Reports of the Commissioners appointed .... respecting the Public Records of Ireland*, Plate 16 and p. 478. The Record Room in the dome is difficult of access, and the consequences of dropping a book over the rail into the Round Hall below would be horrific to contemplate. The space was used for the storage of files, and C.P. Curran recalls seeing a groove where the rope and pulley by which materials had been lowered to the Round Hall had worn a channel in the gallery rail: see C.P. Curran, 'Figures in the Hall', in Costello (ed.) *The Four Courts: 200 Years*, p. 171.
[44] *Old Ireland, Reminiscences of an Irish K.C.*, p. 105.

unused room, in the building, let the huckster ply his trade there, and on his death bought his books and carried on the business for the bar. Larger apartments were given by the authorities as the library and its subscribers increased until the system developed with all its delightful circumstances.

From 1825 until 1897, when the body was absorbed by the Bar Council, there existed a regularly-constituted 'Law Library Society', which has left records.[45] The Society was supported by its members' subscriptions and by grants from the Benchers.

When first glimpsed on a plan of 1813 [left], the Library was accommodated in a first-floor room on the south side of the Chancery Court [Court No. 4], between the upper wall of that court and the 'Court of Appeals'. The room communicated with both these courts, but could also be approached from the western staircase between the Courts of Exchequer and Chancery. The space marked 'Library' was one of the octagonal rooms that Gandon had fitted into the angles between the courts, most of which served as judge's chambers or jury rooms.[46] The room was small, and, apart from housing the books, cannot have received many browsers. The social life of the Bar still took place downstairs in the Round Hall.

In 1835, at the time that the Rolls Courts and first Nisi Prius Court were constructed on the ground floor of the extension to the north of Gandon's building, the profession was allocated the space above, and thereby acquired the first of three purpose-built libraries designed by the Board of Works. The architect in 1835 was Jacob Owen. In his building, a top-lit, 'Soane-like' room, the Law Library was accommodated for some sixty-years, at first contentedly, later

---

[45] Daire Hogan, *The Legal Profession in Ireland 1789-1922* (Dublin, 1986), p. 55-6; Tomás Clancy, 'The Four Courts Buildings and the development of an independent Bar of Ireland', in Costello (ed.), *The Four Courts: 200 years*, pp 80-104, at p. 89.
[46] Daire Hogan, *The Legal Profession in Ireland 1789-1922*, p. 55-6.

with sustained complaint.[47] 'The old library', said Serjeant Sullivan describing Owen's work,[48]

> was a wonderful place. The main room was about sixty feet long and thirty feet wide, lighted by a dome in the centre and a big window at the north end. From the centre of the west wall opened 'the Long Room', a smaller apartment with a door in the far end that led to the Vice-Chancellor's Court; and opening off the south-east corner was a small 'Round Room'. Around the main room ran an impossible gallery to which one climbed by impossible stairs. There were counting-house desks in the large rooms, a small circular table in the south-east room, and beneath the dome was 'the Round Table'.

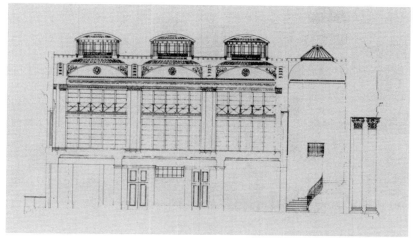

Section through Owen's Law Library, seen from the west.
From the 4th Annual Report on Public Works, Ireland, 1836

The old library had seating accommodation for about seventy persons, and there were about two hundred and fifty subscribers. A newcomer could have no definite place, but every seat whose owner was absent might be occupied by anyone until the owner himself appeared.

The Round Table, which was 'about nine feet in diameter' and which was (in Sullivan's words) 'the resort of the best known *raconteurs* of the profession, who were also the leaders of Nisi Prius', featured similarly in the memory of Lord Carson. He wrote no memoir, but his biography, by Edward Marjoribanks, was an

---

[47] [Architectural Association of Ireland], *Public Works: The architecture of the Office of Public Works 1831-1987* (Dublin, n.d. [1987]), pp 9, 12, 19, 26; Plates 25, 26 and 27 in Caroline Costello (ed.), *The Four Courts: 200 Years*.
[48] The description is derived from passages in two of Sullivan's books: *The last Serjeant*, pp 24-5, and *Old Ireland: Reminiscences of an Irish K.C.*, p. 93.

authorised work published during its subject's lifetime.[49] It contains
this careful description of the first purpose-built Law Library:

> The main room was rectangular, with narrow galleries round the
> sides, under which were the bookshelves, a small octagonal room at
> each corner, and another room, the 'Long Room', running at right
> angles and opening off one side. The entrance used was through one
> of the small rooms, which became an ante-room in which solicitors
> and their clerks could speak to counsel. The barristers sat on forms
> at long desks, or at 'the Round Table', a large table in the centre of
> the main room and opposite the chief fireplace (where twelve men
> sat), or at small round tables or separate desks in the corner rooms,
> or occupied any other available space. The accommodation was
> quite insufficient for the number requiring it, and the Bar were
> packed like children in a poor school of the bad old days, but with
> far more discomfort than would now be tolerated in such a place.
> But it will easily be seen that at such close quarters the members of
> the Bar were a much closer association than their brethren in
> London, that jealousy and backbiting were so uncomfortable as to
> become really impossible, and that friendship and good-fellowship
> were not only general but necessary in such conditions.

Along with the Round Table and the fire, the twin centres of legal
gossip, both Sullivan and Carson remembered the crier, who sat to
the left of the entrance to the main room, possessed of a printed
sheet with the names of the subscribers. In their day, the crier was
an old soldier named Bramley, with a powerful Cockney voice
capable of penetrating into the recesses of the building. Both
Sullivan and Carson commented on the noise in the Law Library.
Carson learned there

> that a general noise, no matter how loud, is not so distressing to the
> worker as two persons in close proximity holding a whispered
> conversation.

The quietest place to be was the 'Long Room', which occupied the
space over the present Court 5, and which, in Sullivan's words, was
'a haven of peace and tranquillity'. It was the abode of
conveyancers and Chancery men. Here Carson, and later John Ross,
sat with their master George Price (M 1859), a tongue-tied
conveyancer, to whom each had paid a fee of fifty guineas for the
privilege of being his devil.

According to Sullivan, 'the legal day commenced in Dublin with
a visitation of the *bagmen'*, a concept that imported the female. 'The
bagmen had admitted women to their guild', said Sullivan, 'and the
women so admitted were dreadful slatterns'. Carson's biographer
used the word 'bagwomen'. When Carson joined the Library, after
his Call in Easter Term 1877, the barristers' black brief bags were

---

[49]   Edward Marjoribanks, *The Life of Lord Carson*, i (London, 1932), pp 19-23.

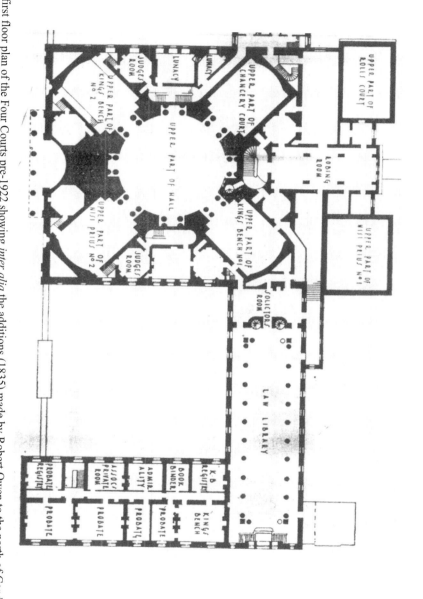

Detail from the first floor plan of the Four Courts pre-1922 showing *inter alia* the additions (1835) made by Robert Owen to the north of Gandon's building and the eastern Wing, as remodelled by Sir Thomas Drew in 1894–97 to include a new Law Library. The 'Robing Room' represents Owen's Law Library of 1835. A corridor and the office attached to the Lunacy Court occupy the site of the Library shown in the plan of 1813 (*cf.* p. 56 *supra*).

[From *100th Annual Report of the Commissioners of Public Works with Appendices. Report for the Year ended 31st March 1932* (Dublin, 1934).]

King's Inns Barristers, 1868-2004, page 59.

still brought from their houses every morning by old women like 'Snuffy Maggie', who carried the loads on their backs or wheeled them in makeshift perambulators. Carson, who spent little more than a decade at the Irish Bar before migrating to London, remembered that the bagwomen were replaced, soon after his coming to the bar, by the 'Legal Express', a service which employed two horse-drawn vans. Denis Johnston, who was born in 1901, remembered the van marked 'O'Connor's Legal Express' which came early in the morning to his parents' home at 54 Wellington Road bearing his father's black bag tied with a black and red rope.[50]

Ultimately, and not without a hint of irony, the old Library was condemned as overcrowded and insanitary, deficient by reference to criteria employed by Factory Act inspectors.[51] In 1897, after three years of planning and building, the Law Library took possession of magnificent accommodation that the Board of Works, aided by a legislative raid on the funds of suitors, had caused to be fashioned out of the two upper floors of the east wing of Gandon's building. The architect was Sir Thomas Drew, who, within the shell of the Georgian building, created a lofty baroque interior. At the eastern end of the wing abutting Chancery Place, where the three-bay Georgian fenestration has since been restored, Drew created a Venetian window, with stained glass representations of Wisdom, Justice and Eloquence, and a grand staircase giving access to a gallery supported by Corinthian columns. Photographs of this Law Library are preserved in the Irish Architectural Archive.[52]

The transfer of the library to the east wing brought additional space and comfort, allowed for the introduction of the telephone and telegraph, and permitted the old accommodation to be turned into a robing room. This last was an improvement. Sullivan, recalling the circumstances of his own call to the Bar, mentions that he had been advised to wear a tall hat. 'If he was a person of great skill', said Sullivan, the candidate for Call

> might not lose or destroy his hat, as so many people did, descending the narrow crooked steps, by which he reached one of the cellars in which he had to robe.

---

[50]   Rory Johnston (ed.), *Orders and Desecrations* (Dublin, 1992), p. 2.
[51]   'Report on the present Sanitary Condition and Ventilation of the Bar Library by Thomas Drew, F.R.I., B.A'., in *I.L.T. & S.J.*, vol. xxviii, 27 Jan. 1894, pp 43-4.
[52]   A view looking east towards the Venetian window is reproduced facing page 117 in Daire Hogan, *The Legal Profession in Ireland 1789-1922*. A close-up of that window, and a view looking west towards the clock over the entrance, are reproduced as Plates 10 and 11 in Caroline Costello (ed.), *The Four Courts: 200 Years*.
The new Library was 123 feet long and 37 feet wide. The room it had replaced (60' x 30') became a Robing Room.

Although a barrister might have no expectation of holding a brief, being dressed in readiness for court was, according to the etiquette, a prerequisite for entering the Library. Sullivan states:

> In the morning the practising members of the bar robed in the cellars beneath the hall of the Four Courts, and then went to the Library.

Matthias Bodkin correctly recognised that the Law Library was 'the fair or market where barristers are hired':[53]

> Business or no busines, he daily robes himself in full legal toggery, climbs a flight of stairs to the law library, and takes his place very literally like a cabman on his hazard, waiting for a fare.

The requirement to be robed doubtless had its origin in the time, before the Law Library was established, when being robed was a necessary advertisement that the wearer was a barrister available for hire. Sullivan imagined how things had been before the library system evolved:[54]

> A hundred years ago the Irish barrister robed at home and walked or drove in his wig and gown to the Four Courts. His uniform was a protection from arrest for debt, and was useful as such to many a counsellor until 1870, when imprisonment for debt was abolished in Ireland. On arrival at the courts, the old practitioner took up his recognised position near a door or near a pillar, and there his clients would find him when not in court. The yet unlocalised junior walked round and round the hall, as his English type had paced the round of the Temple church hundreds of years before.

A trace of the earlier practice of coming robed from home to court lingered in the customs associated with the Lord Chancellor's *levée* on the first day of Easter Term. C.P. Curran described the ceremonial as it had been practised within the memory of older men known to him:[55]

> On the morning of *levée* day the bar in robes called upon the Lord Chancellor at his residence and made their bows to him in his drawing room. The tipstaves, as Mr. Matthew Tayler has told me, took fast trotting horses and cars to the court, followed after a decent interval by the Lord Chancellor and judges, the Lord Chancellor in court dress, velvet suit, long knee breeches with lace ruffles at neck and sleeves, the judges of the Court of Appeal in their black and gold-edged robes, and the High Court judges in red. The Lord Chancellor's carriage stopped at the front entrance and, preceded by the two tipstaves and his mace bearer, and followed by his train bearer, and purse-bearer, the Lord Chancellor entered the

53 M. Bodkin, *Recollections of an Irish Judge*, p. 85.
54 *Old Ireland: Reminiscences of an Irish K.C.*, p. 105.
55 'Figures in the Hall', *loc. cit.*, p. 172.

Hall and passing up on a red drugget carpet took his place opposite the entrance on a scarlet carpet under the clock, his tipstaves and attendants lining up at the side. The other judges then alighted from their carriages and in order of precedence passed before the Lord Chancellor and remained at either side until the Lord Chancellor turned and headed the procession in the same order to the benchers' chamber at the rere of the building.

This ceremony endured in Dublin until 1921, when Lord Glenavy, the penultimate Lord Chancellor, performed it for the last time.[56]

> The Easter Law Sittings were opened at the Four Courts, Dublin, on Wednesday, when the Lord Chancellor held the usual reception associated with the opening of the legal year ... The Central Hall had been carpeted for the ceremony, and crimson cloth was laid from the main entrance to the Benchers' Chambers, where the members of the Bar were received by the Lord Chancellor wearing his State robes of black silk and gold, and attended by his purse-bearer and trainbearer.

Although the ceremony ended in Dublin, the spirit of the Four Courts migrated to Belfast, where Sir Denis Henry conducted an Easter *levée* at the Crumlin Road Courthouse in 1923 and subsequent years.[57] It will be observed that the legal year was still regarded as beginning after Easter. Like the fiscal year, lately abolished in tandem with the introduction of the Euro, the old legal year had survived the calendar reform of 1752 and was reckoned from Lady Day.

The Lord Chancellor's *levée* on the first day of Easter Term has been replaced in Dublin by the simpler ceremonial — a choice of religious services followed by a reception in the hall of King's Inns — that is now associated with the first day of Michaelmas Term. During the period of exile in Dublin Castle no form of ceremony punctuated the legal year. So matters might have remained had not the return of the profession to the Four Courts prompted the feeling that it was proper that this occasion at least should be marked. To the fulfilment of this very reasonable expectation there was an unforeseen obstacle: the Executive Council of the Free State, fearful that 'a formal opening would be a direct incentive to the making of an attempt to wreck the building', decreed that there should be no opening ceremony.[58] The problem was solved by recourse to

---

[56] *I.L.T. & S.J.*, lv (9 April 1921), p. 95. Cf. ibid., liii (26 April 1919), p. 102, and liv (17 April 1920), p. 94, when the ceremony was not held because of a strike.
[57] *I.L.T. & S.J.*, lvii (21 April 1923), p. 100: 'Easter Term was opened on Tuesday [17th] by an imposing procession of judges'; ibid., lviii (19 April 1924), p. 99 [The Lord Chief Justice]'held the customary *levée*; ibid., lix (18 April 1925), p. 95.
[58] See the correspondence between the Minister for Justice and Hugh Kennedy, of which Gerard Hogan has given extracts, in his article in Caroline Costello (ed.), *The Four Courts: 200 Years*, pp 213-5.

religion; and the idea of religious ceremonies, to be in form private and unofficial, had the support of the Minister for Justice and the judges. Hence it is that the celebration of the passage of the legal year is marked *because* of the reopening of the Four Courts in October 1931, but not *in* the building the reopening of which was the occasion of rejoicing. Lawyers, who had not previously gone to church as an adjunct to their professional life, were steered in that direction because it was inexpedient that they should go to court.

The present Law Library, erected to the design of T.J. Byrne on the site of buildings that had previously served the solicitors' side of the profession, was ready for occupation in October 1931 on the occasion of the first of the foregoing annual religious ceremonies. The new building was more spacious but less ornate than its predecessor. Equipped with desks resembling those shown in photographs of Drew's room, it offered facilities and an ambience not dissimilar to those previously enjoyed. The present Library, as creditable to the Board of Works as its predecessors, has now served the Bar for longer than any of its earlier homes.

VIII: The post-1868 barristers

It takes time for a barrister to make his mark. Those, like Palles, who towered over the profession in the second half of Queen Victoria's reign, were men who had been called to the Bar a generation before the first of those whose names are found in the accompanying, post-1868, lists. The accepted wisdom is that it takes a successful man a dozen years before he can aspire to take silk, and twice as many before he should contemplate the bench. The first of the present batch to attain both a silk gown and the bench was John George Gibson (1846-1923; called 1870), who achieved these goals, in near-record time, in 1880 and 1887 respectively: but he was the brother of Lord Ashbourne, and, having fought parliamentary elections, had claims on his family's political friends. It was not until 1884 that a further group of post-1868 barristers obtained silk, and not until 1896 that a second appointment — John Ross (called 1880) — was made to the bench from among the post-1868 men. Then the tempo changed. In the following year one more appointment — Walter Boyd (E 1856) — was made from among earlier men: but after the elevation of William Kenny later in 1897, all judicial appointments were made from among the group in this book.[59]

---

[59]   After Gibson (1887), Ross (1896) and Kenny (1897) came Dunbar Plunkett Barton (appt. 1900); George Wright (appt 1901; d. 1913) Richard Edmund Meredith (appt. 1906, but previously head of the Land Commission); William

---

THE AGES OF QUEEN'S COUNSEL

'There are numerous precedents on both sides of the Channel of calls within the Bar at comparatively early ages. Francis Bacon, the first Queen's Counsel, was appointed, if Lord Macaulay is correct, who fixes 1590 as the date, in his thirtieth year. Again, Philip Yorke, the first Earl of Hardwicke, was Solicitor-General before he attained his twenty-ninth year, and Attorney-General at thirty-four; while his son, the unfortunate Charles Yorke, became Solicitor-General at thirty-four years of age, the same age at which his father was appointed to the post of Attorney-General. At the Irish Bar, in comparatively recent times, in several cases, Queen's Counsel have been appointed at an early period of their professional careers. Thus the late Mr. Butt, Q.C., the leader of the Irish Parliamentary Party, was born in 1813, called to the Irish Bar in 1838, and appointed Queen's Counsel in 1844, in his thirty-second year. So, too, the late Right Hon. William Keogh, one of the Justices of the Irish Court of Common Pleas, was born in 1817, called to the Irish Bar in 1840, and called to the Inner Bar in 1849, in his thirty-third year. The case, however, of Mr. Plunket, Q.C., M.P., beats the record. He "took silk" at an earlier age than any living member of the English or Irish Bars. He was born in 1838, called to the Irish Bar in 1862, and made a Queen's Counsel in 1868, before he had completed his thirtieth year.'

Irish Law Times, xxix, p. 521, 26 Oct. 1895.

How eminent were the post-1868 barristers? As a group they possess considerable interest, especially those who made a splash in public affairs in a turbulent age: yet, in the narrower sphere of the legal profession, they do not seem to have been quite the men their fathers were. Only twenty-two were accorded an entry in the original *Dictionary of National Biography*,[60] an unsatisfactory total considering that the pool of talent stretched over four generations, and extended to some 2,700 candidates When it is recalled that the 1000 barristers on the Roll in 1800 had provided the *D.N.B.* with

---

Huston Dodd (appt. 1907); Richard Robert Cherry (appt. 1909; d. 1923); Redmond John Barry (appt. 1911; retired 1913); Charles Andrew O'Connor (appt. 1912); Ignatius John O'Brien, bart. (appt. 1913); Thomas Francis Molony (appt. 1913); John Francis Moriarty (appt. 1914; d. 1915); Stephen Ronan (appt. 1915; d. 1925); Jonathan Ernest Pim (appt. 1915); James Henry Mussen Campbell (appt. 1916); John Gordon (appt. 1916; d. 1922); William Moore (appt. 1917); James O'Connor (appt. 1918); John Blake Powell (appt. 1918; d. 1923) and Arthur Warren Samuels (appt. 1919; d. 1925). Richard Edmund Meredith (1856-1916), James Owens Wylie (1845-1935) and William Evelyn Wylie (1881-1964) were appointed the Judicial Commissioners of the Irish Land Commission in 1898, 1906 and 1920 respectively.
[60] The *Oxford DNB* (2004) has added a dozen entries, bringing the tally to 34. Other Irish barristers, some still alive, both in the post-1868 and post-1969 categories, are likely to be noticed in future volumes. These include five *Taoisigh* — Lynch, Cosgrave, Haughey, Fitzgerald and Bruton — and two lady-Presidents.

some fifty entries, one is struck by the contrast, and troubled by the sense that the Bar as a profession may have been in decline.

To the extent that it discourages vanity, using the *D.N.B.* as a yardstick of achievement is a wholesome exercise: but the *D.N.B.* is not an ultimate or infallible arbiter of eminence. A couple of innocent factors may account for the fall in the tally of Irish barristers represented in the work. One is that the break-up of the former United Kingdom has made an Irishman's route to inclusion in the *D.N.B.* more difficult. Another is that, both in England and in Ireland, the law has not held its former pre-eminence in public life. In all works of biographical reference, the attainment of high judicial office does not *per se,* as once it did, offer fair prospect of inclusion.

To contemplate the possibility that the Bar might have been in decline is not to say that the profession was in an unhealthy state. Change in a profession, as in an individual, is an inevitable function of the untrimmed course of nature. The profession had been privileged to experience a robust golden age in the 1790s. This was the decade when the Four Courts moved to Inns Quay and when barristers could still cut a figure in the old Parliament on College Green. Assigning boundaries is artificial, but we may reasonably allow the golden gleam to linger until the end of the Georgian era, before permitting gold to yield to silver when Queen Victoria began her long reign, and silver to yield to bronze as that reign entered its closing years. The choice of the metals is as arbitrary as the demarcations are artificial: but there is some virtue in them. The golden age coincides with the years when the professional life of the Bar was acted out in the Round Hall; the silver age with the profession's tenure of the first, Owen-designed, Law Library; and the commencement of the third with the move to Drew's Library in the East Wing, and the establishment of a General Council of the Bar, the latter an event which happened at the time of the move to Drew's Library. In its new quarters, and with its new constitution, the profession was comfortably set to embark on its bronze age. Bronze is not gold or silver, but is still a noble metal. Throughout the period we are surveying the Irish Bar disported itself decently, less rigorously perhaps than the London Bar, but with enough learning and dignity to pass muster, and with an abundance of good nature.

Of the twenty-two persons in these pages who were noticed in the original *D.N.B.* seven were Irish judges, six — Andrews, Campbell [Lord Glenavy], Ignatius O'Brien [Lord Shandon],

Entries for post-1868 King's Inns barristers in works of biographical reference

(i) in the Dictionary of National Biography

Andrews, Sir James 3rd LCJ of N.I. (1877-1951) [by Lord MacDermott]
Bodkin, Thomas Patrick (1887-1961) [by K.J. Garlick]
Campbell, James Henry Mussen, first Baron Glenavy (1851-1931) [by Diarmid Coffey]
Carson, Sir Edward (1854-1935) [by D.L. Savory]
Casey, William Francis (1884-1957) [by A.P. Robbins]
Costello, John Aloysius (1891-1976) [by David Harkness]
Falkiner, Caesar Litton (1863-1908) [by R.H. Murray]
Healy, John Edward (1872-1934) [by R.J.H. Shaw]
Healy, Timothy Michael (1855-1931) [by Joseph Hone]
Johnston, William (1829-1902) [by Alexander Gordon]
MacDermott, John Clarke (1896- 1979) [by Lord Lowry]

MacNeill, John Gordon Swift (1849-1926) [by S.L. Gwynn]
O'Brien, Ignatius John, Baron Shandon (1857-1930) [by T.C. Kingsmill Moore]
O'Higgins, Kevin Christopher (1892-1927) [by James Hogan]
Pearse, Patrick (1879-1916) [by Ruth Dudley Edwards]
Redmond, John Edward (1856-1918) [by Stephen Gwynn]
Redmond, William Hoey Kearney (1861-1917) [by Stephen Gwynn]
Ronan, Stephen (1848-1925) [by T.C. Kingsmill Moore]
Ross, Sir John (1853-1935) [by R.W. Tate]
Shaw, James Johnston (1845-1910) [by Thomas Hamilton]
Sullivan, Alexander Martin (1830-1884) [by Michael MacDonagh]
Sullivan, Alexander Martin (1871-1959) [by F.H. Cowper]

Additional entries first included in the Oxford DNB (2004)

Bastable, Charles Francis (1855-1945) [by R.D. Collison Black]
Cherry, Richard Robert (1859-1923) [by Daire Hogan]
Duffy, George Gavan (1882-1951) [by Mary Kotsonouris]
Henry, Sir Denis Stanislaus (1864-1925) [by aGordon Gillespie]
Heuston, Robert Francis Vere (1923-1995) [by P.R. Glazebrook]
Kelly, Richard John (1860-1931) [by Marie-Louise Legg]

Kettle, Thomas Michael (1880-1916) [by S. Pašeta]
Killen, James Brice (1845-1916) [by Marie-Louise Legg]
Mac Bride, Seán (1904-1988) [by Carla King]
Molony, Sir Thomas (1865-1949) [by Daire Hogan]
Redmond, William Archer (1886-1932) [by Alan O'Day]
Reed, Sir Andrew (1837-1914) [by Elizabeth Malcolm]

(ii) in Henry Boylan, A Dictionary of Irish Biography (Dublin, 1978)

Campbell, James Henry Mussen, first Baron Glenavy (1851-1931)
Carson, Edward Henry (1854-1935)
Costello, John Aloysius (1891-1976)
Duffy, George Gavan (1882-1951)
Harrington, Timothy Charles (1851-1910)
Kettle, Thomas (1880-1916)
Lavery, Cecil (1894-1967)
Maguire, Conor Alexander (1889-1971)
O'Brien, George (1892-1973)

O'Brien, Richard Barry (1847-1918)
O'Grady, Standish James (1846-1928)
O'Higgins, Kevin Christopher (1892-1927)
O'Mahony, Eoin (1904-1970)
Pearse, Patrick (1879-1916)
Redmond, John Edward (1856-1918)
Redmond, William Hoey Kearney (1861-1917)
Sullivan, A.M., senior (1830-1884)
Sullivan, A.M., junior (1871-1959)
Swift MacNeill, J.G.S. (1849-1926)

(iii) in Kate Newman (ed), *Dictionary of Ulster Biography* (Belfast, 1993)

Barton, Dunbar Plunkett (1853-1937)
Brown, Thomas Watters (1879-1944)
Henry, Sir Denis, *Bart.* (1864-1925)
Johnston, William (1829-1902)
MacDermott, John Clarke (1896- 1979)
Maginnis, William Brian (1901-1967)

Moore, William Murphy (1864-1944)
Ross, John (1854-1935)
Sheil, Charles Leo (1897-1968)
Wilson, Daniel Martin (1862-1932)
Wylie, James Owens (1845-1935)
Wylie, William Evelyn (1881-1964)

(iv) in Louis McRedmond (ed.), *Modern Irish Lives: Dictionary of 20th-century Irish Biography* (1996)

Bewley, Charles (1890-1969)
Binchy, Daniel Anthony (1899-1989)
Bodkin, Thomas Patrick (1887-1961)
Bruton, John (1947-)
Budd, Frederick Gardner Orford (1904-1976)
Burke, Richard (1932-)
Carroll, Mella (1934-)
Carroll, Patrick Joseph (1903-1975)
Carson, Edward (1854-1935)
Comyn, Sir James (1921-1997)
Conolly, Thomas J. (1902-1992)
Cosgrave, Liam (1920-)
Costello, Declan (1927-)
Costello, John Aloysius (1891-1976)
Cronin, Anthony (1926-)
Curran, Constantine Peter (1880-1975)
Davitt, Cahir (1894-1986)
Deale, Kenneth Edwin Lee (1907-1974)
Delany, Vincent (1925-1964)
Denham, Susan (1945-)
de Valera, Vivion (1910-1982)
Dillon, James (1902-1986)
Dixon, Kevin (1902-1959)
Duffy, George Gavan (1882-1951)
Finlay, Thomas A. (1922-)
FitzGerald, Garret (1926-)
FitzGerald, William O'Brien (1906-1974)
Hamilton, Liam (1928-2000)
Haughey, Charles (1925-)
Healy, Tmothy (1855-1931)
Hearne, John (1893-1968)
Hederman O'Brien, Miriam (1932-)
Henchy, Seamus (1917-)
Kelly, John Maurice (1931-1991)
Kennedy, Hugh (1879-1936)
Kenny, John (1918-1987)

Kettle, Thomas Michael (1880-1916)
Lavery, Cecil (1894-1967)
Lenihan, Brian (1930-1995)
Lindsay, Patrick (1914-1993)
Lynch, Jack (1917-1999)
McBride, Seán (1904-88)
McCarthy, Niall St John (1925-92)
McDermott, John Clarke (1896-1979)
McDonagh, Donagh (1912-68)
McGilligan, Patrick (1889-1979)
McGuinness, Catherine (1934-)
Marcus, David (1924-)
Mhac an tSaoí, Máire (1922-)
Moore, Theodore Conyngham Kingsmill (1894-1979)
Moran, Frances Elizabeth (1893-1977)
O'Brien, George (1892-1973)
Ó Broin, Leon (1902-1990)
O'Byrne, John (1884-1954)
O'Connor, Sir Charles Andrew (1854-1928)
O'Connor, Ulick (1929-)
Ó Dálaigh, Cearbhall (1911-78)
O'Donovan, Patricia (1953-)
O'Higgins, Kevin Christopher (1892-1927)
O'Higgins, Thomas (1916-2003)
O'Mahony, Eoin (1904-70)
Ó Móráin, Dónall (1923-2000)
Pearse, Patrick Henry (1879-1916)
Redmond, John Edward (1856-1918)
Redmond, William (1861-1917)
Robinson, Mary (1944-)
Sullivan, Alexander Martin (1871-1959)
Sutherland, Peter (1946-)
Walsh, Brian (1918-1998)
Williams, T. Desmond (1921-87)
Wood, Ernest Mountenay (1909-1991)

[72 out of approx. 1400 entries]

Ronan, Ross, and MacDermott — in the superior courts, and J.J. Shaw in the County Court. Shaw, Recorder of Belfast, was prominent at the time of his death because he had lately been chairman of the viceregal enquiry into the disappearance of the Irish crown jewels. Another, Carson, became a Lord of Appeal in Ordinary in London: but he had earned his place in history before he attained judicial rank, and his statue at Stormont was unveiled in his lifetime. Of the others, who were mainly politicians, a couple — Healy and the younger Sullivan — might have merited inclusion as advocates, but were also prominent, beyond the courtroom, in the rough-and-tumble of Nationalist politics. William Johnston of Ballykilbeg, who never practised, attained celebrity purely as an M.P. and Orangeman. Two of those noticed (Casey of *The Times* and Healy of *The Irish Times*) were newspaper editors. Thomas Bodkin, Director of the National Gallery of Ireland, was a lover of the fine arts. Caesar Litton Falkiner, a gifted literary man who died young, wrote history with a grace that testified to the Muses' special favour: but as a young man at the Bar the judicial temper that characterises his historical writing is said not to have prevented his being an effective advocate.

Other works of biographical reference have proved more accommodating to members of the Irish Bar than was the *D.N.B*; and none more so than Louis McRedmond (ed.), *Modern Irish Lives: Dictionary of 20th-century Irish Biography* (1996), which has given space to more than seventy of them. Conspicuous among those to whom all works of reference have accorded recognition are Carson and Pearse, who are coupled in the sense that each became a figure of supreme reverence in the state to the creation of which his career had contributed. Some Irish Party M.P.s — in particular Healy, the Redmonds and Kettle — are also widely recognised, as are J.A. Costello and Kevin O'Higgins.

Recognition of judicial achievements has been uneven, and the listing of judges in works of reference is deficient. Francis Elrington Ball, the magisterial compiler of the two volumes on *The Judges in Ireland 1221-1921*, has had no successor. There is a dearth of readily-available information about several of the mid-twentieth-century Dublin judges. The judges and law officers of Northern Ireland, the earlier of whom, seventeen in all, were King's Inns men, are equally a neglected group.[61]

---

[61] The seventeen judges and law officers of Northern Ireland educated at King's Inns were: Sir James Andrews, Bart.; Anthony Brutus Babington; Richard Best; Arthur Black; Thomas Watters Brown; Lancelot Ernest Curran; Sir Denis Henry, Bart.; William Lowry; Robert Dick Megaw; Lord [John Clarke] MacDermott;

A legal education at King's Inns was lavished on several fellows who, in the end, were happier in the literary world. The 'Pope' O'Mahony was one such, as was Denis Johnston, who practised for a time and had kind things to say about the Law Library: 'The Bar is a very good life, and the most enjoyable profession I ever had'.[62] The names of Máire Mac an tSaoi, Anthony Cronin, David Marcus, and Ulick O'Connor are also included in these pages.

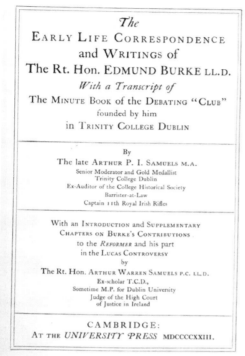

The
EARLY LIFE CORRESPONDENCE
and WRITINGS of
The Rt. Hon. EDMUND BURKE LL.D.
With a Transcript of
The MINUTE BOOK of the DEBATING "CLUB"
founded by him
in TRINITY COLLEGE DUBLIN

By
The late ARTHUR P. I. SAMUELS M.A.
Senior Moderator and Gold Medallist
Trinity College Dublin
Ex-Auditor of the College Historical Society
Barrister-at-Law
Captain 11th Royal Irish Rifles

With an INTRODUCTION and SUPPLEMENTARY
CHAPTERS ON BURKE'S CONTRIBUTIONS
to the *REFORMER* and his part
in the LUCAS CONTROVERSY
by
The Rt. Hon. ARTHUR WARREN SAMUELS P.C. LL.D.
Ex-scholar T.C.D.,
Sometime M.P. for Dublin University
Judge of the High Court
of Justice in Ireland

CAMBRIDGE:
AT THE *UNIVERSITY PRESS* MDCCCCXXIII.

Worthy of celebration among the literary men is a group of historians and antiquarians. C. Litton Falkiner has already been mentioned as a prose writer of consummate grace. The genealogists Burtchaell and Sadleir were likewise King's Inns men.[63] So too were [Richard] Barry O'Brien, Standish O'Grady, and Leon Ó Broin. The younger Arthur Samuels, who fell in the war, showed great promise; and his book on the early life of Edmund Burke (seen through the press by his grieving father, who had become a judge of the King's Bench Division) is scholarship of the first order, a credit alike to father and son. These were gentleman scholars. Others in our group made historical scholarship their profession. Donough Bryan lectured, all too briefly, at Trinity College. George O'Brien long held sway over economic history at U.C.D. More recently Desmond Williams and Oliver MacDonagh have written history at U.C.D. and in Australia. Kevin B. Nowlan,

William Brian Maginnis; Sir William Murphy Moore, Bart.; Samuel Clarke Porter; Charles Leo Sheil; Edward Sullivan Murphy; John Edmond Warnock; and Daniel Martin Wilson.
[62] Rory Johnston (ed.), *Orders and Desecrations: the life of the playwright Denis Johnston* (Dublin, 1992), p. 42.
[63] George Dames Burtchaell and Thomas Ulick Sadleir, whose names are linked as the joint compilers of *Alumni Dublinenses* (Dublin, 1924; 2nd edition, 1935).

as a young barrister, had a role in the celebrated Foyle Fisheries case, where law and history came together for professional profit.[64] Mention of this group of U.C.D. historians prompts recognition of the fact that the Literary and Historical Society of University College Dublin developed close associations with the Irish Bar early in the twentieth century, a time at which that Society may be said to have succeeded to the influence on the profession that Trinity College graduates, and members of the College Historical Society, had enjoyed in the nineteenth century.[65]

IX: The years of transition

The eclipse of the 'Hist' men by those of the 'L & H' is symptomatic of the watershed in the profession that accompanied the transfer of political power after 1922. In 1868 most members of the Bar, like the FitzGibbons, the family chosen to exemplify the spirit of the Bar in the late nineteenth century, were members of the Church of Ireland. At this date the King's Inns made no enquiry as to a man's religion, but the figures from the census of 1871 helpfully establish that Protestants outnumbered Roman Catholics at the Bar by more than 2 to 1. The figures from the 1911 census show that the proportion of Roman Catholics had grown, in forty years, from 30% to 44.5%, but establish that they still did not constitute a majority.[66] Later statistics are not available, but it is clear that the balance afterwards tilted rapidly and decisively. By 1968 the number of Protestants at the Irish Bar had greatly dwindled, and the few who came fresh to the profession from Trinity College were accounted brave.

The point at which the spirit of the Irish Bar ceased to be preponderantly Protestant and Unionist and became Roman Catholic and Nationalist is difficult to identify precisely. This change, which was the most significant of the developments to affect the profession in the course of the century, came about in the early years of the Irish Free State, but was gradual. The appointment of Hugh Kennedy as Chief Justice was an important stage in the process. Kennedy was a forthright nationalist, eager to distance the

[64] *Foyle and Bann Fisheries, Ltd. v. Attorney General and Others*: 83 I.L.T.R. 29.
[65] See, *passim*, James Meenan (ed.), *Centenary History of Literary and Historical Society of University College Dublin 1855-1955* (Tralee, n.d. [1956]).
    T.S.C. Dagg, whose name (like that of James Meenan) appears in this volume, wrote a history of the College Historical Society (Tralee, 1969). Dagg's book was privately printed in an edition of 25. It has been reproduced in part in Declan Budd and Ross Hinds (eds.), *The Hist and Edmund Burke's Club* (Dublin, 1997).
[66] These figures are quoted by W.E. Vaughan and L.P. Curtis in articles in *A New History of Ireland*, v, 741, and vi, 155 respectively. In 1868 Trinity College had 76 Roman Catholic students: ibid., v, 745.

new order from the old, and precipitate in attempting to impose the
Irish language as a condition for Call. His views were in advance of
the general mood, but his appointment to the top job made it clear
that a change had taken place in the criteria for appointment to
judicial office.[67] The spirit of the Bar did not change so abruptly.
Perhaps a telling moment was when the words PRO REGE,
GREGE, LEGE, quietly disappeared from the title page of the *Irish
Law Times*. This elegant little phrase with its succession of Latin
ablatives had been used by the journal since its inception in 1867-8,
the year of the Fenian rebellion. It made its last appearance in the
volume for 1936. Rex Mackey might bravely argue that Edward
VIII never ceased to be King of Ireland:[68] but the proprietors of the
Irish Law Times, perhaps disheartened by the conjuncture of the
Abdication Crisis, and the passage of de Valera's 1937 Constitution,
seem to have recognised the moment as apt to make the change.
Protestant numbers at the Bar were also falling. Judging from the
names, the proportion of Roman Catholics among those called had
increased significantly in the mid-1920s, which was also the
moment at which students for the Northern Ireland Bar ceased to
come to Dublin. Since the 1890s the King's Inns had been exporting
a proportion of its graduates to colonial jurisdictions, and it is likely
that from the 1920s more graduates went abroad who might in an
earlier decade have hazarded practising at home.

X: The barrister M.P.s of the Irish Party

An early harbinger of change, and a curious development of the
later 1880s, was the influx to the Bar of several Irish Party M.P.s.
The spectacle of established M.P.s entering the King's Inns as
students represented the inversion of the usual pattern of a public
career. In this category are found the names of nine, mostly well-
known, members of the Irish Parliamentary Party: A.M. Sullivan,
Tim Healy, Edmund Leamy, Timothy Harrington, J.J. Clancy, John
Deasy, M.J. Kenny, John Redmond, and William Redmond.[69] At

---

[67] Ball commenced the introduction to his catalogue of Irish judges with the
curiously-expressed statement that he treats of the judges in Ireland 'during the
seven centuries that the authority of England was absolute in their appointment'.
[68] Rex Mackey, *Windward of the Law* (1965), Appendix, pp 183-90.
[69] A.M. Sullivan: M.P. for County Louth, 1874-80, County Meath, 1880-2;
student E 1873, called M 1876.
   Tim Healy: M.P. for Wexford, 1880-83; County Monaghan, 1883-5;
Londonderry South, 1885-6; Longford North, 1887-92; Louth North, 1892-1910;
Cork North-East, 1911-180; student T 1881; called M 1884.
   Edmund Leamy: M.P. for Waterford City and other constituencies, 1880-1905;
student E 1884; called T 1885.

King's Inns some of these attended the lectures of J.G. Swift MacNeill, a Protestant Nationalist, who was then Professor of Constitutional and Criminal Law. In 1887 he became an M.P. himself, and sat in the House of Commons alongside his former pupils. In the Parnell Split the ten were evenly divided. Leamy, Harrington, Clancy and the Redmonds sided with the fallen leader. Healy, with Sullivan, Deasy, Kenny, and MacNeill opposed him.[70] Pierce Mahony, 'The O'Mahony,' an M.P. who had supported Parnell, later read for the Bar and was called in 1898. Mathias McD. Bodkin, a member of the Law Library, held a seat for the Anti-Parnellites during the parliament of 1892-5, and was ultimately rewarded in 1907 with a County Court judgeship.[71] Bodkin's case became a *cause célèbre* because at the time of his appointment he had not for some years been attending the Law Library and it was doubted whether he remained in practice.[72] His son, Thomas, who trained as a barrister, became Director of the National Gallery of Ireland, and later Professor of Fine Arts at Birmingham.

MacNeill took silk in 1893, and Bodkin in 1894. It may be surmised that some members of the phalanx of Irish Party M.P.s called in the 1880s may not have blended in easily with their colleagues in practice, but it does not follow that Roman Catholic students of the Royal University called in the ordinary way will have differed appreciably in outlook from their Protestant contemporaries. The French sociologist L. Paul-Dubois, whose book *Contemporary Ireland* was published in translation in 1908 with an introduction by Tom Kettle, characterised the lawyers as

---

Timothy Harrington: M.P. for Westmeath, 1883-5, and Dublin (Harbour), 1885, 1885-1910; student E 1884; called H 1887.

J.J. Clancy: M.P. for Dublin North, 1885; student T 1885; called E 1888. J.J. Clancy's grandson Noel is a current member of the Bar.

John Deasy: M.P. for Cork City, 1884-5, Mayo West, 1885-93; student T 1885; called E 1888.

M.J. Kenny: M.P. for Ennis, 1882-5, Mid-Tyrone, 1885-95; student T 1884; called T 1889.

John Redmond: M.P. for New Ross, 1881-5; Wexford North, 1885-91; Waterford City, 1891-1918; student E 1886; called M 1887.

William Redmond: M.P. for Wexford, 1883-5; Fermanagh North, 1885-92; Clare East, 1892-1917; student T 1887; called H 1891.

[70] Conor Cruise O'Brien, *Parnell and his Party 1880-90* (Oxford, 1957). Also called, at a later time [M 1902], was the English MP and barrister, Richard Rigg.

[71] MP for Roscommon North, 1892 to 1895. County Court Judge for Clare, 1907.

[72] In *Recollections of an Irish Judge* (1914), p. 86, Bodkin wrote: 'It was a mistake to call the House of Commons the best club in Europe. It is only the second best. The Irish law library is the best. I have been for some time a member of both, and ought to know'.

forming part of the 'English oligarchy'.[73] In one phrase (which owes more to what may be Kettle's translation than to the original French) it is alleged that those who belong to the 'Ascendancy' or 'Garrison' 'are all but absolute among the members of the bar':[74]

> The Garrison no longer make the laws, but they apply them, for it is they who control the greater part of the public functions in the State. They dominate the judicial bench, and are all but absolute among the members of the Bar; and they have Trinity College for the education of their sons. They constitute 'society', the 'respectable classes'.

He complained that only three of the 18 High Court judges, and 7 of the 21 County Court judges, were Roman Catholics.[75] Paul-Dubois was justified in complaining about the religious composition of the bench. An imbalance, in the proportion cited, had existed since the end of the nineteenth century. The matter was the subject of an illuminating letter sent to *The Times* in December 1899, when a seat on the bench was vacant following the death of William O'Brien. The writer ascribed the problem to the difficulty of Unionist administrations in finding Roman Catholic candidates for the Bench who adhered to their party:[76]

> The facts I have stated are to be explained — partially at least — by the adoption of Home Rule as the main factor in the Gladstonian policy. A large number of the Roman Catholic lawyers in Ireland, though by no means all, followed their leaders on that disastrous path and went beyond them. Judges ought, of course, to be appointed on purely professional grounds, yet Unionist Governments could hardly be expected to go out of their way to promote men at the Bar who have identified themselves, not only with Separatist schemes for breaking up the United Kingdom, but with an agitation directed against the authority of the law and the judiciary, as well as against the power of the Executive Administration. It is difficult to see how such considerations can be disregarded. Nevertheless, it seems clear that if there are men of distinction at the Irish Bar, born and bred in the faith of the majority, of whose fidelity to the cause of law and order there can be no doubt, and there certainly are such men, it would be expedient, *ceteris paribus*, to choose Mr. Justice O'Brien's successor from among them.

---

[73] L. Paul-Dubois, *Contemporary Ireland. With an Introduction by T.M. Kettle, M.P.* (Dublin, 1908), p. 189. It is not clear from the book, but a recent writer asserts that Kettle was the translator: see Senia Pašeta, 'Thomas Kettle. "An Irish soldier in the army of Europe?" ', in Adrian Gregory and Senia Pašeta (eds), *Ireland and the Great War: 'A war to unite us all'?* (Manchester, 2002), pp 8-27, at p. 11.

[74] Ibid., pp 91, 93. The French reads: 'Elle [meaning 'l'Ascendency' or 'la Garnison'] tient tout le *banc* des juges et presque tout le prétoire des avocats': pp 85-6 of Paris edition of 1907. One may posit that 'le prétoire des avocats' was French for the Law Library.

[75] Ibid., p. 189.

[76] *The Times*, Monday 11 Dec. 1899, p. 4, col. 6.

It is contrary to expectation to find, at the beginning of the twentieth century, that the proportion of Roman Catholics judges was *falling*: but the aspect which is yet more unexpected is that Roman Catholics had briefly, at the beginning of our period, constituted a majority of the bench. The letter-writer set out the facts:

> Now, at the end of 1873, just before the fall of Mr. Gladstone's first administration, the proportion was as follows:- There were ten Roman Catholics on the bench, including the Lord Chancellor (O'Hagan), the Chief Justice of the Common Pleas, the Chief Baron, six puisne judges, and the Landed Estates Court Judge. There were seven Protestant judges, Chief Justice Whiteside, Lord Justice Christian, the Master of the Rolls, three puisne judges, and the Probate Court Judge. Soon after Mr. Gladstone's return to office in 1880 the numbers were eight Roman Catholics against nine Protestants, but in the following year the numbers were made equal by the appointment of Mr. Justice O'Hagan to the newly-created judgeship in the Land Commission. By the end of 1886 the change had gone further. There were twelve Protestants on the bench against six Roman Catholics. Lately, as I have said, the proportion has been fourteen against four.

Paul-Dubois, having levelled his charges against the judges and the members of the Bar, 'le prétoire des avocats', goes on to complain that 'among the higher functionaries not more than one in five or six is a Catholic in religion, or of Nationalist sympathies in politics'. Significantly, he adds that the 'few that one does find in high office are more "loyal" than the king, and more reactionary than their colleagues'. The statement suggests that the fault-line in the upper levels of society was political, and not religious. It may be objected that Paul-Dubois, as a Frenchman, collecting his information at second hand, is not the best witness to the spirit current in the Irish Bar in 1907; but, against that, he is likely to have imbibed perceptions that were current among those to whom he spoke, such as the barrister Tom Kettle, who wrote the introduction for, and may himself have translated, the English edition of the book.

Paul-Dubois's book appeared during a prolonged and uneasy period of political transition. The Law Library had its loyal garrison, but other citadels had fallen. The Land Act of 1881, and subsequent measures facilitating land purchase, had undermined the economic foundations of Anglo-Ireland, although the enactment of these measures brought ample opportunities for professional employment at the Bar. Elizabeth Bowen's father was but one of several members of the Law Library who laboured to compose works on Land Purchase. The widening of the electoral franchise, alas, brought no such consolation, and worked especially to the detriment of Liberal barristers hoping to find a way into the House of

Commons. Power in local government had changed hands decisively in 1898, diminishing the role open to such King's Inns-educated country gentleman as had hitherto been active on the Grand Juries of their counties. After the Liberal election victory in 1905 the Nationalists had the ear of Dublin Castle.[77] The prospect of Home Rule, pushed off the agenda for a time but not dispelled, again overshadowed public affairs.

XI: The Bar and electoral politics

Since prospects of judicial preferment, like influence generally at Dublin Castle and in London, shifted in response to party fortunes at Westminster, it was a time of intensive political organisation. Members of the Bar played a leading role in fighting parliamentary elections. With the exception of the seats in Trinity College (represented in 1906 and 1910 by two K.C.s, Carson and Campbell), and the marginal seats in South County Dublin and the St. Stephen's Green Ward (the latter contested unsuccessfully in January 1910 by Henry Daniel Connor, K.C.), Nationalists monopolised the parliamentary representation outside Ulster. In that province several barristers stood as Unionist candidates in the elections of 1910 — Thomas Stephenson Francis Battersby, K.C., Gerald FitzGibbon Brunskill, James Chambers K.C., Godfrey Fetherstonhaugh, K.C., John Gordon, K.C., Denis Stanislaus Henry, K.C., Andrew Long Horner, K.C., and William Moore, K.C. Many of the Irish Party's M.P.s have been mentioned, stuff gownsmen with the exception of Swift MacNeill (M.P. for South Donegal) and T.M. Healy, who got his silk gown in 1899, and pursued a career as an Independent Nationalist.[78] To the list may be added later the names of Laurence Ginnell, Tom Kettle (an M.P. between 1906 and 1910), John McKean, Thomas O'Donnell, William Archer Redmond (the latter John Redmond's son, who in 1910 succeeded Kettle in the representation of East Tyrone), Daniel Sheehan, and a K.C., Patrick Lynch, de Valera's opponent in the 1917 by-election in East Clare necessitated by Willie Redmond's death. The East Clare election called forth a cartoon by Grace Plunkett (the artist, *née* Gifford, who had married the 1916 leader Joseph Mary Plunkett on the eve of his execution) showing de Valera in the uniform of the Irish Volunteers, and Patrick Lynch in wig and gown holding a brief labelled 'Crown

---

[77] See Lawrence W. McBride, *The Greening of Dublin Castle: The transformation of Bureaucratic and Judicial Personnel in Ireland, 1892-1922* (Washington, D.C., 1991), pp 30-37, and 160-2.
[78] His nephew Maurice, of the Munster Circuit, fought a seat in the family cause, though without success

WHICH?

VOTE FOR DE VALERA, A Felon of Our Land

Grace Plunkett's cartoon from the East Clare election of 1917

prosecutions' (this a reference to the circumstance that Lynch was Crown prosecutor in Kerry). In the election Lynch received 2035 votes, and Dev 5010. The remarkable footnote to the election is that twenty years later the defeated candidate was serving as his opponent's Attorney-General, an outcome which Maurice Healy pronounced to be 'to the honour of both candidates'.[79]

In 1906 William Huston Dodd, K.C. had the distinction of being his party's only successful candidate in Ireland when he was elected as Liberal M.P. for North Tyrone, a marginal constituency where the religious divide was nearly equal. The seat was unique in being held by a succession of Liberal barristers who, with the Irish Party standing aside, managed to garner just enough votes. In the representation of North Tyrone Dodd had succeeded the elderly (and subsequently ennobled) Charles Hare Hemphill, K.C. (1821-1908; called M 1845). Soon afterwards, when Dodd was appointed to the bench, he in turn was succeeded at a by-election by Redmond Barry, K.C., a future Lord Chancellor. Dodd and Barry had defeated

[79] *The Old Munster Circuit*, p. 150. The artist Grace Plunkett (*née* Gifford) [1888-1955] was a solicitor's daughter: see Marie O'Neill, *Grace Gifford Plunkett and Irish Freedom: Tragic Bride of 1916* (Dublin, 2000).

the Unionist candidate, their colleague, Denis Henry K.C., by the narrow margins of nine votes, and seven, respectively.

It is worthy of mention that the defeated Unionist candidate in North Tyrone was a Roman Catholic, and even more remarkable that this person should go on to become the first Lord Chief Justice of Northern Ireland. During the last decades of the old order, notwithstanding political excitement and denominational rancour in the wider world, the Bar accommodated social and political change gracefully. It naturally helped that change was gradual, and that, as in the case of Denis Henry, confessional background and political allegiance did not always conform to stereotype.[80]

Barristers accounted themselves gentlemen, a calling which prescribes not only attention to good manners but disregard of the mercenary. They were nevertheless united in desiring to earn a living, and there are occasional glimpses that this was not easy. In the Easter Term of 1903, for example, there was no Call to the Bar, a circumstance that was the subject of comment in the press:[81]

> Business at the Bar in Ireland (says the *Daily News*) must be in a bad way. Not one solitary recruit for the profession of the law put in an appearance at the opening of the Easter Sittings in Dublin. There was not a single call to the Bar, nor did the Benchers of the King's Inns receive one petition from an intending law student. This boycott of the Bar is said to be unprecedented. But if without precedent, it is very easy to understand. It is notorious that litigation has decreased very materially of late in Ireland, and if the land question is settled in the next score of years or so, the legal business of the country will become further depressed. The prospects of success at the Bar are so doubtful that young Irishmen are turning their thoughts in other directions.

XII: The Bar and the First World War

The cohesion of the profession that was more noticeable than its divisions, is nowhere better observed than at the outbreak of the first world war, when the innately loyal instincts of most members of the profession and the policy of the leaders of the Irish Party coincided. The number of King's Inns barristers that can be shown to have joined up approached 130. This total is large relative to a practising Bar of some 300 members. Not all of those who went to the war were members of the Law Library, but the Library nevertheless

---

[80] But when Cherry (a member of the General Synod) stood for parliament as a Liberal in 1900, his pro-Boer sympathies gave offence: 'Some of his friends refused to speak to him, and often a group chatting at the Library fire would disperse at his approach'. See Maud Cherry's *Memoir* of her father (Dublin, 1924), p. 16.
[81] *I.L.T. & S.J.*, xxxvii, 2 May 1903, p. 184.

contributed a contingent of very creditable size, and practitioners were prominent among the twenty-five[82] who fell and whose names appear on the War Memorial in the corridor of the West Annexe of the Law Library building, a Memorial originally designed for the staircase of Drew's Law Library, but first unveiled, in the time of exile, on the Battle-axe Landing in Dublin Castle.[83] The sculptor was Oliver Sheppard (1865-1941), Professor of Sculpture at the Royal Hibernian Academy, and the designer of a similar Memorial commissioned by the Solicitors,[84] and of the statue of the dying Cúchulain in the General Post Office. The inscription reads:

IN MEMORY OF

THE IRISH BARRISTERS

WHO FELL IN THE GREAT WAR

1914 --------------- 1918

Robert B Burgess	Martin A Lillis
William M Crozier	William A Lipsett
Robert H Cullinan	Cornelius A MacCarthy
John H Edgar	Edmund Meredith
Edmond C Farren	Arthur R Moore
Poole H Hickman	Hubert M O'Connor
Ernest L Julian	Gerald Plunkett
Cecil S Kenny	James C B Proctor
Thomas M Kettle	William Redmond
Joseph B Lee	Arthur P I Samuels
John H F Leland	Rowan Shaw
Frederick H Lewin	George B J Smyth

Herbert Tierney

THEIR NAME LIVETH UNTO GENERATION AND GENERATION

Eight of those honoured died in Flanders, and five on the Somme. Six perished in the Dardanelles campaign. Two, MacCarthy, and Tierney, died in Mesopotomia, where their names may be sought on the British War Memorial in Basra.

---

[82]   The lives of the twenty-five are the subject of A.P. Quinn's forthcoming book, *Wigs and Guns* (Dublin: Irish Legal History Society, 2005).
[83]   *I.L.T. & S.J.*, lviii (31 May 1924), pp 138-9. The Memorial was unveiled by Lord Chief Justice Molony on Tuesday 20 May 1924.
[84]   This had been unveiled on one of the walls of the Solicitors' Building, prior to the destruction of the Four Courts, but was salved [see *I.L.T.& S.J.*, lvi, 12 August 1922, p. 193]. In January 2003, having been in Blackhall Place for more than twenty years, the monument was returned to the Four Courts, and placed on the wall of the corridor of the East Annexe opposite and to the left of the entrance to the Solicitors' Building. For an illustrated description of the solicitors' monument, see Daire Hogan, 'Irish lawyers and the Great War', in *Law Society Gazette*, December 1998, pp 20-1.

NAMES OF 127 MEMBERS OF THE IRISH BAR WHO SERVED IN THE FIRST WORLD WAR.

The 25 who died are indicated thus †

North-west Bar
Atkinson, Thomas J. D
Atkinson, William H.
Dickie, Thomas Wallace
Doherty James Walker
Holmes, Hugh Oliver
Hughes, Thomas
Johnston, J. Weir
Kennedy, Henry Edward
† Lee, Joseph Bagnall
Lemass, Edwin Stephen
Lipsett, Lewis Richard
† Lipsett, William Alfred
Malone, Herbert
Munn, Lionel O. M.
† Plunkett, Gerald
† Proctor, James C.B.
† Samuels, Arthur P.I.
Walsh, Patrick S., K.C.

North-east Bar
Arnold, John Corry
Brett, George Henry
† Burgess, Robert B.
Carvill, Henry John
† Crozier, William Magee
Daly, Oscar B.
Gordon, Alan Samuel
Harbinson, William Dawson
Higgins, Thomas S. Alfred
Kingan, Thomas Davison
† Leland, John Henry F.
Little, James (jun.)
Longworth, Ernest Victor
Macafee, William
MacKeown, W.W.
McNeill, Robert Norman
McWilliam, William
Pringle, James Alexander
† Shaw, Rowan
Sheehy, Eugene
† Smyth, G.B.J.
Warnock, Edmond .
Wilson, Daniel M., K.C.
   (Bencher of King's Inns)

Munster Bar
Conner, Henry Longfield
† Cullinan, Robert Hornige
Cummins, William Ashley

† Farran, Edmond C.
Healy, Joseph
Healy, Maurice F.
† Hickman, Poole Henry
† Lillis, Martin Arthur
Maunsell, Richard J. C
† MacCarthy, Cornelius
McCormick, Hilgrove
Mahony, Edward Ronayne
Mockler, James G.
Mooney, Gerald Kingston
Moriarty, Oliver L.
Murray, John
Naish, Redmond J.
O'Grady, Guillamore
   (Dublin Herald of Arms)
Roche, Christopher
Sheehan, Daniel D., M.P.
Sherlock, David T. J.
† Tierney, Herbert S.
Tyrrell, Robert Leslie
Walsh, James F.

Connaught Bar
Burke, Joseph Bermingham
Campbell, W.P.
FitzGibbon, Frank
† Julian, Ernest L.
† Lewin, Frederick Henry
McCarthy, Gerald F.

Leinster Bar
DeRenzy, Annesley St.G, K.C.
Forsayeth, Gordon William
Miley, John Felix
† Moore, Arthur Robert
† O'Connor, Hubert M.
Thomas, Richard William
White, R. Grove

Others
Barton, Cecil Molyneux
Coghlan, Joseph P.
Corley, Harry Cecil
Courtenay, Arthur H., C.B., D.L. (Master of the King's Bench Division)
Dickinson, Harold Evory
Doherty, Patrick E.
Esmonde, L. Grattan

Filgate, Edward Macartney
FitzGibbon, Harry Macaulay
Gentleman, John Wesley
Gerrard, John D. (R.M.)
Gibson, The Hon. E. Victor
Gill, Roy Anthony F.
Hughes, Thomas W. G.
Jackson, James A. D.
John, Samuel Spedding
Joynt, William R.S. Lane
Kennedy, Frederick Alex.
† Kenny, Cecil Stackpoole
Kenny, Vincent Raymond
† Kettle, Thomas M.
Lidwell, Robert A.
Lowry, Frederick James
Madden, John C.W.
Matthews, Patrick Duff
Matthews, James Stanley
Manders, Richard C.B,
   K.C., Registrar of Deeds and Titles.
Maunder, Stephen T. L.
Mooney, Edmund W. B..
McWalter, James Charles
Newcomen, George A.
Place, Charles Geoffery M.
Plunkett, Oliver
Purcell, Herbert Kevin
† Redmond, William, M.P.
Redmond, William Archer, M.P.
Richey, Henry A.
Ross, Ernest Alexander
Ryan, Leonard Morrogh
Shaw, R.J. Herbert
Shaw, John H. de B.
Swifte, Ernest G.M.
Teeling, Theo. F.
Tighe, Hubert McCartan
Wakely, Ian George

Two names on the Bar War Memorial not found in the above list:-

† Edgar, John H.
† Meredith, Edmund

Source: *The Irish Law Times War Supplement,* 1916. All but 7 of 124 barristers noted as serving were commissioned. The same source named 103 serving solicitors, and 71 solicitors' apprentices. 95 barristers were noted as having sons serving.

Members of the Law Library who were too old or settled to go to France helped the war effort in other ways. There was a 'Four Courts Auxiliary Munitions Association', which Sir John Ross promoted:[85]

> The skilled men in the shell factory and munitions works refused to forgo their Saturday afternoons and Sundays, and the machines stood idle during these times. I had a large meeting assembled in the solicitors' buildings consisting of barristers, solicitors and Civil servants, and set before them a scheme under which they were to form themselves into shifts, to take over the work of making the munitions ... The proposal was enthusiastically taken up, and work commenced at once. Some of the foremost men at the Bar proved themselves the most efficient workers.

Serjeant Sullivan, whom Sir John Ross singled out for praise, recalled:[86]

> The Law Library ran a munition factory from one o'clock on Saturday afternoon till nine o'clock on Monday mornings, until we were objected to as blackleg labour. As we were paid nothing I recognised the fairness of the charge, and we resigned in favour of the trade unions. In our brief spell of activity, we learned something of the conditions of working with machinery, and that is useful for every man to know. Those of us who could use voice and pen devoted ourselves to propaganda.

Sir John Ross did not himself take part in the work at the shell factory, but he did join an ambulance unit:[87]

> I was also much interested in the training of an Ambulance Brigade at the Four Courts, consisting mainly of registrars, court criers, and messengers. As the differences in rank among these volunteers presented difficulties, I was drilled myself as an ordinary private and duly yelled at to keep up my head, throw out my chest, and keep step, like the rest. Some of the company went out to France as stretcher-bearers, and others proved most useful in unloading hospital ships, and conveying patients to hospital.

Others responded to a letter of 1 June 1915, signed jointly by Henry Hanna K.C. and John McGonigal K.C., which appealed for recruits to the various units that made up the Irish Association of Volunteer Training Corps. Ambulance, and supply and transport, duties were the expectation of these older men.[88] The letter promised that 'Motorists, motor cyclists and cyclists will be gladly welcomed as members without having exacted from them any extended period of foot drill or rifle drill'. Lord Justice Molony and Mr. Justice Barton were the honorary officers of the Veterans' Corps, and John

---

[85] *I.L.T. & S.J.*, l, 26 Feb. 1916, p. 54; John Ross, *The Years of my Pilgrimage: Random Reminiscences* (1924), p. 260.
[86] *Old Ireland: Reminiscences of an Irish K.C.*, p. 173.
[87] *The Years of my Pilgrimage*, p. 257.
[88] *I.L.T. & S.J*, xlix, 5 June 1915, pp 138-9.

McGonigal K.C. was its organiser in the Library. This corps, whose members were jocularly known (from their 'G[eorgius] R[ex]' buttons) as the 'Gorgeous Wrecks', came under fire near Beggars Bush Barracks on Easter Monday 1916.[89] F.H. Browning, a barrister-member of the IRFU Corps, and Sub-Commandant of the Volunteer Training Corps, was killed in the attack. Born in 1868 and called to the Bar in 1891, 'Chicken' Browning had used his legal knowledge at the Land Registry, where he was an Examiner of Titles. As President of the Irish Rugby Football Union, he had been a leading organiser of recruitment in Dublin, and a prime mover of the 'Pals' Battalion.

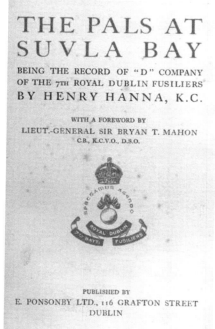

THE PALS AT SUVLA BAY

BEING THE RECORD OF "D" COMPANY OF THE 7TH ROYAL DUBLIN FUSILIERS

BY HENRY HANNA, K.C.

WITH A FOREWORD BY
LIEUT.-GENERAL SIR BRYAN T. MAHON
C.B., K.C.V.O., D.S.O.

PUBLISHED BY
E. PONSONBY LTD., 116 GRAFTON STREET
DUBLIN

Five members of the Law Library joined the celebrated 'Pals' Battalion, a unit of the Royal Dublin Fusiliers that suffered heavy casualties in the Gallipoli landings of August 1915. In 1916 Henry Hanna K.C., who was later to the fore in planning the Bar's war memorial, wrote *The Pals at Suvla Bay*, a history which included photographs of the five barristers, three of whom had been killed.[90] The Pals, being a unit 'composed almost entirely of Dublin gentlemen', had been given the privilege of electing their officers. Ernest Julian, the Reid Professor in Trinity College, 'a man of high character, much learning, and strong individuality', was thus elected to a commission. He died of wounds in a hospital ship off Gallipoli.[91]

To convey the spirit of the opening months of the war Henry Hanna relied on an article in the *Dublin Evening Mail,* which had sent a reporter to the Curragh:[92]

---

[89]   *Sinn Fein Rebellion Handbook* (Dublin, 1916), pp 19-20, 215.
[90]   The five were W.H. Atkinson, Poole H. Hickman, Ernest L. Julian, H. de B. Shaw and Herbert Tierney. Richard Armstrong, the son of the King's Inns Under-Treasurer, was also a member of the Battalion.
[91]   Henry Hanna, *The Pals at Suvla Bay* (Dublin [n.d., 1917]), pp 7, 18.
[92]   Ibid., p. 26.

A soldier came forward to greet me. His name was Atkinson. The
last time I saw him he was wearing a wig and gown in the Four
Courts. He has since been promoted to the rank of lance-serjeant. In
the Officers' Mess ... I came across ... Lieutenant Poole Hickman.
The last time I saw him he, too, was wearing a wig and gown. He,
too, had been promoted to another battle-ground. Then I came
across Lieutenant Julian, formerly Reid Professor of Law in Dublin
University and a member of the Irish Bar. He also has been
promoted to the Irish Brigade.

On 30 April 1915, when the Battalion left Dublin, says Henry
Hanna:[93]

> In front of the Four Courts a large crowd of barristers, solicitors and
> officials gave a cordial send-off to the men. Amongst the crowd
> were judges, whose sittings had concluded for the day, and they
> cheered as spontaneously as the others as the men passed. In the
> ranks were members of the Bar, who had forsaken excellent
> prospects to keep the Old Flag flying, and as they were recognized
> they were cordially cheered.

In November 1914, to protect the interests of those who had
'forsaken excellent prospects', the Bar Council, adopting an English
precedent, passed the following Resolutions:[94]

> RESOLUTIONS OF THE GENERAL COUNCIL OF THE BAR
> OF IRELAND OF NOVEMBER 27TH, 1914.
> That with a view to preserving so far as possible the practice of
> barristers who are unable to attend to their business owing to their
> serving in His Majesty's Forces, or otherwise in connection with the
> war, solicitors be asked to adopt the following procedure in every
> case in which a solicitor would normally have employed a barrister
> so serving:-
> (1) The solicitor to continue to place the name of the barrister so
> serving on brief and papers.
> (2) The solicitor to deliver such briefs and papers, together with the
> fee marked thereon to such barrister as he may, in his own
> discretion, from time to time select, and to invite such barrister to
> hold the brief or attend to the papers so delivered to him on behalf
> of the barrister whose name is placed thereon.
> That with a view to preserving so far as possible the practice of
> every barrister who is unable to attend to his business owing to his
> serving in His Majesty's Forces, or otherwise in connection with the
> war (hereinafter designated as A.B.), the Bar Council recommend:-
> (a) That all barristers should make it a point of honour to do what
> they can to ensure that A.B. may get back his practice intact when
> he resumes work at the Bar.
> (b) That all barristers, whether senior or junior to A.B., should, so
> far as is reasonably practicable, do the work of A.B.

---

[93]   Ibid., p. 31.
[94]   *I.L.T. & S.J.*, xlviii, 5 December 1914, p. 341.

Captain Poole Hickman (left), a member of the Munster Circuit, died on 16 August 1915 leading a bayonet charge at Suvla. From 7 January 1915 he had been Officer Commanding the 'Pals', i.e. 'D' Company of the 7th Royal Dublin Fusiliers. Lieutenant Ernest Julian (right), the Reid Professor of Law at Trinity College, died of wounds on a hospital ship on 7 August 1915.

[From Henry Hanna, *The Pals at Suvla Bay*.]
King's Inns Barristers, 1868–2004, page 83.

Two intellectuals lost in the War: Tom Kettle (left), Professor of National Economics at UCD, who fell at Ginchy on 9 September 1916. His widow Mary was the sister of Eugene Sheehy and the aunt of Conor Cruise O'Brien. Captain Arthur Samuels (right), of the 11th Royal Irish Rifles, who died in Flanders on 24 September 1916, also left a young widow. He was an ex-Auditor of the College Historical Society, and his literary memorial is a work on the young Edmund Burke.

King's Inns Barristers, 1868-2004, page 84.

(c) That any barrister doing the work for A.B. should, after his signature to any pleadings or other documents, add 'for A.B. now serving in His Majesty's Forces' (or as the case may be), and if holding a brief should state to the Court for whom he is holding such brief and for what reason.

The *Irish Law Times* reported on the war service of members of both branches of the profession, and its *War Supplement,* published in its issue of 26 February 1916, is an unrivalled source of information.[95]

In treating of the war it is right to add a footnote about the Indian students at the King's Inns, one of whose number [V.V. Giri; T 1916] became President of India, and a couple of dozen of whom are conspicuous in the Call List of Trinity Term 1917. The Indian students began arriving in Dublin in the first half of 1914. No fewer than fifteen 'natives of our Indian Empire' were among the 32 students who submitted Memorials in November 1915. In Easter Week of the following year, as the *Sinn Fein Rebellion Handbook* acknowledged, the King's Inns Indian students attached themselves to the Rathmines unit of the St. John Ambulance Brigade.[96] In July 1917, when most of the Indians went home, the *Irish Law Times* reported thus on the farewell reception that was accorded to them:[97]

A social gathering was held on Friday evening, 29th ult., in the Gregg Memorial Hall to meet the members of the Dublin Indian Association, especially those lately called to the Irish Bar, on the eve of their departure for India. Mr. Justice Barton, who was in the chair, thanked the Y.M.C.A., on behalf of the legal profession, for the comforts it had extended to the students during their stay in Ireland. The Benchers of King's Inns and others of the legal profession were proud of their Indian students. They were proud of the good conduct which marked them as a body ever since they had come to Ireland. They were proud of the students' good manners. They were proud to congratulate them on their industry and on the distinction which some of them had won in their examinations. The students came from all parts of the Indian Empire. They came from all the provinces and all the presidencies, even from some of the native States. Mr. Justice Dodd was present and said that the Indian students who were going away had succeeded in passing a stiff examination in what was to them a foreign tongue. He hoped that they and the British would be bound together in brotherhood.

---

[95] See *I.L.T. & S.J.*, l, 26 Feb. 1916, p. 53. 'Our War Supplement. The members of the legal profession in Ireland are a comparatively small number, but they have supplied to the ranks of His Majesty's Forces no fewer than 126 barristers, 110 solicitors, 71 solicitors' apprentices, 160 sons of barristers, and 175 sons of solicitors.'
[96] *I.L.T. & S.J.,* xlviii (1914), p. 124; xlix (1915), p. 278; li (1917), p. 164; *Sinn Fein Rebellion Handbook*, p. 166.
[97] *I.L.T. & S.J.*, li, 7 July 1917, p. 164.

XIII: The Bar and the Troubles

In Michaelmas Term 1898 one Patrick Henry Pearse was admitted as a student of the King's Inns, and in Trinity Term 1901, at 31 years of age, he was called to the Irish Bar. A photograph of

him in his wig and gown testifies to the occasion, and the wig and gown have since become the property of the National Museum. Two reported cases, both connected with the Irish language [*McBride v. McGovern* [1906] 2 I.R. 181 and 5 *New Irish Jurist Rep.* 242; and *Buckley v. Finnegan* 40 ILTR 76] show that he twice went to court. He had the experience in the King's Bench of running his case as a junior when the senior (Tim Healy) did not turn up; and, while losing the case, was the recipient of a compliment of sorts from the bench. Mr. Justice Andrews (1832-1924; E 1855) referred to 'the very ingenious, interesting, and, from a literary point of view, instructive arguments of Mr. [P.S.] Walsh and Mr. Pearse'.

The *Sinn Fein Rebellion Handbook,* in a biographical entry for Pearse, places the letters B.L. after B.A. in giving his qualifications. The entry includes the doubtful assertion: 'Evidence exists that Pearse intended to occupy the post of Provost of Trinity College in the event of the rebellion being a success'. His biographer, Ruth Dudley Edwards, says nothing of this claim, which may have been inspired by Pearse's resentment of his treatment by Provost Mahaffy: but it can safely be said that Pearse had no eye on a seat on the judicial bench. Ruth Dudley Edwards reveals that Pearse, once qualified, 'missed no opportunity to sneer at lawyers' and regarded law 'as the most wicked of all professions'. He was nevertheless vain enough to use the letters 'B.L'., and his Gaelic League critic, Father Dinneen the lexicographer, was known to refer to him as 'B-A-B-L'.[98]

---

[98]   Ruth Dudley Edwards, *Patrick Pearse: The Triumph of Failure* (1977; 1979 paperback edition), p. 48.
    The abbreviation 'B.L' signifying Barrister-at-Law, appears to have come into use in the late nineteenth century, not long before Pearse acquired the qualification. Like 'N.T.' for National Teacher, which is of similar origin, it seems to be an abbreviation peculiar to Ireland. The form is habitually used by solicitors in

In 1916 the *Irish Law Times* did not mention Pearse, nor did it advert to the facts that a member of the Irish Bar had put himself at the head of a destructive rebellion, or that he was subsequently shot under the authority of martial law. News of this character was left to 'the lay press'.[99] Part of the charm of the *Irish Law Times* is that it was a discreet and well-mannered publication, speaking ill of no man, reluctant to ventilate matter tending to professional embarrassment. The omission, however, is a cautionary reminder of the extent to which a historian of the Irish Bar is dependent on the materials which the *Irish Law Times* chose to print. Then, as now, much must have been said in the Law Library that posterity will never know.[100]

On Tuesday 11 April 1916, a fortnight before the outbreak of the rebellion, criminal trials had begun at Green Street:[101]

> Mr. Justice Kenny, in opening the proceedings of the Commission for the City of Dublin, referred to a propaganda in the city of an openly seditious character which set all authority at defiance, and seemed to be started in order to counteract the recruiting movement. They had, he said, read of the police, in the execution of their duty, being met and repulsed by men armed with rifle and bayonet, and of street disturbance in which firearms appeared to be freely used. What he regarded as the most serious attempt to paralyse recruiting was the display of large posters, such as 'England's Last Ditch' and 'The Pretence of the Realm Act', which must necessarily have a most mischievous and deterrent influence on certain classes of the population. He called attention to it because continuance of that state of things must have a tendency to create incalculable mischief.

The *Irish Law Times* missed a week as a result of the rebellion, but its first issue after the event reported:[102]

> Easter Term began on Thursday, 27th ult., but on that day the Four Courts was in the hands of the Sinn Feiners, who took possession of the Law Library and other buildings, piling text-books, law reports, and books of record in the windows as barriers behind which to shoot. We understand that the buildings are not damaged seriously,

---

correspondence with barristers. Barristers themselves use it less, and some would disdain to employ it.

[99] To this policy of decorous restraint there was an occasional exception. In the issue of 10 April 1926 (*I.L.T. & S.J.*, vol. lx, p. 92) we read: 'It is reported in the Press that the person who fired the shot which wounded Signor Mussolini, in Rome, on Wednesday, was the Hon. Violet Albina Gibson, the third daughter of the first Lord Ashbourne, twice Lord Chancellor of Ireland. Miss Gibson is described as a lady of eccentric habits.'

[100] Like the *Irish Law Times*, the *Dictionary of National Biography* originally paid no heed to Pearse. He was not included in the volume proper to the decade of his death, but was subsequently included in the *Missing Persons* volume, edited by C.S. Nicholls in 1993.

[101] *Sinn Fein Rebellion Handbook*, p. 6.

[102] *I.L.T. & S.J.*, l, issue of 29 April and 6 May 1916, p. 108.

save in the loss of glass, and that they will be fit for occupation in a few days. Meetings of the Judges and Benchers and of the Library Committee were held on Friday 5th inst., when provisional arrangements were made for opening the Courts and the Law Library on 19th inst.

The effect of the rebellion on the Four Courts was described as follows in the *Sinn Fein Rebellion Handbook*:[103]

> The Courts of Law presented an extraordinary appearance. The gates were closed and barricaded with all kinds of furniture, and inside each was a Volunteer sentry. The buildings within were held by the rebels, whose number could not be ascertained. That many hands had been at work was apparent. Most of the windows were blocked with books and other things taken from the offices, many of which doubtless contained valuable records. Church street Bridge was a centre of interest. It had been barricaded by the Sinn Feiners on Monday. A couple of sentries, marching up and down, did not allow the many inquisitive sight-seers to cross into the space at the end of Church-street. It was possible to go up the Southern quays, but not up the Northern, owing to the position of the Volunteers. The next bridge was open to pedestrians, but was not free from danger. The rebels took in a number of prisoners, and kept them until they surrendered on Saturday. The Mendicity Institute, not far off, had been one of the rebels' fortresses, but had been successfully enfiladed by the soldiers on Monday.
>
> Easter Sittings should have commenced on Thursday, 27th April, but at the time when the Lord Chancellor would, under ordinary circumstances, have been standing, in the Central Hall, wearing his State robes and receiving the judges, the building was in possession of the insurgents, and bloody war had usurped the place of law.
>
> Much anxiety was felt as to what was going on in the Record Office, where thousands of valuable historical documents, wills, deeds, etc., are stored, and great relief was experienced when it was found that the majority of these documents, though much tossed about, had not been seriously damaged. Some bundles containing wills had been thrown out on the adjoining streets, and had been taken away by residents in Church-street, not so much, it is believed, as "loot", but rather as curious souvenirs of the rebellion. When these people learnt that the authorities were again in possession of the Record Office, it is to their credit that many of them brought these documents back to their custodian.

From the occupation of 1916 the Four Courts escaped virtually unscathed; but the event afforded a warning of a disaster waiting to happen. The outcome of the second occupation six years later would forever be rued.

---

[103] Ibid., p. 24.

In 1916 it was not to be foreseen that English authority would collapse so soon or so utterly, or that a small group of younger barristers sympathetic to the revolutionary movement would shortly be the beneficiaries of a change of government. The emergence of a Republican leaven at the Bar can first be detected in 1920, for on 23 June of that year the Bar in general meeting was asked to make a ruling about the Dáil courts. The *Irish Law Times* reported:[104]

THE BAR COUNCIL

At a very largely-attended meeting of the General Council of the Bar of Ireland, held in the Law Library, Four Courts, on Wednesday afternoon, the following question, which was received from a member of the Bar, was considered:- 'I request the opinion of the Bar Council on the question, whether a member of the Irish Bar is guilty of (a) professional misconduct, or (b) breach of professional etiquette in appearing as advocate before a tribunal constituted under the proclamation or submission produced by the Honorary Secretary'. The documents referred to, which were before the meeting, were concerned with an Arbitration Court to be held at Ballinasloe, Co. Galway, and another such court to be held at Tralee for the County of Kerry on July 3rd. These tribunals, the documents stated, were established in accordance with a decree of Dail Eireann. The Bar Council resolved:- 'That it is professional misconduct on the part of any member of the Bar to appear before such tribunals as are constituted under either of the documents laid before the Council'.

This meeting was in June. On 2 November the issue was brought back for consideration at the instance of the party aggrieved by the ruling made in June. This second meeting was adjourned, to preclude acrimony, without coming to a decision on the resolution before it. There is perhaps a hint in the following report that the discussion was in danger of becoming heated, but the implication of the adjournment is that the earlier disapprobation of the Dáil courts held good:[105]

THE IRISH BAR AND REPUBLICAN COURTS

A general meeting of the members of the Irish Bar was held on Tuesday afternoon in the Law Library of the Four Courts. The meeting was called to consider a resolution, of which notice had been given in the Library for some days, to the effect that it was *ultra vires* on the part of Bar Council to have passed a resolution declaring that it was professional misconduct for any barrister to appear before the Sinn Fein Republican Courts.

Mr. R.D. Murray, Father of the Bar, presided. He called upon Mr. Healy, K.C., whose name was attached to the notice on the board, to speak.

Mr. Healy said that he had not drafted the notice, and had not authorised his name to be attached to it; but he held that the Bar

---

[104] *I.L.T. & S.J.*, liv, 26 June 1920, p. 152.
[105] *I.L.T. & S.J.*, liv, 6 November 1920, pp 272-3.

Council had no right to pass judgment upon the conduct of any member of the Bar for his action or non-action. The only body who had that right was the Benchers, who admitted the men to the Bar. He had been thirty-nine years at the Bar, and nothing like this had arisen in his time. He did not know what was to be done, but he felt that the senior members should do what they could to protect the junior members of the Bar.

Mr. S.L. Brown, K.C., suggested that the meeting take no action on the subject matter before them. They had all been a happy family in the Library, and it would be a pity to introduce anything that would cause friction or disagreement. He moved that the meeting adjourn indefinitely.

This motion was seconded, and the meeting dispersed without having come to any decision on the matter before them.

Tim Healy, who moved the November motion, denied being its author. Which members of the 'junior bar' Tim Healy wished to assist and protect is a matter for speculation. Charles Bewley claimed in his Memoirs to have been 'the first barrister to appear in the Republican Courts',[106] and it is possible that indiscretion of his led to the matter's coming before the Bar in general meeting. The number of barristers whose interests were affected by the reference was nevertheless a small one, for we know that Austin Stack complained in August 1921 that he found 'the Irish Bar worthy of the bad traditions it always had; there were scarcely half a dozen patriotic men among them'.[107] To judge, however, from a study of the Dáil Courts published by Mary Kotsonouris,[108] and from scrutiny of the list of those advanced to judicial office by the Free State, Austin Stack could have claimed more than half a dozen but fewer than a score.

Hugh Kennedy, K.C. (M 1902; K.C., 1920) and James Creed Meredith, K.C. (M 1901; K.C., 1918), who in 1924 were appointed respectively Chief Justice and a judge of the High Court of the Irish Free State, were, with Arthur Clery (M 1902), Professor of Law at U.C.D., the most senior Republican sympathisers in the profession. Among the juniors the following names may be suggested, listed here in order of their standing at the Bar:

---

[106] *Memoirs of a Wild Goose* (Dublin, 1989), p. 67; and see also pp 67-70, 89-91, 92-5.

[107] Quoted by Daire Hogan, *The Legal Profession in Ireland*, p. 152.

[108] Mary Kotsonouris, *Retreat from Revolution: The Dáil Courts, 1920-24* (Dublin, 1994). See also: Daire Hogan, *The Legal Profession in Ireland*, pp 151-3; James Casey, 'Republican Courts in Ireland 1919-1922', in *Ir. Jurist*, v (1970), pp 321-42; and *R. (Kelly) v. Maguire and O'Shiel* [1923] 2 I.R. 58, where the defendants were barristers.

William Henry Brayden (T 1894)
St. Laurence Devitt (H 1901)
Joseph Mary Flood (M 1908)
Eugene Sheehy (M 1910)
John O'Byrne (H 1911)
Charles Stewart Kenny (M 1911)
Kevin O'Sheil (M 1913)
Charles Wyse Power (M 1913)

Charles Bewley (H 1914)
Henry Conner (M 1914)
Hector Hughes (T 1915)
Cecil Lavery (M 1915)
Cahir Davitt (H 1916
Jeremiah [alias Diarmuid]
    Crowley (T 1916).
George Gavan Duffy (M 1917)

Several of the above attained judicial office under the Free State. O'Byrne, Lavery, Davitt and Gavan Duffy became judges of the higher Courts. Devitt and Sheehy became judges of the Circuit Court, and Flood a District Justice. Crowley later fell out with his political friends over the amount of his pension for serving as a judge of the Dáil courts, and embarked on an unsuccessful action against the State.[109] Sheehy, who became the Circuit Court judge in Monaghan, wrote a memoir, notable for a story illustrative of the camaraderie of the Bar. His sister, a diehard Republican, found herself a prisoner in Armagh gaol, where Sheehy encountered difficulty in gaining entry to visit her until he persuaded the Governor of the prison to let him make a telephone call to the Attorney-General of Northern Ireland. It suffices to say that the holder of the latter office was Anthony Brutus Babington (M 1900), who not long before had been Sheehy's colleague in the Law Library. The story went on:[110]

> The Governor of the gaol was astonished to find that the prisoner's brother was the Judge of the neighbouring County. I explained to him that that was how things happened ... The criminal of one generation became the judge and law-maker of the next ... Topsyturvy was how the game was played in the field of politics; and I hinted that in a few years the Governor might see my sister sitting as Minister for Justice in an Irish Republic.

From time to time reports in the *Irish Law Times* cast light on the circumstances in which professional life was carried on during the disturbed years. Tim Healy, who failed to sway the meeting called to rule on the Dáil courts controversy, succeeded better on 21 March 1921, an occasion when Eugene Sheehy was associated with his motion:[111]

---

[109] Heard in the High Court by 'Civil Bill' Johnston, Denis Johnston's father, and reported, as *Ó Cruadhlaoich v. Minister for Justice and the Minister for Finance* at [1935] IR 536 and (1934) 68 ILTR 174.
[110] Eugene Sheehy, *May it please the Court*, pp 146-7, at 147.
[111] *I.L.T. & S.J.*, lv, 26 March 1921, p. 83.

BAR MEETING

A general meeting of the members of the Irish Bar was held in the Law Library, Four Courts, Dublin, on Monday, for the purpose of considering the action of Crown Forces in seizing and carrying away from the office of Mr. Michael Noyk, Solicitor briefs for counsel engaged to defend some of the prisoners charged with having taken part in the shooting of military officers in Dublin on the morning of Sunday, the 21st November last. On the motion of Mr. T.M. Healy, K.C., seconded by Mr. Eugene Sheehy, the following resolution was passed unanimously: 'That this meeting of the Bar hereby declare that the privileges of the Bar have been infringed by the action of certain members of the Crown Forces in raiding the office of Mr. Noyk, the solicitor engaged for the prisoners who were then awaiting sentence after their trial for murder, and seizing and carrying away the briefs of the counsel who had been engaged in their defence, which briefs contained the instructions for their defence, and counsel's notes thereon'. Mr. Healy, in proposing the resolution, referred to the inviolable nature of the confidence reposed in a counsel by his client, and to the gravity of an infringement of the privileges of counsel by such an incident as had occurred in this case. On the motion of Mr. T.J. Smyth, seconded by Mr. Vincent Rice, it was decided to send copies of the resolution to the Lord Lieutenant, the Lord Chancellor, the Chief Secretary, and to General Sir Nevil Macready.

Munster, the province in which the people still addressed barristers by their old name of *Counsellor*, was the scene of the greatest disorder during the disturbed years. In the summer of 1920 the Counsellors going south faced sundry inconveniences. Members of the Law Library were afterwards to lose all their possessions, including wigs and gowns, when the Four Courts was destroyed in 1922: but, as this report in the *Irish Law Times* shows, wigs and gowns had already been abandoned in the summer assizes of 1920:[112]

THE BAR AND THE RAILWAY TROUBLE

Owing to the uncertainty of service on the Great Southern and Western Railway at present, the judges going the Munster Circuit for the Summer Assizes, which opened on the 2nd inst. at Ennis, for the County of Clare, arranged to travel by motor cars. The barristers also are hampered in regard to their necessary baggage, including their wigs and gowns. Under these circumstances, the members of the Circuit who intend travelling to the South have obtained permission to appear in court without wig and gown. No difficulty has presented itself so far in regard to the other Circuits.

[112] *I.L.T. & S.J.*, liv, 10 July 1920, p. 163.

XIII: Women

Mention of wigs and gowns prompts a change of theme: the appearance at the Bar of women so attired. In the midst of the turmoil that was interfering with the Bar's travel arrangements to Munster, two young women had entered the King's Inns to read for the Bar, Agnes Deverell in Michaelmas Term 1919 and Frances Kyle in Hilary Term 1920. Mary Dillon-Leech followed at Michaelmas 1920, and Frances Moran, Marion Duggan, and Gretta Flood two years later. In 1919, in the Sex Disqualification (Removal) Act, Parliament had prepared the ground for a social revolution which, by the end of the twentieth century, would see women becoming barristers in numbers comparable with (and in 2001 exceeding) those of men. The beginnings, however, were slow — there are just seventy women among the 2,700 pre-1969 barristers — and the early heroines deserved, and obtained, contemporary recognition.

The fact has fallen out of memory that Dublin called its first women to the Bar six months before London accomplished the feat, and the sequence is worth establishing. *The Times,* reporting on the London Calls of 10 May 1922, published a photograph of 'England's first woman barrister', Miss Ivy Williams of the Inner Temple. It shows a bespectacled solicitor's daughter who was a law lecturer at Oxford. In its report *The Times* elaborated:[113]

> Eight other women students have passed their final examinations, but have not qualified for this call by keeping the requisite number of terms. Miss Williams takes precedence of them because she was awarded a certificate of honour at her examination, and this renders it unnecessary for her to keep the last two terms. She will not be the first woman barrister in the British Isles. Two women, Miss Kyle and Miss Deverell, were called to the Irish Bar in Dublin last November.

This was so. On 1 November 1921 Frances Kyle, from Wellington Park, Belfast, and Agnes Deverell, from Greystones, were called in Dublin, Frances Kyle taking the Brooke Scholarship at the head of a list of twenty. Agnes Deverell was called in fifteenth place, with, but a little behind, her twin brother, a captain returned from the war. The scene was the Court of Appeal, where Chief Justice Molony sat with Lords Justices Ronan and O'Connor. 'These ladies wore the usual wig and gown', reported the *Irish Law Times.*[114]

---

[113] *The Times,* Wednesday May 10, 1922, p. 7 b; Thursday May 11, 1922, pp 7 and 14 (photograph).
[114] *I.L.T. & S.J.,* lv, 5 November 1921, p. 274.

FIRST IRISH PORTIAS,

Ireland's first women barristers, Miss Fay Kyle and Miss A. K. S. Deverell. They were admitted to the Bar on the first call-day in Dublin since the Irish Judiciary has been divided.

Daily Sketch, Thursday 3 November 1921, page 4.

Frances Christian Kyle practised in Belfast until 1944, when she went to live in Hampstead. An obituary in *The Times* called her a 'wonderful conversationalist' and letter-writer: 'The powerful intellect was guided by a spirit so gentle and so generous that it never over-awed those less gifted. Few who have borne the baptismal name of Christian have borne it more worthily.'

Agnes Deverell practised in Dublin for over 40 years. A campaigner for women barristers, she is said to have insisted that a sign on the door of a dressing room which read 'Lady Barristers' should be rendered 'Women Barristers'.

The ceremony attracted attention not only on account of the two ladies, but because it was the first occasion on which a Call to the Bar in Dublin had not been performed by the Lord Chancellor. The judicial provisions of the Government of Ireland Act had come into effect on 1 October 1921, and the jurisdiction of the Dublin courts was now limited to Southern Ireland.[115] This meant that graduates of the King's Inns who desired to practise in Northern Ireland became accustomed, after November 1921, to travel to Belfast to be called a second time.[116] The first Call to the Bar in Northern Ireland took place on Tuesday 8 November 1921, one week after the Dublin Call.[117] Only two of the twenty graduates at the previous week's ceremony made the journey north, but they were arguably the most distinguished members of the group: Frances Kyle, the first woman, and J.C. MacDermott, who went on to become the 4th Lord Chief Justice of Northern Ireland and a member of the House of Lords. Of the ceremony in Crumlin Road Courthouse there is this charming account in Lord MacDermott's memoirs. Sir Denis Henry, whom MacDermott describes as 'a fine lawyer and a great-hearted, kindly man', had never called anybody to the Bar before, and there was an awkward pause:-[118]

> Sir Denis looked at us both, turned this way and that in his great chair, but did not utter a sound. The seconds passed, the pause got longer and longer and more painful as everyone began to wonder what had happened ... Then, after what seemed a very long minute he proceeded with the Call in an assured and confident manner and as though he had been doing it for years.
>
> I don't think either Miss Kyle or myself bothered much about this long pause once it was over, but the matter was raised by Sir Denis himself several weeks later when I happened to meet him on some social occasion. He sought me out and said how sorry he was about the unfortunate hitch which had occurred at the Call. It was, he said, his fault entirely. "You know", he added, "I had got myself word perfect. But when I came in and saw the two of you before me all that would come into my mind were the words 'Do you take this woman to be your lawful wedded wife'. Fortunately something told

---

[115] Government of Ireland Act, 1920, 7th Schedule; S.R.O, 1921, No. 1527. Sir John Ross (who was sworn in on 27 June 1921) had performed the last Call by a Lord Chancellor on 13 July 1921. His office, which carried with it the presidency of the short-lived High Court of Appeal for Ireland, was abolished on 5 December 1922: Irish Free State (Consequential Provisions) Act, 1922, Sch. 1, para. 6 (2).
[116] The need for a second Call was at first in doubt. Sir John Ross told J.C. MacDermott that Sir Denis Henry had agreed to recognise the Dublin Call as 'effectual in the North as in the South'. Lord Justice Moore, however, told Frances Kyle that there was a need to called again by Sir Denis Henry. See J.C. MacDermott, *An Enriching Life* (Belfast: privately printed, 1980), pp 150-2.
[117] *I.L.T. & S.J.*, lv, 12 Nov. 1921, p. 280.
[118] J.C. MacDermott, *An Enriching Life*, pp 152-3.

WOMEN CALLED TO THE BAR
1921-1968

1 Kyle, Frances Christian (M 1921)
2 Deverell, Averil Katherine Statter (M 1921)
3 Dillon-Leetch, Mary (E 1923)
4 Moran, Frances Elizabeth (M 1924)
5 Duggan, Marion Elizabeth (T 1925)
6 McDonnell, Antonia Elizabeth (M 1925)
7 Flood, Gretta Una (H 1926)
8 Phelan, Kathleen (T 1927)
9 Malone, Mary (M 1927)
10 Kimpton, Violet (T 1929)
11 Garrett, Kathleen Butler (E 1930)
12 Caulfield, Anne (M 1930)
13 Martin, Catherine Mary (M 1933)
14 Lysaght-MacGowan, Muriel (T 1934)
15 Wells, Mary Wilhelmina (H 1935)
16 Dockrell, Anne Dorothy (E 1938)
17 Cassidy, Agnes Beatrice (T 1940)
18 Overend, Olive Nancy (M 1940)
19 O'Phelan, Eileen Mary de Riva (M 1941)
20 Walsh, Margaret Mary Patricia (T 1942)
21 O'Toole, Margaret Mary Bermingham (M 1942)
22 Moran, Eileen Mary (M 1943)
23 Costello, Grace Mary (M 1943)
24 MacEntee (Mhac an tSaoi), Máire Caitríona (T 1944)

25 Linehan, Una McAuliffe (M 1944)
26 Walsh, Bridget (M 1945)
27 Blayney, Alice Elizabeth (T 1946)
28 Durkan, Nora (T 1948)
29 Stephenson, Venetia Josephine Mary (H 1949)
30 Donnellan, Mary Josephine Britta (M 1949)
31 Neylon, Mary Josephine (M 1949)
32 Beatty, Ethel Ursula (M 1950)
33 Heslin, Ita Brigid (T 1951)
34 Goodbody, Alys Mary Osterberg (M 1951)
35 Bluett, Maud Cherry (M 1951)
36 Lehane, Leonie Mary (T 1953)
37 Sheehan, Rose Constance (M 1953)
38 Callan, Sylvia Florence (M 1954)
39 Knipe, Joan Clare (M 1954)
40 Hederman, Miriam (M 1954)
41 Bolger, Mary Aingelda Catherine (H 1955)
42 Callery, Mary Patricia (M 1955)
43 Flynn, Ann Mary Gabriel Philomena (M 1956)
44 Keaney, Irene Mary Cecilia (M 1956)
45 Cruess Callaghan, Croasdella (T 1957)
46 Carroll, Mella Elizabeth Laurie (M 1957)
47 Donnelly, Therese Anne (M 1957)
48 McGonagle, Iris Mary (M 1957)

49 Skinner, Geraldine Mary (M 1958)
50 Kinlen, Aideen Patricia (M 1959)
51 O'Conor, Stella Mildred (M 1959)
52 Butler, Anne Kathleen (T 1960)
53 Sheehy, Ruth Mary (M 1960)
54 Riyami, Mrs. Abdullah *née* Soad Mohammad Nasser Lamki (M 1963)
55 McCarthy, Nodlaig Mary Patricia (M 1965)
56 O'Gorman, Martina Louie (M 1965)
57 Johnson, Josephine Mary Philomena (T 1966)
58 Watson, Melissa Rose Mary (T 1966)
59 Hogan, Esther Anne (M 1966)
60 Kelly, Jane Frances (M 1966)
61 Kilduff, Constance Margaret (M 1966)
62 Bourke, Marie Teresa Winifred (T 1967)
63 Kenny, Caroline Elizabeth (T 1967)
64 Wade, Mrs Flavia Margaret (T 1967)
65 Hickey, Clodagh Margaret (M 1967)
66 McHugh, Muireann Caitríona (M 1967)
67 Tormey, Antoinette Catherine (M 1967)
68 Lysaght, Margaret Ann (T 1968)
69 Moore, Helen Therese (M 1968)
70 Gilbert, Jennie Zelda (M 1968

me that they might not be altogether appropriate and I had to wait until the right words came back!"

Frances Kyle never underwent a marriage ceremony, but duly practised at the Bar in Northern Ireland. Her colleague Agnes Deverell, who is commemorated in the Law Library by a small portrait, promptly joined the Dublin Bar, at which she remained for more than forty years.[119] The *Irish Law Times* of 14 January 1922, reporting that there had seldom been 'less bustle in the Central Hall on an opening day', commented:[120]

> An interesting figure amongst the members of the Bar was Miss A. Deverell, who has joined the Law Library. She wears the regulation wig and gown.

Mention of the 'regulation wig and gown' was prompted by controversy in legal circles in London about the forensic attire proper for women barristers. Dublin seems not to have been troubled by the question, but London strained in vain to find an alternative to the horsehair wig. The *Irish Law Times* informed its readers about the thinking in London:[121]

> A committee of His Majesty's Judges is sitting, says *The Justice of the Peace*, on the perplexing question of forensic dress for women, for the time for the first call of women to the Bar is at hand. Already one or two women have been called to the Irish Bar, but apparently the distracted state of their country has prevented the Irish Judges from applying their minds to the matter, for the Irish ladies have donned the horsehair with ludicrous effect. It is generally assumed that no such outrage will occur here, and that women practitioners will be required to substitute for the wig a black biretta. The principle is clear. A woman in Court as in church should have a head-covering, which technically a wig is not.
>
> The women law students, says the *Daily News*, are awaiting with anxiety the decision of the five eminent judges who are to settle the question of wigs or caps for women barristers. This committee, which includes the Lord Chief Justice and the Master of the Rolls, has met more than once, but no decision has yet been reached. The five judges have so far had no feminine adviser to assist them in their deliberations. One of the proposals made by the Judges' Committee is that women barristers should wear a cap similar to that worn by the women graduates and undergraduates at Oxford, but the women students who are reading for the Bar are said to be in favour of wearing wigs, and it is probable that they will be asked their opinion before the judges' decision is made absolute. Some definite rules will also have to be laid down in regard to the dress to be worn under the gown. As it is against etiquette for barristers to wear light suits, it is probable that women will be

---

[119] See the note on Agnes Deverell in Ivana Bacik, Cathryn Costello and Eileen Drew, *Gender InJustice* (Dublin, 2003), p. 57.
[120] *I.L.T. & S.J.*, lvi, 14 January 1922, pp 10-11.
[121] Ibid., lvi, 1 April 1922, p. 81, 'News of the Week'.

prohibited from wearing coloured blouses and skirts, low necks, and short sleeves, when in the courts. The judges must decide these questions very soon for it is expected that the first woman barrister will be called on 10th May, the next call day.

The editor of the *Irish Law Times* commented: 'The question has not created any difficulty in Ireland where lady barristers wear the same style of wig and bands as men. The effect is certainly far from ludicrous. It is regarded as very becoming to the lady wearers.' Soon afterwards the Committee which had been sitting in London accepted wigs for women, and 'expressed a wish' that the dress of women barristers in court should conform to the following rules:-[122]

(1) Ordinary barrister's wigs should be worn and should completely cover and conceal the hair.
(2) Ordinary barrister's gowns should be worn.
(3) Dresses should be plain, black or very dark, high to the neck, with long sleeves, and not shorter than the gown, with high plain white collar and barrister's bands; or plain coats and skirts may be worn, black or very dark, not shorter than the gown, with plain white shirts and high collars and barrister's bands.

From call to the Bar to the attainment of higher station in the profession took time. Frances Moran, fourth to be called to the Outer Bar, was first to be called to the Inner Bar, an event which took place on 9 May 1941. Mella Carroll, the 46th woman to be called to the Outer Bar (M 1957), and second to be called to the Inner Bar (M 1976), was the first woman to be appointed a judge of the High Court (6 October 1980).[123] When this event occurred the profession was unsure how to address a lady on the Bench. The plain form 'Judge' found favour with Miss Justice Carroll, but does not accord parity of deference. 'M'Lord' is widely employed without distinction of sex. 'M' Lady', heard in London, never took root in Dublin.

[122] *I.L.T. & S.J.*, lvi, 15 April 1922, p. 96.
[123] The first woman appointed in England (to the Probate Divorce and Admiralty Division) had been Mrs. Justice Elizabeth Lane in 1965. In 1972 Miss Recorder Heilbron was the first woman judge at the Old Bailey: *The Daily Telegraph*, 4 Jan. 1972 (quoted in *The Gazette of the Incorporated Law Society of Ireland*, 1972, p. 123).

XV: Disaster, exile and a new judicial system

The fate that befell the Four Courts in 1922, and the story of the profession's nine years of exile, falls now to be related as a series of vignettes, by recourse to a selection of contemporary reports. A tragic sequence begins in the issue of the *Irish Law Times* for 22 April 1922:

> We understand that on Thursday night the Four Courts were taken possession of by forces under the independent Executive. About 12.15 a.m. the premises were surrounded by between 300 and 400 armed men, some of whom marched to the scene while others came in motors.
>
> A number of them immediately climbed the railings at the rere, opposite the Bridewell, and a D.M.P. constable, who was on duty in the building, and was walking towards one of the entrances, was held up and taken prisoner. A sergeant and another constable on duty in the vicinity were also captured, and all three were held prisoners till 6.30. a.m. on Friday, when they were released. According to one account, the keys were taken from the police guard by the party who gained entrance at the rere, and the main body then entered by the front gates and occupied the building. All the windows overlooking the principal thoroughfares were sandbagged, and numbers of law books and what appeared to be bags of papers were also utilised for defensive purposes. Armed sentries were stationed at all vantage points, and all through the night men continued to arrive.
>
> Interviewed by a Press representative on Friday, Commandant-General Rory O'Connor, who is in command, declared that they wanted the Four Courts, as the premises they had in Parnell Square were not sufficient to accommodate them. They would find adequate room in the Four Courts, where a publicity office, amongst other things, would be set up. The business of the Courts, he said, would not be allowed to go on, but every care would be taken to preserve all documents, &c.

On the same page the newspaper reported the opening of the Easter Term at the King's Inns, giving the details, as announced by the Lord Chief Justice, of the places to which the Court offices had been relocated. It congratulated the Lord Chief Justice on his arrangements, adding that the 'legal profession, including barristers, solicitors, and a vast number of clerks', had a right to work like other members of the community. In its issue of the following week the *Irish Law Times* published this announcement:[124]

KING'S INNS LIBRARY

> The Library of the King's Inns, Henrietta Street, will be used for the present in lieu of the Law Library at the Four Courts. Solicitors and their clerks should "call" barristers there in the usual way. The books of the King's Inns Library will be used in the Courts established at the King's Inns. An effort, which we hope will be

---

[124] *I.L.T. & S.J.*, lvi, 29 April 1922, p. 104.

successful, is being made to get tramcars to pass Henrietta Street.
This would be a great convenience at the present time.

The destruction of the Four Courts, when the event happened, was
recorded in the *Irish Law Times* in this short paragraph, the more
effective for being so succinct and restrained:[125]

It is with feelings of great sorrow we record the fact that the Four
Courts, the Record Office, the Land Registry, the Solicitors'
Buildings, and many other buildings are now piles of gaunt ruins as
a result of the recent fighting in the city. The magnificent Courts,
with the adjoining Judges' Chambers, the Round Hall with its fine
statues, the Law Library with three or four sets of the reports and of
text-books, the probate office with records of all modern wills, and
perhaps more especially the Record Office, with its priceless
treasures of the past, which are absolutely irreplaceable, are all
gone. Judges have lost their robes, and, doubtless, many personal
belongings in their chambers; Barristers have lost their wigs and
gowns and other possessions, and the Incorporated Law Society has
lost its fine Hall and Library, the Council Chamber, and its fine
suite of Offices. No estimate can he made of the extent of the
damages. The inconvenience resulting from the destruction of the
courts and offices will be felt from day to day. The legal profession
has suffered a blow from which it will not recover for many years to
come.

In the words of Sir Thomas Molony, the last Lord Chief Justice of
Ireland in a line that stretched back to 1209 in the reign of King
John, 'it became necessary to reconstruct the legal system out of the
scanty materials that were left'.[126]

When the Four Courts buildings were destroyed the Courts and
the Law Library had already been functioning for several weeks in
improvised accommodation at the King's Inns. Conditions in these
quarters were cramped, but the profession made do with them until
the end of Hilary Term 1923. The Board of Works selected Dublin
Castle as the best available alternative location. The State
Apartments there were secure and spacious, and not currently being
put to any other use. They had the advantage of being centrally
located in historic surroundings, hard-by the site of the home of the
common law in Ireland, the Great Hall of Henry III, which until the
seventeenth century had occupied the western part of the Upper
Yard. For the eight years between April 1923 and July 1931 the
Law was again at home in the Castle. An insight into how the
profession functioned in these years can be had from the description
of the newly-adapted quarters that was published in the *Irish Law
Times* in April 1923, and is reproduced below.

[125] *I.L.T. & S.J.*, lvi, 1 and 8 July 1922, p. 161.
[126] *I.L.T. & S.J.*, lviiii, 24 Oct. 1924, p. 258; and see [1923] I.R. 13.

Postcard view of the Upper Yard of Dublin Castle c. 1923 showing the entrance, at the State Apartments, to 'the Supreme Court of Saorstát Éireann'. Note the judicial [?] motor cars.

King's Inns Barristers, 1868-2004, page 101.

THE NEW COURTS [AT DUBLIN CASTLE]

The Easter Sittings of the Court of Appeal and the High Court in Saorstát Éireann will commence on Wednesday next [11th] in Dublin Castle. The opening of the Term will not be marked by any ceremony, which will be a departure from the inauguration of the Easter Sittings in the past, when the Lord Chancellor held a levée at which there was a brilliant ceremonial at the Four Courts. The whole of the block of buildings on the south side of the Upper Castle Yard has been allocated for the purposes of the Courts and offices, and portions of the adjoining eastern and western blocks have also been taken over for the same purpose. The main southern block includes what were formerly St. Patrick's Hall, the Throne Room, State Drawingrooms and other apartments. Workmen have been employed by the Board of Works for a considerable time transforming these premises so as to make them suitable as courts and offices.

The old names of the Courts, with one exception, will disappear, and they will henceforth be known as the Court of Appeal and Court No. 1, Court No. 2, and so on to Court No. 5. Later on it is proposed to add a seventh Court, which will be known as Court No. 6.

The Court of Appeal will be in what was formerly the Privy Council Chamber, and will fulfil the functions associated with it at the King's Inns.

Court No. 1 has been placed in one of the State drawingrooms, and in it will be conducted the Chancery business of Mr. Justice Powell's Court.

The Probate Court in Dublin Castle on the last day of sitting there, 31 July 1931. The judge is Henry Hanna; the Registrar, Joseph Hand. [From an article by Eamon Mongey, in *Courts Service News*, iv (Issue 4: October 2002), p. 5.]

Court No. 2, which is also in one of the State drawingrooms, will be used by the Master of the Rolls.

Court No. 3, placed like the other two in a State drawingroom, will be ordinarily used for Common Law motions, and in it will be conducted Probate business on Fridays and Bankruptcy business on another day of the week.

Court No. 4 has been set up in what was formerly the Throne Room, a large and beautiful apartment situated on the first floor — as are all the Courts — over the main entrance. It will be used for the trial of cases by jury and for other business.

Court No. 5, situated at a little distance beyond St. Patrick's Hall, will be used also for the trial of jury cases. It was formerly known as the Round Supper Room.

Court No. 6, whose construction later on is contemplated, will be placed in King George's Supper Hall, and will also be used for the conduct of jury trials.

The internal arrangements of the Courts have been constructed on simple lines. The Judge's Bench, though cut off from the main body of the court, is, unlike the arrangement in the Four Courts, only raised slightly above the general level. In front of the bench is the desk for the Registrar and other officials. In front of this is the accommodation for the members of the inner Bar and the Press, and next are the places for the Junior Bar. The new Courts are well lighted and ventilated and will be attractive and artistic in appearance.

St. Patrick's Hall has been given to the Bar for use as a Law Library, and they will also have the use of apartments close by as consulting rooms. The new library will be a large and spacious apartment immediately adjoining the courts. Other apartments have been transformed into offices. The Lunacy and Probate offices are on the ground floor underneath the courts. The Bankruptcy offices are in the second or top floor. The Taxing Masters' and Chancery Registrars' offices are located on the first floor in what were formerly the State apartments. The Judgments, Record, and Writ offices are at the farthest end of the Castle Yard. A Press room for the accommodation of the journalists attending the Courts has been provided on the second floor. Such provision has been made in the way of a jurors' waiting-room, but full accommodation for the purpose has not yet been provided.

The transformed buildings are well suited for the purpose, and on the whole the profession is to be congratulated on the acquisition of such convenient premises. The Law Library is in process of equipment, and it is expected that the members of the library will have not only large premises but also a good working library. A large number of reports, statutes and text books have been purchased, and several valuable presents of books have been given by judges and barristers.

[*I.L.T. & S.J.*, lvii, p. 88. 7 April 1923.]

The new courts have already been described in these columns. They are fine, spacious Courts, well lighted and ventilated, and when some necessary alterations and improvements are effected, they will be admirably suited for their purpose. St. Patrick's Hall is devoted to the Law Library, and the walls are already partially shelved and filled with books. One great advantage of the arrangement is that the Courts, Law Library, and some of the principal offices are on the same floor. When the public gets acquainted with the premises they will be found very accessible and convenient in every way.

[*ibid*, pp 92-3, 14 April 1923.]

The Courts which sat without ceremony at Dublin Castle on 11 April 1923 were still those of the Supreme Court of Judicature established under the Act of 1877, and such they remained for five legal terms during which the Free State made plans for their replacement. The inauguration, on Wednesday 11 June 1924, of the new judicial order established by the Courts of Justice Act, 1924, was marked by considerable ceremony:[127]

THE IRISH FREE STATE JUDICIARY
NEW COURTS OPENED

The new Supreme and High Courts of the Free State were inaugurated in Dublin Castle on Wednesday morning with an impressive ceremony. Troops were drawn up in the Upper Castle Yard and behind them were ranked a strong contingent of the Dublin Metropolitan Police, both combined to make a Guard of Honour.

There was a large attendance of the general public. President Cosgrave, members of the Government and other distinguished people, including Lord Glenavy, were present. The President of the Incorporated Law Society also attended.

The procession of the judges started in front of the old Privy Council Chambers at the south corner of the quadrangle. At the head came Chief Justice Kennedy, followed by Mr. Justice Sullivan, Mr. Justice O'Connor, Mr. Justice FitzGibbon, Mr. Justice Creed Meredith, Mr. Justice T. O'Shaughnessy, Mr. Justice Wylie, Mr. Justice Johnston and Mr. Justice Murnaghan. It was in this order that they made the oath of declaration. Their lordships wore morning dress, but were not in the customary robes.

King's Counsel and Barristers entered the Court in a body and seated themselves in the places apportioned to the Bar. There was also a representative attendance of solicitors present.

Soon after eleven o'clock the Chief Justice and the other judges entered the Court and took their places on the bench. The Chief Justice at once proceeded with the ceremony of administering the declaration. Commencing with Mr. Sullivan, K.C., President of the High Court of Justice, he addressed him thus:- Timothy Sullivan, the Governor-General, acting on the advice of the Executive Council, has appointed you to he a judge of the High Court of Justice of Saorstát Éireann; you will make and subscribe the declaration accordingly. Mr. Sullivan made and subscribed the declaration and the other judges, in order of priority of appointment, did likewise — namely, Mr. Charles Andrew O'Connor, K.C., and Mr. Gerald FitzGibbon, K.C., Judges of the Supreme Court; Mr. James Creed Meredith, K.C., Mr. Thomas Lopdell O'Shaughnessy, K.C., Mr. William E. Wylie, K.C., Mr. William John Johnston, K.C., and Mr. James Augustine Murnaghan, Judges of the High Court of Justice.

The Chief Justice then addressed Mr. John O'Byrne, the newly-appointed Attorney-General, who sat in Court, wearing a full-

---

[127] *I.L.T. & S.J.*, lviii, 14 June 1924, pp 151-2.

bottom wig and gown, saying — "The Governor-General has, on the advice of the Executive Council, appointed you to be Attorney-General of Saorstát Éireann, and to be a King's Counsel. You will, therefore, now take your place within the Bar accordingly".

Mr. O'Byrne took his place in the Inner Bar and made his declaration.

Addressing the assembled judges, the Attorney-General said that he desired on behalf of the Bar to offer to each of them the heartiest congratulations on the signal honour which had been conferred upon them. The opening of these Courts constituted a culminating factor in the inauguration of a new order in this country. After a long period of stress and suffering, a Treaty was successfully negotiated and concluded between Great Britain and Ireland, whereby the Irish Free State was set up as a self-governing Dominion within the British Empire. A constituent assembly thereupon sat and framed a Constitution, whereby it was declared that all powers of government and all authority, legislative, executive and judicial, in Ireland, was derived from the people of Ireland, and that the same shall be exercised in the Irish Free State through all the organisations established under the Constitution. Of these organisations there were none of greater importance than the Courts of Justice, of which they were the first judges. A great honour had been conferred upon them by the people of this country, acting through the Executive, but it was equally clear that a great task and a great responsibility had been imposed upon them. Very cordial relations had always existed in this country between the Bench and the Bar. It was their desire that these relations might continue. They were both the servants of the law, and the members of the Bar hoped that they might do their part in the establishment and maintenance of a reign of law throughout this country.

The Chief Justice replied, speaking first in Irish and then in English. He said — This is surely a precious moment - the moment when the silence of the Gael in Courts of Law is broken, and that within what was once the Pale - the moment when, after a week of centuries, Irish Courts, fashioned in freedom by an Oireachtas again assembled, are thrown open to administer justice according to laws made in Ireland by free Irish citizens for the well-being of our dearly-loved land and its people. It is for us here in the seat of justice, a moment of compelling emotion, and for me especially, to whom has fallen, under Providence, this unique and sacred favour of presiding at this very time and place, the joy and emotion are well-nigh overwhelming.

Continuing, the Chief Justice said that it would be for them in these newly-established courts to enshrine the ancient inspiration and to evoke again the dormant reverence for the judgment by establishing confidence in its fearless and impartial justice, and the assured expectation that as the law is made by the people, so shall be the judgment. They would look to the legal profession, both of them, without abatement of learning, of courage, and of independence, to cooporate with them in setting firm and paramount the rule of law and justice, upon which rests peace and security for the people. The judicial authority which we shall exercise, said the Chief Justice, is, as has been declared by the

National Constituent Assembly in the second article of the Constitution, derived under God from the people. With that authority these Courts of the nation stand between the people and any and every encroachment upon their constitutional rights and liberties, by whomsoever attempted. Facing these responsibilities, in all humility we pray God to give us strength and to guide us by the light of His wisdom, justice and truth. We will without delay take up the work that lies before us.

The Chief Justice then announced that the rule-making authority would enter immediately upon the work of laying down procedure and devising forms in the spirit of the Act, and according to the requirements of the people, as regards simplicity, efficiency, expedition and economy, without forfeiting anything of the dignity that befits the national Courts of Justice. In the meantime, in order that litigants may not suffer inconvenience or delay, they would probably, for the duration of the present sittings, apply to the business before them, the rules for the regulating the business of the Courts which the Oireachtas had just brought to an end. He congratulated the Attorney-General on being called to the headship of his profession. They knew that he would uphold its position and *prestige* in the new conditions in which it must build up new traditions. He cordially sympathized with him, for he understood only too well the unremitting toil that lay before him.

Mr. James Moore, President of the Incorporated Law Society, on behalf of the solicitors' profession, welcomed the new judges. They would do all that they could to make this new procedure work for the benefit of the community and for the advancement of the land that gave them birth

The Chief Justice thanked Mr. Moore.

Mr. James O'Connor, solicitor, who spoke in Irish, also congratulated the new judges.

The judges then retired to the Benchers' Chambers, where they sat to discuss the business of the Courts. It was stated later that the Probate and Matrimonial Courts had been assigned to Mr. Justice Murnaghan: that he and Mr. Justice Meredith would deal with Chancery business, and that Mr. Justice Johnston would dispose of all business of the Bankruptcy Court.

* * * * *

Seven years pass. It is Monday 12 October 1931. For a reason of secular expediency, previously explained, the members of the legal profession have been encouraged to go to church. The Chief Justice, along with his brethren Sullivan, Murnaghan, and O'Byrne, has been to mass in St. Michan's, Halston Street. There too have been the Master of the High Court (Gerald Horan, K.C.) and six judges of the Circuit Court: O'Brien, Davitt, Roche, Shannon, Gleeson and Moonan. Mr Justice FitzGibbon, with his brethren Hanna, Meredith and Johnston, has been to a service at St. Michan's, Old Church Street. Mr Justice Wylie was not reported to have been at either venue. The moment has come for the Courts to sit again at the Four Courts.[128]

The Michaelmas Law Sittings opened on Monday at the new Courts of Justice. There was a full attendance of the judges. In all the offices associated with the Courts there was considerable activity. Numbers of workmen were busy putting the finishing touches on various parts of the reconstructed buildings. Many visitors, availing of the opening of the Courts, visited them during the day, and were highly impressed with the vast improvements effected. The Supreme Court was greatly admired by all who had the opportunity of seeing it. Before the judges sat in their respective courts a meeting of the Benchers was held in their new chambers.

In the Supreme Court there was an interesting interlude, the following judges being present on the Bench — The Chief Justice, (The Hon. Hugh Kennedy, K.C.), the President of the High Court (the Hon. Timothy Sullivan, K.C.), the Hon. Mr. Justice FitzGibbon, and the Hon. Mr. Justice Murnaghan. The Chief Justice addressing Sir Philip Hanson, chairman of the Board of Works, said that he felt it would be an omission which could never be made good if he failed to express in some way his appreciation, and he thought he could speak for all who along with him took up their work there, of the magnificent work of reconstruction and restoration which had been accomplished through the Office of Public Works. They had been accustomed to hear sung the praises of Gandon, who left his mark on Dublin in a group of notable architectural monuments, but for the future when speaking of three at least of these great buildings the name of Byrne must be inevitably linked with that of Gandon. Everyone who was familiar with the old building from within would be moved with admiration of the manner in which Mr. Byrne, the principal architect of the Board of Works, had restored the main architectural design, in many respects a great feat, as it seemed to the layman. His Lordship said that he felt sure that all of them whose working days would be spent there would find much from day to day for which to thank Mr. Byrne and those working under him, while the people would have there a worthy building wherein to house their Courts of Justice inaugurated in 1924.

XVI: The new order and the rise of the Sullivan clan

At the beginning of this essay the early years of our study were characterised as the age of loyalty and the FitzGibbons. Its closing years may equally be studied by reference to a family, this time one with credentials that are impeccably Nationalist. The Sullivan brothers of Bantry in County Cork, T.D. (1827-1914) and A.M. (1830-1884), gave us respectively 'God save Ireland' and *Speeches from the Dock*. Unlike the FitzGibbons, with their straightforward succession from father to son, the same Christian name being borne in three generations, there is nothing simple about the Sullivan

[128] *I.L.T. & S.J.*, lxv, 17 October 1931, pp 249-50.

family. The genealogical story extends to the Healys and the O'Higgins, and is so complicated that it defies easy exposition.

In this essay we have already met five members of the Clan Sullivan. A.M. Sullivan and Tim Healy were Irish Party M.P.s who joined the Bar in the 1880s. Tim Healy was observed moving a motion at a meeting of the Bar in 1920. The memoirs of Serjeant Sullivan and Maurice Healy, members of their respective families in the following generation, have been fruitful sources of quotation. The name of Timothy Sullivan has been mentioned as first President of the High Court of the Free State.

The painting, a small oil on canvass, which is reproduced as the frontispiece of this book, shows Timothy Sullivan in 1924, when he was in his 50th year. He is wearing a bar wig, which suggests that the sitting preceded his appointment (in June 1924) as the first President of the High Court of the Irish Free State. Sullivan afterwards became Chief Justice in 1936, and died in 1949. The 1924 portrait shows a man with good features, austere perhaps but not unkindly. The sitter is essentially youthful — young-looking for 50 — and he possesses resolution and energy, qualities appropriate to the 1920s, when the affairs of the new state were in the hands of a generation that was notably young and purposeful. The Honorable Society of King's Inns possesses a second portrait of Sullivan, executed by Seán O'Sullivan in 1940, where the sitter is noticeably older.

A label on the back of the earlier picture states that the work was painted by Maev Sullivan at the Viceregal Lodge. Maev Sullivan was well qualified to catch the character of her subject, for she was more than just the artist. She was the wife the sitter had married in 1913. The painting was executed at the Viceregal Lodge because this was the residence of Sullivan's father-in-law. Maev was the second daughter of Tim Healy, who in 1922 became the first Governor General of the Irish Free State. In that capacity he forwarded his son-in-law's warrant of appointment to be President of the High Court.

The relationship between the families of Sullivan and Healy was exceedingly close in successive generations. Tim Healy's mother was Eliza Sullivan of Bantry; and when he married Erina Sullivan, the sister of Timothy Sullivan's father, Timothy Daniel Sullivan, M.P., Healy was marrying his cousin. Timothy Sullivan's mother was Catherine Healy, Tim Healy's father's sister, which made Tim Healy Sullivan's great-uncle as well as his father-in-law. This level of consanguinity, though close, would not appear to be within the forbidden degrees.

Sir Edward Carson and Tim Healy as caricatured in 1919 by the cartoonist Grace Plunket (*née* Gifford) [1888-1955]. The cartoonist was the daughter of a solicitor [Frederick Gifford] and the widow of a barrister's son: Count Plunkett (called M 1886) was the father of her husband, the executed 1916 leader Joseph Mary Plunkett. T.C. Kingsmill Moore (called M 1918) was a pre-1916 visitor to the Gifford home at 8 Temple Villas, Palmerston Road, where he argued politics with Thomas MacDonagh, another executed 1916 leader, who had married Muriel Gifford, Grace's sister. See Marie O'Neill, *Grace Gifford Plunket and Irish Freedom: Tragic Bride of 1916* (Dublin, 2000), p. 30.

The Sullivan connection: (left) Chief Justice Timothy Sullivan (1874-1949; photographed for the *I.L.T. & S.J.* in 1938); (centre) Serjeant A.M. Sullivan (1871-1959), as seen in the frontispiece of his book *The Last Serjeant* (1951); and (right) Thomas Francis O'Higgins (1916-2003), the second Chief Justice in the family, painted for King's Inns in 1977 by James Le Jeune. Tom O'Higgins was called to the Bar by his great-uncle in 1938. *King's Inns Barristers, 1868-2004*, page 110.

The same opinion cannot be advanced about the marriage of Timothy Sullivan, the first President of the High Court and subsequent Chief Justice, to his wife, the artist Maev (*née* Healy). *Burke's Irish Family Records* includes entries for both families, and is consistent on the point. On page 572, *sub* Healy, it states that Maev Healy married her uncle; and on page 1078, *sub* Sullivan, it says that Timothy Sullivan married his niece. The reader of *Burke's Irish Family Records* may be pardoned for blinking: but the lawfulness of this marriage, of which there were no children, may be left for determination in some forum where it may be at issue. Timothy Sullivan died in 1949, his wife (and niece) in 1967.

This complicated story of family relationships does not end here. There is more, much of which is vouched in the genealogical information preserved in the King's Inns records. In his autobiography, *A Double Life*, the late Chief Justice O'Higgins drew attention to the careers in public service and the law of the descendants of his great-grandfather, T.D. Sullivan (died 1914). T.D. Sullivan, an M.P. although not a barrister, was the father of Tom O'Higgins's paternal grandmother. The said T.D. Sullivan was the brother of a barrister (A.M. Sullivan) and the uncle of another (the long-lived Serjeant Sullivan). His son-in-law, Tim Healy, the Governor General of the Irish Free State, was a barrister, as was the latter's son Joseph, a passionate motor-cyclist. Maurice Healy, chronicler of the Old Munster Circuit, was the nephew of the Governor General and a cousin of the Sullivans by various routes. T.D. Sullivan's son Timothy was, as mentioned, a Chief Justice. A grandson, the assassinated Kevin O'Higgins, Vice-President of the Executive Council of the Free State and therein Minister for Justice and for External Affairs, became a barrister by an accelerated process that led to the rift in the King's Inns with the Belfast Benchers. In 1975 T.F. O'Higgins (who had been called to the Bar by his great-uncle, Chief Justice Timothy Sullivan) became the second Chief Justice in the family; and since he wrote his autobiography, another great-grandson, bearing the name of his assassinated uncle, has joined the High Court bench. These nine barristers, called to the Irish Bar between 1876 and 1968, will be found in their due places in this book, under the names of Sullivan, Healy, and O'Higgins.[129] The late Peter Shanley, Tom O'Higgins's sister's son, was likewise a judicial descendant of T.D. Sullivan.

---

[129] Thomas F. O'Higgins, *A Double Life* (Dublin, 1996), pp 70-1. In 1937 Maurice Healy's sister, Frances [Mrs. Dominick O'Connor] was the first married woman to be admitted as a solicitor: *I.L.T.& S.J.*, lxxi, 5 June 1937, p. 147.

The Clan Sullivan offers a spectacular example of a large and successful family: but families in the Ireland of the nineteen-thirties, -forties and -fifties were typically large: as large, or larger, than their predecessors had been in the nineteenth century. The King's Inns records here published disclose fifteen instances of men who described themselves as seventh sons, seven who described themselves as the eighth son, three as the ninth son, and one (Timothy Harrington) who was a tenth son. It was also not unknown for siblings to be put to the Bar simultaneously. In the Michaelmas Call of 1952, for example, we find Fiachra O'Hanrahan taking the Brooke Scholarship of £50 per annum for 3 years and Fachtna O'Hanrahan taking the Society's Exhibition of £21 per annum for 3 years. Fiachra, who was placed first, was the fourth son; and Fachtna, who was placed second, was the eldest son of his family.

More than two hundred, or about 8 per cent, of the 2,700 names in the accompanying list were sons of solicitors. The sons of barristers are scarcely less prominent, and account for nearly seven per cent. Eighty-six gave the profession of their father as 'barrister-at-law'. Among these was the happily-named Edward Patrick Sarsfield Counsel, son of Lawrence Counsel, barrister-at-law, of Athlone, in whose family the imparting of advice would appear to have been hereditary from an early date.[130] In addition, thirty-three were the sons of fathers who had attained the rank of 'Queen's Counsel' and twenty-three the sons of 'King's Counsel'. Some three dozen were the sons of judges, but this total includes colonial appointees,[131] and judges of the County Court.[132] Conspicuous among the names of judges' sons are representatives of the families of Budd, FitzGibbon, Geoghegan, Haugh and McCarthy where the sons have followed their fathers onto the Bench.[133] The Wylies, uncle and nephew, furnish an example of another close family relationship. The uncle, who resigned as judge of the Land Commission to make way for the appointment of his nephew, also made him a present of his judicial robes, which are now the property of King's Inns.

[130] There were three Laws, and two Lawsons; but also two called Lawless!
[131] Keppel Browne, Brian Doyle, John Kernan, Joseph Little, Kanak Roy and Jaja Wachuku.
[132] James Orr, A.K. Overend, James R. Shaw.
[133] C.T. Atkinson, W.P. Ball, Charles Barry, Walter Boyd, Declan Budd, John Casey, Richard Cherry, Jonathan Christian, W.H. Dodd, jun., Richard Dowse, Gerald FitzGerald, Gerald FitzGibbon, Hugh Geoghegan, William Gibson, James and Robert Harrison, Denis Johnston, Samuel and William Lawson, Francis Lynch, Martin and Peter Maguire, John Martley, George May, Edward Sullivan Murphy, Patrick O'Byrne, Fergus O'Connor, A.H. Ormsby, Edward Sullivan, and Henry Warren.

CALLED TO THE BAR, 1ST NOVEMBER 1938

(Front row, left to right): Thomas Francis Kevin Peter O'Higgins (Society's Exhibition of £21 and Certificate of Honour); John Alphonsus Burke (Brooke Scholarship and Certificate of Honour); Richard Noel Cooke (Society's Prize of £21 and Certificate of Honour); James Augustin D'Arcy, B.A., LL.B. (T.C.D.) (Certificate of Honour)

Back row: Patrick Francis Garret Cannon, B.A. (N.U.I.); Arthur Frank Connel Mackey, B.A. (N.U.I.) [alias 'Rex' Mackey]; Denis Synge Stephens B.A. (T.C.D.)

Photo: Lafayette, courtesy of R.N. Cooke, S.C.

King's Inns Barristers, 1868-2004, page 113.

Two sons of the Presbyterian manse: (left) Sir John Ross, last Lord Chancellor of Ireland; and (right) J. C. MacDermott, Lord Mac Dermott of Belmont, 4th Lord Chief Justice of Northern Ireland, and the last head of the Northern Ireland judiciary to have been educated at King's Inns.

King's Inns Barristers, 1868-2004, page 114.

More than a hundred barristers were the sons of clergymen, mostly of the Church of Ireland, but including a representation of Presbyterians. Two of the most eminent judges, Sir John Ross and Lord MacDermott, were sons of the Presbyterian manse. Four, including William Bullick Black (who became a judge after he had contested a parliamentary election for Fianna Fáil) and Sydney Cole (who is mentioned below), have been identified as the sons of Methodist ministers.[134]

Gerald Brunskill had the experience of being called to the Bar *twice*: in 1888, and (after he had been disbarred at his own request to become a solicitor) again in 1901.

Arthur Joseph Donnelly passed the Final Examination in 1918, and was awarded the 1st Victoria Prize. He nevertheless postponed taking his Call until 1966. This was a record gap of 48 years, and, at 82, Arthur Donnelly seems to have been the oldest man called to the Bar in Ireland.

It is notorious that the profession does not require elderly barristers to retire, but it does demand that candidates for Call should have attained the age of 21: this is the rationale for the requirement in the *Memorial* that the candidate for Call should state his age. The youngest person to have been called to the Bar was Arthur Burke Kelly. He was aged just 21 years and one day when he was called in June 1913. Two classmates, Rice and Sullivan, were called on Saturday 18th June, but 'Mr. A.B. Kelly, who did not attain 21 years of age until the 19th', was called on Monday the 20th, an instance which shows that the Benchers were being punctilious.[135]

XVII: The complacent years

The table on the following page shows the numbers called to the Bar annually over the century between 1868 and 1968. It will be seen that the figures fluctuate within limits that are remarkably constant. There is a natural ebb and flow; but in these years one seeks in vain for tempests. The numbers remain small — smallest of all in 1932 and subsequent years, and small again in the early 1960s.

These King's Inns classes were intimate, as was afterwards, for those who joined it, the Law Library itself. The number of subscribers to the Law Library fluctuated in sympathy with the trend in numbers called to the Bar. There were 261 subscribers in 1937, 293 in 1947, 283 in 1952, 242 in 1962, and only 217 in 1968, a year which indeed represented a historic low point. Following the large Call of 1968, membership of the Law Library recovered to 253

---

[134] The others were John Wesley Gentleman and Brian McCracken.
[135] *I.L.T. & S.J.*, xlvii (1913), p. 29].

NUMBERS OF BARRISTERS CALLED TO THE BAR, 1868-1968, BY YEAR AND TERM

Year	Total	H	E	T	M	Year	Total	H	E	T	M
1868	26	7	7	6	6	1919	25	4	3	8	10
1869	18	4	4	4	6	1920	26	6	3	6	11
1870	19	4	4	2	9	1921	34	7	3	4	20
1871	25	4	3	7	11	1922	18	3	2	4	9
1872	32	10	0	14	8	1923	35	8	2	11	14
1873	33	14	2	10	7	1924	21	2	2	5	12
1874	32	10	4	9	9	1925	38	3	0	5	30
1875	26	7	8	7	4	1926	29	4	2	4	19
1876	22	7	3	3	9	1927	41	4	1	9	27
1877	27	5	10	1	11	1928	21	2	3	9	7
1878	21	2	5	3	11	1929	25	1	1	3	20
1879	44	4	15	5	20	1930	20	7	1	1	11
1880	36	10	3	4	19	1931	32	1	3	9	19
1881	30	6	2	2	20	1932	15	0	1	0	14
1882	22	4	2	1	15	1933	16	2	1	3	10
1883	34	4	8	10	12	1934	15	0	0	5	10
1884	26	5	1	6	14	1935	14	1	0	6	7
1885	33	8	4	8	13	1936	22	0	1	11	10
1886	35	6	4	8	17	1937	22	0	0	5	17
1887	47	12	7	10	18	1938	14	0	1	6	7
1888	31	6	9	7	9	1939	16	2	0	0	14
1889	24	4	2	7	11	1940	17	3	1	4	9
1890	25	3	2	12	8	1941	21	0	0	5	16
1891	32	8	4	4	16	1942	13	0	0	7	6
1892	28	5	3	11	9	1943	17	1	0	8	8
1893	23	6	2	7	8	1944	24	0	0	10	14
1894	27	8	4	10	5	1945	26	0	0	15	11
1895	34	9	2	7	16	1946	24	0	0	16	8
1896	24	5	1	9	9	1947	22	0	0	12	10
1897	34	1	2	15	16	1948	28	0	0	20	8
1898	37	10	4	10	13	1949	32	2	0	10	20
1899	29	3	4	9	13	1950	30	4	0	10	16
1900	27	7	2	5	13	1951	29	5	0	8	16
1901	26	5	3	9	9	1952	28	4	1	6	17
1902	35	5	5	11	14	1953	20	0	0	6	14
1903	26	5	0	9	12	1954	36	3	1	16	16
1904	33	8	1	12	12	1955	28	7	0	7	14
1905	30	8	4	11	7	1956	17	0	0	2	15
1906	29	6	2	11	10	1957	26	4	1	6	15
1907	36	5	3	16	12	1958	22	2	0	8	12
1908	25	3	1	14	7	1959	21	0	3	7	11
1909	26	4	2	13	7	1960	24	0	0	14	10
1910	29	5	2	14	8	1961	19	0	0	7	12
1911	31	6	2	12	11	1962	18	0	0	4	14
1912	30	2	1	16	11	1963	15	0	0	8	7
1913	33	3	0	20	10	1964	14	3	1	5	5
1914	35	5	1	21	8	1965	17	0	0	5	12
1915	19	1	1	10	7	1966	37	4	2	12	19
1916	27	5	1	16	5	1967	29	0	0	14	15
1917	46	3	2	29	12	1968	52	4	0	20	28
1918	33	4	1	21	7						
						Total:	2,717	394	209	884	1230

in 1970, and the figures thereafter went on to reach 429 in 1980, 750 in 1990, and 1342 in 2000.[136] It was only in the 1980s that the number of subscribers to the Law Library again equalled (and ultimately surpassed) the membership of the institution in the early nineteenth century.

Earlier in this essay (page 65) it was observed that the period under review might be characterised as the Irish Bar's 'age of bronze', a statement, made in the context of a consideration of the social and intellectual standing of the profession, that implied that there had previously been periods apt to be described by the more precious metals. A similar view might be reached in the context merely of numbers entering the profession. A letter written by the barrister Denis Caulfield Heron (1824-81), and published in *The Times*, preserves valuable information about membership of the Law Library, and offers apt statistical corroboration that the best years of the Irish Bar were over before our period. In January 1868 Heron, who had then been in practice for twenty years, wrote pessimistically:[137]

> Ireland is the only geographical district in Europe diminishing in wealth and population. The population of Ireland is now less than it was in 1805; I believe the rental to be less than it was in 1805. Every county town in Ireland except Belfast and Cork has gone down; county society is vanishing out of Ireland; the ruins of castles and abbeys are everywhere to be seen. There are few gentlemen's houses.
>
> Institution after institution is disappearing. As property vanishes, those who live by the litigation concerning that property also disappear. In the year 1800 there were about 500 practising barristers in Ireland, about 1,000 in England. In the year 1833 the number of barristers and conveyancers in England amounted to 1,290; in 1861, as enumerated in the *Law List*, to 4,630. The number of barristers subscribing to the library of the Four Courts, Dublin, in 1850, was 690; for the last few years it has been about 427. In the year of the Union the number of barristers in Ireland was one-half the number in England; in 1850 it was one-fourth. It is now less than one-tenth. In the year 1800 the population of Ireland was one-third of the population of the United Kingdom; it is now one-sixth of the population of the United Kingdom.

Denis Caulfield Heron
7 Upper Fitzwilliam Street, Dublin. Jan. 31st [1868]

If applied to the century after 1868, and more especially to the burgeoning revival experienced in recent decades, the letter-writer's insight, that the number of barristers is related to national prosperity and self-confidence, has the appearance of a proposition capable of empirical demonstration.

---

[136] Figures abstracted from a table in Ivana Bacik, Cathryn Costello and Eileen Drew, *Gender InJustice* (Dublin, 2003), p. 72.

[137] *The Times*, Monday 3 Feb. 1868, p. 10, col. 6; reproduced in part, under the title 'Decay of the Irish Bar', in *I.L.T. & S.J.*, ii (1868), p. 28. Denis Caulfield Heron was called H 1848. His portrait (by Alfred Gibbs) hangs in King's Inns.

Some overseas students of King's Inns

Bahrain
Salah Jehangir Ali Reza (H 1968)

Bangladesh
Shams-um Alam ((T 1974)

Gold Coast [Ghana]
Kweku Anu Sekyi (T 1952)
Kobina Daniel Gwira (M 1953)

India
Vijay Kumar Arora (T 1967)
Paritosh Mandal (T 1971)
    [West Bengal]
Ricardo Levindo Silverio Xavier
    Falcao e Dourado (M 1971) [Goa]

Kenya
Crispin Beda Nagillah (T 1979)

Malaysia
Aik Wee Goh (T 1985)
Haji Abdul Kadir Haji Abdullah
    (T 1985)
Rathi Selvaratnam (T 1985)
Bimalarajah Kanagasabai (T 1985)
Edwin Boon Chong Tan (M 1993)
Jacqueline Siew Tiong (T 1995)
Kah-Lian Siev (T 1995)
Tze Yen How (T 1999)
Ting Tsuey Yuen (T 1999)
Kuok Ek Ling (M 1999)
Yeow Khoon Loh (M 1999)
Simon K. V Teo (M 2001)
Siva Balan Karupiah (T 2002)

Nigeria
Isaac Ifeanyi Ekwerekwu (M 1959)
Chukwuemeka Udenzwe (conferred
    M 1959)
Arthur Ezeakornobi Okechukwu
    (T 1959)
Jerome Herbert Chukwulozie Okolo
    (T 1960)
Anthony Oye Cukwurah (T 1961)
Linus Obonna (M 1961)
Chukwunonyelu Joseph Metuh
    (M 1961)
Gerard Jombo Ufford (M 1961)
Charles Igboanugo Amasian
    (T 1962)
Franklin Olatunbosun Odumosu
    (conferred T 1962)
Hyacinth Ihezie Anyanwu (H 1966)
Michael Amuziam Omo (M 1968)
Julius Ayodele Olu (M 1971)
Kenneth Boniface Chinedu Ijomah
    (T 1972)

Sierra Leone
Ansumana Philip Conteh (H 1955)

Abraham Joseph Kowa (T 1960)
Lahai Evans Kapindi Daramy
    (M 1963)
Edmond Labib Michael (M 1964)
Alexander Bajulaiye Cotay
    (M 1964)
Jamesina John (née *Rogers-Wright*)
    (T 1974)
Samuel Milton Margai (H 1977)
Desmond Zaidan (T 1990)

South Africa
George Singh (H 1968) [Durban]
Nishar Ahmed Karin (M 1968)
    [Transvaal]
Oothamaseelan Candasamy
    Govender (M 1970) [Natal]
Sirinarain Maharaj (M 1970) [Natal]
Ebrahim Mahomed Kathrada
    (T 1971) [Durban]
Sivalingum Purushothamam
    Govender (T 1971) [Natal]
Idris Mall (M 1971) [Natal]
Nehru Morgan Pillay (T 1972)
Rashid Ahmed Karim (M 1973)
    [Transvaal]
Satchithanathan Moonsamy
    Govender (H 1977) [Natal]
Kikaramjith Sooknanan (M 1978)

Sudan
Edmond S. Malka (T 1962)

Tanzania
Jesse Willibald Kiritta (M 1965)

Thailand
Pinyo Phinainitisatra (T 1963)

Trinidad
*Flavia Margaret Wade (*née *Davis*)
    (T 1967)
Johanna Cornelia Koorn (M 1973)

Uganda
Francis Xavier Oliso-Emingoit
    (H 1977)

Zambia
Edward Chisengalumbwe (M 1969)
James Connolly Heron (M 1974)
Kabika Mukelabai Sibeta (M 1981)

Zanzibar
Mrs Abdullah Riyami (née *Soad
    Mohammad Nasser Lamki*)
    (M 1963)

Zimbabwe
Herbert Sylvester Masiyiwa
    Ushewokunze (M 1989)

The King's Inns has always educated many more students than chose to join the Law Library. Practically-minded parents could reasonably view the King's Inns qualification as an alternative to a university degree, a species of liberal education apt to be useful as a grounding for an administrative career. Máire Cruise O'Brien [*née* MacEntee], who never practised, entered the King's Inns at the suggestion of her father, from whom 'a suggestion ... was, of course, an order'. She recalled that 'the two hours' lectures four afternoons a week' constituted 'numbing boredom'; but she rubbed shoulders with a future Foreign Minister of Nigeria [J.A. Wachuku (M 1944)], and found that 'the qualification came in handy' when she applied to join the Department of External Affairs.[138]

Many graduates of the King's Inns will have been reconciled to going abroad. From the late nineteenth century, Irish barristers regularly took up colonial appointments. In 1909 the Bar Council took credit for having[139]

> brought before the Colonial Office the claims of the Irish Bar to a share in the appointments to Colonial legal offices, and with the assistance of the Attorney-General of Ireland were enabled to secure that the same notification of vacancies should be given to the Irish Bar as is given to the various Inns of Court in England, and these notices have since been sent to the Under Treasurer, King's Inns, who has forwarded them to the Secretaries of the Bar Council to be posted in the Library.

Since the first world war, when an Indian contingent came in force, there has always been a trickle of students from abroad. The names on the page opposite show that King's Inns classes have consistently included individuals from overseas, many of whom, remarkably, were able to satisfy the Chief Justice that they possessed a competent knowledge of the Irish language. The Legal Practitioners (Qualification) Act, 1929, set out to ensure 'that future members of the legal profession[140] shall possess a competent knowledge of the Irish language'. Section 3, which governed the 'Qualification for degree of barrister-at-law', provided (and still provides) that:

> No person shall be admitted by the Chief Justice to practise as a barrister-at-law in the Courts of Saorstát Eireann unless before such person is so admitted he satisfies the Chief Justice, by such evidence as the Chief Justice shall prescribe, that he possesses a competent knowledge of the Irish language: Provided always that nothing in this section contained shall prevent the Chief Justice from admitting to practise as a barrister-at-law in the Courts of Saorstát Éireann any member of three years' standing at any

---

[138] Máire Cruise O'Brien, *The same age as the State* (Dublin, 2003), pp 159-61.
[139] *I.L.T. & S.J.*, xliii, 4 December 1909, p. 299.
[140] Limited to persons 'of the age of fifteen years on the 1st day of October, 1929'.

other Bar who has been admitted to the degree of barrister-at-law by the
Benchers of the Honourable Society of King's Inns, Dublin, pursuant to a
reciprocal arrangement whereby members of the Bar of Saorstát Eireann
may be admitted to practise at such other Bar.

A glance at the text of the statute would suggest that the spirit of
mercy, in prodigious proportions, must have inspired the evidentiary
standards of the Chief Justice. The 1929 statute was clearly not
allowed to prejudice the business of the King's Inns.

After the turmoil of the 1920s, the country, under its new
management, regained an equilibrium that was essentially
conservative. The return to traditional values was congenial to
professional men who had been taught to seek their guidance in
precedent. With the exception of the Supreme Court, which was
beginning under Ó Dálaigh as Chief Justice to discover in the de
Valera Constitution rights that were 'unenumerated', there was no
radical spirit abroad in the law. A journalist in the 1980s, who
purported to reveal the secrets of the Supreme Court, reserved his
special scorn for William O'Brien FitzGerald, who had joined the
bench of that Court in 1966, and was afterwards briefly Chief
Justice. He was damned as 'a Redmondite', and 'an old-fashioned
man'.[141] Billy FitzGerald's sin, in the eyes of the journalist, was that
he decided cases on the basis of his experience, and believed that it
was not the business of the court to change the law. If this be a
correct summary of the views of Mr. Justice FitzGerald in 1968,
then Gerald Fitzgibbon, the author of *Ireland in 1868*, would have
found nothing amiss in them. Fitzgibbon indeed would have
applauded the circumstance that Billy FitzGerald, who had enjoyed
a large Round Hall practice, came to the Bench recommended only
by his standing in the profession, and not as a reward for political
service.

It is not inappropriate that we conclude our story in the year
1968, with its associations of student protest. In the Trinity Term of
1967 a young woman joined the profession who had been active in
student politics under her maiden name of Marie Teresa Winifred
Bourke. In 1969 she would enter the Senate and become the Reid
Professor in Trinity College. Her call to the Bar may be considered
a harbinger of themes to come; but in 1968 her time had not yet
come. When Mary Robinson (*née* Bourke) became the Reid
Professor, her colleagues on the staff of the Law School in Trinity
College included two members of the Bar, who, though a generation
apart in age, were somewhat similar in appearance, not least because

[141] Colm Toibín, 'Inside the Supreme Court', in *Magill*, vol. 8, no. 7 (February
1985), p. 19.

Two Chief Justices who died in office: (left) Hugh Kennedy [1879-1936], the 'Voice of the Gael in the Courts of the Pale'; (right) William O'Brien FitzGerald [1906-74], an 'old-fashioned' disciple of the common law. [Portraits in King's Inns by Leo Whelan (painted in 1925) and Pat Phelan (painted, posthumously, in 1979) respectively.]

King's Inns Barristers, 1868-2004, page 121.

JOHN SYDNEY R. COLE.

WILLIAM BLACK.

Methodist Ministers' sons. A High Court Judge in Dublin (William Black; H 1901); and a colonial civil servant (John Sydney R. Cole; T 1935), who afterwards taught Evidence and Roman Law in Trinity College, Dublin. Photographs from: J.W. Henderson, *Methodist College Belfast 1868-1938* (2 vols.; Belfast, 1939). *King's Inns Barristers, 1868-2004*, page 122.

both wore the black jackets and striped trousers that were the uniform of older members of the profession. One was E.Y. Exshaw (M 1953), who bore the name of a Dublin family eminent in the eighteenth-century book trade. The other was J.S.R. Cole (T 1935), who had been in the colonial service in various countries, including Mauritius, Northern Nigeria and Kenya. [142]

In the years after 1968, as sartorial standards gave way, these figures in their black jackets and striped trousers became conspicuous. Heading for the Common Room, they made a stately and incongruous passage across the Front Square of Trinity College. Their course sometimes brought them past the throng of students assembled in jeans and T-shirts at the Dining Hall steps, the venue for mechanically-assisted oratory. R.F.V. Heuston remembered the scene when he wrote Sydney Cole's obituary.[143] To a man of his age, he mused, the concept of student leader was 'a term almost incomprehensible':

> The young had made the intoxicating discovery that one could have all the excitements of a revolution without any of its dangers. To someone who had survived such dangers in East Africa, the hot-house politics of the Front Square in the early seventies were not worthy of notice.

Fifty years earlier Ireland had experienced its fill of hot-house politics. The Irish Bar had been profoundly affected by the destructive energy of a young generation, which, in overthrowing a form of government that had endured for seven centuries, permitted the Temple of Justice to be destroyed. Inevitably, when the adherents of their revolution came to enter the legal profession, they influenced its tone. Their increasing presence underlay, in 1925, the secession from King's Inns of the Northern Ireland Benchers, and must also have affected, as in the case of Sydney Cole himself, many an individual's choice of career. The requirement to learn Irish was certainly apt to scare away from the profession such as did

---

[142] Sydney Cole's father, the Reverend Richard Lee Cole, wrote a family memoir *The Cole Family of West Carbery* (Belfast, 1943), some sentences on p. 6 of which bear on a general theme suggested by scrutiny of a record volume such as this — the impermanence not only of records but of a family name:

> Many of the papers from which quotation is made here have unfortunately been destroyed in the burning of the Record Office in Dublin. What appears clear, is that in the opening years of the nineteenth century the Coles in West Carbery numbered about one hundred persons, whereas today not one of the name is left in the Barony ... The family which at one time was prolific has now scattered over the world and is represented by scarcely a dozen persons in the whole of Ireland, though it is largely represented in America.

[143] R.F.V. Heuston, obituary of J.S.R. Cole, in *Trinity Trust News*, vol. 14, no. 1 (1989), p. 9.

not dare to believe that their linguistic talents would be sufficient to satisfy the evidentiary standards of the Chief Justice. Although, for old times' sake, a couple of peers — Dunboyne and Hemphill — were called in Dublin, the Irish Bar did not gain in social distinction after 1922.

Yet much less changed than might have changed; and it is notable how easily the newcomers allowed themselves to be moulded by the traditions of their profession. Judicial scarlet was abandoned, but the 'black Irish poplin gown of uniform make and material' and 'white bands as heretofore worn' survived, as, remarkably, did wigs.[144] No more was heard of a proposal of Chief Justice Kennedy, contemplated by him with W.B. Yeats in 1924, that the judiciary should be attired in robes fit for Brehons.[145] The Gael, now that he had the right to be heard *gaelice*, did not often break his silence in the Courts of the Pale. The enthusiasm for innovation waned. A pattern of the routine, characterised by memories of the drab austerity of the war years, is the hallmark of the few legal memoirs that cover the period.[146] The writing of legal textbooks and commentaries, an activity which might be viewed as an index of intellectual vigour, and one in which barristers had been notably energetic in the nineteenth century, became rare.[147] After 1931, once its old home at the Four Courts had been restored to it, the Irish Bar was permitted a respite from change. It entered upon a period of complacency which it was still enjoying in 1968.

---

[144] Rules of the High Court and Supreme Court, 1926, Order XXX. The late Senior Counsel Vincent Davy and Kevin Liston, who remembered Hugh Kennedy's dislike of wigs, confirmed to Chief Justice Keane that 'Chief Justice Kennedy never wore his wig in court: he carried it in his hand and placed it on the bench, presumably regarding this as sufficient compliance with the rules and a defiant gesture that the battle was not over': see Ronan Keane, 'The Voice of the Gael: Chief Justice Kennedy and the emergence of the new Irish court system 1921-1936', in *The Irish Jurist*, xxxi (1996), 204-225, at p. 223.

[145] See Ronan Keane, 'Had I the heavens' embroidered cloths: Yeats's role in robing the judiciary', in *The Irish Times*, Saturday 9 June 1990; also colour illustrations of the proposed robes in [Rónán Kennedy (ed.)], *The Supreme Court of Ireland: a history* (Dublin, 2003), pp 38-9.

[146] e.g., Gerard A. Lee, *A Memoir of the South-Western Circuit* (Dublin, 1990); Patrick MacKenzie, *Lawful Occasions: The old Eastern Circuit* (Cork and Dublin, 1991). See also: Rex Mackey, *Windward of the Law* (1965; 2nd edition, Dublin 1991); Patrick Lindsay, *Memories* (Dublin, 1992); Thomas F. O'Higgins, *A Double Life* (Dublin, 1996).

[147] In response to a question asked in the Dáil on 10 July 1974, the Minister for Justice (Patrick Cooney) said that he was 'well aware of the scarcity of text books on Irish law'. He added that 'the real problem appears to be that there are not enough people in this country who are able and willing to undertake the authorship of text books of this kind' [*Dáil Éireann. Díospóireachtaí Parlaiminte*, vol. 274, cols. 734-5, quoted in *I.L.T. & S.J.*, cix (1975), p. 14]. The complaint cannot be made today.

ALPHABETICAL INDEX
OF BARRISTERS'
MEMORIALS, 1868-1968

Compiled by
JULITTA CLANCY
M.B.E., B.A., Dip. Archival Studies,

assisted by
MARGARET CONNOLLY
B.A., Dip. Archival Studies,

with biographical annotations by
KENNETH FERGUSON
LL. B., Ph. D., Barrister-at-Law.

ALPHABETICAL INDEX
OF BARRISTERS'
MEMORIALS, 1868-1968

A NOTE ON DATES

In the sequences of letters and numbers placed after the personal details and before the note of the number of items of which the record is composed, the first represents the term and year of the candidate's admission to King's Inns as a student; the second (if three dates are given) the identification of an English Inn, with the term and year of admission to that Inn; and the last the year and term, with archival reference number, of Call to the Irish Bar. The elements of the last are separated by the forward slash symbol /.

ABRAHAMSON, MAURICE (b. 28 Oct. 1926) 2nd s. of Professor Leonard Abrahamson, of 40 Fitzwilliam Place, Dublin, and Tillie Nurock; B.A., LL.B. (T.C.D.); M 1946. Awarded 1st Victoria Prize. 1949/M/04 [2 items]. Auditor of the College Historical Society, 1951-2. Stockbroker.

ADAIR, HENRY ROSS WILLIAM (b. 15 May 1847) eld. s. of John Adair, Barrister-at-Law, of 65 Lower Mount Street, Dublin, and Letitia Anne Mahon; B.A. (T.C.D.); E 1870, M.T. E 1871. 1876/H/03 [4 items].

ADAIR, JOHN FREDERICK (b. 20 Jan. 1852) 2nd s. of John Adair (decd.), M.A., Barrister-at-Law, of 65 Lower Mount Street, Dublin, and Letitia Mahon; M.A., Fellow of Pembroke College Cambridge; M 1881, I.T. H 1881. 1885/M/04 [7 items].

ADAIR, JOHN OLPHERT (b. 1 Feb. 1858) only s. of Samuel Frederick Adair J.P., land agent, of 24 Fitzwilliam Square, Dublin, and Letitia Olphert; M 1877, I.T. M 1877. 1880/M/09 [5 items].

ADAMS, RICHARD (b. 6 Jan 1843) eldest s. of Bryan Adams (decd.) of Cork, and Frances Donovan; H 1869; M.T. H 1866. 1873/H/5x [2 items]. Q.C., June 1889. In early life a journalist with the *Cork Examiner*, *Morning Star* (London), *Southern Reporter* (Cork) and *Freeman's Journal*. Prosecuted Parnell for conspiracy, and became Crown Prosecutor for Cork. Appt. County Court Judge for Limerick, 9 March 1894. Died 4 April 1908. Obituary, *I.L.T. & S.J.*, xlii (1908), 89. Mentioned in James Meenan (ed.), *Centenary History of Lit. and Hist. Soc. of U.C.D.*; and in Maurice Healy, *The Old Munster Circuit*, 12, 22-4, 169-70, 217. See *Who's Who*.

ADAMSON, ROBERT St. CLAIRE (b. 23 May 1898) eld. s. of Robert Adamson, of Eden, Ballina, Co. Mayo, and Amy Elizabeth Laing; M 1924. 1927/M/15 [3 items]. Died 16 April 1931. Obituary, *I.L.T. & S.J.*, lxv (1931), 101.

ADEFOLU, OMASANYA (b. 22 Sept. 1881) eld. s. of Chief Oladunjoye Adefolu (decd.), Base of Ake, of Abeokuta, Nigeria, and Sophia Onitande; M 1925. Name crossed out on official list for T 1928. 1928/T/03 [2 items]. Called at E 1929.

ADESANYA, CHARLES OLAYINKA (b. 10 Sept. 1926) eld. s. of Daniel Obi Adesanya, of Oke Agbo, Ijebu Igbo, Nigeria B.W.A., and Christianah Bowale; B.A. (T.C.D.); M 1954, M.T. M 1954. 1957/M/14 [6 items].

ADYE-CURRAN, OLIVER GEORGE VALENTINE (b. 14 Feb. 1928) young. s. of Lieutenant-Colonel F.G. Adye Curran, R.A.M.C. (decd.), of Esker House, 94 Upper Rathmines Road, Dublin, and Julia Cecilia Fair; M 1945. 1952/M/15 [2 items].

Divisional Magistrate, Aden, 1958.

AGASTI, BIJAY NARAIJAN (b. 7 Dec. 1895) 3rd s. of Ram Narayan Agasti, B.A., Prime Minister to H.H. Maharaja of Durbhanga, of Garbheta, Midnapore, Bengal, India; M 1914. 1917/T/29 [2 items].

AGGARWALA, DWARKA NATH (b. 4 May 1897) eld. s. of Bhagat Ram Aggarwala, B.A., LL.B., of Hoshiarpur, Punjab, India; M 1915. 1918/M/04 [2 items].

AHERN, PATRICK SYLVESTER (b. 31 Dec. 1916) 4th s. of James Ahern of Newtown, Cobh, Co. Cork, and Mary Coakley; M 1937. 1943/T/01 [2 items].

ALCOCK, GEORGE (b. 16 July 1849) only s. of George Alcock (decd.) of Crosthwaite Park, Co. Dublin, and Maria Louisa Cooper; H 1878, M.T. M 1881. 1883/E/01 [6 items].

ALCORN, JAMES G. (b. 8 Feb. 1844) 2nd s. of John Alcorn of 101 Leinster Road, Dublin, and Margaret Gunning; M 1875, M.T. T 1877. 1879/M/06 [7 items].

ALEXANDER, GEORGE (b. 20 June 1858) 5th s. of John Alexander of Milford House, Co. Carlow, and Esther Brinkley; B.A. (T.C.D.); M 1877, M.T. H 1880. 1881/H/05 [7 items]. Died 2 Nov. 1930. *Burke's Irish Family Records* (1976), 16.

ALEXANDER, JOHN GEORGE (b. 8 Nov. 1884) eld. surv. s. of John Alexander, of Ellerslie, Enniskerry, Co. Wicklow, and Susan Maguire (decd.); M 1921. 1924/H/01 [2 items]. Chief Examiner of Titles. Died 16 Sept. 1946. Obituary, *I.L.T. & S.J.*, lxxx (1946), 250, 256.

ALLEN, DAVID (b. 18 May 1854) eld. surv. s. of David Allen (decd.), J.P., of Belfast, and Agnes Allen; M.A., B.L. (R.U.I.); H 1901. 1903/M/11 [2 items].

ALLEN, ROBERT (b. 7 Feb. 1848) 4th s. of Joseph Allen of Ashton Lawn, Co. Cork, corn merchant, and Jane Hall; B.A. (Queen's University of Ireland); H 1867, M.T. H 1869. 1871/T/4 [3 items].

ALLEN, ROBERT LOUGHEED (b. 6 Oct. 1864) eld. s. of Joshua Allen, of Stone Park, Dromahair, Co. Leitrim, and Jane McLean; B.A. (R.U.I.); M 1900. 1903/T/07 [3 items].

ALLEN, SAMUEL (b. 22 July 1842) eld. surv. s. of Henry Ellis Allen of Liscomman, Co. Antrim, and Jane Rogan; B.A. (Cambridge and T.C.D.); M 1863, M.T. M 1863. 1869/M/1 [4 items].

ALLEN, WILLIAM KENNEDY ABBOTT (b. 4 June 1878) eld. s. of William Allen (decd.) of Rockhampton, Queensland, Commonwealth of Australia, and Mary Abbott; M 1904. 1907/T/13 [2 items]. Died 1962.

ALLINGHAM, JOHN (b. 24 Sept. 1855) 2nd s. of John Allingham, bank manager, of Waterford, and Eliza Christian; B.A., LL.B (T.C.D.); M 1876, M.T. E 1879. 1880/E/03 [6 items].

ALLISON, EDWIN GEORGE (b. 5 Nov. 1868) 4th s. of the Revd. John William Allison (decd.), B.D., Rector of Sydan and Rathkenny, Co. Meath, and Isabella Collins; B.A. (T.C.D.); M 1891. 1895/E/02 [5 items].

AMASIAN, CHARLES IGBOANUGO (b. 29 Nov. 1928) 3rd s. of Joseph Amasian Ogbo, trader, of Nteje, Nigeria, county of Onitsha and Akaenu Akom; B.C.L. (U.C.D.); M 1957. 1962/T/03 [2 items].

AMBROSE, ROMUALD M. (b. 7 Feb. 1930) eld. s. of Michael Ambrose (decd.), of Ardagh, Co. Limerick, and Stella McFetridge; M 1951. 1955/M/10 [2 items].

ANDERSON, ALFRED HASTINGS (b. 11 Jan. 1888) only s. of Alexander Edmond Anderson (decd.), of 'Kilgour', Dartry Road, Rathmines, Dublin, and Annie Thallon; M 1921. 1922/T/01 [4 items].

ANDERSON, BARCROFT (b. 31 Aug. 1864) only s. of Sir Samuel Lee Anderson, Knight, of Lower Baggot Street, Dublin, and Elizabeth Barcroft; M 1882, M.T. E 1883. 1885/M/09 [6 items]. Advocate of the Supreme Court of South Africa.

ANDERSON, JAMES (b. 12 July 1881) eld. s. of Thomas Anderson of Rockmount Villa, Northland Road, Londonderry, and Susan Wybrants (decd.); M.A. (R.U.I.); M 1904. 1907/M/03 [2 items]. Professor of Jurisprudence and Political Economy at Galway. Reid Professor, T.C.D., 1914-15. Died 19 June 1915. Obituary, *I.L.T. & S.J.*, xlix (1915), 156.

ANDERSON, SAMUEL LEE (b. 14 June 1837) eld. surv. s. of Matthew Anderson, Crown Solicitor, of Knapton House, Dublin, and Mary Lee; M.A. (T.C.D.); E 1874, M.T. T 1874. 1877/H/05 [5 items].

ANDREWS, DAVID PATRICK (b. 15 March 1936) 3rd s. of Dr. Christopher Stephen Andrews, Chairman, Córas Iompair Éireann, of 'Ardeath', Taney Road, Dundrum, Co. Dublin, and Mary Noel Coyle; B.C.L. (N.U.I.); M 1957 1961/M/10 [2 items]. S.C., 13 March 1992. T.D. for Dún Laoghaire, 1965-, and sometime Minister for Foreign Affairs. Listed in Maureen Cairnduff, *Who's Who in Ireland* (1984, 1991 and 1999 editions).

ANDREWS, JAMES (b. 3 Jan. 1877) 3rd s. of Thomas Andrews, of Ardara, Comber, Co. Down, and Eliza [Pirrie]; Mod. B.A.; M 1897. 1900/M/05 [3 items]. Auditor of the College Historical Society, 1902-3. North-East Circuit. K.C., 27 Feb. 1918. Bencher of King's Inns, 1920; a Lord Justice of Appeal in Northern Ireland, 17 Oct. 1921-30 Nov. 1937; Lord Chief Justice of Northern Ireland, 1 Dec.1937-18 Feb. 1951. P.C. (N.I.), 1924. Created a baronet (1942) [baronetcy extinct on his death]. Died 18 Feb. 1951. Obituary, *I.L.T. & S.J.*, lxxxv (1951), 57. See *D.N.B.* [article by Lord MacDermott]; *Burke's Landed Gentry of Ireland*, 4th ed. (1958), 24; and *Who's Who*. Portrait photograph in *I.L.T. & S.J.*, lxii (1938).

ANDREWS, JOHN THOMAS (b. 12 May 1842) eld. s. of Robert Andrews (decd.) of Mountjoy Square, Dublin, and Anne Kennedy; B.A. (T.C.D.); M 1864; M.T. T 1866. 1869/M/2 [4 items].

ANDREWS, THOMAS JOHN (b. 8 July 1855) 2nd s. of Thomas Andrews, M.D., F.R.S., of Belfast, and Jane H. Walker; B.A. (Q.C.B.); E 1878, M.T. E 1877. 1880/M/18 [5 items].

ANYANWU, HYAEINTH IHEZIE (b. 6 Aug. 1933) eld. s. of Frederick Uwawike Anyanwu, merchant, of 43 Aggrey Road, Port Harcourt, Nigeria, and Agnes Nnechioma; M 1959. 1966/H/04 [1 item].

ARMSTRONG, RICHARD (b. 27 April 1856) 2nd s. of Richard Armstrong Q.C., HM First Serjeant-at-Law, of 32 Stephen's Green, Dublin, and Eliza Meurant; M 1875, I.T. M 1877. 1880/H/02 [5 items]. Appt. Under-Treasurer of King's Inns, 1899 in the place of J.D. O'Hanlon (M 1845): *I.L.T. & S.J.*, xxxiii (1899), 479; accident while cycling on Rathmines Road reported, *ibid.*, xxxv, 19 Jan. 1901, 38; retirement noted, *ibid.*, lxiv (1930), 245. Died 21 Oct. 1930. Obituary, *I.L.T. & S.J.*, lxiv (1930), 257.

ARMSTRONG, WILLIAM (b. 31 Dec. 1848) eld. s. of Richard Armstrong Q.C., H.M. First Serjeant-at-Law, of 32 Stephen's Green, Dublin, and Elizabeth Meurant; B.A. (T.C.D.); M 1869; I.T. E 1870. 1872/T/9 [4 items].

ARMSTRONG, WILLIAM REGINALD (b. 25 Feb. 1874) 4th s. of William Armstrong (decd.) of New Ross, Co. Wexford, and Sarah Jeffares; Sen. Mod. B.A., LL.D. (T.C.D.); M 1897. 1900/H/01 [3 items]. S.C., 21 Dec. 1938. Died 22 Nov. 1954. Obituary, *I.L.T. & S.J.*, lxxxviii (1954), 302.

ARNOLD, JOHN CORRY (b. 8 April 1881) only s. of the Revd. R.J. Arnold M.A., of Dunmurry, Co. Antrim, and Eliza Wilson; B.A. (Cambridge); T 1903. 1906/M/10 [2 items]. Q.C. in England. Author of *Covenants relating to Leases and Tenancy Agreements* (London, 1930), *The Settled Land Acts* (London, 1937), *The Marriage Law of England* (London and New York, 1951); and *R.M. Jones of Inst: a Memoir* (Belfast, 1953). Contributor of the essay 'The prospects for constitutional democracy', in John H. Hallowell (ed.), *Prospects for Constitutional Democracy: Essays in honour of R. Taylor Cole* (Durham, N.C., 1976).

ARORA, VIJAY KUMAR (b. 12 Jan. 1932) eld. s. of Hakim Braj Lal Verman Arora (decd.), doctor, of Mathura City, Mathura (W.P.), India, and Krishna Aropa; M.A., LLB; M 1966; Allahabad High Court, Allahabad, India, 1957. 1967/T/14 [1 item].

ATKINS, GEORGE (b. 4 Nov 1867) eldest s. of William Atkins, Dean of Ferns, of Gorey, Co. Wexford and Elizabeth Barrett; B.A. (T.C.D.); T 1865; I.T. E 1866. 1868/T/6 [2 items].

ATKINSON, CECIL THOMAS (b. 22 Oct. 1876) 2nd s. of the Rt. Hon. John Atkinson of 68 Fitzwilliam Square, Dublin, and Rowena Jane [Chute]; B.A. (T.C.D.); M 1898. 1901/T/03 [3 items]. K.C., 27 June 1914. Appt. judge of the High Court of India, 1915:

I.L.T. & S.J., xlix (11 Dec. 1915), 309. Died 1919, as a result of a railway accident on the line between Bombay and Patna. Obituary, *I.L.T. & S.J.*, liii (29 Nov. 1919), 258. Mentioned in Maurice Healy, *The Old Munster Circuit*, 116.

ATKINSON, EDWARD DUPRÉ (b. 2 Feb. 1855) only s. of Richard Atkinson (decd.), solicitor, of Gortmore, Dundrum, Dublin, and Mary Golding; LL.B. (Cambridge); E 1877, L.I. H 1875. 1878/T/03 [7 items]. Took Holy Orders, becoming the Venerable the Archdeacon of Dromore. Author of *An Ulster Parish: being a history of Donaghcloney, Waringstown* (Dublin, 1898); *Dromore: an Ulster diocese* (Dundalk, 1925); *'Science and Health' and Holy Scripture. A contrast* [Parallel passages from Mary Baker Eddy selected and arranged by Atkinson] (London: SPCK, 1930); and *Recollections of an Ulster Archdeacon* (Belfast, 1934). Died 26 April 1937. *Burke's Irish Family Records* (1976), 41; *Who's Who*.

ATKINSON, GEORGE GLANVILLE (b. 5 April 1874) eld. s. of George Atkinson, of Glenvale House, Londonderry, and Margaret McCurdy; B.A. (T.C.D.); M 1900. 1903/M/04 [3 items]. Died Sept. 1945.

ATKINSON, JOSEPH ALBERT NELSON (b. 19 Jan. 1875) 2nd s. of Edward Atkinson (decd.), of Ashfield, Moynalty, Co. Meath, and Lydia Rutherford; B.A. (T.C.D.); M 1899. 1902/M/10 [3 items].

ATKINSON, THOMAS JOHN DAY (b. 4 March 1882) only s. of Thomas John Atkinson, Deputy Lieutenant, of Cavangarden, Co. Donegal, and Elizabeth Day; B.A. (T.C.D.); H 1902. 1904/M/12 [3 items]. President of the University Philosophical Society, T.C.D., 1905-6. N.W. Circuit. One of the founders of the D.U. contingent of the O.T.C., 1909. Captain, 5th Battalion, Royal Irish Fusiliers; wounded at Suvla. Joint Secretary, Commissioners of Charitable Donations and Bequests, 1917-21. K.C. (N.I.), M 1924. Chairman of Caterham and Warlington U.D.C., 1938-9. O.B.E., D.L. Author of Lipsett and Atkinson, *Law of Carriage by Railway in Great Britain and Ireland*. Residences in Devon and at Ballyshannon. Died 11 Dec. 1949. *Who's Who*.

ATKINSON, THOMAS JOYCE (b. 30 Jan. 1878) only surv. s. of Wolsey Richard Atkinson of Eden Villa, Portadown, Co. Armagh, and Alice Joyce; LL.B. (T.C.D.); H 1898. 1900/H/02 [3 items]. Aft. a solicitor. Major, Royal Irish Fusiliers. Died on the Somme, 1 July 1916. See 'A Reminiscence of the King's Inns', in *I.L.T. & S.J.*, li, 14 July 1917, 171. His name is recorded at the Four Courts, not on the Bar's War Memorial, but on the Solicitors'.

ATKINSON, WILLIAM HERBERT (b. 6 Nov. 1876) 2nd s. of Carleton Atkinson of 8 Belgrave Square South, Dublin, and Lucy Hone; B.A. (T.C.D.); E 1897. 1901/E/03 [3 items]. Served as a sergeant in the Pals' battalion, refusing a commission. Photograph (right) in Henry Hanna, *The Pals at Suvla Bay* (1917), 157. Died 21 Dec. 1927. Obituary, *I.L.T. & S.J.*, lxi (1927), 316.

ATWOOL, HENRY RICHARD HERBERT (b. 23 Feb. 1854) eld. s. of Richard Cotten, of Kingstown, Co. Dublin, and Elizabeth Atwool; H 1877, L.I. H 1879. 1880/H/08 [7 items].

AUSTEN, HENRY (b. 17 Dec. 1853) only s. of John Austen of Blair Castle, Co. Cork, and Anne Bennett; LL.B. (Q.C.C.); M 1883. 1886/M/14 [6 items].

AUSTIN, HENRY EVANS (b. 26 Aug. 1857) eld. s. of Thomas Kingston Austin, J.P., of Talbot Lodge, Stillorgan, Co. Dublin, and Octavia Evans; B.A., LL.B (T.C.D.); E 1879, M.T. M 1880. 1882/H/04 [7 items]. Called to English Bar, T 1883. 6 Pump Court, Temple.

AVERGAL, M.R. Ry. T. ADINAVAYANA CHETTIAR (b. 1879) only s. of M.R. Ry. T. Pattabirama Chettiar Avergal, of Salem, Madras, India; M 1914 1917/H/01 [2 items].

AYLMER, FRANCIS (b. 13 Oct. 1930) 2nd s. of Francis P. Aylmer, journalist, of Castledermot, Co. Kildare, and Elizabeth Bradley; M 1954. 1958/M/06 [2 items].

AYLMER, HANS HENDRICK (b. 22 May 1856) 2nd s. of Michael Aylmer, J.P., of Courtown, Co. Kildare, and Charlotte Hendrick; B.A. (T.C.D.); M 1876, M.T. T 1878. 1880/M/06 [6 items].

BABINGTON, ANTHONY BRUTUS (b. 24 Nov. 1877) eld. s. of Hume Babington of Creevagh, Co. Londonderry, and Hester Watt; M 1897. 1900/M/13 [3 items]. North-East Circuit. K.C., 27 Feb. 1918. Attorney-General (N.I.), 24 Nov. 1925-2 Dec. 1937. Appt. Lord Justice of Appeal in N.I., 2 Dec. 1937. Knighted. Retired 26 Feb. 1949. Died 1972. Obituary, *I.L.T. & S.J.*, cvi (13 May 1972), 106. Author of the second edition of R.E. Osborne, *The Jurisdiction and Practice of County Courts in Ireland in Equity and Probate Matters* (Dublin, 1910), the copyright of which he received as a wedding gift from Osborne (see J.C. MacDermott, *An Enriching Life*, 171). Portrait photograph published with the issue of the *I.L.T. & S.J.*, for 14 Jan. 1939. Died 10 April 1972. *Who's Who.*

BACON, EDWARD WILLIAM DELANY (b. 18 Sept. 1924) eld. s. of Thomas Francis Bacon, Barrister-at-Law, of 23 Clyde Road, Ballsbridge, Dublin, and Josephine Mary Dowley; B.A. (N.U.I.); M 1942. 1945/M/01 [2 items]. S.C., 1 March 1996. Chief Parliamentary Counsel, 1970-1985. Died 9 Feb. 2005. Obituary (with photograph) in *The Irish Times*, 19 Feb. 2005.

BACON, THOMAS FRANCIS (b. 17 Sept. 1881) young. s. of William Bacon (decd.) of Carlow, Co. Carlow, and Anne Delany; B.A. (R.U.I.); M 1905. 1908/T/05 [3 items]. Bencher 1946. Died 1964. Mentioned, as 'Father of the Bar', in Patrick MacKenzie, *Lawful Occasions*, 82. Contributor to James Meenan (ed.), *Centenary History of Lit. and Hist. Soc. of U.C.D.*

BAGENAL, PHILIP HENRY (b. 18 June 1850) 2nd surv. s. of Philip Henry Bagenal (decd.) of Benckerry, Co. Carlow, and Georgina Thomasina Boyd; M 1872; I.T. M 1869. 1874/M/9 [2 items]. Author of *A Digest of the Contagious Diseases (Animals) Act, 1878, 41 & 42 Vict., c. 74; and of the Orders of the Lords Justices and Privy Council of Ireland for bringing the same into operation* (Dublin: Stationery Office, 1879); *The Irish Agitator in Parliament and on the Platform* (Dublin, 1880); *A complete history of Irish politics for the year 1879, etc* (Dublin, 1880); *Parnellism Unveiled; or, the land-and-labour agitation of 1879-80, with an index* (Dublin, 1880); *The American Irish and their Influence on Irish Politics* (London, 1882); *Crime in Ireland. The Winter Assizes in Ulster, Munster, Leinster and Connaught* (Dublin, 1880); *Foreign Land Tenures and the Irish Tenant* (Dublin, 1882); *The Life of Ralph Bernal Osborne, M.P.* (London, 1884); *The Priest in Politics* (London, 1893); *The Tory Policy of the Marquis of Salisbury, K.G.* (London, 1895); *Vicissitudes of an Anglo-Irish Family [the Bagenal family], 1530-1800, etc.* (London, 1925); and (privately-printed) *The Annals of the County Carlow Cricket Club*. Died 14 Aug. 1927. *Burke's Irish Family Records* (1976), 46.

BAGGE-HEARN, JOHN WILLIAM (b. 12 Aug. 1851) only surv. s. of John Bagge-Hearn, M.A., Assistant Taxing Master of the Supreme Court, of Kinkora, Clontarf, Dublin, and Rose Roderick; B.A. (T.C.D.); 5 1872, M.T. T 1874. 1878/M/03x [2 items].

BAGWELL, FREDERICK TAYLOR (b. 27 Dec. 1856) eld. s. of John Bagwell of Lisronagh, Co. Tipperary, and Agnes Sarah Lindesay; B.A.; M 1880, I.T. M 1882. 1884/H/03 [5 items].

BAILEY, WILLIAM FREDERICK (b. 9 Feb. 1857) eld. s. of William Bailey (decd.), M.D., of Castletown [conyers], Co. Limerick, and Annie Harding; B.A. (T.C.D.); M 1878, M.T. T 1880. 1881/M/13 [6 items]. Sometime of the Munster Circuit; aft. civil servant. Barrington Lecturer in Political Economy. C.B., 1906. Privy Councillor, 1909. Author of *The Law of Franchise and Registration in Ireland* (Dublin, 1885); *Local and Centralised Government in Ireland: A Sketch of the Existing Systems* (Dublin, 1888); also of *Ireland since the Famine, Report on the Condition of Peasant Purchasers*, and *The Slavs of the War Zone* (1916). Died 16 April 1917. Obituary, *I.L.T. & S.J.*, li (1917), 98.

BAILY, FRANCIS (b. 21 Dec. 1864) 2nd s. of Francis R. Baily (decd.), land agent, of Ring View, Passage West, Co. Cork. 1919/E/02 [2 items].

BAKER, JOSHUA (b. 30 Jan. 1907) eld. s. of Philip Baker (decd.), of 77 Kenilworth Square, Rathgar, Dublin, and Fanny [Berman]; M 1928. 1932/M/04 [2 items]. Educated at Wesley College, Dublin. Reid Professor in Trinity College, Dublin, 1935-40. S.C., 1 Nov. 1963. Bencher.

BAKER, RONALD HEPBURN (b. 9 Nov. 1861) 3rd s. of John Andrew Baker, of Clare Street, Dublin, and Jane McCarthy; B.A. (T.C.D.); H 1883, M.T. H 1884. 1885/M/11 [7 items].

BALL, JOHN WILLIAM (b. 16 Nov. 1868) eld. s. of the Revd. William James Ball, M.A., of Tudor Hall, Monkstown, Dublin, and Julia Frances Hooper; B.A. (T.C.D.); M 1890. 1893/T/06 [5 items].

BALL, WILLIAM PAUMIER (b. 23 Oct. 1858) eld. s. of the Rt. Hon. John Thomas Ball LL.D., Lord Chancellor, of 71 Merrion Square, Dublin, and Catherine Elrington; B.A. (T.C.D.); M 1878, I.T. M 1879. 1883/T/02 [5 items]. North-East Circuit. Died 29 Aug. 1902. Obituary, *I.L.T. & S.J.*, xxxvi (1902), 352.

BARCROFT, RICHARD CECIL (b. 4 March 1871) only s. of Jonathan Hogg Barcroft, J.P., of Grange Lodge, Co. Tyrone, and Margaret Pike; B.A. (T.C.D.); M 1892. 1896/T/01 [5 items]. Lands Compensation Officer attached to the Staff of the Dublin Military Command. Died 25 Dec. 1924. *Burke's Irish Family Records* (1976), 60.

BARLOW, FRANCIS FARIS (b. 27 Dec. 1862) young. s. of Frederick Archer Barlow, solicitor, of North Great Georges Street, Dublin, and Mary Faris; B.A. (T.C.D.); M 1883. 1886/M/12 [6 items].

BARNARD, FRANCIS JOSEPH (b. 30 Jan. 1899) eld. s. of Patrick Michael Barnard, of Cnoc Seoirse (George's Hill), Dublin, and Jane Foster; M 1925. 1928/M/06 [2 items]. Local Government Auditor.

BARNES, EAMONN M. (b. 15 Sept. 1934) 3rd s. of John A. Barnes, B.A., teacher, of 'Grianain', Ballymote, Co. Sligo, and Brigid Coleman; B.A.; M 1954. 1958/M/12 [2 items]. First holder of the office of Director of Public Prosecutions, 1974-99. See also: Louis McRedmond (ed.), *Modern Irish Lives*; and Maureen Cairnduff, *Who's Who in Ireland* (1984, 1991 and 1999 editions).

BARNHILL, WILLIAM WILSON (b. 1 Jan. 1867) 2nd s. of William Barnhill (decd.), of Brickfield House, Strabane, Co. Tyrone, and Frances Anne Wilson; LL.B. (T.C.D.); M 1888. 1891/T/04 [5 items]. Died 1950. Obituary, *I.L.T. & S.J.*, lxxxv (1951), 4-5.

BARR, ROBERT PAUL (b. 28 June 1930) eld. s. of William Barr (decd.), of Middlesex, and Eileen Mary Mulhern; M 1953. Awarded 3rd Victoria Prize. 1957/T/02 [2 items]. S.C., 15 July 1972. Judge of the High Court, 30 Jan. 1985-27 June 2002. Listed in the 1991 and 1999 editions of Maureen Cairnduff, *Who's Who in Ireland*.

BARRAGRY, RICHARD M. (b. 22 Sept. 1915). 4th s. of John Barragry, of 121 Hollybank Road, Drumcondra, Dublin, and Bridget Higgins; B. Comm; M 1955 1958/T/07 [3 items].

BARRETT, JOHN SAMUEL (b. 28 July 1842) eld. s. of John Samuel Barrett of Greenhills, Co. Galway and Jane Hare; B.A. (T.C.D.); M 1864, MT H 1865. 1868/H/5 [4 items].

BARRETT, STEPHEN DECLAN (b. 26 Dec. 1913) only s. of George F. Barrett (decd.), journalist, of 4 York Terrace, Summerhill, Co. Cork, and Alice O'Sullivan; M 1942. 1946/T/14 [2 items]. T.D. 1954-69. Lord Mayor of Cork 1960. Judge of the Circuit Court, 1973. Died 1976. Obituary, *I.L.T. & S.J.*, cx (23 Oct. 1976), 259.

BARRETT, WILLIAM (b. 3 Dec. 1870) eld. s. of Joseph Barrett of 6 Parliament Street, Cork, and Catherine Harrington; M 1899. 1902/T/08 [4 items]. Died 26 May 1935. Obituary, *I.L.T. & S.J.*, lxix (1935), 148.

BARRINGTON, CROKER (b. 18 Aug. 1851) 2nd s. of Sir Croker Barrington, solicitor, of Glenstal, Co. Limerick, and 10 Ely Place, Dublin, and Anna West; B.A. (T.C.D.); H 1873, I.T. H 1875. 1876/M/06 [5 items].

BARRINGTON, DONALD P.M. (b. 20 Feb. 1928) young. s. of Thomas Barrington (decd.), of 26 Iona Crescent, Glasnevin, Dublin, and Eileen Bracken; B.A., LL.B.(N.U.I.); M 1947. 1951/M/10 [2 items]. Known as 'Donal'. S.C., 10 Oct. 1968. Judge of the High Court, 1 Oct. 1979; retired 31 Aug. 1989; Judge of the European Court of Justice, 1989-95; Judge of the Supreme Court, 12 Jan. 1996; retired 18 Feb. 2000. Listed in the 1984 and 1991 editions of Maureen Cairnduff, *Who's Who in Ireland*.

BARRINGTON, MANLIFF (b. 2 July 1861) eld. s. of Charles Barrington, merchant, of Gt. Britain Street, Dublin, and Louisa Grubb; B.A. (Cambridge); M 1884. 1887/M/06 [6 items].

BARRINGTON, RICHARD MANLIFFE (b. 22 May 1849) 8th s. of Edward Barrington, J.P., of Fassaroe, Bray, Co. Wicklow, and Huldah Strongman; B.A. (T.C.D.); E 1872, I.T. E 1873. 1875/T/05 [2 items].

BARRON, EUSTACE JOHN FITZGERALD (b. 24 June 1847) 5th s. of Pierse Marcus Barron of Belmont Park, Co. Waterford, D.L. and Catherine Crowe; H 1866; M.T. E 1869. 1871/T/3 [2 items].

BARRON, HENRY DENIS (b. 25 May 1926) only s. of Harrie Barron, of 19 Green Park, Rathgar, Dublin, and Lena Ellis; B.A. (T.C.D.); M 1947; M.T. E 1950. 1951/H/01 [2 items]. S.C., 6 March 1970. Judge of the High Court, 5 March 1982; of the Supreme Court, 19 March 1997. Retired 24 May 2000. Listed in the 1991 and 1999 editions of Maureen Cairnduff, *Who's Who in Ireland.*

BARRON, NICHOLAS (b. 27 Nov. 1907) only s. of Pierce Barron, accountant (retd.), of San Francisco, California, USA, formerly of Dungarvan, Co. Waterford, and Frances Anna Sheehan; M 1936 1942/T/04 [2 items]. Mentioned in Patrick MacKenzie, *Lawful Occasions,* 98-9.

BARROR, CECIL JOHN (b. 12 Aug. 1911) 2nd s. of John Joseph Barror, retired civil servant, of 16 Carlisle Avenue, Donnybrook, Co. Dublin, and Sarah Mannion; M 1949. 1954/H/03 [2 items]. Died 15 Oct. 1999. Obituary, *The Irish Times,* 30 Oct. 1999.

BARRY, CHARLES DAVID (b. 27 Sept. 1859) 2nd s. of the Rt. Hon. Charles Robert Barry, Justice of the Queen's Bench Division of the High Court of Justice, of Fitzwilliam Square, Dublin, and Kate FitzGerald; B.A. (T.C.D.); M 1878, I.T. T 1882. 1884/M/05 [7 items]. K.C., 29 June 1920. Irish Local Government Board. Died at Nice, 7 Feb. 1928. Obituary, *I.L.T. & S.J.,* lxii (1928), 43.

BARRY, IVOR HENRY HARTE (b. 20 Aug. 1909) eld. s. of Arthur Patrick Harte Barry, of 12 Fitzwilliam Place, Dublin, and Helena Mary Plunkett; M 1927. 1931/H/01 [2 items].

BARRY, JAMES J. McCARTHY (b. 17 April 1869) eld. s. of John McCarthy Barry of Belvidere, Tivoli, Cork, and Emily Cooke; M 1890. 1893/M/04 [6 items].

BARRY, KEVIN (b. 3 May 1923) 3rd s. of Richard Barry (decd.), of 27 St. Joseph's Terrace, Limerick, and Margaret Tobin; M 1952. Awarded 1st Victoria Prize. 1956/T/01 [2 items]. Civil servant; registrar.

BARRY, MICHAEL FRANCIS (b. 9 Oct. 1844) 2nd s. of Thomas Barry of No. 7 George's Quay, Cork, and Ellen Harding; H 1866; M.T. H 1868. 1871/E/2 [2 items]. Justice of the Peace, 1876. Died 23 July 1908. Obituary, *I.L.T. & S.J.,* xlii (1908), 194.

BARRY, RALPH BRERETON (b. 2 Oct. 1899) young. s. of Ralph Brereton Barry, K.C., County Court Judge (decd.), of Langara, Glenageary, Co. Dublin, and Claire Roche; M 1920. Awarded Society's Prize. 1922/M/02 [2 items]. Auditor of the College Historical Society, 1921-2. Contested parliamentary elections unsuccessfully in 1923 (Wexford, as Independent: 500 votes) and 1943 (Wicklow, Fine Gael: 3,452 votes). S.C., 12 April 1935. Died of typhoid fever on circuit in Letterkenny, 2 Dec. 1943. Obituary (and photograph) in *I.L.T. & S.J.,* lxxvii (1943), 308-9. Mentioned by T. de V. White in *A Fretful Midge* (1957) and by V.T.H. Delany [q.v.], in 'The Bench and Bar in Ireland', xxxiv. Remembered as an actor by Garrett Gill (q.v.). See biographical note in Joachim Fischer and John Dillon (eds.), *The Correspondence of Myles Dillon 1922-1925* (Dublin, 1999), 279. Portrait by Leo Whelan in T.C.D. in the possession of the College Historical Society: see Anne Crookshank and David Webb, *Paintings and Sculptures in Trinity College Dublin* (Dublin, 1990), 154.

BARRY, RALPH WESTROPP BRERETON (b. 7 June 1856) eld. s. of James Barry, solicitor, of Rathgar, Dublin, and Elizabeth Brereton; B.A.; M 1876, M.T. H 1879. 1880/M/05 [6 items]. Q.C., 22 April 1899. Appt. County Court Judge for Kildare, Carlow, Wicklow and Wexford, 1 April 1902. Died 16 March 1920. Obituary, *I.L.T. & S.J.,* liv (1920), 71; *Who's Who.*

BARRY, REDMOND JOHN (b. 14 Sept. 1866) 2nd surv. s. of Patrick Barry (decd.) of Hill View, St. Luke's, Cork, and Mary Anne Murphy; B.A. (R.U.I.); M 1885. 1888/T/06 [5 items]. Q.C., 22 April 1899. Liberal M.P. for North Tyrone, 1907-11. Solicitor-General, 1905-9; Attorney-General, 1909-11; Lord Chancellor, 1911-13. Died 11 July 1913. See: Ball, *Judges,* ii, 383; *Who's Who.*

BARRY-WALSH, JAMES OWEN (b. 15 June 1915) 2nd s. of Eugene Barry-Walsh, of Tremlewis House, Kilmallock, Co. Limerick, and Katherine Carroll; M 1934 1937/M/04 [2 items].

BARTLEY, CHARLES (b. 18 Dec. 1882) eld. s. of Charles Bartley, of Enniskillen, Co. Fermanagh, and Louisa Murray; Sen. Mod., B.A. (T.C.D.); T 1924. 1924/M/08 [2 items]. Indian Civil Service, 1907; District and Sessions Judge, Bengal, 1921; Assam, 1929; Legal Remembrancer, Bengal, 1931. Judge of the High Court, Calcutta, 1932-42. Knighted 1942. Died 2 Sept. 1968. *Who's Who*. Mentioned in J.W. Henderson, *Methodist College Belfast 1868-1938* (2 vols.; Belfast, 1939), 187.

BARTLEY, GERALD: see MAC PHARTALAIN, GEARÓID.

BARTLEY, JOHN (b. 10 Sept. 1858) young. s. of Charles Bartley, farmer, of Ternaneal, Co. Monaghan, and Anne Douglas; H 1887. 1889/M/09 [9 items]. Presbyterian, and former teacher. Died 26 June 1931. Obituary, *I.L.T. & S.J.*, lxv (1931), 161-2. Mentioned in Maurice Healy, *The Old Munster Circuit*, 51-3.

BARTON, CECIL MOLYNEUX (b. 11 Oct. 1883) eld. s. of Molyneux Barton, B.L., of 38 Upper Fitzwilliam Street, Dublin, and Charlotte Frances Yates Peel; M 1903. 1906/T/07 [3 items]. Resident Magistrate, Kenya, 1914-22; Adviser, Gambia, 1922-9; Circuit Judge, Ashanti Territories, Gold Coast, 1929-34; aft. puisne judge of the Supreme Court of the Gold Coast. Retired to Cornwall. Died 29 March 1962. *Who's Who*.

BARTON, DUNBAR PLUNKET (b. 29 Oct. 1853) eld. s. of Thomas Henry Barton (decd.), of Longford Terrace, Monkstown, Dublin, and the Hon. Charlotte Plunket; M 1876, I.T. T 1875. 1880/H/06 [7 items]. Q.C., June 1889. Judge of the High Court, King's Bench Division, 1900-1904; Chancery Division, 1904-18. Retired 1 Jan. 1918. President of the Law Students' Debating Society of Ireland. Honorary Officer of the Dublin Veterans' Corps, and chairman of the Executive Committee of the Irish National War Memorial. Senator of the National University of Ireland, 1909-; Commissioner of Irish Lights, 1918-; M.R.I.A., F.R. Hist. Soc. Published on the Irish Land Act (1896), and contributed to the 1st edition of *Halsbury's Laws of England* the articles on Perpetuities and Partnership. Author, *inter alia*, of *Bernadotte: the First Phase* (1914), *Bernadotte and Napoleon* (1920), and *Bernadotte, Prince and King, 1810-1844* (1925); *Links between Ireland and Shakespeare* (1919), and *Links between Shakespeare and the Law* (1929); *The Story of our Inns of Court* (1924), and *Timothy Healy* (1933). [Barton's learned interest in Shakespeare was shared with his brother judge, Dodgson Hamilton Madden, author of *The Diary of Master William Silence: a study of Shakespeare & of Elizabethan sport* (London, 1897) and *Shakespeare and his Fellows: an attempt to decipher the man and his nature* (London, 1916)]. Died 11 Sept. 1937. Obituary, *I.L.T. & S.J.*, lxxi (1937), 257-8. See: Ball, *Judges*, ii, 381; *Vanity Fair*, 1898; *Who's Who*; *Burke's Irish Family Records* (1976), 81. Mentioned in Maurice Healy, *The Old Munster Circuit*, 37-9, 238. Portrait by Lander in King's Inns: see Wanda Ryan-Smolin, *King's Inns Portraits* (1992), 6.

BARTON, MOLYNEUX (b. 1 Nov. 1846) only s. of John Barton of 37 Mespil Road, Dublin, and Mary Nicholson; B.A. (T.C.D.); M 1868; M.T. E 1870. 1874/H/1 [2 items]. Leinster Circuit. Professor of Real Property at King's Inns. Landowner. Died July 1917. Obituary, *I.L.T. & S.J.*, li (14 July 1917), 171.

BASTABLE, BARTHOLOMEW JOHN (b. 8 Nov. 1920) 3rd s. of Thomas J. Bastable, of 8 Marlborough Road, Donnybrook, Dublin, and Elizabeth Connolly; M 1952. 1956/M/03 [2 items]. Broadcaster, whose resonant voice on Telefís Éireann long intoned the words 'To whom it may concern … it's the Late Late Show'. Died in Florida, *c.* 1995.

BASTABLE, CHARLES FRANCIS (b. 26 Sept. 1856) only s. of Robert Bastable, clerk, of Rathgar, Dublin, and Louisa Little; B.A. (T.C.D.); M 1879, M.T. M 1880. 1882/M/02 [5 items]. Professor of Political Economy, T.C.D., 1882-1932; Regius Professor of Laws, T.C.D., 1908-32. Professor of Jurisprudence and International Law, Queen's College, Galway, 1883-1903. Fellow of the British Academy, 1921. Author, *inter alia*, of *The Theory of Intenational Trade* (1887); *The Commerce of Nations* (1892; 9th edition, 1923); *Public Finance* (1892); and contributions to the *Encyclopoedia Britannica*. Died 3 Jan. 1945. Obituary in *I.L.T. & S.J.*, lxxix (1945), 11. Photograph [facing p. 241] with obituary (by G.A. Duncan) in *Proceedings of the British Academy*, xxxi (1945), 241-4. Here G.A. Duncan observed: 'It is remarkable how many of his distinguished predecessors in the Whately Chair were also lawyers ... Mountifort Longfield, J.E. Cairnes and Isaac Butt. The man [R.R. Cherry] whom Bastable surpassed in 1882 ultimately became Lord Chief Justice of Ireland.' *Who's Who*; *Oxford DNB* (2004) [article by R.D.C. Black].

BASUDEV, BANSI LALL (b. 1891) 3rd s. of Pandit Mela Ram Basudev, of Adampur, Jullundur, Punjab, India; M 1915. Awarded John Brooke Scholarship, Oct. 1917. 1918/H/01 [2 items].

BATES, ARTHUR HENRY (b. 8 Oct. 1853) 7th s. of John Bates (decd.), solicitor, of Belfast, and Jane Anne Victor; M 1876; G. I. H 1875. 1879/H/01 [5 items]. Q.C., 22 April 1899. Appt. County Court Judge for Co. Down, 20 Sept. 1919. Died 2 April 1947. Obituary, *I.L.T. & S.J.*, lxxxi (1947), 88. *Who's Who*.

BATTERSBY, THOMAS STEPHENSON FRANCIS (b. 17 April 1855) only s. of Francis Battersby, M.B., F.R.C.S.I., of 15 Warrington Place, Dublin, and Elizabeth Crooke; B.A. (T.C.D.); M 1876, M.T. M 1878. 1879/M/12 [6 items]. President of the University Philosophical Society, T.C.D., 1878-9. Leinster Circuit. K.C., March 1904. Unionist candidate in South Fermanagh, 1900 and January 1910. Author of *The Pocket Pleader, or Compendium of practical precedents of Civil Bills in Contract and Tort: for practitioners in county courts* (Dublin, 1907; 2nd edition 1911) and other legal works, including a second edition (with J.N. Gerrard) of Charles H. Foot's *The Grand Jury Laws of Ireland* (Dublin, 1884) and editions (also with John N. Gerrard) of *Carleton on Parliamentary Elections in Ireland* (10th edition, Dublin, 1885; 11th edition, Dublin, 1892; Supplements, 1899). Author also of *The Fiscal Question in the United States*. On 22 July 1884 he swam from Bray Head to Dalkey Island, a distance of 5½ miles, in a record time of 121 minutes. Died 31 Oct. 1933. Obituary, *I.L.T. & S.J.*, lxvii (1933), 302, 307; *Who's Who*.

BATTLEY, JOHN D'OYLY (b. 12 Oct. 1904) only s. of Charles Battley, of Belvedere Hall, Bray, Co. Wicklow, and Louisa Battley; [n.d.] 1926/M/08 [2 items]. LL.D. Died Jan. 1962.

BATTY, ESPINE FITZHERBERT (b. 18 Nov. 1862) only s. of Espine Batty (decd.), Barrister-at-Law, of 59 Stephen's Green, Dublin, and Maria Wilson; B.A. (Cambridge); M 1884, I.T. M 1884. 1891/M/05 [9 items].

BAXTER, JAMES SINCLAIR (b. 25 May 1870) eld. s. of John A. Baxter, engineeer, of Belfast, and Jeanie A. Sinclair; LL.B. (Univ. London), B.A. (R.U.I.); M 1891, M.T. T 1892. 1895/M/01 [9 items]. K.C. 1922. Reid Professor, T.C.D., 1899-1904. Professor of English Law, Q.U.B., 1900-33. Professor of Civil Law and General Jurisprudence, T.C.D., 1908-9; Regius Professor of Feudal and English Law, T.C.D., 1909-33. Holding both the Trinity College, Dublin and Queen's University, Belfast chairs for twenty-four years, R.B. McDowell and David Webb observe, in their *Trinity College Dublin 1592-1952: An academic history* (Cambridge, 1982), 414, 'that the Great Northern Railway must have seen almost as much of him as either of the universities at which he taught between train journeys'. Assistant editor of Strahan's *A general view of the Law of Property* (1895); joint editor (with W.C. Stubbs) of *Irish Forms and Precendents being a Supplementary Volume to 'Encyclopedia of Forms and Precedents'* (London: Butterworth, 1910). Speaker's Counsel in the Parliament of Northern Ireland. Died 24 Aug. 1933. Obituary, *I.L.T. & S.J.*, lxvii (1933), 233-4, 264-5; *Who's Who*.

BAYLOR, RICHARD PATRICK (b. 19 May 1931) 2nd s. of John Baylor, of 146 Old Youghal Road, Cork, and Nora McSweeney; M 1952. Awarded 2nd Victoria Prize. 1956/T/02 [2 items].

BEATTIE, WILLIAM (b. 22 May 1870) 4th s. of William Beattie (decd.), of 24 Marlboro' Avenue, Londonderry, and Eliza Jane Boal; T 1913. 1913/M/08 [2 items]. Formerly a solicitor. North-East Circuit. K.C., 12 July 1921. Appt. Recorder of Belfast, 1921. Mentioned in J.C. MacDermott, *An Enriching Life*, 170. Died 1941. Obituary, *I.L.T. & S.J.*, lxxv (29 Nov. 1941), 300.

BEATTY, CYRIL JOSEPH (b. 13 Aug. 1890) 4th s. of Christopher Beatty of 6 Sandford Terrace, Ranelagh, Dublin, and Ellen Corr; M 1907. 1911/M/05 [2 items]. Appt. District Justice, Nov. 1922: *I.L.T. & S.J.*, lvi (4 Nov. 1922), 266. Mullingar (District No. 11): see *Thom's Directory* (Biographies).

BEATTY, EDWARD FREDERICK (b. 20 Nov 1845) 3rd s. of Frederick Beatty of Lake Park, Co. Wicklow, and Mary Anne Bryan; B.A. (T.C.D.); H 1867, MT T 1867. 1870/E/4 [4 items].

BEATTY, ETHEL URSULA (b. 18 Sept. 1925) only d. of John Joseph Beatty (decd.), solicitor, of 'Tullyvin', Merrion Road, Dublin, and Ethel Violet Boyle; B.A. (Mod.), LL.B (T.C.D.); M 1947. Awarded John Brooke Scholarship. 1950/M/01 [2 items]. Mrs. Exshaw.

BEATTY, FRANCIS CHRISTOPHER (b. 12 Oct. 1926) only s. of Cyril J. Beatty, D.J., B.L., of 8 Earlsfort Mansions, Dublin, and Iva Mary Golding; M 1944. 1947/M/04 [2 items]. Killed in an aeroplane accident 15 July 1955. Obituary, *I.L.T. & S.J.*, lxxxix (1955), 189.

BEAUMONT, JOHN NELSON (b. 21 Nov. 1893) 3rd s. of William Beaumont, of Ballinrobe, Co. Mayo, and Helen Mayne; Sch. Sen. Mod., B.A. (T.C.D.); M 1916. 1919/M/08 [2 items]. Died 11 Dec. 1959.

BEDI, HARI DASS (b. 20 March 1894) 2nd s. of Bawa Salamat Rai Bedi, of Jullundur City, Punjab, India; M 1914. 1917/T/14 [2 items].

BEGLEY, MARCUS DILL (b. 10 Aug. 1881) only s. of Marcus Dill Begley (decd.), of Limavady, Co. Londonderry, and [Samina] Begley; M 1902. 1905/H/03 [2 items]. K.C., 16 June 1921. Editor of *The Northern Ireland Reports*, 1930-39. County Court Judge for County Down. Died 10 March 1962. Obituary, *I.L.T. & S.J.*, xcvi (1962), 76.

BEHL, BHAWANI DAS (b. 15 Sept. 1896) eld. s. of Lala Chuni Lal Behl, of Multan, Punjab, India; M 1915. 1918/T/16 [2 items].

BELFORD, ALFRED JAMES (b. 10 June 1904) 3rd s. of William Henry Belford, J.P., of Fleurville, Ballycastle, Co. Antrim, and Margaret L. Ruske; M 1923. 1926/M/19 [3 items]. K.C. (N.I.), T. 1950.

BELL, DESMOND EDWARD (b. 2 July 1912) only s. of Hamilton Paul Bell, of 2 Packenham Villas, Monkstown, Dublin, and Mary Long; M 1934. 1937/M/03 [2 items]. S.C., 2 March 1948. Died 20 March 1969. Obituary, *I.L.T. & S.J.*, ciii (1969), 139.

BELL, Captain PHILIP SYDNEY (b. 24 Feb. 1884) only s. of Richard Bell (decd.); [removed from roll of solicitors at own request, 29 March 1920] 1920/E/03 [4 items].

BELL, STEPHEN JOSEPH (b. 5 Oct. 1897) only s. of Henry Bell, of 16 Lower Sherrard Street, Dublin, and Delia Hannan; M 1923. 1926/M/06 [2 items].

BELTON, JOHN (b. 6 Nov. 1903) 2nd s. of John Belton, of Longford, Co. Longford [and 14 Essex Road, Leyton, London E 10], and Margaret Farrell; M.A., LL.B. (N.U.I.); M 1924. 1927/M/13 [2 items]. Department of External Affairs, Dublin. Ambassador to Sweden and Canada.

BENNER, JOHN (b. 8 March 1863) 3rd s. of John Benner (decd.) of Tralee, Co. Kerry, and Rosina McCarthy (decd.); undergraduate (R.U.I.); T 1883. 1909/T/02 [2 items].

BENNETT, FRANCIS PATRICK (b. 20 Oct. 1925) eld. s. of Francis Joseph Bennett (decd.), of 29 Seaview, Warrenpoint, Co. Down, and Mary Christina O'Neill; M 1945. 1949/T/08 [2 items].

BERNARD, JAMES SYMES (b. 18 April 1859) 2nd s. of George Bernard, solicitor, of Rathgar, Dublin, and Nannie Symes; B.A. (T.C.D.); H 1881, M.T. H 1883. 1884/H/05 [5 items]. Disbarred at own request and 'his name removed from the Roll of Irish Barristers', 20 Feb. 1901: K.I. Benchers' Minute Book 1885-1901, 473-4.

BERNARD, WILLIAM LEIGH (b. 1 Jan. 1845) eld. s. of Michael Charles Bernard, M.B., L.R.C.S.I., of Elm Lawn, Dundrum, Dublin, and Jane Leigh; E 1871, G.I. T 1871. (Clerk of the Commissioners of Church Temporalities in Ireland) 1875/E/05 [7 items].

BERRY, HENRY FITZPATRICK (b. 12 May 1847) eld. s. of Parsons Berry of Mallow, Co. Cork, surgeon, and Isabella FitzPatrick; B.A. (T.C.D.); M 1869, G.I. H 1870. 1872/M/7 [2 items]. Editor of *Statutes and Ordinances*, and *Statute Rolls of the Parliament of*

Ireland (3 vols., Dublin, 1907, 1910, 1914); and of *A History of the Royal Dublin Society* (London, 1915). Died 1920s. *Who's Who.*

BEST, RICHARD (b. 11 Dec. 1869) young. s. of Robert Best (decd.) of Richhill, Co. Armagh, and Annie Leamon; Scholar, gold medallist in mathematics, gold medallist in ethics and logics, B.A. (T.C.D.); M 1892. 1895/T/04 [6 items]. North-East Circuit. K.C., 24 Feb. 1912. Unionist M.P. for Armagh, 1921-5. Attorney-General, N.I., Feb. 1922-Nov. 1925. Appt. Lord Justice of Appeal in N.I., 5 Nov. 1925. Died 23 Feb. 1939. Obituary, *I.L.T. & S.J.*, lxxiii (1939), 70-1; *Who's Who.*

BEVERIDGE, JOHN FRANCIS BARRY (b. 30 April 1845) eldest surviving s. of William Beveridge (decd.) of Tralee, Co. Kerry, and Barbara Barry; M 1869; M.T. M 1871. 1874/T/3 [2 items].

BEWLEY, CHARLES HENRY (b. 12 July 1888) eld. s. of Henry Theodore Bewley of 89 Merrion Square, Dublin, and Eveleen Pim; B.A. (Oxon); M 1911. 1914/H/01 [2 items]. S.C., 30 March 1926. Trade representative to Germany, 1921-3. Irish Minister in Rome, 1929-33, and in Berlin, 1933-9: see Ronan Keating, Michael Kennedy, Dermot Keogh and Eunan O'Halpin (eds.), *Documents on Irish Foreign Policy. Volume I. 1919-1922* [&c.] (Dublin. 1998-). Died in Italy in 1969. Claimed to be the first barrister to appear in the Dáil courts: see his *Memoirs of a Wild Goose* (Dublin, 1989), 67-70, 89-91, 92-5; Louis McRedmond (ed.), *Modern Irish Lives.*

BEWLEY, EDWARD DAWSON (b. 9 July 1868) eld. s. of Sir Edmund Bewley, LL.D., J.P., of 40 Fitzwilliam Place, Dublin, and Anna Sophia Colles; B.A. (Oxford); H 1902; M.T. M 1890. 1902/T/10 [4 items]. Called to English Bar, T 1902.

BHAN, FREDERICK JAMES (n.d.) eld. s. of Ephraim Tej Bhan, of Lahore, Punjab, India; M 1914. 1918/T/04 [2 items].

BHATIA, AUTAR SINGH (b. 31 March 1895) only s. of S. Amrik Singh Bhatia (decd.), of Gujranwala, Punjab, India; T 1914. 1917/T/04 [2 items].

BHATIA, JAGDISH SINGH (b. 25 Dec. 1895) 3rd s. of Gopal Singh Bhatia Rais, of Quetta, Baluchistan, India; M 1915. 1918/T/11 [2 items].

BINCHY, DANIEL ANTHONY (b. 3 June 1899) 2nd s. of William P. Binchy (decd.), of Charleville, Co. Cork, and Anne Browne; M 1917. 1920/M/04 [2 items]. Professor of Roman Law and Jurisprudence, U.C.D., 1924-46. Entered Department of External Affairs, 1929, and served as first Irish Minister to Berlin, July 1929 - March 1932. Author of *Church and State in Fascist Italy* (1941). As Professor at the Dublin Institute for Advanced Studies, the foremost expert of his day on Brehon Law, and editor of *Corpus Iuris Hibernici* (1979; 6 vols.). Died 4 May 1989. Obituary (by Morfydd E. Owen) in *Studia Celtica* (Cardiff), xxiv/xxv (1989-90), 153-7. Bibliography of his writings in *Peritia*, v, 468-477. See *Who's Who*; Louis McRedmond (ed.), *Modern Irish Lives.*

BINCHY, MICHAEL (b. 25 Aug. 1893) 2nd s. of James Binchy, solicitor, of Gortokagh, Charleville, Co. Cork, and Katie Fitzgibbon; B.A. (N.U.I.); M 1913. 1916/M/01 [2 items]. S.C., 25 June 1930. Bencher of King's Inns, E 1937. Judge of the Circuit Court, 1950-63 (Midland Circuit, 1950-9; Dublin 1959-63). Died 20 Feb. 1971. Obituary, *I.L.T. & S.J.*, cv (1970), 83-4.

BINCHY, WILLIAM FRANCIS (b. 25 Nov. 1907) young. s. of William Patrick Binchy (decd.), of Charleville Park, Charleville, Co. Cork, and Annie Binchy (decd.); M 1927. 1931/M/03 [2 items]. Mentioned in Gerard A. Lee, *A Memoir of the South-Western Circuit* (Dublin, 1990), 15-16. Died 1971. Obituary, *I.L.T. & S.J.*, cv (1971), 263-4.

BINCHY, WILLIAM THOMAS (b. 11 March 1947) only s. of William Binchy, Barrister-at-Law, of Eastmount, Dalkey, Co. Dublin, and Maureen Blackmore (decd.); B.A. (N.U.I.); M 1965. Awarded John Brooke Scholarship. 1968/M/01 [1 item]. Counsellor with the Law Reform Commission. Regius Professor of Laws, T.C.D., July 1992. Author (with Bryan McMahon) of *Irish Law of Torts* (Abingdon, Oxon., 1981), *Irish Conflicts of Laws* (1988), and (with Raymond Byrne) the *Annual Review of Irish Law.*

BIRCH, MICHAEL (b. 22 Feb. 1848) only s. of Patrick Birch of Kilkenny, and Elizabeth Hanrahan; M 1870; M.T. H 1872. 1874/T/5 [2 items].

BIRD, JAMES WILLIAM (b. 14 Jan. 1858) eld. s. of William Bird of Keenogue, Co. Tyrone, and Ellen Ashinhurst; LL.B. (T.C.D.); H 1879, M.T. M 1880. 1881/M/18 [8 items]. Died 7 July 1917. Obituary, *I.L.T. & S.J.*, li (1917), 171.

BIRD, WILLIAM SEYMOUR (b. 22 May 1846) eld. s. of John James Bird (decd.) of Banagher, King's Co, Doctor, and Hannah Moore; B.A. (T.C.D.); T 1867, MT E 1868. 1870/M/5 [2 items]. Q.C., June 1889. Appt. County Court Judge for the West Riding of Cork, 27 Feb. 1892-1919. Died 1 June 1919. Obituary, *I.L.T. & S.J.*, liii (1919), 138; *Who's Who*.

BLACK, ARTHUR (b. 6 Feb. 1888) only s. of Arthur Black of Lyndhurst, Bloomfield, Belfast, and Mary Guy; M 1912. 1915/H/01 [4 items]. Son of a National School headmaster in Ballymacarrett. Classical scholar and double first at Sidney Sussex College, Cambridge. K.C. (N.I.) H 1929. Attorney-General (N.I.), 1939-42; Recorder of Belfast, 1942; Judge of the Chancery Division (N.I.), 20 Nov. 1943 - 2 March 1949; a Lord Justice in N.I., 3 March 1949 - 31 Aug. 1964. P.C. Mentioned in J.C. MacDermott, *An Enriching Life*, 167. 'By nature a shy, unsophisticated man, something of a recluse': see Basil McIvor, *Hope Deferred: Experiences of an Irish Unionist* (Belfast, 1998), 33-4. See *Who's Who*.

BLACK, ARTHUR EDWARD (b. 6 March 1876) young. s. of James Black, of Carrick House, Boyle, Co. Roscommon, and Margaret Robinson; cand. bachelor (T.C.D.); M 1901. 1906/M/02 [3 items].

BLACK, WILLIAM (b. 6 June 1853) eld. s. of the Revd. Thomas Black (decd.) of Armagh [Ballynahinch, Co. Down], and Agnes Mary Black; B.A., LL.B. (Q.C.B.); H 1876; M.T. H 1878. 1879/H/04 [7 items].

BLACK, WILLIAM BULLICK (b. 22 Sept. 1879) only s. of the Revd. James Black of Dromore, Co. Down, and Sarah Edith Bullick; M 1897. 1901/H/03 [3 items]. S.C., 12 April 1935. Son of a Methodist minister, and educated at Methodist College, Belfast. Mentioned (with photograph) in J.W. Henderson, *Methodist College Belfast 1868-1938* (2 vols.; Belfast, 1939), 182-3. Fianna Fáil parliamentary candidate (with Seán MacEntee), Dublin Townships, 1938. Judge of the High Court, 1939-42; of the Supreme Court, 1942-51. Retired 1951. Vice-President of the Law Students' Debating Society of Ireland. Delegate to Council of Europe. Died 11 March 1967. Obituaries: *Irish Times* (with photograph), Monday 13 March 1967, 9; *I.L.T. & S.J.*, ci (1967), 119-20.

BLACKALL, HENRY WILLIAM BUTLER (b. 19 June 1889) eld. s. of Henry Blackall, solicitor, of 93 George Street, Limerick, and Isabella Emily Butler; B.A. (Sen. Mod.); M 1909. 1912/M/01 [2 items]. Colonial Service in Kenya, Nigeria, Cyprus, Gold Coast. Knighted (1945) as President of the West Indian Court of Appeal, 1943-6; Chief Justice of Hong Kong, 1946-8; President of the West African Court of Appeal, 1948-51. Genealogist. Died 1 Nov. 1981. *Who's Who*.

BLACKMORE, THOMAS MAITLAND (b. 11 Nov. 1895) eld. s. of Thomas Maitland Blackmore, of 60 Whitworth Road, Glasnevin, Dublin, and Annie Gertrude Bleakley; M 1921. 1923/T/10 [2 items].

BLAKE, JOHN HUBERT (b. 7 Oct 1848) 3rd s. of Peter Blake J.P. of Holly Park, Craughwell, Co. Galway and Kate Kernan; B.A. (T.C.D.); M 1868; M.T. T 1869. 1872/T/4 [2 items].

BLAKE, THOMAS JOSEPH (b. 27 May 1849) 5th s. of Valentine O'Connor Blake of Towerhill, Co. Mayo, and the Hon. Margaret Ffrench; B.A. (T.C.D.); M 1870; M.T. H 1872. 1873/M/4 [4 items].

BLAYNEY, ALICE ELIZABETH (b. 13 Feb. 1924) youngest d. of Alexander Blayney, FRSI (decd.), of 15 Merrion Square, Dublin, and Mary Stanton; M 1943. 1946/T/02 [2 items]. Wife of T.A. Finlay, C.J.

BLAYNEY, JOHN JOSEPH PATRICK (b. 13 March 1925) 2nd s. of Alexander Blayney (decd.), of 15 Merrion Square, Dublin, and Mary Stanton; B.A. (N.U.I.); M 1944. Awarded 3rd Victoria Prize. 1948/T/04 [2 items]. S.C., 28 Feb. 1974. Judge of the High Court, 20 Jan. 1986; of the Supreme Court, 19 Oct. 1992. Retired 13 March 1997. Listed in the 1991 edition of Maureen Cairnduff, *Who's Who in Ireland*.

BLOOD, ALEXANDER FINDLATER (b. 25 May 1853) 3rd s. of John Lloyd Blood, brewer, of 6 Longford Terrace, Monkstown, Co. Dublin, and Margaret Findlater; B.A. (T.C.D.); M 1873, M.T. M 1874. 1877/E/05 [4 items]. Q.C., 22 April 1899. Died 13 June 1933. Obituary, *I.L.T. & S.J.*, lxvii (1933), 174, 179-80, 190, 232.

BLOOD, LANCELOT IVAN LLOYD (b. 9 Feb. 1896) eld. s. of Adam Lloyd Blood, solicitor, of Leeson Park, Dublin, and Helena Geoghegan (decd.); M 1920; [solicitor of Supreme Court of Judicature; removed from roll at own request] 1920/M/12 [2 items]. Died 6 Nov. 1951. [For this man's son, see below, under Lloyd-Blood, Nevil]

BLOOD-SMYTH, JOHN LOWE (b. 21 Feb. 1858) 4th s. of Matthew Blood Smyth, Barrister-at-Law, J.P., of Castle Fergus, Co. Clare, and Mary Vincent; B.A., LL.B (T.C.D.); M 1878, M.T. M 1880. 1881/M/15 [6 items].

BLUETT, MAUD CHERRY (b. 6 June 1895) only d. of the Rt. Hon. R.R. Cherry (decd.), of 92 St. Stephen's Green, Dublin, and Mary Wilhemina Cooper; M.A. (T.C.D.); M 1949. 1951/M/03 [2 items]. Author (as Maud H. Cherry) of *A Short memoir of the Rt. Hon. Richard Robert Cherry, sometime Lord Chief Justice of Ireland* (Dublin, 1924). As 'Blake Scholar' of T.C.D. and 'lecturer in history' at Alexandra College, author of a slight text *Scenes from Irish History* (Dublin, 1927). Permitted to be disbarred at her own request with intention of becoming a solicitor, 25 July 1956 (Benchers' Minute Book, 437). Died Jan. 1963.

BODEN, IVAR McGRATH (b. 26 April 1923) 4th s. of Peter Joseph Boden, of 6 Belgrave Square, Monkstown, Dublin, and Anna [?]; M 1943. 1946/M/05 [2 items].

BODKIN, MATTHIAS McDONNELL GEORGE (b. 22 July 1850) 2nd s. of Thomas Bodkin, F.R.C.S.I., physician and surgeon, of Eastland House, Co. Galway, and Maria McDonnell; B.A. (Catholic University); M 1872, M.T. M 1874. 1877/M/03 [2 items]. Connaught Circuit. Q.C., 30 June 1894. M.P. 1892-5. Leader-writer of the *Freeman's Journal*. Appt. County Court Judge for Clare, 7 Nov. 1907 (*I.L.T. & S.J.*, xli (1907), 303). The story of his appointment is mentioned in Maurice Healy, *The Old Munster Circuit*, 175-80, and in Serjeant Sullivan's *Old Ireland*, 155. Author of *Grattan's Parliament, before and after* (London, 1912); *Recollections of an Irish Judge* (London, 1914); *Famous Irish Trials* (Dublin, 1918; new ed. 1928); *When Youth meets Youth* (Dublin, 1920); *A County Court Judge on the Lawlessness of the Forces of the Crown in Ireland* (London, 1921), and several other works, including novels. Died 7 June 1933. Obituary, *I.L.T. & S.J.*, lxvii (1933), 167, 327; *Who's Who*. Mentioned in James Meenan (ed.), *Centenary History of Lit. and Hist. Soc. of U.C.D.*

BODKIN, THOMAS (b. 21 July 1887) eld. s. of Mathias McD Bodkin of 52 Upper Mount Street, Dublin, and Arabella Norman; B.A. (R.U.I.); M 1909. 1912/E/02 [2 items]. Secretary to the Commissioners of Charitable Donations and Bequests. Aft. Director of the National Gallery of Ireland, 1927-35. Barber Professor of Fine Arts at Birmingham, 1935-52. Author of *Hugh Lane and his Pictures, The Paintings of Jan Vermeer*, &c., and of *May it Please Your Lordships*. Died at Birmingham, 24 April 1961. Contributor to James Meenan (ed.), *Centenary History of Lit. and Hist. Soc. of U.C.D.* See *Who's Who; D.N.B.*; Louis McRedmond (ed.), *Modern Irish Lives*.

BOHAN, BRIAN (b. 25 July 1942) 4th s. of Dominick Bohan, corporation official, of 40 Fitzroy Avenue, Drumcondra, Dublin, and Mary O'Brien; M 1961. 1965/M/10 [1 item].

BOLAND, JOHN ANTHONY (b. 23 Jan. 1931) only s. of Daniel Boland, M.B.E., of 12 Cullenswood Gardens, Ranelagh, Dublin, and Hannah Barton; M.A., LLB; M 1965, M.T. M 1950. 1967/T/12 [1 item]. Public Trustee in England, 1980. Assistant editor of the *Supreme Court Practice*, 1984. Accountant General of the Supreme Court. Died 14 Nov. 2001. Obituary, *The Irish Times*, 15 Dec. 2001; *The Times*, 17 Dec. 2001.

BOLES, WILLIAM (b. 11 Oct. 1898) eld. s. of William Boles, merchant, of 83 Castle Street, Belfast, and Agnes Boyd; B.A., LL.B. (Q.U.B.); M 1923. Awarded 2nd Class Certificate of Honour. 1925/M/07 [2 items].

BOLGER, MARY AINGELDA CATHERINE (b. 30 April 1933) 3rd d. of David Joseph Bolger, of Millmount, Gorey, Co. Wexford, and Mercedes McGrath; M 1952. 1956/H/02 [2 items].

BOLTON, ALBERT DENNE (b. 29 May 1873) young. s. of Samuel H. Bolton (decd.), J.P., of Grove House, Rathmines, Dublin, and Rath-na-Seer, Bray, Co. Wicklow, and Emma Denne; M.A., LL.D. (T.C.D.); H 1899. 1902/E/03 [3 items]. S.C., 25 June 1930. Father of the Leinster Bar. Editor of the *Irish Reports*. Author of *The Labourers (Ireland) Acts 1883-1906* (Dublin, 1907). Died 2 Feb. 1947. Obituary, *I.L.T. & S.J.*, lxxxi (1947), 35.

BOLTON, JOHN FREDERICK (b. 10 Nov. 1850) eld. s. of George Bolton, solicitor, of 16 Merrion Square North, Dublin, and Anna Cashel; M.A., LL.B (T.C.D.); H 1873, M.T. T 1877. 1880/E/01 [8 items].

BONASS, GEORGE JOSEPH (b. 30 April 1886) 2nd surv. s. of Henry Bonass (decd.), solicitor to Dublin Corporation, of 62 Grosvenor Road, Rathmines, Dublin, and Teresa Hudson; M 1905. 1908/T/14 [3 items]. Died 24 July 1942. Obituary, *I.L.T. & S.J.*, lxxvi (1942), 192.

BONNAR, HUGH (b. 7 Oct. 1887) 2nd s. of John Bonnar, of 14 Edward Street, Portadown, Co. Armagh, and Sarah Rooney. 1927/M/23 [2 items].

BOTTING, JOHN GEORGE GRINSTEAD (b. 13 April 1912) only s. of George Henry Botting (decd.), of 37 Landseer Road, Hove, Sussex, and Mary Ellen Grinstead; M 1951, M.T. 1937. 1952/T/03 [2 items]. Called to English Bar, T 1940.

BOUGHEY, CHARLES (b. 18 March 1845) eld. s. of William Boughey of 33 Hardwicke Street, Dublin, Solicitor, and Ellen Killeen; B.A. (T.C.D.); H 1866, MT H 1867. 1869/H/4 [4 items].

BOURKE, ARTHUR EDWARD DESBOROUGH (b. 3 Dec. 1852) 3rd s. of the Revd. John Bourke of Kilmeaden, Co. Waterford, and Louisa Maria Potts; B.A. (T.C.D.); H 1876, G.I. M 1878. 1879/M/09 [6 items].

BOURKE, GEOFFREY THEOBALD JOSEPH (b. 5 Dec. 1866) eld. s. of Surgeon Lieut.-Colonel Joseph Bourke of [Oldtowne] Claremorris, Co. Mayo, and Margaret Gray; M 1894. 1897/T/11 [3 items].

BOURKE, JOHN FRANCIS (b. 1 Dec. 1889) only s. of Matthew John Bourke, K.C., Recorder of Cork, of The Lodge, Banteer, Cork, and Annie Binchy; M 1913. 1916/M/03 [2 items]. G.I., T 1922. Practised on the Oxford Circuit. Justice of the Peace in Worcestershire, and Chairman of Quarter Sessions there, 1942-65. Recorder of Shrewsbury, 1945-63. Died 27 Nov. 1967. *Who's Who.*

BOURKE, JOHN OLIVER PAGET (b. 19 Feb. 1937) eld. s. of Paget John Bourke, Barrister-at-Law, of Amana, Ballina, Co. Mayo, and Susan Dorothy Killeen; B.C.L; M 1955. 1958/M/04 [2 items]. Businessman. Chairman of Irish Permanent plc. Listed [with photograph] in the 1984 edition of Maureen Cairnduff, *Who's Who in Ireland*; and also mentioned in the 1999 edition.

BOURKE, JOHN ULICK (b. 8 July 1845) eld. s. of Richard Bourke of Thornfields, Co. Limerick, Poor Law Inspector, and Anne O'Grady; B.A. (Cambridge); T 1868; I.T. H 1867. 1870/H/4 [3 items].

BOURKE, MARCUS: see DE BÚRCA, MARCUS.

BOURKE, MARIE TERESA WINIFRED (b. 21 May 1944) only d. of Dr. Aubrey de Vere Bourke, of Victoria House, Ballina, Co. Mayo, and Dr. Teresa O'Donnell; M 1963 1967/T/03 [2 items]. Christened Marie, but calls herself Mary. Married Nicholas Robinson. S.C., 29 Feb. 1980. Reid Professor, T.C.D., 1 Oct. 1969-1975. Senator (Dublin University) 1969-89. President of Ireland, 1990-7. United Nations High Commissioner for Human Rights, 1997-2002. Listed [with photographs] in the 1984, 1991 and 1999 editions of Maureen Cairnduff, *Who's Who in Ireland*. See Louis McRedmond (ed.), *Modern Irish Lives*. Biographies by Fergus Finlay (Dublin, 1990) Michael G. O'Sullivan (Dublin, 1993), Deirdre McQuillan (Dublin, 1994), John Horgan (Dublin, 1997), Lorna Siggins (Edinburgh, 1997) and Olivia O'Leary (London, 1998).

BOURKE, MATTHEW JOHN (b. 15 July 1849) 2nd s. of John Bourke of Kanturk, Co. Cork, and Margaret Nunan; M.A. (Queen's University); M 1869; I.T. E 1872. 1874/T/1 [2 items]. Q.C., 1 July 1892. 3rd Serjeant, 5 Dec. 1907. Recorder of Cork, 18 April 1908-1924. Died 21 April 1926. Obituary, *I.L.T. & S.J.*, lx (1926), 105; *Who's Who.* Mentioned in Maurice Healy, *The Old Munster Circuit*, 65-7.

BOURKE, PAGET JOHN (b. 8 Oct. 1906) eld. s. of Henry Charles Bourke, of 'Amena', Ballina, Co. Mayo, and Eleanor Doreen Macaulay; Mod., B.A., LL.B. (T.C.D.); M 1925. 1928/M/05 [2 items]. S.C., 2 March 1961. Colonial Service in Seychelles, Palestine and Kenya. Chief Justice of Sierra Leone, 1955-7, and Cyprus, 1957-60. Knighted 1957. Died 7 Nov. 1983. See *Who's Who*.

BOURKE, PATRICK (b. 25 Aug. 1893): see DE BÚRCA, PÁDRAIG.

BOURKE, PATRICK (b. 24 Aug. 1899) eld. s. of James Bourke, of 'Lisbrin', Terenure Park, Dublin, and Hanora Bourke; M.A., ex-Scholar, Sen. Mod. (T.C.D.); H 1923. 1929/M/01 [2 items]. Auditor of the College Historical Society, 1923-4. Banker.

BOURKE, WILLIAM CAMPBELL (b. 18 Sept. 1853) only s. of Michael Bourke, of Fermoy, Co. Cork, and Caroline Campbell; B.A. (Cambridge); H 1876, I.T. T 1875. 1879/T/03 [6 items].

BOURNE, THOMAS MORGAN RICHARD (b. 27 Feb. 1857) only surv. s. of Richard Edwards Bourne J.P., of Ashbourne, Co. Meath, and Isabella Mangan; B.A. (T.C.D.); M 1880, M.T. H 1881. 1883/T/09 [6 items].

BOWEN, BARTHOLOMEW PATRICK (b. 29 July 1891) 3rd s. of John Bowen (decd.), of 13 Main Street, Howth, Co. Dublin, and Catherine McEvoy; A.R.C.Sc.I; M 1925. 1928/M/02 [2 items].

BOWEN, HENRY CHARLES COLE (b. 21 Jan. 1862) eld. s. of Robert St John Cole Bowen, M.A., J.P., of Bowen's Court, Co. Cork, and Elizabeth Jane Clarke; B.A., scholar and Senior Moderator (T.C.D.); M 1883, M.T. E 1885. 1887/E/06 [7 items]. Examiner of Titles at the Land Commission. Author of *Statutory Land Purchase in Ireland* (1928). One of the judges of the Court of the General Synod of the Church of Ireland. Father of Elizabeth Bowen. Died 27 May 1930. Obituary, *I.L.T. & S.J.*, lxiv (1930), 137. See the chapter 'Henry VI', in Elizabeth Bowen, *Bowen's Court* (1940), 270-332, esp. 278-9, 293, 303, 325-6, 329-30.

BOYD, ADOLPHUS JAMES (b. 22 Feb. 1856) eld. s. of Arthur Joshua Boyd, solicitor, of Parade House, Kilkenny, and Susanna Maria Gladwell; M 1876, L.I. H 1879. 1880/E/02 [6 items].

BOYD, PATRICK GEORGE CARDWELL (b. 23 Oct. 1925) young. s. of Patrick Russell Boyd, solicitor, of 'Saul', Newtown Park Avenue, Blackrock, Co. Dublin, and Mary Sharples; B.A. (N.U.I.); M 1946. Awarded Society's Prize. 1949/M/03 [2 items]. S.C., 10 Oct. 1968.

BOYD, WALTER HERBERT (b. 31 March 1867) eld. s. of Walter Boyd, Judge of the Court of Bankruptcy in Ireland, of 66 Merrion Square, Dublin, and Anne C. Anderson; B.A. (T.C.D.); M 1888. 1891/M/08 [5 items]. K.C., 1918. Succeeded his father as 2nd Baronet, 1918. Chief Registrar in Bankruptcy, 1912-37. Died 17 April 1948. *Who's Who*.

BOYLAN, GERALD JOHN (b. 5 Feb. 1918) 3rd s. of Richard Joseph Boylan (decd.), bank manager, of 3 Longford Terrace, Monkstown, Co. Dublin, and Agnes Norah Coldough; M 1945. 1951/M/04 [2 items].

BOYLE, ALEXANDER (b. 8 Aug 1845) eld. s. of Edward Boyle (decd.) of Newtownlimavady, Co. Londonderry, and Mary Ann Park; B.A. (T.C.D.); M 1865; M.T. T 1867. 1870/E/1 [4 items].

BOYLE, CHARLES VESEY (b. 2 July 1915) 2nd s. of Charles Benjamin Whitley Boyle, solicitor, of Temple House, Temple Road, Rathmines, Dublin, and Margaret Edith Alice McCullagh; B.A. (T.C.D.); M 1933. 1937/T/01 [2 items].

BRACKEN, JOHN FRANCIS (b. 6 Oct. 1945) eld. s. of Thomas Christopher Bracken, stationery stock controller, of 46 Copeland Grove, Clontarf, Dublin, and Agnes O'Connor; M 1964. Awarded 2nd Victoria Prize. 1968/T/01 [1 item].

BRADFIELD-ENGLAND, AUSTEN St. JAMES (b. 13 January 1913) 4th s. of St. James Bradfield-England, of 11 Rostrevor Terrace, Rathgar, Co. Dublin, and Maud Dobbyn; E 1936. Awarded Society's Prize. 1939/M/03 [1 item]. His eldest brother is here listed under England, William Henry Philip.

BRADLEY, MICHAEL KIERAN (b. 13 Nov. 1921) only s. of John Bradley, journalist, of Athy, Co. Kildare, and Sheila Loughnane (decd.); LL.B.(London); M 1965. 1968/T/15 [1 item].

BRADY, ANDREW NEWTON (b. 24 Sept. 1849) eld. s. of Thomas Francis Brady, Inspector of Irish Fisheries, of 11 Percy Place, Dublin, and Sarah Bridgford; B.A. (Q.C.G.); M 1871, M.T. E 1875. 1878/H/01 [2 items].

BRADY, CHARLES WILLIAM RAWSON (b. 12 Jan. 1852) 2nd s. of Thomas Francis Brady, Inspector of Irish Fisheries, of 11 Percy Place, Dublin, and Sarah [Bridgford]; B.A. (T.C.D.); H 1873, M.T. E 1875. 1876/M/07 [6 items]. Died 1922. Obituary, *I.L.T. & S.J.*, lvi (15 and 22 July 1922), 172.

BRADY, GEORGE ANTHONY (b. 8 May 1942) young. s. of George E. Brady, BL, of 'Villa Rapallo', Nutley Lane, Dublin, and Hannah O'Sullivan; B.A. (N.U.I.); M 1964. Awarded 2nd Victoria Prize. 1967/T/02 [1 item]. S.C., 1 Oct. 1984.

BRADY, GEORGE EDWARD (b. 1 May 1906) eld. s. of Owen Brady (decd.), of 1 Patrick Street, Dublin, and Josephine Carroll (decd.); M 1945. 1950/T/06 [2 items].

BRADY, HORACE NEWMAN (b. 12 Aug 1843) eld. s. of the Revd. Francis Tempest Brady of Clonmel, Co. Tipperary, and Fanny Susan Norman; B.A. (T.C.D.); M 1865; M.T. T 1866. 1870/M/9 [2 items].

BRADY, JOHN COCHRANE (b. 1 March 1870) only s. of John Cochrane Brady (decd.), of Johnstown, Clones, Co. Monaghan, and Annie Louisa Johnston; B.A. (T.C.D.); E 1893. 1896/M/06 [4 items].

BRADY, ROBERT SAMUEL (b. 2 Oct 1845) 3rd s. of John Brady J.P. of Johnstown Co. Fermanagh, and Isabella McMurray; B.A. (T.C.D.); H 1866; M.T. T 1867. 1869/E/3 [2 items].

BRANIGAN, PATRICK FRANCIS (b. 30 Aug. 1906) eld. s. of Daniel Branigan (decd.), of Drogheda, Co. Louth, and Teresa A.B. Clinton (decd.); Cand. Bach. (T.C.D.); M 1925. Awarded 2nd Class Cert. of Honour. 1928/T/01 [2 items]. Practised at the Irish Bar, 1928-30. Aft. served as a colonial administrator in Africa and Malta. Minister of Justice and Attorney-General of the Gold Coast, 1948-54. Knighted upon retirement, 1954. Chairman of the Pensions Appeal Tribunal, 1955-81. Recorder, 1972-75. Died 2 Nov. 2000. Obituary, *The Times*, 6 Nov. 2000. *Who's Who*.

BRAYDEN, WILLIAM HENRY (b. 30 Sept. 1865) eld. s. of William H. Brayden, of Armagh, Co. Armagh, and Elizabeth Windrum; M 1891. 1894/T/05 [7 items]. Reporter in the Gallery of the House of Commons, 1885-7. Editor of the Dublin *National Press*, 1890-2, and of the *Freeman's Journal*, 1892-1920. O.B.E., 1920. Practitioner in the Dáil courts: author of 'Republican Courts in Ireland', in *Journal of the American Bar Association*, Sept. 1920. Died 17 Dec. 1933. Obituary, *I.L.T. & S.J.*, lxvii (1933), 351; *Who's Who*.

BREAKEY, WILLIAM ALEXANDER (b. 11 March 1845) 2nd s. of John Breakey (decd.), gentleman, of Ballybay, Co. Monaghan, and Margaret Jane Levers; M 1889. 1890/M/08 [2 items]. A former Petty Sessions clerk. Author of *Handbook for Magistrates' Clerks of Petty Sessions, Solicitors, Coroners* (Dublin, 1895). Died 1919. Obituary, *I.L.T. & S.J.*, liii (29 Nov. 1919), 288. Mentioned in Maurice Healy, *The Old Munster Circuit*, 127.

BREATHNACH, SEÁN (b. 14 March 1911) only s. of Cormac Breathnach, of 384 Clontarf Road, Dollymount, Dublin, and Kathleen Ryan; B. Comm (N.U.I.); M 1944. 1947/T/08 [2 items]. District Justice. Died 1974. Obituary, *I.L.T. & S.J.*, cviii (22 June 1974), 154. Mentioned in Patrick MacKenzie, *Lawful Occasions*, 60.

BREEN, GERARD VINCENT (b. 30 Aug. 1941) young. s. of Charles Breen, retired clerk (Guinness), of 20 O'Leary Road, Kilmainham, Co. Dublin, and Cathleen Clarke; M 1962. 1967/M/02 [3 items].

BRENNAN, CHARLES JOSEPH (b. 19 Sept. 1915) eld. s. of Joseph Brennan, of Bartra, Dalkey, Co. Dublin, and Ita Ryan; M 1943. 1947/M/09 [2 items].

BRENNAN, GABRIEL JOSEPH (b. 1928) 6th s. of Senator Joseph Brennan (decd.), of Bartra, Dalkey, Co. Dublin, and Ita Ryan; B.A. (N.U.I.); M 1947. 1950/T/04 [2 items].

BRENNAN, IAN GERARD MARY (b. 2 Dec. 1945) eld. s. of Senan John Brennan (decd.), school teacher, of 44 South Avenue, Mount Merrion, Co. Dublin, and Madeline McGrotty; B.A. (N.U.I.); M 1964. 1968/T/18 [1 item].

BRENNAN, PATRICK JAMES (b. 3 Oct. 1899) 4th s. of Joseph Brennan (decd.), of Dublin, and Jane McDonnell (decd.); M 1952; M.T. T 1949. 1953/T/02 [4 items].

BRENNAN, PETER JAMES (b. 14 Nov. 1921) 2nd s. of Joseph Brennan, of 27 Pembroke Road, Ballsbridge, Dublin, and Evelyn Slimcox; B.A. (N.U.I.); M 1940. 1945/T/06 [2 items].

BRENNAN, THOMAS JOSEPH (b. 31 Aug. 1870) young. s. of William Joseph Brennan of Holly Ville, Cabra Road, Dublin, and Mary Harkness; M 1890. 1894/H/02 [7 items].

BRETT, GEORGE HENRY (b. 11 Feb. 1872) 2nd s. of Charles Henry Brett, solicitor, of Belfast, and Margaret Neill; cand. bach. (R.U.I.); M 1895, M.T. M 1896. 1898/T/07 [4 items]. Died 17 Feb. 1938. Obituary, *I.L.T. & S.J.*, lxxii (1938), 69, 174. See C.E.B. Brett, *Long Shadows Cast Before* (Edinburgh and London, 1978), 120-1, 141.

BRETT, JOSEPH PATRICK (b. 12 Oct. 1856) young. s. of Henry Brett, C.E., County Surveyor of Wicklow, of Rosemount, Booterstown, Dublin, and Mary Henry; B.A. (T.C.D.); M 1876, M.T. E 1878. 1879/M/16 [7 items].

BREW, THOMAS STUDDERT (b. 2 Nov 1840) 2nd s. of William Brew of Leadmore House, Co. Clare, and Elizabeth Studdert; E 1862; M.T. M 1867. 1869/T/1 [8 items].

BRIDGEMAN, JOSEPH KIRWAN (b. 9 May 1874) only s. of Joseph Bridgeman, civil engineer, of 82 Summerhill, Dublin, and Margaret Kirwan; B.A. (R.U.I.); M 1893. 1896/T/07 [3 items].

BRISCOE, HENRY WHITBY (b. 19 April 1873) eld. s. of Arthur Wellesley Briscoe of 34 Leinster Road, Dublin, and Frances Keon; M 1890. 1894/E/01 [6 items]. Civil servant. Drowned, 1917.

BROSNAN, JOHN ANTHONY (b. 20 Feb. 1916) eld. s. of Patrick Brosnan (decd.), of Dingle, Co. Kerry, and Ellen Moriarty; M 1951. 1955/M/11 [2 items].

BROWN, HERBERT MACAULAY (b. 2 Feb. 1897) only s. of William Herbert Brown, of 28 Sydney Avenue, Blackrock, Co. Dublin, and Elizabeth Rose Sandes; M 1919. 1921/M/03 [2 items]. Royal Marines. Administrative Service, Nigeria, 1924. Magistrate, 1934. Assistant Judge, 1943. Judge of the High Court, Eastern Nigeria, 1945. Died 19 Dec. 1987. *Who's Who*

BROWN, HUGH DUNLOP (b. 12 Feb. 1858) y. s. of Hugh Brown (decd.), J.P., of Oakland, Rathgar, Dublin, and Marianne Riddle; B.A. (T.C.D.); H 1880, M.T. T 1882. 1883/H/03* [5 items]. Became Pastor of the Baptist church at 46-48 Harcourt Street. Died 1918. See 'The story of the Harcourt Street Baptist Church Dublin', in *Irish Baptist Historical Society Journal*, vol. 14 (1981-82), pp 23-34.

BROWN, SAMUEL LOMBARD (B. 10 Jan. 1856) eld. s. of Samuel Brown, LL.D., of Dundrum, Dublin, and Isabella Lombard; M 1875; M.T. M 1877. 1881/H/03 [6 items]. Q.C., 22 April 1899. 1899. Senator of the Irish Free State, 1924. Regius Professor of Laws, T.C.D., 1934-9. Died 14 Dec. 1939. Obituary, *I.L.T. & S.J.*, lxxiii (1939), 367, 374-5.

BROWN, THOMAS WATTERS (b. 17 March 1879) 2nd s. of James A. Brown of Newtownards, Co. Down, and Mary Anne Watters; B.A.; M 1904. 1907/T/10 [2 items]. K.C., 27 Feb. 1918. Unionist M.P. for North Down, 1918-22. Attorney-General for N.I. P.C., 1921. Judge of the N.I. High Court, 1922. Died 7 Oct. 1944. Obituary, *I.L.T. & S.J.*, lxxviii (1944), 262. See Kate Newmann, *Dictionary of Ulster Biography* (Belfast, 1993).

BROWN, WILLIAM H. (b. 13 April 1860) 2nd s. of the Revd. Nathaniel M. Brown, D.D., of Fairy Fort, Limavady, Co. Londonderry, and Isabella J. Irwin; B.Sc (London), M.A. (R.U.I.); M 1884; Exhibition at Honor Examination, Oct. 1886. 1887/T/01 [5 items]. K.C., 28 Oct. 1911. Appt. County Court Judge for Cavan and Leitrim, 20 Feb. 1914. Died 7 Feb. 1927. Obituary, *I.L.T. & S.J.*, lxi (1927), 41; *Who's Who*

BROWNE, AIDAN FRANCIS (b. 29 Jan. 1937) 4th s. of Daniel Joseph Browne (decd.), Land Commissioner, of 'San Antoine', Cross Avenue, Blackrock, Co. Dublin, and Kathleen Savage; B.C.L.; M 1958. 1961/M/05 [2 items]. S.C., 4 Oct. 1976.

BROWNE, DANIEL FRANCIS (b. 15 Sept. 1858) 3rd surv. s. of Michael Browne (decd.) of Limerick, and Bridget Meehan; M 1878, M.T. M 1880. 1881/M/10 [6 items]. Munster Circuit. K.C., 19 Feb. 1902. Appt. County Court Judge of Kerry, 2 Dec. 1909. Died at Central Hotel, Tralee, 21 Jan. 1913. Obituary, *I.L.T. & S.J.*, xlvii (1913), 29; *Who's Who*

BROWNE, DILLON AUGUSTUS (b. 17 June 1903) only s. of Joseph Dillon Browne, of Narrow Water, Raheny, Dublin, and Florence Maud White; M 1944. 1947/T/03 [2 items].

BROWNE, HARVEY (b. 15 Dec. 1867) only s. of Thomas Harvey Browne of Sydney, Australia, and Matilda Rigney; M 1889. 1892/T/05 [5 items].

BROWNE, JAMES SWAN (b. 9 Dec. 1864) only s. of Joseph Swan Browne (decd.) of Kingstown, Co. Dublin, and Mary [?]; B.A. (T.C.D.); M 1889. 1901/T/01 [5 items]. Captain, 2nd Brabant's Horse. Died 7 April 1902. *I.L.T. & S.J.*, xxxvi (1902), 148.

BROWNE, JOHN HENRY (b. 8 Jan 1844) eldest s. of Henry Browne of Banna, Ardfert, Co. Kerry, and Mary Stack; B.A. (T.C.D.); E 1871; M.T. T 1871. 1874/H/10 [2 items].

BROWNE, KEPPEL GLENNY DODWELL (b. 15 Aug. 1873) 2nd s. of Dodwell F. Browne, Judge of the District Court of Colombo, Ceylon, and Arabella Glenny; B.A.; H 1893. 1896/H/05 [6 items].

BROWNE, MATTHEW BARRY CHARLES (b. 1 Nov 1844) eld. s. of Matthew Browne, solicitor, of Dublin, and Margaret Delaney; B.A. (T.C.D.); H 1869; L.I. E 1871. 1873/E/2 [4 items].

BROWNING, FRANCIS HENRY (b. 22 June 1868) eld. s. of Jeffrey Browning (decd.), solicitor, and Julia Mary Smart; B.A. (T.C.D.); M 1888. 1891/T/02 [6 items]. Examiner of Titles in the Land Registry. Joint author of *Local Registration of Title in Ireland* [1st edition, with W.E. Glover (Dublin, 1901); 2nd edition, with Raymond Smith (Dublin, 1912)]. 2nd in command of the I.A.V.T. Corps. Shot while returning to Beggars Bush Barracks, 26 April 1916. Obituary, *I.L.T. & S.J.*, l (1916), 111, 150. Photograph (right) in Henry Hanna, *The Pals at Suvla Bay* (1917).

*BRUNSKILL, GERALD FITZGIBBON (b. 4 April 1866) 2nd s. of Thomas Richardson Brunskill of 2 Grosvenor Square, Dublin, and Anna Jane Tully; B.A. (T.C.D.); M 1885. *1888/T/01 [9 items]. *1901/H/02x [2 items]. Auditor of the College Historical Society, 1889-90. Disbarred at own request T 1900 to become a solicitor (for family reasons); struck off roll of solicitors at own request [personal memorial], and called a *second time in 1901. Briefly Unionist M.P. for Mid-Tyrone, 1910. K.C., 28 Nov. 1914. Died in Trim Court House, 3 Oct. 1918, while acting as Deputy for His Honour Judge Fleming. Obituary, *I.L.T. & S.J.*, lii (1918), 250; *Who's Who*.

BRYAN, JOHN DONOUGH OWEN (b. 26 Oct. 1904) 3rd s. of Loftus Anthony Bryan, Colonel, of Bornmount Manor, Enniscorthy, Co. Wexford, and Annie Ryan; Sch. (Mod.) B.A.; M 1926. 1929/M/06 [2 items]. Auditor of the College Historical Society, 1928-9. Lecturer in history, T.C.D. Died (from influenza contracted while learning Irish on the Blasket Islands) 9 Oct. 1932. Obituary, *I.L.T. & S.J.*, lxvi (1932), 259. Author of *The Great Earl of Kildare* (Dublin, 1933).

BUCHANAN, JOHN GERARD (b. 27 Aug. 1926) only s. of Hugh Johnston Buchanan (decd.), bank manager, of the Northern Bank Ltd, Derry, and Gladys Gilmore; B.A. (Mod.) (T.C.D.); M 1944. 1949/M/16 [2 items]. S.C., 2 Oct. 1972. Judge of the Circuit Court, 1978-96.

BUCKHALTER, SIMON WILLIAM (b. 19 March 1904) eld. s. of Henry Buckhalter (decd.), of 42a Clanbrassil Street, Dublin, and Nechama Miller; M 1925. 1929/T/01 [2 items].

BUCKLEY, CORNELIUS THOMAS VAUGHAN (b. 13 Nov. 1944) 3rd s. of Francis Vaughan Buckley, Senior Counsel, of 'Montrose', Thormanby Road, Howth, Co. Dublin, and Margaret Crowley; B.C.L. (N.U.I.); M 1962. 1967/T/11 [1 item].

BUCKLEY, DANIEL CHRISTOPHER JOSEPH [Domhnall C. Ó Buachalla] (b. 3 Dec. 1933) 4th s. of Timothy Buckley, of Main Street, Cashel, Co. Tipperary, and Mary Kiely; D.P.A; M 1952. 1957/H/02 [2 items]. Department of Justice.

BUCKLEY, DENIS JOSEPH VAUGHAN (b. 10 Nov. 1942) 2nd s. of Francis Vaughan Buckley, Senior Counsel, of 'Montrose', Asgard Road, Howth, Co. Dublin, and Margaret Crowley; B.C.L. (N.U.I.); M 1962. 1965/M/07 [1 item]. S.C., 5 Oct. 1987.

BUCKLEY, FRANCIS BERNARD VAUGHAN (b. 17 Sept. 1910) eld. s. of Denis Joseph Buckley, of Elmvale, Mallow, Co. Cork, and Beatrice Vaughan; M 1928. 1931/M/06 [2 items]. S.C., 30 June 1943. Died 24 Dec. 1968. Obituary, *I.L.T. & S.J.*, ciii (1969), 20.

BUCKLEY, JEREMIAH (b. 16 Nov. 1862) 2nd s. of John Buckley (decd.), gentleman, of Millstreet, Co. Cork, and Ellen Mullane; M 1890. 1893/M/05 [6 items]. A chartered accountant, and proprietor of the *Limerick Leader*. Died 15 Sept. 1937. Obituary, *I.L.T. & S.J.*, lxxi (1937), 264.

BUCKLEY, JOHN MARY (b. 8 Sept. 1919) only s. of John M. Buckley (decd.), of Laurelmount, Highfield, West Co. Cork, and K.R. McNamara; B. Comm (N.U.I.); D.P.A. (T.C.D.); M 1942. 1946/T/16 [2 items]. District Justice.

BUDD, DECLAN NICHOLAS ORFORD (b. 27 July 1943) only s. of Frederick Gardner Orford Budd, Judge of the Supreme Court, of 73 South Hill, Dartry, Co. Dublin, and Oonah Blennerhassett; B.A. (Mod.), LL.B. (T.C.D.); M 1964. 1968/M/06 [1 item]. S.C., 12 March 1981. Judge of the High Court, 1 Oct. 1991. President of the Law Reform Commission, 2000-2005. Listed in the 1991 and 1999 editions of Maureen Cairnduff, *Who's Who in Ireland*.

BUDD, FREDERICK GARDNER ORFORD (b. 11 April 1904) 2nd s. of Samuel Duguid Budd, of 18 Herbert Park, Dublin, and Fanny Beatrice Orford; B.A., Sen. Mod., LL.D. (T.C.D.); M 1924. Awarded 2nd Class Certificate of Honour. 1927/H/02 [2 items]. S.C., 5 March 1943. Senator (Dublin University), 1951. Judge of the High Court, Oct. 1951; of the Supreme Court, 1966-75. Retired 18 Dec. 1975. Died 9 Feb. 1976. Appreciation on retirement and obituary, *I.L.T. & S.J.*, cx (1976), 37-8 and 75-6. See Louis McRedmond (ed.), *Modern Irish Lives*.

BULLOCH, ALEXANDER MILLER (b. 8 May 1874) eld. s. of Alexander Bulloch, merchant, of Eversleigh, Belfast, and Mary Lytle; Sch. Mod. B.A. (T.C.D.); H 1897, G.I. E 1898. 1900/H/03 [7 items].

BURGESS, ROBERT BALDERSTON (b. 25 Dec. 1890) eld. s. of Henry Givens Burgess of Eglinton House, Kingstown, Co. Dublin, and Agnes Balderston; M 1910. 1914/H/05 [2 items]. Captain, Royal Engineers. Died in France, 9 Dec. 1915 [Name on the Bar War Memorial].

BURKE, ANTHONY (b. 23 June 1914) 5th s. of Thomas Francis Burke (decd.), solicitor, of 4 Belgrave Square, Monkstown, Co. Dublin, and Marcella Flynn. 1939/M/08 [1 item].

BURKE, ARTHUR ULICK (b. 25 Sept. 1881) 4th s. of Chevalier John Burke, J.P., of Ravensdale, Strandtown, Belfast, and Elizabeth Charlotte French; M 1915. 1918/T/07 [2 items].

BURKE, CORMAC PATRICK (b. 21 March 1927) 3rd s. of Patrick Joseph Burke, medical practitioner, of 'St. Colm's', Sligo, and Nora Costelloe; B.A. (N.U.I.); M 1946. 1950/H/03 [2 items].

BURKE, DANIEL (b. 10 Feb. 1892) 3rd s. of Daniel Burke, of 42 Ormond Road, Rathmines, Dublin, and Margaret Maher; M 1914. 1917/T/03 [2 items].

BURKE, FITZSTEPHEN (b. 14 July 1885) 6th s. of Chevalier John Burke, J.P., of 75. 77. Corporation Street, Belfast, and Elizabeth French; M 1906. 1910/T/05 [3 items].

BURKE, JAMES ALOYSIUS (b. 15 June 1893) eld. s. of Tobias Henry Burke of Rockforest, Roscrea, Co. Tipperary, and B.A. Quinlan; M 1913. 1916/T/07 [2 items]. M.P. for Mid-Tipperary, Dec. 1918-1921; T.D. for Tipperary constituencies, 1921-1938. Minister for Local Government, 1923-27; Parliamentary Secretary to Minister for Finance, 1927. See *Thom's Directory* (Biographies). Name rendered Séamus Aloysius Bourke in Brian Walker (ed.), *Parliamentary Election Results in Ireland 1918-92* (Dublin, 1992).

BURKE, JAMES MICHAEL (b. 4 Nov. 1873) 7th s. of Patrick Burke of Skibbereen, Co. Cork, and Mary Gallagher; M 1897. 1900/M/01 [3 items]. Cumann na nGael T.D. for Cork West, 1933-6. Died 10 Sept. 1936. Obituary, *I.L.T. & S.J.*, lxx (1936), 243.

BURKE, JOHN ALPHONSUS (b. 3 Sept. 1915) 3rd s. of James Burke (decd.), of Carrick-on-Shannon, Co. Leitrim, and Mary Grey. 1938/M/01 [2 items]. Mentioned, as 'Shane Burke', the Brooke Scholar, who 'took a teaching post in England and never practised', in T.F. O'Higgins, *A Double Life* (Dublin, 1996), p. 70.

BURKE, JOSEPH BERMINGHAM (b. 20 Nov. 1867) 3rd s. of Joseph Burke, Sessional Crown Solicitor, of The Abbey, Co. Roscommon, and Matilda Kirwan; B.A., LL.B. (T.C.D.); M 1887. 1890/T/05 [8 items]. Under-Treasurer at King's Inns, 12 April 1932-1944. Died 5 June 1954. Obituary, *I.L.T. & S.J.*, lxxxviii (1954), 162.

BURKE, MARTIN JOHN (b. 26 Aug 1848) eld. s. of James Milo Burke J.P., of Khyber Pass [Queenstown Lodge], Dalkey, Co. Dublin and Elizabeth Eiffe; B.A. (T.C.D.); M 1868; M.T. T 1870. 1872/T/2 [4 items]. Q.C., 1 July 1892.

BURKE, MATTHEW ALEXANDER (b. 4 Oct. 1867) 3rd surv. s. of William Hamilton Burke (decd.), of Hill View, Belfast, and Ann Wilson; M 1885. 1888/M/07 [9 items].

BURKE, MICHAEL C. (b. 6 June 1884) 2nd s. of Edmond Burke of Coolclough, Hospital, Co. Limerick, and Catherine Canty; M 1903. 1908/H/02 [2 items].

BURKE, SEÁN OILIBHEAR (b. 14 Jan. 1938) eld. s. of Thomas Gerard Burke, Barrister-at-Law, District Justice, of Cnoc Muire, St. Mary's Road, Galway, and Charity Margaret Jordan; B.A. (Hons) (N.U.I.); M 1957. 1961/T/05 [2 items]. Department of External Affairs. Ambassador to Portugal.

BURKE, THOMAS (b. 15 Jan. 1873) young. s. of Samuel Burke, merchant, of Killemnee, Cahir, Co. Tipperary, and Katherine Rice; M 1891. 1898/T/01 [4 items].

BURKE, THOMAS GERARD ANTHONY (b. 7 May 1901) only s. of William Burke (decd.), of Hollyville Park, Monkstown, Co. Dublin, and Annie Luby; M 1919. 1922/M/03 [2 items]. Registrar in the Dáil courts. Aft. District Justice, Galway. Died 1997. See Mary Kotsonouris, *The Winding-up of the Dáil Courts, 1922-1925*: *an obvious duty* (Dublin, 2004), p. 248.

BURKE, WILLIAM ANTHONY (2 April 1866) 3rd s. of Sir Thomas Burke (decd.) of Marble Hill, Co. Galway; and Lady Mary Nugent; T 1885, M.T. T 1885. 1890/M/03 [8 items]. Died 8 Feb. 1939. *Burke's Peerage* (107th ed., 2003), 590.

BURKE, WILLIAM (b. 21 July 1871) only s. of Lawrence Burke of Tuam, Co. Galway, and Julia Clancy; M 1906; H 1893. 1907/E/03 [2 items].

BURNE, ARTHUR HENRY (b. 22 July 1874) eld. surv. s. of Joseph Graham Burne, M.D. (decd.), of 38 Westland Row, Dublin, and Sarah Wilson; [called *in absentia*] 1920/H/06 [2 items]. Died 1960. Obituary, *I.L.T. & S.J.*, xciv (23 April 1960), 101.

BURROWES, PAUL (b. 7 Aug. 1877) 3rd s. of Thomas Burrowes of Rehoboth, South Circular Road, Dublin, and Julia Mitchell; B.A. (T.C.D.); M 1900. 1903/T/05 [3 items]. Registrar of Titles, N.I.

BURTCHAELL, GEORGE DAMES (b. 12 June 1853) eld. s. of Peter Burtchaell, engineer, of Larchfield, Co. Kilkenny, and Maria Isabella Foot; LL.B. (T.C.D.); E 1875, M.T. T 1876. 1879/M/03 [6 items]. K.C., 5 June 1918. Went the home circuit, but ultimately confined himself to peerage cases. Suffered from epilepsy. Athlone Pursuivant, assistant to Sir Arthur Vicars: mentioned in Kevin Hannafin and John Cafferky, *Scandal and Betrayal*: *Shackleton and the Irish Crown Jewels* (Cork, 2002), 70. Fellow (and holder of sundry offices) of the Royal Society of Antiquaries of Ireland; Inspector of Historical MSS, 1899-1903; member of the Council of the Royal Irish Academy, 1915-18. Died, having been knocked down by a motor-car, 18 Aug. 1921. Obituary, *I.L.T. & S.J.*, lv (1921), 213; *Who's Who*. Joint author (with T.U. Sadleir) of *Alumni Dublinenses* (Dublin, 1924; 2nd editiion, 1935).

BURY, AMBROSE UPTON GLEDSTANES (b. 1 Aug. 1869) 4th s. of Charles Michael Bury, J.P., of Downings House, Co. Kildare, and Margaret Aylmer; M.A. (T.C.D.); M 1904. 1907/T/14 [2 items]. Judge. Died 1951.

BUSHE, ARTHUR PLUNKET (b. 24 Nov. 1873) 2nd s. of Charles Percy Bushe, of 2 St. Joseph's Terrace, Sandford Road, Dublin, and Dorcas Mary Atkinson; B.A.; M 1894. 1897/T/06 [3 items].

BUSHE, SEYMOUR COGHILL (5 April 1853) 4th s. of the Revd. Charles Bushe (decd.), Rector of Castlehaven, Co. Cork, and Emmeline Coghill; B.A. (T.C.D.); M 1877, I.T. M 1874. 1879/E/15 [7 items]. Q.C., 1 July 1892. Bencher, 1896. Senior Crown Prosecutor for Dublin. Called to English Bar, 1899 (and K.C. 1904). Travelled in Australasia and Central America. Died Jan. 1922. Obituary, *I.L.T. & S.J.*, lvi (4 Feb. 1922), 32, 38-9; *Who's Who*. Mentioned, tantalisingly, in Joyce's *Ulysses* (Penguin edition, 140: 'He would have been on the bench long ago ... only for ...'), and in Maurice Healy, *The Old Munster Circuit*, 238.

BUSTARD, GEORGE (b. 31 Dec. 1855) eld. s. of Ebenezer Bustard, of Belleville House, Co. Donegal, and Margaret Lynch; LL.B. (T.C.D.); M 1876, M.T. H 1879. 1880/H/05 [6 items].

BUTLER, ANNE KATHLEEN (b. 8 April 1931) eld. d. of John Christopher Butler (decd.), of Miltonfields, Swords, Co. Dublin, and Elizabeth Black; M 1956. 1960/T/12 [2 items].

BUTLER, DAVID ARTHUR SETON (b. 3 July 1940) only s. of the Right Revd. Arthur Hamilton Butler, Lord Bishop of Tuam, Killala and Achonry, of Bishop's House, Crossmolina, Co. Mayo; B.A. (T.C.D.); M 1960. 1963/T/03 [1 item]. S.C., 9 March 1979. Chairman of the Employment Appeals Tribunal. Died 1990. Obituary in *The Irish Times*.

BUTLER, EDWARD GERALD (b. 22 Sept. 1866) eld. s. of Gerald Villars Butler of Ballyadams, Queen's Co., and Mary Whitestone; ex-Scholar and Sen. Mod., B.A. (T.C.D.); M 1895. 1898/M/12 [3 items].

BUTLER, JOHN PIERS (b. 17 Feb. 1870) only s. of John Kilkelly, J.P., solicitor, of 46 Upper Mount Street, Dublin and of Rathilig, Queen's Co., and Maria Elizabeth Butler; M 1888, I.T. M 1890. 1891/M/10 [8 items].

BUTLER, PASCHAL BAYLON (b. 27 May 1932) 2nd s. of Patrick Butler, of 41 Charleville Road, Dublin, and Monica Redmond; M 1954. 1958/T/05 [2 items].

BUTLER, SEÁN (b. 9 May 1921) eld. s. of Edward Patrick Butler, of Ferrybank, Arklow, Co. Wicklow, and Mary Murphy; (Mod.) B.A., LL.B.(T.C.D.); M 1948. 1951/M/12 [2 items]. S.C., 21 Jan. 1963. Judge of the High Court, 1966. Retired, 6 July 1980. Mentioned in Patrick MacKenzie, *Lawful Occasions*, 134-9.

BUTLER, WILLIAM BILBIE (b. 5 Nov. 1891) only s. of Arthur Frederic Butler of 20 Oakley Road, Rathmines, Dublin, and Annie Fitzpatrick; M 1914. 1917/E/01 [2 items]. Called to English Bar, G.I., 1923.

BUTLER, WILLIAM JAMES (b. 4 June 1876) eld. s. of William Butler, C.E., of 58 Mountjoy Square, Dublin, and Ellen Mary Davidson; H 1902. 1904/T/11 [3 items].

BYRNE, ALFRED PATRICK (b. 12 June 1913) 2nd s. of Alfred Byrne, T.D., of 48 Palmerston Road, Dublin, and Elizabeth Heagney; M 1940. 1945/M/08 [2 items]. Independent T.D. for Dublin North-West, 1937-May 1944, 1948-52. Alderman of the City of Dublin. Died 1952. See *Thom's Directory* (Biographies).

BYRNE, COLEMAN MICHAEL (b. 17 Oct.1863) 2nd s. of William Louis Byrne, of Glenconnor House, Co. Tipperary, and Winifred J. Coleman; B.A. (T.C.D.); M 1882, M.T. H 1884. 1886/T/03 [8 items].

BYRNE, EDWARD LE CESNE (b. 20 Jan. 1883) only s. of Bernard Byrne (decd.), of 70 North Gate, London N.W.8, and Laura Charlotte Le Cesne; M.A. (Oxon); K.I. 1925; I.T. H 1902. Barrister-at-Law, of the Inner Temple, called 1905. 1926/E/02 [2 items].

BYRNE, GERALD (b. 14 April 1884) only surv. s. of John Byrne (decd.), of Armagh, Co. Armagh, and Mary Monahan; M 1913. 1914/M/03 [2 items].

BYRNE, JAMES BENJAMIN (b. 19 Dec. 1862) only s. of John Alexander Byrne, Q.C., of 85 Lower Leeson Street, Dublin, and Sarah Frend; B.A.; M 1882, M.T. M 1884. 1885/M/05 [6 items].

BYRNE, JAMES PATRICK (b. 19 Feb. 1909) 2nd s. of Michael Byrne, livestock exporter, of Glentague House, Arklow, Co. Wicklow, and Margaret Lenehan; M 1932. 1935/M/05 [2 items].

BYRNE, JOHN JOSEPH (b. 23 Sept. 1878) eld. s. of James Byrne (decd.), of Clonskeagh House, Clonskeagh, Co. Dublin, and Catherine Farrell; B.A. (T.C.D.); M 1923. 1927/T/09 [2 items]. Fine Gael T.D. for Dublin City North, 1927-33. Died 29 July 1942. Obituary, *I.L.T. & S.J.*, lxxvi (1942), 198.

BYRNE, JOHN MYLES (b. 15 May 1931) 2nd s. of Patrick A. Byrne, of 19 Greygates, Blackrock, Co. Dublin, and Nora Ring; B.A. (N.U.I.); M 1950. 1953/M/03 [2 items].

BYRNE, JOHN OUSELEY (b. 12 Jan 1846) 2nd s. of John Byrne of 10 Lombard Street, Dublin and Errislannan Co. Galway, and Prudence Henderson; B.A. (T.C.D.); E 1865; M.T. T 1865. 1868/E/7 [4 items].

BYRNE, JOHN P. (b. 1 Dec. 1859) eld. s. of John Byrne, J.P., Divisional Commissioner, of Old Court, Athlone, Co. Roscommon [sic], and Maria Jones; LL.B. (T.C.D.), District Inspector, R.I.C.; M 1885. 1891/M/06 [7 items].

BYRNE, PATRICK (b. 22 Jan. 1905) only s. of Joseph Byrne, merchant (decd.), of Athlone, Co. Westmeath, and Ellen Galvin; M.A. (N.U.I.); E 1933. 1933/T/03 [3 items].

BYRNE, WILLIAM J. (b. 5 Sept. 1862) eld. s. of William Louis Byrne, late of Glenconnor House, Co. Tipperary, and Winifred Coleman; B.A. (T.C.D.); M 1885, G.I. E 1886. 1894/T/01 [5 items]. Mentioned in Lawrence W. McBride, *The Greening of Dublin Castle: The Transformation of Bureaucratic and Judicial Personnel in Ireland, 1892-1922* (Washington, D.C.: 1991), and in Keith Jeffery (ed.), *The Sinn Fein Rebellion as they saw it: Mary Louisa and Arthur Hamilton Norwa*y (Dublin, 1999), 122. Sir William Byrne, 'a barrister with a long record of public service', was Under-Secretary to the Irish Office, 1916-18.

CAHILL, EDWARD FRANCIS (b. 29 April 1845) 1st s. of Michael Cahill of Ballyconra, Co. Kilkenny and Margaret Magan; B.A. (T.C.D.); H 1864; M.T. T 1864. 1868/E/2 [2 items].

CALDWELL, JOHN FOSTER (b. 3 May 1892) eld. s. of Charles Sproule Caldwell, of Londonderry, Co. Londonderry, and Jeanie Hamilton Foster; M 1923. 1925/M/17 [2 items]. K.C. (N.I.), M 1946.

CALLAGHAN, ALFRED JOHN (b. 29 Oct. 1864) 3rd s. of James Walter Callaghan of 11 Northumberland Road, Dublin, and Anna Louisa O'Dowd; LL.D. (T.C.D.), Barrister-at-Law, called to the I.T. 1896; H 1911. 1911/M/10 [2 items]. Sometime secretary to the City of Dublin Steam Packet Company. Principal proprietor of the *Church of Ireland Gazette*. Died 3 June 1940. Obituary, *I.L.T. & S.J.*, lxxiv (1940), 144, 259.

CALLAGHAN, FREDERICK WILLIAM (b. 6 Aug. 1864) eld. s. of James Walker Callaghan (decd.), of 11 Northumberland Road, Dublin, and Anna Louisa O'Dowd; M 1911. 1914/T/13 [3 items].

CALLAN, PAUL (b. 10 Feb. 1931) eld. s. of Denis Callan (decd.), farmer, of Longfield, Carrickmacross, Co. Monaghan, and Annie Duffy N.T.; B.A. (N.U.I.); M 1950. Awarded Society's Exhibition prize. 1953/M/02 [2 items]. S.C., 4 Oct. 1976

CALLAN, SYLVIA FLORENCE (b. 12 Nov. 1932) 3rd d. of Christopher E. Callan, solicitor, of The Warren, Boyle, Co. Roscommon, and Molly Dillon-Leetch, Barrister-at-Law; B.A. (N.U.I.); M 1951. Awarded Society's Exhibition prize. 1954/M/02 [2 items]. Aft. a solicitor, and wife of James Joseph O'Connor [q.v.].

CALLAN, WALTER ERNEST EVERARD (b. 10 June 1874) 2nd s. of Philip Callan (decd.), Barrister-at-Law, sometime M.P. for Dundalk, of Cookstown House, Ardee, Co. Louth, and Jane Frances McDonnell; M 1900. 1903/T/06 [3 items].

CALLANAN, DENIS JOSEPH (b. 17 Oct. 1889) 3rd s. of Eugene Callanan, of Dunleary, Magazine Road, Cork, and Anne Dunne; M 1926. 1931/M/18 [2 items].

CALLERY, MARY PATRICIA JOSEPHINE (b. 9 March 1930) 2nd d. of Patrick Joseph Callery (decd.), solicitor, of Elphin, Co. Roscommon, and Gertrude Flynn; M 1949. 1955/M/02 [2 items].

CALLINAN, BRIAN PATRICK CHRISTOPHER (b. 14 Sept. 1926) only s. of Patrick Callinan, architect, chartered surveyor, of 15 Mespil Road, Ballsbridge, Dublin, and Margaret Alice McElligott; (Mod.) B.A. (T.C.D.); M 1946. 1951/M/07 [2 items].

CALVERT, ROBERT HENRY (b. 28 July 1875) 3rd surv. s. of Henry Calvert late of Armagh, Co. Armagh, and Jane Menary; M 1896. 1899/E/01 [3 items]. Died of pneumonia, 27 Oct. 1914. Obituary, *I.L.T. & S.J.*, xlviii (1914), 311.

CALWELL, JOHN TORRENS (b. 27 July 1847) eld. s. of Andrew Calwell of Ballyreagh House, Co. Antrim, and Elizabeth Torrens (Q.C.B.); M 1870, M.T. E 1872. 1878/E/03 [2 items].

CAMPBELL, CHARLES HENRY GORDON (b. 22 Oct. 1885) eld. s. of Sir James H.M. Campbell, Bart., Lord Chancellor of Ireland, of Glenavy, Milltown, Dublin, and Emily MacCullagh; E 1920; G.I. T 1909. 1920/E/02 [2 items]. 2nd Lord Glenavy, and also a Baronet (created 1917). Lieutenant, Royal Engineers, 1905-10. Assistant Controller,

Ministry of Munitions, 1915-18. Secretary, Irish Department, Ministry of Labour, 1919-22, and Department of Industry and Commerce, 1922-32. Director of the Bank of Ireland (1932-; Governor, 1945) and other companies. Died 30 July 1963. See *Burke's Peerage*; *Who's Who*. Portrait in F.S.L. Lyons (ed.), *Bicentenary Essays: Bank of Ireland 1783-1983* (Dublin, 1983), 87.

CAMPBELL, CHARLES STEWART PARNELL (b. 16 April 1887) 2nd s. of Henry Campbell of 'Home', Shankill, Co. Dublin, and Jane Anne Brewis; M 1908. 1912/T/03 [2 items]. S.C., 24 April 1933. Bencher of King's Inns, 1948.

CAMPBELL, DAVID ROBB (b. 26 Sept. 1874) eld. s. of Josiah Campbell (decd.), of Donegall Street, Belfast, and Elizabeth Robb; M 1923. 1927/M/14 [2 items]. Died 14 Jan. 1934. Obituary, *I.L.T. & S.J.*, lxviii (1934), 21, 39.

CAMPBELL, HARPER (b. 11 April 1857) 2nd s. of Harper Campbell, J.P., of Hermitage, Sligo, and Ellen Steen; B.A. (T.C.D.); M 1876; L.I. H 1879. 1879/M/13 [6 items]. Sometime captain of artillery in Australia. Died 1940. Obituary, *I.L.T. & S.J.*, lxxiv (14 Dec. 1940), 328.

CAMPBELL, HENRY (b. 29 March 1880) 4th s. of Thomas Campbell, J.P., of 11 Vesey Place, Kingstown, Co. Dublin, and Margaret Warren; E 1907. 1907/M/11 [4 items].

CAMPBELL, JAMES ALEXANDER (b. 27 Oct. 1928) 2nd s. of Robert John Campbell, company director, of The Mall, Ramelton, Co. Donegal, and Sarah Jane Patterson; B.A. (Mod.), LL.B.(T.C.D.); M 1948. 1952/H/03 [2 items].

CAMPBELL, JAMES HENRY MUSSEN (b. 4 April 1852) young. s. of William Mussen Campbell of Prospect House, Terenure, Dublin, and Sarah Armstrong; B.A. (T.C.D.); H 1875, G.I. H 1877. 1878/E/02 [5 items]. Auditor of the College Historical Society, 1876-7. Q.C., 1 July 1892. M.P. for St. Stephen's Green Division of Dublin, 1898-1900, for Dublin University, 1903-17. Privy Councillor 1905. Solicitor-General for Ireland, 1901-5; Attorney-General, Dec. 1905 (for 3 weeks) and 1916. Lord Chief Justice, 1916. Baronet 10 Jan. 1917. Lord Chancellor of Ireland, 1918-21. Created a peer as Lord Glenavy, 26 July 1921. Chairman of the Senate of the Irish Free State, 1922-8. Vice-Chancellor of Dublin University, 1919-31. Died 22 March 1931. Obituary, *I.L.T. & S.J.*, lxv (1931), 77-8. See: *Burke's Peerage*; *Who's Who* (sub Glenavy); *D.N.B* (article by Diarmid Coffey); Ball, *Judges*, ii, 385; and Henry Boylan, *A Dictionary of Irish Biography* (1978). Portrait by Sir William Orpen at Gray's Inn; portrait by Leo Whelan in T.C.D.: see Anne Crookshank and David Webb, *Paintings and Sculptures in Trinity College Dublin* (Dublin, 1990), 34.

CAMPBELL, JOHN HUGH HAMILTON (b. 6 June 1892) young. s. of Edward Campbell, of Katesbridge, Co. Antrim, and Catherine Magenis; M 1914. 1917/M/11 [2 items]. K.C. (N.I.), T. 1939.

CAMPBELL, MICHAEL MUSSEN (b. 25 Oct. 1924) 2nd s. of [2nd] Lord Glenavy, of Rockbrook House, Rathfarnham, Dublin, and Beatrice Elvery; B.A. (T.C.D.); M 1944. 1948/M/01 [2 items]. Author of *Peter Perry* (1956), *Oh Mary This England* (1959), *Across the Water* (1961), *The Princess in England* (1964), *Lord Dismiss Us* (1967) and *Nothing Doing* (1970). In 1980 succeeded his brother Patrick in the peerage as 4th (and last) Baron Glenavy. Died s.p., June 1984. See *Burke's Peerage*; *Who's Who*.

CAMPBELL, ROBERT SEYMOUR (b. 26 March 1848) 3rd s. of William Campbell (decd.), gentleman, of Trot Hill, Co. Monaghan, and Mary Ann Smyth; M 1891. 1894/M/04 [8 items].

CAMPBELL, THOMAS JOSEPH (b. 14 Dec. 1871) 2nd s.of Joseph Campbell of Belfast, and Sarah Morrow; M.A., LL.B; E 1898. 1900/M/02 [5 items]. North-East Circuit. K.C., 27 Feb. 1918. Editor of *The Irish News*, 1895-1906. Practised in Dublin 1910-22. First secretary of the Circuit of Northern Ireland, 1922. Bencher of King's Inns (the last before the setting up of the Inn of Court of N.I.), 1924. Nationalist Senator at Stormont, 1929-34. M.P. for Belfast Central, 1934-45. Author of three N.I. statutes [Wild Birds Protection Act, 1931, Slaughter of Animals Act, 1932, and Dogs Protection Act, 1934] and of *Workmen's Compensation*, and *Fifty Years of Ulster, 1890-1940*. Appt. County Court Judge for Tyrone, Dec. 1945. Died 3 May 1946. Obituary, *I.L.T. & S.J.*, lxxx (1946), 121; *Who's Who*. Photograph in *The Collegian: The Magazine of St. Malachy's College, Belfast, Centenary Number* (Belfast, 1933), 142.

CAMPBELL, WILLIAM (b. 25 April 1876) young. s. of Harper Campbell (decd.), of The Hermitage, Sligo, Co. Sligo, and Harriet Becket Davidson; B.A. (Cambridge); T 1899. 1902/T/05 [2 items]. Captain. Died 17 June 1938. Obituary, *I.L.T. & S.J.*, lxxii (1938), 191, 320.

CAMPBELL, WILLIAM BERNARD (b. 4 Oct. 1865) 2nd s. of William Campbell of Gardiner's Place, Dublin, and Kate Rorke (decd.); candidate bachelor (T.C.D.); T 1885, M.T. E 1886. 1888/E/07 [7 items]. Died May 1911: *I.L.T. & S.J.*, xlv (1911), 167.

CAMPBELL-GAUSSEN, PERCEVAL DAVID WILLIAM (b. 22 July 1862) eld. s. of D. Campbell-Gaussen, B.L., J.P., of Shanemullagh House, Castle Dawson, Co. Londonderry, and Annie Catherine Ottiwell; B.A. (T.C.D.); M 1882, M.T. M 1884. 1885/M/07 [8 items].

CANNON, JOHN HUGH GERALD TANDY (b. 29 Dec. 1892) young. s. of Harry Tandy Cannon, of Clare Hall, Raheny, Dublin, and Emily Elliott; B.A. (T.C.D.); M 1914. 1917/M/08 [2 items]. Died in a motor accident, 13 April 1949.

CANNON, PATRICK FRANCIS GARRETT (b. 30 Dec. 1908) eld. s. of Patrick Cannon, of Moneymore, Ballintra, Co. Donegal, and Annie H. Murphy; M 1935. 1938/M/05 [2 items]. Headmaster of Sandymount High School.

CARBERY, JOHN HUGH (b. 24 Jan. 1939) 1st s. of Austin Hugh Carbery, agent of Bank of Ireland (retired), of 53 St. Kevin's Park, Dartry, Co. Dublin, and Josephine Mary Heffernan; B.A. (U.C.D.), Diplome de l'Université de Strasbourg; M 1957. 1962/T/01 [2 items]. Department of External Affairs, and Commission of the European Communites.

CARBERY, WILLIAM JOSEPH (b. 22 Jan. 1870) eld. s. of James Sarsfield Carbery, J.P., of Knockane, Co. Cork, and Margaret Matthews; E 1890. 1893/M/08 [6 items].

CAREY, CECIL WILLIAM VICTOR (b. 6 Oct. 1887) 2nd s. of William Percival Carey, solicitor, of 44 Grosvenor Square, Rathmines, Dublin, and Rhoda L. Loverock; B.A. (T.C.D.); M 1907. 1910/T/11 [2 items].

CAREY, PATRICK JOSEPH (Padhraic Ó Ciardha) (b. 27 January 1907) eld. s. of John Carey, of Mough, Ballinamore, Co. Leitrim, and Anne Quinn; 1936. 1940/E/01 [2 items].

CAREY, PATRICK PAUL (b. 4 May 1918) eld. s. of John Augustine Carey, of 11 Adelaide Street, Dún Laoghaire, Co. Dublin, and Catherine Keogh; M 1936. 1940/T/03 [2 items].

CARMICHAEL-FERRALL, JOHN (b. 8 Nov. 1855) only s. of John Jervis O'Ferral Carmichael-Ferrall, Captain, R.N., of Aughercastle, Co. Tyrone, and Margaret Humble; M 1876, M.T. H 1878. 1878/M/06 [6 items].

CARNEY, JOHN FRANCIS (b. 23 Sept. 1892) 2nd s. of John Carney (decd.) of Killarney, Co. Kerry, and U. O'Donoghue; M 1912. 1915/T/08 [2 items].

CARNEY, PAUL (b. 27 April 1943) only s. of James Patrick Carney, professor, of 45 Garville Avenue, Rathgar, Dublin, and Mary Ellen Morrissey; M 1961. 1966/H/01 [1 item]. S.C., 6 Oct. 1980. Judge of the High Court, 30 April 1991. Listed (with photograph) in the 1991 and 1999 editions of Maureen Cairnduff, *Who's Who in Ireland*.

CARNEY, THOMAS PATRICK (b. 22 Jan. 1941) 3rd s. of Richard G. Carney (decd.), pharmaceutical chemist, of Bellevue, Ballaghaderreen, Co. Roscommon, and Frances Howley; B.C.L. (N.U.I.); M 1963; I.T. H 1965. 1966/M/09 [1 item].

CAROLAN, THOMAS JAMES RUPERT (b. 30 Jan. 1928) only s. of Andrew James Carolan, of 33 York Lane, Belfast and Eleanor Theresa Hayes; M 1948. 1953/M/12 [2 items].

CARR, GEORGE WHITMORE (b. 17 Feb. 1846) eld. s. of Edward Carr of Camlin, New Ross, Co. Wexford, solicitor, and Sarah Carr; B.A.; E 1865, M.T. T 1866. 1868/E/6 [2 items].

CARRIGAN, WILLIAM (b. 19 Oct. 1865) eld. s. of John Carrigan, merchant, of Tipperary, Co. Tipperary, and Elizabeth O'Donnell; T 1897. Former solicitor practising in Thurles. 1897/M/04 [3 items]. K.C., 16 Dec. 1909. Died 25 Jan. 1951. Obituary, *I.L.T. & S.J.*, lxxxv (1951), 27.

CARROLL, ADRIAN FRANCIS (b. 25 Oct. 1937) eld. s. of Francis Carroll, L.D.S.I., of 34 Gladstone Street, Clonmel, Co. Tipperary, and Eleanor O'Brien; B.C.L.; M 1955. 1959/M/07 [2 items].

CARROLL, JAMES (b. 15 May 1927) only s. of John Carroll (decd.), cattle exporter and farmer, of Kickham Street, Carrick-on-Suir, Co. Tipperary, and Eleanor Cahill; M 1955. 1959/T/06 [2 items]. S.C., 3 Oct. 1977. Judge of the Circuit Court. Died 6 December 2002. Appreciation, *The Irish Times*, 12 February 2003.

CARROLL, JUSTIN EDWARD EMMANUEL (b. 28 Dec. 1942) only s. of Edward Joseph Carroll, chartered accountant, of 7 Grove Avenue, Blackrock, Co. Dublin, and Priscilla Darby; B.A. (T.C.D.); M 1961. 1966/T/13 [1 item]. Department of Foreign Affairs.

CARROLL, MELLA ELIZABETH LAURIE (b. 6 March 1934) youngest d. of Patrick Carroll, Chief Superintendent, Garda Síochána, Barrister-at-Law, of 15 Cowper Drive, Rathmines, Dublin, and Agnes Mary Caulfield; B.A. (U.C.D.); M 1954. Awarded Brooke Scholarship. 1957/M/01 [2 items]. S.C., 4 Oct. 1976. Chairman of the Bar Council, 1979. Judge of the High Court, 6 Oct. 1980. Listed in the 1984, 1991 and 1999 editions of Maureen Cairnduff, *Who's Who in Ireland*; and in Louis McRedmond (ed.), *Modern Irish Lives*.

CARROLL, PATRICK JOSEPH (b. 15 Sept. 1903) 3rd s. of Michael Carroll (decd.), of Ballyrider, Stradbally, Leix, and Julia Scully; M 1928. 1932/M/02 [2 items]. Adapted the Royal Irish Constabulary Guide for use in the Garda Síochána, 1934. Garda Commissioner, 1967-8. Portrait in Garda Museum. Died 6 Dec. 1975. See Louis McRedmond (ed.), *Modern Irish Lives*.

CARROLL, REDMOND FRANCIS (b. 4 Sept. 1846) young. s. of Redmond Carroll (decd.), solicitor, of Summer Hill, Dublin, and Helen Taaffe; H 1880, M.T. H 1880. 1882/M/13 [7 items].

CARSON, EDWARD HENRY (b. 9 Feb. 1854) 2nd s. of Edward Henry Carson, architect, of 25 Harcourt St, Dublin, and Isabella Lambert; B.A. (T.C.D.), H 1874, M.T. M 1875. 1877/E/06x [5 items]. Q.C., June 1889; at English Bar, 1894. Solicitor-General for Ireland, 1892; for England, 1900-6. Knighted, 1900. Attorney-General (England), 1915; First Lord of the Admiralty, 1917; Lord of Appeal in Ordinary, 1921-9. Died 22 Oct. 1935. Obituary, *I.L.T. & S.J.*, lxix (1935), 306-8, 313. See also *I.L.T. & S.J.*, lxi, 84, lxvi, 202, and lxix, 51; *Who's Who*; *D.N.B.*; *The Life of Lord Carson*, Vol. 1 by E. Marjoribanks (1932), Vols. 2 and 3 by Ian Colvin (1934 and 1936); Lord Lowry, 'The Irish lords of appeal in ordinary' [with which Sir John Lavery's portrait of Carson is reproduced] in D.S. Greer and N.M. Dawson (eds.), *Mysteries and Solutions in Irish Legal History* (Dublin, 2001), 193-216; and Louis McRedmond (ed.), *Modern Irish Lives*. Statue at Stormont, sculpted by Leonard Stanford Merrifield, unveiled in July 1933. Sketch (2003) by Thomas Ryan in King's Inns.

Sir John Ross [M 1879] on Carson [E 1877], his contemporary in the College Historical Society

'Edward Carson, now Lord Carson, was very able in debate, and his speeches were remarkable for their sincerity. While in College his mind never rose to the great intellectual height he was to reach in later years. We used to say of him at the Bar that he improved every year, and probably the highest type of mind is one that is always growing. The one thing about him that impressed us all was his transparent integrity and courage.

An eminent man, connected with Trinity College, once complained in my presence that, while representing Dublin University, Carson had agreed to the partition of Ireland. I said that if I ceased to believe in Carson, whom I had known from my youth, I must cease to believe in men; that I was convinced that neither power, nor money, nor any other inducement would make him swerve from what he thought just and right.'

From Sir John Ross, *The Years of my Pilgrimage* (London, 1924)

CARSON, WILLIAM HENRY WEBSTER (b. 2 Feb. 1882) young. s. of Robert Carson of Belmullet, Co. Mayo, and Eliza Jane Wood; B.A. (T.C.D.); M 1902. 1905/T/05 [3 items]. Called to English Bar, M.T., T 1922. S.C., 14 July 1924. Bencher of King's Inns, H 1935. Died unmarried 18 Jan. 1965. Obituary, *I.L.T. & S.J.*, xcvix (1965), 56.

CARSON, WILLIAM ROLAND (b. 18 June 1896) s. of Robert Hugh Carson, of 85 Tritonville Road, Sandymount, Dublin, and Annie Norewood; M 1920. 1923/H/06 [2 items].

CARTER, JASPER JAMES (b. 17 Aug. 1862) 3rd surv. s. of Hugh Carter (decd.) of Sherborne Street, Islington, London, and Susan Kelly; H 1897. 1900/H/06 [4 items].

CARTER, SAMUEL RICHARD (b. 1 Jan 1841) only s. of William Carter (decd.) of Monawee, Queen's County and of Letitia Brennan; B.A. (T.C.D.); H 1869; M.T. T 1870. 1872/H/7 [4 items].

CARTER, WILLIAM SEYMOUR JESSOP (b. 27 March 1908) young. s. of Thomas Henry Carter, of The Lodge, Mountrath, Queen's Co., and Mabel Elizabeth Jessop; B.A. (T.C.D.); M 1926. 1929/M/11 [2 items].

CARTON, JOSEPH JOHN (b. 12 May 1867) eld. s. of Richard Paul Carton [d. 24 Feb. 1907], one of Her Majesty's Counsel, of 35 Rutland Square, Dublin, and Mary Hoey; B.A., LL.B. (T.C.D.); M 1887. 1891/H/02 [7 items]. Succeeded James MacIvor as Librarian of King's Inns, serving from 11 Jan. 1901 to his death on 9 April 1935. Obituary, *I.L.T. & S.J.*, lxix (1935), 107. Mentioned in Maurice Healy, *The Old Munster Circuit*, 59; and in J.C. MacDermott, *An Enriching Life*, 142.

CARTY, FRANK (b. 3 April 1897) only s. of John Carty, of Clooncunny, Ballinacarrow, Ballymote, Co. Sligo, and Ellen Rice; M 1932. 1936/T/02 [3 items]. Fianna Fáil T.D. for Sligo and other constituencies, 1921-42. Died 10 Sept. 1942. Obituary, *I.L.T. & S.J.*, lxxvi (1942), 235, 265.

CARUANA, ROBERT JOSEPH (b. 31 May 1923) eld. s. of Joseph William Caruana, H.B.M's Consul, of Tripoli, Africa, and Josephine [?], of Paris; (Mod.) B.A. (T.C.D.); M 1948. 1952/H/04 [2 items]

CARUTH, ALEXANDER (b. 24 Aug. 1870) eld. s. of Alexander Caruth, solicitor, of Drumard, Ballymena, Co. Antrim, and Deborah Mary Cordukes; M 1893. 1896/T/06 [3 items].

CARVILL, JOHN HENRY (b. 1 July 1891) 2nd s. of Louis Edward Carvill (decd.), of Rathgar House, Dublin, and Minnie McKinley; M 1911. 1914/T/21 [2 items].

CASEY, CHARLES FRANCIS (b. 2 Jan. 1895) 2nd s. of Dr. Charles Casey, of 33 Upper Ormond Quay, Dublin, and Mary Teresa Conran; M 1920. 1923/M/07 [2 items]. Served with the 16th (Irish) Division in the Great War. S.C., 28 Oct. 1941. Attorney-General, 1950-1. Judge of the High Court, 15 June 1951. Died 6 Nov. 1952. Obituary, *I.L.T. & S.J.*, lxxxvi (1952), 287.

CASEY, HENRY EDWARD MACMAHON (b. 5 Sept. 1837) 2nd s. of Edward Macmahon Casey (decd.) of Drumboe, Co. Monaghan, and Catherine Heath; M 1880, M.T. T 1880. 1883/T/06 [7 items].

CASEY, JOHN CHARLES (b. 17 May 1932) 2nd s. of the Hon. Mr. Justice Charles Francis Casey (decd.), of 'Jerpoint', Elton Park, Sandycove, Co. Dublin, and Helen Hanlon; M 1950 1954/M/06 [2 items].

CASEY, PATRICK JOSEPH (b. 11 Jan. 1923) 2nd s. of Timothy Casey, of Hamilton Terrace, Glin, Co. Limerick, and Margaret Leahy (decd.); M 1943. 1946/T/13 [2 items].

CASEY, THOMAS JULIAN SMITH (b. 16 April 1845) eld. s. of Edmund Henry Casey of the Donaghies, Co. Dublin and Mary [?]; B.A. (T.C.D.); T 1865, L.I. E 1867. 1869/H/3 [4 items].

CASEY, WILLIAM FRANCIS (b. 2 May 1884) only s. of Patrick Joseph Casey of Adderly Street, Capetown, South Africa, and 2 Sunbury Gardens, Dublin, and Margaret Lennon; B.A. (T.C.D.); M 1906. 1909/T/01 [2 items]. Practised for a year: 'one year, one brief, one guinea' (I. McDonald, *History of The Times*, v (1984), 165). Author of two plays, 'The Suburban Groove' and 'The Man who Missed the Tide', produced at the Abbey Theatre in 1908. Joined the staff of *The Times* in 1914, and served as editor, 1948-52. LL.D. (Dubl., *h.c.*, 1949). Died 20 April 1957. See *D.N.B.* Mentioned in Maurice Healy, *The Old Munster Circuit*, 62.

CASSEDY, JAMES (b. 22 July 1877) 4th s. of Michael Cassedy (decd.), of Tigh Chluana, Berkeley Street, Dublin, and Nora Manning; B.A. (N.U.I.); M 1910. 1915/T/01 [2 items].

CASSIDY, AGNES BEATRICE (b. 7 April 1918) eld. daughter of John Price Cassidy, Barrister-at-Law, of 11 Whitehall Road, Terenure, Co. Dublin, and Elizabeth McDonagh; B.A., LL.B. (T.C.D.); M 1936. 1940/H/01 [2 items]. Reid Professor, T.C.D., 1 July 1950; aft. Lecturer in Law, T.C.D., 1 Oct. 1964; Examiner at King's Inns. Appt. District Justice, 1975. Died c. 2001.

CASSIDY, JOHN BERNARD (b. 13 May 1929) 2nd s. of Eugene Cassidy, licensed vintner, of 'Waterside House', Howth, Co. Dublin, and Kathleen Whittle; B.A. (N.U.I.); M 1947. 1950/M/05 [2 items]. S.C., 1 Oct. 1973. Appt. a Judge of the Circuit Court, 1987; killed in a road accident, Oct. 1995: see *Gazette of the Incorporated Law Society of Ireland*, November 1995, 321.

CASSIDY, JOHN PRICE (b. 24 Oct. 1885) eld. s. of John Armstrong Cassidy, of 36 Ormond Road, Rathmines, Dublin, and Mary McManus; M 1922 [incl. Student's memorial for M 1922; employed as civil servant in Land Registry]. 1925/T/04 [4 items]. Died 18 Nov. 1945. Obituary, *I.L.T. & S.J.*, lxxix (1945), 285-6.

CATHCART, ROBERT (b. 17 Oct. 1862) eld. s. of Robert Cathcart (decd.), merchant, of Drogheda, Co. Louth, and M.A. Hobson; M 1885. 1888/T/02 [4 items].

CAULFIELD, ANNE (b. 4 Nov. 1905) eld. d. of John P. Caulfield, of Hollymount, Lee Road, Cork, and Jane Cudmore; M 1927. 1930/M/09 [2 items].

CAWLEY, FRANCIS JOSEPH (b. 10 May 1890) young. s. of Thomas Cawley, of Temple Street, Sligo, and Bridget Igoe; M 1921. 1924/T/01 [2 items; missing]. Department of Industry and Commerce. Died 5 Nov. 1938. Obituary, *I.L.T. & S.J.*, lxxii (1938), 341.

CAWLEY, JAMES JOSEPH (b. 25 Feb. 1887) 4th s. of Thomas Cawley (decd.), of Temple Street, Sligo, and Bridget Igoe; M 1914. 1919/M/05 [2 items]. S.C., 12 April 1937. Died 28 April 1944. Obituary, *I.L.T. & S.J.*, lxxviii (1944), 123.

CHADWICK, ROBERT St. JAMES (b. 26 Feb. 1871) eld. s. of the Very Revd. Geo. A. Chadwick, DD., Dean of Armagh, and Emma Browning; B.A. (T.C.D.); M 1892. 1895/T/02 [6 items]. S.C., 25 June 1930. Editor of *The Irish Law Times and Solicitors' Journal*, 1930-31. Died 23 July 1947. Obituary, *I.L.T. & S.J.*, lxxxi (1947), 184.

CHAMBERS, JAMES (b. 19 April 1861) 4th s. of Joseph Chambers of Belfast, and Margaret Shilliday; M 1883. 1886/M/13 [5 items]. North-East Bar. K.C., 19 Feb. 1902. M.P. for Belfast South, 1901-17. Briefly Solicitor-General. Died in that office, 11 June 1917. Obituary, *I.L.T. & S.J.*, li (1917), 146-7, 152-4; *Who's Who*. Mentioned in Maurice Healy, *The Old Munster Circuit*, 248; and by V.T.H. Delany [q.v.], who, in his article 'The Bench and Bar in Ireland', named him as one of 'those who were at the forefront of their profession during the period'.

CHAMBERS, JOHN DESMOND (b. 17 Oct. 1899) 2nd s. of James Chambers, of Grove House, Foxrock, Co. Dublin, and Esther Wallis; M 1919. 1923/M/08 [2 items]. Recorder of Belfast, 1943-4. Died 2 April 1945. Obituary, *I.L.T. & S.J.*, lxxix (1945), 89-90.

CHARLETON, AENGUS (b. 23 March 1946) eld. s. of Joseph Charleton, accountant, of 54 Landscape Road, Churchtown, Co. Dublin, and Una Ó Dálaigh; B.C.L. (N.U.I.); M 1965. 1968/M/21 [1 item]. S.C., 3 Oct. 1983.

CHAYTOR, DAVID GRAINGER (b. 11 May 1868) 3rd s. of Charles Henry Chaytor (decd.), of Marino, Killiney, Dublin, and Mary Grainger; M 1886. 1890/T/03 [8 items]. K.C., 22 Jan. 1906. Author of *The Law and Practice relating to the Variation of Tithe-Rent Charges in Ireland* (Dublin and London, 1897). Died 14 July 1913. Obituary, *I.L.T. & S.J.*, xlvii (1913), 202.

CHEEKE, Major WILLIAM ALEXANDER, Royal Engineers (b. 31 March 1873) 2nd s. of George A. Cheeke, of Charlton Court, Cheltenham, Gloucestershire, and Selina Long; M 1915. 1919/T/03 [2 items].

CHERRY, RICHARD ROBERT (b. 19 March 1859) 2nd s. of Robert William Cherry, solicitor, of Waterford, and Susan Emily Briscoe; B.A. (T.C.D.); M 1878, M.T. H 1880; John Brooke Scholarship. 1881/M/01 [6 items]. Auditor of the College Historical Society, 1882-3. 1st holder of the Reid professorship in Trinity College, Dublin, 1888-

94. Q.C., 1896. Author, assisted by John Wakely, of *Irish Land Law and Land Purchase Acts 1881, 1885, 1887* (Dublin, 1888; 2nd edition (with Wakely and J.W. Brady Murray), Dublin 1893; 3rd edition (with Wakely and T. H. Maxwell), Dublin, 1903, with Supplements in 1906 and 1910). Author also of *Lectures on the growth of criminal law in ancient communities* (London and New York, 1890) and of *An outline of criminal law as regards offences against individuals* (Dublin, 1892). During the Boer War perceived by his colleagues at the Bar as pro-Nationalist and pro-Boer. In a *Memoir* written in 1924, his daughter Maud recalled: 'It is difficult, perhaps, to realise at the present day the strength of the Conservative tradition in the Dublin of twenty-five years ago. In those days the learned professions were almost entirely filled by men of Protestant and Unionist upbringing ... Some of his friends refused to speak to him, and often a group chatting at the Library fire would disperse at his approach': Maud H. Cherry, *A Short memoir of the Rt. Hon. Richard Robert Cherry, sometime Lord Chief Justice of Ireland* (Dublin, 1924), 15-6. Liberal M.P. for Liverpool (Exchange) 1906-9. Attorney-General for Ireland, 1905-9. Lord Justice of Appeal (in succession to FitzGibbon), 1909-14. Lord Chief Justice of Ireland (in succession to Peter O'Brien), 1914-16. Retired because of ill health, 22 Dec. 1916. Died 10 Feb. 1923. Obituary, *I.L.T. & S.J.*, lvii (1923), 46; *Who's Who*. Mentioned in Maurice Healy, *The Old Munster Circuit*, 105. See: Maud Cherry's *Memoir* (which has as its frontispiece a photograph of her father in 1906), Ball, *Judges*, 382; and Daire Hogan, 'R.R. Cherry, lord chief justice of Ireland, 1914-1916', in D.S. Greer and N.M. Dawson (eds.), *Mysteries and Solutions in Irish Legal History* (Dublin, 2001), 161-92; *Oxford DNB* (2004) [article by Daire Hogan].

CHERRY, RICHARD THEODORE (b. 17 June 1896) eld. s. of the Rt. Hon. Richard Robert Cherry, ex-Lord Chief Justice, of 92 Stephen's Green, Dublin, and Mary Wilhelmina Cooper; M 1919. 1921/H/01 [2 items]. Died 2 Feb. 1948. Obituary, *I.L.T. & S.J.*, lxxxii (1948), 34. Richard Cherry sang bass in the Dublin University Choral Society. Since 1949 that society has held in his memory an annual competition for vocal quartet. A 'Cherry Cup', presented by his sisters Wilna and Kitty, bears the inscription 'Tune thy music to thy heart, sing thy joy with thanks'.

CHOPRA, IQBALCHAND (b. 1 Dec. 1896) 2nd s. of Lala Gangaram Pleader (decd.), of Gujranwala, Punjab, India; M 1915. 1918/T/10 [2 items].

CHOWDHURY, KAHAN SINGH (b. 28 April 1889) young. s. of Sirdar Atma Singh Chowdhury, of Rawalpindi, Punjab, India, and Shirimati Chanan Devi; C.S. Assistant Commr. and Administrative officer (Colonial); M 1919. 1921/M/16 [2 items].

CHOWDHURY, RAJENDATAL (b. 7 May 1877) 1st s. of Chand[hebar] Chowdhury of Beltali, Dacca, India, and Bidyasundari Chowdhurani; M 1913. 1916/T/10 [2 items].

CHRISTIAN, JONATHAN (b. 13 Aug. 1861) 2nd s. of the Rt. Hon. Jonathan Christian, Privy Councillor [previously Lord Justice of H.M. Court of Appeal in Ireland], of 53 Merrion Square, Dublin, and Mary Thomas; M 1881, G.I. T 1884. 1886/H/05 [8 items].

CHRISTIE, DAVID WILSON (b. 29 June 1859) eld. s. of Robert Christie of Bracklamont, Ballymena, Co. Antrim, and Annie Wilson; B.A. (T.C.D.); M 1880, M.T. M 1882. 1884/T/02 [5 items].

CHRISTIE, MICHAEL (b. 31 March 1887) s. of Patrick Christie, of 3 Spence's Terrace, Cork Street, Dublin, and Rose Butler; B.A., LL.B; M 1915. 1920/T/02 [2 items]. Clerk of the Senate, Dublin.

CHRISTLE, COLMCILLE PASCHAL (b. 15 June 1932) 7th s. of James Christle (decd.), labourer, of 132 Carrow Road, Drimnagh, Co. Dublin, and Johanna O'Keeffe (decd.); M 1951. 1960/T/14 [2 items].

CHRISTLE, JOSEPH PATRICK (b. 4 Nov. 1927) 4th s. of James Christle (decd.), labourer, of 132 Carrow Road, Drimnagh, Co. Dublin, and Johanna O'Keeffe (decd.); M 1952. 1960/T/06 [2 items].

CHUTE, CHARLES GEORGE FALKINER (b. 16 July 1866) young. s. of the Revd. John Lindsay Chute (decd.), M.A., late Rector of Dingle, Co. Kerry, and Josephine Haines; M.A. (T.C.D.); M 1892. 1895/T/03 [8 items].

CLAMPETT, GEORGE JOSEPH TRAVIS (b. 26 Oct. 1885) eld. s. of George A. Clampett, of Waterford, Co. Waterford, and Frances Hatchett; M 1920. 1923/T/03 [2 items].

CLANCY, HERBERT EDGAR (b. 18 May 1903) 3rd s. of Aubrey Edgar Clancy, of 1 Gracepark Gardens, Drumcondra, Dublin, and Kathleen Harrington; M 1921. 1924/M/04x [2 items]. Mentioned in Patrick MacKenzie, *Lawful Occasions*, 61.

CLANCY, JOHN JOSEPH, M.P. (b. 15 July 1847) eld. s. of William Clancy (decd.), gentleman, of Carragh, Co. Galway, and Mary Burke; M.A. (R.U.I.); E 1884, M.T. E 1884. 1887/E/07 [7 items]. K.C., 30 June 1906. M.P. for Dublin North, 1885-1918. Representative of the Irish Parl. Party at the Irish Convention, 1917. Died 25 Nov. 1928. Obituary, *I.L.T. & S.J.*, lxii (1928), 288-9; *Who's Who*. Author of *A Year of Unionist Coercion* (London, 1888) and *The Irish Question. The Voice of Ireland* (London, 1896).

CLANCY, NOEL AUBREY (b. 3 March 1933) only s. of Aubrey Clancy (decd.), chief rate collector, Dublin Corporation, of 86 Marlborough Road, Ballsbridge, Dublin, and Brigid Hegarty; M 1962. 1966/T/04 [1 item]. S.C., 5 Oct. 1981. Died 19 Oct. 2004.

CLARKE, EDWARD STANLEY (b. 1 Jan. 1879) only s. of George Henry Clarke of Lisburn, Co. Antrim, and Kate [Dunsterville]; M 1901; M.T. M 1899. 1904/T/03 [3 items].

CLARKE, GERARD ANTHONY (b. 15 January 1919) 2nd s. of James Vincent Clarke, bank official, of 21 Sandford Road, Dublin, and Mary Mac Hugh; B.A. (N.U.I.); M 1938. 1941/M/06 [2 items]. S.C., 4 March 1960. Judge of the Circuit Court.

CLARKE, MARSHAL NEVILLE (b. 10 Jan. 1897) eld. s. of Charles Neville Clarke (decd.), J.P., D.L., of Graiguenoe Park, Thurles, Co. Tipperary, and Bertha Cross (decd.); H 1949; L.I. M 1921, Barrister-at-Law of Lincoln's Inn, 1924. 1949/T/09 [9 items]. Name does not appear on the Supreme Court Roll. *Burke's Irish Family Records* (1976), 240.

CLARKE, MATTHEW JOHN (b. 7 March 1863) eld. s. of James Clarke, solicitor, of Belfast, Co. Antrim, and Mary McQuillan; T 1883. 1886/T/05 [9 items].

CLEARY, EDWARD A. (b. 21 April 1898) 2nd s. of Peter Cleary (decd.), of 12 Annesley Park, Rathmines, Dublin, and Margaret Byrne; M 1924. Awarded 2nd Class Certificate of Honour. 1925/M/06 [2 items].

CLEMENTS, ROBERT NATHANIEL (b. 7 July 1910) 3rd s. of Henry John Beresford Clements, of Killadoon, Celbridge, Co. Kildare, and Eleonore Wickham; M 1933. Includes letter from Clements explaining his absence at November call. 1939/H/01 [3 items]. *Burke's Irish Family Records* (1976), 246.

CLERY, ARTHUR EDWARD (b. 25 Oct. 1879) only s. of Arthur Patrick Clery, K.C., of 58 Albert Street, London, and Kathleen Moylan (decd.); B.A., LL.B. (R.U.I.); M 1900. 1902/M/03 [3 items]. Professor of Law at U.C.D. Judge of the Dáil's Supreme Court, 1920-2. Author, *inter alia*, of *The Idea of a Nation* (essays), and of contributions to *Studies*. A co-author of commentaries on the Town Tenants (Ireland) Act, 1906; and the Public Health (Amendment) Act, 1907. Contributed the chapter on Public Health to Hennessy's *Justice of the Peace*. Died 20 Nov. 1932. Obituary, *I.L.T. & S.J.*, lxvi (1932), 289-90, 308; *Who's Who*. Mentioned in James Meenan (ed.), *Centenary History of Lit. and Hist. Soc. of U.C.D*; and in C.S. Andrews, *Man of No Property* (Dublin, 1982), 43-5. Portrait by Leo Whelan in U.C.D. [reproduced (No. 2, between pp 148-9), in Mary Kotsonouris, *The Winding-up of the Dáil Courts, 1922-1925: an obvious duty* (Dublin, 2004), in which work there is also (p. 248) a biographical note].

CLERY, GERALD FRANCIS HOGAN (b. 24 Dec. 1930) 2nd s. of Anthony Burton Clery, President R.C.S.I., of 59 Fitzwilliam Square, Dublin, and Mary Gabrielle Hogan, F.R.C.S.I; B.A., LL.B.(N.U.I.); M 1952. 1956/M/08 [2 items]. Department of Foreign Affairs (as Gearóid Ó Cléirigh).

COBBE, WILLIAM ARTHUR THOMPSON (b. 2 April 1892) 2nd s. of Thomas Cobbe, of Arnagharvey, Elton Park, Sandycove, Dublin, and Alice Thompson; M 1917. 1927/M/11 [2 items]. Registrar in Bankruptcy.

COFFEY, ALFRED (b. 3 June 1872) eld. s. of Thomas P. Coffey (decd.), solicitor, of 136 Tritonville Road, Dublin, and Marion Madden; T 1904. 1905/E/03 [2 items].

COFFEY, DONOUGH J. (b. 13 Feb. 1909) young. s. of Denis J. Coffey, M.A., MB, LL.D., President, U.C.D., Chevalier de la Légion d'Honneur, of 41 Fitzwilliam Square, Dublin, and Maude Quin; M.A., LL.B. (N.U.I.); M 1931; [includes letter] 1934/T/04 [3 items]. Called to English Bar, T 1938. Author of *Digest of Cases decided by the Courts in Ireland under the Increase of Rent and Mortgage Interest (Restrictions) Acts, 1915-30, to end Hilary Term 1938* (Dublin, 1938).

COFFEY, GEORGE (b. 2 July 1857) 3rd s. of James Charles Coffey (decd.), Q.C., County Court Judge, of 72 Lower Baggot Street, Dublin, and Anna Maria Wilkinson; B.A., BE (T.C.D.); E 1880, G.I. E 1882. 1883/T/04 [7 items]. President of the University Philosophical Society, T.C.D., 1888-9. Superintendent of the Royal Irish Academy's collection of Irish Antiquities at the National Museum, 1890-1914. Member of the Royal Irish Academy, and Officer of the Académie Française. Author, *inter alia*, of *Guide to the Christian Antiquities in the National Museum, Newgrange, The Bronze Age in Ireland.* Died 29 Aug. 1916. *Burke's Irish Family Records* (1976), 254. Described by G.F. Mitchell, in Tarlach Ó Raifeartaigh (ed.), *The Royal Irish Academy: a bicentennial history 1785-1985* (Dublin, 1985), p. 147, as 'one of the makers of modern European archaeology'. Photograph in ibid., p. 148. Portrait plaque by Oliver Sheppard in the central court of the National Museum.

COFFEY, HUGH DIARMID JAMES (b. 24 Dec. 1888) only s. of George Coffey of 5 Harcourt Terrace, Dublin, and Jane L'Estrange; Sen. Mod. B.A. (T.C.D.); M 1909. 1912/M/05 [2 items]. Better known as Dermot Coffey. Member of the secretariat of the Irish Convention, 1917. Assistant Clerk of the Senate of the Irish Free State, 1923-35; and Assistant Keeper on staff of the Public Record Office of Ireland, 1935-56. Author of *O'Neill and Ormond* (1914); *The Cooperative Movement in Jugoslavia Rumania and North Italy during and after the World War* (1922); *D.N.B.* entry for Lord Glenavy; and *Douglas Hyde* (Dublin, 1938). Died 7 July 1964. *Burke's Irish Family Records* (1976), 254.

COFFEY, PATRICK JOSEPH (b. 12 March 1923) 3rd s. of James Coffey (decd.), farmer, of Borrisoleigh, Thurles, Co. Tipperary, and Mary Small; M 1956. 1959/T/02 [2 items].

COFFEY, TIMOTHY JOSEPH (b. 2 Nov. 1913) eld. s. of Patrick Coffey, hardware merchant, of 9 Mount Pleasant, College Road, Cork, and Hanorah Bailey; M.D., B.Ch., B.A.O. (N.U.I.), L.M; M 1961. 1966/H/03 [1 item].

COGAN, OWEN (b. 20 Aug 1845) eld. s. of Patrick Owen Cogan (decd.) of North Great Georges Street, Dublin, barrister, and Helena Waldron; B.A. (T.C.D.); M 1863, M.T. E 1866. 1869/H/1 [2 items].

COGHLAN, DANIEL (b. 11 Feb. 1884) 2nd s. of Daniel Coghlan (decd.), of Skibbereen, Co. Cork, and Ellen Collins; M 1926; [Colonel, O.B.E.] 1929/M/15 [2 items].

COGHLAN, JOHN RICHARD CHARLES (b. 27 May 1905) only s. of Charles M. Coghlan, of 25 Iona Road, Glasnevin, Dublin, and Mary Haveron; Mod., B.A., LL.B. (T.C.D.); M 1924. 1927/M/18 [2 items]. District Justice (Waterford). Author of *The Law of Rent Restriction in Eire* (1944; 2nd edition, 1950; 3rd edition, *The Law of Rent Restriction in the Republic of Ireland* (1979).

COGHLAN, JOSEPH PATRICK (b. 18 Jan. 1885) young. s. of David Coghlan (decd.), of Cussane House, Carrick-on-Suir, Co. Tipperary, and Anastasia O'Shee; M 1912. 1915/T/10 [3 items].

COLCLOUGH, JOHN GEORGE (b. 8 Jan. 1869) eld. s. of John Richard Colclough, of Bic, Rimouski, Canada, and Philomena Lavoir; B.A. (Laval Univ. Quebec); E 1890. 1893/E/02 [8 items]. Called to English Bar, M 1905. Middle Temple.

COLE, JOHN COPELAND (b. 1 Jan. 1912) only s. of John James Cole, of Nahillah Park, Cloverhill, Co. Cavan, and Jeanie M.E. James; M 1936. 1936/T/03 [2 items]. District Justice. Author of commentary on the Rent Restrictions Acts. Mentioned in Patrick MacKenzie, *Lawful Occasions*, 61.

COLE, JOHN SYDNEY RICHARD (b. 24 Jan. 1907) only s. of the Revd. Richard Lee Cole, M.A., B.D., of 71 Brighton Road, Rathgar, Dublin, and Selina Kelly (decd.); Sch. Mod., B.A. (T.C.D.); M 1928. Obtained 3rd Victoria Prize. 1935/T/01 [2 items]. Colonial Office lecturer in Classics at the Royal College in Mauritius, 1930; superintendent of education at King's College, Nigeria, 1937. Crown Counsel in the colonial service. Attorney-General of Nigeria, the Bahamas, Somaliland and (1957) Tanganyika. Reid Professor, T.C.D., 1 Oct. 1965. Senior Lecturer in Law, T.C.D., 1 Oct. 1972. Died 15 Aug. 1989. *Who's Who.* Obituary (by R.F.V. Heuston) in *Trinity Trust News*, vol. 14 no. 1 (1989), p. 9. Author of *Irish Cases on Evidence* (Dublin,

1972; 2nd edition, 1982) and *Irish Cases on Criminal Law* (Dublin, 1975). Mentioned (with photograph) in J.W. Henderson, *Methodist College Belfast 1868-1938* (2 vols.; Belfast, 1939), 301.

COLEMAN, JAMES GERARD (b. 17 Oct. 1910) 2nd s. of Patrick Charles Coleman, of Tyone, Nenagh, Co. Tipperary, and Josephine Barron; M 1947. 1951/M/06 [2 items]. Secretary of the Pharmaceutical Society of Ireland.

COLEMAN, JOHN VINCENT (b. 26 March 1919) only s. of James P. Coleman (decd.), of 13 North Mall, Cork, and Margaret M. Cronin; M 1937. 1941/M/08 [2 items]. S.C., 7 Oct. 1974. Author of *An Employer's Duties at Common Law in Ireland* (Dublin, 1961).

COLL, EDMOND CHRISTOPHER (b. 24 Dec. 1872) eld. s. of Patrick Coll, C.B., Chief Crown Solicitor for Ireland, of 54 Fitzwilliam Square, Dublin, and Clara Rosetta D'Arcy; B.A. (T.C.D.); E 1891. 1895/H/04 [8 items]. Called to English Bar, E 1902. Counsel to Inland Revenue and Board of Trade.

COLLES, ABRAHAM RICHARD (b. 4 Feb. 1863) only s. of William Colles, M.D., of 21 Stephen's Green, Dublin, and Penelope Waddy; B.A., LL.B. (T.C.D.); M 1883. 1887/M/04 [6 items].

COLLES, JOHN DAWSON MAYNE (b. 9 Nov. 1857) 2nd s. of Henry J.C. Colles (decd.), Barrister-at-Law, of 14 Ely Place, Dublin, and Elizabeth Mayne; B.A. (T.C.D.); H 1878, I.T. H 1879. 1880/M/14 [6 items]. K.C., 6 March 1915. Registrar in Lunacy, and author of *The Lunacy Act and Orders, with Forms, and the County Court Act and Rules* [2nd edition] *containing a synopsis of the law as to establishments for the insane* (Dublin and London, 1895). Author also of: *A Daughter of Rome. A romance of the Fatherland. From the German of L. Pichler* (1893) and *The Journal of John Mayne* [called H 1816] *during a tour on the Continent upon its reopening after the fall of Napoleon, 1814. Edited by his grandson John Mayne Colles. With numerous illustrations* (London, 1909).

COLLINS, CHARLES MACCARTHY (b. 30 Dec. 1850) 3rd s. of Joseph Tenison Collins, bank manager, of Ballinasloe, Co. Galway, and Sarah Louisa MacCarthy; H 1875, M.T. E 1875. 1879/M/02 [4 items].

COLLINS, EAMONN FLANNERY (b. 9 Oct. 1918) 3rd s. of Edmund Collins, of Johnstown House, Cabinteely, Co. Dublin, and Margaret Creedon; B. Comm. (N.U.I.); M 1942. 1945/T/03 [2 items]. Registrar.

COLLINS, EDWARD ALPHONSUS (b. 15 Nov. 1875) eld. s. of George Collins, solicitor, of 30 North Frederick Street, Dublin, and Jane Fagan; B.A. (R.U.I.); M 1893. 1897/M/03 [4 items]. K.C., 16 June 1921. Divisional Magistrate for the Dublin Metropolitan District, and later a District Justice. Died 17 April. 1930. Obituary, *I.L.T. & S.J.*, lxiv (1930), 101.

COLLINS, EDWARD TENISON (b. 8 Jan. 1845) eld. s. of Joseph Tenison Collins of Ballinasloe, Co. Galway, and Mary Reardon; M 1889. 1892/M/06 [6 items]. Died 1923. Obituary, *I.L.T. & S.J.*, lvii (25 Aug. 1923), 212.

COLLINS, JOHN JOSEPH MARY (b. 22 May 1944) eld. s. of Patrick Collins, company director, of Orlock, Killiney Avenue, Killiney, Co. Dublin, and Mary O'Brien; M 1961. 1966/M/19 [1 item].

COLLINS, SEÁN (b. 10 July 1918) 3rd s. of Seán Collins, Chief Inspector, Irish Land Commission, of Inchidoney, Booterstown Ave, Blackrock, Co. Dublin, and Catherine Hurley; M 1936. 1940/T/02 [2 items]. Fine Gael T.D. 1948-57 and 1961-9. Died 1975. Obituary, *I.L.T. & S.J.*, cix (10 May 1975), 122.

COLLUM, ARTHUR PERCIVAL TOD (b. 26 Feb. 1866) eld. s. of Captain William Collum, J.P., D.L., of Bellevue, Co. Fermanagh, and Mary Jane Nixon; H 1889. 1892/T/03 [8 items].

COLLUM, RUPERT FRANCIS (b. 23 Sept 1849) young. s. of John Collum, solicitor, of Bellevue, Co. Fermanagh, and Catherine Jane Deering; B.A. (T.C.D.); E 1869; L.I. M 1870. 1872/T/7 [2 items].

COLQUHOUN, DAVID WILLIAM SPROULE (b. 25 June 1873) 2nd s. of David Colquhoun, County Court Judge and Chairman of Quarter Sessions, Co. Down, of 66 Leeson Street, Dublin, and Mary Porter Du Bedat (decd.); B.A. (T.C.D.); M 1901. 1904/M/11

[2 items]. Office of the Supreme Court. Died 18 Nov. 1937. Obituary, *I.L.T. & S.J.*, lxxi (1937), 334.

COLTHURST, HERBERT BALDWIN (b. 20 March 1845) eld. s. of James Colthurst, of Underwood, Co. Cork, and Eliza Carson; M.A. (T.C.D.); H 1869, M.T. H 1870. 1875/T/02 [2 items].

COMBER, THOMAS (b. 21 May 1920) eld. s. of Eamon Comber (decd.), civil servant, of 18 Iona Villas, Glasnevin, Co. Dublin, and Katherine Finn; M 1951. 1955/M/05 [2 items].

COMYN, EDWARD FREDERICK (b. 13 Sept. 1929) only s. of Denis F. Comyn, of Gort-na-Locha, Strand Road, Merrion, Co. Dublin, and Teresa Mary Conlan; M 1948. 1952/M/08 [2 items]. S.C., 27 Feb. 1975. Listed (with photograph) in the 1999 edition of Maureen Cairnduff, *Who's Who in Ireland*.

COMYN, JAMES GERARD PETER (b. 8 March 1921) only s. of James Comyn, Senior Counsel, of 15 Waterloo Road, Dublin, and Mary Moloney; M 1942; I.T. M 1939. 1945/M/11 [3 items]. President of the Oxford Union 1940 (when he defeated Roy Jenkins by 4 votes). Called to the English Bar, I.T., Nov. 1942. Irish Call delayed until T 1947. Subsequently practised a little in Ireland. Q.C. in England, 1961; but twice refused silk by the Irish Government. Chairman of the Bar Council in England, 1973-4. Judge of the High Court in England, 1977-85; and knighted. Co. Meath home destroyed by the I.R.A., 1981. In retirement took an interest in Irish legal publishing (member of the editorial board of the *Irish Law Reports Monthly*). Died 5 Jan. 1997. Obituary, *The Times*, 9 Jan. 1997. Appreciation [by Charles Lysaght] in the *Irish Law Times*, new series, xv (1997), 46-7. Joint author, with Robert Johnson, of *Wills and Intestacies* (Oxford, 1970) and *Contract* (Chichester, 1975). Author, *inter alia*, of *Their Friends at Court* (Chichester, 1973), a memoir of his father and uncle (see below); *Irish at Law: A selection of famous and unusual cases* (London, 1981); *Lost Causes* (London, 1982); and of four volumes of memoirs: *Summing it Up: Memoirs of an Irishman at the English Bar* (Dublin, 1991); *Watching Brief: Further Memoirs of an Irishman at Law in England* (Dublin, 1993); *Leave to Appeal: Further Legal Memoirs* (Dublin, 1994); and *If your Lordship Pleases: Legal Recollections* (Dublin, 1996). See Louis McRedmond (ed.), *Modern Irish Lives*.

COMYN, JAMES JOSEPH (b. 25 Dec. 1880) young. s. of James Comyn, of Kilshanny, Co. Cork, and Ellen Quin; B.A.; E 1904. 1907/H/04 [2 items]. S.C., 21 Dec. 1938. Died 4 June 1953. Obituary, *I.L.T. & S.J.*, lxxxvii (1953), 173. See his son's memoir *Their Friends at Court* (Chichester, 1973).

COMYN, MICHAEL (b. 3 June 1871) eld. s. of James Comyn of Kilshanny, Co. Clare, and Ellen Quinn; H 1896. 1898/M/05 [3 items]. K.C., 27 June 1914. Senator of the Irish Free State, 1928-36. Judge of the Circuit Court (Eastern Circuit). Interest in geology. Died 6 Oct. 1952. *Who's Who*. See his nephew's memoir, *Their Friends at Court* (Chichester, 1973). Mentioned in Maurice Healy, *The Old Munster Circuit*, 114-5; by Garrett Gill (q.v.); and in Patrick MacKenzie, *Lawful Occasions*, 6-9, 25-7, 41-5, 47.

CONAN, ALAISTAIR STEWART (b. 8 Jan. 1946) eld. s. of John Stewart Conan, schoolmaster, of Graigueconna, Old Conna, Bray, Co. Wicklow, and Maureen Murphy; M 1963. 1968/T/20 [1 item].

CONCANNON, JAMES PATRICK MCDONNELL (b. 30 June 1916) 4th s. of John Concannon, of St. Louis, Missouri, USA, and Glenamaddy, Co. Galway, and Sarah McDonnell; M 1934. 1939/H/02 [2 items].

CONDON, COLUMBA (b. 16 July 1921) 3rd s. of Thomas Condon, of Cloonand House, Ashbourne, Co. Meath, and Margaret Maguire; B.A. (N.U.I.); M 1941. 1944/M/05 [2 items]. Known as 'Colm' Condon. S.C., 7 Dec. 1959. Attorney-General, 1965-73. Listed in the 1984 and 1991 editions of Maureen Cairnduff, *Who's Who in Ireland*.

CONDON, DENIS FITZGERALD (b. 8 Dec. 1870) 4th s. of James Condon (decd.) of Corrogorm, Mitchelstown, Co. Cork, and Ellen Fitzgerald; M 1903. 1906/T/08 [3 items].

CONDON, JAMES EDMUND SMITH (b. 28 Oct. 1852) 2nd s. of Michael Smith Condon, gentleman, of Palmerston Place, Dublin, and Catherine Anderson-Crawford; B.A. (R.U.I.); E 1885. 1888/H/04 [7 items]. LL.D. Sometime (briefly) City Sub-Sheriff.

President of the Court of Referees. Died 20 Jan. 1919. Obituary, *I.L.T. & S.J.*, liii (1919), 23. Mentioned in Maurice Healy, *The Old Munster Circuit*, 250.

CONDON, JOHN PATRICK (b. 10 Nov. 1863) 3rd s. of Michael Smith Condon of 12 Middle Mountjoy Street, Dublin, gentleman, and Catherine Jane Anderson Crawford; M 1891. 1897/M/05 [10 items]. Died 26 Jan. 1936. Obituary, *I.L.T. & S.J.*, lxx (1936), 34.

CONDY, JOHN DEVENISH (b. 1 Feb. 1903) only s. of John Condy, of Clonsilla, Antrim Road, Belfast, and Mary Bradley; M 1923. 1925/M/16 [2 items].

CONLAN, PETER (b. 30 September 1913) 2nd s. of Thomas Conlan (decd.), of Belfast, and Mary Conlan, widow of Francis Connery, *née* McGowan; M 1935. 1941/M/11 [2 items]. First Officer on S.S. *Irish Ash*. Drowned at sea 16 Jan. 1947. Obituary, *I.L.T. & S.J.*, lxxxi (1947), 23.

CONLAN, WILLIAM (b. 18 Feb. 1863) only s. of William Joseph Conlan (decd.), of Ellerslie, Lancashire, and Anastasia Bullen; B.A. (T.C.D.); E 1882, G.I. M 1883. 1885/H/07 [6 items]. Resident in Brisbane, Queensland.

CONNER, HENRY DANIEL (b. 3 Oct. 1859) only s. of Daniel Conner, J.P., of Manch, Co. Cork, and Patience Longfield; B.A. (T.C.D.); M 1879, M.T. M 1881. 1882/M/06 [6 items]. Q.C., 22 April 1899. Bencher, 1910. The first of the eight original judges of the Circuit Court, appointed in June 1924 for Dublin (sitting in Green Street to replace O'Shaughnessy), then (in August 1924) for Cork. Died 23 July 1925. Obituary, *I.L.T. & S.J.*, lix (1925), 184; *Who's Who; Burke's Irish Family Records* (1976), 266. Joint editor for Ireland of the *English and Empire Digest*. Author of *The Fishery Laws of Ireland* (1892; 2nd ed. 1907).

CONNER, HENRY LONGFIELD (b. 7 Nov. 1887) 2nd s. of Henry Daniel Conner, of Manch, Co. Cork, and Anne Purcell; M 1911. 1914/M/04 [2 items]. Served in the Royal Flying Corps and R.A.F. in the 1st World War. Associated with the Dáil courts: see Daire Hogan, *The Legal Profession in Ireland*, 152. Legal Officer, Irish Free State Army, 1922-5. Appt. District Justice, 1929. Father of Patience, wife of Seán Mac.D. Fawsitt, Judge of the Circuit Court [q.v.]. Died 20 Oct. 1972. *Burke's Irish Family Records* (1976), 267.

CONNIFFE, PATRICK (b. 25 Sept. 1900) 5th s. of Patrick Conniffe, of Mt. Talbot, Co. Roscommon, and Mary Smyth; M 1926. 1929/M/13 [2 items].

CONNOLLY, CYRIL (b. 12 June 1883) eld. s. of Patrick Shelton Connolly, solicitor, of 86 O'Connell Street, Limerick, and Ada Julian; B.A. (T.C.D.); M 1903. 1907/T/02 [3 items].

CONNOLLY, EDWARD (b. 13 May 1856) 4th s. of John Connolly (decd.), of Kilmore, Co. Dublin, and Elizabeth O'Brien; M 1879, I.T. T 1879. 1883/H/04* [5 items]. Land Commission (retired 1921). Died 1933. Obituary, *I.L.T. & S.J.*, lxvii (17 June 1933), 167, 214.

CONNOLLY, JAMES MATTHEW (b. 9 Feb. 1923) 2nd s. of Matthew Connolly, M.A., LL.B., O.B.E., of Highgate, Middlesex, England, and Margaret Gogarty; M.A., LL.B; M 1943. 1950/M/06 [2 items].

CONNOLLY, MARTIN JOSEPH (n.d.) 5th s. of Edward Connolly, of Roundstone, Co. Galway, and Ellen King; T 1918. 1918/M/05 [1 item]. S.C., 12 April 1935. Appt. a permanent judge of the Circuit Court, and sworn in on 28 July 1947. Mentioned in Patrick MacKenzie, *Lawful Occasions*, 87.

CONNOLLY, PATRICK JOSEPH (b. 25 May 1927) eld. s. of Patrick Joseph Connolly, of Oldtown, Co. Dublin, and Ellen O'Hara; M 1946 1949/M/18 [2 items]. S.C., 4 Oct. 1971. Attorney-General, March-August 1982. See Dublin newspapers of August 1982. Listed in the 1984 and 1991 editions of Maureen Cairnduff, *Who's Who in Ireland*.

CONNOR, ARTHUR ERNEST (b. 27 July 1867) 2nd s. of John J. Connor (decd.), Collector of Inland Revenue and Receiver of Crown and Quit Rents for Cork, of Monkstown, Dublin, and Maria J. O'Neil; B.A. (R.U.I.), M 1894. 1897/M/13 [4 items].

CONOLLY, THOMAS JAMES (b. 4 Jan. 1902) 2nd s. of Thomas Conolly, of 'Fernville', Glasnevin, Dublin, and Teresa McQuaid; M.A. (N.U.I.); M 1923. 1927/M/03 [2 items]. S.C., 3 July 1946. Bencher. Died 21 Sept. 1992. Exercised immense influence as an advocate. Appreciation [by Donal Barrington] in the *Irish Law Times*, new series, x (1992), 294. See Louis McRedmond (ed.), *Modern Irish Lives*.

CONROY, JAMES GERVE (b. 20 April 1839) [Carlow College] 2nd s. of Luke Malachi Conroy (decd.) of Clonkea [Aughrim], Co. Roscommon, and Sarah Garvey; B.A. (London University); M 1869; M.T. T 1866. 1872/T/8 [4 items]. District Judge, Newfoundland.

CONROY, JOHN CHARLES (b. 14 Jan. 1906) 3rd s. of Patrick D. Conroy, of Garafin, Co. Galway, and Jane Joyce; M 1926. 1930/M/02 [2 items]. S.C., 21 Dec. 1948. Judge (Dublin Circuit) and (1973) President of the Circuit Court.

CONROY, PATRICK DOMINIC (b. 11 July 1934) eld. s. of John Charles Conroy, Circuit Court judge, of 11 Mount Eden Road, Donnybrook, Dublin, and Mary Frances Alison; B.A. (Hons); M 1955. Awarded Brooke Scholarship. 1958/M/01 [2 items]. Parliamentary draftsman. Died c. 1990.

CONTEH, ANSUMANA PHILIP (b. 16 Aug. 1928) 2nd s. of the Hon. Paramount Chief Alhadil Alimani S. Conteh, of Freetown, Sierra Leone, and of Doctor Yomho Kanu; M 1951. 1955/H/03 [2 items].

CONVERY, DENIS BRENDAN (b. 21 July 1939) eld. s. of Francis Joseph Convery (decd.), managing director, of 35 Richmond Park, Belfast, and Agnes Dowling; M 1962. 1966/T/07 [1 item]. Died 1990s.

CONVERY, JOHN GERARD PLUNKET (b. 24 Dec. 1910) 2nd s. of Francis Convery, of Bellaghy, Maghera, Co. Derry, and Mary MacGowan; B.A. (N.U.I.); M 1930 [Dublin address: 80 Merrion Road,] 1934/M/10 [2 items].

CONWAY, JOHN EDWARD (b. 19 Oct. 1880) 4th s. of John Conway, of Cootehall, Boyle, Co. Roscommon, and Catherine Farry; B.A., LL.D. (N.U.I.); M 1923. 1925/M/21 [2 items]. Teacher of mathematics in Wesley College, Dublin, 1920-57.

CONWAY, JOSEPH AUGUSTINE MICHAEL (b. 28 Sept. 1924) only s. of John Alphonsus Conway (decd.), of Howth View, Blackrock, Co. Dublin, and Brigid Tynan; M 1944. 1948/T/09 [2 items].

COOGAN, EDWARD JAMES (b. 30 November 1896) only s. of Timothy Coogan, of Castlecomer, Co. Kilkenny, and Bridget Joyce; B. Comm; B.A., LL.B. (N.U.I.); M 1934. 1941/M/07 [2 items]. Assistant Commissioner, Garda Síochána. T.D. for Kilkenny, 1944-8. Died 22 Jan. 1948. Obituary, *I.L.T. & S.J.*, lxxxii (1948), 27.

COOKE, FREDERICK GEORGE (b. 28 Oct. 1915) 4th s. of Charles Alexander Cooke, solicitor, of Corrib House, Galway, and Sarah Ann Barnett; B.A. (T.C.D.); M 1941. 1944/M/11 [2 items].

COOKE, JOHN (b. 24 Oct. 1854) 3rd s. of Joseph Cooke of Boom Hall, Londonderry, and Francis Walker; LL.B. (T.C.D.); H 1878, M.T. T 1877. 1878/M/07 [6 items]. K.C. 1907. Appt. County Court Judge for Donegal, 7 Nov. 1903. Died 12 Dec. 1930. Obituary, *I.L.T. & S.J.*, lxiv (1930), 306. *Burke's Irish Family Records* (1976), 271.

COOKE, JOHN DONAL (b. 7 May 1944) eld. s. of Richard Cooke, Senior Counsel, of 9 Whitebeam Avenue, Clonskeagh, Dublin, and Kathleen O'Reilly; B.C.L. (N.U.I.); M 1963. 1966/M/03 [1 item]. S.C., 6 Oct. 1980. Judge of the Court of First Instance of the European Union, 1995-.

COOKE, RICHARD NOEL (b. 22 Aug. 1912) eld. s. of Michael Cooke, of 1 St. Mobhi Drive, Glasnevin, Dublin, and Eleanor Croly; M 1935. 1938/M/03 [2 items]. S.C., 7 Dec. 1959. Contributor to James Meenan (ed.), *Centenary History of Lit. and Hist. Soc. of U.C.D.*

COONEY, GARRETT FRANCIS (b. 6 Jan. 1935) 3rd s. of Dr. Mark Cooney, of Lisdarn, Cavan, Co. Cavan, and Margaret Blake (decd.); B.A. (N.U.I.); M 1954. 1960/M/05 [2 items]. S.C., 3 Oct. 1977.

COOPER, JOSEPH JAMES (b. 19 June 1880) 4th s. of Patrick Cooper, of Whitehead, Belfast, Co. Antrim, and Agnes Davis; M 1923. Awarded 2nd Class Certificate of Honour. 1925/M/08 [2 items]. Chief superintendent of the Belfast Post Office. Died 19 June 1940. Obituary, *I.L.T. & S.J.*, lxxiv (1940), 167.

COOPER, MARK BLOXHAM (b. 16 Sept. 1855) 2nd s. of Austin Damer Cooper of 5 Palmerston Road, Dublin, and Caroline Ann Bloxham; T 1882, M.T. T 1882. 1885/H/01 [6 items]. K.C., 14 May 1919. Police magistrate in Dublin. Senior District Justice in Dublin. Died 1 Nov. 1929. Obituary, *I.L.T. & S.J.*, lxiii (1929), 268.

COOPER, THOMAS KENNAN (b. 28 Feb. 1926) 3rd s. of John Kennan, solicitor, of Birchgrove, Wexford, and Rachel Margaret White; B.A. (Mod.), LL.B. (T.C.D.); M 1946. 1949/M/09 [2 items].

COPELAND, ISAAC (b. 15 Oct. 1889) 3rd s. of Isaac Copeland, of Glenanne, Armagh, Co. Armagh, and Marianne Johnston; M 1917. Awarded Society's Prize. 1920/H/02 [2 items]. K.C. (N.I.), H 1945. Recorder of Londonderry.

COPINGER, RICHARD HENRY (b. 17 Dec. 1847) 2nd s. of William Richard Copinger, solicitor, of Webbville, Co. Cork, and Harriet Neal; M 1870, M.T. H 1874. 1876/H/05 [11 items].

COPINGER, WILLIAM FREDERICK (b. 2 Oct. 1876) only s. of Richard Henry Copinger (decd.) of 64 Northumberland Road, Dublin, and Harriette Elizabeth Isabella Mangan; M.A., LL.B. (T.C.D.); M 1904. 1907/T/01 [2 items]. Resided in retirement in Florence. Died 23 May 1959.

CORBET, JOHN DERMOT MULHALL (b. 2 Sept. 1902) 2nd s. of Thomas Mulhall Corbet, L.R.C.P.S.I. (decd.), of 92 Mount Clarence, Dún Laoghaire, Co. Dublin, and Josephine McDermott; M 1925. 1929/M/08 [2 items]. Died 1969.

CORBETT, ARTHUR EDWARD (b. 16 Feb. 1881) 4th s. of Martin Corbett of Bunratty House, Co. Clare, and Susan Mary Burke; B.A. (Cambridge); M 1905. 1908/T/07 [3 items].

CORBOY, DENIS (b. 1 Sept. 1934) 2nd s. of Thomas J. Corboy, company director, of Fort Prospect, Co. Limerick, and Nora Trant; B.A.; M 1953. 1958/M/09 [2 items]. European Commission.

CORCORAN, OWEN FRANCIS (b. 3 Sept. 1930) 3rd s. of William Morris Corcoran, newspaper proprietor, of Riversfield, Wexford, and Margaret Mary Ryan; B.A. (T.C.D.); M 1949. 1954/H/02 [2 items].

CORDUFF, PHILIP EDWARD JOSEPH (b. 30 March 1922) 2nd s. of James Corduff (decd.), of Drinark House, Donegal, Co. Donegal, and Catherine Melley; B.A. (N.U.I.); M 1945. 1948/M/04 [2 items].

CORLEY, HARRY CECIL (b. 15 Aug. 1878) 2nd s. of Henry Hagarty Corley, B.L., Probate Registrar, Belfast, of 54 Elmwood Ave, Belfast, and Kate Anne Heney; B.A. (T.C.D.); E 1899. 1902/E/04 [3 items].

CORLEY, HENRY HAGARTY (b. 12 Jan. 1839) eld. s. of Hugh Corley of 30 Lower Baggot Street, Dublin, and Frances Hagarty; H 1877, M.T. H 1878. 1880/H/09 [7 items]. Probate Registrar, Belfast.

CORRIGAN, JOHN F. (b. 30 Oct. 1942) eld. s. of Francis Kevin Corrigan, fruit importer, of 'Glenhazel', St. Clare's Avenue, Cork, and Sarah O'Flaherty; M 1960. 1965/M/12 [1 item].

CORVAN, CLARENCE WILLIAM (b. 1 Aug. 1860) only s. of the Revd. W.W. Corvan, M.A., of Bannow Vicarage, Co.Wexford, and Jane Boyce; B.A. (T.C.D.); M 1883, M.T. M 1884. 1887/E/03 [8 items]. Leinster Circuit. K.C., 24 Feb. 1912. Died 7 Jan. 1945.

COSGRAVE, LIAM MICHAEL GOBBIN (b. 13 April 1920) eld. s. of William Thomas Cosgrave, of Beechpark, Templeogue, Co. Dublin, and Louisa Flanagan; M 1939. 1943/T/03 [2 items]. S.C., 18 July 1958. Bencher (wrote about the King's Inns in the *Dublin Historical Record*, xxi (1967), 45-52). T.D., 1943-81. Leader of Fine Gael, 1965-77. Taoiseach, 1974-7. See Louis McRedmond (ed.), *Modern Irish Lives*.

COSGRAVE, MAURICE (b. 29 March 1868) eld. s. of John Cosgrave of Cahergal, Cork, and Ellen O'Regan; Cand. Bachelor (R.U.I.); M 1898. 1902/E/02 [3 items]. Died 5 March 1937. Obituary, *I.L.T. & S.J.*, lxxi (1937), 70.

COSTELLO, CORNELIUS (b. 4 July 1925) 2nd s. of Timothy Costello, postmaster (retired), of Borrisoleigh, Thurles, Co. Tipperary, and Margaret Kennedy (decd.); M 1949. 1961/T/09 [2 items].

COSTELLO, DAVID DECLAN (b. 1 Aug. 1926) 2nd s. of John A. Costello, of 20 Herbert Road, Ballsbridge, Co. Dublin, and Ida O'Malley; B.A. (N.U.I.); M 1944. 1948/M/03 [2 items]. S.C., 30 April 1965. Attorney-General, 1973-77. Judge of the High Court, 20 May 1977; President of the High Court, 11 Jan. 1995. Retired 1 Jan. 1998. Listed [with photographs] in the 1984 and 1991 editions of Maureen Cairnduff, *Who's Who in Ireland*. See Louis McRedmond (ed.), *Modern Irish Lives*.

COSTELLO, GRACE MARY (b. 22 Nov. 1921) eld. d. of John A Costello, of 20 Herbert Park, Dublin, and Ida O'Malley; B.A. (N.U.I.); M 1940. 1943/M/06 [2 items]. Died 1973.

COSTELLO, JOHN ALOYSIUS (b. 20 June 1891) 2nd s. of John Costello, of 32 Rathdown Road, Dublin, and Rose Callaghan; LL.B. (N.U.I.); M 1911. 1914/M/02 [2 items]. S.C., 6 May 1925. Attorney-General, 1926-32. T.D., 1933-69. Taoiseach, 1948-51 and 1954-7. Died 5 Jan. 1976. Obituaries, *I.L.T. & S.J.*, cx (1976), 49; *The Times*, 7 Jan. 1976. Portrait by Leo Whelan in King's Inns: see Wanda Ryan-Smolin, *King's Inns Portraits* (1992), 17. See *D.N.B. 1971-80* (article by David Harkness); Louis McRedmond (ed.), *Modern Irish Lives*.

COTAY, ALEXANDER BAJULAIYE (b. 26 Jan. 1913) 3rd s. of Lamin Comateh Cotay, merchant, of Freetown, Sierra Leone, West Africa, and Serah Kamara; B.Sc. (Lincoln, USA), D.P.A. Part 1 (Exeter University); M 1959. 1964/M/03 [1 item].

COTTER, FRANCIS MacCARTHY (b. 26 May 1886) eld. s. of Jeremiah Cotter, M.D., of 8 Sidney Place, Cork, and Mary MacCarthy; B.A. (R.U.I.); M 1906. 1909/T/12 [2 items].

COUGHLAN, ARTHUR (b. 30 Nov. 1877) 2nd s. of William Coughlan (decd.) of Mitchelstown, Co. Cork, and Mary Dinneen; T 1911. 1911/M/11 [2 items].

COUNIHAN, FRANCIS (b. 21 Oct. 1845) 2nd s. of Francis Counihan of Limerick, newspaper proprietor, and Susanna Nolan; B.A. (T.C.D.); E 1867; M.T. E 1869. 1871/M/5 [4 items].

COUNIHAN, ROGER AMBROSE (b. 20 Aug. 1927) young. s. of Jerome Henry Counihan, M.B., of River View, Ennis, Co. Clare, and Mary Catherine O'Mara; (Mod.) B.A. (T.C.D.); M 1947. 1951/T/06 [2 items]. Lawyer in Uganda.

COUNSEL, EDWARD PATRICK SARSFIELD (b. 16 Jan. 1851) 2nd s. of Lawrence Counsel, Barrister-at-Law, of Craggan House, Athlone, Co. Westmeath, J.P., and Kate Meares; LL.B (T.C.D.); H 1870, M.T. H 1873. 1875/E/02 [7 items]. Stood forlornly as a Home Ruler in the Dublin University constituency in 1886, obtaining 55 votes.

COURTENAY, ARTHUR HENRY (16 Oct. 1852) 3rd surv. s. of Thomas Lefroy Courtenay (decd.), J.P., of 14 Fitzwilliam Sq, Dublin, and Jane Caroline Morris; J.P.; H 1878, I.T. E 1878. 1880/M/17 [6 items]. Master of the Common Pleas, 1883. Lieutenant, Lanark Militia, 1871, rising to be Colonel of the Cameronians in the Boer War. Service at HQ in 1st World War. C.B. Master of the High Court, King's Bench Division, -1918. J.P. High Sheriff of Co. Galway, 1887 and 1909. Died at Tunbridge Wells, 1927. Obituary, *I.L.T. & S.J.*, lxi (28 May 1927), 130; *Who's Who*.

COWDY, HENRY LLOYD (b. 6 April 1880) 5th s. of Anthony Cowdy of Millmount, Banbridge, Co. Down, and Sara Frances Jones; B.A. (T.C.D.); M 1900. 1903/M/03 [3 items].

COWL, RICHARD PAPE (b. 25 Dec.1871) 2nd s. of Richard Pape Cowl of 46 Sandycove Road, Dublin, and Hannah Bull; Sch., Sen. Mod. B.A. (T.C.D.); M 1894. 1897/M/12 [3 items]. President of the University Philosophical Society, T.C.D., 1895-6. Professor. Died May 1950.

COX, VINCENT AEDAN (b. 1 July 1887) eld. s. of Michael F. Cox, M.D., of 26 Merrion Square, Dublin, and Elizabeth Nolan; M 1908. 1911/H/04 [3 items]. Died 1921.

COX, WILLIAM HUMPHREYS (b. 18 Nov. 1876) eld. s. of William Cox (decd.) of Carrick-on-Shannon, Co. Leitrim, and Jane Humphreys; B.A. (T.C.D.); M 1907. 1911/H/06 [2 items]. Died 9 March 1946. Obituary, *I.L.T. & S.J.*, lxxx (1946), 79.

COYLE, GEOFFREY DAVID (b. 7 Jan. 1925) 2nd s. of David Coyle, of Avonmore, Stillorgan, Co. Dublin, and Madeline Cantwell; M 1944. 1947/M/08 [2 items]. Secretary to the Bar Council, 1966. Died during the legal year 1990/91.

COYLE, JAMES VINCENT (b. 15 Dec. 1864) eld. s. of Charles Coyle, of Laranda, Grosvenor Road, Rathmines, Dublin, and Anne Duggan; cand. bachelor (T.C.D.); M 1885. 1896/M/05 [7 items]. Collector General's Office, Dublin, 1884-99; Department of Agriculture and Technical Instruction, 1900-21; Assistant Secretary, Ministry of Agriculture, N.I., 1922-30. C.B.E., 1926. Chairman of the committee of management of Peamount Sanatorium, 1934-43. Died 5 July 1948. Obituary, *I.L.T. & S.J.*, lxxxii (1948), 174; *Who's Who.*

COYNE, THOMAS JOSEPH (b. 22 Feb. 1901) 3rd s. of William Patrick Coyne, B.L., M.A., LL.D. (decd.), of Saval Villa, Glenageary, Co. Dublin, and Agnes Martin; B.A. (N.U.I.); M 1919. 1922/E/01 [2 items]. Civil servant. Private secretary to the Minister for Jome Affairs/Justice, 1923-9. Seconded to the Department of External Affairs, 1929-34, serving at the Vatican and League of Nations. Principal Officer, Department of Justice, 1934-9. Wartime censor, 1939-46: see Donal Ó Drisceoil, *Censorship in Ireland 1939-1945* (Cork, 1996). Assistant-Secretary of the Department of Justice, 1946-9; Secretary,1949-1961. Died 1961. Photograph (No. 9, between pp 148-9) and biographical note (p. 248) in Mary Kotsonouris, *The Winding-up of the Dáil Courts, 1922-1925: an obvious duty* (Dublin, 2004).

COYNE, WILLIAM PATRICK (b. 18 May 1866) 2nd s. of Edward Coyne of Nenagh, Co. Tipperary, and Maria Hayes; M.A. (R.U.I.); M 1891. 1895/M/15 [6 items]. Also known as Liam Coyne or Ua Cadhain. One of the first District Justices. Author of *The Law Courts in Eire* (n.d.): Kotsonouris, *Retreat from Revolution*, 120, n. 48. Died 3 Sept. 1953. Obituary, *I.L.T. & S.J.*, lxxxvii (1953), 238.

CRAIG, JOHN WALKER (b. 22 Aug. 1847) 4th s. of Thomas Henry Craig (decd.), of Ardcoen, Strabane, Co. Tyrone, and Martha Smith; M.A. (QUI); E 1870; L.I. M 1868. 1871/T/6 [2 items]. Q.C., June 1889. County Court Judge of Monaghan and Fermanagh, 18 March 1897-1911; of Antrim, 1911-19. A Commissioner of Education. Knighted 1920. Died 21 April 1926. Obituary, *I.L.T. & S.J.*, lx (1926), 186; *Who's Who.*

CRAMSIE, ROBERT (b. 17 Sept. 1852) 3rd s. of James Cramsie (decd.), solicitor, of Ballymoney, Co. Antrim, and Eliza Murray; B.A. (T.C.D.); M 1873, I.T. H 1876. 1881/H/02 [5 items].

CRAWFORD, ALEXANDER ROSS (b. 15 Sept. 1843) young. s. of Robert Crawford (decd.) of Belfast, and Elizabeth Thompson; M.A., LL.D (R.U.I.); H 1886. 1889/H/03 [7 items].

CRAWFORD, ALFRED (b. 1 Aug. 1878) 5th s. of Robert Crawford, Deputy Lieutenant, of Stonewold, Ballyshannon, Co. Donegal, and Anna Stubbs; M.A. (T.C.D.); M 1899. 1913/T/02 [2 items].

CRAWFORD, ALFRED DOUGLAS (b. 10 June 1868) 3rd s. of Thomas Douglas Crawford, J.P., of [Fort Reda], Co. Down, and Eleanor Sharman; B.A., LL.B. (T.C.D.); M 1887. 1890/T/06 [9 items].

CRAWFORD, THOMAS HENRY (b. 9 Dec. 1933) eld. s. of Lieut.-Colonel Henry Crawford, of 15 Blackheath Gardens, Clontarf, Dublin, and Bridget Barry; B.A. (T.C.D.); M 1959. 1962/M/11 [1 item].

CRAWFORD, WILLIAM ERNEST (b. 16 Nov. 1891) eld. s. of Henry Edward Crawford, of 'Arigna', St. John's Park, Belfast, and Catherine Sadleir; M 1921. 1923/M/03 [2 items].

CRAWLEY, HERBERT CAPEL (b. 1 March 1879) 3rd s. of William Chetwoode Crawley, LL.D., of Merton Park, Sandyford, Co. Dublin, and Ellen Mary McCarthy; B.A. (T.C.D.); M 1904. 1908/M/05 [2 items].

CRAWLEY, WILLIAM STOKER CHETWODE (b. 17 Aug. 1873) 2nd s. of William John Chetwode Crawley LL.D, D.C.L, of 50 Stephen's Green, Dublin, and Ellen McCarthy; B.A. (T.C.D.); M.A. (Cantab.). 1897/M/09 [4 items].

CREAN, BERNARD A. (b. 11 July 1880) 5th s. of Michael Crean (decd.), of Bloomfield, Belfast, and Mary O'Kane; M 1909. 1912/T/10A [2 items]. Colonial Service, 1920. Chief Justice of British Guiana, 1934-8, and of Cyprus, 1938-43. Knighted. Died 10 Oct. 1956. Obituary, *I.L.T. & S.J.*, xc (1956), 245-6; *Who's Who.*

CREAN, JOHN BERCHMANS (b. 6 Feb. 1872) eld. s. of Michael Theobald Crean, Barrister-at-Law, Asst. Legal Commissioner, Irish Land Commission, of Harcourt Street, Dublin, and Emma Dunn; H 1896. 1899/H/02 [3 items]. Land Commission. Died 21 Oct. 1948. Obituary, *I.L.T. & S.J.*, lxxxii (1948), 362-3.

CREED, JOHN PERCY (b. 20 Aug. 1861) eld. s. of Richard Creed, J.P., of Cloyne House, Co. Cork, and Olivia Percy; B.A. (T.C.D.); M 1880, M.T. M 1882. 1883/M/02 [7 items].

CREEDON, TIMOTHY (b. 29 Dec. 1918) young. s. of Timothy Creedon, of Parkgarriffe House, Monkstown, Co. Cork, and Mary Ellen O'Leary; M.A. (N.U.I.); M 1937 1943/T/05 [2 items].

CRESSWELL, JOHN VICTOR PEACOCK (b. 8 August 1919) 2nd s. of James Robert Cresswell, solicitor, of Sorrento House, Dalkey, Co. Dublin, and Bessie Jane Seymour; B.A. (T.C.D.); M 1938 [endorsed 'disbarred at own request to become solicitor as from 1/XI/60'] 1941/M/12 [2 items].

CRIVON, SAMUEL (b. 16 Sept. 1906) eld. s. of Joseph Crivon, of 37 Longwood Avenue, Dublin, and Leah Verikofski; M 1928. 1931/T/03 [2 items]. S.C., 1 Nov. 1963.

CROCKETT, ROBERT WILLIAM McDOWELL (b. 18 Aug. 1913) only s. of the Revd. John Scott Crockett, M.A., of The Manse, Sandymount, Dublin, and Alice Mary McDowell; Mod. B.A., LL.B. (T.C.D.); M 1933. Awarded Certificate of Honour. 1936/M/04 [2 items]. Died 6 May 1950.

CROMIE, ALFRED ALBERT (b. 5 Dec. 1900) eld. s. of Andrew Cromie, solicitor, of Mount Royal, Banbridge, Co. Down, and Maude Cunninghamme; B.A., LL.B. (Q.U.B.); M 1921. 1923/M/01 [2 items]. Died in Sierra Leone, 1937. Obituary, *I.L.T. & S.J.*, lxxi (7 April 1937), 212.

CRONHELM, EDWARD WILLIAM (b. 3 Jan. 1854) 2nd s. of Theodore Cronhelm, solicitor, of Luneburg, Sandymount, Dublin, and Mary Louise Crosbie; B.A. (T.C.D.); H 1874, M.T. H 1875. 1877/H/04 [6 items].

CRONIN, ANTHONY GERARD RICHARD (b. 28 Dec. 1923) 2nd s. of John Cronin, solicitor's assistant, of 20 Slaney Street, Enniscorthy, Co. Wexford, and Josephine Barren; B.A. (N.U.I.); M 1944. 1948/M/02 [2 items]. Writer and literary critic: author, *inter alia*, of *The Life of Riley* (London, 1964); *Dead as Doornails* (Dublin and London, 1976); *'No laughing matter': the life of Flann O'Brien* (London, 1989); and a biography of *Samuel Beckett* (London, 1996). Listed in the 1984 and 1991 editions of Maureen Cairnduff, *Who's Who in Ireland*. See Louis McRedmond (ed.), *Modern Irish Lives*.

CRONIN, DAVID WATKINS (b. 9 March 1930) 3rd s. of Doctor Thomas Mary Cronin, of Willowfield, Ballynorcorgy, Mullingar, Co. Westmeath, and Susan Dorothea O'Keeffe; B. Arch. (N.U.I.), A.R.I.B.A; M 1953. 1956/T/03 [2 items].

CRONIN, DOMINIC (b. 23 Sept. 1863) eld. s. of Dominic Cronin, merchant, of Belgrave Place, Cork, and Kate Lyons; B.A. (T.C.D.); M 1883, M.T. T 1884. 1887/E/04 [7 items].

CRONIN, EDMOND MATTHEW JUDE (b. 15 Oct. 1933) 2nd s. of Commandant E.J. Cronin (decd.), of St. Jude's, Fortfield Road, Co. Dublin, and Bridget McMahon; B.A., LL.B.(T.C.D.); M 1958. 1962/M/07 [1 item]. Lawyer in U.S.A.

CRONIN, THOMAS EUGENE (b. 21 Nov. 1907) 2nd s. of John Patrick Cronin, of Rock Cottage, Mallow, Co. Cork, and Margaret Josephine Molloy; M 1927. 1931/M/07 [2 items].

CROOKSHANK, CHARLES HENRY (b. 11 April 1859) only s. of Robert Crookshank, solicitor, of Glenmanus House, Portrush, Co. Londonderry, and Olivia Chambre; B.A.; M 1879, M.T. M 1881. 1883/E/03 [5 items]. K.C., 5 June 1918. Judicial Commissioner (N.I.). Died 19 May 1927. Obituary, *I.L.T. & S.J.*, lxi (1927), 131.

CROSBIE, DONAL PHILOMENA (b. 1 April 1927) 2nd s. of George Crosbie, of Garrydare, Tivoli, Cork, and Maureen Lyons; M 1946. 1950/T/01 [2 items].

CROSBIE, GEORGE (b. 7 May 1864) 2nd s. of Thomas Crosbie, of Lee Bank, Sunday's Well, in the City of Cork, and Mary Anne Callaghan; M 1886. 1889/T/05 [6 items].

CROSBIE, JAMES (b. 27 Aug. 1902) only s. of James G. Crosbie, of Ballybrack, Douglas, Co. Cork, and Meta Nelson; M 1920. 1925/H/02 [2 items]. Senator.

CROSS, WILLIAM PENNELL (b. 8 Dec 1849) only s. of Colonel William Cross J.P., of Dartan, Co. Armagh, and Frances Jane Cole; LL.B (T.C.D.); E 1870; I.T. E 1872. 1873/M/3 [4 items].

CROTTY, RICHARD DEMSY (b. 4 Oct. 1842) eld. s. of the Revd. William Crotty (decd.), of Galway, and Catherine Demsy; B.A. (Q.C.G.); M 1874, M.T. T 1876. 1879/H/03 [6 items].

CROWE, HENRY (b. 7 Oct. 1868) 4th s. of Wainwright Crowe (decd.), J.P., of Cahircalla, Co. Clare, and Annie M. Spaight; B.A. (T.C.D.); M 1889. 1892/T/09 [7 items]. Death noted, without date, in T.C.D. *Register of Alumni*, 7th ed., 1962.

CROWLEY, JEREMIAH (b. 30 April 1875) young. s. of John Crowley (decd.), of Glanduff, Kilbrittain, Co. Cork, and Ellen Grace (decd.); M 1913. 1916/T/06 [2 items]. Judge of the Dáil's Circuit Court, 1920-2. See under 'Crowley (Ó Cruadhlaoich), Diarmuid' in Mary Kotsonouris, *Retreat from Revolution: The Dáil Courts, 1920-24* (Dublin, 1994), esp. 31-2, 121-6; *O'Crowley v. The Minister for Justice and the Minister for Finance* [1935] I.R. 536 and (1934) 68 ILTR 174.

CROZIER, WILLIAM MAGEE (b. 5 Dec. 1875) 2nd s. of Francis Rawdon Moira Crozier of Carrickbrennan, Monkstown, Dublin, and Katherine Sophia Magee; Sch., B.A.; M 1895. 1898/M/08 [3 items]. Lieutenant, Royal Inniskilling Fusiliers. Died in France, 1 July 1916 [Name on the Bar War Memorial, and at Thiepval].

CRUESS CALLAGHAN, CROSADELLA (b. 5 May 1932) eld. d. of George Cruess Callaghan, of Ferndene, Stradbrook, Blackrock, Co. Dublin, and Ita Senior; H 1954. 1957/T/04 [2 items].

CRUISE, HENRY ERNEST RALEIGH (b. 12 Feb. 1874) eld. s. of Richard Joseph Cruise, (decd.), C.E., M.R.I.A., of Rahood, Co. Meath, and Elizabeth Raleigh; H 1904. 1909/H/03 [2 items]. Land Judge's Office. Died 3 Feb. 1940. Obituary, *I.L.T. & S.J.*, lxxiv (1940), 43.

CRUMP, PATRICK JOSEPH (b. 21 March 1882) 2nd s. of John J. Crump (decd.), of Blessington Street, Dublin, and Mary Griffin; M 1924. 1928/T/02 [2 items]. A solicitor's clerk in Maxwell Weldon & Co., who in January 1922 went to work for the Dáil courts, where he became senior official. Aft. transferred to the High Court office. See Mary Kotsonouris, *The Winding-up of the Dáil Courts, 1922-1925: an obvious duty* (Dublin, 2004), p. 249.

CUDDON, BERNARD ERIC DOUGHBY (b. 18 Jan. 1905) only s. of Bernard Cuddon (decd.), of Mullbarton Court, Chislehurst, Kent, and Margaret Charlotte Browne (decd.); M 1951, I.T. M 1928. 1952/E/01 [2 items]. Called to the English Bar, M 1928.

CULLIGAN, MICHAEL PATRICK JOSEPH (b. 10 March 1933) only s. of John Joseph Culligan, of Bonnie Doon, Kilrush, Co. Clare, and Kathleen Dooley; B.A. (N.U.I.); M 1950. 1954/M/10 [2 items].

CULLINAN, Captain BRENDAN PETER (b. 24 July 1926) young. s. of Patrick Joseph Cullinan (decd.), of Botanic Road, Glasnevin, Dublin, and Elizabeth O'Connor (decd.); B.Comm.(N.U.I.); M 1960. 1963/T/04 [1 item].

CULLINAN, CHARLES BARTHOLOMEW (b. 3 July 1879) eld. s. of Bartholomew Cullinan of Woodlands, Leap, Co. Cork, and Honoria Eleanor O'Donohoe; B.A. (R.U.I.); M 1903. 1906/H/01 [3 items].

CULLINAN, GEORGE CRITCHLEY (b. 11 Dec. 1885) 4th s. of John Cullinan, solicitor, of Bindon-street, Ennis, Co. Clare, and Martha Frances Faris; M 1910. 1913/T/10 [3 items]. S.C., 12 April 1937. Died 12 March 1943. Obituary, *I.L.T. & S.J.*, lxxvii (1943), 75.

CULLINAN, HENRY COOKE (b. 22 Aug. 1866) young. s. of John Cullinan of Ennis, Co. Clare, and Ellen Burton; B.A., LL.B. (T.C.D.); M 1887. 1890/T/09 [7 items]. President of the University Philosophical Society, T.C.D., 1888-9. Died 11 April 1908. *I.L.T. & S.J.*, xlii (1908), 98.

CULLINAN, ROBERT HORNIDGE (b. 9 Aug. 1881) 2nd s. of John Cullinan of Ennis, Co. Clare, and Martha Faris; Sen. Mod. (T.C.D.); M 1901. 1904/T/01 [3 items]. Captain, Royal Munster Fusiliers. Died at Gallipoli, 8 Aug.1915: *I.L.T. & S.J.*, xlix (1915), 206. [Name on the Bar War Memorial; also on the Helles Memorial, Gallipoli].

CUMING, EDWARD (b. 18 July 1852) 4th s. of Edward Cuming, merchant, of Markethill, Co. Armagh, and Agnes O'Callaghan; B.A. (Queen's); H 1875, M.T. H 1874. 1876/M/01 [7 items]. K.C., 22 Jan. 1906. Mentioned in Maurice Healy, *The Old Munster Circuit*, 267-270.

CUMING, FRANCIS EDWARD (b. 18 June 1863) only s. of James Cuming, physician, of Wellington Place, Belfast, and Harriet McLaughlin; B.A. (Oxford); M 1885; I.T. M 1884. 1887/M/17 [8 items].

CUMMINS, WILLIAM ASHLEY (b. 31 Aug. 1886) 2nd s. of William Edward Ashley Cummins, M.D., of 17 St. Patrick's Place, Cork, and Jane Constable Hall; B.A., LL.B; M 1905. 1908/M/07 [3 items].

CUNNIAM, PATRICK THOMAS (b. 19 July 1895) 2nd s. of Thomas Cunniam, of 1 Werburgh Street, Dublin, and Margaret Kenny; M 1918. 1921/M/11 [2 items].

CUNNINGHAM, ADRIAN ANTHONY BERNARD (b. 20 Aug. 1944) young. s. of Edward C. Cunningham (decd.), director, of 17 Woodbine Road, Blackrock, Co. Dublin, and Mary B.C. Deering; B.C.L. (N.U.I.); M 1963. 1966/M/07 [1 item].

CURLEY, THOMAS JOSEPH (b. 26 Nov. 1897) eld. s. of Thomas Curley (decd.), of Classaghroe, Ballyhaunis, Co. Mayo, and Catherine Finn; B.A., B. Comm, H. Dip. Ed (U.C.D.); M 1938. 1942/T/08 [2 items].

CURRAN, CONSTANTINE PETER (b. 30 Jan. 1883) 2nd s. of Patrick Curran of 6 Cumberland Place, N.C.R., Dublin, and Mary McGahan; M 1906. 1910/T/04 [3 items]. S.C., 21 Dec. 1938. Registrar of the Supreme Court, 1946-52. LL. D. (*h.c.*), N.U.I., April 1949. Contributor of historical essays to the *New Ireland Review*; Irish correspondent of the *Nation* (1916-22), and drama critic of the *Irish Statesman* (1925-30). Author, *inter alia*, of 'Cooley, Gandon and the Four Courts', in *Journal of the Royal Society of Antiquaries of Ireland*, vol. lxxix (1949), 20-5; 'The White Cross Inn, Dublin', in *ibid.*, lxxv (1945), 56, and plate facing page 55; *Dublin Decorative Plasterwork of the Seventeenth and Eighteenth Centuries* (1967); *James Joyce Remembered* (1968); and 'Figures in the Hall', in *Record of the Centenary of the Charter of the Incorporated Law Society of Ireland 1852-1052* (Dublin, 1953), 75-82; reprinted in *Gazette of the Incorporated Law Society of Ireland*, vol. lxvi (1972), 45-7; and in Caroline Costello (ed.), *The Four Courts: 200 Years* (Dublin, 1996), 105-112. Died 1972. See an Appreciation in *Gazette of the Incorporated Law Society of Ireland*, vol. lxvi (1972), 32, and Louis McRedmond (ed.), *Modern Irish Lives*.

CURRAN, LANCELOT ERNEST (b. 8 March 1899) 4th s. of Myles Curran, of Myrtlefield Park, Belfast, and Edith Bruce; B.A., LL.B. (Q.U.B.); M 1920. 1923/T/11 [2 items]. M.P. (Northern Ireland Parliament). K.C. (N.I.), T 1943. M.P. (N.I. Parl.) for Carrick, 1945-9. Attorney-General (N.I.), 6 June 1947-9 Nov. 1949; Judge of the King's Bench Division, 4 Nov. 1949, and Lord Justice of Appeal, 1 Nov. 1956-31 Aug. 1975. The murder of his daughter was a *cause célèbre* in 1953. Died 20 Oct. 1984. *Who's Who.*

CURTIN, Revd. JEROME KEVIN (b. 17 June 1918) 5th s. of Maurice J. Curtin (decd.), of Tournafulla, Newcastlewest, Co. Limerick, and Margaret Maher; B.A., B.D., DCL; M 1955. Awarded 1st Victoria Prize. 1958/T/01 [2 items]. Professor, U.C.D.

CUSACK, JOHN (b. 22 July 1865) eld. s. of James Cusack of Newry, Co. Down, and Anna Christian; H 1889. 1893/H/02 [6 items]. North-East Circuit. Contested the Newry constituency, 1910. Member of the Bar Council, 1913-15. K.C, 27 Feb. 1918. Served as County Court Judge for Limerick, 1919-20; appt. for Kerry, 9 April 1920, retiring in 1924. Lived thereafter in England. Visiting Justice for Wormwood Scrubs, 1929-32; Mayor of Twickenham, 1929-30. Died 2 April 1940. Obituary, *I.L.T. & S.J.*, lxxiv (1940), 96, 143; *Who's Who.*

DAGG, THOMAS SIDNEY CHARLES (b. 25 Dec. 1875) young. s. of George William Jackson (decd.), of 7 Airefield Terrace, Rathgar, Dublin, and Mary Barbara Kellett; B.A. (T.C.D.); M 1906. 1909/M/05 [2 items]. Auditor of the College Historical Society, 1906-7. Worked for the Congested Districts Board and the Department of Finance (see Ronan Fanning, *The Irish Department of Finance, 1922-58* (Dublin, 1978), pp 522, 534-5, 547). Author of *Hockey in Ireland* (1942) and *College Historical Society: A History* (Tralee, 1969) [reprinted in part in Declan Budd and Ross Hinds (eds.), *The Hist and Edmund Burke's Club* (Dublin, 1997), on p. xx of which is reproduced a photograph of Dagg]. Died 29 Dec. 1964. Obituary, *I.L.T. & S.J.*, xcix (1965), 19.

DALTON, JAMES JOSEPH (b. 6 Feb. 1861) 2nd s. of James Dalton of Orange, New South Wales, and Margaret Collins; E 1885. 1888/E/05 [7 items]. Nationalist M.P. for West Donegal, 1890-92; unsuccessful Parnellite candidate in South Meath, 1892 and 1893. Brother-in-law of John Redmond. Went to Australia.

DALTON, JOHN (b. 19 June 1943) only s. of John Dalton, civil servant, of 125 Swords Road, Whitehall, Dublin, and Mary O'Gorman; M 1961. 1965/M/08 [1 item]. Registrar of the Supreme Court. Retired 2003.

DALY, GEORGE FRANCIS ALEXANDER (b. 4 Oct. 1924) 2nd s. of Charles Daly (decd.), of 3 Inniscarrig, Western Road, Cork, and Anita McCarthy; B.A. (N.U.I.); M 1947. 1951/T/05 [2 items].

DALY, GEORGE JOSEPH (b. 6 Sept. 1877) 4th s. of John Daly of Inniscarrig house, Cork, and Katherine Sutton; M 1904. 1907/T/08 [3 items]. Father of the Munster Bar. Died 25 May 1941. Obituary, *I.L.T. & S.J.*, lxxv (1941), 134, 141.

DALY, JAMES DERMOT (b. 11 May 1868) only s. of James Daly, of Castle Daly, Co. Galway, and Christina O'Kelly; M.A. (R.U.I.); M 1894. 1897/T/10 [4 items]. Died 11 Oct. 1914.

DALY, MARCUS JAMES ALBERT (b. 15 Nov. 1937) 2nd s. of Marcus John George Daly (decd.), farmer, of Ballygaddy House, Tuam, Co. Galway, and Harriet Mylotte; M 1955. 1959/M/04 [2 items]. S.C., 6 Oct. 1975.

DALY, MICHAEL BERNARD (b. 24 Feb. 1900) only s. of James Daly, J.P., of Esmond Hall, Carrickmacross, Co. Monaghan, and Mary McCaul; M 1918. 1922/T/03 [3 items]. Office of the Attorney-General.

DALY, OSCAR BEDFORD (b. 2 Sept. 1880) 2nd s. of Robert Bedford Daly (decd.) of Drogheda, Co. Louth, and Amelia King; B.A.; M 1900. 1904/H/05 [3 items]. Son of a County Inspector of the R.I.C., and educated at schools in Pau and Leipzig. North-East Circuit. Admitted to the Bar of Kenya Colony, 1910. Commissioned 9th South Wales Borderers, 1915. Returned to practise in Kenya Colony, 1919. K.C. (N.I.), T 1938. Chief Justice of the Bahamas, 1939-45. Knighted 1942. Hon. LL.D. (T.C.D.), 1944. Died 29 June 1953. Obituary, *I.L.T. & S.J.*, lxxxvii (1953), 191; *Who's Who*.

DAMES-LONGWORTH, EDWARD TRAVERS (b. 23 May 1861) eld. s. of Francis Travers Dames Longworth, Q.C., of Glynwood, Co. Westmeath, and Frances Noble; B.A. (Oxford); H 1883, M.T. E 1882. 1885/M/12 [6 items].

DANAHER, MAURICE young. s. of William Philip Danaher (decd.), of Glenagower, Athea, Co. Limerick; M.A., LL.B. (N.U.I.). Awarded First Class Certificate of Honour. 1925/M/03. Memorial missing; receipt only. Mentioned in Gerard A. Lee, *A Memoir of the South-Western Circuit* (Dublin, 1990), 13, 16.

DANE, RICHARD MARTIN (b. 4 Dec. 1852) 3rd s. of William Auchinleck Dane, solicitor, Secretary to Fermanagh Grand Jury, of Killyreagh, Enniskillen, Co. Fermanagh, and Sarah Foster; M.A. (T.C.D.); M 1873, M.T. T 1875. 1877/E/04 [4 items]. Unionist M.P. for North Fermanagh, 1892-8. County Court Judge for Mayo, 30 Sept. 1898-1903. Died 22 March 1903. Obituary, *I.L.T. & S.J.*, xxxvii (1903), 133-4; *Who's Who*; *Burke's Irish Family Records* (1976), 319.

DANIELL, ROBERT GEORGE (b. 2 July 1870) 2nd s. of Robert George Daniell, J.P., of New Forest, Co. Westmeath, and Ellen O'Brien; M 1894. 1897/M/11 [4 items]. Court Registrar in Bankruptcy, King's Bench Division. Died unmarried. See *Burke's Irish Family Records* (1976), 321.

DARAMY, LAHAI EVANS KAPINDI (b. 24 Oct. 1925) eld. s. of Chief Kapindi Sepeh (decd.), of Panguma, Lower Bambara, Kenema District, Sierra Leone, and Merci Manye; B.C.L. (N.U.I.); M 1956. 1963/M/03 [1 item].

D'ARCY, JAMES AUGUSTINE (b. 4 April 1915) eld. s. of James F. D'Arcy, of 'Gleneden', Tipperary, Co. Tipperary, and Agnes Duggan; B.A., LL.B. (T.C.D.); M 1935. 1938/M/04 [2 items]. S.C., 29 Jan. 1954. Judge of the High Court, 24 June 1977. Retired 5 Jan. 1986. Listed in the 1984 edition of Maureen Cairnduff, *Who's Who in Ireland*. Obituary (by Roman Keane) in *The Irish Times*.

DARDIS, PATRICK GREGORY (b. 11 March 1890) 4th s. of Michael Dardis, of 51 North Circular Road, Dublin, and Mary Daly; M.A., LL.B. (N.U.I.); M 1917. Awarded Society's Exhibition. 1920/H/01 [2 items].

DARKO, JOSEPH ANTHONY (b. 31 Dec. 1931) 2nd s. of Kwadwo Fordwuo, farmer, of Bekwai, Ashanti, Ghana, and Akosua Nyarko; B.A. (T.C.D.); E 1957. 1962/M/13 [7 items].

DARLEY, CECIL HASTINGS (b. 13 Sept. 1878) 2nd surv. s. of John Henry Darley (decd.), Chief Clerk in the Court of Chancery, of Ferney, Stillorgan, Co. Dublin, and Marie Cerise Lees; Sen. Mod. B.A. (T.C.D.); M 1899. 1903/H/04 [3 items]. Died 12 July 1955. Obituary, *I.L.T. & S.J.*, lxxxix (1955), 183.

DAS, RAM KRISHNA (b. 24 July 1912) eld. s. of Pirthipal Das of V. Ekma P. Unwal, Gorakhpur (U.P.), India, landowner, and Kabutani Das; T 1938. 1944/M/14 [2 items].

DAVEY, WILLIAM HAMILTON (b. 15 Aug. 1880) only s. of Robert Davey of Carrickfergus, and Jane Hamilton; M.A. (R.U.I.); M 1902. 1906/H/05 [5 items]. Major, Tyeside Irish Brigade. Opponent of Sir Edward Carson in the Belfast (Duncairn) Constituency, 1918. Sued Sir Edward Carson for slander: see panel. Died 1920. Obituary, *I.L.T. & S.J.*, liv, 30 Oct. 1920, 266.

AN ACTION FOR SLANDER AGAINST SIR EDWARD CARSON

Major W.H.E. Davey of the Tyneside Irish Brigade, who is a member of the Irish Bar and who was associated with the Irish Recruiting Committee during the last three months has brought on an action for slander against Sir Edward Carson. The latter is being opposed in the Duncairn Division of Belfast by Major Davey and by a Dr. McNab, a Sinn Feiner. In the course of one of his speeches Sir Edward said that he was being opposed by two Sinn Feiners; but in a subsequent speech he explained that he was wrong in having referred to Major Davey in such a way, and expressed regret. Section 1 of the Corrupt and Illegal Practices Act, 1898, empowers the Court to restrain the publication of 'any false statement of fact' in relation to the personal character or conduct of a candidate at a parliamentary election. Recourse was had to that section in 1906 by the late Mr. T.M. Kettle, who was alleged by the *Northern Whig* to have 'formed one of a gang of hobbledehoys who created a disturbance and exhibited their disloyalty at the Royal University on last degree days'. (In re T.M. Kettle, 40 ILTR 234).

[*I.L.T. & S.J.*, lii, p. 302, 14 Dec. 1918].

In the poll in the Duncairn constituency Sir Edward was elected as a Unionist with 11,637 votes. Major Davey, standing as a Nationalist, obtained 2,449 votes. Dr Russell McNab[b], the Sinn Feiner, obtained 271 votes.

Sir Edward Carson, says the *Law Times*, recently paid his second visit to the Four Courts in Dublin since he quitted these precincts to try his fortunes at the English Bar. The previous occasion was fourteen years ago, when, in the course of the Dunlop Tyre litigation, he came over specially to represent Mr. Du Cros, sen. in an action in the Division of the Master of the Rolls. That was his last professional appearance at the Irish Courts. On the present visit the right hon. Gentleman was defendant in a slander action entitled *Dav*[e]*y v. Carson*. He delivered a speech at the General Election in which he made a sustained attack upon Sinn Fein, and then said he was opposed by two Sinn Fein candidates. The plaintiff, who had attained the rank of major, felt aggrieved at these words and commenced proceedings. The defendant tendered an apology, and from the point of view of frankness and fullness it certainly left nothing to be desired.

[*I.L.T. & S.J.*, liii, p. 114, 10 May 1919].

DAVIDSON, JOHN CRAIG NELSON (b. 2 March 1877) only s. of James Davidson of Windsor Park, Belfast, and Alice Maude Mary Nelson; M 1896. 1899/T/07 [3 items].

DAVIS, CHARLES STEWART PARNELL (b. 13 Nov. 1891) only s. of Francis Davis (decd.), of Dunlevy, Upper Beechwood Avenue, Ranelagh, Dublin, and Catherine Rutherford; M 1914. 1921/H/06 [2 items].

DAVISON, ARTHUR BOLDEN (b. 19 March 1837) only s. of David Davison (decd.) of Gardiner Place, Dublin, and Alice Jane Bolden; B.A. (T.C.D.); H 1867; I.T. M 1866. 1869/M/6 [7 items].

DAVISON, JOHN CLARKE (b. 19 April 1875) eld. surv. s. of Samuel Davison, merchant, of Scotch Street, Armagh, and Mary McKinley; B.A. (T.C.D.); M 1895, G.I. M 1897.

1898/M/02 [3 items]. K.C. (N.I.), M 1926. Unionist M.P. for Armagh constituencies, 1925-38; Deputy Speaker, Parl. of N.I., 1937, and Parliamentary Secretary to Ministry of Home Affairs, 1937-8. P.C. Recorder of Londonderry, 1938. Died 19 Feb. 1946. Obituary, *I.L.T. & S.J.*, lxxx (1946), 60; *Who's Who*.

DAVITT, CATHAR (b. 15 Aug. 1894) 2nd s. of Michael Davitt (decd.), of Dalkey, Co. Dublin, and Mary Yore; B.A. (N.U.I.); M 1913. 1916/H/02 [2 items]. First name more often rendered 'Cahir'. Judge of the Dáil's Circuit Court, 1920-22; member of the Judiciary Committee, 1923; Judge Advocate of the Defence Forces, 1922-6. Bencher of King's Inns, 1927. Judge of the Circuit Court, 1926-45; of the High Court, 1945-51. President of the High Court, 1951-66. Died 1 March 1986. Contributor to James Meenan (ed.), *Centenary History of Lit. and Hist. Soc. of U.C.D.* See Mary Kotsonouris, *Retreat from Revolution: The Dáil Courts, 1920-24* (Dublin, 1994), 31-2. Louis McRedmond (ed.), *Modern Irish Lives*.

DAVY, THOMAS VINCENT (b. 23 Aug. 1900) eld. s. of Thomas Davy (decd.), of Beaumont, Terenure, Dublin (decd.), and Alice O'Donnell; T 1929. 1929/M/19 [2 items]. S.C., 3 March 1950. Died, as 'Father of the Bar', *c.* 1995.

DAWSON, WILLIAM (b. 5 Dec. 1877) 2nd s. of Charles Dawson of 74 Northumberland Road, Dublin, and Catherine Carroll; M 1901. 1904/M/08 [3 items]. Examiner of Title, Land Commission. Honorary secretary of the United Arts Club. Died mid-September 1934. Obituary, *I.L.T. & S.J.*, lxviii (29 Sept. 1934), 274, 284. Contributor to James Meenan (ed.), *Centenary History of Lit. and Hist. Soc. of U.C.D.*

DAY, JOSEPH MICHAEL (b. 22 Oct 1852) 2nd s. of Arthur Magee Day of Rathgar, Dublin, and Charlotte Dunne; B.A. (T.C.D.); T 1871; M.T. E 1873. 1874/T/7 [4 items]. North-East Bar. Died 15 July 1915. Obituary, *I.L.T. & S.J.*, xlix (1915), 181.

DE BLAGHD, EARNÁN PÁDRAIG (b. 19 March 1925) only s. of Ernest Blythe, of 50 Kenilworth Square, Rathmines, Dublin, and Annie McHugh; M 1946. 1949/T/01 [2 items].

DE BÚRCA, MARCUS (b. 15 Jan. 1927) eld. s. of Patrick Bourke, Barrister-at-Law, of 52 Grace Park Road, Drumcondra, Dublin, and Hannah Moreton; B.A. (N.U.I.); M 1947. Awarded Society's Exhibition Prize. 1949/M/02 [2 items]. Parliamentary draftsman. As Marcus Bourke, author of *The O'Rahilly* (Tralee, 1967); *John O'Leary: a study in Irish separatism* (Tralee and Athens, Georgia, 1967); and *Murder at Marlhill: was Harry Gleeson innocent?* (Dublin, 1993). As Marcus De Búrca, author of works on the history of the Gaelic Athletic Association (1980-1999).

DE BÚRCA, PÁDRAIG (Patrick Bourke) (b. 25 Aug. 1893) only surv. s. of John Bourke (decd.), of Tipperary, Co. Tipperary, and Ellen Keating; B.A. (N.U.I.); M 1927. 1930/M/01 [2 items]. S.C., 3 July 1950.

DE BURGH, HUBERT JOHN (b. 1 Aug 1845) only s. of Major John de Burgh, late 93rd Sutherland Highlanders, of 2 Warwick Terrace, Dublin and Emma Maria Hunt; B.A. (T.C.D.); T 1870; M.T. M 1866. 1872/H/8 [4 items]. Died unmarried 1877. *Burke's Irish Family Records* (1976), 339.

DE BUTTS, GEORGE (b. 11 June 1844) only surviving s. of the Revd. George De Butts of 35 Leeson Park, Dublin and Anna Maria Locker; B.A. (T.C.D.); E 1871; L.I. T 1866. 1872/M/9 [2 items]. Called to English Bar, E 1869.

DE COURCY, CYRIL NOEL (b. 10 Dec. 1931) 2nd s. of Louis de Courcy, auctioneer, of Mount Catherine House, Clonlara, Co. Clare, and Kathleen Gillespie; B.A. (N.U.I.); M 1950. 1953/T/04 [2 items]. Aft. an auctioneer in Limerick.

DE COURCY, JOHN ALOYSIUS FRANCIS (b. 4 Oct. 1930) eld. s. of Louis de Courcy, auctioneer, of Mount Catherine House, Clonlara, Co. Clare, and Kathleen Gillespie; B.A. (N.U.I.); M 1949. 1952/T/02 [2 items].

DE LA COUR, ROBERT WILLIAM (b. 3 Dec. 1861) eld. s. of the Revd. Robert William de la Cour (decd.), of Kilowen Rectory, Co. Cork, and Elizabeth Hyde; student of Charles Hall College, Oxford; E 1892, M.T. M 1884. 1894/T/09 [3 items].

DE RENZY, ANNESLEY St. GEORGE (b. 28 Dec. 1868) only s. of Surgeon-General C.C. De Renzy, of 18 Clyde Road, Dublin, and Mary Whitty; Scholar, B.A. (T.C.D.); M 1890. 1893/T/03 [6 items]. Leinster Circuit. K.C., 24 Feb. 1912. Died at Burnham, Somerset, 6 Aug. 1921. Obituary, *I.L.T. & S.J.*, lv (1921), 201.

DE VALERA, VIVION (b. 13 Dec. 1910) eld. s. of Eamon de Valera, of Cross Avenue, Blackrock, Co. Dublin, and Sinéad Ní Fhlannagáin; M 1934. 1937/T/02 [2 items]. S.C., 5 July 1951. T.D. 1945-81. Managing Director of Irish Press Ltd., 1959-81. Died 1982. See Louis McRedmond (ed.), *Modern Irish Lives; Burke's Irish Family Records* (1976), 359.

DE VERSAN, JOHN RICHARD RAOUL COUTURIER (b. 22 Nov 1848) eldest s. of Edward Couturier de Versan (decd.) of Paris, and Anne Clancy; B.A. (T.C.D.); E 1869; I.T. H 1871. 1874/H/2x [2 items]. K.C., 5 June 1918. Senior Registrar in Chancery; sometime Clerk of the Errors (Exchequer Chamber). Retired 1921. Died 14 April 1936. Obituary, *I.L.T. & S.J.*, lxx (1936), 109.

DEALE, KENNETH EDWIN LEE (b. 17 Jan. 1907) 3rd s. of Edwin Deale, merchant, of 11 Effra Road, Rathmines, Dublin, and Minnie Hill Martin; M 1930; [incl. letter from Deale to Under-Treasurer Burke, 6 June 1935; postage stamp removed] 1935/T/02 [3 items]. Educated at Wesley College, Dublin. Part-time broadcaster ('Information Please') with Radio Éireann. S.C., 3 July 1950. Judge of the Circuit Court (Eastern Circuit), 1951-74. Appt. Judge of the High Court, 8 May 1974. Died 21 Oct. 1974. Obituary, *I.L.T. & S.J.*, cviii (1974), 266. Author, *inter alia*, of: *Guide to High Court Practice*; *Landlord and Tenant Acts 1931 and 1943* [known to practitioners as the 'Blue Deale']; *The Law of Landlord and Tenant in Ireland* [the 'Black Deale', a work commissioned by the Incorporated Council of Law Reporting for Ireland at the then handsome fee of £500]; *Memorable Irish Trials*; *Beyond Reasonable Doubt?*; and 'The Conspiracy', a play performed at the Abbey Theatre in 1966. See Louis McRedmond (ed.), *Modern Irish Lives*.

DEASY, JOHN, M.P. (b. 29 June 1855) only s. of Michael Deasy (decd.), of Bishopstown, Co. Cork, and Mary Murray; T 1885. 1888/E/06 [6 items].

DELANEY, PATRICK (b. 22 March 1873) young. s. of Patrick Delaney (decd.) of 7 Cumberland Place, North Circular Road, Dublin, and Maria Roland; T 1893. 1897/T/01 [5 items].

DELANY, VINCENT THOMAS HYGINAS (b. 11 Jan. 1923) 2nd s. of Vincent Sylvester Delany, of Longford, Co. Longford, and Anna Higgins; M.A., LL.B. (T.C.D.); M 1945. 1950/T/05 [2 items]. Auditor of the College Historical Society, 1946-7. Lecturer in Law, Q.U.B., 1953; Reader in Law, Q.U.B., 1960. Professor of Laws, T.C.D., 1962. Died 17 Jan. 1964. Obituary, *I.L.T. & S.J.*, xcviii (1964), 66. Editor of the revived *Irish Jurist*. Author of *The Law relating to Charities in Ireland* (Dublin, 1956; 2nd edition, 1963); *The Holmes Reader*; *Christopher Palles. His Life and Times* (Dublin, 1960); *The Administration of Justice in Ireland* (Dublin, 1963; 4th edition (ed. Charles Lysaght, 1975); also, 'The Bench and Bar in Ireland', in L.G. Pine (ed.), *Burke's Genealogical and Heraldic History of the Landed Gentry of Ireland*, 4th edition, 1958, xxx-xxxiv, an article frequently cited in this listing. See Louis McRedmond (ed.), *Modern Irish Lives*.

DELMEGE, ARTHUR JAMES (b. 27 Oct. 1851) 6th s. of Julius Delmege (decd.) of 36 Fitzwilliam Sq, Dublin, and Rathkeale, Co. Limerick, and Belinda Leake; M.A. (T.C.D.); H 1874, M.T. M 1874. 1877/E/06 [4 items]. Died 1 March 1944.

DEMPSEY, DAVID BRIAN PAUL (b. 25 June 1942) eld. s. of William Peter Dempsey, company director, of Hatley, Kerrymount Avenue, Foxrock, Co. Dublin, and Mary Christina Murray; B.C.L., LL.B. (N.U.I.); M 1963. 1967/M/11 [1 item]. S.C., 7 Oct. 1985.

DEMPSEY, FREDERICK JEROME (b. 30 Sept. 1890) 2nd s. of Sir Alexander Dempsey, M.D., of Coldagh, Fortwilliam Park, Belfast, and Jane Smyth; Mod. B.A., LL.B. (T.C.D.); M 1910. 1914/T/01 [2 items]. Rea's Buildings, Royal Avenue, Belfast.

DEMPSEY, PATRICK JOSEPH (b. 13 Jan. 1893) 3rd s. of Patrick Dempsey, of Herbert Road, Bray, Co. Wicklow, and Annie Scully; M 1915. 1918/T/09 [2 items].

DEMPSEY, PAUL RONAN (b. 9 March 1936) eld. s. of Paul J. Dempsey (decd.), chief executive officer, Vocational Education Committee, N.R. Tipperary, of Nenagh, Co. Tipperary, and Sinead O'Shea; M 1957. 1968/H/01 [1 item]. Ambassador to India, Sweden, Canada.

DENNING, FREDERICK FFOLLIOTT (b. 25 Nov. 1862) 5th s. of Frederick Benson Denning, agent to the Bank of Ireland, of Tullamore, Kings Co., and Isabella Waddle; B.A. (T.C.D.); M 1880, G.I. M 1882. 1884/H/04 [5 items]. K.C., 27 June 1914. Died 30 Dec. 1938. Obituary, *I.L.T. & S.J.*, lxxiii (1939), 7-8. Long 'Father of the Bar'. Mentioned by Patrick MacKenzie, *Lawful Occasions*, 15; by V.T.H. Delany [q.v.], in 'The Bench and Bar in Ireland', xxxiii; and by Garrett Gill [q.v.] in his short memoir.

DENNISON, THOMAS ANDREWS (b. 18 Sept. 1906) eld. s. of Robert John Dennison, of Belfast, and Emma Rachael Foster; M 1926. 1931/E/03 [2 items]. Puisne Judge of the Gold Coast.

DESMOND, TIMOTHY NOEL (b. 28 November 1915) only s. of William Desmond, alderman, of 2 Pembroke Street, Cork, and Bridget Mary Murnane; M 1936. 1940/T/04 [2 items]. Judge of the Circuit Court, 1977. S.C., 3 Oct. 1986. Mentioned in Gerard A. Lee, *A Memoir of the South-Western Circuit* (Dublin, 1990), 12.

DEVENISH-MEARES, JOHN FREDERICK (b. 18 Feb. 1866) eld. s. of Joseph Leycester Devenish-Meares, M.A., of Newry, Co. Armagh, and Frances Georgina Brooke; B.A. (T.C.D.); M 1888, called to the Bar, M.T. 11 May 1892. 1897/T/14 [2 items]. Died 5 March 1935.

DEVERELL, AVERIL KATHERINE STATTER (b. 2 Jan. 1893) only d. of William Deverell, of Ellesmere, Greystones, Co. Wicklow, and Ada Kate Statter Carr; M 1919. 1921/M/15 [2 items]. 2nd woman to be called to the Bar, and first to practise in Dublin, where she is reported to have insisted that a sign on the door of the dressing room which read 'Lady Barristers' should be rendered 'Women Barristers'. See a biographical note (derived from information from R.N. Cooke, S.C.) in Ivana Bacik, Cathryn Costello and Eileen Drew, *Gender InJustice* (Dublin, 2003), 57. Portrait in the Law Library. Died 1979. Bequest to the T.C.D. Law School.

DEVERELL, WILLIAM BERENGER STATTER (b. 2 Jan. 1893) only s. of William Deverell, of Greystones, Co. Wicklow, and Ada Kate Statter Carr; M 1913. 1921/M/05 [3 items]. Brigadier. Died Feb. 1966.

DEVITT, St. LAWRENCE ERNEST JOSEPH (b. 21 Dec. 1873) 2nd s. of Michael Devitt (decd.) of Ballina, Co. Mayo, and Nina Ffrench Mullen; LL.B. (R.U.I.); M 1898. 1901/H/01 [2 items]. Judicial Commissioner under the Dáil Éireann Courts (Winding-Up) Act, 1923. One of the eight original judges of the Circuit Court, 1924, appointed for the Northern Circuit, 1924-8; Eastern Circuit, 1928-36. Died 14 Feb. 1936. Obituary, *I.L.T. & S.J.*, lxx (1936), 56, 138. See Mary Kotsonouris, *Retreat from Revolution: The Dáil Courts, 1920-24* (Dublin, 1994), 101, 107.

DEVLIN, JOHN JOSEPH LEE (b. 16 Aug. 1897) eld. s. of Joseph Walker Devlin, of Molesworth Street, Cookstown, Co. Tyrone, and Amy O'Hanlon; B.A. (T.C.D.); M 1916. 1919/M/06 [2 items]. Mentioned, as 'the double of Billy Bunter', in Patrick MacKenzie, *Lawful Occasions*, 55-60. Died 10 Jan. 1961.

DHALL, ACHRAJRAM (b. 15 March 1895) eld. s. of Lalla Atma Ram Dhall Sahib, of Peshawar, North-West Frontier, India; M 1915. 1918/T/20x [2 items].

DIAMOND, DAVID (b. 6 June 1942) 5th s. of William Diamond, company director, of 42 Woodbine Road, Blackrock, Co. Dublin, and Martha Graham; M 1964. 1968/T/02 [1 item].

DICK, WILLIAM (b. 5 April 1874) eld. s. of James Fairweather Dick of Dundee, Scotland, and Mary Couper; M.A. (R.U.I.); M 1899. 1902/T/01 [3 items]. K.C., 13 July 1921.

DICKIE, ALEXANDER ALFRED (b. 3 Feb. 1868) 3rd s. of Alexander Dickie of Roachdale, Co. Louth, and Anna McCulla; B.A. (R.U.I.); H 1890. 1893/H/01 [9 items]. K.C., 27 June 1914. Died 1 June 1933. Obituary, *I.L.T. & S.J.*, lxvii (1933), 161-2, 166, 172.

DICKIE, THOMAS WALLACE (b. 23 April 1887) 2nd s. of J.C. Dickie, solicitor, B.A., of Clonavon, Omagh, Co. Tyrone, and M.K.E. MacNeice; B.A. (T.C.D.); M 1906. 1909/M/04 [2 items]. K.C. (N.I.), T 1943.

DICKINSON, CYRIL HENRY (b. 15 July 1876) 3rd s. of the Very Revd. H.H. Dickinson, Dean of the Chapel Royal, of the Vicarage, Dawson Street, Dublin, and Mary Kennedy; M 1895. 1898/M/13 [3 items].

DICKINSON, HAROLD EVORY (b. 26 June 1872) 2nd s. of the Very Revd. H.H. Dickinson (decd.), D.D., Dean of the Chapel Royal, Dublin, and Mary Mabel Kennedy; cand. bachelor (T.C.D.); H 1893. 1909/T/03 [2 items].

DICKSON, JOHN MacGEAGH (b. 26 April 1860) 2nd s. of Thomas Alexander Dickson MP, of Dungannon, Co. Tyrone, and Elizabeth MacGeagh; LL.B. M 1883, L.I. M 1882. 1885/T/08 [6 items]. Resident Magistrate.

DIFFIN, JOHN (b. 18 Nov. 1873) eld. s. of John Diffin (decd.), of Tullyserran, Co. Armagh, and Margaret Flanaghan; M 1920. 1924/M/03 [2 items]. Died 1949. Obituary, *I.L.T. & S.J.*, lxxxiii (28 May 1949), 142.

DIGBY, EVERARD (b. 3 June 1854) eld. s. of George Digby (decd.), J.P., of Kilrooskey, Co. Roscommon, and Catherine Hawkes; H 1878, M.T. H 1880. 1880/M/16 [6 items].

DIGGES LA TOUCHE, JOHN JAMES. See: LA TOUCHE, JOHN JAMES DIGGES.

DIGGIN, CHRISTOPHER VALENTINE BERNADETTE (b. 24 March 1928) 5th s. of Patrick Diggin, publican, of Atlantic View Hotel, Ballybunion, Co. Kerry, and Hannah O'Connor; M 1947. Awarded Society's Exhibition prize. 1951/M/01 [2 items]. Appeal Commissioner of Income Tax.

DILLON, BRIAN FRANCIS (b. 13 March 1905) 5th s. of John Dillon, of 2 North Great George's Street, Dublin, and Elizabeth Mathew; B.A. (N.U.I.); M 1924. Awarded John Brooke Scholarship and 1st Class Cert. of Honour. 1927/H/01 [2 items]. Practised for two years before studying for the priesthood (Benedictine Order). Known as Father Matthew. Headmaster of Glenstal Abbey. Died 25 Oct. 1979. See Joachim Fischer and John Dillon (eds.), *The Correspondence of Myles Dillon 1922-1925* (Dublin, 1999), 281; *Burke's Irish Family Records* (1976), 365.

DILLON, CHARLES (b. 19 March 1863) 2nd s. of Michael Dillon of Sydney Parade, Dublin, and Maria MacCabe; B.A. (T.C.D.); H 1883, M.T. H 1885. 1886/M/09 [7 items].

DILLON, HENRY JOSEPH (b. 3 Sept. 1857) 4th s. of John Blake Dillon (decd.), M.P., Barrister-at-Law, of Fitzwilliam Square, Dublin, and Adelaide Hart; BL (M.T.); M 1877, M.T. E 1880. 1883/M/04 [8 items]. Afterwards entered the Franciscan Order, and was known as Father Nicholas. Minister-Provincial, 1912-18. Author of religious books. Died 1939. See Joachim Fischer and John Dillon (eds.), *The Correspondence of Myles Dillon 1922-1925* (Dublin, 1999), 281. *Burke's Irish Family Records* (1976), 364, decribes Henry as the 3rd son of John Blake Dillon, and gives his dates as 1856-1938.

DILLON, JAMES (b. 4 April 1922) eld. s. of James Dillon, railway employee, of Limerick, Co. Limerick, and Clare Ahern; M 1954. 1958/T/03 [2 items].

DILLON, JAMES MATHEW (b. 26 Sept. 1902) 4th s. of John Dillon, of 2 North Great Georges Street, Dublin, and Elizabeth Mathew; M 1928. 1931/T/06 [2 items]. T.D. for Donegal, 1932-7; for Monaghan, 1937-69. Co-founder of the Centre Party, 1933, aft. merged in Fine Gael. Sat as an Independent, March 1942-May 1952. Minister for Agriculture, 1948-51, and 1954-7. Leader of Fine Gael, 1959-65. Died 10 Feb. 1986. Obituary, *The Times*, 11 Feb. 1986. See Joachim Fischer and John Dillon (eds.), *The Correspondence of Myles Dillon 1922-1925* (Dublin, 1999), 281; *Burke's Irish Family Records* (1976), 363; and Louis McRedmond (ed.), *Modern Irish Lives*.

DILLON, LUKE PLUNKETT (b. 15 Oct. 1850) eld. s. of Andrew Dillon, M.D., of Ballaghaderin, Co. Mayo, and Arabella Plunkett; M 1871, M.T. T 1873. 1875/H/07 [2 items].

DILLON, Sir ROBERT WILLIAM CHARLIER, Bart. (b. 17 Jan. 1914) only s. of Robert Arthur Dillon, of 7 Tavistock Place, London, and Laura Maud Reese; B.A. (T.C.D.); M 1933. 1936/T/04 [2 items]. 8th (and last) Baronet [1801]; Baron [1782] of the Holy Roman Empire. Died *sine prole* 25 Dec. 1982. *Who's Who*; *Debrett*.

DILLON, THEOBALD AUGUSTUS (b. 11 Dec. 1894) eld. s. of Theobald Augustus Dillon (decd.), of Mount Dillon, Co. Roscommon, and Bertha Victoria Mulhall; B.A. (Cambridge); M 1920; [late Captain, 4th Bn. Connaught Rangers] 1922/T/04 [2 items].

DILLON, WILLIAM (b. 10 July 1850) eld. s. of John Blake Dillon (decd.), M.P., barrister-at-law, of 51 Fitzwilliam Square, Dublin, and Adelaide Hart; M 1869, M.T. M 1871. 1875/H/02 [2 items]. Emigrated to America, 1883, and practised as an attorney in

Chicago and Castle Rock, Colorado. A grandson has lately practised law in Chicago in the firm of Concannon, Dillon & Snook. *Burke's Irish Family Records* (1976), 364.

DILLON-LEETCH, MARY (b. 21 Nov. 1900) 2nd d. of Thomas Dillon-Leetch (decd.), solicitor, of Ballyhaunis, Co. Mayo, and Margaret O'Connor; B.A., LL.B. (T.C.D.); M 1920. 1923/T/05 [2 items]. 3rd woman to be called to the Irish Bar, and, under her twice-hyphenated married name of Molly Dillon-Leetch-Callan, the 2nd to practise in Dublin. Mother of Sylvia Callan [q.v.]; and aunt of the late Tom Dillon-Leetch [T 1987; (1939-2004)]. Died 8 Feb. 1959.

DIXON, BENJAMIN JOSEPH (b. 8 June 1922) eld. s. of Benjamin Joseph Dixon, B.Sc. (Eng.), A.R.Sc.I., civil engineer, of 62 Dartmouth Square, Dublin; M 1947. 1950/T/09 [2 items]. Died 1975.

DIXON, GEORGE YEATES (b. 9 Nov. 1856) 2nd s. of George Dixon (decd.), merchant, of 30 Holles Street, Dublin, and Rebecca Yeates; B.A. (T.C.D.); M 1877, G.I. M 1879. 1880/M/10 [6 items]. K.C., 25 Feb. 1919. Assistant Examiner, Land Commission. Author (with W. Gilliard) of *The Law relating to Sheriffs in Ireland* (Dublin, 1888); and compiler for the Council of the Incorporated Law Society of Ireland of *Reported Cases on Costs, 1867-1891* (Dublin, 1892).

DIXON, JOSEPH HENRY (b. 24 Oct. 1890) eld. s. of Henry Dixon of 19 Cabra Road, Dublin, and Mary Gillis; M 1908. 1913/M/04 [2 items].

DIXON, KEVIN JOSEPH (b. 22 June 1902) 4th s. of Martin G. Dixon, of 124 Rock Road, Booterstown, Co. Dublin, and Ellen Sheridan; B.Sc. (N.U.I.); M 1923. 1926/M/01 [2 items]. S.C., 2 April 1940. Attorney-General, 1942-6. Bencher, M 1942. Judge of the High Court, April 1946-Oct. 1959. Died 25 Oct. 1959. Obituary, *I.L.T. & S.J.*, xciii (1959), 264; *Who's Who*. Author (with Hector Hughes) of a commentary on the Landlord and Tenant Act 1931. See Louis McRedmond (ed.), *Modern Irish Lives*.

DIXON, MARTIN JOSEPH (b. 4 Feb. 1890) eld. s. of Martin Dixon, of 124 Rock Road, Booterstown, Co. Dublin, and Ellen Sheridan; B.A. (N.U.I.); M 1923. 1923*/M/03 [placed in 1924 bundle].

DOBBIN, FRANCIS KNOWLES (b. 30 Aug. 1863) 4th s. of the Revd. W.P.H. Dobbin (decd.), chaplain of Steven's Hospital, Dublin, and Fanny Knowles; B.A. (T.C.D.); M 1886. 1893/H/04 [5 items]. Died 10 April 1936.

DOBBIN, JAMES SHERIDAN KNOWLES (b. 20 May 1857) 2nd s. of the Revd. W.P.H. Dobbin, late chaplain of Steeven's Hospital, Dublin, and Frances Knowles; B.A.; H 1883. 1886/M/08 [6 items].

DOBBIN, WILLIAM TERTIUS (b. 18 Nov. 1875) eld. s. of William Dobbin, M.A., F.R.C.S.I, of Banbridge, Co. Down, and Margaret Robson; B.A. (R.U.I.); M 1898. 1901/T/08 [3 items].

DOBBYN, GEORGE LANCELOT (b. 30 May 1906) 5th s. of William Alexander Dobbyn, of Riverdale, Waterford, and Eleanor Adelaide Nelson; M 1924. 1927/M/19 [2 items]. Editor of the *Irish Reports*. Died 15 June 1949. Obituary, *I.L.T. & S.J.*, lxxxiii (1949), 167.

DOCKRELL, ANNE DOROTHY (b. 6 Jan. 1891) only d. of Sir Maurice Dockrell, D.L. (decd.), of Camolin, Monkstown, Dublin, and Margaret Sarah Shannon; M.B., LL.B; M 1928. 1938/E/01 [2 items]. Died *c*. 1975.

DOCKRELL, KENNETH BROOKS (b. 9 Jan. 1888) 6th s. of Sir Maurice Dockrell of Camolin, Monkstown, Co. Dublin, and Margaret Sarah Shannon; B.A.; M 1906. 1910/H/05 [3 items]. S.C., 14 July 1924. Died 11 March 1937. Obituary, *I.L.T. & S.J.*, lxxi (1937), 76.

DODD, WILLIAM HUSTON (b. 28 March 1844) only s. of Robert Dodd, of Woodville, Bangor, Co. Down, and Letitia Huston; M.A. (Queen's College Belfast); H 1870; M.T. H 1871. 1873/H/11 [8 items]. North-East Circuit. Q.C., 5 July 1884. 3rd Serjeant 1892. Crown prosecutor at Green Street. M.P. for North Tyrone 1906-7. Judge of the King's Bench Division, 1907-24. Privy Councillor 1913. Retired 1924. Died 17 March 1930. Obituary, *I.L.T. & S.J.*, lxiv (1930), 71; *Who's Who*. See Ball, *Judges*, ii. 382. Mentioned in Maurice Healy, *The Old Munster Circuit*, 40-42.

DODD, WILLIAM HUSTON (b. 8 Sept. 1875) only s. of Mr. Serjeant Dodd of 26 Fitzwilliam Square, Dublin, and Ellen Hunter; M 1896. 1899/M/08 [3 items]. Registrar to his father. Died 23 Jan. 1923. Obituary, *I.L.T. & S.J.*, lvii (1923), 24.

DOHERTY, JAMES COLUMBA (b. 9 June 1940) eld. s. of James Doherty, of 31 Clonmacnoise Road, Kimmage, Dublin, and Mary Friel; M 1959. Awarded 1st Victoria Prize. 1963/T/01 [1 item].

DOHERTY, JAMES WALKER (b. 15 July 1873) only s. of Edward Doherty of Glen House, Co. Donegal, and Emily Roper; B.A. (T.C.D.); M 1893. 1897/M/08 [4 items]. Died 1 Feb. 1925. Obituary, *I.L.T. & S.J.*, lix (1925), 34.

DOHERTY, PATRICK EDWARD (b. 1 April 1864) only s. of William J. Doherty, C.E., J.P., of St. Mura's, Fahan, Co. Donegal, and Bridget Scarry; E 1888. 1891/E/04 [8 items].

DOIG, HENRY STUART (b. 27 April 1874) eld. s. of James Doig of Kinloch, Cupar-Angus, Perthshire, and Anne Black; M 1910. 1912/E/01 [2 items]. 'Preferred the field of literature to that of law'. Served as editor of the Dublin *Daily Express* and *Evening Mail*, and was Irish correspondent of the *Daily Chronicle* and London *Daily Express*. Died, Middlesex, 3 April 1931. Obituary, *I.L.T. & S.J.*, lxv (1931), 89-90; *Who's Who*.

DOLAN, JOHN HENRY GEOFFREY (b. 30 Nov. 1926) only s. of James J. Dolan (decd.), architect, and Susan Mary White. See LOVATT-DOLAN, JOHN HENRY GEOFFREY.

DOLMAGE, CECIL GOODRICH JULIUS (b. 24 Feb. 1870) 2nd s. of Austin J. Dolmage of Rathkeale, Co. Limerick, and Frances Millicent Shedden; M.A., LL.D. (T.C.D.); H 1894. 1897/H/01 [5 items].

DONALDSON, JOHN (b. 1 June 1861) 4th s. of the Revd. Joseph Donaldson (decd.), Presbyterian clergyman, of The Manse, Fermoy, Co. Cork, and Mary Dickie; M.A. (QUI); M 1882, M.T. E 1884. 1885/M/01 [8 items]. North-East Circuit. K.C., 26 April 1913. Died 12 July 1913. Obituary, *I.L.T. & S.J.*, xlvii (1913), 201-2.

DONEGAN, CORNELIUS O'KANE (b. 21 Nov. 1861) young. s. of James Donegan (decd.), colliery contractor, of Airdrie, Lanark, and Marie O'Kane (decd.); B.A. (R.U.I.); M 1889; G.I. H 1894 [address at Withersfield, Braintree, Essex] 1910/T/02 [3 items].

DONNELLAN, MARY JOSEPHINE BRITTA (b. 11 April 1928) 3rd d. of Thomas Donnellan, farmer, of Taghadoe, Maynooth, Co. Kildare, and Mary Josephine Fahy; B.A. (N.U.I.); M 1946. 1949/M/07 [2 items].

DONNELLY, ARTHUR JOSEPH (b. 26 Feb. 1885) only s. of Augustine Donnelly (decd.), of 53 Lower Drumcondra Road, Dublin, and Mary Jeanne Broughall; M.A., B.Sc. (N.U.I.); M 1915. Awarded 1st Victoria Prize at the Final Examination in May 1918. 1966/E/01 [1 item]. In 1918 a civil servant in the Chief Secretary's Office, this man waited for 48 years before taking his Call. He was present when the Union flag was lowered at the Viceregal Lodge, and left Ireland in 1922: but returned to assist in the formation of the Irish civil service, from which he retired as a Revenue Commissioner in 1951. See 'Man of 82 called to the Bar', in *The Irish Times*, 17 May 1966, 11.

DONNELLY, HENRY GRATTAN (b. 8 Dec. 1884) 3rd s. of John Donnelly of Lower Clifton, Bangor, Co. Down, and Sara McConnell; M 1904. 1907/T/11 [4 items].

DONNELLY, JOHN ANDREW (b. 1 Oct. 1908) only s. of John Donnelly, of 7 Merrion View Avenue, Dublin, and Elizabeth Donnelly (decd.); M 1934. 1937/M/05 [2 items].

DONNELLY, JOHN (b. 28 Jan. 1929) 2nd s. of John Donnelly (decd.), chartered accountant, of St. Mary's Cowper Road, Dublin, and Mary Mehegan; M 1962. 1967/T/10 [1 item]. Chartered accountant. Listed in the 1984 edition of Maureen Cairnduff, *Who's Who in Ireland.*

DONNELLY, JOHN DESMOND MARY (b. 17 April 1916) eld. s. of Henry Grattan Marie Donnelly, of The Abbey, Athy, Co. Kildare, and Monica Mary O'Shaughnessy; E 1946 [*in absentia*] 1947/T/07 [2 items]. Actually called H 1948.

DONNELLY, JOSEPH ALOYSIUS (n.d.) only s. of Joseph Donnelly (decd.), of Ailesbury Road, Dublin, and Isabella Connolly. 1921/E/03 [1 item].

DONNELLY, THERESE ANNE (b. 6 Nov. 1934) 3rd d. of Kieran Donnelly, of 27 St. Kevin's Park, Dartry Road, Co. Dublin, and Nora Mary Rea; B.A., LL.B.(N.U.I.); M 1954. 1957/M/03 [2 items].

DONNELLY, THOMAS FEIDHLIM (b. 27 Feb. 1915) only s. of Daniel Donnelly (decd.), of Dungannon, Co. Tyrone, and Gertrude MacManus; M.A. (N.U.I.); M 1941. 1944/M/01 [2 items]. District Justice, aft. President of the District Court. Died 2005. Photograph and appreciation in *Courts Service News*, Vol. 7, No. 1 (March 2005), p. 12.

DONOGHUE, FLORENCE (b. 12 Feb. 1928) eld. d. of John Donoghue, of 10 York Road, Killarney, Co. Kerry, and Deborah O'Sullivan; B.A. (T.C.D.); M 1945. 1955/H/04 [2 items].

DONOHUE, FREDERICK JOSEPH (b. 6 Oct. 1925) eld. s. of Frederick Donohue, farmer, of Northyard, Scramogue, Co. Roscommon, and Brigid Cox; LL.B; M 1956. 1959/M/05 [2 items].

DONOVAN, JOHN THOMAS (b. 12 Dec. 1885) 9th s. of William Donovan (decd.), of Galway, Co. Galway, and Bridget Hurley; B.A. (R.U.I.); T 1925. 1925/M/29 [2 items].

DONOVAN, JOHN THOMAS (b. 22 Sept. 1877) eld. s. of Daniel Donovan of 2 Lonsdale Street, Belfast, and Anne McGrath; T 1913. 1914/E/01 [2 items].

DONOVAN, PHILIP JOSEPH (b. 1 June 1897) only s. of Patrick Donovan, of 49 Cabra Road, Dublin, and Francis Mary Giffney; B.A. (N.U.I.); M 1922. 1926/H/03 [2 items]. Registrar of Wards of Court.

DONOVAN, TERENCE DESMOND (b. 7 Nov. 1920) 3rd s. of John Joseph Donovan, of Glenbower, Dundrum, Co. Dublin, and Bridget Murnane; M 1941. 1945/T/13 [4 items].

DONOVAN, THOMAS JOSEPH ANTHONY (b. 4 July 1910) 3rd s. of St. John Henry Donovan, of Seafield, Spa, Tralee, Co. Kerry, and Eileen O'Connor; M 1928. 1931/M/17 [2 items]. Mentioned in Gerard A. Lee, *A Memoir of the South-Western Circuit* (Dublin, 1990), 37.

DONOVAN, TIMOTHY (b. 1 March 1888) eld. s. of John Donovan (decd.), of Courtmacsherry, Co. Cork, and Mary Driscoll; H 1928. 1931/M/14 [2 items].

DOOLIN, EUGENE JOSEPH (b. 21 Sept. 1926) eld. s. of Paul J. Doolin (decd.), merchant, of 1 Brookeville Park, Coolock, Co. Dublin, and Catherine Brennan; B.A., B.Comm. (T.C.D.); M 1962. 1965/T/02 [1 item].

DOONER, LAWRENCE (b. 7 Oct. 1845) young. s. of John Dooner of Barton Lodge, Rathfarnham, Dublin, and Georgina Dundas; B.A. (Oxford); T 1873, I.T. H 1869. 1876/H/02 [4 items].

DORAN, CHARLES FREDERICK GARFIELD young. s. of William Thomas Doran of Montpelier House, Malone Road, Belfast. 1913/T/14 [Memorial and papers missing]. Practised in Belfast, where he shared a room in Rea's Buildings with J.C. MacDermott: see J.C. MacDermott, *An Enriching Life*, 165.

DORAN, MICHAEL JOSEPH (b. 15 Feb. 1946) 3rd s. of Michael Joseph Doran, director, of 128B Merrion Road, Ballsbridge, Dublin, and Maureen Barker; B.C.L., LL.B.(N.U.I.); M 1965. 1968/M/27 [1 item].

DORGAN, JOSEPH (b. 19 April 1872) 3rd s. of John Nicholas Dorgan of Janeville, Sunday's Well, Co. Cork, and Ellen Keyes; M 1902. 1905/T/11 [3 items]. Chancery Division, Four Courts. Died 1942. Obituary, *I.L.T. & S.J.*, lxxvi (13 June 1942), 152.

DOUGAN, JAMES HAMILTON (b. 31 Oct. 1895) eld. s. of William Dougan, of 25 Great James Street, Londonderry, Co. Londonderry, and Elizabeth Orr; M 1924. 1925/M/25 [2 items].

DOUGHERTY, JOHN GERALD (b. 19 Oct. 1882) only s. of Sir James Brown Dougherty, C.V.O., C.B., of 6 Fitzwilliam Place, Dublin, and Mary Donaldson; B.A.; M 1904. 1907/T/15 [2 items]. Auditor of the College Historical Society. Secretary to the Lord Chancellor (1915). Died 25 March 1951. Obituary, *I.L.T. & S.J.*, lxxxv (21 April 1951), 98-9.

DOWNING, DANIEL McCARTHY (b. 14 Feb. 1875) 4th s. of Francis Creagh Downing, solicitor, of Lohercanon, Tralee, Co. Kerry, and Marie Cormack; M 1894. 1898/H/04 [9 items]. Called to Madras Bar, 1907.

DOWSE, RICHARD (b. 27 Aug. 1859) only s. of the Rt. Hon. Richard Dowse, Baron of the Exchequer, High Court of Justice, of 38 Mountjoy Square, Dublin, and Kate Moore; M 1880, M.T. T 1882. 1883/T/07 [5 items].

DOYLE, ARTHUR JOSEPH PETER (b. 24 May 1927) eld. s. of Arthur Peter Doyle, of Knockmullin House, Co. Wexford, and Kathleen O'Hara; (Mod.) B.A., B.L. (T.C.D.); M 1948. 1952/H/02 [2 items].

DOYLE, BRIAN ANDRE JAMES (b. 10 May 1911) 2nd s. of John Patrick Doyle, Judge of the High Court of Burma, and of 18 Elgin Road, Ballsbridge, Dublin, and Louise Amelie Renard; B.A. (T.C.D.); M 1929. 1932/M/14 [2 items].

DOYLE, CHARLES (b. 23 Jan. 1844) only s. of Denis Doyle, of Dublin (decd.), merchant, and Rosetta Kennedy; E 1862; I.T. 1869. 1871/T/1a [4 items].

DOYLE, CHARLES FRANCIS (b. 18 June 1863) 2nd s. of Daniel Doyle (decd.), solicitor, of 56 Georges Street, Limerick, and Eliza Simpson; B.A., Sch., Sen. Mod. (T.C.D.); M.A. (R.U.I.); M 1884. 1888/M/04 [6 items]. Auditor of the College Historical Society, 1889-9. K.C., 22 Jan. 1906. Appt. County Court Judge for Mayo, 7 Nov. 1910. One of the eight original judges of the Circuit Court, 1924, appointed to the Eastern Circuit. Died 29 Sept. 1928. Obituary, *I.L.T. & S.J.*, lxii (1928), 241; *Who's Who*.

DOYLE, CHARLES GERARD (b. 17 Aug. 1930) 2nd s. of Charles Doyle, of Ballysax, Co. Kildare, and Mary Eleanor Clarke; B.A. (N.U.I.); M 1949. 1952/M/14 [2 items]. Went Western Circuit. Contributor to James Meenan (ed.), *Centenary History of Lit. and Hist. Soc. of U.C.D.*

DOYLE, DENIS CONOR (b. 26 Oct. 1945) only s. of Thomas Francis Doyle, company director, of Ardmanagh, Glenbrook, Co. Cork, and Elizabeth Mary Walsh; B.A. (N.U.I.); M 1964. 1968/M/07 [1 item].

DOYLE, DONALD F.P. (b. 1 Oct. 1943) 3rd s. of Raymond Doyle (decd.), farmer and publican, of Broadway, Wexford, Co. Wexford, and Mary Ellen Stafford; B.Comm. (N.U.I.); M 1965. 1968/M/04 [1 item].

DOYLE, JOHN GERRARD (b. 26 July 1912) eld. s. of Michael Doyle, of 25 Vernon Grove, Clontarf, Dublin, and Julia Murphy (decd.); M 1933. 1937/M/06 [2 items].

DOYLE, JOHN PATRICK (b. 14 July 1882) eld. s. of James John Doyle, of 138 University Street, Belfast, and Mary Adelaide Joyce; B.A. (N.U.I.); M 1919. 1920/H/05 [2 items]. Judge of the High Court in Burma. Died at Tavoy, Burma, 22 June 1934. Obituary, *I.L.T. & S.J.*, lxviii (1934), 181. James Meenan (ed.), *Centenary History of Lit. and Hist. Soc. of U.C.D.*

DOYLE, LAURENCE (b. 28 May 1844) eld. s. of Laurence Doyle of Enniscorthy Co. Wexford, and Catharine Roche; B.A. (T.C.D.); E 1864; M.T. H 1866. 1868/H/3 [4 items].

DOYLE, MAURICE FRANCIS (b. 14 Dec. 1931) only s. of Valentine Doyle, builder, of 212 Collins Avenue, Drumcondra, Dublin, and Agnes O'Growney; B.A. (N.U.I.); M 1950. 1953/T/05 [2 items]. Aft. Secretary of the Department of Finance and Governor of the Central Bank. Listed in the 1984 and 1991 editions of Maureen Cairnduff, *Who's Who in Ireland*.

DOYLE, ROBERT JOSEPH (b. 1 June 1864) 2nd s. of Hugh Doyle, Registrar in Bankruptcy, of Melrose, Dalkey, Co. Dublin, and Christina Mary Byrne; M 1885, M.T. H 1887. 1889/M/02 [7 items]. K.C., 16 Dec. 1909. Appt. Recorder of Galway, 24 Nov. 1913, serving until 1924. Mentioned in Maurice Healy, *The Old Munster Circuit*, 243-5.

DOYLE, THOMAS ALOYSIUS (b. 14 June 1912) 2nd s. of Thomas Joseph Doyle, P.C., of 133 North Circular Road, Dublin, and Mary Margaret Treacy (decd.); M 1932. 1935/M/06 [2 items]. S.C., 29 Jan. 1954. Judge of the High Court, 17 Dec. 1974. Retired 13 June 1984. An incident in Naas Courthouse in 1947 is mentioned in Patrick MacKenzie, *Lawful Occasions*, 100-4. Listed in the 1984 edition of Maureen Cairnduff, *Who's Who in Ireland*.

DRENNAN, JOHN THOMAS (b. 7 Oct. 1873) 2nd s. of William H. Drennan, Assistant Registrar of Deeds in Ireland, of Henrietta Street, Dublin, and Elizabeth Trimble; B.A. (T.C.D.); M 1895. 1898/M/10 [3 items]. President of the University Philosophical Society, T.C.D., 1898-9. Died 7 Nov. 1942. Obituary, *I.L.T. & S.J.*, lxxvi (1942), 283-4.

DROMGOOLE, CHARLES (b. 29 July 1865) only surv. s. of Charles Dromgoole (decd.) of Newry, Co. Armagh, and Catherine Collins; M.A., LL.D. (R.U.I.); M 1888. 1894/H/04 [8 items]. K.C., 28 Feb. 1910. Appt. County Court Judge for Kerry; 28 Feb. 1913; aft.

(1920) for Carlow, Kildare, Wexford and Wicklow. Bencher 1924. One of the eight original judges of the Circuit Court, 1924, appointed for Dublin. Died 27 Jan. 1927. Obituary, *I.L.T. & S.J.*, lxi (1927), 34; *Who's Who*. Mentioned in Maurice Healy, *The Old Munster Circuit*, 158-60.

DRUMMOND, MICHAEL (b. 19 Dec 1846) 2nd s. of Michael Drummond of Ballyshannon, Co. Donegal and Jane Kelly; M.A. (Queen's University); M 1869; M.T. E 1871. 1872/M/6 [2 items]. Q.C., Jan. 1891. County Court Judge for Cavan and Leitrim; and aft. (1914-8) for Meath, Westmeath, King's and Longford, Author, jointly with Judge Law Smith, of a work on High Court procedure. Died 25 May 1921. Obituary, *I.L.T. & S.J.*, lv (1921), 136; *Who's Who*.

DRURY, THOMAS CHALMERS (b. 4 May 1847) 3rd s. of Thomas Drury (decd.), J.P., of Dartry, Co. Dublin, and Marion [Girdwood]; M.A., LL.B. (T.C.D.); E 1880, M.T. H 1882. 1883/E/05 [6 items]. K.C., 5 June 1918. Police Magistrate, Dublin. Died 10 April 1925. Obituary, *I.L.T. & S.J.*, lix (1925), 95.

DUFF, JOHN EDWIN (b. 27 Jan. 1895) 2nd s. of John Duff (decd.), of 55 St. Patrick's Road, Dublin, and Susan Letitia Frehill; B.Sc; M 1920. 1923/T/11 [2 items]. Secretary of the Department of Justice. Died 20 Aug. 1949.

DUFF, LIAM B. (b. 17 Dec. 1924) eld. s. of Christopher Duff (decd.), of Old Cabra Road, Dublin, and Ellen Murphy; M 1944. 1947/T/05 [2 items].

DUFFY, BERNARD JOSEPH (b. 20 June 1882) 2nd s. of James Joseph Duffy of Carrickmacross, Co. Monaghan, and Mary Anne McEntegart; B.A. (T.C.D.); M 1904. 1907/T/16 [3 items]. Manager of mineral water business. Author of the novels *Oriel* (1918) and *The Rocky Road* (1929); and of a treatise *Food for Thought* (1944). Died 31 Mar. 1952. Obituary, *I.L.T. & S.J.*, lxxxvi (1952), 111.

DUFFY, FRANCIS JOSEPH (b. 15 Oct. 1932) eld. s. of Francis Joseph Duffy, of Dublin Street, Monaghan, and Lucy McDonald; B.A. (N.U.I.); M 1955. 1960/M/06 [2 items].

DUFFY, FREDERICK MYLES (b. 11 April 1895) 2nd s. of Myles Duffy (decd.), of Kingscourt, Co. Cavan, and Rose Daniel; T 1925. 1926/M/18 [2 items].

DUFFY, GEORGE GAVAN. see Gavan Duffy, George

DUFFY, PATRICK (b. 22 Dec. 1890) 2nd s. of Patrick Duffy, of Castletown, Dundalk, Co. Louth, and Rose Griffin; M 1925. 1928/E/02 [3 items].

DUGGAN, JAMES STEPHEN (b. 11 Aug. 1862) 3rd s. of Thomas Raphael Duggan (decd.) of St. Helen's, Clonliffe, Dublin, and Eleanor Murphy (decd.); cand. bachelor (N.U.I.); M 1908 [address at 'Winton Villa', Rathgar, Dublin]. 1911/T/11 [2 items].

DUGGAN, MARION ELIZABETH (b. 27 July 1884) only child of James Duggan, of 11 Brighton Avenue, Rathgar, Dublin, and Elizabeth E. Denham; B.A., LL.B. (T.C.D.); M 1922. 1925/T/01 [3 items]. Dáil court official: mentioned in Mary Kotsonouris, *Retreat from Revolution: The Dáil Courts, 1920-24* (Dublin, 1994), 132. Died 24 June 1943.

DUNBOYNE, Rt. Hon. Lord (PATRICK THEOBALD TOWER BUTLER) (b. 27 Jan. 1917) only s. of Captain the Rt. Hon. Lord Dunboyne (Fitzwalter Geo. Butler) (decd.), of Knoppogue Castle, Quin, Co. Clare, and Dowager Lady Dunboyne (Dora Isolde Tower); M 1964; M.T. 1964. 1966/E/02 [9 items]. Irish Guards, 1939; POW in Germany until 1943. In 1945 succeeded his father in the peerage as 28th Baron Dunboyne; 'on terms of hospitality with the Queen all his life'. English barrister, 1949; expert on ecclesiastical law (adviser to two successive Archbishops of Canterbury) and the law of the peerage (in 1965 one of the petitioners before the Committee of Privileges of the House of Lords for the holding of an election of Irish representative peers). Recorder of Hastings; and (in 1972) circuit judge. Founder of the English Bar's lawn tennis club. President of the Irish Genealogical Research Society. Lord Dunboyne told *The Irish Times* (17 May 1966, p. 11): 'One of my ancestors, the jovial Sir Toby [Theobald] Butler [Solicitor-General to James II], was one of the people who negotiated a reasonably good settlement following the Siege of Limerick'. Died 19 May 2004. Obituary in *The Times*, 25 May 2004.

DUNCAN, JOHN COLLEY (b. 31 Dec. 1884) only s. of George Duncan of 1 Fortfield Terrace, Upper Rathmines, Dublin, and Charlotte Maria Delaney; M.A. (T.C.D.); M 1909. 1911/M/01 [2 items].

DUNCAN, SAMUEL JOSEPH (b. 30 June 1878) eld. s. of Samuel Duncan of Newry, Co. Down, and Mary Macdowell; Sen. Mod. B.A. (T.C.D.); M 1897. 1900/T/05 [3 items].

DUNLOP, JAMES MARCUS MUNTZ (b. 24 Dec. 1865) young. s. of Joseph Dunlop (decd.) of Mount Hamilton, Co. Antrim, and Mary Robertson Munnis; LL.D. (T.C.D.); H 1895. 1900/H/02x [5 items].

DUNLOP, ROBERT ALEXANDER (b. 10 April 1866) eld. s. of Andrew Dunlop, of Westminster, Grosvenor Road, Dublin, and Isabella Bond; M 1893. 1896/M/07 [4 items].

DUNN, MICHAEL JOSEPH (b. 14 May 1850) 2nd s. of Michael Patrick Dunn (decd.), merchant, of Watercourse, Cork, and Mary Anne Kearney; B.A. (T.C.D.); M 1870, M.T. H 1872. 1875/E/04 [4 items]. K.C. , 22 Jan. 1906. Died 22 May 1907. Obituary, *I.L.T. & S.J.*, xli (1907), 148.

DUNNE, CHARLES WILLIAM HENRY (b. 8 Sept. 1862) only s. of William Dunne (decd.), of Londonderry, and Rebecca Dupré Lindsay; M 1882. 1887/T/02 [6 items].

DUNNE, FRANCIS (b. 17 Aug. 1938) 5th s. of Christopher Dunne, CIÉ employee, of 113 Ballymun Avenue, Ballymun, Dublin, and Norah Lyons; M 1959. 1963/T/02 [1 item].

DUNNE, FRANCIS WILLIAM BRADNEY (b. 11 June 1850) 2nd s. of Revd. John Henry Dunne (decd.) of Dunshaughlin, Co. Meath, and Augusta Bockett; B.A. (T.C.D.); M 1870; M.T. H 1872. 1874/M/2 [4 items].

DUNNE, RICHARD PATRICK (b. 2 April 1910) eld. s. of Patrick Dunne, accountant, Revenue Department, of 63 Lower Drumcondra Road, Dublin, and Agnes Mary Brougham; B.A. (N.U.I.); M 1930. 1933/M/06 [3 items]. Went Midland Circuit. Aft. worked in London for the Foreign Office, Inland Revenue, and commercially. Died 22 Dec. 1962. Obituary, *I.L.T. & S.J.*, xcvi (1962), 342. Contributor to James Meenan (ed.), *Centenary History of Lit. and Hist. Soc. of U.C.D.*

DUNS, WILLIAM (b. 28 Jan. 1888) only s. of William Duns (Sr.), of Newcastle-on-Tyne, and Isabella Oliver; M 1919; [includes record of war service; awarded military cross, July 1917] 1921/H/04 [3 items].

DURCAN, JOHN JAMES (b. 9 May 1907) 3rd s. of John Durcan, of Turlough, Castlebar, Co. Mayo, and Julia Barrett; M 1933. 1936/T/05 [2 items]. Judge of the Circuit Court (Western Circuit); and President of the Court, 1975-7. Father of the poet, Paul Durcan.

DURKAN, NORA (b. 2 Feb. 1921) only d. of Thomas Durkan, of Culmore, Swinford, Co. Mayo, and Bridget Durkan; M 1943. Awarded 2nd Victoria Prize. 1948/T/02 [2 items].

DUTT, DHAN RAJ (b. 7 May 1900) eld. s. of Mehta Gukhramdas Dutt, of Gujrat, Punjab, India, and Nehal Devi Bhanwal; M 1921. 1924/T/03 [2 items].

DWYER, MATTHEW JOSEPH FRANCIS (b. 2 April 1923) only s. of Michael John Dwyer, County Registrar, of 16 St. Mary's Road, Ballsbridge, Dublin, and Mary Josephine Hannan; B.A., Mod. (T.C.D.); M 1948. 1951/M/15 [3 items].

EAMES, ROBERT (b. 15 June 1837) 4th s. of William James Eames (decd.) of Londonderry, and Elizabeth Anne Comyns; B.A. (T.C.D.); E 1870, I.T. M 1871. 1873/H/12 [4 items].

EARLY, DANIEL PATRICK (b. 5 Jan. 1928) 4th s. of John J. Early (decd.), solicitor, of 'Belvedere', 132 Howth Road, Dublin, and Imelda Josephine Dowling; M 1947. 1951/M/08 [2 items].

EARLY, JAMES (b. 31 Oct. 1879) 3rd s. of Peter Early (decd.) of Swords, Co. Dublin, and Mary Anne Reilly; M 1908. 1910/T/08 [3 items]. Died at Ballarat, Australia, 1920. Obituary, *I.L.T. & S.J.*, liv (13 Nov. 1920), 277.

EASON, CHARLES (b. 10 April 1853) 2nd s. of Charles Eason of 30 Kenilworth Square, Rathgar, Dublin, and Caroline Birks; M.A. (T.C.D.); M 1879, M.T. H 1881. 1883/E/02 [6 items].

ECCLES, WILLIAM (b. 1 July 1847) eld. s. of Samuel Eccles (decd.) of Coleraine, Co. Londonderry, and Ann Robb; H 1883, M.T. T 1882. 1885/M/10 [9 items].

EDGAR, JOHN HAMMOND (b. 23 Oct. 1879) only s. of Robert Smyth Edgar of Dromore, Co. Down, and Eliza Jane Jardine; M.A. (R.U.I.); M 1901; M.T. M 1902. 1904/M/01

[10 items]. Lieutenant, 9th Batt., Durham Light Infantry. Died in Flanders, 24 Feb. 1916. [Name on the Bar War Memorial]

EDGE, JOSEPH SAW (b. 11 July 1848) young. surv. s. of John Edge (decd.) of Crettyard House, Queen's Co., and Sarah Jane Edge; B.A. (T.C.D.); M 1868, M.T. M 1870. 1881/T/01 [1 item]. North-East Circuit. K.C., 13 July 1921. Died 18 Jan. 1922. Obituary, *I.L.T. & S.J.*, lvi (1922), 23-4.

EGAN, DONAL BRIAN (b. 14 Sept. 1937) eld. s. of Thomas Egan, company managing director, of 'Drumcora', Blackrock, Co. Cork, and Molly Power; B.C.L.; M 1955. 1960/T/08 [3 items].

EGAN, JAMES FRANCIS (b. 1 Dec. 1923) 2nd s. of James Sergius Egan. of 3 Greygates, Stillorgan Road, Co. Dublin, and Christina O'Donnell; B.A. (N.U.I.); M 1942. 1945/M/02 [2 items]. Also known as Séamus Egan, S.C., 16 March 1962. Judge of the High Court, 13 Dec. 1984; of the Supreme Court, 22 April 1991. Retired 1 Dec. 1995. Died 23 Jan. 2004. Obituary, *The Irish Times*, 31 Jan. 2004; Appreciation (by T.A. Finlay) in ibid., 23 Feb. 2004. Listed in the 1984 and 1991 editions of Maureen Cairnduff, *Who's Who in Ireland*.

EGAN, PATRICK JOSEPH (b. 24 March 1915) young. s. of Thomas Egan (decd.), farmer, of Knockgrafton, Cahir, Co. Tipperary, and Bridget Condon (decd.); BA(N.U.I.); M 1962. 1965/M/02 [1 item].

EIFFE, LUKE SWEETMAN (b. 23 Sept 1846) only s. of Patrick Eiffe (decd.) of Donoughmore Lodge, Co. Meath, and Grace Roe; B.A. (T.C.D.); H 1872, M.T. H 1870. 1873/T/1 [2 items]. Author (aided by his colleagues A. Houston and J.O. Wylie) of *The Judicature Acts, Ireland, 1877 and 1878, and orders, rules, and forms ...* (Dublin, 1881)

EKWEREKWU, ISAAC IFEANYI (b. 5 Feb. 1930) 5th s. of Joseph Anara Ekwerekwu, landowner, of 14 Court Road, Onitsha, Nigeria, and Elizabeth Nwerie Okonkwo; M 1955. 1959/M/10 [2 items].

ELLIS, ARTHUR CHARLES (b. 12 Jan. 1885) eld. s. of William Edward Ellis, M.A., LL.D., Barrister-at-Law, of 3 Dartmouth Road, Dublin, and Edith Anne Graves; B.A., LL.B. (T.C.D.). 1911/T/05 [3 items]. Auditor, Local Government Board, Died April 1963.

ELLIS, HENRY (b. 3 Dec. 1917) 2nd s. of Thomas John Ellis, of Omeath, Co. Louth, and Mary Hardy; M 1943. 1947/T/04 [2 items].

ELLIS, MALCOLM HENRY GRAEME (b. 8 Dec. 1909) 3rd s. of Ernest Albert George Ellis (decd.), of 21 Palmerston Park, Dublin, and Mildred Nash Ellis; B.A., LL.B. (T.C.D.); M 1929. 1933/H/02 [2 items]. S.C., 3 March 1955.

ELLIS, WILLIAM EDWARD (b. 30 Nov. 1853) eld. s. of Malcolm Graeme Ellis of 8 Ontario Tce, Rathmines, Dublin, and Mildred Webb; B.A., LL.B. (T.C.D.); M 1877; M.T. M 1879. 1881/H/04 [6 items]. Called to the English Bar, M.T., H 1900. Auditor, Local Government Board, Justice of the Peace for Dublin City and Co. Clare.

ELLIS, WILLIAM ROCHE DENNY (b. 9 April 1920) 2nd s. of Frederick Bruce Ellis, of Chagrin Falls, Ohio, SA, and Aileen Roche; B.A. (N.U.I.); M 1941. 1944/T/07 [2 items]. S.C., 3 Oct. 1961. Judge of the High Court, 1 Oct. 1979. Died 16 Dec. 1983. Obituary [by R.G.S.] in the *Irish Law Times*, new series, ii (1984), 10.

ELLISON, MARTIN GORE (b. 7 Sept. 1871) 3rd s. of John Ellison of Lisburn, Co. Antrim, and Elizabeth Edmondson; M.A., LL.B. (R.U.I.); M 1892. 1897/E/01 [4 items]. K.C. (N.I.), E 1938. Editor of *The Northern Ireland Reports*, 1940-45. County Court Judge for Armagh and Fermanagh, and acting Recorder of Londonderry (1947).

ELYAN, ISIDORE VICTOR (B. 5 Sept. 1909) 2nd s. of Jacob Elyan (decd.), of 'Ormeau', Newtownsmith, Dún Laoghaire, Co. Dublin, and Olga [?]; E 1949. 1949/T/10 [3 items]. Colonial Legal Service. Resident Magistrate, Accra, Gold Coast.

ENGLAND, WILLIAM GEORGE (b. 27 Nov. 1856) only s. of Thomas England (decd.), gentleman, of Hacknahay, Co. Armagh, and Jane Wilson; B.A. (Q.C.G.); M 1881, M.T. M 1883. 1885/H/03 [4 items].

ENGLAND, WILLIAM HENRY PHILIP (b. 20 May 1898) eld. s. of St. James Bradfield England, solicitor, of St. Michael Street, Tipperary, Co. Tipperary, and Maud Dobbyn; E 1961. 1965/T/05 [1 item]. His younger brother is here listed as Bradfield-England.

ENNIS, EDWARD ARMSTRONG Jnr. (b. 6 July 1865) 2nd s. of Edward A. Ennis, solicitor, of 8 Grosvenor Road, Rathgar, Dublin, and Lydia Byrne; B.A. (T.C.D.); M 1882. 1886/M/06 [5 items].

ENNIS, EDWARD HENRY (b. 20 June 1855) 2nd surv. s. of James Ennis (decd.), merchant, of Belfast, and Ellen Greer; H 1884. 1886/M/16 [8 items]. Assistant Under Secretary to the Lord Lieutenant. Died (as the result of an accident) 18 Aug. 1908. Obituary, *I.L.T. & S.J.*, xlii (1908), 218.

ENNIS, JOHN JOSEPH [n.d.] eld. s. of Nicholas Ennis (decd.) of Claremount, Julianstown, Co. Meath, and Mary Louisa Kieran; M 1889. 1893/M/03 [6 items]. District Commissioner in the Colonial Service. Died at Sekondi, Gold Coast, 16 March 1907. Obituary, *I.L.T. & S.J.*, xli (1907), 90.

ENRIGHT, DANIEL DOMINIC (b. 28 Aug. 1925) eld. s. of Daniel John Enright, farmer, of Doonaghboy, Kilkee, Co. Clare, and Anna Costelloe; M 1947. 1951/M/11 [2 items].

ESMONDE, JOHN HENRY GRATTAN (b. 27 June 1928) eld. s. of Anthony Charles Esmonde, medical practitioner, of St. Osmond's, Gorey, Co. Wexford, and Eithne Grattan Esmonde; M 1945. 1949/M/20 [2 items]. S.C., 4 Oct. 1971. Fine Gael T.D. for Wexford, 1973-7. Judge of the Circuit Court, 1977-87. Succeeded his father as 16th Baronet, 1981. Died 16 May 1987. Obituary, *The Times*, 13 June 1987. *Who's Who*; *Debrett's Illustrated Baronetage*.

ESMONDE, JOHN LYMBRICK (b. 15 Dec. 1893) eld. s. of John Joseph Esmonde, M.D., M.P. (decd.), of Drominagh, Borrisokane, Co. Tipperary, and Rose Magennis; H 1919. Captain, late of R.D.F. 1921/E/02 [1 item]. 14th Baronet. Nationalist M.P. for N. Tipperary, 1915-1918. Fine Gael T.D. for Wexford, 1937-44 and 1948-51.S.C., 14 Oct. 1942. Bencher, 1948. Died 6 July 1958. Obituary, *I.L.T. & S.J.*, xcii (1958), 203-4; *Who's Who*; *Debrett's Illustrated Baronetage*.

ESMONDE, LAURENCE GRATTAN (b. 3 Nov. 1863) 2nd s. of Sir John Esmonde, M.P., late of Ballynastragh, Co. Wexford, and Louise Grattan; E 1886. 1890/T/01 [7 items]. Died 1 Feb. 1943. Obituary, *I.L.T. & S.J.*, lxxvii (1943), 37-8; *Debrett's Illustrated Baronetage*.

EVANS, FRANCIS NICHOLAS (b. 14 Jan 1846) 2nd s. of Nicholas Evans of Newtown, Co. Cork, Captain R.N., and Katherine Gervais; B.A. (T.C.D.); H 1867; I.T. T 1868. 1870/M/3 [4 items].

EVANS, ROBERT BRENDAN (b. 28 Oct. 1902) eld. s. of Edward Hugh Evans, of 'Silveracre', Howth Road, Clontarf, Dublin, and Sarah Clinton; M 1928. 1931/T/04 [2 items].

EVANS, ROBERTS WALTER (b. 30 Nov. 1873) 3rd s. of John Westropp Evans of Doneraile, Co. Cork, and Annie Connor; M 1897. 1900/M/04 [5 items]. Died 19 Oct. 1932. Obituary, *I.L.T. & S.J.*, lxvi (1932), 265.

EVANS, SAMUEL WILLIAM (b. 27 Sept. 1860) 2nd s. of William Evans of Leeson Park Avenue, Dublin, and Catherine Curry; M 1899. 1902/M/13 [3 items].

EVERARD, JAMES PATRICK (b. 18 Aug. 1911) eld. s. of James Everard, farmer, of Churchill, Navan, Co. Meath, and Jane Denning; M 1945. 1951/H/05 [2 items].

EWART, FREDERICK WILLIAM (b. 14 Oct. 1858) young. s. of Sir John Ewart, M.P., of Glenmachan, Co. Down, and Isabella Kelso Matthewson; B.A. (Oxford); M 1885. 1888/T/03 [7 items].

EXSHAW, ELDON YOUNG (b. 5 June 1930) only s. of Charles Eldon Exshaw, of Springfield, Elphin, Co. Roscommon, and Isobel Cameron Hagan; M 1950. Awarded Brooke Scholarship. 1953/M/01 [3 items]. Reid Professor, T.C.D., 21 Sept. 1955; aft Lecturer in Law, T.C.D., 21 Sept. 1964. Died 2001. *Burke's Irish Family Records* (1976), 395.

FAHY, BRIAN VINCENT DE PAUL (b. 18 Jan. 1923) eld. s. of John Vincent Fahy, District Justice, of Avenue House, Gorey, Co. Wexford, and Mary O'Brien; B.A. (N.U.I.); M 1940. 1944/M/02 [2 items]. S.C., 27 Feb. 1975.

FAHY, EDWARD (b. 20 June 1913) only s. of Edward Fahy, Barrister-at-Law, of Riverside House, Islandbridge, Dublin, and Violet Tunstead; M 1933. 1936/M/05 [2 items]. Reid

Professor, T.C.D., 1940-5. Examiner at King's Inns. Wrote on penal reform in *Hermathena*. Died 26 Dec. 1970. Obituary, *I.L.T. & S.J.*, cv (1971), 19.

FAHY, EDWARD (b. 30 June 1876) 2nd s. of William Wall Fahy, of Kilcrea, Ovens, Co. Cork, and Margaret Leary; M 1902. 1905/M/07 [3 items]

FAHY, FRANCIS PATRICK [Proinnsias Ó Fathaigh] (b. 23 May1880) eld. s. of John Fahy, N.T. (decd.), of Kilchreest, Loughrea, Co. Galway, and Mary Fahy (decd.); M 1924. 1931/M/05 [2 items].

FALCONER, JOHN BOURSIQUOT (b. 12 Sept 1844) eld. s. of John Falconer, printer and publisher, of Sackville Street, Dublin, and Ellen Bradshaw; B.A., LL.D (T.C.D.); T 1868, I.T. M 1869. 1872/T/2x [2 items]. Q.C. , 22 April 1899. Died, as Father of the Irish Bar and of the Leinster Circuit, 31 August 1924. Obituary, *I.L.T. & S.J.*, lviii (1924), 228-9; *Who's Who*.

FALKINER, CAESAR LITTON (b. 26 Sept. 1863) 2nd s. of Frederick Richard Falkiner, Q.C., Recorder of Dublin, of Killiney, Co. Dublin, and Adelaide Sadleir; B.A. (T.C.D.); M 1883. 1887/H/05 [6 items]. President of the University Philosophical Society, T.C.D., 1885-6. Assistant Legal Land Commissioner. Author *inter alia* of *Illustrations of Irish History and Topography* (1904). Died 5 August 1908. Obituary, *I.L.T. & S.J.*, xlii (1908), 197; notice, *ibid.*, 260, 'The late Mr Litton Falkiner and Fair Rent Applications'. See *D.N.B.*; and memoir by Edward Dowden prefixed to Falkiner's *Essays relating to Ireland* (1909).

FALLON, WILLIAM (b. 13 Feb. 1881) 2nd s. of John Fallon (decd.), of 10 Fitzgibbon Street, Dublin, and Alicia Fallon; B.A. (N.U.I.); M 1913. 1920/T/01 [2 items]. S.C., 19 Oct. 1964. Contributor to James Meenan (ed.), *Centenary History of Lit. and Hist. Soc. of U.C.D.*

FANNING, ARNOLD F. (b. 5 May 1942) eld. s. of J.G. Fanning, proprietor, Midland Tribune, of 9 St. John's Mall, Birr, Co. Offaly, and Elizabeth Hickey; B.C.L. (N.U.I.); M 1961. 1966/H/02 [1 item].

FARRAN, EDMOND CHOMLEY (b. 2 Oct. 1879) 2nd s. of Edmond Chomley Farran (decd.) of Knocklyon House, Co. Dublin, and Annie Hume Ryan; B.A., LL.B. (T.C.D.); M 1901. 1904/H/02 [3 items]. Editor (with R.A. Walker) of *First Supplement to the Law Relating to Land Purchase in Ireland* (Dublin: Hodges & Figgis, 1907). Captain, Royal Irish Rifles. Died in Flanders, 16 June 1915. [Name on the Bar War Memorial (the spelling Farren on which is erroneous) and on the Menin Gate at Ypres].

FARRELL, GERALD PATRICK (b. 24 Oct. 1890) eld. s. of James Patrick Farrell, M.P., of Market Square, Longford, and Bridget Maria Fitzgerald; B.A. (University College Galway); M 1909. 1912/M/02 [2 items].

FARRELL, HENRY WILLIAM (b. 2 Nov. 1873) young. s. of Henry Farrell (decd.), of Mountjoy Square, Dublin, and Susan Farrell; E 1913. 1918/M/01 [2 items].

FARRELL, JOHN JOSEPH (b. 12 July 1900) eld. s. of John Joseph Farrell, of 9 Iona Drive, Glasnevin, Dublin, and Mary Josephine Redmond; M 1918. 1921/M/12 [2 items]. District Justice 1943. Contributor to James Meenan (ed.), *Centenary History of Lit. and Hist. Soc. of U.C.D.*

FARRELL, JOHN MICHAEL (b. 27 Feb. 1938) eld. s. of John Farrell, District Justice, of 'Glenaulin', Foster Avenue, Stillorgan Road, Dublin, and Kathleen Eveleen Tynan; B.A. (N.U.I.); M 1957. 1960/M/02 [3 items]. S.C., 2 Oct. 1978. Author of *Irish Law of Specific Performance* (Dublin, 1994).

FARRELL, NIALL CHRISTOPHER (b. 8 Feb. 1940) only s. of Francis Joseph Farrell, of Ballymahon, Co. Longford, and Beatrice Connolly; M 1959. 1964/T/05 [5 items].

FARRELLY, MICHAEL JAMES (B. 27 Jan. 1856) 3rd s. of P. Farrelly (decd.) of Drogheda, Co. Louth, and Ellen [Waters]; M.A., LL.D. (R.U.I.); M 1888, M.T. T 1887. 1891/H/08 [9 items].

FARRELLY, PHILIP (b. 13 Feb. 1842) 5th s. of Thomas Farrelly (decd.) of Bailieboro, Co. Cavan and Elizabeth O'Reilly; H 1860; M.T. T 1864. 1868/T/1 [6 items].

FARUQI, SHEIKH MOHAMMAD MUMTAZ (b. 28 Oct. 1884) eld. s. of Sheikh Mohammad Nasir ud Din, of Gujrat City, India; M 1914. 1917/T/11 [2 items].

FAULKNER, THOMAS PATRICK (b. 16 Dec. 1865) 2nd s. of James Faulkner, merchant, of Castlebar, Co. Mayo, and Maria Teresa Walshe; B.A. (R.U.I.); M 1886. 1890/M/04 [7 items].

FAWCETT, JASPER EVELYN (b. 17 Feb. 1867) eld. s. of John Fawcett, B.L., J.P., of 39 Raglan Road, Dublin and Friars Park, Co. Roscommon, and Tridora Fawcett; M 1886. 1889/M/08 [9 items].

FAWSITT, DIARMAID (b. 7 May 1884) 2nd s. of Boyle Fawsitt (decd.), of Bandon, Co. Cork; M 1925. 1928/T/07 [2 items]. Irish Republican consul in U.S. 1919-21. Former civil servant. S.C., 21 Dec. 1938. Judge of the Circuit Court (South-Eastern Circuit). Died 27 April 1967. Obituary, I.L.T. & S.J., ci (1967), 190. Obituary (by Hugh O'Flaherty) in The Irish Times. Mentioned in Patrick MacKenzie, Lawful Occasions, 48-52, 100-4.

FAWSITT, SEÁN MACDIARMAID (10 May 1918) 4th s. of Diarmaid Fawsitt, of 'St. Petroc', Stillorgan, Co. Dublin, Senior Counsel, and Cathleen M. Kenny; B.A. (N.U.I.); M 1936. Awarded Society's Exhibition. 1939/M/02 [1 item]. S.C., 5 March 1953. Judge of the Circuit Court. Retired 1988. Died 2001.

FAY, WILLIAM PATRICK (b. 17 April 1909) eld. s. of Henry Edward Fay, of St. Michael's, Dalkey, Co. Dublin, and Helene Magdalen; M 1928. 1931/M/01x [2 items]. Department of External Affairs. Irish ambassador to France, Canada and the United States. Died 1970.

FEEHAN, MICHAEL A. (b. 28 May 1931) eld. s. of John J. Feehan, of Cashel, Co. Tipperary, and Nora A. Ryan; B.A. (N.U.I.); M 1950. 1953/M/04 [2 items]. S.C., 6 Oct. 1975. Died 12 April 2002.

FEELY, EDWARD MAURICE (2 Sept. 1858) 2nd s. of James Feely of Tramore, Co. Waterford, and Mary Anne O'Riordan; E 1877, M.T. E 1879. 1880/T/03 [7 items].

FEELY, RICHARD J. (b. 10 Sept. 1886) eld. s. of Thomas Feely (decd.), of 6 Orchard Terrace, Grangegorman, Dublin, and Anne Cully (decd.); M 1924. 1926/M/04 [2 items].

FENNELL, MICHAEL JOHN (b. 23 Sept. 1924) eld. s. of Thomas Fennell, of 29 Park Drive, Cowper Gardens, Rathmines, Dublin, and Nora Hennigan; B.A. (N.U.I.); M 1947. 1950/M/08 [2 items].

FENNELLY, MICHAEL PATRICK (b. 3 May 1942) 7th s. of William Francis Fennelly, veterinary surgeon, of Callan, Co. Kilkenny, and Josephine Pollard; B.A. (N.U.I.); M 1960. Awarded Society's Exhibition Prize. 1964/H/02 [1 item]. Known as 'Nial' Fennelly. S.C., 24 Feb. 1978. Chairman of the Legal Aid Board, 1983-90. Advocate-General, European Court of Justice, 1995-2000. Appt. a judge of the Supreme Court, 16 Oct. 2000. Listed [with photograph] in the 1991 edition of Maureen Cairnduff, Who's Who in Ireland.

FERGUSON, GEORGE JOSEPH NAPIER (b. 1 Feb. 1853) 3rd surv. s. of William Ferguson, Barrister-at-Law, of 48 Mountjoy Square, Dublin, and Charlotte Fitzpatrick; B.A.; E 1874, I.T. M 1875. 1877/E/07 [7 items]. Author, jointly with his father, of A Treatise on the Supreme Court of Judicature Act (Ireland), 1877 (Dublin, 1878).

FERNANDO, W.S.C. (b. 23 Oct. 1895) young. s. of W.L. Fernando, planter, of Winifred House, Marawila, Colombo, Chilan, Ceylon, and Agnes Lowe; M 1916. 1920/T/03 [2 items].

FERRISS, ALFRED (b. 21 Jan. 1913) 4th s. of John Patrick Ferriss, of 19 Eglantine Avenue, Belfast, and Julia O'Keeffe; M 1931. 1935/T/03 [2 items]. Died Oct. 1969.

FETHERSTONHAUGH, GODFREY (b. 11 April 1858) eld. s. of Stephen Radcliff Fetherstonhaugh of Eccles Street, Dublin, and Jane Boyce; B.A. (T.C.D.); E 1883, M.T. H 1882. 1883/M/01 [5 items]. Q.C., 30 Nov. 1898. Called to English Bar, 1895. Bencher of King's Inns, 1900. Secretary of the Connaught Circuit. M.P. for Fermanagh North, 1906-16. Died 12 Sept. 1928. Obituary, I.L.T. & S.J., lxii (1928), 222; Who's Who. Mentioned by V.T.H. Delany [q.v.], in his article 'The Bench and Bar in Ireland', as one of 'those who were at the forefront of their profession during the period'.

FFORDE, CECIL ROBERT (b. 24 June 1875) 2nd s. of Arthur Brownlow Fforde of St. Jean-de-Luz, France, and Mary Carver Pope; M 1899. 1903/M/06 [3 items]. K.C., 20 Feb. 1920. President of the Special Courts in Swaziland and Bechuanaland.

FFRENCH, DANIEL O'CONNELL (b. 26 Oct 1832) [Leinster Road, Dublin] eld. s. of Nicholas Joseph Ffrench (decd.) of Ffrenchlawn, Co. Roscommon, J.P., and Elizabeth Mary O'Connell; M 1863, M.T. M 1866. 1872/H/3 [6 items]. Assistant Registar of Deeds.

FIGGIS, EDWARD ALLEN KEENE (b. 9 Feb. 1876) young. s. of Samuel Figgis (decd.), J.P., of 'Newlands', Bray, Co. Wicklow, and Mary Anne Cuttle; B.A. (T.C.D.); M 1897. 1901/M/04 [4 items]. K.C., 6 April 1920. Advocate in Nairobi. Died 27 Nov. 1948. Obituary, *I.L.T. & S.J.*, lxxxiii (1949), 4.

FIGGIS, HERBERT BENJAMIN (b. 2 Sept. 1861) 6th s. of Edmund Johnstone Figgis of Glen-na-Smoil, Co. Dublin, and Frances Anna Hicks; B.A. (T.C.D.); H 1880, M.T. H 1883. 1884/M/06 [5 items]. Died 1943. Obituary, *I.L.T. & S.J.*, lxxvii (30 Jan. 1943), 33.

FINDLATER, ADAM SEATON (b. 21 Jan. 1855) eld. s. of John Findlater, J.P., of Melbeach, Monkstown, Co. Dublin, and Mary Johnston; M.A. (T.C.D.); M 1878. 1906/T/02 [2 items]. Proprietor of the well-known Dublin grocery and wine business. Subject of the chapter entitled 'A Southern Unionist Businessman: Adam Findlater (1855-1911)', pp 143-260 in Alex. Findlater, *Findlaters: The Story of a Dublin Merchant Family 1774-2001* (Dublin, 2001) [photograph, p. 144; caricature, p. 180]. Aged 51 when called to the Bar, and never practised. Died 18 Jan. 1911. Obituary in *The Irish Orchard and Forest Glade* (reproduced on p. 229 of the family history). *Burke's Irish Family Records* (1976), 415.

FINLAY, THOMAS ALOYSIUS (b. 11 Oct. 1893) only s. of William Finlay of Killynebber, Co. Cavan, and Margaret Mary O'Hanlon; B.A. (N.U.I.); M 1912. 1915/M/03 [2 items]. Appt. District Justice, Oct. 1924. S.C., 25 June 1930. T.D. for Dublin County, 1930-3. Died 22 Nov. 1932. Obituary, *I.L.T. & S.J.*, lxvi (1932), 290. Photograph (No. 10, between pp 148-9) and biographical note (p. 250) in Mary Kotsonouris, *The Winding-up of the Dáil Courts, 1922-1925: an obvious duty* (Dublin, 2004).

FINLAY, THOMAS ALOYSIUS (b. 17 Sept. 1922) 2nd s. of Thomas Aloysius Finlay, S.C., of 43 Pembroke Road, Ballsbridge, Dublin, and Eva Fegan; B.A. (N.U.I.); M 1941. 1944/T/01 [2 items]. Fine Gael TD, 1954-7. S.C., 3 Oct. 1961. Judge of the High Court, 10 Oct. 1972. President of the High Court, 17 Dec. 1974. Chief Justice, 16 Jan. 1985. Retired, 16 Sept. 1994. Appreciation on retirement by Brian Walsh in *Gazette of the Incorporated Law Society of Ireland*, Aug./Sept. 1994, 246; also assessment of his career in *The Irish Times*, 1 Aug. 1994. Portrait by John F. Kelly in King's Inns: see Wanda Ryan-Smolin, *King's Inns Portraits* (1992), 26. Listed [with photograph] in the 1984 and 1991 editions of Maureen Cairnduff, *Who's Who in Ireland*. See Louis McRedmond (ed.), *Modern Irish Lives*.

FINLAY, WILLIAM DENIS (b. 6 Feb. 1921) eld. s. of Aloysius Finlay, K.C., T.D. (decd.), of 43 Pembroke Road, Dublin, and Eva Fegan; B.A., M 1939. 1942/M/03 [2 items]. S.C., 1 March 1956. Sometime Professor of Law at University College, Dublin and Governor of the Bank of Ireland. Co-founder of the relaunched *Irish Jurist* (1965). Listed in the 1984 edition of Maureen Cairnduff, *Who's Who in Ireland*.

FINN, DENIS (b. 13 April 1882) eld. s. of Thomas Finn, of 5 Shamrock Villas, Drumcondra, Dublin, and Mary Twomey; M 1918. 1921/M/07 [2 items].

FINNY, WILLIAM WATSON (b. 22 April 1876) eld. s. of John Magee Finny, M.D., of 36 Merrion Square, Dublin, and Agnes Anne Watson; M 1898, I.T. E 1897. 1900/M/10 [2 items].

FIRTEAR [Ferriter], MICHAEL PATRICK (b. 4 Oct. 1912) 2nd s. of Thomas Firtear, of Caherquinn, Ballyferriter, Dingle, Co. Kerry, and Máire Bácaéir; M 1951. 1956/M/11 [2 items].

FITZ GERALD, HERBERT GERALD (b. 18 Aug. 1894) only s. of Gerald Fitz Gerald, J.P., of 74 Grosvenor Road, Rathgar, Dublin, and Frances Quinlan; M 1914. 1917/M/01 [2 items].

FITZ-HENRY, WILLIAM ALBERT (b. 10 April 1862) eld. s. of Robert Fitz-Henry, of 2 Cowper Road, Rathmines, Dublin, and Catherine Laird; M.A., LL.B. (R.U.I.); T 1902. 1902/M/02 [2 items].

FITZGERALD, ALBERT VICTOR STEWART (b. 8 April 1885) only s. of Francis Creighton Fitzgerald, High Sheriff, L.R.C.P. & S.I., of Newtown Butler, Co. Fermanagh, and Lucie Stewart; M 1911. 1914/M/05 [2 items].

FITZGERALD, DAVID (b. 14 Jan 1847) eld. s. of the Rt. Hon. J.D. Fitzgerald, of 7 Merrion Square East, Dublin, and Rose Donohoe; B.A. (Cambridge University); E 1870, L.I. T 1865. 1872/T/12 [4 items]. Called to the English Bar, M. 1871. Appt. County Court Judge for Queen's County, Kilkenny and Waterford, 5 Aug. 1892. Died 5 March 1920. Will noted, *I.L.T. & S.J.*, liv (1920), 155; *Who's Who*.

FITZGERALD, EDWARD MARTIN (b. 27 Aug. 1886) 2nd s. of Edward FitzGerald, J.P., of Khyber Pass, Dalkey, Co. Dublin, and Margaret Hughes; cand. bachelor (T.C.D.); M 1904. 1907/M/08 [2 items]. Practised in London. Died 1965. Obituary, *I.L.T. & S.J.*, xcix (6 March 1965), 19.

FITZGERALD, GARRET MICHAEL DESMOND (b. 9 Feb. 1926) 4th s. of Thomas Desmond FitzGerald, of Airfield, Donnybrook, Dublin, and Mabel McConnell; M 1944. 1947/M/05 [2 items]. Worked in Aer Lingus, 1947-58. Lecturer in economics, U.C.D., 1959-73. Senator 1965-9. T.D. 1969-92. Leader of Fine Gael, 1977-87. Taoiseach 1981-2, 1982-7. Chancellor of the National University of Ireland. His autobiography, *All in a Life* (Dublin, 1991) is silent about his call to the Bar. Listed [with photograph] in the 1984 and 1991 editions of Maureen Cairnduff, *Who's Who in Ireland*. See Louis McRedmond (ed.), *Modern Irish Lives*.

FITZGERALD, GERALD (b. 12 Aug. 1849) 3rd s. of the Rt. Hon. Mr Justice FitzGerald, of Kilmarnock House, Co. Dublin, and Rose Donohoe (decd.); B.A. (T.C.D.); M 1868; I.T. E 1868. 1871/M/9 [2 items]. Q.C., June 1889. County Court Judge for King's County, Longford, Meath and Westmeath, 1886-90. Land Commission, 1890- (Judicial Commissioner, 1893-1922). Died 30 Oct. 1925. Obituary, *I.L.T. & S.J.*, lix (1925), 267; *Who's Who*.

FITZGERALD, JAMES DERMOT JOSEPH (b. 13 June 1934) eld. s. of Dr John FitzGerald, of Mental Hospital, Mullingar, Co. Westmeath, and Dr. Nora May O'Connell; B.A.; M 1955. 1958/M/05 [2 items].

FITZGERALD, JAMES JOHN FOSTER VESEY (b. 15 Nov. 1846) eld. s. of James Thomas Lester Vesey Fitzgerald of Moyriesk, Co. Clare, and Henrietta Mahon; B.A. (T.C.D.); E 1868, M.T. H 1870. 1871/M/6 [2 items]. Munster Circuit. K.C., March 1904. Author of *A Practical Guide to the Valuation of Rent in Ireland* (Dublin, 1881).

FITZGERALD, JOHN MARY (b. 17 July 1882) eld. s. of William J. FitzGerald, solicitor, Clerk of the Crown and Peace for the County of Cork, of Montenotte, Cork, and Eily C. Harrington; B.A. (T.C.D.); M 1901. 1904/T/02 [3 items]. Auditor of the College Historical Society, 1903-4. S.C., 14 July 1924. Died 28 May 1946. Personal tribute (by J.J.H.), in *I.L.T.& S.J*, lxxx (1946), 150-1. Mentioned by V.T.H. Delany [q.v.], in 'The Bench and Bar in Ireland', xxxiii.

FITZGERALD, JOHN SOUTHWELL (b. 17 June 1933) only s. of John David FitzGerald, of 7 Leeson Park, Dublin, and Freda Anquetil; M 1952. 1957/M/12 [2 items].

FITZGERALD, MAURICE V. (b. 10 Feb. 1904) eld. s. of Maurice Fitzgerald, of Limerick, Co. Limerick, and Mary Walshe; B.A. (N.U.I.); M 1923. 1926/M/07 [2 items]. Mentioned in Gerard A. Lee, *A Memoir of the South-Western Circuit* (Dublin, 1990), 15.

FITZGERALD, PIERCE (b. 26 March 1914) 2nd s. of Desmond Fitzgerald, of Montpelier Manor, Monkstown, Dublin, and Mabel McConnell; M 1935. 1938/T/03 [2 items]. Worked for the U.N. Food and Agriculture Organisation. Died in Rome, 1986.

FITZGERALD, RICHARD VALENTINE (b. 14 Feb. 1847) eld. s. of Richard Augustine Fitzgerald, of 29 Upper Merrion Square, Dublin, Taxing Officer Landed Estates Court, and Anabella Decy; B.A. (T.C.D.), M 1866, I.T. E 1868. 1870/M/2 [4 items].

FITZGERALD, THOMAS EDWARD (b. 30 June 1915) only s. of Thomas W. Fitzgerald (decd.), of 19 Pembroke Park, Dublin, and Kathleen H. Markey; M 1933. 1937/M/17 [6 items].

FITZGERALD, WILLIAM (b. 5 Oct. 1852) 3rd s. of William, Bishop of Killaloe, of Clarisford House, Co. Clare, and Anne Francis Stoney; B.A. (T.C.D.); E 1874, I.T. E 1876. 1877/M/07 [5 items].

FITZGERALD, WILLIAM JAMES (b. 19 May 1894) eld. s. of Joseph Fitzgerald, of Cappawhite, Co. Tipperary, and Mary Teresa Quinlan; B.A. (T.C.D.); H 1923. 1923/H/08 [3 items]. Served in the Durham Light Infantry and XV Corps Mounted Troops. M.C. and *Croix-de-Guerre*. M.T. 1921. Nigerian administrative service, 1920. Crown counsel in Nigeria, 1924. Solicitor-General of Northern Rhodesia, 1932 (Attorney-General, 1933). Attorney-General of Palestine, 1937-43. Chief Justice of Palestine, 1944-8. President of the Lands Tribunal, 1950-65. Died 4 July 1989. *Who's Who*.

FITZGERALD, WILLIAM O'BRIEN (b. 26 March 1906) 3rd s. of William Joseph FitzGerald (decd.), Clerk of the Crown and Peace for Co. of Cork, of Dundesmond, Cork, and Mary Frances Dorman; M 1924. Awarded 3rd Class Cert. of Honour. 1927/M/08 [2 items]. S.C., 6 March 1944. Bencher T 1950. Judge of the Supreme Court, 1966. Chief Justice, Dec. 1972-Oct. 1974. Died 17 Oct. 1974. Portrait by Pat Phelan in King's Inns: see Wanda Ryan-Smolin, *King's Inns Portraits* (1992), 27. See Louis McRedmond (ed.), *Modern Irish Lives*.

FITZGERALD-KENNEY, JAMES C. (b. 30 April 1878) 2nd surv. s. of J.C. Fitzgerald-Kenney (decd.), J.P. of Kilclogher, Co. Galway, and Helena Crean-Lynch; M 1896. 1899/M/05 [3 items]. S.C., 21 Oct. 1926. Bencher, 1928. T.D. for Mayo South, June 1927-1948. Parliamentary Secretary, 1927; Minister for Justice of the Irish Free State, 1927-1932. Died 21 Oct. 1956. Obituary, *I.L.T. & S.J.*, xc (1956), 258-9; *Who's Who*. Mentioned in James Meenan (ed.), *Centenary History of Lit. and Hist. Soc. of U.C.D.*

FITZGERALD-LOMBARD, ROGER EDWARD (b. 22 May 1878) 2nd s. of James Fitzgerald-Lombard (decd.), J.P., Chevalier of the Legion of Honour, of South Hill, Co. Dublin, and Sarah Barry; M.A. (T.C.D.); Capt., 5th Batt. Rifle Brigade; M 1899. 1912/H/01 [2 items]. Major. Chevalier of the Order of the Holy Sepulchre, of the Ordre de Mérite, and of the Order of the Crown of Stuart. B.A.I., M.A. Died 11 Jan. 1951. See *Thom's Directory* (Biographies).

FITZGIBBON, EDWARD M. (b. 12 Oct. 1909) only s. of Cornelius M. FitzGibbon, of Rock Abbey, Askeaton, Co. Limerick, and Helen Cussen; M 1928. 1934/T/05 [3 items]. Went Munster Circuit. Died 26 Sept. 1936. Obituary, *I.L.T. & S.J.*, lxx (1936), 261. See James Meenan (ed.), *Centenary History of Lit. and Hist. Soc. of U.C.D.*

FITZGIBBON, FRANK (b. 10 Nov. 1881) 3rd s. of Henry Fitzgibbon, M.D., of 49 Merrion Square, Dublin, and Meta Adelaide Foot; B.A. (T.C.D.); M 1901. 1904/M/02 [2 items]. K.C., July 1919. After war service, judge of the Egyptian courts. Returned to practise in Ireland, 1925. Died 1970. Nephew of Lord Justice FitzGibbon. Obituary, *I.L.T. & S.J.*, civ (25 July 1970), 304-5. Remembered by Garrett Gill (q.v.), and mentioned in Patrick MacKenzie, *Lawful Occasions*, 147-51.

FITZGIBBON, GERALD (b. 8 Oct. 1866) eld. s. of the Rt. Hon. Gerald FitzGibbon of 10 Merrion Square, Dublin, and Margaret Anne FitzGerald; B.A. (T.C.D.); M 1887. 1891/M/03 [6 items]. Munster Circuit. K.C., 24 June 1908. Bencher, 1912. T.D. (Dublin University), 1921-3. The last holder (1917) of the office of King's Advocate General [in admiralty cases]: see *Irish Law Times* 3 Nov. 1917, 264, and R.B. McDowell, *The Irish Administration 1801-1914* (1964), 120. Judge of the Supreme Court of the Irish Free State, 1924-38. Died 6 Dec. 1942. Obituary, *I.L.T. & S.J.*, lxxvi (1942), 306, 311; appreciation on retirement in ibid., lxxii (1938), 311, 324; *Who's Who*. Mentioned in Maurice Healy, *The Old Munster Circuit*, 261. Portrait by Dermot O'Brien in King's Inns: see Wanda Ryan-Smolin, *King's Inns Portraits* (1992), 29.

FITZGIBBON, HENRY MACAULAY (b. 30 June 1855) only s. of Henry FitzGibbon, Q.C., of 15 Merrion Sq, Dublin, and Georgina Macaulay; B.A. (T.C.D.); M 1876, L.I. E 1878. 1879/M/20 [6 items]. Private secretary to his kinsman, Lord Justice FitzGibbon. Captain 4th (old 5th) Connaught Rangers; Musketry Staff Officer, 1914-18. Editor of the *Irish Law Times & Solicitors' Journal*, 1892-1906. Author of *Early English and Scottish Poetry* (1887); an edition of Thomas Campbell's *Gertrude of Wyoming* (1889), *Famous Elizabethan Plays expurgated and adapted for modern readers* (1890); an edition of George Farquhar's *The Beaux-Stratagem* (1898); and *The story of the flute, being a history of the flute and everything connected with it* (1914; 2nd ed., 1929). Author (with W.J. Johnston [q.v.]), of *The Law of Local Government in Ireland including the Local Government Act, 1898, the Orders in Council, the Orders of the Local Government Board, and the Rules of Court, with forms and table* (Dublin, 1899). Died 3 Feb. 1942. Obituary, *I.L.T. & S.J.*, lxxvi (1942), 48; *Who's Who.*

FITZPATRICK, FINTAN (b. 26 Feb. 1889) only s. of Fenton Fitzpatrick, of 50 Upper Rathmines, Dublin, and Mary Cheevers (decd.); H 1922; [practising solicitor from 1911 to 1917] 1922/H/03 [3 items]. District Justice. Died 9 Jan. 1959. Obituary, *I.L.T. & S.J.*, xciii (1959), 32.

FITZPATRICK, JOHN IGNATIUS (b. 27 July 1914) 2nd s. of John Fitzpatrick, company director, of Ballyclough, Co. Limerick, and Mary Kelly; Ph.D. (T.C.D.), B.Comm. (N.U.I.); M 1952. 1956/M/06 [2 items].

FITZPATRICK, RICHARD ANTHONY (b. 17 Jan. 1926) eld. s. of Michael Fitzpatrick, Garda Síochána, of 25 Upper Northbrook Ave, North Strand, Dublin, and Margaret McCrossan; M 1946. 1950/M/02 [2 items].

FITZSIMON, BARTHOLOMEW KEVIN (b. 7 Aug. 1929) eld. s. of Bartholomew Fitzsimon, of Churchtown Park, Churchtown, Dublin, and Mary Kavanagh; M 1954. 1958/T/06 [2 items].

FITZSIMON, ROBERT LOUIS PATRICK (b. 13 March 1874) 4th s. of James Charles FitzSimon (decd.), merchant, of Longford Square, Monkstown, Dublin, and Augusta Rutter; M 1896. 1899/T/08 [3 items].

FITZSIMON, Major SAMUEL ERNEST SYDNEY (b. 6 Feb. 1892) eld. s. of Charles Edmund FitzSimon, of Belfast, and Jeanie Harrison. M.B.E.; M 1924. 1926/M/13 [2 items]. Lieutenant-Colonel. S.C., 23 Feb. 1967.

FITZSIMONS, CHARLES B. (b. 8 May 1924) eld. s. of Charles Stewart Parnell Fitzsimons, of 13 Churchtown Road, Rathgar, Dublin, and Marguerita Lilburn; B.A. (N.U.I.); M 1941. 1945/T/01 [2 items].

FITZSIMONS, EOGHAN (b. 13 June 1943) eld. s. of James Fitzsimons, general manager, director of Hibernian Bank Ltd, of Clonenagh, Greenfield Road, Sutton, Co. Dublin, and Eithne O'Dwyer; B.C.L. (N.U.I.); M 1962. 1965/T/01 [1 item]. S.C., 6 Oct. 1980. Attorney-General, 11 Nov.1994-15 Dec. 1994. See J.P. Casey, *The Irish Law Officers* (Dublin, 1996), 347-66.

FLANAGAN, DESMOND DAVID (b. 4 Feb. 1919) eld. s. of Desmond Flanagan, merchant, of 11 Leighlin Road, Dublin, and Mary McIntyre; M 1949. 1953/M/06 [2 items].

FLANAGAN, JAMES WOULFE (b. 27 Jan. 1864) 4th s. of the Rt. Hon. Stephen Woulfe Flanagan of 20 Fitzwilliam Place, Dublin, and Mary Corballis; B.A. (Oxford); M 1887, M.T. M 1888. 1890/M/07 [8 items]. Called to English Bar, M 1891. For 10 years Resident Magistrate at Newry, where he was shot dead, 4 June 1922: see *I.L.T. & S.J.*, lvi (1922), 143. See also Penny Bonsall, *The Irish RMs* (Dublin, 1997), 154-74.

FLANAGAN, MARTIN JOSEPH (b. 18 July 1894) 7th s. of Timothy Flanagan (decd.), of Oldcastle, Co. Meath, and Bridget MacDonagh; B.A., LL.B; M 1914. Awarded Society's Exhibition, Oct. 1917. 1918/E/01x [2 items].

FLANAGAN, STANISLAUS (b. 18 Nov. 1887) 3rd s. of Michael Flanagan, of Borth y Gest, Portmadoc, Caernarvon, and Mary Morley; M 1913 [Colour Sergt. 3rd Royal Irish Rifles] 1919/T/04x[?] [3 items].

FLEMING, FREDERICK (b. 12 Oct. 1845) 3rd s. of George Fleming (decd.) of Surock House, Co. Westmeath, and Margaret Whitley; M.A. (T.C.D.); E 1874, L.I. M 1874. 1877/E/01 [4 items]. Q.C., 22 Feb. 1896. Bencher 1900. Died 31 Dec. 1922. Obituary, *I.L.T. & S.J.*, lvii (1923), 4.

FLEMING, PATRICK DAVID (b. 1 Feb. 1857) eld. s. of David Fleming of Charleville, Co. Cork, and Johanna Leahy; B.A. (T.C.D.); M 1878, M.T. M 1880. 1881/M/16 [6 items]. Munster Circuit. K.C., March 1904. Appt. County Court Judge for King's County, Longford, Meath and Westmeath, 11 March 1918. Died 3 April 1928. Obituary, *I.L.T. & S.J.*, lxii (1928), 84; *Who's Who.* Mentioned in Maurice Healy, *The Old Munster Circuit*, 133-9.

FLEMING, PATRICK DAVID (b. 5 Jan. 1910) 3rd s. of John Fleming, of Sunville, Kilmallock, Co. Limerick, and Annie Daly; B.A., LL.B.; M 1931. 1934/M/02 [2 items]. Registrar of the Bahamas.

FLEMYNG, WILLIAM WESTROPP (b. 13 May 1849) only s. of Revd. Robert Flemyng of 18 Upper Fitzwilliam Street, Dublin, and Charlotte Westropp; B.A. (T.C.D.); H 1871, M.T. E 1872. 873/M/6 [5 items].

FLOOD, BENJAMIN THOMAS BRADLEY (b. 9 July 1849) eld. s. of Frederick Leopold Flood (decd.), solicitor, of Dame Street, Dublin, and Maria [Moyers]; Lieut. 82nd Regiment; H 1877, G.I. H 1879. 1879/M/19 [7 items].

FLOOD, FEARGUS MICHAEL (b. 10 July 1928) only s. of Michael Flood, of Kenlis, Dublin Road, Sutton, and Dora Frances McBreen; B.A. (N.U.I.); M 1946. 1949/M/14 [2 items]. S.C., 7 Oct. 1974. Judge of the High Court, 1 Oct. 1991. Retired. 7 July 2000. Continued in retirement as chairman of a tribunal. See Courts (Supplemental Provisons) (Amendment) Act, 2000. Listed in the 1991 edition of Maureen Cairnduff, *Who's Who in Ireland*.

FLOOD, GRETTA UNA (b. 4 Dec. 1904) eld. d. of Michael Francis Flood, M.A., of 65 Grosvenor Road, Rathgar, Dublin, and Mary Elizabeth Flood; M 1922. 1926/H/04 [2 items].

FLOOD, JOSEPH MARY (b. 2 April 1882) 3rd s. of Peter Flood (decd.) of Rockspring House, Co. Longford, and Marcella Atkinson; B.A. (R.U.I.); M 1905. 1908/T/13 [3 items]. Appt. District Justice, Oct. 1924. Author of 'The Old Law Library: resort of wits and scholars', in *The Irish Times*, Monday 11 October 1961, p. 7.

FLYNN, ANDREW IGNATIUS (b. 7 March 1925) only s. of John Francis Flynn, publisher, of 268 North Circular Road, Dublin, and Elizabeth Mary Foley; M 1944. 1948/T/17 [2 items].

FLYNN, ANN MARY GABRIEL PHILOMENA (b. 2 Feb. 1934) only d. of James P. Flynn (decd.), of 'Carnacon', Ailesbury Road, Dublin, and Ina Noone; B.A., LL.B.(N.U.I.); M 1953. 1956/M/05 [2 items].

FLYNN, WILLIAM (b. 4 May 1907) eld. s. of William Flynn, of Abbeyside, Dungarvan, Co. Waterford, and Margaret Griffin; B.A. (N.U.I.); E 1942. 1945/T/02 [2 items].

FOOT, ALBERT REVELL (b. 9 Nov. 1854) young. s. of William Foot, J.P., of Raglan Road, Dublin, and [?]; B.A. (T.C.D.); H 1881, M.T. E 1881. 1883/M/10 [5 items].

FORBES, TADHG (b. 23 Sept. 1905). see Mac Firbhisigh, Tadhg

FORD, JOHN FOWLER (b. 24 Aug. 1883) eld. s. of Alexander Ford, M.D., of 31 Catherine Street, Waterford, and Maria Louisa Fowler (decd.); M 1908. 1911/H/03 [2 items].

FORDE, DANIEL PETER (b. 28 March 1890) 6th s. of Timothy Forde, Snr., of Ballymurphy, Upton, Co. Cork, and Kate Whelton; B.A. (N.U.I.); M 1920. 1923/M/11 [2 items].

FORDE, HENRY (b. 24 July 1845) only son of Henry Forde (decd.) of 56 Harcourt Street, Dublin, and Jannet Fraser; B.A. (T.C.D.); M 1866, M.T. E 1868. 1869/M/5 [6 items].

FORDE, PATRICK BERNARD (b. 25 Feb. 1950) eld. s. of Thomas Forde, merchant, of The Square, Ballyhaunis, Co. Mayo, and Dora Neary; B. Comm. (N.U.I.); M 1948. 1951/M/09 [2 items].

FORSAYETH, GORDON WILLIAM (b. 19 April 1885) eld. s. of Richard William Forsayeth, Colonel R.A.M.C., of Whitechurch House, Cappagh, Co. Waterford, and Margaret Baird; B.A. (T.C.D.); M 1909 1912/T/07 [3 items]. Captain. Died July 1963.

FOX, BERNARD JOSHUA (b. 3 Feb. 1885) only s. of Herman Fox of 19 Twickenham Street, Belfast, and Dora Fox; B.A. (N.U.I.); M 1911. 1914/T/11 [2 items]. K.C. (N.I.), T 1939. County Court Judge for Antrim and Recorder of Belfast, 1944-60. Died 25 Dec. 1977. See *Who's Who*.

FOY, HENRY BERTRAM (b. 12 Dec. 1932) only s. of Major H.B. Foy, R.E. (decd.), of Inane House, Roscrea, Co. Tipperary, and Mary Tubridy of Janemount, Limerick; M 1952. 1955/M/08 [2 items].

FRAHER, PATRICK (b. 15 April 1905) 3rd s. of John Fraher (decd.), of Ballinamuddagh, Galbally, Co. Limerick, and Ellen Hanrahan; M 1926. 1929/M/09 [2 items].

FREWEN, GERARD L. (b. 4 Feb. 1926) 2nd s. of Robert Frewen, of 96 Castle Avenue, Clontarf, Co. Dublin, and Sarah O'Neill; M 1952. 1957/H/03 [2 items]. Registrar of the High Court. Editor of two volumes of *Judgments of the Court of Criminal Appeal*, *1924-1978* and *1979-1983* (1984). Died *c*. 1990.

GAFFNEY, MAURICE PATRICK (b. 11 Oct. 1916) 2nd s. of Patrick Joseph Gaffney (decd.), civil servant, of Tolka Lodge, Finglas Bridge, Co. Dublin, and Margaret Fennell; B.A. (N.U.I.); M 1950. 1954/H/01 [2 items]. S.C., 3 July 1970.

GAHAGAN, JAMES HENRY (b. 30 Nov. 1888) only s. of the Revd. John Richard Gahagan of The Rectory, Athleague, Co. Roscommon, and Harriet Jane Stock; M 1909. 1912/M/07 [2 items]. Died 5 March 1946. Obituary, *I.L.T. & S.J.*, lxxx (1946), 73.

GAHARWAR, THAKUR RAM LAL SINGH (b. 27 Nov. 1879) 4th s. of Thakur Mukund Singh Gaharwar, of Hoshangahad District, Central Provinces, India; M 1914. 1917/T/17 [2 items].

GALLAGHER, DERMOT CHARLES ARTHUR (b. 3 Sept. 1898) 4th s. of Daniel Patrick Gallagher, of Dernasesk, Vernon Avenue, Clontarf, Dublin, and Elizabeth Haughey; M 1918. 1925/M/24 [2 items].

GALLAGHER, EDWARD STANISLAUS (b. 20 July 1900) young. s. of Patrick Gallagher (decd.), of 34 Chief Street, Ardoyne, Belfast, and Mary Macauley; M 1927. 1930/M/07 [2 items].

GALLAGHER, JOHN (b. 17 Feb. 1865) 8th s. of Patrick Gallagher, J.P., of Ardloher, Co. Donegal, and Margaret O'Boyle; T 1883. 1886/M/10 [6 items]. Appt. District Justice, Nov. 1922: *I.L.T. & S.J.*, lvi (4 Nov. 1922), 266.

GALLAGHER, PATRICK (b. 25 April 1940) 2nd s. of John Gallagher, of Kinlough, Co. Leitrim, and Mary Coll. 1966/T/05 [1 item].

GALVIN, BARRY St. JOHN (b. 1 Nov. 1943) eld. s. of Francis Patrick Galvin, solicitor, of St. Aubyn's, Monkstown, Co. Cork, and Anne Mary O'Sullivan; B.C.L. (N.U.I.); M 1963. Awarded Society's Prize. 1966/M/01 [3 items]. Subsequently (1969) admitted as a Solicitor. State Solicitor for Cork, 1983. Since 1996 Chief Legal Officer of the Criminal Assets Bureau. Listed in the 1999 edition of Maureen Cairnduff, *Who's Who in Ireland*.

GALVIN, THOMAS EUSTACE (b. 20 Sept. 1874) 3rd s. of Thomas Galvin, J.P. (decd.), of Ballyard House, Tralee, Co. Kerry, and Eily O'Connell; M 1894. 1927/M/10 [2 items]. Department of Agriculture. Died 24 Nov. 1941. Obituary, *I.L.T. & S.J.*, lxxv (1941), 309.

GAMBLE, RICHARD KEENE (b. 3 Aug. 1860) 2nd s. of Richard Wilson Gamble, Barrister-at-Law, County Court Judge, of 51 Fitzwilliam Square, Dublin, and Charlotte Keene; B.A. (T.C.D.); M 1882, L.I. H 1885. 1886/H/06 [7 items]. Chairman of Brooks Thomas & Co., Ltd. Died 20 March 1921. Obituary, *I.L.T. & S.J.*, lv (1921), 83.

GANNON, JOHN MARY JOSEPH (b. 5 December 1918) younger s. of John Gannon, of 181 Griffith Avenue, Dublin, and Mary Ellen Costello; B.A. (N.U.I.); M 1938. Awarded Certificate of Honour. 1941/M/04 [2 items]. S.C., 8 July 1966. Judge of the High Court, 19 Sept. 1973. Retired 4 Dec. 1990. Listed in the 1984 edition of Maureen Cairnduff, *Who's Who in Ireland*.

GARDNER, WILLIAM CHARLES (b. 31 July 1862) eld. s. of Robert Gardner, J.P., of Clyde Road, Dublin, and Sarah Dale; M 1882, M.T. E 1884. 1886/M/04 [7 items].

GARGAN, JOHN GILBERT (b. 29 Aug. 1910) eld. s. of John Patrick Gargan, of 51 Lower Beechwood Avenue, Dublin, and Bridget Mary McCabe; M 1938. 1942/T/07 [2 items]. Head of the Electricity Supply Board.

GARLAND, JAMES NOEL (b. 28 Dec. 1907) 2nd s. of Thomas Ignatius Garland (decd.), of 59 Northumberland Road, Dublin, and Elizabeth Lyons; B.A. (T.C.D.); M 1932. Awarded Society's Exhibition. 1936/T/01 [2 items]. Bencher.

GARLAND, RICHARD CHARLES (b. 3 Sept. 1873) young. s. of Edward Garland (decd.) of 34 Carlisle Tce, N.C.R., Dublin, and Elizabeth Garland; B.A. (R.U.I.); M 1896. 1899/M/04 [3 items].

GARRETT, KATHLEEN BUTLER (n.d.) only d. of Robert Bruce Garrett, of Bryon, Oklahoma, and Cherrie E. Cherikee; M 1927. 1930/T/01 [2 items]. Actually called in Hilary Term 1930.

GARTLAN, GEORGE HENRY (b. 5 Nov 1848) eld. s. of George Henry Gartlan J.P. of Cabra House, Newry, Co. Down, and Mary McMullan; B.A. (T.C.D.); H 1867, M.T. E 1868. 1870/M/4 [2 items].

GARTLAN, JAMES (b. 2 June 1845) only s. of Peter McEvoy Gartlan of Mountjoy Square, Dublin, Assistant Taxing Master, and Margaret Hamill; B.A. (T.C.D.); H 1867, M.T. E 1868. 1872/H/4 [4 items].

GAUSSEN, STEWART MACNAGHTEN PENNEFATHER ASH (b. 4 July 1866) 2nd s. of David Campbell Gaussen, Barrister-at-Law, of Shanemullagh, Co. Londonderry, and Annie Ottiwell; E 1892. 1895/M/09 [6 items]. K.C., 16 Dec. 1909. Died 1928. Obituary, *I.L.T. & S.J.*, lxii (3 Nov. 1928), 246.

GAVAN DUFFY, GEORGE (b. 21 Oct. 1882) eld. s. of Sir Charles Gavan Duffy (decd.), of Villa Guillory, Nice, France, and Louise Hall; T 1917. 1917/M/03 [2 items]. Sinn Féin M.P., 1918. Resigned seat 1923. Briefly Minister for Foreign Affairs in the first government of the Irish Free State, 1922. S.C., 29 May 1929. Judge of the High Court, 1936-46; and President of the High Court, 1946-51. Officer of the Légion d'Honneur. Died 10 June 1951. Obituary, *I.L.T. & S.J.*, lxxxv (1951), 146. See G.M. Golding, *George Gavan Duffy 1882-1951* (Dublin, 1982); *Oxford DNB* (2004) [article by Mary Kotsonouris]; and Louis McRedmond (ed.), *Modern Irish Lives*. George Gavan Duffy was the eldest child of his father's third marriage. A half-brother, Sir Frank Gavan Duffy (1857-1936), was a Justice of the High Court of Australia, 1913-31; and the latter's son, Sir Charles Gavan Duffy (1882-1961), was a Justice of the Supreme Court of Victoria, 1933-61.

GAY, KEVIN PATRICK (b. 28 March 1922) only s. of Colonel Thomas T. Gray (decd.), of 15 Grantham Street, S.C. Road, Dublin, and Eileen O'Shaughnessy (decd.); M 1952. 1956/H/03 [2 items]. Probate Officer. Died 2 Nov. 2000. Obituaries, *The Irish Times*, 18 Nov. 2000; *Courts Service News*, vol. 2 (5), Dec. 2000, p. 10.

GAYNOR, JOHN PATRICK (b. 23 July 1864) eld. s. of Patrick Gaynor (decd.) of Belfast, and Ellen Kelliher; M 1893. 1896/M/08 [4 items]. Journalist. Died 5 March 1940. Obituary, *I.L.T. & S.J.*, lxxiv (1940), 66,

GAYNOR, JOSEPH EDWARD (b. 21 Jan. 1862) eld. s. of George Gaynor of Tully Baylin, Athlone, Co. Westmeath, and Anne Hagan; B.A. (T.C.D.); M 1881, M.T. H 1884. 1885/H/04 [6 items].

GAYNOR, LIAM ANTHONY (b. 26 June 1943) eld. s. of Liam Gaynor, company director, of The Grove, Killiney, Co. Dublin, and Lena Mary Rochford; B.A. (Economics) (N.U.I.); M 1961. 1964/M/01 [1 item]. S.C., 4 Oct. 1982. Bencher.

GEARY, COLM EAMONN (b. 9 June 1928) only s. of Robert Charles Geary, D.Sc., of 27 Leeson Park, Dublin, and Mida O'Brien; B.A. (N.U.I.); M 1946. 1950/H/04 [2 items].

GENTLEMAN, JOHN WESLEY (b. 7 June 1881) eld. s. of the Revd. Benson E. Gentleman of 1 Epworth Terrace, North Circular Road, Dublin, and Jane Hill (decd.); B.A. (T.C.D.); M 1910. 1913/T/19 [3 items]. Admitted as a solicitor, H 1928. Died Feb. 1968.

GEOGHEGAN, GERALD (b. 11 March 1852) 3rd s. of Arthur Gerald Geoghegan of 27 Addison Road, West Kensington, Middlesex, and Anne Wilson; B.A. (T.C.D.); H 1871, M.T. M 1872. 1876/M/03 [2 items].

GEOGHEGAN, HANBURY CLEMENTS (b. 7 Dec. 1847) 5th s. of Thomas Geoghegan (decd.), solicitor, of 55 Stephen's Green W. Dublin, and Margaret Maria Hebden; T 1902. 1902/M/05 [2 items]. Died 8 May 1910: *I.L.T. & S.J.*, xliv (1910), 118.

GEOGHEGAN, HUGH (b. 16 May 1938) eld. s. of James Geoghegan (decd.), Judge of the Supreme Court, of Carne Lodge, Cowper Gardens, Rathmines, Dublin, and Eileen Murphy; B.C.L.; M 1959. Awarded Society's Exhibition Prize. 1962/M/02 [1 item]. S.C., 3 Oct. 1977. Judge of the High Court, 14 Dec. 1992; of the Supreme Court, 13 March 2000. Listed in the 1999 edition of Maureen Cairnduff, *Who's Who in Ireland*.

GEOGHEGAN, JACOB THOMAS (b. 25 Nov 1846) 6th s. of Thomas Grace Geoghegan M.D. (decd.), of Merrion Street, Dublin, and Frances Anne Purser; B.A. (T.C.D.); H 1872, M.T. T 1868. 1873/H/1 [2 items]. Called to the English Bar, M 1871. Assistant-Registrar of the Probate and Matrimonial Division. Died 14 Dec. 1918. Obituary, *I.L.T. & S.J.*, lii (1918), 310.

GEOGHEGAN, JAMES (b. 8 Dec. 1886) eld. s. of Thomas Geoghegan (decd.), of Walshestown, Co. Westmeath, and Bridget Carney; T 1915. 1915/M/06 [2 items]. English Bar, 1923. S.C., 6 May 1925. Fianna Fáil T.D. for Longford-Westmeath, 13

June 1930-1936. Minister for Justice, 1932-3. Attorney-General, 2 Nov.-22 Dec. 1936.
Judge of the Supreme Court, Dec. 1936. Retired 1950. Died 27 March 1951. Obituary,
I.L.T. & S.J., lxxxv (1951), 87.

GEOGHEGAN, JAMES JOSEPH (b. 7 June 1926) 2nd s. of Thomas Geoghegan, of 558 North
Circular Road, Dublin, and Ellen Deenihan; M 1945. 1949/T/06 [2 items].

GERAGHTY, JOSEPH SEBASTIAN (b. 20 Jan. 1888) eld. s. of Patrick Geraghty (decd.), of
25 Longwood Avenue, Dublin, and Margaret Mangan; B.A., LL.B. (N.U.I.); M 1922.
1924/M/11 [2 items]. Died in Hilary Term, 1974. Obituary, *I.L.T. & S.J.*, cviii (1974),
166.

GERAGHTY, PATRICK JOSEPH (b. 10 Nov. 1921) 2nd s. of John Christopher Geraghty,
retired head postmaster, of Baymount, Putland Road, Bray, Co. Wicklow, and Eily
Malone; M 1947. 1951/T/02 [2 items]. S.C., 6 Oct. 1975. Bencher.

GERRARD, JOHN DENISON WARDELL (b. 28 Dec. 1875) 3rd s. of Thomas Gerrard
(decd.) of 28 Fitzwilliam Square, Dublin, and Eliza Jane Wardell; E 1897. 1900/E/02
[3 items]. Home Circuit. Q.C., 5 July 1884.

GERRARD, JOHN NETTERVILLE (b. 24 Feb. 1843) 3rd s of Samuel Gerrard of Batchelor
Hall, Rathfarnham, Dublin and Hannah Monsarrat; B.A. (T.C.D.); M 1865, M.T. E
1867. 1868/M/1 [2 items].

GHANTAMRAJU, KAPALLY (n.d.) s. of Kapally Somaraju, of Gudivada, Krishna District,
Madras, India; M 1914. 1917/T/05 [2 items].

GHARPURAY, PARSHURAM VYANKATRAO (b. 10 Dec. 1883) 3rd s. of Vyankatrao
Malhar Gharpuray of Wardha, Central Provinces, India; M 1913. 1916/T/08 [2 items].

GIBLIN, BARTHOLOMEW AUGUSTINE (b. 30 Sept. 1924) only s. of Luke Giblin, of 31
Bunting Road, Walkinstown, Co. Dublin, and Julia O'Shaughnessy; B.A. (N.U.I.); M
1945. 1949/M/12 [2 items]. Died 22 March 2002.

GIBSON, EDWARD GRAVES MAYNE (b. 28 July 1873) 3rd s. of Edward Gibson, 1st Baron
Ashbourne, of 12 Merrion Square, Dublin, and Frances Maria Adelaide Colles; E 1898.
1901/E/01 [3 items]. J.P. Died 26 April 1928.

GIBSON, JOHN GEORGE (b. 14 Feb. 1846) 5th s. of William Gibson of Merrion Square,
Dublin, Taxing Master in Chancery, and Louisa Grant; B.A., M.A. (T.C.D.); H 1868,
L.I. H 1869. 1870/T/1 [2 items]. Auditor of the College Historical Society, 1870-1.
QC, 1880. 3rd Serjeant and Solicitor-General, 1885. M.P. for Liverpool (Walton) 1885.
Solicitor-General 1886, Attorney-General, 1887-8. Judge of the Queen's Bench
Division, 1888. Retired 1921. Died at Colwyn Bay, 28 June 1923. Obituary, *I.L.T. &
S.J.*, lvii (1923), 166-7; *Who's Who*. See Ball, *Judges*, ii, 377-8. Anecdote in Maurice
Healy, *The Old Munster Circuit*, 28.

GIBSON, THOMAS HENRY (b. 3 Feb. 1865) 5th s. of George Gibson, linen merchant, of
Belfast, and Ellen Hanna; LL.D., M 1887 [John Brooke Scholarship]. 1892/H/01 [8
items].

GIBSON, Hon. VICTOR (b. 3 Jan. 1875) 4th s. of the Rt. Hon. Edward Gibson, Lord
Ashbourne, Lord Chancellor of Ireland, of 12 Merrion Square, Dublin, and Frances
Maria Adelaide [Colles]; T.C.D., Cambridge; M 1896. 1899/T/04 [3 items]. Served
with the Imperial Yeomanry in the Boer War: see *I.L.T. & S.J.*, xxxiv (1900), 440.

GIBSON, WILLIAM GEORGE (b. 13 Feb. 1874) 2nd s. of the Rt. Hon. John George Gibson,
Justice of Queen's Bench Div., of 38 Fitzwilliam Place, Dublin, and Anna [?]; B.A.
(T.C.D.); M 1894. 1897/T/08 [4 items]. Leinster Circuit. K.C., 24 Feb. 1912. Called to
the English Bar, H 1912. Bencher, T 1916. Mentioned by V.T.H. Delany [q.v.], as one
of 'those who were at the forefront of their profession during the period'.

GILBERT, HENRY (b. 27 Dec. 1870) 6th s. of William John Gilbert (decd.), merchant, of
Belfast, and Ellen Orr Killen; B.A. (R.U.I.); M 1892. 1896/T/02 [6 items].

GILBERT, JENNIE ZELDA (b. 16 Jan. 1907) young. d. of Mark Rubinstein (decd.), retired
photographer, of 94 South Circular Road, Portobello, Dublin, and Annie Cowan; M
1962. 1968/M/28 [1 item].

GILL, GARRETT EDWARD (b. 11 Jan. 1909) only s. of Garrett Gill, of 68 Pembroke Road,
Ballsbridge, Dublin, and Elizabeth O'Hara; M 1928. 1933/H/01 [2 items]. S.C., 1 Nov.
1963. Contributed a short memoir, 'A Half-century in the Law Library', to the *Irish
Law Times* (new series), x (1992), 46-7.

GILL, ROY ANTHONY FURLONG (b. 10 Oct. 1883) eld. s. of Thomas Patrick Gill of 19 Herbert Street, Dublin, and Anne Hennell; M 1905. 1908/T/11 [2 items]. Died 17 May 1949.

GILLESPIE, Captain JOHN eld. s. of John Gillespie, of The Lodge, Castleblayney, Co. Monaghan, and Mary Elizabeth Duff; B.A., LL.B. (T.C.D.); M.C. and Bar. T 1921. 1921/T/04 [1 item].

GILLILAND, WILLIAM LOUIS (b. 21 May 1855) 3rd s. of Samuel Gilliland (decd.), J.P., of Brook Hall, Co. Londonderry, and Frances Knox; LL.B. (T.C.D.); M 1877, L.I. T 1879. 1880/M/03 [5 items]. Author of *The Law relating to Sheriffs in Ireland with an Appendix of Statutes and Forms* (Dublin, 1888).

GILMORE, JOHN EDWARD (b. 31 March 1859) only s. of Thomas Spotswood Gilmore, J.P., of Bellaghy House, Co. Londonderry, and Rose Bruce; B.A. (T.C.D.); M 1880, M.T. H 1882. 1883/M/08 [5 items].

GILROY, SEÁN LAURENCE (b. 8 Nov. 1931) only s. of Thomas Gilroy (decd.), of 412 Clogher Road, Dublin, and Anne Kavanagh; M 1961. 1965/M/06 [1 item].

GINNELL, LAWRENCE (b. April 1852) 3rd s. of Lawrence Ginnell (decd.) of Crowenstown, Delvin, Co. Westmeath, and Mary Monaghan; H 1906; M.T. 1893. 1906/T/11 [4 items]. M.P. for Westmeath North 1906-18, and Westmeath County 1918-22 (Nationalist -1909, when expelled; Independent Nationalist, 1909-; after 1916 supported Sinn Fein); Sinn Féin T.D. for Longford-Westmeath 1921-3. Author of *Brehon Laws* (1894); *Doubtful Grant of Ireland* (1899) [a work personally presented to Pope Leo XIII]; *Land and Liberty* (Dublin: Duffy, 1908) [written in Kilmainham Gaol while imprisoned for contempt of the Land Judge's Court]; and *The Irish Republic. Why? Non-Official Statement. Prepared for Submission to the Peace Conference by Laurence Ginnell, Barrister of the Middle Temple and Irish Bar, Representative of North Westmeath in the Dáil Éireann* (New York, [n.d.]). Died 17 April 1923. *Who's Who*.

GIRI, VARAHAGIRI VENKATA (b. 10 Aug. 1894) eld. s. of V.V. [Jogiah], of Berhampore, Madras, India; M 1913. 1916/T/04 [2 items]. Indian nationalist leader, whose contacts with Sinn Féin are said to have led to his deportation from Ireland. In India he became a trade union organiser (1927) and member of the Central Legislative Assembly (1934). Minister of Labour in Nehru's government, 1952-4. Vice-President of India, 1967-9 and 4th President of India, 1969-74. Father of 11 children. Died at Madras, 24 June 1980. Obituary (with photograph) in Richard Turner (ed.), *The Annual Obituary 1980* (New York: 1981), pp 370-3. Photograph in Benchers' Room at King's Inns.

GLEESON, DONOUGH PATRICK (b. 6 March 1932) 4th s. of Dermot Florence Gleeson, District Justice, of Carnelly, Clarecastle, Co. Clare, and Aileen O'Dwyer; M 1950. 1954/T/15 [2 items]. Aft. a magistrate in Surrey.

GLEESON, EDWARD (b. 5 April 1926) 3rd s. of Martin Gleeson, of Lackin, Birdhill, Co. Tipperary, and Anne Flynn; M 1951. 1954/T/14 [2 items]. S.C., 13 Jan. 1986.

GLEESON, JOHN (b. 2 October 1918) eld. s. of Jeremiah Gleeson, auditor, Department of Local Government, of Wilton House, Wilton, Co. Cork, and Mary Murphy; B.A., LL.B. (N.U.I.: U.C.C. and U.C.D.); M 1938. Awarded Society's Exhibition. 1941/M/02 [2 items]. S.C., 5 March 1953. In 1968 he left the Bar to become a solicitor, in which role he took on Mary Finlay [H 1980] as an apprentice. He returned to the Bar, and was appointed a judge of the Circuit Court, serving from 1978 to 1988. See Eamonn G. Hall and Daire Hogan (eds.), *The Law Society of Ireland 1852-2002* (Dublin, 2002), 119. Died 4 Feb. 2004. Death noted: *Courts Service News*. Volume 6, No. 1 (March 2004), 8.

GLEESON, PAUL (b. 19 Sept. 1874) only s. of Patrick Michael Gleeson, merchant, of Kilcolman, Glenageary, Co. Dublin and Margaret Clare Purcell; T 1906. 1906/M/09 [2 items]. Died 4 Sept. 1940. Obituary, *I.L.T. & S.J.*, lxxiv (1940), 237.

GLEESON, WILLIAM JOSEPH (b. 24 Nov. 1878) eld. s. of Joseph Gleeson of Frankfort Lodge, Inchicore, Dublin, and Frances Nolan; T 1908. 1908/M/03 [2 items]. S.C., 6 May 1927. Judge of the Circuit Court (Midland Circuit). Died 3 Feb. 1953. Obituary, *I.L.T. & S.J.*, lxxxvii (1953), 63. Mentioned in Patrick MacKenzie, *Lawful Occasions*, 75.

GLENNON, CHRISTOPHER PATRICK (b. 9 March 1884) only s. of Patrick Glennon (decd.) of Anfield House, Booterstown, Co. Dublin, and Annie C. Byrne; B.A. (R.U.I.); M 1903. 1906/M/07 [3 items].

GLOVER, WILLIAM ERSKINE (b. 23 Feb. 1872) 3rd s. of John Glover (decd.), solicitor, of Magherafelt, Co. Londonderry, and Mary Hastings; B.A. (T.C.D.); M 1892. 1895/M/04 [5 items]. Registrar, Land Commission. Author of *Registration of Ownership of Land in Ireland* (Dublin, 1933); and (with F.H. Browning) of *Local Registration of Title in Ireland* (Dublin, 1901; 2nd edition, 1912). Died 1956. Obituary, *I.L.T. & S.J.*, xc (21 Jan. 1956), 22.

GLYNN, DAVID KEVIN (b. 18 Jan. 1947) eld. s. of John Glynn, local government official (retired), of 'The Croft', Cross Avenue, Blackrock, Co. Dublin, and Josephine Corbett; B.Comm. (N.U.I.); M 1965. 1968/T/07 [1 item].

GLYNN, PATRICK McMAHON (b. 25 Aug. 1855) 3rd s. of John McMahon Glynn (decd.), merchant, of Gort, Co. Galway, and Ellen Walsh; B.A. (T.C.D.); M 1875, M.T. M 1877. 1879/E/11 [6 items]. 'A not altogether empty brief bag during ... sixteen months membership of the Irish Bar' did not prove 'a sufficient inducement to remain at home'. Emigrated to Australia. Called to the Bar in Victoria, 1880, and also in New South Wales and South Australia. K.C. in Australia, 1913. Member of the South Australia Legislative Assembly, 1887-9, 1895-9, and of the Commonwealth Parliament, 1901-19. Attorney-General in South Australia, 1899; in Federal Ministry, 1909-10. Minister for External Affairs, 1913-4; Minister of Home Affairs, and Territories, 1917-20. Author of numerous political tracts (including a 32-page Melbourne-printed pamphlet entitled *Irish State Trials*) and of Shakespearian studies. Died in North Adelaide, 28 Oct. 1931. Obituary, *I.L.T. & S.J.*, lxv (1931), 268, and lxvi (1932), 5. See the biography by Gerald O'Collins, *Patrick McMahon Glynn, a founder of Australian Federation* (Melbourne, 1976). Papers in National Library of Australia, Camberra, MS 4,653. *Who's Who*; Bede Nairn and Geoffrey Serle (eds.), *Australian Dictionary of Biography*, ix (Melbourne, 1983), 30-32 [article by Gerald O'Collins].

GODLEY, JOHN (b. 21 June 1861) only s. of William G.R.J. Godley, J.P., of Forthill, Co. Dublin, and Mary Anne Farley; cand. bachelor (T.C.D.); T 1883, M.T. H 1885. 1886/E/04 [6 items].

GOGARTY, HENRY HAMILL DEVEREUX (b. 15 Nov. 1882) 2nd s. of Henry J.H. Gogarty, F.R.C.S.I., of 5 Rutland Square, and Glasnevin, Dublin, and Margaret M. Oliver; B.A. (T.C.D.); M 1900. 1905/H/07 [3 items].

GOGARTY, OLIVER DUANE (b. 23 July 1907) eld. s. of Oliver St. John Gogarty, M.D., of 15 Ely Place, Dublin, and Mary Martha Duane; M 1928. 1931/T/01 [2 items]. Son of 'stately, plump Buck Mulligan' of Joyce's *Ulysses*. S.C., 2 March 1948. Interview (with photograph) in *The Irish Times*, 23 June 1994. Died 25 Dec. 1999. Obituary, *The Times*, 19 Jan. 2000; Appreciation (by T.A. Finlay) in *The Irish Times*, 14 Feb 2000. *Burke's Irish Family Records* (1976), 475.

GOLDBERG, DAVID SIMON (b. 17 Aug. 1945) 3rd s. of Gerald Yael Goldberg, solicitor, of Ben-Truda, Douglas, Cork, and Sheila Beth Smith; M 1963. 1967/M/04 [1 item]. S.C., 1 Oct. 1999. Photograph (with his father) in *The Irish Times*, 10 Jan. 2004. Editor of *Consolidated Criminal Legislation* (Dublin, 2002).

GOLIGHER, WILLIAM ALEXANDER (b. 30 Dec. 1870) 3rd s. of John Goligher, J.P., of Londonderry, and Matilda Hunter; F.T.C.D.; M 1902. 1905/T/09 [3 items]. S.F.T.C.D. Vice-Provost. Professor of Ancient History, 1904-9; Professor of Classical Archaeology, 1909-34. Author of articles in *Kottabos, Hermathena, Classical Review*, and *English Historical Review*. Died 15 Aug. 1941. Obituary, *I.L.T. & S.J.*, lxxv (1941), 211; *Who's Who*.

GOOD, DONAL BERNARD WATERS (b. 13 April 1907) eld. s. of William John Good, of 'Drynan', Bushy Park Gardens, Dublin, and Kathleen Mary Waters (decd.); M.A. (T.C.D.); M 1932. 1935/M/02 [2 items]. Called to the English Bar, G.I., 1948. Puisne Judge, Federation of Malaya.

GOODBODY, ALYS MARY OSTERBERG (b. 21 March 1925) only d. of Harald A.V. Osterberg, company director, of Watford, Shrewsbury Road, Dublin, and Ethel Mary Davenport; B.A. (T.C.D.); M 1944. 1951/M/02 [2 items].

GOOLD-VERSCHOYLE: see VERSCHOYLE.

GORDON, ALAN SAMUEL (b. 11 Dec. 1888) only s. of John Gordon, K.C., MP, of 25 Upper Fitzwilliam Street, Dublin, and Dorothy May Clay; B.A. (Cantab.); M 1909, I.T. M 1908. 1912/T/11 [2 items].

GORDON, JOHN (b. 23 Nov. 1849) eld. s. of Samuel Gordon of Shankill House, Co. Down, and Arabella Barclay; B.A., LL.B (Queen's University); E 1874, G.I. M 1875. 1877/E/08 [4 items]. Q.C., 1 July 1892. Bencher 1898. Liberal Unionist M.P. for South Londonderry, 1900-1916. Attorney-General 1915. Judge of the King's Bench Division, 1916-22. Died 26 Sept. 1922. Obituary, *I.L.T. & S.J.*, lvi (1922), 236-7, 243; *Who's Who*. See Ball, *Judges*, ii, 385.

GORDON, RICHARD MAYBERRY (b. 6 April 1853) 2nd s. of Stephen Gordon, solicitor, of 2 Burlington Road, Dublin, and Mary Duckett; B.A. (T.C.D.); T 1871, M.T. H 1874. 1875/M/02 [4 items].

GORHAM, ALFRED (b. 21 Nov. 1856) eld. s. of the Revd. George Martyn Gorham, late Fellow of Trin. Coll. Cambridge, of Masham, York, and Mary Ann Holmes; B.A. (T.C.D.); M 1884. 1887/M/03 [5 items]. Death noted, without date, in T.C.D. *Register of Alumni*, 6th ed., 1955.

GOWAN, JAMES ROBERT (b. [Cahore, Co. Wexford] [22 Dec.] 1815 [3rd surviving s. of Henry Hatton Gowan and Elizabeth Burkitt]) Late Local Judge of the H.C. of Justice for Ontario, and Senr. Judge of the Judicial Distr. of Simcoe, Canada; Law Society of Canada, June 1834, called Aug. 1839. [personal memorial] 1889/M/11 [4 items]. Emigrated to Canada, 1832, where his judicial career extended for over sixty years. Founded the *Canada Law Journal*, 1855. Senator for life, 1885. C.M.G., 1893; K.C.M.G., 1905. Died 18 March 1909; *Who's Who*; Ramsay Cook (ed.), *Dictionary of Canadian Biography*, xiii (1994), 391-5 [article by Desmond H. Brown].

GRAHAM, HENRY GEORGE DUNNE (b. 5 June 1940) only s. of George Carson Graham, solicitor, of Hopefield, Castleblaney, Co. Monaghan, and Helen Hannah Molloy; M 1958. 1963/T/08 [2 items]. English Bar. Birmingham

GRANT, CHARLES WILLIAM (b. 26 May 1881) only s. of Thomas Grant of 24 Rathgar Road, Dublin, and Marie Watson; M 1912. 1915/E/01 [2 items].

GRANT, JAMES (b. 24 June 1853) 2nd s. of Edward Grant, merchant, of Carndonagh, Co. Donegal, and Mary McConalogue; H 1881, M.T. M 1882. 1883/M/11 [6 items].

GRAVES, ARNOLD FELIX (b. 17 Nov 1847) 2nd [3rd] s. of the Rt. Revd. Charles Graves, Bishop of Limerick, and Selina Cheyne; B.A. (T.C.D.); E 1871, I.T. M 1866. 1872/T/13 [2 items].

GRAY, DAVID (b. 20 Aug. 1878) eld. s. of David Gray, of 2 West Street, Portadown, Co. Armagh, and Sarah Kegan; M.A. (T.C.D.); M 1917. 1920/T/04 [2 items].

GRAY, EDWARD JOSEPH (b. 2 May 1925) eld. s. of Commandant Michael Gray, of 118 Grace Park Road, Drumcondra, Dublin, and Mary Power; M 1944. Awarded 1st Victoria Prize. 1948/T/03 [2 items].

GRAY, JOHN (b. 14 June 1854) only s. of Joseph Gray (decd.) of Rockfield House, Co. Monaghan, and Elizabeth Smith; B.A. (T.C.D.); M 1877, L.I. T 1880. 1886/H/01 [7 items].

GREALY, MICHAEL EUCHARIA (b. 23 Dec. 1932) 2nd s. of John Francis Grealy, of Rathcoffey, Co. Kildare, and Mary Healy; B. Comm. (U.C.D.); M 1955. 1960/T/13 [2 items].

GREEN, JAMES MAXWELL SULLIVAN (b. 24 September 1913) 2nd s. of Max Sullivan Green (decd.), Chairman of Prisons Board, of 9 Appian Way, Dublin, and Joanna Redmond; B.A. (T.C.D.); M 1934. 1939/M/06 [1 item]. Leinster Circuit. Called to English Bar, L.I., 1947. Grandson of John Redmond. See *Thom's Directory* (Biographies).

GREEN, WILLIAM (b. 8 May 1845) only s. of Murdoch Green of Youghal Co. Cork, and Adelaide O'Neill; B.A. (T.C.D.); M 1864, I.T. E 1866. 1868/H/4 [4 items]. Editor of the *Law Reports, Ireland*, from 1877 to his death. Died as Father of the Bar, 3 Aug. 1913. Obituary, *I.L.T. & S.J.*, xlvii (1913), 219, 260.

GREENE, ARTHUR ALEXANDER (b. 16 July 1860) eld. s. of Edward Jonas Greene of 10 Lansdowne Road, Dublin, and Adelaide Reid; B.A. (T.C.D.); T 1883, M.T. T 1884

[Exchequer Office]. 1887/T/03 [7 items]. Court official, 1885-1930. Died 31 Jan. 1932. Obituary, *I.L.T. & S.J.*, lxvi (1932), 37.

GREENE, BENJAMIN (b. 9 Jan 1846) only s. of John Butler Greene of Prospect Hill, Galway, and Ellen Casey; B.A. (T.C.D.); E 1866, M.T. H 1868. 1869/M/4 [4 items].

GREENE, DONAL (b. 12 March 1894). see Mac Grianna, Dómhnall.

GREENE, ERNEST HENRY (b. 4 Oct. 1862) 2nd s. of Edward J. Greene, Common Pleas Division, of 10 Lansdown Road, Dublin, and Adelaide Reid; B.A. (T.C.D.); T 1883, M.T. T 1884. 1887/H/04 [7 items].

GREENE, GEORGE COMERFORD (b. 19 Jan. 1863) 3rd s. of James Sullivan Green, Q.C., of Air Hill, Co. Cork, and Annie Comerford; B.A. (T.C.D.); M 1882, M.T. E1884. 1886/M/05 [8 items]. Appt. County Court Judge for Armagh and Louth, 25 Sept. 1909; after 1921 for Armagh and Fermanagh. Died 7 Feb. 1940. Obituary, *I.L.T. & S.J.*, lxxiv (1940), 49, 143.

GREENE, GEORGE COURTENAY BALL (b. 25 Nov. 1870) eld. s. of Sir John Ball Greene, C.B., Commissioner of Valuation, of Landour, 53 Raglan Road, Dublin, and Charlotte Mary Courtenay; B.A. (T.C.D.); M 1890, I.T. H 1892. 1893/M/06 [7 items]. Munster Circuit. K.C., 24 June 1908. Died Jan. 1958.

GREENE, IAN RAWDON (b. 3 March 1909) only s. of Rawdon Greene, of Rahan, Bray, Co. Wicklow, and Marie Louise Greene; M 1928. 1931/M/08 [2 items]. Judge of the High Court, Somaliland.

GREENE, MAURICE CHERRY (b. 4 Nov. 1881) 4th s. of the Revd. Thomas Robert Greene (decd.), of 25 Eccles Street, Dublin, and Kathleen Dalton Cherry; B.A. (T.C.D.); M 1910. Formerly political and administrative officer in West Africa. 1919/M/10 [5 items]. Nigeria, 1912-1927; President, District Court, Cyprus, 1928; Puisne Judge, Palestine, 1937; Chief Justice of Gibraltar, 1941-2; Proper Officer of the Crown Prize Court, Bermuda, 1945-9. Died 6 Dec. 1959. *Who's Who.*

GREER, EDWARD (b. 4 Feb. 1832) eld. s. of Robert Greer, late of Newry, Co. Down, and Mary Bell; T 1897. 1897/M/15 [2 items].

GREER, FRANK NUGENT (b. 24 Feb. 1869) 3rd s. of Samuel McCurdy Greer (decd.), County Court Judge, of Springvale, Co. Londonderry, and Sara Thomas Nugent; Sch., Sen. Moderator, B.A. (T.C.D.); M 1890. 1893/T/04 [6 items]. Auditor of the College Historical Society, 1893-4. K.C., 27 Feb. 1918. Parliamentary draftsman at the Irish Office, Arundel House, The Bank, Highgate, 1908-23. K.C.B., 1923. Died Feb. 1925. Obituary, *I.L.T. & S.J.*, lix (1925), 40; *Who's Who.*

GREER, GEORGE (b. 26 Nov 1849) eldest s. of John Waite Greer J.P. of Woodville, Lurgan, Co. Armagh, and N.F. Gofslin; B.A. (T.C.D.); M 1870, I.T. E 1872. 1874/T/6 [4 items].

GREGG, JAMES REALI (b. 16 Nov. 1899) eld. s. of Captain James Gregg, O.B.E., V.S., 20 Chlorine Gardens, Belfast, and Beatrice Hannah Wells; Harvard University (USA); B.A. (Cambridge); M 1921, G.I. M 1920. 1923/T/09 [2 items]. Called to English Bar, G.I., 1939; K.C. (Uganda), 1944; Law Officer in Nyasaland (1939) and Uganda (1943); Puisne Judge in Nigeria, 1948, Puisne Judge, Hong Kong, 1953-61. Died 16 Dec. 1978; *Who's Who.*

GRIFFIN, CHARLES JAMES (b. 25 Dec. 1875) young. s. of John Griffin, solicitor, Clerk of the Peace, Castlebar, Co. Mayo, and Anna M. Daly; ex-Scholar, B.A. (R.U.I.); M 1894. 1898/T/02 [5 items]. Elected first Auditor of the revived 'L. & H.', 1897: see James Meenan (ed.), *Centenary History of Lit. and Hist. Soc. of U.C.D.*, 42-4, 52. Went Connaught Circuit. Crown Prosecutor in the British Central Africa Protectorate (Nyasaland), Blantyre, 1901; Attorney-General of Nyasaland, 1905; Judge of the High Court there, 1906. Attorney-General, Gibraltar, 1914-19; Chief Justice of the Leeward Islands, 1919-21; and Chief Justice of Uganda Protectorate, 1921-32. K.C., 14 Dec. 1920 [not noted in *Thom*, but see *I.L.T. & S.J.*, liv, 306]. Knighted 1923. Published the *Revised and Consolidated Laws of Nyasaland* (1913); the *Revised Statutes of the Presidency of Montserrat* (1921), and ibid. of Antigua (1921) and Uganda (1923). Resided in retirement in Suffolk. Last cited in *Thom's Directory* for 1950, but did not die until 3 Jan. 1962. *Who's Who.*

GRIFFIN, GERALD (b. 30 April 1854) 3rd and only surv. s. of Daniel Griffin (decd.) of George's Street, Limerick, and Anna Leake; M 1881, M.T. E 1883. 1884/M/12 [4 items]. Nephew of the novelist. Died 26 May 1933. Obituary, *I.L.T. & S.J.*, lxvii (1933), 155-6. James Meenan (ed.), *Centenary History of Lit. and Hist. Soc. of U.C.D.*

GRIFFIN, MARTIN (b. 20 Nov. 1895) 4th s. of Michael Griffin, of The Square, Kildysart, Co. Clare, and Beidget MacCarthy; M 1929. 1933/M/07 [2 items].

GRIFFIN, MICHAEL FRANCIS (b. 12 March 1919) 2nd s. of Michael Griffin, insurance broker, of 11 Palace Street, Drogheda, Co. Louth, and Mary Sullivan; M 1942. 1946/T/01 [2 items]. S.C., 28 Feb. 1964. Judge of the High Court, 11 Oct. 1971; of the Supreme Court, 3 Jan. 1973. Retired 11 March 1991. Retrospect (by T.K. Liston) in *Gazette of the Incorporated Law Society of Ireland*, March 1991, 55-6. Listed in the 1984 edition of Maureen Cairnduff, *Who's Who in Ireland*.

GRIFFIN, PATRICK (b. 18 June 1903) 3rd s. of John Griffin, farmer (decd.), of Glenmore, Kilmihill, Co. Clare, and Catherine Griffin; M 1926; [incl. letter from P. Griffin to R. Armstrong] 1929/M/12 [3 items].

GRIFFITH, NAOMHAN MICHAEL (b. 7 Sept. 1911) only s. of Arthur Griffith, journalist (decd.), of 36 Eaton Square, Terenure, Dublin, and Mary Sheehan; B.A. (N.U.I.); M 1932. 1935/T/04 [2 items]. Known as Nevin Griffith. Son of the founder of Sinn Féin. Registrar of Deeds and Titles, 1975-8. Died 2 June 1984. Appreciation [by J.B.F.] in the *Irish Law Times*, new series, ii (1984), 132.

GROGAN, BRENDAN JOSEPH (b. 23 Nov. 1944) 2nd s. of Vincent Grogan, Senior Counsel, of 'Grace Dieu', Trimleston Avenue, Booterstown, Co. Dublin, and Mary Bell; B.C.L. (N.U.I.); M 1965. 1968/M/22 [1 item]. Died 10 Sept. 2002. Appreciation (by N.J. Kearns) in *The Irish Times*, 7 Oct. 2002. See also *Sunday Independent*, 15 Sept. 2002.

GROGAN, VINCENT BENEDICT (b. 10 April 1915) only s. of Captain Vincent Grogan (decd.), of Lytham-St. Anne's, Lancashire, and Eleanor Kirwan (decd.); B.A. (N.U.I.); M 1934. 1937/M/01 [2 items]. S.C., 8 July 1966. Parliamentary draftsman. Died 1997. Obituary (by E.W.D. Bacon) in *The Irish Times*, 22 Sept. 1997.

GRUBB, RICHARD (b. 29 July 1880) 2nd s. of Frederic Ernest Grubb of Berkeley, Alameda County, State of California, and Edith Going; M 1905. 1908/T/10 [3 items].

GUINEY, CORNELIUS (b. 7 Feb. 1942) eld. s. of John Guiney, farmer, of Corbetstown House, Killucan, Co. Westmeath, and Mary Doherty; B.A. (N.U.I.); M 1963. 1967/M/14 [1 item].

GUINEY, THOMAS JARLATH (b. 4 Sept. 1925) eld. s. of Edward Joseph Guiney, of 1 Burgh Quay, Dublin, and Aileen Mangan; B.A. (N.U.I.); M 1945. 1948/T/15 [2 items].

GUISE-BROWN, GERALD EDWARD (b. 1 May 1898) eld. s. of William Guise-Brown, of The Grove, Rathgar, Dublin, and Isabel McElwaine; B.A. (T.C.D.); M 1919. 1923/H/04 [2 items].

GUPTA, POLISETTY HANUMAYYA (b. 21 Nov. 1893) only s. of Polisetty Ramamoorti (decd.), of Guntur, Madras, India; M 1913. 1917/H/02 [2 items].

GWIRA, DANIEL ESSUON (b. 12 June 1891) 3rd s. of Kobina Daniel Gwira, of Elmina, Gold Coast, Africa, and Elizabeth Gwira; M 1916. 1919/E/01 [2 items].

GWIRA, KOBINA DANIEL (b. 2 Jan. 1923) eld. s. of Danniel Essuon Gwira, of Sekondi, Gold Coast, and Jane McClaren Amondo; M 1949 1953/M/14 [2 items].

GYAW, MAUNG HLA (B. 11 May 1904) only s. of U San Dun, of Maubin, Burma, and Daw Myat Shwe; M 1927. 1930/E/01 [2 items]. Name does not appear on the Supreme Court Roll.

GYLES, WILLIAM THOMAS McGWIRE (b. 17 March 1846) 2nd s. of Revd. Walter Gyles, of 24 Elgin Road Dublin, and Mary Vaughan; B.A. (T.C.D.); M 1868; I.T. E 1867. 1870/T/2 [4 items].

HACKETT, ARTHUR FREDERICK (b. 5 July 1867) 2nd s. of James Hackett (decd.) of Bellair, Co. Cork, and Jane Helen; B.A. (T.C.D.); M 1886. 1890/T/02 [8 items].

HACKETT, JOHN WINTHRUP (b. 4 Feb. 1848) eldest s. of John Winthrup Hackett of 72 Harcourt Street, Dublin, and Jane Mason; H 1872, I.T. E 1872. 1874/M/7 [2 items]. Emigrated to Australia, where he became a member of the Bars of Western Australia,

New South Wales, and Victoria. Editor and proprietor of the *West Australian* and *Western Mail* newspapers. Member of the Legislative Council of Western Australia from 1890. Delegate to the National Australian Federal Convention, 1891, and to the Federal Convention, 1897-8, in which capacity he helped to formulate the Commonwealth Constitution. Married (3 Aug. 1905) an 18-year-old bride; and became the father of General Sir John Hackett (1910-97) and four daughters. LL.D., *h.c.*, T.C.D., 1902. Knighted 1911 (K.C.M.G. 1913). First Chancellor of the University of Western Australia (which has a posthumous portrait done by William Dargie). Registrar of the Diocese of Perth. Died at Perth, 19 Feb. 1916. His great personal wealth went chiefly to the University of Western Australia (£425,000), and to the Church of England. Obituary, *I.L.T. & S.J.*, 1 (26 Feb. 1916), 55. *Burke's Irish Family Records* (1976), 540; Bede Nairn and Geoffrey Serle (eds.), *Australian Dictionary of Biography*, ix (Melbourne, 1983), 150-3 [article by Lyall Hunt].

HADOKE, WILLIAM CLARK (b. 24 July 1876) young. s. of Charles George Haddock (decd.), of Grosvenor Square, Rathmines, Dublin, and Eleanor Mary Clark; M 1913; [Captain, Royal Welch Fusiliers] 1917/M/12 [2 items].

HAG, MOHAMMED ABDUL (b. 14 Sept. 1886) eld. s. of Mian Ala-ud-Din of Ferozepore City, Punjab, India; M 1912. 1915/T/05 [2 items].

HAGUE, WILLIAM VESEY (b. 22 Jan. 1877) eld. s. of William Hague (decd.), J.P., architect, F.R.I.A.I., of 21 Upper Mount Street, Dublin, and Anne Frances Vesey Daly; M.A .(R.U.I.); M 1896. 1902/E/01 [2 items].

HALL, REGINALD (b. 18 April 1906) only s. of Samuel Hall (decd.), of Belfast, and Margaret Ann Getty; H 1926. 1928/T/08 [2 items].

HALL, WILLIAM CLARKE (b. 26 May 1866) eld. s. of the Revd. William Hall, M.A, of Folkestone, Kent, and Sarah Jane Clarke; Scholar of Christ Church College (Oxford); M 1887, G.I. M 1886, called to the English Bar. 1889/M/10 [6 items].

HALLINAN, ERIC (b. 27 Oct. 1900) 4th s. of Edward Hallinan, of Avoncore, Midleton, Co. Cork, and Elizabeth Denachy. Sen. Mod. B.A., LL.B. (T.C.D.); M 1920. 1924/H/02 [2 items]. Called to English Bar, G.I., 1927. Practised at Irish Bar, 1924-9. Colonial Administrative (1930-6) and Legal (1936-40) Service, Nigeria; Attorney-General of the Bahamas, 1940-4; Puisne Judge Trinidad, 1944-8; Nigeria, 1948-52; Chief Justice of Cyprus, 1952-7; of the West Indies, 1958-61; Justice of Appeal, Bahamas and Bermuda, 1966-8. Knighted 1955; LL.D. (*jure. dig.*, Dubl.), 1958. Died 13 April 1985. *Who's Who*.

HAMILL, ARTHUR JOHN (b. 3 March 1850) eldest s. of Arthur Hamill Q.C. of Eccles Street, Dublin, and Mary Hamilton; B.A. (T.C.D.); M 1870, M.T. E 1872. 1873/M/5 [4 items].

HAMILL, WILLIAM INGRAM (b. 18 July 1900) eld. s. of Goodleth Hamill, solicitor, of Castletown House, Dundalk, Co. Louth, and Annie Ingram; Cand. Bachelor (T.C.D.); Awarded Certificate of Honour. 1930/H/02 [2 items]. oxo

HAMILTON, ALFRED H. ORMSBY: see ORMSBY, ALFRED HAMILTON.

HAMILTON, ANDREW BREAKEY (b. 22 Dec. 1857) 3rd s. of the Revd. Samuel Hamilton of Saintfield, Co. Down, and Elizabeth Breakey; M.A., LL.B. (QUI); M 1882, M.T. T 1883. 1885/T/07 [5 items]. Subsequently a Presbyterian Minister, ordained by the Presbytery of Armagh for the charge of First Banbridge. Died 1905. Obituary, *I.L.T. & S.J.*, xxxix (5 August 1905), 236.

HAMILTON, DAVID PAUL IGNATIUS (b. 28 June 1929) 2nd s. of Richard Hamilton, of Church Street, Mitchelstown, Co. Cork, and Mary Ellen Lyons; B.Comm., M.Econ.Sc. (N.U.I.); M 1961. 1964/T/02 [1 item]. S.C., 9 March 1990.

HAMILTON, EDMUND HARDY (b. 1 April 1863) young. s. of William Hardy Hamilton of Ailesbury Road, Dublin, and Annie Stark; B.A. (Oxon); H 1885. 1887/M/12 [5 items].

HAMILTON, EDWARD BLAYNEY (b. 1 Jan 1845) eld. s. of the Revd. Edward James Hamilton of Desertmartin, Co. Londonderry [Rector of Kilcronaghan Glebe], and Georgina Susan Hart; B.A. (T.C.D.); M 1865, M.T. E 1867. 1869/T/2 [2 items]. Auditor of the College Historical Society, 1869-70.

HAMILTON, EDWIN (b. 14 April 1849) only s. of the Revd. Hugh Hamilton (decd.), of 40 York Street, Dublin, and Mary Ormsby; M.A. (T.C.D.); M 1884. 1887/T/09 [6 items].

Humorous writer, resident in Donaghadee, author of *Mongrel Doggrells, Waggist Tales* and other works, including plays. Chairman of the Dublin District of the Institute of Journalists, 1900. MRIA, 1879; JP, 1896. Died June 1919. *Who's Who.*

HAMILTON, FREDERICK ALEXANDER POLLOCK (b. 20 Aug. 1852) eld. s. of Alexander Hamilton, J.P., of Innistioge, Co. Kilkenny, and Emma Hamilton; B.A. (Cambridge); T 1875, I.T. M 1872. 1877/M/11 [5 items]. Author of: *The Law relating to Charities in Ireland* (2nd edition. Dublin, 1881); (with A.W. Quill) of the 8th edition of Thomas De Moleyns' *The Landowner's and Agent's Practical Guide* (Dublin, 1899); and (with A.W. Quill and E.V. Longworth) of *The Irish Land Acts of 1903, 4, with Appendix of Rules and Forms and a Commentary* (Dublin, 1904) and *The Town Tenants (Ireland) Act, 1906, with Commentary, Rules and Forms* (Dublin, 1907).

HAMILTON, GUSTAVUS EVERARD (b. 14 March 1882) only s. of Everard Hamilton, solicitor, of Balinteer Lodge, Dundrum, Co. Dublin, and Elinor Nolan; B.A. (T.C.D.); M 1902. 1905/M/02 [3 items]. Author of *Solicitors' Costs and Fees in the Superior Courts in Ireland* (Dublin, 1911), being the 2nd edition of 'Baker on Costs' [Sir Augustine Fitzgerald Bakers's *The Schedule of Costs and Fees in use in Ireland, with the General Order and Statutes relating thereto* (Dublin, 1890)], and of *Early History of the Society of King's Inns, Dublin* (Dublin, 1915). Died 2 May 1918. Obituary, *I.L.T. & S.J.*, lii (1918), 112.

HAMILTON, HUBERT CHARLES (b. 12 Jan. 1886) 2nd s. of Charles P. Hamilton (decd.), Barrister-at-Law, of Roundwood, Mountrath, Queen's Co., and Emily L. Smyth-King; B.A., LL.B. (T.C.D.) 1908/T/08 [3 items]. S.C., 30 March 1926. District Justice. Died 21 Feb. 1946. Obituary, *I.L.T. & S.J.*, lxxx (1946), 60, 61.

HAMILTON, JOHN MILLER (b. 23 Sept. 1875) only s. of Captain John Miller Hamilton (decd.), R.M.L.I., of Bonds Hill, Londonderry, and Elizabeth Sarah Lyster; B.A. (T.C.D.); M 1901. 1904/T/09 [3 items].

HAMILTON, WILLIAM JOSEPH LYONS (b. 30 Jan. 1928) eld. s. of Richard Hamilton, of Mitchelstown, Co. Cork, and Mary Ellen Lyons; M 1951. Awarded Brooke Scholarship. 1956/H/01 [2 items]. Known as 'Liam' Hamilton. S.C., 1 March 1968. Judge of the High Court, 23 Oct. 1974. President of the High Court, 16 Jan. 1985. Chief Justice, 19 Sept. 1994. Retired 28 Jan. 2000. Died 29 Nov. 2000. Obituary, *The Times*, [with photograph] 6 Dec. 2000. Appreciation (by Ronan Keane), *Courts Service News* , vol. 3 (1), March 2001, p. 8. Listed in the 1984, 1991 [with photograph] and 1999 editions of Maureen Cairnduff, *Who's Who in Ireland*. See also: Louis McRedmond (ed.), *Modern Irish Lives.*

HAN, MAUNG B.A. (b. 4 May 1906) 4th s. of U. Aung Gyaw, of Rangoon, Burma, and Daw [Moy?]; M 1927. 1931/T/07 [2 items].

HANBURY, HUBERT [Thornburgh] (b. 11 Sept. 1888) only s. of Hubert James Hanbury of Somerstown, Laracor, Co. Meath, and Amelia Kate [Askin]; B.A. (T.C.D.); M 1909. 1912/M/08 [3 items].

HAND, GEOFFREY JOSEPH (b. 25 June 1931) young. s. of Joseph Anthony Hand, Barrister-at-Law, of Woodburn, Sydney Avenue, Blackrock, Co. Dublin, and Mary Josephine Macaulay; M.A. (N.U.I.), D.Phil. (Oxon); M 1954. 1961/T/06 [2 items]. Aft. university lecturer and professor, U.C.D. Author of *English Law in Ireland, 1290-1324* (Cambridge, 1967). Volume xxxi (1996) of *The Irish Jurist*, a festschrift dedicated to him, contains biographical details, a photograph, and a bibliography of his writings.

HAND, JOSEPH ANTONY (b. 7 Dec. 1891) 3rd s. of James J. Hand, of 9 Waltham Terrace, Blackrock, Co. Dublin, and Mary Sweeney; M 1914. 1917/T/08 [2 items]. Assistant Probate Officer, seen in a photograph of 31 July 1931 taken on the occasion of the last day of sitting in Dublin Castle (*Courts Service News*, vol. 4 (4), Oct. 2002, p. 5).

HAND, WILLIAM JOSEPH (b. 25 March 1882) eld. s. of William J. Hand (decd.) of Percy Place, Dublin, and Mary Lambe; M 1910. 1913/T/11 [3 items]. Died 10 Nov. 1962. Obituary, *I.L.T. & S.J.*, xcvi (1962), 302.

HANLEY, EAMONN (b. 4 Aug. 1919) 3rd s. of Hugh Hanley, civil servant, of 6 Newtown Terrace, Athlone, Co. Westmeath, and Mary Josephine Finn (decd.); E 1957. Awarded 2nd Victoria Prize. 1961/T/03 [2 items]. District Court Clerk. Died c. 2004.

HANLY, DERMOT JOSEPH (b. 20 Oct. 1910) eld. s. of Joseph Francis Hanly, of Knockboyne, Navan, Co. Meath, and Margaret [?]; E 1945. 1945/M/09 [4 items].

HANLY, JOHN BARRY (b. 6 Dec. 1926) 5th s. of Francis Joseph Hanly, F.R.C.S.I., M.Sc., M.R.I.A. (retired chief science inspector), of 'Eagle Lodge', 36 Rathgar Avenue, Dublin, and Margaret Healy; B.A. (N.U.I.); M 1945. 1950/M/07 [2 items].

HANNA, GEORGE BOYLE (b. 17[?] Dec. 1877) 5th s. of Robert Hanna, auctioneer, of Ballymena, Co. Antrim, and Mary Jane Kennedy; 1920. 1920/M/09 [2 items]. Unionist M.P. at Westminster, 1919-22; at Stormont, 1921-37. K.C. (N.I.). County Court Judge for Tyrone, 1937. Died 30 Oct. 1938. Obituary, *I.L.T. & S.J.*, lxxii (1938), 335, 340; *Who's Who*.

HANNA, HENRY (b. 4 Jan. 1871) 3rd s. of John Hanna, merchant, of Belfast, and Elizabeth Robinson; LL.B. (London Univ.), B.A.; M 1893, M.T. H 1894. 1896/M/03 [6 items]. K.C., 28 Oct. 1911. Called to the English Bar, E 1913. Bencher 1915, 3rd Serjeant, 29 Oct. 1919. Judge of the High Court 1925-42. Retired 18 Dec. 1942. Author of *The Pals at Suvla Bay* (1917) and *The Statute Law of the Irish Free State 1922 to 1928* (1929). Member of the Executive Committee of the International Academy of International Law at The Hague. President of the Photographic Society of Ireland and of the Irish Kennel Club. Died 21 March 1946. Obituary, *I.L.T. & S.J.*, lxxx (1946), 84; appreciation on retirement, ibid., lxxvi (1942), 320; *Who's Who*. Portrait in King's Inns: see Wanda Ryan-Smolin, *King's Inns Portraits* (1992), 32.

HANNAN, JOHN JAMES (b. 24 Oct. 1936) eld. s. of Leo Patrick Hannan, company director, of South Hill, Mount Merrion Avenue, Blackrock, Co. Dublin, and Sylvia Lee; B.A. (N.U.I.); M 1957. 1961/T/04 [2 items]. Businessman.

HANNAN, MATTHEW JOSEPH (b. 11 Dec. 1893) eld. s. of James Hannan, J.P., of Ballymote, Co. Sligo, and Ellen Hayden; B.A. (N.U.I.); M 1912. 1915/M/04 [2 items]. Appt. District Justice, Oct. 1924. At Cavan, 1929-30; at Dublin, 1930-.

HANNIGAN, DENIS FRANCIS (b. 25 Jan. 1855) only s. of Declan Hannigan, merchant, of Main Street, Dungarvan, Co. Waterford, and Hanora Curran; B.A., LL.B. (Q.U.I.); H 1876, M.T. T 1877. 1878/M/08 [6 items].

HANNIN, THOMAS JOHN BERCHMANS STEEN (b. 5 May 1910) only s. of Berchmans Hannin, of Mullingar, Co. Westmeath, and Margaret Steen; M 1929. 1932/M/06 [3 items]. S.C., 3 March 1950.

HARBINSON, JAMES MAGOFFIN (b. 30 Nov. 1880) 2nd s. of Thomas Kilpatrick Harbinson, J.P., of Warrenpoint, Co. Down, and Annie Magoffin; M.A. (T.C.D.); M 1919. 1923/H/03 [2 items].

HARBINSON, WILLIAM DAWSON (b. 6 Aug. 1874) eld. s. of Thomas Kilpatrick Harbinson of Cornascribe, Co. Armagh, and Annie McGaffin; M 1902. 1905/H/05 [2 items]. Called to the English Bar, M 1910.

HARDY, WILLIAM JOHNSTON (b. 27 March 1865) young. s. of Alexander Hardy (decd.) of Londonderry, and Charlotte McKnight; Sen. Mod., LL.B. (T.C.D.); E 1888. 1891/E/03 [9 items]. Auditor of the College Historical Society, 1890-1.

HARE, HERBERT HAMILTON (b. 29 Dec. 1893) 2nd s. of William Hare, of 61 North Strand, Co. Dublin, and Sarah Jane Stafford; M 1919. 1922/M/04 [2 items]. Editor of *The Irish Law Times and Solicitors' Journal*, 1931-49. Died 17 Nov. 1953. Obituary, *I.L.T. & S.J.*, lxxxvii (1953), 302.

HARLEY, THOMAS TURNER (b. 27 Feb. 1856) 3rd s. of James Austin Harley (decd.), ship owner, of Clarence House, Cork, and Mary Turner; M 1892, M.T. M 1894 [includes certificates of attendance at lectures in Inner Temple]. 1895/T/06 [12 items]. Died 1934. Obituary, *I.L.T. & S.J.*, lxviii (13 Jan. 1934), 11.

HARNETT, MICHAEL JOSEPH (b. 7 Oct. 1915) 3rd s. of Timothy Harnett, of New Street, Abbeyfeale, Co. Limerick, and Hanorah Collins; M 1943. 1946/T/15 [2 items].

HARREL, ALFRED GISBORNE WHARTON (b. 17 Feb. 1865) eld. s. of David Harrel, C.B., J.P., Chief Commissioner, Dublin Metropolitan Police, of 10 Ailesbury Road, Dublin, and Juliana Horner; B.A. (T.C.D.), District Inspector, R.I.C.; M 1888. 1891/M/13 [5 items].

ALPHABETICAL INDEX 1868-1968   201

HARRINGTON, MICHAEL JOHN (b. 9 Nov. 1914) young. s. of James Harrington, of Holybrook Road, Clontarf, Co. Dublin, and Ellen McCarthy; M 1946. 1950/T/08 [2 items].
HARRINGTON, TIMOTHY (b. 20 Sept. 1852) 10th s. of Denis Harrington (decd.) of Castletown Bere, Co. Cork; E 1884. 1887/H/10 [7 items]. M.P. 1883-1910. Counsel for Parnell in *The Times* Parnell Commission, 1888-9. Lord Mayor of Dublin, 1901-4. Author of *A Diary of Coercion* (3 parts; Dublin, 1888-90). Died 12 March 1910. See *Who's Who*; and Henry Boylan, *A Dictionary of Irish Biography* (Dublin, 1978).
HARRIS, EDWIN (b. 7 July 1867) 3rd s. of John Frederick Harris of Bessbrook, Co. Armagh, and Elizabeth Green; LL.B., H 1888. 1891/H/05 [8 items].
HARRIS, FRANCIS WILLIAM FITZGERALD (b. 7 June 1847) eld. surv. s. of William Wallace Harris, LL.D, Barrister-at-Law, of 24 Mountjoy Square, [26 Eccles Street] Dublin, and Caroline Parker; LL.B (T.C.D.); M 1870, I.T. E 1872. 1873/T/10 [4 items].
HARRIS, LESLIE GERALD EYRE (b. 16 May 1906) eld. s. of John Leslie Harris, solicitor, of 3 Connaught Place, Clonskeagh, Dublin, and Annie Margaret Hunter; M 1924. 1927/T/03 [2 items]. Author of *A Treatise on the Law and Practice in Lunacy in Ireland* (Dublin, 1930). Practised in Nairobi.
HARRIS, REGINALD THOMAS (b. 5 April 1861) young. s. of William Wallace Harris, LL.D., Barrister-at-Law, of 24 Mountjoy Square, Dublin, and Caroline Frances Sydney Parker; B.A. (T.C.D.); M 1882, M.T. 1885/T/04 [6 items]. Died 2 Oct. 1946.
HARRISON, ANTHONY CLEPHANE (b. 5 Feb. 1916) young. s. of Lieut.-Colonel Robert William George Harrison, of Johnstown, Kill, Co. Kildare, and Helena Cecilia Houghton; B.A.; M 1937. 1942/T/01 [2 items].
HARRISON, JAMES WHITELAW STRONGE (b. 31 May 1868) 2nd s. of the Hon. Michael Harrison of 3 Mountjoy Square, Dublin, Judge of the High Court of Justice in Ireland, and Sophia Mary Stronge; B.A. (T.C.D.); M 1888. 1893/H/06 [6 items].
HARRISON, REGINALD ALFRED (b. 2 March 1908) 3rd s. of William John Harrison, Chief Clerk, Dublin Circuit Court, of Homestead, Iona Road, Glasnevin, Dublin, and Florence Rich; M 1926. 1929/M/07 [2 items]. S.C., 28 July 1965. Librarian of the Law Library, and editor of the *Irish Reports*, 1950-66, and of *The Irish Digest, 1939-48* and *The Irish Digest, 1949-58*. Died 7 Feb. 1968. Obituary, *I.L.T. & S.J.*, cii (1968), 109.
HARRISON, ROBERT FRANCIS (b. 26 Dec. 1858) eld. s. of the Hon. Michael Harrison, Judge of the Common Pleas Division of H.M. High Court of Justice in Ireland, of 3 Mountjoy Square, Dublin, and Frances Davison; B.A. (T.C.D.); M 1879, M.T. T 1880. 1882/M/01 [5 items]. Q.C., 22 April 1899. Bencher, 1904. Died 24 Nov. 1927. Obituary, *I.L.T. & S.J.*, lxi (1927), 286. *Who's Who*.
HARRISON, THOMAS (b. 27 Nov. 1859) eld. s. of William Harrison of Bally[cowen], Co. Down, and Sarah [McKee]; LL.B (Q.C.B.); M 1882. 1886/M/02x [4 items]. Died 4 Feb. 1920. Author of *The Law and Practice relating to Ejectments in Ireland in the Superior Courts, Civil Bill Courts, and Petty Sessions together with Appendices of Statutes, Rules and Forms* (Dublin, 1903; reprinted, 1981). Obituary, *I.L.T. & S.J.*, liv (1920), 37.
HART, GEORGE VAUGHAN (b. 31 Aug. 1877) eld. s. of George Vaughan Hart, K.C. of Woodside, Howth, Co. Dublin, and Mary Elizabeth Hone; H 1898. 1901/T/02 [3 items]. Land Commission. Died (in a drowning tragedy in which two of his sons also perished) 8 Sept. 1928. Obituary, *I.L.T. & S.J.*, lxii (1928), 223.
HARTNETT, MAURICE NOEL (b. 21 Dec. 1909) 4th s. of William Joseph Hartnett, LPSI (decd.), of the Medical Hall, Kenmare, Co. Kerry, and Kathleen Barbery; B.A. (T.C.D.); M 1937. 1943/M/05 [2 items]. Senator 1951-4. Joint founder (with Seán MacBride) of Clann na Poblachta. Died 25 Aug. 1960. Obituary, *I.L.T. & S.J.*, xciv (1960), 242-3.
HARTY, DONAL JOACHIM (b. 17 Aug. 1930) eld. s. of Daniel Harty, of 25 Lambay Road, Drumcondra, Dublin, and Lilian Linnane; D.P.A. (T.C.D.); M 1950. 1954/T/07 [2 items].
HARVEY, ALBERT WILLIAM (b. 3 April 1863) 3rd s. of Samuel Harvey, J.P., of Weston-Super-Mare, Somerset, and Petronell Jane Perrett Luscombe; M 1895. 1898/T/08 [3 items].

HARVEY, EDWARD AUGUSTINE (b. 30 Aug. 1865) 4th s. of Richard Harvey, J.P., of 45 Ailesbury Road, Dublin, and Mary Anne King; E 1890. 1892/T/11 [8 items].
HARVEY, ERNEST LOUIS (b. 31 March 1866) 2nd s. of William Harvey (decd.), of University Square, Belfast, and Louisa Leathem; B.A. (R.U.I.); M 1888. 1892/H/05 [7 items].
HASAN, SAYED NAZIR (b. 16 May 1873) eld. s. of Sayed Haji Hazder Hasan, of Chilkana District, Saharanpur, United Province, India; T 1913. 1917/T/01 [2 items].
HASSARD, WILLIAM (b. 3 March 1856) eld. s. of Michael Dobbyn Hassard of Glenville, Co. Waterford, and Anne Hassard; B.A. (T.C.D.); H 1876, I.T. E 1878. 1879/M/08 [6 items].
HASTINGS, PATRICK ANTHONY (b. 26 Jan. 1942) 3rd s. of James Joseph Hastings (decd.), Garda officer, of 85 St. Helen's Road, Booterstown, Co. Dublin, and Julia Kathleen Thornton; M 1964. 1968/M/09 [1 item].
HASTINGS, SAMUEL HENRY (b. 28 Sept. 1891) only s. of Samuel Henry Hastings (decd.), of Bangor, Co. Down, and Elizabeth McCloy; B.A. (London); M 1919. 1922/H/01 [2 items]. Assistant Legal Adviser, Department of Local Government. Died 30 March 1943. Obituary, I.L.T. & S.J., lxxvii (1943), 93.
HAUGH, JOSEPH D. (b. 22 Nov. 1938) young. s. of John Haugh (decd.), national teacher, of Bridgetown, O'Brien's Bridge, Co. Clare, and Nora Lucid; M 1958. Awarded 2nd Victoria Prize. 1962/M/04 [1 item]. Became a solicitor, E 1974. A. & L. Goodbody.
HAUGH, KEVIN JOHN (b. 1 June 1944) eld. s. of the Hon. Mr. Justice Kevin C. O'Hanrahan Haugh, of 10 Airfield Park, Donnybrook, Dublin, and Brenda Cullen; B.C.L. (N.U.I.); M 1963. 1966/T/11 [1 item]. Judge of the Circuit Court, 1996.
HAUGH, KEVIN O'HANRAHAN (b. 17 Nov. 1901) 2nd s. of Professor John Joseph Haugh (decd.), of Castlenau, Merrion, Dublin, and Kathleen O'Hanrahan; M 1922. 1925/M/26 [2 items]. S.C., 21 Dec. 1938. Bencher, E 1940. Attorney-General 1940-2. Judge of the High Court, 1942-61; of the Supreme Court, 1961-9. Died 5 April 1969. Obituary, I.L.T. & S.J., ciii (1969), 179-80.
HAUGHEY, CHARLES JAMES (b. 16 Sept. 1925) 2nd s. of Commandant John Haughey (decd.), of 12 Belton Park Road, Dublin, and Sarah McWilliams; B. Comm. (N.U.I.); M 1946. 1949/M/11 [2 items]. Fianna Fáil T.D., 1957-1992. Minister for Justice, 1961-4; for Agriculture, 1964-6; for Finance, 1966-70; for Health, 1977-9. Taoiseach, 1979-81, 1982, 1987-1992. Acquitted of charge of conspiring to import arms illegally, 1970: see Tom MacIntyre, Through the Bridewell Gate: A Diary of the Dublin Arms Trial (London, 1971). Listed in the 1984 and 1991 editions of Maureen Cairnduff, Who's Who in Ireland. See Louis McRedmond (ed.), Modern Irish Lives. Biographies, inter alia, by Raymond Smith (Dublin, 1983), John M. Feehan (Cork, 1985), T. Ryle Dwyer (Dublin, 1987; Cork, 1997; Dublin, 1999), and Bruce Arnold (London, 1993).
HAWKINS, ALEXANDER BRUCE (b. 18 Oct 1848) 2nd surv. s. of Henry Hawkins of Belfast, Co. Antrim, Merchant, and Eliza Bruce; M.A. (Queen's College Belfast); M 1869, M.T. H 1871. 1873/M/2 [7 items].
HAYDEN, JAMES JOSEPH (b. 11 July 1883) eld. s. of Michael Hayden, of 54 South Great George's Street, Dublin, and Katherine Dooley; T 1926. 1926/M/17 [2 items]. LL.D. Died 29 March 1936. Obituary, I.L.T. & S.J., lxx (1936), 91.
HAYES, FRANCIS MAHON (b. 2 March 1930) 2nd s. of Francis Mahon Hayes, bank manager, of Munster & Leinster Bank, Castletownbere, Co. Cork, and Aileen Walsh; B.A. (N.U.I.); M 1949. 1952/M/11 [2 items]. Legal adviser and deputy secretary, Department of Foreign Affairs; ambassador to U.N.
HAYES, MICHAEL (b. 1 Dec. 1889) eld. s. of John Hayes (decd.), of Tipperary, Co. Tipperary, and Jane Finn; M.A. (N.U.I.); H 1924. 1929/M/20 [2 items].
HAYES, ROGER (b. 16 March 1918) first s. of Edward Hayes (decd.), farmer, of Clonconaur, North Liberties, Co. Limerick, and Anna Kiely; B.A. (N.U.I.); M 1937. 1940/M/09 [2 items]. Assistant Secretary, Department of Justice; Law Reform Commissioner, 1977-84.
HAYES, SAMUEL (b. 26 April 1875) 4th s. of William Hayes (decd.), solicitor, of Kingstown, Co. Dublin, and Susan Mathews; B.A. (T.C.D.); M 1896. 1899/M/10 [4 items].

HEALY, FRANCIS JEROME BURKE (b. 29 Aug. 1869) only s. of Jeremiah Healy, Contractor to Her Majesty's Royal Navy, of The Beach, Queenstown, Co. Cork, and Mary Theresa Burke; E 1890, L.I. M 1891. 1893/E/01 [8 items]. Died 7 August 1931. Obituary, *I.L.T. & S.J.*, lxv (1931), 196.

HEALY, JOHN (b. 20 Sept. 1866) eld. s. of Michael Healy, J.P., of Ballinglen, Co. Wicklow, and Margaret Jane Savage; B.A. (N.U.I.); M 1901. 1919/M/09 [2 items].

HEALY, JOHN CRICHTON (b. 22 March 1869) only s. of John Healy (decd.), accountant, of Cork, and Mary Baldwin M'Creight; H 1906, G.I. H 1900. 1906/T/10 [5 items].

HEALY, JOHN EDWARD (b. 17 March 1872) only s. of James Stanislaus Healy, solicitor, of Drogheda, Co. Louth, and Kate Mary Appleyard; B.A. (T.C.D.); M 1902. 1906/M/05 [2 items]. In 1898 joined staff of the Dublin *Daily Express*, of which he became editor. Editor of *The Irish Times*, 1907-34, and Dublin correspondent of *The Times*. Died 30 May 1934. Obituary, *I.L.T. & S.J.*, lxviii (1934), 154; *Who's Who*; *D.N.B.* See Tony Gray, *Mr Smyllie, Sir* (Dublin, 1991; 1994), 28-31 (and photograph).

HEALY, JOHN J.C. (b. 19 May 1867) 2nd s. of William Healy, Inspector of Schools, of Longford, Co. Longford, and Catherine Cunningham; BA(R.U.I.); M 1888. 1891/T/03 [4 items]. Died 1947. Obituary, *I.L.T. & S.J.*, lxxxi (13 Dec. 1947), 88.

HEALY, JOSEPH (b. 17 Dec. 1889) eld. s. of Timothy Michael Healy, K.C. of Glenaulin, Chapelizod, Dublin, and Erina Sullivan; B.A. (R.U.I.); M 1909. 1912/T/10 [2 items]. S.C., 15 March 1943. Died 25 Dec. 1955. Obituary, *I.L.T. & S.J.*, xc (1956), 5.

HEALY, MAURICE FRANCIS (b. 16 Nov. 1887) eld. s. of Maurice Healy of Ashton Lawn, Cork, and Anne Mary Sullivan; M 1907. 1910/T/12 [3 items]. Called to the English Bar, 1914; K.C. (Eng.), 1931. Recorder of Coventry, 1941-43. Died 9 May 1943. Obituary, *I.L.T. & S.J.*, lxxvii (1943), 121, 140-1, 148; *Who's Who*. Author of *The Old Munster Circuit: A book of memories and traditions* (1939) [reprinted, with a biographical introduction by Charles Lysaght (London: Wildy, 2001)]. Author also of *Claret and the White Wines of Bordeaux* (1934) and *Stay me with Flagons* (1939). Mentioned in James Meenan (ed.), *Centenary History of Lit. and Hist. Soc. of U.C.D.*; in Charles Bewley, *Memoirs of a Wild Goose* (Dublin, 1989), 46-7; and as teetotal cellarer of the Munster Circuit in *I.L.T. & S.J.*, lxii (1938), 47. C.N. Kough's 1913 caricature of the author as 'The Jackdaw of Rhymes' forms the frontispiece to *The Old Munster Circuit*.

Of Maurice Healy

'He was brought up in the law, for his grandfather, a grand-uncle, his father and five uncles, his sister and brother and six first cousins, all became members of one or other branch of the legal profession'.

From 'London Letter', in *The Irish Times*, 11 May 1943

HEALY, RICHARD (b. 13 May 1870) eld. surv. s. of William Healy, gentleman, of Ballymee, Doneraile, Co. Cork, and Mary O'Brien; M.A. (R.U.I.); M 1893. 1896/M/02 [4 items]. Munster Circuit. Died June 1900: *I.L.T. & S.J.*, 16 June 1900, 254.

HEALY, ROWLAND HENRY SAVAGE (b. 13 Nov. 1905) only s. of John Healy, Barrister-at-Law, Examiner of the High Court, of Alderley, Glenageary, Co. Dublin, and Alyce Katherine O'Brien; B.A. (T.C.D.); M 1928; [Indian Civil Service, Burma] 1936/E/01 [4 items]. Actually called at E 1946. His Memorial was misfiled at K.I. under E 1936.

HEALY, TIMOTHY MICHAEL (b. 17 May 1855) 2nd s. of Maurice Healy of Lismore, Co. Waterford, and Eliza Sullivan; T 1881, G.I. T 1880 [M.P. for Monaghan]. 1884/M/08 [7 items]. Q.C., 22 April 1899. M.P. (for numerous constituencies) 1883-1918. Governor General of the Irish Free State, 1922-8. Died 26 March 1931. Obituary, *I.L.T. & S.J.*, lxv (1931), 83-4; *Who's Who*. For an appreciation on his retirement, see *I.L.T. & S.J.*, lxii (1928), 12. Bronze by Joseph Davidson in King's Inns: see Wanda Ryan-Smolin, *King's Inns Portraits* (1992), 79. See his *Letters and Leaders of my Day* (2 vols., 1928) and the memoir by his daughter, Maev, *No Man's Man;* the description 'T.M. Healy as advocate', in J.B. Hall, *Random Records of a Reporter* (Dublin, n.d.), 106-7; the biography by Frank Callanan, *T.M. Healy* (Cork, 1996); *D.N.B.*; chapter 3 in Brendan Sexton, *Ireland and the Crown 1922-1936* (Dublin, 1989); and Louis

McRedmond (ed.), *Modern Irish Lives*. Author of numerous political and historical publications, including *Stolen Waters: a page in the conquest of Ulster* (1913), a work prompted by knowledge acquired in the Lough Neagh fishery litigation: O'Neill v. Johnston [1908] 1 I.R. 358, [1909] 1 I.R. 237, [1912] 1 I.R. 61 (and 1911 A.C. 552).

HEARN, Lieutenant THOMAS EDMUND (b. 4 Sept. 1894) eld. s. of Michael Louis Hearn, solicitor, of Waterloo, Temple Gardens, Rathmines, Dublin, and Mary Josephine Molony; M 1913. 1919/H/03 [2 items]. Died, as Lieutenant-Colonel, 27 March 1959.

HEARNE, JOHN J. (b. 4 Nov. 1893) 5th s. of Richard Hearne, Alderman, J.P., of Waterford, Co. Waterford, and Alice Power; B.A., LL.B. (N.U.I.); M 1916. 1919/M/03 [2 items]. Assistant parliamentary draftsman 1923-9; legal adviser to the Department of External Affairs 1929-39. S.C., 20 June 1939. High Commissioner to Canada, 1939-49, and ambassador to USA, 1950-60. Influential in drawing up the heads of the 1937 Constitution. Died 1968. See Louis McRedmond (ed.), *Modern Irish Lives*.

HEAVEY, AIDAN (b. 1 Feb. 1927) eld. s. of Andrew Heavey (decd.), commercial agent, of Ashley Crescent, Athlone, Co. Westmeath, and Mary Scott; B.Comm. (N.U.I.); M 1965. 1968/M/12 [1 item].

HEAVEY, JAMES RICHARD (b. 24 April 1916) eld. s. of Martin Joseph Heavey, of Inniscorrig, Dalkey, Co. Dublin, and Joanna O'Neill; B.A. (T.C.D.); M 1934. 1937/M/07 [2 items]. S.C., 9 July 1953. Died 14 April 1971. Obituary, *I.L.T. & S.J.*, cv (1971), 147.

HEDERMAN, ANTHONY JAMES JOSEPH (b. 11 Aug. 1921) 2nd s. of William Patrick Hederman, of Glenville, Naas, Co. Kildare, and Milly Jones; B.A. (N.U.I.); M 1941. 1944/M/07 [3 items]. S.C., 30 April 1965. Attorney-General, 5 July 1977-1981. Judge of the Supreme Court, 1 July 1981. Retired 31 July 1993. President of the Law Reform Commission, 1992-7. Listed in the 1984 and 1991 editions of Maureen Cairnduff, *Who's Who in Ireland*.

HEDERMAN, MIRIAM (b. 6 June 1932) only d. of William Hederman, of Glenville, Naas, Co. Kildare, and Mary Jones; M 1950. 1954/M/11 [2 items]. Mrs. Hederman O'Brien. Ph. D. (T.C.D.), 1981. Policy consultant, with interests in fiscal reform and the European movement; Chairman of the Commission on Taxation, 1980-5; Chancellor of the University of Limerick, 1998-2002. See Dónal de Búitléir and Frances Ruane (eds.), *Governance and Policy in Ireland. Essays in honour of Miriam Hederman O'Brien* (Dublin: I.P.A., 2003), a volume which carries her photograph on its dustjacket; and Louis McRedmond (ed.), *Modern Irish Lives*.

HEGARTY, PATRICK HUBERT (b. 2 July 1941) eld. s. of Peter V. Hegarty, insurance official, of Kevinsfort, Sligo, and Gertrude Kelly; M 1963. 1967/T/07 [1 item].

HEGARTY, THOMAS LAURENCE OSWALD (b. 27 Oct. 1885) only s. of Maurice Hegarty (decd.) of Bolanstown, Delvin, Co. Westmeath, and Oswaldina Neilson; T 1911. 1911/T/08 [2 items].

HEMPHILL, Hon. MARTYN (b. 17 Feb. 1901) eld. s. of the Rt. Hon. Lord Hemphill, of 28 Fitzwilliam Place, Dublin, and Lady Hemphill; B.A. (New College, Oxford); M 1927. 1930/H/03 [2 items]. Practised on the Western Circuit. M.T. 1933. Suceeded to the peeerage as the 4th Baron Hemphill. S.C., 3 July 1946. Died 19 March 1957; *Who's Who*.

HEMPHILL, STANHOPE CHARLES JOHN (b. 13 March 1853) eld. s. of Charles Hemphill, Q.C., of Merrion Sq, Dublin, and Augusta Stanhope; MA; E 1877, M.T. H 1874. 1878/M/09 [4 items]. K.C., 30 June 1906. Called to the English Bar, E 1877. Succeeded to the peerage as the 2nd Baron Hemphill. Died *sine prole* 26 March 1919; *Who's Who*.

HENCHY, SÉAMUS: see Ó hINNSE, SÉAMUS.

HENDERSON, JAMES (b. 26 April 1848) eld. s. of James Alexander Henderson J.P., of Norwood Tower, Strandtown, Belfast, Co. Down, and Agnes Mackay; B.A. (T.C.D.); M 1870, M.T. M 1868. 1872/T/10 [8 items]. Editor of the *Newry Telegraph*; 1883-manager-proprietor of the *Belfast News-Letter*. Knighted 1899. Died 1914. Obituary, *I.L.T. & S.J.*, xlviii (1914), 133.

HENDERSON, JAMES (b. 16 Feb. 1889) eld. s. of Sir James Henderson, D.L., of Oakley House, Belfast, and Martha Ann Pollock; B.A. (T.C.D.); M 1908. 1911/T/02 [2 items]. D.L. Died July 1963.

HENDERSON, JOSEPH DUNLOP (b. 27 Dec. 1878) eld. s. of John Henderson of Carrickue, Co. Londonderry, and Annie Reid; M 1909. 1912/T/13 [3 items].

HENN, FRANCIS BLACKBURNE (b. 28 Feb. 1848) 2nd s. of Thomas Rice Henn, Q.C., Barrister-at-Law, of Paradise, Co. Clare, and J. Blackburne; H 1870, M.T. E 1872. 1875/H/03 [2 items]. Resident Magistrate and Justice of the Peace, Co. Sligo. Died 15 Nov. 1915. *Burke's Irish Family Records* (1976), 573.

HENNESSY, RICHARD MARTIN (b. 5 Oct. 1853) 2nd s. of John B. Hennessy, J.P., of Ballindeasig House, Co. Cork, and Mary Hennessy; M 1873, M.T. H 1876. 1877/M/06 [5 items]. Munster Circuit. K.C., 19 Feb. 1902. Bencher, 1913. Died 23 Oct. 1926. Obituary, *I.L.T. & S.J.*, lx (1926), 259; *Who's Who*. Mentioned in Maurice Healy, *The Old Munster Circuit*, 139-44.

HENNESSY, WILLIAM CHARLES (b. 28 June 1858) only s. of William M. Hennessy of Pembroke Road, Dublin, and Anne O'Callaghan; E 1879, M.T. M 1880. 1882/H/03 [6 items].

HENRION, PETER WILLIAM (b. 21 July 1875) only s. of Peter Joseph Henrion (decd.), of Coobroe, Graig-na-managh, Co. Kilkenny, and Catherine Agnes Jones; M 1923. 1926/T/01 [*recte* 1926/E/03] [2 items]. Died 3 Nov. 1953. Obituary, *I.L.T. & S.J.*, lxxxvii (1953), 290.

HENRY, ALEXANDER PATTERSON (b. 23 Dec. 1868) 8th s. of James Henry (decd.) of Draperstown, Co. Londonderry; and Ellen Kelly; M 1891. 1894/T/04 [8 items]. Died 3 Sept. 1935. Obituary, *I.L.T. & S.J.*, lxix (1935), 257.

HENRY, DENIS STANISLAUS (b. 7 March 1864) 6th s. of James Henry (decd.), of Cahore, Co. Londonderry, and Ellen Kelly; M 1881, M.T. M 1883. 1885/E/02 [6 items]. Q.C., 23 June 1896. Unionist M.P. for South Londonderry, 1916-21. Solicitor-General, 1918, and Attorney-General, 1919. Lord Chief Justice of Northern Ireland, 15 Aug. 1921. Knighted. Died 1 Oct. 1925. Obituary, *I.L.T. & S.J.*, lix (1925), 238-9, 262; *Who's Who*; Kate Newmann, *Dictionary of Ulster Biography* (Belfast, 1993). See A.D. McDonnell, *The Life of Sir Denis Henry: Catholic Unionist* (Belfast: Ulster Historical Foundation, 2000); *Oxford DNB* (2004) [article by Gordon Gillespie].

HENRY, GEORGE HEWITT (b. 16 Feb. 1861) 2nd s. of Thomas Henry, merchant, of Monaghan, Co. Monaghan, and Jane Hewitt; B.A. (R.U.I.); H 1887. 1890/H/02 [11 items].

HENRY, Captain HERBERT GEORGE (b. 25 June 1889) young. s. of Thomas Henry (decd.), of Emlaghnaghten, Ballymote, Co. Sligo, and Catherine Mooney; M 1920. 1923/M/10 [2 items].

HENRY, JAMES (b. 23 Sept. 1864) eld. surv. s. of Thomas Henry of [Aighen], Co. Donegal, and Jane Colvin; B.A., LL.D. (R.U.I.); M 1893. 1899/M/02 [5 items]. Formerly principal of the Foote Memorial School in Lisburn. S.C., 15 June 1927. Editor of *The Irish Law Times and Solicitors' Journal*, Nov. 1911-April 1930. Standing counsel to the Methodist Church in Ireland. Died 3 April 1930. Obituary (with photograph), *I.L.T. & S.J.*, lxiv (1930), 84, 89-90. Mentioned in R. Lee Cole, *History of Methodism in Ireland 1860-1960* (Belfast, 1960), 120.

HENRY, JAMES JOSEPH ERIC (b. 4 Sept. 1913) only s. of Thomas Martin Henry, dentist (decd.), of Banbridge, Co. Down, and Teresa O'Hare; B.A. (N.U.I.); M 1933. 1936/M/06 [2 items].

HENRY, WESLEY PETTIGREW (b. 4 March 1861) eld. s. of Robert Henry of 10 North Vincent Street, Dublin, and Anne Pettigrew; B.A. (T.C.D.); M 1885. 1888/M/09 [6 items]. Chief Secretary's Office. Died 27 June 1952.

HERBERT, DANIEL NICHOLAS (b. 30 Nov. 1944) only s. of James Joseph Herbert, national teacher, of Cahir, Co. Tipperary, and Helen Rita Crane; B.A. (N.U.I.); M 1964. 1967/T/09 [1 item]. S.C., 10 March 1995. Judge of the High Court, 8 May 2000.

HERDMAN, JOHN OCTAVIUS (b. 22 May 1862) 8th s. of John Herdman (decd.), merchant, of Belfast, and Elizabeth Finlay; B.A. (T.C.D.); M 1884, I.T. E 1887. 1887/M/11 [7 items]. Gold Medallist of T.C.D., and Auditor of the College Historical Society, 1887-

8. Member of the English Bar whose career was marred by deafness. Coached in law. Died 1930 or 1931, when about to take up a lectureship in law at Cambridge. Mentioned in J.W. Henderson, *Methodist College Belfast 1868-1938* (2 vols.; Belfast, 1939), 47, 49.

HERLIHY, JOHN (b. 20 July 1889) 3rd s. of Patrick Herlihy (decd.), of 42 Millmount Ave, Drumcondra, Dublin, and Ellen O'Keeffe; B.A. (N.U.I.); M 1925. 1928/H/01 [2 items]. Commissioner of Valuation. Died 26 Aug. 1941. Obituary, *I.L.T. & S.J.*, lxxv (1941), 218, 224.

HERON, CHARLES BERNARD (b. 8 Dec. 1899) 3rd s. of Charles Heron (decd.), of Armagh, Co. Armagh, and Annie McKenna; M 1928. Includes 3 letters between Heron and Under-Treasurer Burke, June 1932 ? 2 with postage stamps. 1932/M/05 [6 items].

HERON, SÉAMUS CONNOLLY (b. 31 July 1921) eld. s. of Archibald Heron, of 63 Park Avenue, Sandymount, Dublin, and Ina Connolly; M 1939 1945/M/10 [2 items]. Grandson of James Connolly, executed in 1916.

HERRICK, JOHN HENRY BEAMISH (b. 15 June 1843) 2nd s. of Henry Herrick (decd.), of Bellmount, Co. Cork, and Elizabeth Beamish; M.A. (T.C.D.); H 1874, M.T. M 1869. 1879/E/04 [4 items].

HERRICK, JOHN THEODORE FRANCIS (b. 6 Nov. 1885) young. s. of John Henry Beamish Herrick (decd.), Barrister-at-Law, of Burlington House, Burlington Road, Dublin, and Fanny Robinson; LL.B. (T.C.D.); M 1908. 1911/T/07 [3 items].

HESLIN, ITA BRIGID (b. 23 May 1925) 2nd d. of Francis Heslin (decd.), of Druminbawn, Carrigallen, Co. Leitrim, and Katie Canning (decd.); M 1947. Awarded 3rd Victoria Prize. 1951/T/01 [2 items].

HEUSTON, ROBERT FRANCIS VERE (b. 17 Nov. 1923) eld. s. of Vere Douglas Heuston, of 18 Vergemount Park, Clonskeagh, Co. Dublin, and Dorothy Helen Coulter; B.A. (T.C.D.); M 1943. Awarded John Brooke Scholarship. 1947/T/01 [3 items]. Auditor of the College Historical Society, 1945-6. Fellow of Pembroke College, Oxford, Regius Professor of Laws, T.C.D., 1970. Editor (from the 11th edition, 1953) of *Salmond on Torts*. Author, *inter alia*, of the *Lives of the Lord Chancellors, 1885-1940* (1964) and *1940-1970* (1987). Q.C., *honoris causa* [*The Times*, 13 April 1995]. Died 21 Dec. 1995. Obituary, *The Times*, 27 Dec. 1995. *Oxford DNB* (2004) [article by P.R. Glazebrook].

HEWSON, JOHN GILBERT (b. 24 May 1875) 2nd s. of John Brownrigg Hewson of Castle Hewson, Co. Limerick, and Harriet Gardiner; H 1898. 1900/M/09 [4 items]. Died Feb. 1951.

HEWSON, THOMAS (b. 3 March 1844) [1 Leeson Park, Dublin] 2nd s. of Falkiner Minchin Hewson (decd.) of 60 Upper Baggot Street, Dublin, wine merchant, and Mary Brownrigg; B.A. (T.C.D.); T 1870, M.T. M 1866. 1872/H/9 [9 items].

HICKEY, CLODAGH MARGARET (b. 14 Dec. 1947) eld. d. of Dr. Garrett Hickey, of 37 South Street, New Ross, Co. Wexford, and Irene Liston-Murphy; B.C.L. (N.U.I.); M 1964. 1967/M/01* [1 item].

HICKEY, DENIS JOHN BORROMEO GIDEON (b. 2 Nov. 1934) eld. s. of Daniel G. Hickey, of Cappawhite, Co. Tipperary, and Lillie O'Byrne; B.A.; M 1954. 1957/M/09 [3 items].

HICKEY, HENRY MAURICE (b. 4 Aug. 1933) 2nd s. of James Joseph Hickey, solicitor, 7 Rathdown Park, Terenure, Dublin, and Marcella Wren (decd.); M 1952. 1955/M/04 [2 items]. S.C., 4 Oct. 1971.

HICKEY, JOHN M. (b. 22 May 1849) only s. of John Hickey of 131 Leinster Road, Dublin, and Maria O'Reilly; B.A. (T.C.D.); M 1869; M.T. M 1871. 1874/H/4 [2 items].

HICKIE, CHARLES VALENTINE (b. 14 Feb. 1856) 2nd s. of Wm. Creagh Hickie, J.P., D.L., of Kilelton, Ballylongford, Co. Kerry, and Mary A.C. Scott; B.A. (London); M 1886, M.T. H 1877. 1888/E/08 [8 items]. English Bar. Died 7 Dec. 1928. *Burke's Irish Family Records* (1976), 589.

HICKMAN, POOLE HENRY (b. 8 June 1880) 2nd s. of Francis William Hickman, D.L., of Kilmore House, Knock, Ennis, Co. Clare, and Elizabeth O'Brien; B.A. (T.C.D.); M 1906. 1909/E/01 [2 items]. Captain, Royal Dublin Fusiliers. Died 15 Aug. 1915: *I.L.T. & S.J.*, xlix (1915), 216. Photograph in Henry Hanna, *The Pals at Suvla Bay* (1917),

197. Mentioned in Maurice Healy, *The Old Munster Circuit*, 62. [Name on the Bar War Memorial; also on the Helles Memorial, Gallipoli].

HICKSON, EDWARD FITZGERALD (b. 17 Feb. 1849) 5th s. of William Murray Hickson (decd.) of [Drumkelly] House, Co. Cavan, and Louisa Hickson; M 1875, M.T. M 1876. 1879/E/10 [6 items].

HIGGINS, KEVIN: see O'HIGGINS, KEVIN CHRISTOPHER.

HIGGINS, PATRICK ROBERT (b. 15 May 1914) eld. s. of Martin Joseph Higgins (decd.), of Catherine Street, Waterford, and Margaret O'Keeffe; M 1939. 1943/T/04 [2 items]. Probate Office.

HIGGINS, THOMAS ALFRED (b. 25 Feb. 1869) eld. s. of John Higgins, builder and contractor, of Divis Street, Belfast, and Harriette Carey; M 1901. 1904/T/07 [3 items]. Died 1 March 1944. Obituary, *I.L.T. & S.J.*, lxxviii (1944), 73.

HILL, HUGH (b. 4 June 1917) 3rd s. of Edward Hill (decd.), trader, of 7 St. James Road, Belfast, and Margaret Savage (decd.); M 1959. 1963/T/07 [1 item]. Author of *Outlines of Irish Taxation (as applicable to the Republic of Ireland): covering income tax, surtax and corporation profits tax and including legislation* (Dublin, 1970-75).

HILL, RICHARD COTTON WALKER (b. 4 July 1858) only s. of Benjamin Hill, R.M., of Helenville, Co. Longford, and Harriet Walker; Barrister-at-Law of Lincoln's Inn; Member of the Royal Irish Academy; M 1883; L.I. E 1884. 1889/T/02 [7 items].

HILL, WILLIAM HARRY (b. 2 March 1931) 2nd s. of Harry Hill, engineer, of 30 Oaklands Park, Ballsbridge, Dublin, and Ann Glennon; B.A. (N.U.I.); M 1950. 1953/M/07 [2 items]. S.C., 24 Feb. 1978. Master of the High Court, 19 Jan. 1984-2001. Photograph upon appointment in the *Irish Law Times*, new series, ii (No. 2, Feb. 1984), 34.

HIME, MAURICE CHARLES (21 Nov. 1843) 2nd s. of John Rhames Hime (decd.), solicitor, of Gardiner Street, Dublin, and Susan Black; MA; LL.D. (T.C.D. and Foyle College, Londonderry); H 1862, M.T. T 1863. 1884/H/01 [3 items].

HINKSON, ALEXANDER LIONEL (b. 21 Sept. 1922) only s. of Captain Theobald Henry Hinkson, of Budaire, Highampton, Beaworthy, Devon, and Monica Pilkington; B.A. (N.U.I.); M 1941. 1944/M/10 [2 items].

HITCHCOCK, HENRY EDWARD (b. 20 Dec 1843) 2nd s. of William Hitchcock of 10 Prince of Wales Terrace, Bray, Co. Wicklow, Solicitor, and Mary Fitzgerald; B.A. (T.C.D.); T 1865; M.T. E 1866. 1869/E/4 [2 items].

HOARE, THOMAS EDWARD, (b. 27 April 1865) eld. s. of Edward Hoare, of Glenanore, Co. Cork, and Cornelia Shaw; B.A. (T.C.D.); M 1886. 1889/T/07 [8 items].

HODDER, FRANCIS GEORGE (b. 28 July 1846) eld. s. of George Francis Hodder (decd.), Barrister, of Fountainstown, Co. Cork, and Elizabeth Roberts; T 1868; M.T. M 1869. 1871/T/1 [3 items].

HODNETT, GEORGE POPE (b. 4 Sept. 1890) 3rd s. of William M. Hodnett, of Youghal, Co. Cork, and Mary Josephine Curran; E 1923. 1923/E/02 [2 items].

HODNETT, WILLIAM GEORGE (b. 3 Sept. 1933) 2nd s. of George Pope Hodnett, of Maretimo, Blackrock, Co. Dublin, and Laure Olga Fasnacht; M 1951. 1955/M/14 [2 items].

HOGAN, CHRISTOPHER (b. 19 July 1943) eld. s. of John Hogan, CIÉ employee (goods section), of 43 Caseyville, Dungarvan, Co. Waterford, and Mary Murphy; M 1962. 1966/T/06 [1 item].

HOGAN, CONNOR (b. 1 April 1892) eld. s. of Mortimer Hogan, of Cooga, Corofin, Co. Clare, and Bridget Hogan; M 1925. 1929/T/03 [2 items].

HOGAN, ESTHER ANNE (b. 17 April 1945) only d. of Terence F. Hogan (decd.), race horse trainer, of Templehoolen, Pallasgreen, Co. Limerick, and Mary Neylon; M 1962. 1966/M/05 [1 item].

HOGAN, GABRIEL PATRICK (b. 18 March 1901) eld. s. of Patrick Hogan, of Longwood, Herbert Park, Dublin, and Catharine Murphy. 1923/H/02 [2 items].

HOGAN, MICHAEL JOSEPH PATRICK (b. 15 March 1908) only s. of Timothy Hogan, of 29 Sydney Parade Avenue, Dublin, and Mary Lyons; E 1936; [formerly solicitor, struck off roll at own request; called *in absentia*] 1936/T/07 [3 items]. Colonial Legal Service in Palestine, Aden, Malaya. Attorney-General of Malaya, 1950-55. Chief Justice of Hong Kong, 1955, and of Brunei, 1964-70. British Member of the Anglo-

Japanese Property Commission, 1960. Knighted, 1958. LL.D. (*h.c.*, Dubl.), 1962. Died 27 Sept. 1986. Obituary, *The Times*, 29 Sept. 1986; *Who's Who*.

HOGAN, PATRICK (b. 8 Oct. 1891) only s. of Patrick Hogan, of Culleen, Kilmalley, Co. Clare, and Bridget O'Connor; M 1932. 1936/T/06 [3 items].

HOGAN, PATRICK JOSEPH (b. 16 Jan. 1868) only s. of James W. Hogan of 237 Clonliffe Road, Dublin, and Margaret Roche; M.A., jun. fellow (R.U.I.); ex university scholar; H 1894. 1897/M/02 [4 items].

HOGAN, PATRICK JOSEPH (b. 23 Jan. 1911) eld. s. of Thomas Hogan, of 83 Mount Prospect Ave, Clontarf, Dublin, and Mary Ryan; M 1947. 1950/M/14 [2 items].

HOGAN, ROBERT SIMON (b. 21 May 1902) 3rd s. of William Hogan, of 24 Lansdowne Road, Dublin, and Alice Dowse; B.A. (T.C.D.); M 1919. 1923/M/09 [2 items]. S.C., 11 Oct. 1943. Died 28 May 1944. Obituary, *I.L.T. & S.J.*, lxxviii (1944), 148. Mentioned in Patrick MacKenzie, *Lawful Occasions*, 75.

HOGAN-MAGEE: see MAGEE.

HOLLAND, PATRICK COLUMBA (b. 2 Nov. 1917) 3rd s. of Patrick Francis Holland, of 24 Iona Drive, Glasnevin, Dublin, and Bridget Fagan; B. Comm (N.U.I.); T 1943. 1946/T/04 [2 items]. Wine merchant.

HOLLAND, ROBERT SMITH (b. 19 July 1890) 4th s. of Daniel Holland (decd.), of Londonderry, Co. Londonderry, and Mary Jane Smith; T 1922. 1926/H/02 [2 items].

HOLMES, ALEXANDER (8 July 1851) 4th s. of Samuel Crawford Holmes (decd.), of Synge Street, Dublin, and Elizabeth Stephenson; M.A. (T.C.D.); M 1874, M.T. M 1876. 1879/E/06 [5 items].

HOLMES, HUGH OLIVER (b. 12 Jan. 1886) 2nd s. of the Rt. Hon. Hugh Holmes of 3 Fitzwilliam Place, Dublin, and Olivia Moule; B.A. (T.C.D.); M 1907. 1910/M/01 [2 items]. K.C., 27 July 1920. Knighted (1946) K.B.E.; C.M.G., M.C., Belgian Croix de Guerre. Served in the 1st World War, returning to the Irish Bar with the rank of Major. Counsel to the Crown in Ireland, 1919-20. Judge in the Native Court, Cairo, 1920-3; in the Mixed Court, 1924-9; Procurator-General of the Mixed Court of Appeal, Alexandria, 1929-49. Died at Nairobi, 1 Oct. 1955. Obituary, *I.L.T. & S.J.*, lxxxix (1955), 252; *Who's Who*.

HOLMES, ROBERT FRANCIS (b. 25 Feb. 1878) only s. of Major Robert Holmes of 8 Uxbridge Terrace, Dublin, and M.O. Power; M 1899. 1902/M/01 [3 items]. Died 8 Jan. 1950. Obituary, *I.L.T. & S.J.*, lxxxiv (1950), 21-2. Mentioned by V.T.H. Delany [q.v.], in his article 'The Bench and Bar in Ireland', as one prominent among those who never took silk. Recalled also by Garrett Gill [q.v.]. Died 8 Jan. 1950.

HOLMES, ROBERT WILLIAM ARBUTHNOT (b. 25 Dec. 1843) eld. s. of Robert Holmes (decd.) of Moycashel, Kilbeggan, Co. Westmeath, and Jane Henn; M.A. (T.C.D.); E 1868, M.T. H 1875. 1876/T/01 [4 items].

HOLMES, WILLIAM (b. 19 June 1871) eld. s. of the Rt. Hon. Hugh Holmes, Judge, Queen's Bench, of Fitzwilliam Place, Dublin, and Olivia Moule; B.A. (Oxon); M 1892. 1895/M/12 [5 items]. Fought in the Boer War with the Dublin Hunt contingent of the Imperial Yeomanry, losing a leg at Lindley: see *I.L.T. & S.J.*, xxxiv, 20 Oct. 1900, 440, 'Return of Irish Barristers from the War'.

HOLMES, WILLIAM JOHN LONGFORD CURRAN (b. 16 Nov. 1874) eld. s. of Arthur Holmes, J.P., of 'Hazelbrook', Ballyholme, Bangor, Co. Down; M 1916. 1920/M/03 [2 items].

HOLT, HENRY (b. 13 Dec. 1831) only surv. s. of Thomas Holt (decd.), civil engineer, of Cork, and Mary Thomas; [BA?] Queen's University of Ireland; E 1868, I.T. M 1870. 1875/E/01x [2 items]. Secretary to Chief Baron Palles. Died 2 July 1916. Obituary, *I.L.T. & S.J.*, l (1916), 172.

HOOPER, JOHN JOSEPH (b. 7 May 1906) eld. s. of Patrick Joseph Hooper, of 102 Morehampton Road, Dublin, and Margaret Ryan; B.A. (N.U.I.); M 1924. 1927/M/22 [2 items]. S.C., 12 Feb. 1945. A prime mover of the petition to the Benchers for the disbarring of Serjeant Sullivan [q.v.], 13 April 1956. Died 15 April 1961. Obituary, *I.L.T. & S.J.*, xcv (1961), 104-5.

HORAN, GERALD (b. 3 May 1879) 3rd s. of Michael Lane Horan, solicitor, of Belgrave House, Belgrave Square, Rathmines, Dublin, and Theresa Flanagan; B.A. (T.C.D.); H

1898. 1901/M/05 [4 items]. President of the University Philosophical Society, T.C.D., 1901-2. North-East Circuit. Crown Prosecutor for Meath and Louth, 1913-15. K.C., 6 March 1915. Clerk of the Crown and Hanaper, and Permanent Secretary to the Lord Chancellor, 1915-21. First Master of the High Court of the Irish Free State. Author of a commentary of the Courts of Justice Act, 1924, and of *Circuit Court Practice containing Statutes, Rules, Orders and Forms relating to the general procedure and jurisdiction of the Circuit Court*. (Dublin: Irish Law Times & Solicitors' Journal, 1932). Died 10 May 1949. Obituary, *I.L.T. & S.J.*, lxxxiii (1949), 142; *Who's Who*.

HORGAN, JOHN CHRISTOPHER (b. 8 Dec. 1917) eld. s. of Denis Horgan, of Park Road, Killarney, Co. Kerry, and Abina Cahill; M 1944. 1948/M/05 [2 items].

HORNER, ANDREW LONG (b. 7 April 1862) eld. s. of Jacob Henry Horner, gentleman, of Limavady, Co. Londonderry, and Hester Long; B.A. (R.U.I.); M 1884, L.I. E 1886. 1887/M/09 [7 items]. North-West Circuit. K.C., March 1904. Bencher, 1912. Unionist M.P. for South Tyrone, Jan. 1910-16. Died, at Crewe Station Hotel, 26 Jan. 1916. Obituary, *I.L.T. & S.J.*, l (1916), 28; *Who's Who*.

HOUSTON, ARTHUR HENRY (b. 20 Dec. 1872) eld. s. of Arthur Houston, Q.C., of 22 Lancaster Gate, London, and Mary Banks; H 1896. 1898/M/04 [3 items]. Died 25 Feb. 1937. Obituary, *I.L.T. & S.J.*, lxxi (1937), 76.

HOUSTON, FREDERICK HENRY (b. 5 Oct. 1848) 2nd s. of Thomas Houston (decd.) of Belfast, and Elizabeth Cornelius; H 1882, G.I. T 1883. 1884/M/14 [6 items].

HOUSTON, JOHN JAMES (b. 19 April 1877) eld. s. of Thomas Houston, of 'Craigmore', College Ave, Bangor, Co. Down, and Mary McNaught. 1925/M/11 [2 items].

HOUSTON, ROSS (b. 19 Dec. 1868) eld. surv. s. of James Houston of 20 Oaklands Park, Ballsbridge, Dublin, and Dorcas O'Hara (decd.); M 1903. 1907/E/02 [2 items]. Died 29 Aug. 1948.

HOWE, GERARD LEWIS (b. 3 June 1899) only s. of Gerard Augustus Howe, solicitor, of Kingstown, Co. Dublin, and K.J. Beaslay; M 1920. 1923/T/02 [2 items]. Resident Magistrate, Kenya, 1930; Crown Counsel, Gold Coast, 1934, Straits Settlement, 1937. Solicitor-General, Nigeria, 1941-6; Attorney-General 1946-50. Knighted 1949. Chief Justice of Hong Kong, 1950. Died 25 May 1955. *Who's Who*.

HOWLEY, EDWARD (b. 31 Oct 1834) eld. s. of Patrick Culkin Howley (decd.) of Rathellen, Co. Sligo, and Margaret Shiel; M 1853, M.T. M 1852. 1874/M/1 [1 item].

HOWLEY, JOHN GERARD (b. 22 Dec. 1866) 2nd s. of Lieut.-Colonel John Howley, J.P., D.L., of Rich Hill, Co. Limerick, and Helena Mary White; M 1887. 1892/E/03 [7 items].

HOY, EDWARD MARK (b. 4 June 1888) 2nd s. of John Hoy, solicitor, of Dungannon, Co. Tyrone, and Elizabeth Teresa Mooney; M 1905. 1914/H/02 [2 items].

HUBAND, WILLIAM GEORGE (b. 8 March 1845) eld. s. of George Huband (decd.), Captain 8th Hussars, of 39 Upper Mount Street, Dublin, and Marianne Croft; B.A. (T.C.D.); E 1867, I.T. T 1866. 1869/T/3 [4 items]. Called to English Bar, H 1870. Sometime private secretary to the Lord Chancellor. Died 6 April 1912. Obituary, *I.L.T. & S.J.*, xlvi (1912), 91. Author of *A Practical Treatise on the Law relating to Juries in Ireland* (London, 1910).

HUGGARD, WALTER CLARENCE (b. 18 April 1884) eld. s. of John Turner Huggard, land agent, of 13 Palmerston Road, Rathmines, Dublin, and Susan Martin; B.A. (T.C.D.); M 1904. 1907/T/04 [3 items]. LL.D. (T.C.D.), 1908. Colonial Service. Magistrate in Nigeria, 1914. Solicitor-General, Trinidad and Tobago, 1920-; Kenya, 1926-9; Straits Settlement, 1929-33. Chief Justice, Straits Settlement, 1933-6. President of the Special Courts of Swaziland and the Bechuanaland Protectorate, and Judicial Commissioner in Basutoland, 1937-48. Knighted 1933. Mentioned in J.W. Henderson, *Methodist College Belfast 1868-1938* (2 vols.; Belfast, 1939), 189. Died 21 June 1957. *Who's Who*.

HUGHES, BERNARD EDWARD (b. 10 June 1869) only s. of Edward Hughes (decd.), J.P., of 11 College Square North, Belfast, and Mary Frances Hughes; M 1904. 1910/M/05 [2 items]. 'Barney Hughes', mentioned in Maurice Healy, *The Old Munster Circuit*, 61-2.

HUGHES, BRIAN M. (b. 3 May 1923) young. s. of James Laurence Joseph Hayes (decd.), F.C.R.A., B.L., of 12 Seafield Road, Stillorgan, Co. Dublin, and Kathleen Mary Hayden; M 1948. 1952/M/12 [2 items].

HUGHES, GEORGE SPENCER (b. 1 Jan. 1887) young. s. of Mayor Pierce Edward Hughes of Lurganbrae, Shankill, Co. Dublin, and Lucy Adamthwaite; B.A. (T.C.D.); M 1907. 1910/M/07 [2 items]. Died 8 Nov. 1957.

HUGHES, HECTOR SAMUEL JAMES (b. 14 Aug. 1887) eld. s. of Alexander Wilson Hughes of Beach House, Irishtown, Co. Dublin, and Elizabeth Anne Dempsey; M 1912. 1915/T/03 [2 items]. S.C., 21 Nov. 1927. Educated at St. Andrew's College, and boy chorister at St. Ann's Church, Dawson Street, Dublin. Mentioned in James Meenan (ed.), *Centenary History of Lit. and Hist. Soc. of U.C.D*, 100. A founder of the Socialist Party of Ireland, 1918. Associated with the Dáil courts: see Daire Hogan, *The Legal Profession in Ireland*, 152. Author of *Select Cases in Registration of Title in Ireland* (Dublin, 1916) and of several commentaries on statutes, and joint author (with Kevin Dixon) of a commentary on the Landlord and Tenant Act, 1931. Called to the English Bar, 1923, and K.C. in England, H 1932. Labour Party M.P. for Aberdeen North, 1945-70. Died 23 June 1970. See *Who's Who*.

HUGHES, HENRY CHARLES (b. 24 July 1861) 2nd s. of Nicholas Hughes, merchant, of Coleraine, Co. Londonderry, and Sarah O'Doherty; B.A. (R.U.I.); M 1883, G.I. M 1885. 1887/E/02 [7 items].

HUGHES, JAMES LAWRENCE JOSEPH (b. 16 Nov. 1864) 2nd surv. s. of James Hughes (decd.), merchant, of Lower Summerhill, Dublin, and Margaret Kavanagh; M 1899. 1903/T/04 [3 items].

HUGHES, JOHN (b. 18 June 1894) 3rd s. of Michael Hughes of Claremorris, Co. Mayo, and Honor Joyce; M 1929. 1934/T/03 [3 items].

HUGHES, THOMAS (b. 27 Aug. 1884) eld. s. of William J. Hughes (decd.) of 15 Raglan Road, Dublin, and Marietta Neale; B.A. (T.C.D.); M 1906. 1909/M/03 [2 items]. Captain. Died Jan. 1967.

HUGHES, THOMAS WILLIAM GILLILAN JOHNSON (b. 30 March 1889) only s. of Edwin Hughes of Dalchoolin, Craigavad, Co. Down, and Emma Sophia Rhodes; B.A. (Pembroke College, Cambridge); M 1911. 1914/T/04 [4 items].

HUGHES, VINCENT PHILIP (b. 19 Jan. 1908) 2nd s. of Patrick Hughes, Assistant Secretary to the Revenue Commissioners, and Registrar of Joint Stock Companies, of 26 Clyde Road, Dublin, and Mary Agnes Murphy; M 1926. 1929/M/05 [2 items].

HUME, GEORGE ALEXANDER (b. 11 Jan. 1859) 2nd s. of George Alexander Hume, M.D. of Crumlin, Dublin, and Christina Oakman; M.A., LL.B. (QUI); M 1878, M.T. H 1880. 1881/M/02 [5 items]. Q.C., 22 April 1899. Died 9 Jan. 1905. Obituary, *I.L.T. & S.J.*, xxxix (1905), 20-1.

HUME, WALTER OAKMAN (b. 8 Sept. 1890) only s. of George Alexander Hume, K.C. (decd.), of 47 Fitzwilliam Square, Dublin, and Blanche Carr; Sen. Mod. B.A., LL.B. (T.C.D.); M 1911. 1914/T/17 [3 items]. K.C. (N.I.), H 1933. Died 30 June 1939. Obituary, *I.L.T. & S.J.*, lxxiii (1939), 195-6.

HUMPHREYS, DERMOT SIGERSON (b. 10 Feb. 1944) only s. of Emmet Humphreys, architect, of 36 Ailesbury Road, Ballsbridge, Dublin, and Eileen Pratt; B.C.L. (N.U.I.); M 1963, I.T. H 1965. 1966/M/14 [3 items]. Legal adviser, Department of the Environment.

HUMPHREYS, JOHN THOMAS CONOLLY (b. 22 Sept. 1855) eld. s. of Thomas William Drummon Humphreys, J.P., of Milltown House, Co. Tyrone, and Isabella Caroline Thomson; B.A. (T.C.D.); M 1877, M.T. T 1879. 1881/H/06 [7 items]. As 'Jack Humphreys', son of the Duke of Abercorn's principal agent, and nephew of Mrs. Cecil Frances Alexander, mentioned by Sir John Ross as his companion in Henrietta Street: 'Though called to the Bar, he took no interest in the profession, but he was a poet and a gifted writer': *The Days of my Pilgrimage: Random Reminiscences* (1924), 39.

HUMPHREYS, RICHARD (b. 23 April 1896) eld. s. of Dr. David Humphreys, of The Crescent, Limerick, and Mary Ellen O'Reilly; M 1916. 1920/M/02 [2 items].

HUMPHRIES, ROBERT PERCY (b. 6 Jan. 1910) 3rd s. of Edward Humphries (decd.), of 2 Mountain View Road, Ranelagh, Dublin, and Margaret Sheridan; E 1945. 1945/T/14 [5 items]. Bencher.

HUNGERFORD, WINSPEARE CAMPBELL AUGUSTUS (b. 28 Aug. 1871) eld. s. of Winspeare Toye Hungerford (decd.) of Shanakiel House, Co. Cork, and Isabella Fishbourne; M 1906. 1909/T/09 [2 items]. Served in the Royal Canadian Mounted Police before coming to the Bar, and emembered by Garrett Gill (q.v.). Died 31 Aug. 1945. Obituary, *I.L.T. & S.J.*, lxxix (1945), 256.

HUNT, FREDERICK JOHN ROBERT (b. 5 Jan. 1871) eld. s. of Surgeon Major General S.B. Hunt, Madras Command, Secunderabad, India, and Emma Matilda Clarke; E 1894. 1897/T/04 [4 items]. Puisne Judge, and aft. Chief Justice of Travancore, South India. Retired to Dublin. Died c. 1952 [last entry in *Thom's Directory* of that year].

HUNT, HENRY (b. 21 Sept. 1849) eld. s. of Henry Hunt (decd.), gentleman, of Cashel, Co. Tipperary, and Mary Hayes; H 1881, M.T. E 1882. [prize winner at Honor Examination]. 1883/M/03 [7 items]. Revising Barrister for the City of Dublin. Author of *A Guide to the Representation of the People Act, 1884* (3rd edition, Dublin, 1885), and of *Franchise and Registration Law: A Practical Guide for Officials, Voters & Revising Barristers* (Dublin, 1885). Died 7 Nov. 1918. Obituary, *I.L.T. & S.J.*, lii (1918), 281.

HUNTER, ROBERT JOHN (b. 20 Aug. 1864) 2nd s. of Johnston Hunter of Bachelor's Walk, Lisburn, Co. Antrim, and Anna Hunter; M 1907. 1910/T/10 [2 items].

HURLEY, JOHN ANTHONY (b. 24 Aug. 1946) 2nd s. of James Hurley, sugar company employee, of Lacknalooka, Mallow, Co. Cork, and Catherine Hurley; M 1964. 1968/T/10 [1 item].

HURLEY, JOHN GORDON (b. 17 Oct. 1913) eld. s. of Peter John Hurley, civil servant (decd.), of Bayvilla Strand, Youghal, Co. Cork, and Susan Reynolds; M 1931; [incl. letter from Hurley's mother to Burke, Oct. 1936 with stamp] 1936/M/10 [3 items]. District Justice.

HURLEY, WILFRID HUGH (b. 16 Oct. 1910) eld. s. of Henry Hutchings Hurley, solicitor, of Castle Park Road, Sandycove, Dublin, and Elizabeth Louise Maguire; B.A., LL.B. (T.C.D.); M 1932. 1935/M/03 [3 items]. Long Colonial Legal Service career in Nigeria, beginning as a magistrate in 1940, and ending as Chief Justice of the High Court of Northern Nigeria, 1960-7. Knighted 1963. Died 13 July 1984. *Who's Who.*

HURLEY, WILLIAM MICHAEL MARY (b. 29 Sept. 1897) 6th s. of Patrick J. Hurley, of Glenbrook, Glasnevin, Co. Dublin, and Delia Sweeney; B.A., LL.B; M 1953. Awarded Brooke Scholarship. 1956/M/01 [2 items]. Group Captain. Appt. Librarian of the Law Library, 1968: see *I.L.T. & S.J.*, cii (18 May 1968). Died 1989: see obituary, *Irish Law Times*, new series, vii (1989), 147.

HUSAIN, SHEIKH AJMAL (b. 13 Feb. 1893) 4th s. of Sheikh Ahmad Husain of Sasaram, Shahabad District, Bengal, India; M 1913. 1916/T/16 [2 items].

HUSEIN, CHOUDHRI ZOFAR (b. 15 Oct. 1898) 2nd s. of Choudhri Gazanfar Husein, of Barahbanki, India; B.A., LL.B., D.C.L. (T.C.D.); M 1924. 1927/T/07 [2 items].

HUSSAIN, JAVAD (b. 11 Feb. 1893) only s. of the Hon. Mr. Nawal Mohammed Razakhan Khan Bahaharni[es], of Saidapet, Madras, South India, and Lahara Begum; M 1912. 1915/T/04 [2 items].

HUSSEY, PAUL ANTHONY (b. 15 Feb. 1933) eld. s. of Francis Patrick Hussey, university lecturer, B. Econ.Sc., of Grianan, Albert College, Glasnevin, Dublin, and Aileen Houlihan; M 1952. 1956/M/12 [2 items].

HYLAND, ARTHUR C. (b. 6 April 1895) only s. of John Swift Hyland, J.P., of Maxwell Road, Rathgar, Dublin, and Francis Masterson; B.A. (N.U.I.); M 1918. 1921/M/18 [2 items].

HYNES, JOHN WILLIAM (b. 28 Oct. 1856) eld. s. of William Hynes, J.P., of 28 Elgin Road, Dublin, and Maria Caulfield; B.A., LL.B. (T.C.D.); M 1883. 1888/E/02 [6 items]. Connaught Circuit. K.C., 26 April 1913. Bencher 1915. Appt. County Court Judge for the West Riding of Cork, 21 Sept. 1915. Retired 1924. At cricket, captain of the D.U. Eleven and of the Gentlemen of Ireland. Died 16 July 1930. Obituary, *I.L.T. & S.J.*, lxiv (1930), 179; *Who's Who.*

IGOE, FRANCIS GERARD (b. 11 December 1909) first s. of John Igoe, of Summerhill, Nenagh, Co. Tipperary, and Delia Igoe; M 1937. 1940/M/08 [1 item].

INGHAM, RICHARD PATRICK (b. 1 March 1854) eld. surv. s. of Charles David Ingham, solicitor, of Fitzgibbon Street, Dublin, and Helen Anne Day; B.A. (T.C.D.); E 1873, M.T. T 1875. 1877/E/03 [5 items]. Chief Registrar of the Appeal Court of the Irish Land Commission. Died 26 April 1939. Obituary, *I.L.T. & S.J.*, lxxiii (1939), 128.

JACKSON, DAVID (b. 28 June 1933) eld. s. of Jacob Jackson, of 'Beechwood', College Road, Cork, and Rachel Elyan; (Mod.) B.A., LL.B; M 1950. 1955/H/02 [2 items].

JACKSON, HENRY WILLIAM (b. 3 Nov. 1853) 3rd s. of Henry Jackson, of Cara, Co. Fermanagh, and Ellen Kidd; LL.B (T.C.D.); M 1876, L.I. T 1878. 1879/M/11 [6 items]. Q.C., 22 April 1899. Master of the King's Bench Division, 1918-26. Died 28 Dec. 1930. Obituary, *I.L.T. & S.J.*, lxv (1931), 6. Biographical note in Mary Kotsonouris, *The Winding-up of the Dáil Courts, 1922-1925: an obvious duty* (Dublin, 2004), p. 250.

JACKSON, JAMES ALFRED (b. 21 Nov. 1878) only s. of Thomas Stuart Jackson of Glenluce, Ballycastle, Co. Antrim, and Jane Anderson; Mod. B.A. (T.C.D.); M 1910. 1913/T/12 [2 items]. Registrar to Judge W.E. Wylie. Died 1957. Obituary, *I.L.T. & S.J.*, xci (2 Nov. 1957), 264.

JAMESON, JAMES ALGERNA DURAND (b. 31 Oct. 1887) only s. of J.S. Jameson (decd.) of London, and the Countess de Contardone; M 1909. 1913/T/06 [2 items].

JEFFARES, ALFRED SHAUN (b. 14 Aug. 1906) eld. s. of John Lett Sealy Jeffares, of Ballykelly, Drinagh, Co. Wexford, and Caroline Anne Seale; B.A. (T.C.D.); M 1925. 1929/M/10 [2 items].

JEFFERSON, JAMES FULTON (b. 13 Oct. 1871) eld. surv. s. of William John Jefferson of Belfast, and Margaret Kidd; cand. bachelor (T.C.D.); M 1892. 1895/T/05 [5 items].

JEFFERSON, WOOD GIBSON (b. 9 July 1859) only s. of Thomas Ross Jefferson (decd.) of Corroboy House, Co. Roscommon, and Mary Corrigan; B.A. (T.C.D.); M 1879, M.T. T 1881. 1882/M/10 [5 items]. K.C., 30 June 1906. Crown Counsel for the City of Limerick. Died 12 Sept. 1912. *Who's Who.* Mentioned in Maurice Healy, *The Old Munster Circuit*, 98-102.

JELLETT, WILLIAM MORGAN (b. 19 May 1857) eld. s. of the Revd. John Hewitt Jellett, Provost of Trinity College, Dublin, and Dora C. Morgan; B.A. (T.C.D.), Scholar (T.C.D.); M 1878, M.T. M 1880. 1882/M/05 [5 items]. Q.C., 22 April 1899. Candidate (1918), and M.P. for Dublin University, 1919-22. Died as 'Father of the Bar', 26 Oct. 1936. Obituary, *I.L.T. & S.J.*, lxx (1936), 289, 317; *Who's Who.* Mentioned in Maurice Healy, *The Old Munster Circuit*, 189 *et seq.*; and by V.T.H. Delany [q.v.], in 'The Bench and Bar in Ireland', xxxiii-iv. Remembered by Garrett Gill (q.v.) for saying to a solicitor, 'no cheque, no Jellett'. He is remembered working on his briefs by night in the uncurtained front room of 36 Fitzwilliam Square. See the memoir of his grandson, Michael Purser: *Jellett, O'Brien, Purser and Stokes: Seven Generations, Four Families* (Dublin: Prejmer Verlag, 2004), 129-132, 154-5, 165-8 (photographs nos. 10 and 11 between pp 128-9).

JENNINGS, BRENDAN JOSEPH (b. 29 Aug. 1911) 5th s. of Joseph Daniel Jennings, timber merchant (decd.), of Seatown Place, Dundalk, Co. Louth, and Frances Josephine Murphy; H 1934. 1937/T/03 [2 items]. District Judge, Penang, Malaya.

JOHN, SAMUEL SPEDDING (b. 30 Jan. 1891) only s. of Abraham Spedding John of Roseville House, Bray, Co. Dublin [Wicklow?], and Kathleen Mortimer Murray; B.A. (T.C.D.); M 1911. 1914/T/03 [3 items]. Resided in Nigeria.

JOHNS, EDWARD HENRY (b. 18 Dec. 1865) 2nd s. of Thomas Digby Johns, solicitor, of Carrickfergus, Co. Antrim, and Henrietta French; B.A. (T.C.D.); M 1885. 1888/T/07 [8 items].

JOHNSON, EDWARD PHILIP (b. 26 April 1851) eld. s. of Thomas Henry Johnson (decd.) of Ballymacash, Co. Antrim, and Isabella Garnett; B.A. (Cambridge); H 1872, I.T. E

1872. 1876/M/05 [2 items]. Died 16 April 1939. Obituary, *I.L.T. & S.J.*, lxxiii (1939), 118, 216.

JOHNSON, GARRET ANTHONY (Gearoid Mac Eoin) (b. 12 June 1909) 3rd s. of William Johnson, of Curry, Co. Sligo, and Bridget Burke; M 1940. Retired civil servant; awarded Society's Exhibition Prize. 1943/M/02 [2 items].

JOHNSON, JOHN DANIEL ANDREW (b. 5 Feb. 1863) only s. of Andrew John Johnson of Glenbrook, Co. Cork, and Kate [McAlester]; B.A., LL.D. (R.U.I.); M 1884, M.T. M 1886. 1887/M/10 [7 items]. Member of the Irish Selection Board of the Inns of Court Officers' Training Corps.

JOHNSON, JOSEPHINE MARY PHILOMENA (b. 5 Sept. 1942) 4th d. of Richard Johnson, businessman, of Main Street, Kiltimagh, Co. Mayo, and Agnes Gallagher; M 1963. Awarded 3rd Victoria Prize. 1966/T/02 [1 item].

JOHNSON, RICHARD PARNELL FITZGIBBON (b. 27 Oct. 1937) only s. of Richard D.F. Johnson, District Justice, of Curraghroigue, Tralee, Co. Kerry, and Anne Shortis; B.C.L., LL.B.(N.U.I.); M 1957. 1960/M/03 [2 items]. S.C., 3 Oct. 1977. Judge of the High Court, 19 Jan. 1987. Listed in the 1991 edition of Maureen Cairnduff, *Who's Who in Ireland*.

JOHNSON, WILLIAM (b. 1 April 1903) only s. of William Johnson, C.B.E., solicitor, of Newry, Co. Down, and Nellie Stewart; Cand. Bach. (T.C.D.). 1924/E/01 [2 items]. Appt. County Court Judge for County Tyrone, 1947.

JOHNSTON, FREDERICK WILLIAM (b. 22 Dec. 1899) eld. s. of Frederick William Johnston, of Hazelbrook, Upper Kimmage Road, Terenure, Dublin, and Janie Hobson; B.A. (T.C.D.); M 1922. 1925/M/15 [2 items].

JOHNSTON, GEORGE EDWARD PATRICK (b. 16 March 1920) eld. s. of David James Johnston, of Castlemorris, Ballymullen, Tralee, Co. Kerry, and Elizabeth Anne Kelly; M 1940. 1944/M/04 [2 items].

JOHNSTON, HENRY AUGUSTUS (b. 10 Nov 1851) 4th s. of the Revd. Richard Johnston, Rector of Kilmore, Co. Armagh, and Augustus Sophia Hamilton; B.A. (T.C.D.); M 1870, I.T. E 1871. 1873/T/9 [4 items].

JOHNSTON, HENRY THOMAS GERRARD STUART (b. 3 Feb. 1869) eld. s. of Colonel Henry Stuart Johnston of Stirling, Co. Meath, and Elizabeth Mary Gerrard; M 1889. 1892/M/07 [6 items].

JOHNSTON, JAMES GRAYDON (b. 1 Feb. 1848) only s. of Francis Graydon Johnston of Cleveland Square, London, and St Angelo, Co. Fermanagh, and Sarah Johnston; M.A. (Queen's University); M 1867; M.T. 1868. 1871/T/5 [2 items].

JOHNSTON, JOHN ALEXANDER WEIR (b. 17 Nov. 1879) only s. of John Barr Johnston, Knt. of Boom Hall, Londonderry, and Isabella Weir; B.A. (T.C.D.); M 1899. 1903/H/03 [4 items]. K.C. (N.I.), M. 1923.

JOHNSTON, ROBERT (b. 15 March 1835) 3rd s. of W. John Johnston, farmer, of Derrymene, Co. Fermanagh, and Margaret Coulter; E 1872, M.T. H 1873. 1878/M/02 [2 items].

JOHNSTON, WILLIAM (b. 22 Feb. 1829) eld. s. of John Brett Johnston of Ballykilbeg, Co. Down, and Thomasina Scott; B.A., M.A. (T.C.D.); M 1868, M.T. E 1869. 1871/H/5 [3 items]. Associated with the phrase that equated Home Rule with Rome Rule, this robust Orangeman was a Co. Down landowner (a descendant of Francis Marsh, the seventeenth-century Archbishop of Dublin), newspaper-proprietor (*The Downshire Protestant*, 1855-62) and novelist, and was widely renowned in his day as 'Johnston of Ballykilbeg'. He acquired celebrity in March 1868 when Morris J. at Downpatrick sentenced him to two months' imprisonment for a calculated contravention of the Party Processions Act, 1850. Held high office in the Orange Order, and was an Independent Conservative (later Unionist) M.P. for Belfast, 1868-78, and Belfast South, 1885-1902; and for a time held an official post as an inspector of fisheries. He never practised. Died 17 July 1902. See his novel *Nightshade* (1857) and later writings; a biography by Aiken McClelland, *William Johnston of Ballykilbeg* (Lurgan, 1990: portrait and photographs between 54-5); *Who's Who*; *D.N.B.*; and Kate Newmann, *Dictionary of Ulster Biography* (Belfast, 1993). His portrait is painted on Orange banners borne on the Twelfth of July, *inter alia* on that of Ballykilbeg L.O.L. No. 1040.

JOHNSTON, WILLIAM DENIS (b. 18 June 1901) only s. of William Johnston, Judge of the High Court, of Etwall, Lansdowne Road, Dublin, and Kathleen King; B.A., LL.B. (Cambridge); M 1924, I.T. H 1922. Awarded 2nd Class Cert. of Honour. 1925/M/05 [2 items]. The playwright Denis Johnston, President of the Union at Cambridge, was author *inter alia* of *The Old Lady says 'No'* and (using King's Inns materials) of the biography *In Search of Swift* (Dublin: 1959). Bencher of the Inner Temple. Died 8 Aug. 1984. Obituary, *The Times*, 10 Aug. 1984; appreciation (by Terence de Vere White), *The Irish Times*, 10 Aug. 1984. See: *Orders and Descecrations: the life of the playwright Denis Johnston* (ed. Rory Johnston. Dublin, 1992), 42-9; Bernard Adams, *Denis Johnston: A Life* (Dublin, 2002); *Who's Who*; and Louis McRedmond (ed.), *Modern Irish Lives*.

JOHNSTON, WILLIAM JOHN (b. 18 Jan. 1868) eld. s. of James Johnston, merchant, of Dunarnon, Belfast, and Sarah Davidson; M.A., LL.B. (R.U.I.); M 1889, G.I. H 1892. 1892/M/01 [13 items]. N.E. Circuit. K.C., 28 Oct. 1911. Editor of *The New Irish Jurist*, 1900. Joint author with H.M. FitzGibbon [q.v.] of *The Law of Local Government in Ireland* (1899), and his successor as editor of *The Irish Law Times and Solicitors' Journal*, 1906-Nov. 1911. Author of commentaries on Land Purchase (1903) and the Labourers (Ireland) Acts (1906). Liberal parliamentary candidate for Londonderry South, Dec. 1910. Appt. County Court Judge for Monaghan and Fermanagh, 15 Nov. 1911; after 1921 for Monaghan and Louth. Appt. a Judge of the High Court of the Irish Free State, 5 June 1924; advanced to the Supreme Court, 7 March 1939. Retired 17 Jan. 1940. Died 29 Nov. 1940. Obituary, *I.L.T. & S.J.*, lxxiv (1940), 320, 329; *Who's Who*. Recalled in the memoirs of his son, Denis: see *Orders and Desecrations: the life of the playwright Denis Johnston* (ed. Rory Johnston. Dublin, 1992), 6-15. Mentioned (with photograph) in J.W. Henderson, *Methodist College Belfast 1868-1938* (2 vols.; Belfast, 1939), 70-1. See also Kotsonouris, *Retreat from Revolution*, page 161, note 76. Portrait by Seán O'Sullivan reproduced in Brand, Costello and Osborough (eds.), *Adventures of the Law* (Dublin, 2005), xiv. Portrait photograph published with the issue of the *I.L.T. & S.J.* for 14 Jan. 1939.

JOHNSTONE, EUSTACE MEREDYTH MARTIN (b. 15 Aug. 1845) 7th s. of Andrew Johnstone (decd.) of Corboy House, Co. Longford, and Grace A. Martin; H 1875, G.I. E 1881. 1884/T/01 [6 items].

JOHNSTONE, ROBERT STEWART (b. 23 July 1855) 2nd s. of William John Johnstone of Dunensk, Co. Antrim, and Lucinda Stewart; B.A., LL.B. (T.C.D.), and 'Holt' scholar of the Honourable Society of Gray's Inn for 1885; E 1884, G.I. E 1885. 1887/H/12 [8 items]. Called to the English Bar, H 1889. District Commissioner, Lagos, 1889; Stipendiary Magistrate, Bahamas, 1894; Chief Justice of Grenada, 1909-14. Knighted. Died 31 Dec. 1936. Obituary, *I.L.T. & S.J.*, lxxi (9 Jan. 1937), 12; *Who's Who*.

JOLY, JASPAR JOHN (b. 27 April 1865) eld. s. of Henry Charles Joly of Clonbologue, King's Co., and Rebecca Read; B.A. (T.C.D.); M 1887. 1891/H/01 [7 items].

JONES, BOLTON C. (b. 2 Nov. 1863) eld. s. of John Jones of Kilmore House, Co. Roscommon, and Charlotte Browne; cand. bachelor (T.C.D.); H 1891. 1894/T/02x [6 items]. Called to the English Bar, 1899. 24 Chancery Lane. Lectured in Cambridge and Oxford, Died at Buxton 20 May 1942. Obituary, *I.L.T. & S.J.*, lxxvi (1942), 145.

JONES, FRANCIS JOHN (b. 14 Oct. 1848) eld. s. of the Revd. A. Armstrong Jones of Kilmore, Nenagh, Co. Tipperary, and Charlotte Smythe; B.A. (T.C.D.); M 1874, M.T. M 1875. 1879/E/07 [5 items].

JONES, HERBERT WILLIAM (b. 29 May 1866) 5th s. of William Robertson Jones (decd.), Barrister-at-Law, of Tudor House, Monkstown, Dublin, and Amelia Florence Kilgrey; B.A. (T.C.D.); E 1888. 1891/E/02 [7 items]. Died 1919. Obituary, *I.L.T. & S.J.*, liii (19 April 1919), 95.

JONES, HUME RIVERSDALE (b. 21 June 1866) eld. s. of Richard Bathoe Jones, Archdeacon of Killaloe and Rector of Roscrea, Co. Tipperary, and Angel Babington; LL.D. (T.C.D.); T 1889, District Inspector, Killarney [incl. special memorial]. 1898/E/01 [4 items]. Died 5 Feb. 1949.

JONES, PERCY JAMES COLVILL (b. 22 Nov. 1872) eld. s. of Ormsby Colvill McClintock Jones, J.P., of Mount Edward, Co. Sligo, and Margarette Anna Adams; M 1900. 1903/T/09 [3 items].

JONES, WORDSWORTH FILOMENO (b. 29 Aug. 1939) eld. s. of Filomeno Jones, of 3 Ross Road, Freetown, Sierra Leone, and Kezia Finch; M 1962. 1966/M/16 [1 item].

JORDAN, AUGUSTUS CHRISTOPHER (b. 4 Sept. 1865) young. s. of Myles Jordan (decd.), Crown Solicitor, of Castlebar, Co. Mayo, and Margaret Graham; B.A., LL.B. (T.C.D.); E 1886. 1889/E/01 [9 items]. Died 12 Sept. 1895: Notice, *I.L.T. & S.J.*, xxix (1895), 469.

JORDAN, Captain PATRICK (b. 28 March 1919) eld. s. of Martin Jordan (decd.), farmer, of Lisacul, Ballaghaderreen, Co. Roscommon, and Margaret Jordan; M.A., LLB, B. Comm., Dip. Pub. Adm. (T.C.D.); M 1954. 1957/M/13 [2 items].

JOYCE, JOHN ANTHONY (b. 2 May 1936) 2nd s. of John Vincent Joyce, of 116 Tritonville Road, Dublin, and Marion Fogarty; M 1953. 1959/E/03 [2 items].

JOYCE, JOHN (b. 22 Oct. 1852) 4th s. of Pierce Joyce of Mervue, Co. Galway, and Jane Blake; B.A. (T.C.D.); M 1873, M.T. M 1875. 1877/T/01 [7 items].

JOYCE, PATRICK SIMON (b. 16 July 1898) 2nd s. of James Joyce, of 51 Eccles Street, Dublin, and Mary Burke; M 1922. 1925/M/18 [2 items].

JOYCE, PATRICK WESTON (b. 13 March 1905) young. s. of Garrett Joyce, M.D. (decd.), of 20 Lower Baggot Street, Dublin, and Anne Teresa Smith; M 1924. Awarded Society's Exhibition and 1st Class Certificate of Honour. 1927/M/02 [2 items]. Parliamentary draftsman.

JOYNT, ALBERT EDWARD RUSSELL (b. 7 March 1863) 3rd s. of William Lane Joynt, D.L., solicitor, of 43 Merrion Square, Dublin, and Janet Russell; B.A. (T.C.D.); M 1886, M.T. M 1886. 1889/M/01 [6 items]. Munster Circuit. Excellent shorthand writer. Died 27 Dec. 1902. Obituary, *I.L.T. & S.J.*, xxxvii (1903), 13.

JOYNT, WILLIAM LANE (b. 24 Aug. 1886) only s. of Wm Lane Joynt, Barrister-at-Law, of Carisbrook House, Pembroke Road, Dublin, and Annie Quin; M 1906. 1909/M/06 [2 items].

JOYNT, WILLIAM RUSSELL (b. 27 March 1855) eld. s. of Wm. Lane Joynt, Crown and Treasury Solicitor for Ireland, of Grange Abbey, Raheny, Dublin, and Jane Russell; LL.B. (T.C.D.); H 1876, M.T. H 1878. 1879/E/12 [6 items].

JUDGE, JOHN FRANCIS WILLIS (b. 13 Jan. 1928) only s. of Dominick Walter Willis Judge, of Bank of Ireland House, Arklow, Co. Wicklow, and Emaline Mary McGuire; M 1948. 1952/M/07 [2 items].

JULIAN, ERNEST LAWRENCE (b. 28 July 1879) 2nd s. of John Julian, of Frankfort, Dundrum, Co. Dublin, and Margaret Parsons; B.A. (T.C.D.); M 1900. 1903/M/10 [2 items]. Captain (in 1901) and subsequent stalwart of Dublin University Boat Club: see Raymond Blake, *In Black and White: A History of Rowing at Trinity College, Dublin* (Dublin, 1991), pp 101-6. Reid Professor, T.C.D., 1909-14. Lieutenant, Royal Dublin Fusiliers. Died at Gallipoli, 8 August 1915. Photograph in Henry Hanna, *The Pals at Suvla Bay* (1917), 203. [Name on the Bar War Memorial; also on the Helles Memorial, Gallipoli]. *Who's Who*. Prize founded in his memory at Law School, T.C.D.

JULIAN, JAMES EDWARD JOHN (b. 22 Sept. 1854) eld. s. of Samuel Julian (decd.), J.P., of Kilfeighny, Co. Kerry [and Somersetshire], and Georgina Mary Hornblow Griffiths; B.A. (Oxford); E 1899, I.T. H 1876, called to Engl. Bar, E 1879. 1899/M/11 [4 items]. Mentioned in Maurice Healy, *The Old Munster Circuit*, 154-5.

KALIA, DAULAT RAM (b. 19 Feb. 1887) 2nd s. of Pandit Daya Ram Kalia, of Ferozepore City, Ferozepore, India; M 1914. 1917/E/02 [2 items].

KANE, AKBA BAILEY ALEXANDER (b. 28 Oct. 1893) only s. of Frederick Alexander Kane (decd.), of Quetta, India, and Alice Bailey (decd.); H 1920. 1923/M/13 [2 items].

KANE, WILLIAM VINCENT (b. 11 Jan. 1856) 4th s. of William Joseph Kane (decd.), merchant, of 38 North Great Georges Street, Dublin, and Mary McDonell; B.A. (T.C.D.); M 1874, L.I. H 1877. 1879/E/01 [5 items]. Called to the English Bar, M 1889.

KANGLEY, JOHN (b. 22 Jan. 1904) eld. s. of John Kangley, of Fairhill, Dundalk, Co. Louth, and Mary Hanlon; M 1923. Awarded 3rd Class Certificate of Honour. 1927/H/03 [2 items].

KAPUR, VAISHNA DASS (b. 8 Dec. 1878) 2nd s. of Lalla [?] Ram Kapur, of Peshawar, North-West Frontier, India; M 1914. 1917/T/23 [2 items].

KARIM, NISHAR AHMED (b. 23 April 1943) 4th s. of Malek Karim (decd.), merchant, of Bank Street, Transvaal, South Africa, and Ayesha Bibi Pierbhai; B.C.L. (N.U.I.); M 1965. 1968/M/13 [1 item].

KAUL, PANDIT PARMESHUR NATH (b. 10 Oct. 1895) 2nd s. of Rai Behadur Diwan Pandit Manmohan Nath Kaul, Deputy Commissioner of Misrwali, Punjab, India, and Radika Rance Tuthe[?]. 1921/T/03 [1 item?; missing].

KAVANAGH, EUGENE RUPERT (b. 10 Jan. 1878) 2nd s. of Morgan Butler Kavanagh (decd.), Barrister-at-Law, of 20 Merrion Square, Dublin, and Kate Beatrice Shine; B.A. (R.U.I.); H 1899. 1907/H/02 [2 items].

KAVANAGH, JOSEPH (Captain) (b. ?) eld. s. of Patrick Joseph Kavanagh, solicitor, of Ardfallen House, Cork; Connaught Rangers. 1922/M [?] [n.a. ?].

KAVANAGH, PATRICK GLADSTONE (b. 3 Nov. 1877) 2nd s. of Patrick Kavanagh (decd.), of 'Killeen', Victoria Road, Clontarf, Dublin, and Rosanna Rush; M 1915. 1918/T/13 [2 items].

KEADY, DERMOT (b. 20 Jan. 1906) 4th s. of Patrick Keady of 143 Lower Road, Cork, and Mary Angela Buttimer; M 1934. 1938/T/04 [2 items]. Examiner, Estate Duty Office.

KEANE, CHARLES OWEN (b. 14 Feb. 1912) eld. s. of Charles Owen Keane (decd.), of The Hermitage, Ennis, Co. Clare, and A. O'Gorman; M 1930. 1934/M/06 [2 items].

KEANE, JOHN JOSEPH (b. 23 Sept. 1879) 2nd s. of Martin Keane (decd.), of Maam, Co. Galway, and Barbara Conroy; M 1928. 1933/M/08 [2 items].

KEANE, RONAN COLMAN (b. 20 July 1932) 3rd s. of John Patrick Keane, of 1 St. Helen's Villas, Booterstown, Co. Dublin, and Katherine Boylan; B.A. (N.U.I.); M 1951. Awarded Brooke Scholarship. 1954/M/01 [2 items]. S.C., 3 July 1970. Judge of the High Court, 16 July 1979; of the Supreme Court, 15 April 1996. Chief Justice, 31 Jan. 2000. Ret. 19 July 2004; assessment of career by Edward Honohan, *The Irish Times*, 20 July 2004. Author of *The Law of Local Government in the Republic of Ireland* (Dublin, 1982); *Equity and the Law of Trusts in the Republic of Ireland* (Dublin, 1985); and *Company Law in the Republic of Ireland* (London, 1985; 2nd ed. 1991). Listed in the 1984, 1991 and 1999 editions of Maureen Cairnduff, *Who's Who in Ireland*.

KEANEY, IRENE MARY CECILIA (b. 7 Jan. 1914) eld. d. of Joseph Keaney, of Earlsfield, Manorhamilton, Co. Leitrim, and Agnes Bonner; M 1952. 1956/M/07 [2 items].

KEARNEY, EDWARD HENRY (b. 13 Dec. 1845) 2nd s. of Henry Kearney (decd.), merchant, of Castlebar, Co. Mayo, and Sarah Doyle; T 1880, M.T. T 1881. 1883/E/08 [6 items]. Chief Clerk in the Lunacy Department. Died 13 April 1911. Obituary, *I.L.T. & S.J.*, xlv (1911), 95-6.

KEARNEY, FRANCIS JOSEPH (b. 29 Jan. 1928) 4th s. of Jeremiah Francis Kearney, civil servant, of Glasnevin, Dublin, and Josephine Tancred; M 1956. 1960/T/07 [2 items].

KEARNS, JAMES DESMOND (b. 25 Oct. 1912) young. s. of James Kearns (decd.), solicitor, of Portumna, Co. Galway, and Bridget Murphy; E 1950. Formerly a solicitor. 1950/M/03 [5 items].

KEARNS, NICHOLAS JAMES (b. 13 April 1946) eld. s. of William Kearns, civil servant, of 26 Dartry Park, Dartry, Dublin, and Joan Welland; M 1964. 1968/T/09 [1 item]. S.C., 5 March 1982. Appt. a judge of the High Court, 8 May 2000; of the Supreme Court, 17 Nov. 2004. Listed in the 1999 edition of Maureen Cairnduff, *Who's Who in Ireland*.

KEATING, MICHAEL (b. 29 Sept. 1856) 4th s. of Michael James Keating of Glanmire Road, Cork, and Margaret Hannigan; B.A. (Q.C.C.); H 1877, M.T. T 1878. 1880/H/10 [6 items].

KEATING, MICHAEL JOSEPH (b. 2 Jan. 1895) eld. s. of William Keating, of Kelso, Killester, Dublin, and Elizabeth Mary Doyle; M 1924. 1927/T/05 [2 items].

KEEGAN, BERNARD JAMES (b. 1 Aug. 1919) 3rd s. of Bernard Keegan (decd.), of Edmondstown, Killucan, Co. Westmeath, and Mary Anne Wilson; M 1948. 1956/M/13 [2 items].

KEELEY, JAMES ROBERT (b. 5 Nov. 1865) eld. s. of Michael Keeley (decd.) of 12 Hannan Road, Kensington, Liverpool and Catherine Galvin; B.A., LL.B. (T.C.D.); M 1909. 1912/T/01 [2 items].

KEELY, JAMES PATRICK (b. 28 Dec. 1890) 2nd s. of John Keely, of Kilcrimple, Gort, Co. Galway, and Bridget Scully; M 1924. Awarded Certificate of Honour. 1927/T/01 [2 items]. Fianna Fáil T.D. for Galway, 1933-37. District Justice for No. 6 District, 1923-44; for No. 10 District after 1944.

KEELY, JOHN JOSEPH MARY (b. 28 Nov. 1937) only s. of James P. Keely, District Justice, of Rushbrooke, Cobh, Co. Cork, and Margaret Mohilly; B.C.L. (N.U.I.); M 1955. 1962/M/06 [2 items].

KEENAN, NORBERT MICHAEL (b. 31 Jan. 1864) eld. s. of the Rt. Hon. Sir Patrick Keenan, P.C., K.C.M.G., C.B., Resident Commissioner of National Education, of Delville, Glasnevin, Dublin, and Elizabeth Quinn; B.A. (T.C.D.); M 1884, M.T. E 1886. 1890/E/01 [7 items].

KEHILY, CORNELIUS FRANCIS (b. 1 Aug. 1942) 2nd s. of Jeremiah Kehily, farmer, of Scrahane, Enniskeane, Co. Cork, and Ellen O'Halloran; M 1963. Awarded 2nd Victoria Prize. 1967/T/01 [1 item].

KEHOE, DANIEL (b. 3 April 1854) 2nd s. of Miles Kehoe (decd.) of Pembroke Road, Dublin, and Margaret Treacy; B.A. (T.C.D.); H 1879, M.T. M 1880. 1881/M/20 [7 items]. Auditor of the College Historical Society, 1881-2.

KEHOE, MILES VINCENT (b. 19 July 1847) eld. s. of Miles Kehoe of 48 Pembroke Road, Dublin, and Margaret Treacey; B.A. (T.C.D.); M 1867, M.T. M 1869. 1873/H/3 [2 items]. Munster Circuit. Q.C., 30 June 1894. County Court Judge for Clare. Died 12 Oct. 1907. Obituary, *I.L.T. & S.J.*, xli (1907), 268; *Who's Who*.

KEHOE, PATRICK THOMAS (b. 3 March 1938) twin young. s. of Joseph Kehoe, merchant, of Glynn, Enniscorthy, Co. Wexford, and Margaret Wadding; B.Comm., D.P.A. (N.U.I.); M 1961. 1964/T/04 [1 item].

KEIGHTLEY, SAMUEL ROBERT (b. 13 Jan. 1857) eld. s. of Samuel Keatley, merchant, of Elmwood Avenue, Belfast, Co. Antrim, and Katherine Brennan; LL.B. (Q.C.B.); E 1880, M.T. T 1881. 1883/E/06 [6 items].

KEILY, JOHN TOWNSEND (b. 14 Dec. 1867) only s. of J. Keily of Clarebeg, Co. Dublin, and Augusta Bell; M 1888. 1891/M/09 [5 items].

KELLEHER, JAMES (b. 7 April 1846) young. s. of Mortimer Kelleher (decd.) of Bridgemount, Co. Cork, and Margaret Corkery; H 1890, I.T. H 1880. [District and Sessions Judge, Bengal] 1890/T/11 [2 items]. Called to the English Bar, I.T., E 1880.

KELLY, ARTHUR BURKE (b. 19 Jan. 1892) eld. s. of William Peter Kelly, solicitor, of The Park, Athlone, Co. Westmeath, and Julia Mary Blake-Burke; M 1909. 1913/H/02 [2 items].

KELLY, BERNARD DOWELL (b. 10 Aug 1849) only s. of Tobias Joseph Kelly (decd.) of Clondayle, Co. Galway, and Anna Maria Dowell; B.A. (T.C.D.); M 1870, M.T. H 1872. 1874/H/7 [4 items]. Died (as O'Kelly), 12 July 1924. Obituary, *I.L.T. & S.J.*, lviii (1924), 180.

KELLY, DENIS BERNARD (b. 6 July 1891) 4th s. of John Kelly, of Main Street, Killarney, Co. Kerry and Bridget Cronin; Sen. Mod. B.A., LL.B. (T.C.D.); M 1911. 1914/T/05 [2 items]. Identified in *Thom*'s biographical section as a judge of the Dáil Courts, 1920. Became 'Father of the Kerry Bar'. Acting District Justice. Mentioned in Gerard A. Lee, *A Memoir of the South-Western Circuit* (Dublin, 1990), 36.

KELLY, EDWARD JOSEPH (b. 31 March 1883) 2nd s. of Peter Kelly, J.P. (decd.), of Ballyshannon, Co. Donegal, and Rose Kelly; M.A. (N.U.I.); 1916. 1917/H/01x [2 items]. S.C., 25 June 1930. Nationalist M.P. for East Donegal 1910-22. Died 25 Sept. 1944. Obituary, *I.L.T. & S.J.*, lxxviii (1944), 250, 256. See also James Meenan (ed.), *Centenary History of Lit. and Hist. Soc. of U.C.D.*; and V.T.H. Delany [q.v.] 'The Bench and Bar in Ireland', xxxiii.

KELLY, FRANCES DECLAN (b. 28 Dec. 1938) 3rd s. of Charles Edward Kelly, journalist, of 27 Frascati Park, Blackrock, Co. Dublin, and Kathleen Esther Hayden (decd.); B.C.L. (N.U.I.); M 1958. 1966/T/12 [1 item]. Actor.

KELLY, GEORGE ALEXANDER PATRICK (b. 21 Jan. 1848) 2nd s. of John Kelly of Essex Lawn, Co. Roscommon, civil engineer, and Mary Patricia O'Connor; B.A. (T.C.D.); E 1867, M.T. E 1869. 1871/E/3 [4 items]. Died, as father of the Connaught Bar, 10 April 1914. Obituary, *I.L.T. & S.J.*, xlviii (1914), 115.

KELLY, HENRY GREENE (b. 21 July 1863) eld. s. of Henry Greene Kelly, solicitor, of 4 Belgrave Square East, Monkstown, Dublin, and 39 Lower Ormond Quay, Dublin, and Anna [C]rangey; B.A., LL.B. (T.C.D.); M 1881, I.T. T 1882. 1884/M/11 [6 items]. Chief Justice of Southern Nigeria. Knighted 1906. Retired 1908. Died in London, 1934. Obituary, *I.L.T. & S.J.*, lxviii (16 June 1934), 160-1.

KELLY, IGNATIUS JOSEPH (b. 4 July 1895) only s. of Sir Malachi John Kelly (decd.), of Thorndale, Temple Road, Rathmines, Dublin, and Annie Coll; M 1914. 1922/E/02 [2 items]. Professor of Common Law at King's Inns. Died 13 Sept. 1955. Obituary, *I.L.T. & S.J.*, lxxxix (1955), 242.

KELLY, JANE FRANCES (b. 13 Jan. 1945) 2nd d. of Martin Kelly (decd.), solicitor, of 35 Parliament Street, Kilkenny, and Bridget McGrath; B.A. (N.U.I.); M 1963. 1966/M/06 [1 item].

KELLY, JOHN MAURICE DOMINIC (b. 31 Aug. 1931) eld. s. of Joseph Kelly, of Lucan, Co. Dublin, and Mary Boyle; M.A., Dr. Jur. (Heidelberg); M 1950. 1957/E/01 [2 items]. Professor of Jurisprudence and Roman law at U.C.D., 1965-91. Fine Gael TD, 1973-89. S.C., 19 May 1977. Attorney-General for 48 days, May 1977-4 July 1977. Minister for Industry and Commerce (and briefly for Foreign Affairs), 1981-2. Died 24 Jan. 1991. Author of numerous legal works, listed at 351-2 of *The Irish Jurist*, vols. xxv-xxvii (1990-1992), dedicated, with photograph, as a '*liber memorialis* John M. Kelly'. *A Short History of Western Legal Theory* (Oxford: Clarendon Press, 1992) and John Fanagan (ed.), *Belling the Cats: Selected speechs and articles of John Kelly* (Dublin: [1992]) were published posthumously. *The Irish Constitution* (3rd edition, ed. Hogan and Whyte, 1994) has become an enduring textbook. Writing under the *nom-de-plume* of John Boyle, John Kelly was the author of *Matters of Honour* (1964; a novel). Obituary, *The Times*, 26 Jan. 1991; Appreciation [by G.H.] in the *Irish Law Times*, new series, ix (1991), 68. Listed in the 1984 edition of Maureen Cairnduff, *Who's Who in Ireland*. See also: Louis McRedmond (ed.), *Modern Irish Lives*.

KELLY, JOSEPH FRANCIS (b. 3 Dec. 1853) young. s. of Darby Kelly (decd.) of Ardnaglue, Co. Westmeath, and Maria Byrne; M 1884. 1892/H/03 [6 items].

KELLY, LAWRENCE JOHN O'BRIEN (b. 30 July 1871) eld. s. of John George Kelly, J.P., of Fedamore House, Bruff, Co. Limerick, and Mary Josephine O'Neill; B.A. (T.C.D.); M 1891. 1895/H/02 [5 items]. Crown Counsel for the City of Limerick. Mentioned in Maurice Healy, *The Old Munster Circuit*, 155-7. Died 26 Oct. 1950.

KELLY, LOUIS O'SULLIVAN (b. 23 March 187[9]) eld. s. of William Kelly of [Persse] Park, Co. Galway, and Eveleen O'Sullivan; undergraduate (Univ. of London); M 1899. 1903/T/02 [2 items].

KELLY, MICHAEL JOSEPH (b. 26 Nov. 1910) 2nd s. of Michael Kelly, accountant, of 7 Ashbrook Terrace, Leeson Park, Dublin, and Annie Ryan (decd.); M 1943. Awarded 2nd Victoria Prize. 1947/T/02 [2 items].

KELLY, PATRICK (b. 15 March 1861) eld. s. of Michael Kelly of Ardagh, Co. Limerick, and Bridget Kevin; M 1890. 1895/H/01 [7 items]. Died 16 Jan. 1931. Obituary, *I.L.T. & S.J.*, lxv (1931), 23, 59. Mentioned in Maurice Healy, *The Old Munster Circuit*, 48-51.

KELLY, PATRICK (b. 5 May 1909) 2nd s. of James Kelly, of Millbrae House, Carndonagh, Co. Donegal (decd.), and R. Gibbons; B. Comm (N.U.I.); M 1943. 1946/T/06 [2 items].

KELLY, PATRICK JOSEPH (b. 26 Sept. 1850) eld. s. of Michael Kelly of Down, Co. Londonderry, and Mary Hagan; LL.B; H 1884. 1886/M/15 [7 items].

KELLY, RICHARD (b. 28 April 1848) 3rd s. of John William Kelly of 32 Gardiner Place, Dublin, Civil engineer, and Mary Scott; B.A. (T.C.D.); H 1870, M.T. M 1870. 1873/H/10 [4 items].

KELLY, RICHARD JOHN (b. 20 Jan. 1856) only s. of Jasper Kelly (decd.) of Tuam, Co. Galway, and Delia Daly; H 1883, M.T. M 1884. 1886/E/02 [10 items]. K.C., 27 June

1914. Prolific legal writer and pamphleteer, and for fifty years editor of the *Tuam Herald*. Author, *inter alia*, of *The Statutes relating to the Law of Landlord and Tenant and Land Purchase in Ireland from 1860 to 1896* (Dublin: Ponsonby, 1898. 5th edition; a work containing also material by Francis Nolan, Q.C., and Robert Romney Kane). Chevalier of the Order of the Star of Roumania. Died 3 Sept. 1931. Obituary, *I.L.T. & S.J.*, lxv (1931), 220-1; *Who's Who*; *Oxford DNB* (2004).

KELLY, ROBERT JAMES (b. 16 Sept. 1890) eld. s. of Charles Kelly (decd.), of 13 Leinster Road, Rathmines, Dublin, and Frances Dunne; M 1921. 1923/T/06 [2 items].

KELLY, THOMAS (b. 31 Jan 1844) 6th s. of James Kelly of Castle Bagot, Co. Dublin [Cahircon, Co. Clare] and Frances Roche; M 1868, M.T. E 1870. 1872/M/5 [2 items].

KEMMIS, EDWARD BERNHARD (b. 11 June 1873) 4th s. of Colonel William Kemmis, J.P., of Ballinacor, Co. Wicklow, and Ellen Gertrude de Horne Christy Steinmann; B.A. (Oxford); E 1895 [includes special memorial]. 1898/E/03 [10 items].

KENNEDY, ALFRED St. J. (b. 15 Oct. 1886) 3rd s. of John Kennedy of Bridge House, Dingle, Co. Kerry, and Sarah Collier; M 1906. 1910/T/03 [3 items].

KENNEDY, ANTHONY (b. 24 Nov. 1941) 6th s. of Thomas Bernard Kennedy, building contractor, of 14 Castle Countess, Tralee, Co. Kerry, and Mary Catherine Dee; B.A. (N.U.I.); M 1965. 1968/T/04 [1 item]. S.C., 4 Oct. 1982. Author, with H.R. McWilliam, of *The law on compensation for criminal injuries in the Republic of Ireland* ([Clonsilla, Co. Dublin]: [1979]). Judge of the Circuit Court (Midland Circuit), 1996-.

KENNEDY, CHARLES MICHAEL (b. 31 Jan. 1897) 2nd s. of Francis Charles Kennedy, of 25 Wellington Place, Clyde Road, Dublin, and Nina Kennedy; M 1918. 1921/H/07 [2 items].

KENNEDY, DESMOND (b. 31 Oct. 1922) 4th s. of Denis Kennedy, of 30 Parkgate Street, Dublin, and Kathleen Lawler; M.A., B. Comm. (N.U.I.); M 1951. 1955/M/01 [2 items].

KENNEDY, EDWARD THOMAS (b. 21 Oct. 1843) 2nd s. of James Birch Kennedy, of Cara, Co. Kerry, and 1 Albert Terrace, Blackrock, Co. Dublin and Charlotte Brunker; B.A. (T.C.D.); M 1867, M.T. E 1869. 1875/M/01 [4 items].

KENNEDY, FRANCIS CHARLES (b. 13 July 1867) 3rd s. of Patrick Kennedy (decd.), of 8 Ailesbury Road, Dublin, and Mary McCann; E 1896, L.I. E 1897. 1899/T/03 [5 items]. Registrar to Chief Baron Palles (his uncle). Died 5 April 1929. Obituary, *I.L.T. & S.J.*, lxiii (1929), 88.

KENNEDY, FREDERICK ALEXANDER (b. 2 Jan. 1879) 2nd s. of George O'Brien Kennedy, solicitor, of Bloomfield, Merrion, Dublin, and Clara Jane Abercrombie; B.A. (T.C.D.); H 1898. 1902/M/08 [3 items].

KENNEDY, HENRY EDWARD (b. 22 Aug. 1881) young. s. of Hugh Peter Kennedy, Crown Solicitor of Cavan, and Rose Magennis; M 1901, M.T. M 1902. 1904/T/06 [6 items]. Died in accident at the Swiss frontier, 8 Jan. 1921. Obituary, *I.L.T. & S.J.*, lv (1921), 16.

KENNEDY, HUGH (b. 11 July 1879) eld. s. of Hugh Boyle Kennedy L.R.C.S.I, of Dublin, and Mary Kate Kennedy; H 1900. 1902/M/14 [2 items]. Munster Circuit. Q.C., 20 Feb. 1920. Attorney-General, 1922-4. Cumann na nGaedheal T.D. for Dublin South, Oct. 1923-1924. Appointed first Chief Justice of the Irish Free State, 5 June 1924. Died 12 Dec. 1936. Obituaries, *I.L.T. & S.J.*, lxx (1936), 341-3, 346; and *Irish Jurist*, iii (1937), 6. Mentioned (with photograph) in James Meenan (ed.), *Centenary History of Lit. and Hist. Soc. of U.C.D.* See: Ronan Keane, 'The voice of the Gael: Chief Justice Kennedy and the emergence of the new Irish court system 1921-1936', in *The Irish Jurist*, vol. xxxi (1996), 205-25; *Who's Who*; and Louis McRedmond (ed.), *Modern Irish Lives*. Portrait by Leo Whelan in King's Inns: see Wanda Ryan-Smolin, *King's Inns Portraits* (1992), 37.

KENNEDY, JOSEPH MARY (b. 25 March 1848) 3rd s. of James Barron Kennedy, solicitor, of Mountjoy Square, Dublin, and Margaret Mulcahy; M 1873, M.T. T 1875. 1877/H/03 [6 items].

KENNEDY, JOSEPH PATRICK (b. 23 Nov. 1894) eld. s. of Francis Charles Kennedy, B.L. (decd.), of 3 DeVesci Terrace, Monkstown, Dublin, and Nina Geoghegan (decd.); M.A. (T.C.D.); T 1939. 1942/T/02 [3 items].

KENNEDY, KENNETH ARTHUR (b. 3 April 1894) young. s. of Doctor J.M. Prior
Kennedy, J.P., of Elmfield, Tullamore, King's County, and Anchoretta H. Jacob; M
1914. 1917/M/04 [2 items].

KENNEDY, MARTIN JOSEPH ALEXANDER (b. 22 Oct. 1931) 2nd s. of Patrick Joseph
Kennedy, of 1 Elm Park Villa, Ennis Road, Limerick, and May Frances Ratcliffe; B.A.
(N.U.I.); M 1950. 1954/T/02 [2 items]. S.C., 1 June 1973.

KENNEDY, THOMAS (b. 3 Dec. 1862) eld. s. of James Kennedy of Castletown Bere, Co.
Cork, and Mary Regan; B.A. (R.U.I.); M 1890. 1895/E/01 [6 items].

KENNEY, JAMES C. FITZGERALD: see FITZGERALD-KENNEY, JAMES C.

KENNY, BERNARD HARVEY (b. 28 July 1939) only s. of Charles Kenny, clerk, Bank of
Ireland, of Yorkville, Summerhill, Co. Cork, and Hope Harvey; B.C.L. (N.U.I.); M
1960. 1967/M/12 [1 item]. Judge of the Circuit Court (Western Circuit), 1995-.

KENNY, CAROLINE ELIZABETH (b. 22 Sept. 1945) 2nd d. of Kevin M. Kenny (decd.),
Senior Counsel, of Wyattville, Ballybrack, Co. Dublin, and Lilian Morrison; B.C.L.
(N.U.I.); M 1964. 1967/T/05 [1 item].

KENNY, CECIL STACKPOOLE (b. 20 Oct. 1891) 3rd s. of Thomas Hugh Kenny, solicitor,
of 55 George Street, Limerick, and Louise Mary Dunne; M 1909. 1912/M/06 [2 items].
2nd Lieutenant, Shropshire Light Infantry. Drowned at sea 11 Nov. 1915.[Name on the
Bar War Memorial, and on the Hollybrook Memorial, Hampshire].

KENNY, CHARLES STEWART (b. 10 July 1888) eld. s. of Matthew Joseph Kenny of
Freagh Castle, Miltown Malbay, Co. Clare, and Elizabeth Stewart; B.A. (T.C.D.); M
1908. 1911/M/06 [3 items]. Judicial Commissioner under the Dáil Éireann Courts
(Winding-Up) Act, 1923. District Justice (Limerick). Died 1978. See Mary
Kotsonouris, *Retreat from Revolution: The Dáil Courts, 1920-24* (Dublin, 1994), 107;
and biographical note in ibid., *The Winding-up of the Dáil Courts, 1922-1925: an
obvious duty* (Dublin, 2004), p. 251.

KENNY, EDWARD HENRY (b. 1 May 1874) eld. s. of William Kenny, Q.C., MP, Solicitor-
General for Ireland, of 35 Fitzwilliam Place, Dublin, and Mary Coffey; M 1893.
1897/M/07 [6 items]. Probate Officer. Died 15 Oct. 1944. Obituary, *I.L.T. & S.J.*,
lxxviii (1944), 266.

KENNY, GEORGE GORDON (b. 7 Dec. 1898) 2nd s. of Matthew Joseph Kenny, of Freagh,
Miltown-Malbay, Co. Clare, and Elizabeth Stewart; M 1917. 1921/M/06 [2 items].
'Father of the Clare Bar'. Mentioned in Joachim Fischer and John Dillon, *The
Correspondence of Myles Dillon 1922-1925* (Dublin, 1999), 180; and in Gerard A.
Lee, *A Memoir of the South-Western Circuit* (Dublin, 1990), 13-14.

KENNY, JAMES DAVID (b. 13 May 1857) 2nd s. of M. Kenny of [Freagh] Co. Clare, and
Clare Frost; B.A., LL.B. (T.C.D.); M 1875, M.T. H 1878. 1879/M/05 [6 items].

KENNY, JOHN JOSEPH (b. 19 April 1917) eld. s. of John Kenny of 14 Green Park, Rathgar,
Co. Dublin, and Lucy O'Dea; B.A. (N.U.I.); Dipl. Kms (Vienna); M 1937. 1940/M/01
[1 item]. S.C., 6 March 1958. Judge of the High Court, 1960-75; and of the Supreme
Court, 1975-81. Retired because of ill health, 26 April 1982. Died 25 March 1987.
Obituary (by Ronan Keane) in *The Irish Times*. See Louis McRedmond (ed.), *Modern
Irish Lives*.

KENNY, JOSEPH PATRICK (b. 29 May 1884) 4th s. of William Kenny (decd.), of
Beechmount, Merrion, Dublin, and Angela Sheridan; B.A. (R.U.I.); M 1906.
1909/H/02 [3 items]. Legal Officer in the Army of the Irish Free State. Appt. a
Commissioner for the Winding-up of the Dáil Courts, June 1924; and a District Justice,
August 1924. Biographical note in Mary Kotsonouris, *The Winding-up of the Dáil
Courts, 1922-1925: an obvious duty* (Dublin, 2004), p. 251.

KENNY, KEVIN MICHAEL (b. 15 Sept. 1911) eld. s. of Kevin J. Kenny, publisher and
advertising agent, of 279 North Circular Road, Dublin, and Annette Murphy; M 1931.
1934/M/05 [2 items]. S.C., 3 July 1950. Professor of Equity, U.C.D. Died 1966.
Obituary, *I.L.T. & S.J.*, c, 16 July 1966, 293.

KENNY, MATTHEW JOSEPH, M.P. (b. 1 Feb. 1861) 3rd s. of Michael Kenny, solicitor, of
[Freagh] Castle, Co. Clare, and Bridget Frost; E 1888, G.I. E 1883; member of English
Bar [E 1886] on call in Ireland. 1889/H/04 [8 items]. K.C., 27 June 1914. Voted
against Parnell in Committee Room 15. M.P. for Ennis, 1882; for Mid-Tyrone, 1885-

95. Crown Prosecutor for Co. Kerry, 1916. Judge of the Circuit Court (Cork), August 1925-33. Breeder of pedigree horses, cattle and sheep. Died 8 Dec. 1942. Obituary, *I.L.T. & S.J.*, lxxvi (1942), 311, 318; *Who's Who*. Mentioned in Maurice Healy, *The Old Munster Circuit*, 145-8.

KENNY, MICHAEL EDWARD (b. 23 Oct. 1855) only s. of George C. Kenny of 4 Aylesbury Road, Dublin, and of Longford Castle, Co. Galway, and Mary Martin; B.A. (T.C.D.); M 1878, M.T. M 1880. 1881/M/12 [6 items].

KENNY, PATRICK BERCHMANS (b. 17 May 1893) eld. s. of John Kenny (decd.), Director of Agriculture of Hyderabad State, of Hyderabad, India, and Cecilia O'Donnell; M 1915. 1918/T/14 [2 items].

KENNY, VINCENT RAYMOND (b. 21 Feb. 1882) 3rd s. of William Kenny (decd.) of Beechmount, Merrion, Co. Dublin, and Angela G. Sheridan; M 1904. 1907/M/06 [3 items]. Honorary Brigadier, Royal Engineers. C.B., M.B.E. Director of Army Postal Services, 1940-4. Invalided out of the Army, 1944. Died 3 Dec. 1966. *Who's Who*.

KENNY, WILLIAM (b. 14 Jan. 1846) only s. of Edward Kenny of Kilrush, Co. Clare, Solicitor, and Catherine Murphy; B.A. (T.C.D.); H 1865; M.T. T 1866. 1868/T/4 [4 items]. Munster Circuit. Q.C., 1885. Bencher, 1890. Elected Liberal Unionist M.P. for the Dublin (St. Stephen's Green) constituency, 1892 and 1895. Solicitor-General, 1895. Judge of the Queen's Bench Division of the High Court, 1897-1921. Died 4 Feb. 1921. Obituary, *I.L.T. & S.J.*, lv (1921), 44-5; *Who's Who*. See Ball, *Judges*, ii, 380-1. Mentioned in Maurice Healy, *The Old Munster Circuit*, 35-6. Portrait by Sarah Purser in King's Inns: see Wanda Ryan-Smolin, *King's Inns Portraits* (1992), 38.

KENNY, WILLIAM FREDERICK (b. 3 Oct. 1856) eld. s. of Matthew Kenny, solicitor, of 17 Middle Gardiner Street, Dublin, and L. MacNamara; B.A. (T.C.D.); T 1876, M.T. T 1877. 1879/M/10 [5 items]. Munster Circuit. Junior Crown Prosecutor for Cork City. K.C., March 1904. Died 24 Aug. 1929. Obituary, *I.L.T. & S.J.*, lxiii (1929), 209. Mentioned in Maurice Healy, *The Old Munster Circuit*, 144.

KENT, JOHN (b. 15 Oct. 1908) eld. s. of Pierce Kent, Commissioner of Public Works, of 13 Rostrevor Terrace, Rathgar, Dublin, and Mary Connolly; M.A., LL.B; M 1933. 1936/M/07 [2 items]. Auditor of the 'L. & H.', 1930-1: see James Meenan (ed.), *Centenary History of Lit. and Hist. Soc. of U.C.D.*, 347. Private secretary to W.T. Cosgrave. Died 12 Dec. 1941. Obituary, *I.L.T. & S.J.*, lxxv (1941), 320.

KEOGH, DESMOND JOSEPH BERNARD (b. 27 Feb. 1935) only s. of Stephen Keogh, bank manager (retired), of 'Ashleigh', Foxrock Park, Co. Dublin, and Maura O'Connor; B.A. (N.U.I.); M 1954. 1966/M/17 [1 item]. Actor and broadcaster. Listed in the 1984 edition of Maureen Cairnduff, *Who's Who in Ireland*.

KEOGH, EDWARD JOSEPH LOREAN (b. 26 June 1870) eld. s. of Surgeon Major J.R. Keogh, High Sheriff, Co. Kildare, and Margaret [?]. 1897/E/02 [3 items].

KEOGH, GEORGE DARRELL (b. 14 March 1859) 2nd s. of George Keogh, J.P., solicitor, of Glencourt, Co. Wicklow, and Teresa Carroll; LL.B. (T.C.D.); T 1881, I.T. E 1883. 1884/E/01 [7 items].

KEOGH, HENRY (b. 19 Aug. 1830) [Carlisle Road, Londonderry] 3rd s. of William Lucas Keogh (decd.), of Kilkenny, and Mary Ffrench; M 1851, M.T. E 1857. 1871/T/2 [5 items].

KEOGH, WILLIAM (b. 20 Sept. 1844) [Bushy Park, Co. Wicklow] only s. of the Rt. Hon. William Keogh, of 38 Elgin Road, Co. Dublin, Justice of Court of Common Pleas in Ireland, and Kate Roney; B.A. (T.C.D.); M 1864; I.T. E 1866. 1871/M/3 [3 items].

KEOGH-NOLAN, ALFRED ARTHUR MYLES (b. 7 Oct. 1911) younger s. of Anthony Keogh Nolan, Secretary, Co. Council General Council, of 46 St. Lawrence Road, Clontarf, Dublin, and Maria Elizabeth Albury; B.A. (N.U.I.); M 1930. 1934/M/01 [2 items].

KEPPLE, SIMON (b. 29 Sept. 1906) young. s. of John Kepple, solicitor (decd.), of Bank Place, Mallow, Co. Cork, and Elizabeth Mary [Tyner]; M.A., LL.B; M 1944. Awarded Society's Exhibition. 1947/M/02 [2 items].

KERNAN, JOHN GEORGE (b. 8 May 1855) eld. s. of the Hon. James Kernan, Judge of the Supreme Court of Madras, and Mary Donohoe; LL.B (T.C.D.); H 1875, I.T. E 1874. 1878/M/05 [6 items].

KERR, JAMES PATRICK (b. 14 Sept. 1864) eld. surv. s. of James Kerr (decd.) of Belfast, and Elizabeth Connolly; B.A., LL.D. (R.U.I.); M 1890. 1894/H/01 [9 items]. Called to English Bar, M.T., M 1906.

KETTLE, THOMAS MICHAEL (b. 9 Feb. 1880) 3rd s. of Andrew Joseph Kettle, of Newtown House, St. Margaret's, Co. Dublin, and Margaret McCourt; B.A. (R.U.I.); H 1903. 1906/E/02 [3 items]. M.P. for East Tyrone, 1906-10. Professor of National Economics at U.C.D. Killed at Ginchy during the battle of the Somme, 9 Sept. 1916. Bust in St. Stephen's Green, Dublin. Name on the Bar War Memorial, and at Thiepval. Author of *The Day's Burden* (1910), *The Open Secret of Ireland, Poems and Parodies* (1916) and *The Ways of War* (1917). Mentioned (with photograph of bust) in James Meenan (ed.), *Centenary History of Lit. and Hist. Soc. of U.C.D.* For litigation linked to the 1906 election and to Kettle's alleged participation in the 'storming the organ' incident at the U.C.D. conferring ceremony of 27 Oct. 1905, see: *In re* Kettle [1906] ILTR, 234-7, *The Irish Times* of 8 Nov. 1905, and Meenan (ed.), *Centenary History*, 72-3. Photograph (in wig and gown) in Eugene Sheehy, *May it Please the Court* (Dublin, 1951), facing. p. 38, and in Conor Cruise O'Brien, *Memoir: My Life and Themes* (Dublin, 1998), after p. 156. See J.B. Lyons, *The Enigma of Tom Kettle* (Dublin, 1983); Louis McRedmond (ed.), *Modern Irish Lives*; *Oxford DNB* (2004); *Burke's Irish Family Records* (1976), 1020.

KIERNAN, BRENDAN JOSEPH (b. 7 Aug. 1913) young. s. of Francis Kiernan, of 65 Upper Rathmines Road, Dublin and Katherine Hurley; B.A. (N.U.I.); M 1933. Awarded Society's Prize and Certificate of Honour. 1936/M/03 [2 items]. Secretary of the Department of Local Government; European Commission of Human Rights.

KILBRIDE, JOSEPH (b. 8 March 1864) young. s. of Thomas Kilbride (decd.) of Luggacurren, Queen's Co., and Maria Ryan; M 1883. 1888/E/01 [6 items]. Died 28 Jan. 1936. Obituary, *I.L.T. & S.J.*, lxx (1936), 43.

KILDUFF, CONSTANCE MARGARET (b. 7 July 1944) only d. of Arthur Joseph Kilduff, bank manager, of 14 Knocknacree Park, Dalkey, Co. Dublin, and Constance Bergin; B.C.L. (N.U.I.); M 1963. 1966/M/12 [1 item].

KILFEDDER, JAMES ALEXANDER (b. 16 July 1928) 2nd s. of Robert Kilfedder, of 15 Rosetta Avenue, Belfast, and Elizabeth Johnston; B.A. (T.C.D.); M 1947. 1952/T/05 [2 items]. M.P. for North Down, 1970-1995. Died 20 March 1995. Obituary, *The Times*, 22 March 1995.

KILLEEN, PROINNSIAS PÁDRAIG. See Ó CILLÍN, PROINNSEAS PÁDRAIG.

KILLEEN, Major TIMOTHY (b. 19 Dec. 1896) 5th s. of Patrick Killeen (decd.), of Moloskey House, Co. Clare, and Susan Blackall; M 1924. 1927/M/17 [2 items].

KILLEN, JAMES BRYCE (b. 14 Aug 1842) 4th s. of Samuel Killen of Kells, Co. Antrim (decd.) and Mary Jane Shaw; B.A., LL.B.(Queen's University); T 1865, MT E 1866. 1869/E/2 [2 items]. Nationalist journalist, imprisoned on sundry occasions during the 'Land War' of 1879-81. Died in poverty in Dublin, 26 Dec. 1916. *Oxford DNB* (2004) [article by Marie-Louise Legg].

KILPATRICK, WILLIAM ARCHIBALD (b. 15 June 1857) eld. s. of Hugh Alexander Kilpatrick (decd.) of Ballylane, Co. Armagh, and Mary Anne Armstrong; B.A. (T.C.D.), M 1879, M.T. M 1881. 1882/M/03 [5 items].

KILROY, MICHAEL GERARD (b. 13 Dec. 1922) eld. s. of Thomas Kilroy, livestock dealer, of Green View, Callan, Co. Kilkenny, and Mary Devine; M 1963. 1967/M/09 [1 item].

KIMPTON, VIOLET (b. 10 Nov. 1903) only d. of Alfred Charles Kimpton, of 118 Lower Baggot Street, Dublin, and Helena McSweeney; M 1926. 1929/T/02 [2 items]. Mrs. Bloomer.

KINAHAN, HENRY (b. 18 Jan. 1879) young. s. of Frederic Kinahan (decd.) of Low Wood, Co. Antrim, and Marion E. Hannay; B.A. (Oxford); H 1902, I.T. E 1899. 1904/T/10 [3 items].

KINAHAN, ROBERT JOSEPH IGNATIUS (b. 24 March 1881) only s. of Christopher Kinahan of Dublin, and Margaret Manning; B.A., LL.B. (R.U.I.); H 1903. 1906/H/06 [3 items]. Went Leinster Circuit. Died 21 July 1921. Obituary, *I.L.T. & S.J.*, lv (1921), 182. See James Meenan (ed.), *Centenary History of Lit. and Hist. Soc. of U.C.D.*

KING, FREDERICK CHARLES (b. 6 Jan. 1888) eld. s. of John Charles King, of Castlepollard, Co. Westmeath, and Christina Cecilia Deehan; Sen. Mod. B.A. (T.C.D.); T 1921. 1921/M/17 [2 items]. Had served in Indian civil service. Author of *Town and Regional Planning in Ireland* and editor of *Public Administration in Ireland*. Died 8 Nov. 1958. Obituary, *I.L.T. & S.J.*, xcii (22 Nov. 1958), 288.

KING, GEORGE GORDON (b. 26 Sept. 1912) eld. s. of John Alexander King (decd.), of 10 Sunbury Gardens, Rathmines, Dublin, and Emily Charlotte Gordon; E 1957. 1958/T/04 [3 items].

KING, Captain LEO ALOYSIUS (b. 1 June 1898) 2nd s. of John Joseph King, of Clifden, Co. Galway, and Helena Casey; M 1921; [Captain, Regular Army Reserve of Officers] 1923/T/07 [2 items]. Electricity Supply Board, Died 28 July 1935. Obituary, *I.L.T. & S.J.*, lxix (1935), 216.

KING, ROBERT MacFARLAND (b. 18 Feb. 1862) 4th s. of Francis King, Archdeacon, of Newry, Co. Down, and Jane Jelly; B.A., ex-Scholar (T.C.D.); M 1885. 1888/M/01 [7 items].

KINGAN, THOMAS DAVISON (b. 7 Nov. 1879) 2nd s. of Samuel Kingan, D.L., of Glenganagh, Bangor, Co. Down, and Jane Sinclair (decd.); B.A. (Oxford); M 1902. 1905/M/01 [3 items].

KINGSMILL MOORE, THEODORE CONYNGHAM (b. 16 March 1893): see MOORE, THEODORE CONYNGHAM KINGSMILL.

KINLEN, AIDEEN PATRICIA (b. 13 June 1937) only d. of Louis P. Kinlen (decd.), contractor, of 69 Merrion Road, Dublin, and Aileen O'Donnell; B.A.; M 1956. Awarded Brooke Scholarship. 1959/M/01 [2 items]. Practised on the South Western Circuit, later joining the Sacred Heart nuns, and becoming a headmistress.

KINLEN, DERMOT PATRICK (b. 24 April 1930) eld. s. of Louis P. Kinlen, of 200 Rathfarnham Road, Dublin, and Aileen O'Donnell; B.A. (N.U.I.); M 1949. 1952/M/05 [2 items]. S.C., 12 March 1971. Judge of the High Court, 7 Oct. 1993. Retired in April 2002, when appointed the State's first Inspector of Prisons. See *The Irish Times*, 3 July 2003.

KINNEAR, THOMAS JOHN (b. 19 Oct. 1870) 2nd s. of Alexander Kinnear (decd.), of Ballybay, Co. Monaghan, and Ballsbridge, Dublin, and Jane Wright; M 1913. 1916/T/15 [2 items].

KINSELLA, GERALD STEPHEN (b. 29 July 1945) eld. s. of Richard Joseph Kinsella (decd.), trade union official, of 21 Fortfield Park, Terenure, Co. Dublin, and Margaret Daly; M 1964. 1968/M/20 [1 item].

KIRITTA, JESSE WILLIBALD (b. 27 Aug. 1937) eld. s. of Willibald D.P. Kiritta, magistrate, of Kilimanjaro, Tanzania, and Laurentia J. Kinyaiye; M 1960. 1965/M/11 [1 item].

KIRKPATRICK, HENRY CLARE (b. 25 Sept 1842) eldest s. of the Revd. William Baillie Kirkpatrick, of 48 North Great Georges Street, Dublin, and Elizabeth Clare; B.A. (T.C.D.); M 1867, L.I. M 1864. 1869/T/4 [2 items]. English Bar.

KIRKPATRICK, STANLEY VICTOR (b. 27 March 1897) only s. of William George Kirkpatrick (decd.), of Carlisle, Cumberland, and Isabel Henderson; M 1934. 1938/T/02 [2 items].

KIRKWOOD, ANDREW TORTON (b. 28 Aug. 1871) 2nd s. of Andrew Samuel Kirkwood, of Clongoonagh, Co. Roscommon, and Mary Harriet MacMunn; M 1908. 1925/H/01 [2 items]. *Cf.* David Thomson's *Woodbrook*.

KIRWAN, JAMES St. LAWRENCE (b. 31 Dec. 1916) only s. of James St. Lawrence Kirwan, medical doctor, of Ballinasloe Mental Hospital, Co. Galway, and Kathleen O'Connor; M 1937. 1960/M/08 [2 items].

KIRWAN, PATRICK JOSEPH (b. 23 June 1893) 2nd s. of Thomas Kirwan (decd.), of Goresbridge, Co. Kilkenny, and Anna Mary Phelan; M 1921. 1924/M/05 [2 items].

KIRWAN, SAMUEL VALENTINE (b. 1 June 1895) eld. s. of Valentine Francis Kirwan, solicitor, of 4 Ormond Terrace, Rathmines, Dublin, and Hannah Narcissa Barber; M 1920. 1923/T/04 [2 items].

KISSANE, EDWARD (EAMON) (b. 4 Jan. 1899) 7th s. of James Kissane, of Ahalapana, Newtownsandes, Co. Kerry, and Bridget Doherty; M 1933. 1938/T/06 [2 items].

KISSEADOO, WILLIAM ASSAH ASARE (b. 25 Nov. 1886) 2nd s. of John William
    Kisseadoo (decd.), of Gold Coast, West Africa, and Sophia Ampeah Kisseadoo; M
    1917. 1920/E/01 [2 items].
KNIPE, JOAN CLARE (b. 25 Aug. 1931) eld. d. of James Knipe, company director, of 'The
    Dell', Carrickbrennan Road, Monkstown, Co. Dublin, and Alice Morris; B. Comm.
    (N.U.I.); M 1951. 1954/M/07 [2 items].
KOHLI, GOKAL CHAND (b. 25 April 1885) 2nd s. of Jawala Sahai Kohli, of Peshawar,
    North-West Frontier, India; M 1914. 1917/T/12 [2 items].
KOTHARE, KHANDERAS GAJANAN (b. 2 Dec. 1884) 2nd s. of Gajanan Bapoojee
    Kothare, of Bombay, India; M 1915. 1918/T/06 [2 items].
KOUGH, CHARLES NORMAN (b. 25 July 1879) only s. of Charles Kough, B.A., Indian
    Civil Service (retd.), of 7 Alma Road, Monkstown, Dublin, and Jane Mary Elizabeth
    White; B.A. (T.C.D.); E 1901. 1903/M/12 [3 items]. Artist and caricaturist of legal
    contemporaries [e.g., of Maurice Healy, and the three King's Serjeants]. Died 17 Nov.
    1926. Obituary, *I.L.T. & S.J.*, lx (1926), 289.
KOWA, ABRAHAM JOSEPH (b. 6 July 1932) eld. s. of Robert Booma Kowa, administrative
    secretary, of Bo District Council, Bo, Sierra Leone, and Martha Tucker; B.C.L.; H
    1956. 1960/T/10 [2 items].
KUMA, ALEXANDER CUTHBERT (b. 24 Feb. 1928) eld. s. of Thomas Kuma, of Leklebi-
    Duga, Gold Coast, and Kate Abra; B.A. (Mod.); M 1953. 1956/M/04 [2 items].
KYLE, FRANCES CHRISTIAN (b. 30 Oct. 1894) young. d. of Robert Alexander Kyle, of 17
    Wellington Park, Belfast, and Kathleen Frances Bates; Sen. Mod., B.A., LL.B.
    (T.C.D.); H 1920. Awarded Brooke Scholarship. 1921/M/01 [2 items]. First woman to
    be called to the Bar in Ireland, 1 Nov. 1921. Photograph in the *Daily Sketch* of 3 Nov.
    1921, p. 4. Practised in Belfast until 1944; thereafter resided with her sister (Mrs.
    Kathleen McCloy) at 41 The Pryors, Hampstead. Died 22 June 1958. Obituary, *The
    Times*, 25 June 1958. Mentioned in J.C. MacDermott, *An Enriching Life* (Belfast,
    1980), 152-3, and in Ivana Bacik, Cathryn Costello and Eileen Drew, *Gender InJustice*
    (Dublin, 2003), 56. In 2001 her John Brooke Gold Medal and a collection of
    newspaper clippings relating to her Call were donated to the Law School of Trinity
    College by her niece, Dr. Elinor Meynell. Remembered as a wonderful
    conversationalist, as 'surely one of the best letter-writers of her day', and for her
    kindness. *The Times* obituary said of her: 'Goodness indeed was the quality which
    stood out above all others. The powerful intellect was guided by a spirit so gentle and
    so generous that it never over-awed those less gifted. Few who have borne the
    baptismal name of Christian have borne it more worthily.'
KYLE, WILLIAM (b. 7 April 1849) younger s. of Henry Kyle J.P. of Laures Hill, Coleraine,
    Co. Londonderry, and Elizabeth Mary Thompson (decd.); B.A. (T.C.D.); T 1870, I.T.
    E 1872. 1874/T/4 [4 items].

LA TOUCHE, JOHN JAMES DIGGES (b. 13 Jan 1838) 4th s. of Peter Digges La Touche
    (decd.) of Portarlington, Queen's County, and Marianne Browne; B.A. (T.C.D.); M
    1858, G.I. H 1860. 1870/M/2* [4 items]. Died 1899. *Burke's Irish Family Records*
    (1976), 694.
LABIB-MICHAEL: see MICHAEL, EDMOND LABIB.
LAKSHMINARAYANA, VUNNAVA (b. 4 Dec. 1879) eld. s. of Vunnava Greeramulu, of
    Guntur, Madras, India; M 1913. 1916/H/04 [2 items].
LALOR, EDWARD FINBARR JOHN (b. 9 April 1944) young. s. of Edward Lalor, farmer,
    of Ballybride, Roscommon, Co. Roscommon, and Johanna Dillon; B.C.L. (N.U.I.); M
    1962. 1966/M/10 [1 item].
LAMB, BENJAMIN (b. 22 Oct. 1892) eld. s. of Benjamin Lamb (decd.), of Belfast, and
    Minnie Millar; M 1922. 1925/M/10 [2 items].
LAMBAH, DIWAN CHAND (b. 26 July 1891) 3rd s. of Rai Bahadur Lala Mool Chand
    Lambah, Honorary Magistrate of Peshawar City, North-West Frontier, India; M 1914.
    1917/M/07 [2 items].

LANDY, ANDREW VINCENT (b. 9 Oct. 1917) only s. of Vincent Landy (decd.), of Convent Avenue, Skerries, Co. Dublin, and Agnes Branagan; B.A. (Mod.), LL.B; M 1944. Awarded John Brooke Scholarship. 1947/M/01 [2 items]. S.C., 7 March 1969. Died 7 Jan. 2000. Obituary [with photograph], *The Irish Times*, 29 Jan. 2000.

LANE, HUGH DILLON (b. 5 Aug. 1852) 3rd s. of Hugh Lane, Master of Her Majesty's Court of Queen's Bench, of 13 Mountjoy Square, Dublin, and Mary Moody; B.A. (T.C.D.); T 1877, M.T. H 1875. 1876/T/03 [4 items].

LANE, JAMES CLARKE (b. 22 Jan 1842) eld. s. of Richard James Lane, Q.C., of 84 Lr Baggot Street, Dublin and Catherine Tydd; B.A. (T.C.D.); E 1867, M.T. 1865. 1868/E/1 [2 items]. Auditor of the College Historical Society, 1867-8. Munster Circuit. Q.C. 5 July 1884.

LANE, RICHARD DONAL (b. 25 Sept. 1885) 3rd s. of Patrick Richard Lane of Boulder City, Western Australia, and Bridget Carrucan; [n.d.]. 1913/T/18 [2 items].

LANGAN, PETER St. JOHN HEVEY (b. 1 May 1942) only s. of Frederick Hevey Langan, farmer, of Mounty Hevey, Hill of Down, Co. Meath, and Myrrha Jephson; B.A. (T.C.D.); M 1961. Awarded 1st Victoria Prize. 1964/T/01 [1 item]. Q.C. Circuit Judge in Leeds. Contributor to the *Northern Ireland Legal Quarterly*.

LANIGAN-O'KEEFFE, ARTHUR JOHN (b. 22 Dec. 1912) 2nd s. of Arthur Lanigan O'Keeffe (decd.), of Cratloe, Merrion Road, Dublin, and May Borough; M 1940. 1944/M/13 [2 items]. District Justice, 1956.

LANKTREE, Captain CHARLES JOSEPH (b. 20 Nov. 1896) 4th s. of Barnaby Lanktree, of Gweedore, Ballintemple, Cork, and Mary Fogarty; M 1913. Captain, 5th Royal Munster Fusiliers. 1920/H/04 [3 items].

LARDNER, GERARD JOSEPH WILLIAM (b. 23 Sept. 1921) eld. s. of James Carrig Rushe Lardner, K.C. (decd.), of 22 Ailesbury Road, Dublin; M 1939. Awarded Society's Exhibition prize. 1943/M/04 [2 items]. Reid Professor, T.C.D., 1945-50. S.C., 5 March 1965. Judge of the High Court, 7 March 1985. Retired, 31 July 1993. Listed in the 1991 edition of Maureen Cairnduff, *Who's Who in Ireland*.

LARDNER, JAMES C.R. (b. 22 May 1879) eld. s. of Hugh William Lardner, gentleman, of Swan Park, Monaghan, Co. Monaghan, and Annie Loughran; T 1913. Formerly a solicitor. 1913/M/10 [2 items]. North-East Circuit. K.C., 12 July 1921. Nationalist M.P. for North Monaghan, 1907-18. Died 3 May 1925. Obituary, *I.L.T. & S.J.*, lix (1925), 113.

LAVAN, MICHAEL GIBSON (b. 23 May 1875) eld. s. of Martin Lavan of Portumna, Co. Galway, and Harriet Gibson; cand. bachelor (R.U.I.); M 1893. 1896/T/05 [3 items]. K.C. Died at Perth, Western Australia, 1937. Obituary, *I.L.T. & S.J.*, lxxi (16 June 1937), 167.

LAVERY, CECIL PATRICK LINTON (b. 6 Oct. 1894) 2nd s. of Patrick Lavery, solicitor, of Melvale, Armagh, Co. Armagh, and Rose Vallelly; B.A. (N.U.I.); M 1912. 1915/M/01 [2 items]. Judge of the Dáil Circuit Court, 1921-2. S.C., 21 Nov. 1927. Bencher, E 1933. Fine Gael TD, 1935-8. Attorney-General and Senator, 1948-50. Judge of the Supreme Court, 1950-66. Died 16 Dec. 1967. Obituary, *I.L.T. & S.J.*, cii (1968), 19; Appreciation in *The Irish Times* by T.A. Doyle; *Who's Who*. Contributor to James Meenan (ed.), *Centenary History of Lit. and Hist. Soc. of U.C.D.* Portrait by Leo Whelan in King's Inns: see Wanda Ryan-Smolin, *King's Inns Portraits* (1992), 40. See Louis McRedmond (ed.), *Modern Irish Lives*.

LAW, ARTHUR GERALD SIDNEY (b. 28 Nov. 1872) 3rd surv. s. of the Revd. Robert S. Law (decd.), M.A., of Drumconrath, Ardee, Co. Meath, and Eleanor Callwell; M 1897. 1902/H/04 [2 items].

LAW, HUGH ALEXANDER (b. 28 July 1872) 2nd s. of the Rt. Hon. Hugh Law (decd.), Q.C., LL.D., sometime Lord Chancellor of Ireland, of 9 Fitzwilliam Square, Dublin, and Helen Mary White; M 1897, I.T. M 1898. 1919/E/04x [2 items]. Called to English Bar. Convert to Catholicism, 1912, becoming a Knight of Grace of the Sovereign and Military Order of Malta. Nationalist M.P. for West Donegal, 1902-18. Ministry of Munitions, 1915-16; News Department of the Foreign Office, 1916-18. Member of the Congested Districts Board, 1919; of the Housing Committee of the Local Government Board, 1919-22. Fine Gael TD, 1927-32. Author of *Why is Ireland at war?* (Dublin,

1915; 2nd edition, 1916) and of *Anglo-Irish Literature, with a foreword by A.E.* (London, 1926). Died 2 April 1943. Obituary, *I.L.T. & S.J.*, lxxvii (1943), 93; *Who's Who*.

LAW, ROBERT KENNETH (b. 21 June 1906) only s. of Frederick William Law, of Evington, Carlow, Co. Carlow, and Eveleen Edith Dockeray; B.A. (Mod.), LL.B. (T.C.D.); M 1924. 1929/H/01 [2 items].

LAWLESS, EDMUND CONSTANTINE (b. 10 Aug 1850) only s. of Edmund Byrne Lawless Q.C. of 13 Upper Temple Street, Dublin, and Rose Maguire; B.A. (T.C.D.); H 1871, M.T. T 1872. 1874/E/4 [5 items]. Vancouver, British Columbia.

LAWLESS, HENRY HAMILTON (b. 15 June 1857) 4th s. of John Lawless, solicitor, of Leinster Lodge, Rathmines (Dublin), and Louise Van Laer; B.A. (T.C.D.); M 1876, M.T. T 1878. 1880/T/02 [6 items].

LAWRENCE, GEORGE (b. 10 Oct 1843) eld. s. of George Joseph Lawrence (decd.) of Midleton, Co. Cork, and Catherine O'Leary; M 1868, M.T. T 1867. 1874/E/2 [2 items]. Died at Cork, 23 Feb. 1912: *I.L.T. & S.J.*, xlvi (1912), 64. Mentioned in Maurice Healy, *The Old Munster Circuit*, 74-5.

LAWSON, SAMUEL ARNOLD (b. 17 Oct 1847) 2nd s. of the Rt. Hon. Mr. Justice Lawson of 27 Upper Fitzwilliam Street, Dublin, and Jane Merrick; B.A. (T.C.D.); M 1869; G.I. H 1871. 1873/M/1 [7 items].

LAWSON, WILLIAM (b. 11 Dec. 1850) 3rd s. of the Rt. Hon. James Anthony Lawson, Justice of the Court of Common Pleas in Ireland, of 27 Upper Fitzwilliam Street, Dublin, and Jane Margaret Merrick; B.A., LL.M. (Cambridge); E 1873, L.I. M 1871. 1881/M/04 [2 items]. Called to the English Bar, T 1875. Revising Barrister for Co. Dublin. Law reporter. Joint author, with R.J. Kelly K.C., of an edition of *The Representation of the People Act, 1918*. Died at Llandidrod Wells, 1918. Obituary, *I.L.T. & S.J.*, lii (16 Nov. 1918), 281.

LE FANU, WILLIAM JOSEPH HENRY (b. 13 April 1843) young. s. of the Revd. W.J.H. Le Fanu, Rector of St Paul's and Chaplain of the Marshalsea, Co. Dublin, and Charlotte Mary [Purdon*]; B.A. (T.C.D.); M 1871; M.T. H 1864. 1872/H/10 [2 items].

LE FANU, WILLIAM RICHARD (b. 26 April 1861) 3rd s. of William Richard Le Fanu of Enniskerry, Co. Wicklow, and Henrietta Barrington; B.A. (Cambridge); M 1881, M.T. M 1881. 1884/M/01 [5 items]. Secretary and Treasurer to the Governors of Queen Anne's Bounty. Died 22 March 1925. *Who's Who*.

LE POER TRENCH, FREDERICK NETTERVILLE: see TRENCH, FREDERICK NETTERVILLE LE POER.

LEAHY, DANIEL VINCENT (b. 7 April 1869) young. s. of Patrick Leahy (decd.) of Schull, Co. Cork, and Mary Coughlan; cand. bachelor (R.U.I.); M 1889. 1894/H/05 [7 items].

LEAHY, MICHAEL (b. 11 Feb. 1886) 2nd s. of Timothy Leahy, of Tipperary, Co. Tipperary, and Margaret Dwyer; M 1924; [Chief Superintendent, Garda Síochána] 1927/T/08 [2 items]. Died 8 April 1932. Obituary, *I.L.T. & S.J.*, lxvi (1932), 97.

LEAMY, EDMUND (b. 25 Dec. 1848) 2nd s. of James Leamy, merchant, of 14 Beresford Street, Waterford, and Margaret Meahger; E 1884, M.T. T 1884; MP. 1885/T/01 [2 items].

LEDWICH, FREDERICK FRANCIS (b. 3 March 1857) 4th s. of William Ledwich of 23 Upper Leeson Street, Dublin, and Elizabeth L'Estrange; E 1877, M.T. E 1879. 1880/M/08 [7 items].

LEDWITH, JAMES (b. 26 April 1932) only s. of James Ledwith (decd.), of 20 Wellpark Avenue, Drumcondra, Dublin, and Síobhán Ní Mhurchadh; M 1953. 1957/T/05 [2 items].

LEE, GERARD ANTHONY (b. 17 Oct. 1917) young. s. of William P. Lee, M.D. (decd.), of Glen-Dove House, Kilfinane, Co. Limerick, and Agnes Mary Condon; M.A. (N.U.I.); M 1938. 1942/T/05 [2 items]. S.C., 9 March 1979. Author of *A Memoir of the South-Western Circuit* (Dublin, 1990). Died 15 Nov. 2003. Appreciation (by Charles Lysaght) in the *Sunday Independent*, 23 Nov. 2003.

LEE, JOSEPH BAGNALL (b. 3 May 1888) 3rd surv. s. of Edward Lee of The Grange, Stillorgan, Co. Dublin, and Annie Shackleton; B.A., LL.B. (T.C.D.); M 1905. 1909/T/04 [3 items]. Lieutenant, Royal Munster Fusiliers. Died at Gallipoli, 7 Aug.

1915: *I.L.T. & S.J.*, xlix (1915), 206. [Name on the Bar War Memorial; also on the Helles Memorial, Gallipoli].

LEECH, ARTHUR GRAVES (b. 17 Sept. 1877) eld. s. of Henry Leech, LL.D., of Yew Park, Clontarf, Dublin, and Annie Louisa Garbois; B.A. (T.C.D.); M 1897. 1901/H/05 [2 items].

LEECH, HENRY BROUGHAM (b. 15 Nov. 1843) 2nd s. of the Revd. John Leech, of Mitchelstown, Co. Cork, and Mary Darley; B.A. (T.C.D.); E 1868, M.T. H 1866. 1871/M/7 [2 items]. Fellow of Caius College, Cambridge, 1873. Professor of Jurisprudence and International Law, T.C.D., 1877-88; Regius Professor of Laws, T.C.D., 1888-1908. Registrar of Deeds and Registrar of Titles. Retired 1908. R.B. McDowell and David Webb observe, in their *Trinity College Dublin 1592-1952: An academic history* (Cambridge, 1982), 413, that Leech 'spent two-thirds of his time in an administrative post unconnected with the university'. Author, *inter alia*, of *Essay on Ancient International Law* (1878); *The Irish Landowners' Convention. Registration of Title v. Registration of Assurances* (London, 1891); *The South African Republics, their History and International Position* (Dublin, 1901); *The Irish University Question: its History and its Solution* (1905); *A Handbook for Unionist Speakers* (1910); *1848 and 1887: The Continuity of the Irish Revolutionary Movement* (Dublin: 1887; 2nd edition,'1848 and 1912', with foreword by Carson, London, 1912). Died 2 March 1921. Obituary, *I.L.T. & S.J.*, lv (1921), 71; *Who's Who*. Portrait in T.C.D. (purchased for the Law School as a memorial to Mr. Justice Kingsmill Moore): see Anne Crookshank and David Webb, *Paintings and Sculptures in Trinity College Dublin* (Dublin, 1990), 83. See also Alan Denson's biography of his son, the artist William John Leech (Kendal, 1968).

LEECH, HUNT WALSH CHAMBRE (b. 20 Dec. 1847) eld. surv. s. of George Williams Leech (decd.), Barrister-at-Law, J.P., of Rathkeale Abbey, Co. Limerick, and Katherine Chambre (decd.); LL.D.; H 1883, M.T. M 1882. 1883/M/12 [4 items].

LEECH, JOHN (b. 22 May 1857) young. s. of Charles Leech Q.C., of 40 North Great George's Street, Dublin, and Anna Maria Chambre; B.A. (T.C.D.); M 1878, M.T. M 1880. 1881/M/17 [7 items]. K.C., 28 Feb. 1910. Recorder of Belfast. Retired in 1926 to join the British-Israel World Federation: see *I.L.T. & S.J.*, lx (1926), 175. Died 1942. Obituary, *I.L.T. & S.J.*, lxxvi (8 Aug. 1942), 198.

LEET, ERNEST FLEETWOOD (b. 4 Feb. 1869) 3rd s. of the Revd. A. W. Leet, D.D., Canon of Christ Church Cathedral and incumbent of Baggotrath Church, Dublin and Mary Henry; M 1893. 1896/M/04 [4 items]. President of the University Philosophical Society, T.C.D., 1892-3. Institute of Bankers. Died 28 May 1952.

LEHANE, CORNELIUS (b. 23 Dec. 1871) only s. of Matthew Lehane (decd.), of Macroom, Co. Cork, and Ellen Dromey; M 1899. 1902/T/07 [2 items].

LEHANE, LEONIE MARY (b. 23 Nov. 1931) eld. d. of Patrick Lehane (decd.), of Arranthrue, 2 The Rise, Stillorgan Road, Co. Dublin, and Eileen O'Flaherty; B.A. (N.U.I.); M 1950. 1953/T/06 [2 items]. Mrs. Maurice Gaffney.

LELAND, JOHN HENRY FREDERICK (b. 17 Sept. 1884) eld. s. of Henry Leland, of Blackrock, Co. Dublin, and Laura Jane Leland; B.A. (T.C.D.); M 1907. 1911/E/01 [2 items]. 2nd Lieutenant, Royal Welch Fusiliers. Died at Gallipoli, 10 Aug. 1915. [Name on the Bar War Memorial; also on the Helles Memorial, Gallipoli].

LEMASS, EDWIN STEPHEN (b. 26 Dec. 1890) eld. surv. s. of Peter Edmund Lemass, L.R.C.S.I., Secretary, Board of National Education, of 3 Clifton Terrace, Monkstown, Dublin, and Maria Patricia Scallan; B.A. (T.C.D.); M 1909. 1912/M/03 [2 items]. Auditor of the College Historical Society, 1913-4. Practised on the North-West Circuit before going to the war, serving in France and with the Archangel Force in northern Russia. Appointed to Ministry of Justice, Egypt, 1920, and aft. Judge of various courts in Egypt. British Judge of the International Court, Tangier, 1949-57. Died 12 April 1970. *Who's Who*.

LENIHAN, BRIAN JOSEPH (b. 17 Nov. 1930) eld. s. of Patrick Joseph Lenihan, of Hodson Bay Hotel, Athlone, Co. Westmeath, and Ann Scanlon; B.A. (N.U.I.); M 1949. 1952/M/16 [2 items]. Senator, 1957-61, 1973-7; T.D. 1961-73, 1977-95. Minister for Education 1968-9, Transport and Power 1969-73, Foreign Affairs 1973, 1979-81,

1987-9, Agriculture, March-Nov. 1982, Defence 1989-90. Unsuccessful candidate for the presidency of Ireland, 1990. Died 1 Nov. 1995. Obituary, *The Times*, 3 Nov. 1995. Listed [with photographs] in the 1984 and 1991 editions of Maureen Cairnduff, *Who's Who in Ireland*. See also: Louis McRedmond (ed.), *Modern Irish Lives*.

LENNON, MICHAEL JOHN (b. 18 May 1891) eld. s. of Daniel Lennon, of 6 Longwood Avenue, Dublin, and Margaret Reardon; M 1919. 1922/H/02 [2 items]. Also known as Micheál Ó Leannáin. Irish-speaker and District Justice, 1937-57, who 'resigned at the request of the Government, following an inquiry by a High Court judge into handling of a case involving political offences'. Died 1966. Obituary, *I.L.T. & S.J.*, c (1966), 103.

LENTAIGNE, JOSEPH HUSSEY NUGENT (b. 30 May 1847) eld. s. of John Francis Lentaigne of Tallaght, Co. Dublin, Inspector General of Prisons, and Mary Magan; B.A. (T.C.D.); H 1867, M.T. E 1868. 1870/H/3 [2 items]. Clerk of the Crown and Hanaper, and Permanent Secretary to the Lord Chancellor. Justice of the Peace for County Dublin. Died unmarried 1915. Uncle of the following entry. *Burke's Irish Family Records* (1976), 717

LENTAIGNE, JOSEPH IGNATIUS NUGENT (b. 31 July 1889) 3rd s. of Sir John Lentaigne of 42 Merrion Square, Dublin, and Phillis Coffey; B.A., LL.B. (T.C.D.); M 1911. 1911/T/09 [2 items]. Barrister in Rangoon, Burma. Died 9 Sept. 1921. *Burke's Irish Family Records* (1976), 717.

LEONARD, PATRICK FRANCIS XAVIER (b. 28 December 1919) 4th s. of Peter Paul Leonard, merchant, of 238 North Circular Road, Dublin, and May Connolly; B.A. (N.U.I.); M 1938. Awarded John Brooke Scholarship. 1941/M/01 [2 items]. Judge of the High Court in Hong Kong.

LEONARD, ROBERT GALLOWAY LOUIS (b. 25 Oct. 1878) only surv. s. of Hugh Leonard, Geological Survey of Ireland (retd.), of Mount Merrion Avenue, Blackrock, Co. Dublin, and Katherine Stuart Kinahan; cand. LL.B. (London), M 1895. 1899/M/03 [3 items]. Went Connaught Circuit. K.C., 27 Feb. 1918. Reid Professor, T.C.D., 1904-9. Judge of the Court of the General Synod of the Church of Ireland. Died 22 June 1957. Obituary, *I.L.T. & S.J.*, xci , 172. Mentioned by V.T.H. Delany [q.v.], in 'The Bench and Bar in Ireland', xxxiv.

LEPPER, JOHN HERON (b. 3 Oct. 1878) only s. of Alfred Adolphus Lepper of Carrickfergus, Co. Antrim, and Margaret Louisa [Herdman]; B.A. (T.C.D.); M 189[7]. 1903/T/01 [3 items]. Died Dec. 1951.

LESLIE, WILLIAM MOUTRAY (b. 29 June 1847) only s. of William Leslie, J.P. and High Sheriff for Co. Cavan, of Cootehill, Co. Cavan, and Mary Erskine; B.A. (T.C.D.); E 1872, M.T. E 1873.1875/M/03 [2 items].

LEWIN, FREDERICK HENRY (b. 26 Aug. 1877) 3rd s. of Frederick Thomas Lewin, D.S. of Castlegrove, Co. Galway, and Lucy Emily Corrie; E 1899. 1902/T/04 [2 items]. Corporal, 3rd Batt., Connaught Rangers. Died of wounds received in a bomb-throwing practice at Kinsale, 8 Dec. 1915, and buried in Holy Trinity Church of Ireland Churchyard, Kilmaine, Co. Mayo: see *I.L.T. & S.J.*, War Supplement, p. 8. [Name on the Bar War Memorial, and on the Screen Wall at Grangegorman].

LEWIS, FRANCIS WILLIAM (b. 11 May 1893) eld. s. of Richard Lewis, of Bagenalstown, Co. Carlow, and Lucy Hughes; M 1923. 1925/M/30. Note attached stating 'The date within will probably have to be altered'. Name not on official list. [3 items].

LEWIS-HEATH, FREDERICK RONALD (b. 4 June 1911) only s. of Eng[ineer] Commander Frederick John Lewis-Heath (decd.), of 'Byrsa', Egg Buckland Road, Hartley, Plymouth, Devon, and Lilian Constance Austin; M 1949. 1953/M/10 [2 items].

LIDDY, JAMES DANIEL REEVES (b. 1 July 1934) only s. of James Liddy, M.B., of Coolgreany, Co. Wexford, and Margaret Reeves; B.A. (N.U.I.); M 1953. Awarded Society's Exhibition Prize. 1956/M/02 [2 items]. Author of more than a dozen volumes of prose and verse, including the Dolmen Press titles *Esau my kingdom for a drink*: *homage to James Joyce on his 80th birthday* (1962) [a memorial address delivered at King's Inns on 13 Feb. 1962], *In a blue smoke* (1964) and *Blue Mountain* (1968): see Brian Arkins, *James Liddy: A Critical Study* (Arlen House, 2001). Professor in the English Department at the University of Wisconsin-Milwaukee, teaching creative writing, and Irish and Beat literature: see *The Doctor's House*: *An Autbiography* (Co. Clare, 2004), the cover of which bears a photograph of the author with his father.

LIDDY, MICHAEL (b. 17 July 1945) eld. s. of Patrick Liddy, Barrister-at-Law, of the King's Inns and the Inner Temple, and Judge Advocate to the Defence Forces, of Newtownpark Avenue, Blackrock, Co. Dublin, and Maud Lennox; B.A. (N.U.I.); M 1964. 1968/T/19 [1 item].

LIDDY, PATRICK JOSEPH (b. 17 Mar. 1916) only s. of John Liddy of Earlswood Road, Belfast, and Susan Farrelly; B.A. (Q.U.B.); M 1944. 1947/M/10 [2 items].

LIDWILL, ROBERT ARTHUR (b. 15 April 1871) 2nd s. of Major George Lidwill of Dromard, Co. Tipperary, and Edith Adams; B.A. (T.C.D.); M 1896. 1899/M/13 [3 items]. Colonel. Died 19 Jan. 1954.

LILLIS, MARTIN ARTHUR (b. 21 Sept. 1890) 3rd s. of Thomas Barry Lillis of Carrig, Queenstown, Co. Cork, and Nannie M. [Goggin]; B.A. (T.C.D.); M 1911. 1914/T/18 [2 items]. Lieutenant, Royal Irish Regiment, attached to the Royal Flying Corps (Feb. 1916) and killed in action, 11 April 1917. [Name on the Bar War Memorial].

LILLIS, RICHARD JOSEPH (b. 13 Feb. 1882) 3rd s. of Thomas Barry Lillis, J.P., of Janeville, Ballintemple, Co. Cork, and Anne Victoria Goggin; B.A. (T.C.D.); M 1901. 1904/T/05 [3 items]. Died 30 March 1909. Obituary, *I.L.T. & S.J.*, xliii (1909), 94.

LINDSAY, PATRICK JAMES (b. 18 Jan. 1914) 1st s. of Patrick Lindsay, of Geesala, Ballina, Co. Mayo, and Mary Keegan; M 1943. 1946/M/04 [2 items]. S.C., 9 Dec. 1954. Fine Gael T.D., 1954-61, 1965-9, serving in Cabinet as first Minister for the Gaeltacht, 1954-57. Appt. Master of the High Court, 1 Nov. 1975. Retired 18 Jan. 1984. Author of *Memories* (Dublin, 1992; paperback edition with epilogue, 1993). Died 29 June 1993. See Louis McRedmond (ed.), *Modern Irish Lives*.

LINEHAN, DANIEL CORNELIUS (b. 7 June 1928) eld. s. of Michael P. Lenihan, Treasurer, INTO, President, ICPSA, of 146 Upper Drumcondra Road, Dublin, and Christina Margaret Crimmins; M.A., H.Dip; M 1957. Awarded 3rd Victoria Prize. 1960/T/01 [2 items]. Department of Justice. Data Protection Commissioner. Author of a foreword to Robert Clark's *Data Protection Law in Ireland* (Dublin, 1990).

LINEHAN, JOHN (b. 11 June 1865) eld. s. of Matthew Linehan (decd.), of South Mall, Cork, and Mary Blake; M 1888. 1891/E/01 [9 items]. Began life as a journalist, and worked in the Press Gallery of the House of Commons, 1888-9. Munster Circuit. Prosecutor in Co. Clare, aft. Cork. Permanent Revising Barrister for Dublin. K.C., 24 Feb. 1912. Twice acted as Deputy Recorder of Londonderry. Appt. County Court Judge for Tyrone, 12 Sept. 1912. Died 31 Jan. 1935. Obituary, *I.L.T. & S.J.*, lxix (1935), 47, 129; *Who's Who*.

LINEHAN, MATTHEW FRANCIS (b. 30 May 1867) 2nd s. of Matthew Linehan (decd.) of South Mall, Cork, and Mary Blake; B.A. (R.U.I.); H 1903. 1907/H/03 [2 items]. Died 20 March 1939. Obituary, *I.L.T. & S.J.*, lxxiii (1939), 99.

LINEHAN, UNA McAULIFFE (b. 4 Aug. 1923) only d. of William Linehan, director of education of Singapore, Straits Settlements, and Mary O'Sullivan; B.A. (N.U.I.); M 1941. 1944/M/08 [2 items].

LIPSETT, LEWIS RICHARD (b. 16 Aug. 1876) eld. s. of Robert Lipsett (decd.), of Ballyshannon, Co. Donegal, and Martha Elizabeth Bowker; M.A., LL.D. (T.C.D.); T 1912. 1912/M/11 [2 items]. Formerly a solicitor. North-West Circuit. K.C., 13 July 1921. Called to English Bar, H 1918. LL. D. (Dubl.). Died 12 Oct. 1957.

LIPSETT, WILLIAM ALFRED (b. 29 Jan. 1886) 4th s. of Robert Lipsett (decd.) of Ballyshannon, Co. Donegal, and Martha Elizabeth Bowker; M 1904. 1907/T/05 [3 items]. Grenadier, 10th Batt., Alberta Regiment, 1st Canadian Infantry Division; killed in action at Ypres, 22 April 1915. [Name on the Bar War Memorial, and on the Menin Gate at Ypres].

LISTON, JEREMIAH LOUIS VINCENT (b. 19 Sept. 1940) eld. s. of Terence Kevin Liston, Senior Counsel, of 'Glaunsharoon', Eglinton Road, Donnybrook, Dublin, and Margaret Slattery; B.A. (N.U.I.); M 1959. Awarded Society's prize. 1962/M/03 [1 item]. Businessman. Chief Executive of United Drug plc. Listed in the 1999 edition of Maureen Cairnduff, *Who's Who in Ireland*.

LISTON, KEVIN DENIS MARY (b. 18 June 1943) 2nd s. of Terence Kevin Liston, Senior Counsel, of 'Glaunsharoon', 29 Eglinton Road, Dublin, and Margaret Slattery; B. Comm. (N.U.I.); M 1964. 1967/M/13 [1 item]. Became a solicitor, 1976. Legal Aid Board.

LISTON, TERENCE KEVIN (b. 3 July 1903) eld. s. of Terence Joseph Liston, of Ballard House, Tralee, Co. Kerry, and Annie Galvin; M 1922. 1928/M/01 [2 items]. S.C., 26 June 1944. Died 1992. Appreciation [by J. McM.] in the *Irish Law Times*, new series, x (1992), 147.

LITTLE, EDWARD DAVID (b. 2 April 1938) eld. s. of Cornelius Joseph Patrick Little, chartered civil engineer, of Limbo, Nyasaland, and Lily Doris Henderson; B.C.L. (N.U.I.); M 1960. 1963/M/05 [1 item].

LITTLE, Captain EDWARD GERALD (b. 18 Feb. 1897) 5th s. of William Little, of Una Lodge, Sandycove, Co. Dublin, and Catherine Harriet Currie; M 1924; [M.C. late Royal Dublin Fusiliers and Indian Army] 1927/H/04 [2 items].

LITTLE, EDWARD JOSEPH (b. 8 Dec. 1870) 5th s. of Philip Francis Little, ex Judge, Supreme Court of Newfoundland, of Monkstown, Dublin, and Mary Jane Holdwright; B.A. (T.C.D.); H 1892. 1895/T/01 [6 items]. Appt. District Justice, Oct. 1924. Died 20 March 1952. Obituary, *I.L.T. & S.J.*, lxxxvi (1952), 99-100.

LITTLE, ESMONDE WILLIAM (b. 6 Aug. 1886) eld. s. of William Little, of 22 Mountjoy Square, Dublin, and Katherine Harriet Currie; M 1920. 1923/M/02 [2 items].

LITTLE, ISAAC (b. 30 June 1863) young. s. of James Henry Vos Little (decd.), solicitor, of Belfast, and Sarah Hardy; B.A. (T.C.D.); H 1886. 1889/M/05 [9 items].

LITTLE, JAMES (b. 4 Aug. 1872) eld. s. of James Little, M.D., of 14 Stephen's Green, Dublin, and Anna Murdock; B.A. (Oxford); M 1894, I.T. M 1892. 1896/T/09 [5 items]. Death noted, without date, in T.C.D. *Register of Alumni*, 7th ed., 1962.

LITTLE, JOSEPH CHRISTOPHER (b. 3 May 187[2]) 6th s. of the Hon. Philip Francis Little (decd.), Judge of the Supreme Court of Newfoundland and of No. 6, New Brighton, Monkstown, Dublin, and Mary Jane [Holdnight]; M 1896, G.I. E 1898. 1899/T/06 [3 items].

LITTLEDALE, RICHARD WILLIAM WHALEY (b. 25 Aug. 1862) 2nd surv. s. of William Francis Littledale, J.P., of Whaley Abbey, Rathdrum, Co. Wicklow, and Jane Cross; B.A., LL.B. (T.C.D.); H 1885. 1887/M/15 [7 items]. K.C., 22 Jan. 1906. King's Advocate. Registrar in Chancery. Mentioned in Maurice Healy, *The Old Munster Circuit*, 251.

LITTON, EDWARD DE L'ESTABLIRE (b. 19 Nov. 1864) 2nd s. of Edward Falconer Litton, Q.C., Irish Land Commissioner, of 47 Merrion Square, Dublin, and Eliz. Clarke (decd.); B.A. (T.C.D.); M 1884, L.I. E 1885. 1888/M/03 [8 items]. Died 27 June 1902. *I.L.T. & S.J.*, xxxvi (1902), 258.

LLOYD, HUMPHREY WILMOT (b. 28 Feb. 1848) 3rd s. of B.C. Lloyd (decd.), Q.C., of 22 Lower Leeson Street, Dublin, and Caroline H. Brooke; E 1884. 1887/H/09 [6 items].

LLOYD-BLOOD, LANCELOT IVAN: see: BLOOD, LANCELOT IVAN LLOYD.

LLOYD-BLOOD, NEVIL (b. 1 July 1921) eld. s. of Lancelot Ivan Neptune Lloyd-Blood, Barrister-at-Law, of 9 Winton Road, Leeson Park, Dublin, and Constance Elizabeth Byrne; B.A., LL.B. (T.C.D.); M 1940. 1950/M/13 [2 items]. Editor of *The Irish Reports* 1968-1984, and of *Irish Law Log* (5 vols., 1988-92). Died 1996.

LOCKHART, HENRY (b. 16 Feb. 1865) 2nd s. of Alexander Lockhart. solicitor, of Belfast, and Margaret Agnew; B.A. (T.C.D.); E 1887. 1890/E/02 [10 items].

LOFTUS, JOHN DANIEL (b. 26 Nov. 1927) eld. s. of Doctor J.J. Loftus, of 29 Ailesbury Road, Ballsbridge, Dublin, and Margaret McCarthy; H 1954. 1958/M/08 [2 items].

LOKKO, CHRISTIAN CHARLES (b. 26 Aug. 1882) eld. s. of Andrew Frederick Lokko (decd.), of Christiansberg, Accra, Gold Coast Colony, West Coast Africa; M 1915. 1918/T/17 [2 items].

LONG, JOHN GERARD (b. 5 Oct. 1903) only s. of John Alexander Long (decd.), of 74 Dame Street, Dublin, and Mary Mullan; M 1922. 1926/M/03 [2 items].

LONG, JOHN OLIVER HORNER (b. 15 Aug. 1902) only s. of John Andrew Long, of Ballinamore, Co. Londonderry, and Margaret Jackson Horner; M 1921. 1924/M/04 [2 items]. Killed on 12 Sept. 1941 in an air raid on Malta, where he held an educational appointment. Obituary, *I.L.T. & S.J.*, lxxv (1941), 242, 248.

LONG, WALTER EDWARD (b. 25 Sept. 1850) eld. s. of William Long of 61 Victoria Terrace, Belfast (Randalstown, Hermitage, Co. Armagh), and Elizabeth Pasley; B.A. (T.C.D.); E 1875, I.T. E 1876. 1878/H/02 [6 items].

LONGFIELD, HENRY FOSTER (b. 19 July 1867) only s. of Henry Longfield, J.P., of Broadview, Mallow, Co. Cork, and Elinor Ware; B.A. (T.C.D.); M 1888. 1891/M/12 [6 items]. Died 28 Oct. 1937. Obituary, *I.L.T. & S.J.*, lxxi (1937), 315.

LONGFIELD, MOUNTIFORT GEORGE (b. 4 June 1864) only s. of the Revd. George Longfield (decd.), D.D., F.T.C.D., of Earlsfort Terrace, Dublin, and Church Hill, Bandon, Co. Cork, and Mary Ware; B.A. (T.C.D.); M 1885. 1888/M/08 [7 items]. Died 25 April. 1930. Obituary, *I.L.T. & S.J.*, lxiv (1930), 106. Author (with D.G. Chaytor) of the Supplement to *Chaytor on Tithe Rent Charge*.

LONGWORTH, EDWARD TRAVERS: see DAMES-LONGWORTH, EDWARD TRAVERS.

LONGWORTH, ERNEST VICTOR (b. 13 July 1874) eld. s. of Daniel Longworth, M.I.M.E. of Villa Verani, Avenue Malanssena, Nice, France, and Emily Hatte; H 1900. 1903/H/05 [3 items]. Auditor of the College Historical Society, 1899-1900. Called to the English Bar, June 1912. K.C., 14 Dec. 1920 [taking silk not noted in *Thom*, but see *I.L.T. & S.J.*, liv, 306]. Joint author (with F.P. Hamilton and A.W. Quill) of *The Irish Land Acts of 1903, 4, with Appendix of Rules and Forms and a Commentary* (Dublin, 1904) and *The Town Tenants (Ireland) Act, 1906, with Commentary, Rules and Forms* (Dublin, 1907).

LOUDEN, JOHN JAMES (b. 12 Sept 1842) eld. s. of John Louden of Westport, Co. Mayo and Bridget Mulholland; B.A. (Queen's College, Galway); M 1862, M.T. E 1864. 1871/H/1 [3 items].

LOUDEN, THOMAS (b. 3 Sept. 1874) young. s. of David Louden, merchant, of Holmslea, Knock, Co. Down, and Jane MacPhail; B.A. (R.U.I.); M 1895. 1899/M/07 [6 items].

LOUGHNAN: see MAHER-LOUGHNAN, JOHN.

LOUGHREY, MARTIN CHARLES (b. 2 Nov. 1910) 2nd s. of Martin A. Loughrey (decd.), merchant, of Killala, Co. Mayo, and Ellen Timlin; B.A. (N.U.I.); M 1944. 1950/M/12 [2 items].

LOVATT-DOLAN, JOHN HENRY GEOFFREY (b. 30 Nov. 1926) only s. of James J. Dolan (decd.), architect, of 68 Palmerston Road, Rathmines, Dublin, and Susan Mary White; B.A. (N.U.I.); M 1945. 1949/M/06 [2 items]. S.C., 5 March 1965. Law Reform Commissioner. Died 1985.

LOWE, JOHN (b. 22 Sept. 1932) 3rd s. of John Lowe (decd.), company director, of Hollywell, Carrick-on-Shannon, Co. Leitrim, and Brigid Carney; M.A. (N.U.I.); M 1959. 1963/T/05 [1 item]. Accountant, banker.

LOWEY, MICHAEL JAMES ANTHONY (b. 24 April 1939) only s. of Harold Lowey, (decd.), Officer R.N., of 'Devonia', Kiln Road, Fareham, Hampshire, and Maud Gordon; B.C.L.; M 1957. 1960/T/03 [2 items]. Management consultant. Contributor to Frank Callanan (ed.), *The Literary and Historical Society 1955-2005* (Dublin, 2005), 39-40.

LOWRY, FREDERICK JAMES SHARPLES (b. 10 Sept. 1859) 3rd surv. s. of John Lowry (decd.) of Belfast, and Jane Harper; H 1901. 1904/H/01 [2 items].

LOWRY, GEORGE TREVOR (b. 20 April 1906) 2nd s. of George Herbert Lowry, of Kells, Co. Meath, and Margaret Millar; M 1927, M.T. M 1928. 1933/M/10 [2 items].

LOWRY, HENRY EDGAR (b. 3 Oct. 1874) young. s. of Joseph Lowry, of Bachelors Lodge, Navan, Co. Meath, and Mary Kilroy; B.A. (T.C.D.); M 1897. 1902/T/03 [3 items]. Died at Buenos Aires, 1926. Obituary, *I.L.T. & S.J.*, lx (14 Aug. 1926), 206.

LOWRY, JAMES MOODY (b. 31 Oct. 1849) eld. s. of Thomas Kennedy Lowry (decd.), Q.C., Prothonotary of the Duchy of Lancaster, of Ballytrim, Co. Down, and Isabella Moody; B.A. (T.C.D.); M 1882, L.I. H 1870. 1885/H/08 [5 items]. Clerk of the Judgements, Records and Writs, Chancery Division. Author, *inter alia*, of *A Book of Jousts* (London [1888]); *House of Keys* and *The Book of Trusts*; *The Lay of Kilcock, with other Lays and Relays* (Dublin and London, 1906). Died at Birmingham, 29 July

1922. Obituary, *I.L.T. & S.J.*, lvi (1922), 186. Mentioned, as composer of a ballad, in Maurice Healy, *The Old Munster Circuit*, 180-2.

LOWRY, JOHN (b. 20 Jan. 1846) 2nd s. of Michael Lowry (decd.), farmer, of Killismeestha, Queen's Co., and Catherine Ryan; T 1872, G.I. H 1878. 1881/H/01 [2 items].

LOWRY, WILLIAM (b. 19 March 1884) 3rd s. of Samuel Lowry of White Hill, Limavady, Co. Londonderry, and Margaret J. Gibson; B.A. (R.U.I.); M 1904, G.I. T 1906. 1907/H/01 [2 items]. Reid Professor, T.C.D., 1915-20. Organiser of a coaching class for Bar students (see J.C. MacDermott, *An Enriching Life*, 147). K.C. (N.I.), M 1926. M.P. (N.I. Parliament) for Londonderry City, 1939. Minister of Home Affairs, 1943-4. Attorney-General for N.I., 3 Nov. 1944 - 5 June 1947. Judge of the King's Bench Division in Northern Ireland, 5 June 1947-11 Oct. 1949. Died 14 Dec. 1949. Obituary, *I.L.T. & S.J.*, lxxxiii (31 Dec. 1949), 328-9; *Who's Who*.

LUCAS, ROBERT WILLIAM (b. 16 Sept. 1857) eld. s. of Edward William Lucas of Raconnell, Co. Monaghan, and Louisa Johnston; B.A. (T.C.D.); M 1879, M.T. M 1881. 1882/M/08 [5 items]. Died 26 Feb. 1919. Obituary, *I.L.T. & S.J.*, liii (1919), 59.

LUKE, EDWARD HARRIS (b. 14 Sept. 1865) eld. s. of William J. Luke of Hollymount, Belfast, and Elizabeth Harris; B.A., scholar (T.C.D.); H 1888. 1892/M/04 [6 items].

LUPTON, EDMOND (b. 26 March 1877) eld. s. of Robert Lupton (decd.) of Liverpool, Lancashire, and Kate Concannon; T 1904. 1907/M/10 [4 items]. K.C., 25 Feb.1919. Last Chief Magistrate of the Dublin Police Courts, 1921-4. Afterwards returned to practise. Died 19 Nov. 1942. Obituary, *I.L.T. & S.J.*, lxxvi (1942), 296.

LYHANE, CORNELIUS (b. 13 April 1871) young. s. of Cornelius Lyhane (decd.), gentleman, of Lackadune, Macroom, Co. Cork, and Catherine Kelleher; B.A., LL.B. (R.U.I.); M 1894, M.T. M 1895. 1899/T/01 [3 items].

LYNAM, WILLIAM (b. 18 Feb. 1850) young. s. of John Lynam (decd.), medical doctor, of Jersey City, New Jersey, USA, and Eliza Byrne; T 1878, M.T. E 1881. 1883/M/05 [5 items].

LYNCH, FIONÁN: see: Ó LOINGSIGH, FIONÁN.

LYNCH, FRANCIS (b. 10 May 1851) 5th s. of David Lynch (decd.), Judge of the Landed Estates Court, Ireland, of Merrion Sq, Dublin, and Margaret Kennedy; B.A. (T.C.D.); E 1872, I.T. E 1873. 1879/T/01 [2 items]. Examiner, Land Judge's Court. Died 2 Jan. 1903. *I.L.T. & S.J.*, xxxvii (1903), 35.

LYNCH, HENRY CHARLES (b. 7 June 1863) 3rd s. of Stanislaus T. Lynch, J.P., Registrar Landed Estates Court, of 24 Clyde Road, Dublin, and Helen Briscoe; E 1881, M.T. E 1883. 1884/M/07 [6 items].

LYNCH, HENRY RAPHAEL (b. 22 Oct. 1923) 2nd s. of Michael Lynch, farmer, of Killafinla House, Ballyjamesduff, Co. Cavan, and Mary O'Connell; M 1948. 1951/M/14 [2 items].

LYNCH, JAMES DOMINIC (b. 30 July 1937) 4th s. of Michael Lynch, farmer, of Killafinla House, Ballyjamesduff, Co. Cavan, and Mary O'Connell; M 1957. 1964/M/05 [1 item]. S.C., 29 Feb. 1980. Judge of the Circuit Court.

LYNCH, JOHN MARY (b. 15 Aug. 1917) 5th s. of Daniel Lynch, of Clonard, Farrenferris, Cork, and Nora O'Donoghue; M 1941. 1945/T/15 [2 items]. Fianna Fáil T.D. 1948-81. Minister for Education 1957-9, Industry and Commerce 1959-65, Finance 1965-6. Leader of Fianna Fáil 1966-79. Taoiseach 1966-73, 77-79. Died 20 Oct. 1999. Obituary, *The Times*, 21 Oct. 1999; *The Irish Times*, 23 Oct. 1999. See Louis McRedmond (ed.), *Modern Irish Lives*; and biographies by T.P. O'Mahony (Dublin, 1991), T. Ryle Dwyer (Cork, 2001), and Bruce Arnold (Dublin, 2001).

LYNCH, JOSEPH EDWARD (b. 6 July 1916) eld. s. of James Joseph Lynch, solicitor, of Kells, Co. Meath, and Elizabeth Scully; B.A., LL.B. (T.C.D.); E 1937. Awarded John Brook Scholarship. 1939/M/01 [1 item]. Died 10 Feb. 1967. Described in Patrick MacKenzie, *Lawful Occasions*, 111, as 'the most taciturn man at the Bar'. Died Feb. 1967.

LYNCH, KEVIN (b. 15 Dec. 1927) 4th s. of His Hon. Judge Fionán Lynch, of Minore, Orwell Park, Rathgar, Dublin, and Brighid Lynch; B.A. (N.U.I.); M 1946. Awarded John Brooke Scholarship. 1949/M/01 [2 items]. S.C., 5 Oct. 1970. Judge of the High Court,

24 Jan. 1984; of the Supreme Court, 15 April 1996. Retired 14 Dec. 1999. Listed in the 1984 and 1991 editions of Maureen Cairnduff, *Who's Who in Ireland*.

LYNCH, MICHAEL BREEN (b. 27 Sept. 1881) 3rd s. of Michael P. Lynch of 17 Longford Terrace, Monkstown, Dublin, Barrister-at-Law, and Annie Josephine McKone; B.A. (T.C.D.); H 1901. 1904/H/07 [3 items]. Died at Singapore, 14/15 Aug. 1941. Obituary, *I.L.T. & S.J.*, lxxv (1941), 288.

LYNCH, MICHAEL PALLES (b. 3 June 1850) 5th s. of Joseph Lynch J.P. (decd.) of Roebuck, Co. Cavan, and Belinda Jane Breen; B.A. (T.C.D.); M 1870, M.T. M 1871. 1874/H/8 [4 items].

LYNCH, PATRICK GREGORY (b. 10 Feb. 1866) 4th s. of John Lynch (decd.) of Latoon, Co. Clare, and Elizabeth Kelly; B.A. (R.U.I.); M 1885. 1888/T/04 [7 items]. K.C., 30 June 1906. Defeated by de Valera in the East Clare by-election of 1917 occasioned by the death of Willie Redmond. Senator, 1934-36. Appointed by de Valera Attorney-General, 1936-40. Author of *Some members of the Munster Bar* (Cork, 1946). Died 9 Dec. 1947. Obituary, *I.L.T. & S.J.*, lxxxi (1947), 291; *Who's Who*. Mentioned in James Meenan (ed.), *Centenary History of Lit. and Hist. Soc. of U.C.D.*; in Maurice Healy, *The Old Munster Circuit*, 149-51; and by V.T.H. Delany [q.v.], in 'The Bench and Bar in Ireland', xxxiii.

LYNCH, VINCENT JAMES (b. 18 April 1895) 4th s. of Philip Lynch (decd.), of College Road, Cork; M 1946. 1950/T/02 [2 items].

LYNN, ALEXANDER (b. 17 Aug. 1882) 2nd s. of John Lynn, of Belfast, and Sarah Doyle; B.A. (Q.U.B.); M 1918. 1921/M/10 [2 items].

LYSAGHT, CHARLES EDWARD (b. 23 Sept. 1941) eld. s. of Dr. Charles Edward Lysaght, of Merrion, Dublin, and Margaret Durnien; B.A. (Cantab.), M.A. (N.U.I.); M 1959. 1962/M/05 [1 item]. Professor of Company Law at King's Inns, 1970-75; aft. legal adviser, Department of Foreign Affairs; counsellor, Law Reform Commission. Editor of the 4th edition of V.T.H. Delany's *The Administration of Justice in Ireland* (Dublin, 1975). Author *inter alia* of the biography *Brendan Bracken* (London, 1979), and of *Edward MacLysaght, 1887-1986: a Memoir* (Dublin, 1988). *Burke's Irish Family Records* (1976), 742 (and contributor of the article, 'The Irish Peers and the House of Lords – The Final Chapter', to Charles Mosley (ed.), *Burke's Peerage and Baronetage*, 106th Edition (2 vols., 1999), vol. i, xli-xliii).

LYSAGHT, MARGARET ANN (b. 28 April 1946) eld. d. of Owen Joseph Lysaght, business executive, of St. Ronan's, Salthill, Galway, and Patricia Shaffrey; B.C.L. (N.U.I.); M 1964. 1968/T/17 [1 item]. Mrs. George Anthony Brady [q.v.]

LYSAGHT-MacGOWAN, MURIEL (b. 13 Jan. 1912) only d. of John Lysaght-MacGowan, of 8 Martello Terrace, Bray, Co. Wicklow, and Lucinda Hall; M 1928. 1934/T/01 [2 items].

MHAC FHIONNLAOICH, DUBHGLAS COLM (b. 14 May 1907) 5th s. of Peadar T. Mhac Fhionnlaoich, of 108 Drumcondra Road, Dublin, and Eibhlis Woods; M 1926. Awarded Certificate of Honour. 1930/H/05 [2 items].

MAC FIRBHISIGH [Forbes], TADHG (b. 23 Sept. 1905) only s. of Stephen Forbes of 16 Chapel Street, Cork, and Ellen O'Sullivan; M 1927. 1932/M/10 [2 items]. S.C., 3 July 1946. Chairman, Court of Referees (National Health Insurance) 1933-52. Lay Commissioner, Irish Land Commission. Died 6 Sept. 1954. Obituary, *I.L.T. & S.J.*, lxxxviii (1954), 242. Mentioned in James Meenan (ed.), *Centenary History of Lit. and Hist. Soc. of U.C.D.*

MAC GRIANNA, DOMHNALL [Donal Greene] (b. 12 March 1894) eld. s. of Frank Greene, of Annagry, Letterkenny, Co. Donegal, and Rose Duffy; M 1924. 1937/M/12 [2 items].

MACAFEE, WILLIAM (b. 22 Feb. 1875) eld. s. of Thomas Macafee, Assistant Land Commissioner, Currysisken House, Ballymoney, Co. Antrim, and Mary Jane Dunne; undergrad.(T.C.D.); M 1898, G.I. M 1899. 1901/M/01 [3 items]. K.C. (N.I.), E 1922.

McALEER, PETER (b. 2 Feb. 1943) only s. of Charles Vincent McAleer, travel agent, of 2 Campsie Road, Omagh, Co. Tyrone, and Kathleen McCanny; B.Comm. (N.U.I.); M 1965. 1968/T/16 [1 item].

MACALISTER, ROBERT (b. 23 April 1849) 3rd s. of Robert Macalister of 9 Great Charles Street, Dublin, and Margaret Boyle; LL.B. (T.C.D.); E 1876, I.T. E 1878. 1879/E/13 [6 items].

MACAN, ARTHUR VERNON (b. 23 May 1882) eld. s. of Sir Arthur Vernon Macan (decd.) of 53 Merrion Square, Dublin, and Mary Agnes Wauklyn; cand. bachelor (T.C.D.); M 1905. 1908/M/08 [2 items].

McARDLE, EAMON (b. 23 Aug. 1920) eld. s. of Thomas McArdle (decd.), of Dublin Road, Skerries, Co. Dublin, and Hannah W. McGrath; B.A. (N.U.I.); M 1941. 1944/M/06 [2 items]. Registrar.

McARDLE, JOSEPH ARDLE FRANCIS (b. 29 Sept. 1934) 2nd s. of John James McArdle, surgeon, of Hillsboro House, Monaghan, and Margaret Breen; B.A. (N.U.I.); M 1952. 1956/M/09 [2 items]. English Bar, M.T., 1966. Legal consultant in various overseas countries, including Russia. Contributor to Frank Callanan, *The Literary and Historical Society 1955-2005* (Dublin, 2005), 41-2. Author of the novels *Closing Time* (Dublin, 1982) and *Sin Embargo* (Dublin, 1987).

MACARTNEY-FILGATE, EDWARD (b. 17 March 1865) 2nd s. of Townley Macartney-Filgate, Registrar General, Bombay Residency, of Lowtherstone, Balbriggan, Co. Dublin, and Tryphena Seymour Fitzgerald; M 1885. 1890/T/12 [6 items]. Colonel of the 12th Battalion, Lancashire Fusiliers, 1915. Died at Gibraltar, 10 June 1927. *Burke's Irish Family Records* (1976), 413.

MACAULAY, ANDREW ALFRED (b. 8 June 1872) 2nd s. of Peter Macaulay, of Rupert Lodge, Belfast, and Lucy Garland; M 1922. 1923/M/12 [2 items]. Died 1926. Obituary, *I.L.T. & S.J.*, lx (11 Sept. 1926), 228-9.

MACAULAY, ARTHUR HAROLD (b. 13 Dec. 1883) 6th s. of Peter Macaulay, LL.D., solicitor, of Rupert Lodge, Malone Road, Belfast, and Lucy Garland; H 1907. 1909/M/07 [2 items].

MACAULAY, RODERICK MUREDACH (b. 18 Nov. 1904) 5th s. of Roderick Macaulay (decd.), of Ballina, Co. Mayo, and Louisa Treston; M 1926. 1929/M/18 [2 items].

McAULEY, DENIS ROBERT (b. 21 June 1923) only s. of Thomas A. McAuley, of 31 Newbridge Avenue, Sandymount, Dublin, and Eva M. O'Neill; M 1944. 1948/T/07 [2 items].

McAULEY, JOSEPH (b. 20 July 1865) 6th s. of Bernard McAuley, decd., late of Randalstown, Co. Antrim, and Jane Smith; B.A. (R.U.I.); M 1886. 1889/T/04 [6 items].

MACAULEY, MAURICE SCOTT (b. 10 May 1891) 2nd s. of Thomas Henry Macauley (decd.), manufacturer, of 21 Camden Street, Belfast, and Jessie Scott; M 1922. 1925/T/02 [3 items]. Also called to N.I. Bar, T 1925. Assistant to Parliamentary Counsel, N.I.

McAULIFFE, MICHAEL JOSEPH (b. 27 Sept. 1870) 2nd s. of Simon McAuliffe of Knock, Co. Clare, and Anne O'Brien; cand. bachelor (T.C.D.); H 1890. 1894/T/02 [7 items].

MACBETH, JAMES DAXELHOFFER (b. 22 Feb. 1831) eld. s. of John Macbeth of Green Lawn, Ennis, Co. Clare, and Elise Daxelhoffer; M.A. (T.C.D.); E 1864, M.T. E 1873. 1876/E/01 [8 items].

MACBRIDE, SEÁN (b. 26 Jan. 1904) only s. of John MacBride (decd.), of Westport, Co. Mayo, and Maud Gonne; M 1932. 1937/M/08 [2 items]. A prominent Irish Republican in the 1920s and '30s, at one time chief of staff of the I.R.A. S.C., 11 Oct. 1943. T.D. (Clann na Poblachta), 1948-57. Minister for External Affairs, 1948-51. Afterwards active in international organisations. Recipient of the Nobel Peace prize in 1974, and of the Lenin peace prize in 1977. Practised in the Law Library (of which he became an honorary member) into old age. Died 15 Jan. 1988. Obituary, *The Times*, 16 Jan. 1988. Appreciation (by Hugh O'Flaherty) in the *Irish Law Times*, new series, vi (1988), 42-3. Listed in the 1984 edition of Maureen Cairnduff, *Who's Who in Ireland*. See also: A. J. Jordan, *Seán MacBride: a biography* (Dublin, 1993); Louis McRedmond (ed.), *Modern Irish Lives*; *Oxford DNB* (2004) [article by Carla King].

MACCABE, NIALL FRANCIS (b. 2 Dec. 1923) 2nd s. of Francis MacCabe, District Justice, of Park House, Waterford, and Ilene Mooney; B.A. (N.U.I.); M 1942. 1945/M/03 [2 items].

McCAMMON, THOMAS ANDREW (b. 3 Sept 1849) only s. of Thomas McCammon (decd.), of Tudor Lodge, Holywood, Co. Down, and Susanna K. Davis; AB (T.C.D.); M 1869; I.T. H 1872. 1873/T/7 [2 items].

McCANCE, JOHN STOUPPE FINLAY (b. 12 Feb. 1865) only s. of Finlay McCance, J.P., of Suffolk, Co. Antrim, and Annie L. Macaulay; B.A. (Oxon); E 1886. 1889/E/02 [11 items].

McCANN, DERMOT PAUL (b. 29 June 1912) young. s. of Thomas S. McCann, K.C., of Frankfield, Foxrock, Co. Dublin, and Alice Murphy; M 1931. 1934/M/04 [2 items].

McCANN, HUGH JOSEPH LAWRENCE (b. 27 March 1876) eld. s. of John McCann of 15 Nottingham Street, Dublin, and Emma Dowling; M 1904. 1904/M/06 [3 items]. District Justice.

McCANN, THOMAS S. (b. 5 Feb. 1868) only s. of Thomas S. McCann of 84 Harcourt Street, Dublin, and [Dorinda] Harrington; B.A. (T.C.D.); M 1889, I.T. M 1890. 1892/T/02 [8 items]. North-East Circuit. K.C., 24 June 1908. Died 1 Feb. 1942. Obituary, *I.L.T. & S.J.*, lxxvi (1942), 43. Mentioned by V.T.H. Delany [q.v.], in his article 'The Bench and Bar in Ireland', as one of 'those who were at the forefront of their profession during the period'.

McCANN, THOMAS STANISLAUS (b. 13 May 1940) only s. of John Baldwin McCann, solicitor, of Wakefield House, York Road, Dún Laoghaire, Co. Dublin, and Maura O'Dwyer; M 1958. Awarded Brooke Scholarship. 1962/M/01 [2 items]. S.C., 2 Oct. 1978. Bencher.

McCARRON, EDWARD PATRICK (b. 1 March 1881) 3rd s. of Edward McCarron (decd.), of Carrowblagh, Co. Donegal, and Catherine McGowan; M 1911. Local Govt. auditor. File includes certificate from Cork Street Fever Hospital. 1914/T/15 [4 items]. Secretary of the Department of Local Government, 1922-36. Obituary (by Frank Duff) in *The Irish Times*.

McCARTHY, Captain ANDREW J. (b. 25 Nov. 1894) 1st s. of Cornelius McCarthy, of Killarney, Co. Kerry, and Julia Dinneen (decd.); M.B.E; M 1923. 1924/T/06 [2 items].

McCARTHY, CHARLES (b. 25 Jan. 1924) eld. s. of John George McCarthy (decd.), merchant, of Bellevue Park, Passage West, Co. Cork, and Agnes O'Donoghue; M 1948. 1956/M/15 [2 items]. Professor of Industrial Relations at T.C.D., 1979. Died 8 Sept. 1986. Obituary, *Trinity Trust News*, vol. 11, no. 1 (November 1986), 6-7. Listed in the 1984 edition of Maureen Cairnduff, *Who's Who in Ireland*. See also: Louis McRedmond (ed.), *Modern Irish Lives*.

MacCARTHY, CORNELIUS ALOYSIUS (b. 15 June 1889) only s. of Patrick Joseph MacCarthy of Kilbrogan House, Bandon, Co. Cork, and Charlotte Moynihan; M 1910. 1913/T/15 [2 items]. 2nd Lieutenant, Royal Dublin Fusiliers. Drowned at sea, 19 July 1917. Obituary, *I.L.T. & S.J.*, li (11 Aug. 1917), 193. [Name on the Bar War Memorial; also on the Memorial at Basra].

MacCARTHY, DERMOT (b. 6 Nov. 1940) eld. s. of Joseph Alphonsus MacCarthy, medical practitioner, of Valetta, Kildare, Co. Kildare, and Mary Jean Nyhan; B.A. (N.U.I.); M 1958. 1964/H/03 [4 items]. S.C., 16 March 1984. Vice-Chairman, Employment Appeals Tribunal.

McCARTHY, DERMOT JOSEPH THADDEUS (b. 29 March 1918) 2nd s. of Judge Joseph A. McCarthy, of 6 Trafalgar Terrace, Monkstown, Co. Dublin, and Rose A. O'Neill; M 1941. 1946/T/09 [2 items]. Chief Magistrate, Northern Region, Nigeria.

McCARTHY, DONAL TIMOTHY (b. 11 April 1946) 2nd s. of Donald Thaddeus McCarthy, solicitor, of 3 Clarence Terrace, St. Luke's, Cork, and Mary Sybil Moxly Wright; B.C.L. (N.U.I.); M 1964. Awarded 1st Victoria Prize. 1968/M/02 [1 item].

McCARTHY, GERALD FLORENCE (b. 28 July 1886) 2nd surv. s. of Jeremiah McCarthy, solicitor, of Baymount, Sligo, Co. Sligo, and Mary Louisa Rice; B.A. (T.C.D.); M 1907. 1910/H/01 [3 items]. Died 9 Jan. 1961.

MacCARTHY, GERARD BRIAN (b. 14 Sept. 1923) 3rd s. of Michael Joseph McCarthy, physician, of 'Teavenagrena', Alma Road, Monkstown, Co. Dublin, and Carmen Kennedy; M 1951. 1954/M/12 [2 items].

McCARTHY, HENRY AUGUSTINE (b. 16 May 1895) 3rd s. of Charles McCarthy of Emmet Place, Cork, and Annie Roche; M 1913. 1916/T/09 [2 items]. District Justice.

McCARTHY, JEREMIAH CHRISTOPHER (b. 4 Jan. 1935) 2nd s. of Jeremiah McCarthy (decd.), retired headmaster, of 17 Glenarm Avenue, Drumcondra, Dublin, and Mary Sheehy; M 1954. Awarded 3rd Victoria Prize. 1958/T/02 [2 items].

McCARTHY, JEREMIAH GERALD (b. 29 Dec. 1912) only s. of John McCarthy, railway officer (retd.), of 39 North Street, Skibbereen, Co. Cork, and Mary Ellen Cotter; M 1946. 1950/T/10 [2 items].

McCARTHY, JOHN EUGENE (b. 3 Jan. 1916) eld. s. of Thomas J. McCarthy, of The Square, Charlestown, Co. Mayo, and Kitty Gallagher; M 1939. 1943/T/06 [2 items]. District Justice.

MacCARTHY, JOHN HENRY (b. 29 Jan. 1868) 2nd s. of John George MacCarthy of 19 Aylesbury Road, Dublin, and Maria J. Hanrahan; M 1887. 1890/T/08 [7 items]. Land Commission. Died 15 May 1944. Obituary, *I.L.T. & S.J.*, lxxviii (1944), 136.

McCARTHY, JOSEPH ANDREW (b. 25 Nov. 1884) young. s. of Patrick McCarthy (decd.), of Timoleague, Co. Cork, and Johanna Dempsey (decd.); M 1914. File includes undertaking not to practise as engineer, surveyor or architect. 1917/T/30 [2 items]. S.C., 24 April 1933. Judge of the Circuit Court.

McCARTHY, MICHAEL JOHN (b. 24 July 1862) eld. s. of Denis McCarthy, merchant, of Midleton, Co. Cork, and Catherine Fitzgerald; B.A. (T.C.D.); M 1886. 1889/M/07 [7 items].

McCARTHY, NIALL St JOHN (b. 25 May 1925) 4th s. of Judge Joseph A. McCarthy, of 6 Trafalgar Terrace, Monkstown, Dublin, and Rose A. O'Neill; B.A. (U.C.D.); M 1943. 1946/T/03 [2 items]. S.C., 7 Dec. 1959. Judge of the Supreme Court, 1 Nov. 1982. Died at Seville, 1 Oct. 1992. Obituary, *The Times*, 12 Oct. 1992. Appreciations [by T.A. Finlay and P.S.] in the *Irish Law Times*, new series, x (1992), 263-4. Bronze bust in the Reading Room of the National Archives, Dublin, and at King's Inns. Listed in the 1984 and 1991 editions of Maureen Cairnduff, *Who's Who in Ireland*. See also: Louis McRedmond (ed.), *Modern Irish Lives*. For a King's Inns bursary established in his memory, see *The Irish Times*, 1 Oct. 2002.

McCARTHY, NODLAIG MARY PATRICIA (b. 9 Dec. 1939) only d. of Dr Denis McCarthy (decd.), of St. Kevin's Hospital, James Street, Dublin, and Johanna Mary Josephine Leahy; M 1959. 1965/M/05 [1 item]. Barrister in London.

McCARTHY, THOMAS PAUL (b. 23 June 1888) 3rd surv. s. of Jeremiah McCarthy, solicitor (decd.), of Union Place, Sligo, and Mary Louisa Rice; T 1922. 1922/T/02 [2 items]. S.C., 12 April 1935. Died 1961. Obituary, *I.L.T. & S.J.*, xcv (17 June 1961), 146.

McCARTHY, TIMOTHY JOSEPH (b. 17 April 1929) eld. s. of Gerald McCarthy (decd.), merchant, of James Street, Dublin, and Bridget Donegan; B.E., A.M.I.C.E.I; M 1953. 1958/H/01 [3 items].

MacCARTHY-MORROGH, FRANCIS DENIS M.A.J. (b. 7 Jan. 1902) 2nd s. of Denis James MacCarthy-Morrogh, of Shanakiel, Co. Cork, and Mary Murphy; B.A., LL.B. (T.C.D.); M 1926. G.I. E 1923. Barrister-at-Law, English Bar, April 1926. 1927/M/09 [2 items]. Member of Cork County Council, 1934-42; a forlorn Fine Gael candidate in Cork Borough in the 1943 general election. Described himself in Thom's biographical entry as 'Father of the West Cork Bar, 1944'.

MacCARTIE, GERALD FALKINER (b. 8 Nov 1848) eld. s. of Justin MacCartie J.P., Barrister-at-Law, of Carrignavar, Co. Cork, and Louisa Fitzgerald; B.A. (T.C.D.); M 1869, M.T. H 1872. 1873/T/6 [2 items].

McCAULEY, LEO THOMAS (b. 29 Dec. 1895) 3rd s. of William Joseph McCauley, of 150 Lakedale Road, Woolwich, London, and Agnes Heaney; M.A. (N.U.I.); M 1918. 1921/T/01 [2 items]. Entered Department of Finance, 1922-9; then changed to Irish Free State Diplomatic Service, serving in Berlin, 1929-33. He was acting Minister in Berlin, 1932-3, filling the gap between D.A. Binchy and Charles Bewley [qq.v; and see Mervyn O'Driscoll, *Ireland, Germany and the Nazis: Politics and Diplomacy, 1919-39* (Dublin: 2004)]; subsequently Consul General in New York (1934-46), Assistant-Secretary in Dublin (1946-9), and Ambassador to Spain (1949-55), Canada (1955-6) and the Vatican (1956-62). Died 1974. See *Thom's Directory* (Biographies); Ronan Keating, Michael Kennedy, Dermot Keogh and Eunan O'Halpin (eds.), *Documents on*

Irish Foreign Policy. Volume III. 1926-1932 [&c.] (Dublin. 2002-). Mentioned in James Meenan (ed.), *Centenary History of Lit. and Hist. Soc. of U.C.D.*

McCAY, JOHN HEDLEY DOUGLAS (b. 22 Oct. 1924) only s. of William Joseph Kilpatrick McCay, of Buttevant, Co. Cork, and Margaret McHugh; B.A. (Q.U.B.); M 1947. 1950/T/03 [2 items]. District Justice. Author of *Patrick Pearse: a new biography* (Cork, 1966).

McCOMAS, RICHARD HENRY ARCHIBALD (b. 23 Sept. 1847) 3rd s. of Archibald McComas, of Cliff Castle, Dalkey, Co. Dublin, and Jane Jones; E 1871, M.T. M 1872. 1875/H/06 [2 items].

McCONNELL, JAMES ADAMS (b. 20 Sept. 1877) eld. s. of Andrew McConnell of 12 College Square North, Belfast, and Margaret Adams; B.A. (T.C.D.); T 1902. 1906/M/03 [3 items]. Died 10 May 1947. Obituary, *I.L.T. & S.J.*, lxxxi (1947), 118.

McCONNELL, JAMES (b. 25 Feb. 1880) 3rd s. of James McConnell of Stranmillis House, Belfast, and Ellen Frances Crawford; B.A., LL.B. (R.U.I.); M 1899. 1902/M/11 [5 items].

McCORKELL, DAVID BROWNE (b. 20 Oct 1845) eld. s. of Bartholomew McCorkell of Londonderry, Co. Londonderry, merchant, and Elizabeth Browne; B.A. (T.C.D.); T 1864, MT E 1866. 1869/H/2 [4 items].

MacCORMACK, FRANCIS JOSEPH (b. 25 Nov. 1883) eld. s. of Charles Joseph MacCormack of Fry Place, Athlone, Co. Westmeath, and Mary Duff; B.A. (R.U.I.); M 1905. 1908/H/01 [3 items]. Went Connaught Circuit; practised later in Egypt. Died 1921. James Meenan (ed.), *Centenary History of Lit. and Hist. Soc. of U.C.D.*

McCORMACK, Captain LIAM CAOIMGEIN (b. 23 Feb. 1922) 5th s. of William John McCormack, of Wicklow, Co. Wicklow, and Germaine Plunkett; M 1950. 1954/T/01 [2 items].

McCORMICK, HILGROVE (b. 5 Sept. 1888) 3rd s. of Samuel Smith McCormick of Shandon, Monkstown, Dublin and Emily Gardiner; B.A. (T.C.D.); M 1909. 1913/T/05 [2 items]. Major. MC. Died 19 Jan. 1952. Obituary, *I.L.T. & S.J.*, lxxxvi (1952), 44. '

McCORRY, PATRICK LEO (n.d.) young. s. of Francis McCorry of 8 [Ardmoulin] Street, Belfast, and Letitia Liddy; M 1906. 1912/H/02 [4 items].

McCOTTER, FRANK (b. 9 Nov. 1859) eld. s. of Samson McCotter of Dunmanway, Co. Cork, and Eleanor Mary Cosgrave; B.A. (R.U.I.); M 1885. 1891/M/07 [6 items].

McCOURT, JOHN DECLAN KEVIN (b. 15 April 1946) only s. of Kevin Colum McCourt, business executive, of Simmonscourt Castle, Ballsbridge, Dublin, and Margaret McMahon; B.A. (N.U.I.); M 1965. 1968/T/13 [1 item]. Prominent businessman.

McCOY, Major RICHARD PATRICK JOSEPH (b. 16 March 1890) 2nd s. of Richard Francis McCoy, of 'Clare House', Kilcolman, Ardagh, Co. Limerick, and Marion Teresa Reynolds; M 1919; [late Royal Air Force] 1921/M/19 [2 items].

McCOY, WILLIAM FREDERICK (b. 19 Jan. 1885) 2nd s. of William McCoy, of Knockballymore, Clones, Co. Fermanagh, and Charlotte L. Murphy; T 1920. 1920/M/08 [2 items]. K.C. (N.I.), T. 1939. Unionist M.P. for Tyrone South (N.I. Parl.), April 1945-1965.

McCRACKEN, BRIAN MOORE (b. 13 July 1934) only s. of Thomas McCracken, medical doctor, of 'Albany', Albany Avenue, Monkstown, Co. Dublin, and Anne Frances Moore; B.A. (T.C.D.); M 1954. 1957/M/06 [2 items]. S.C., 27 Feb. 1975. Judge of the High Court, 27 Jan. 1995; of the Supreme Court, 4 Nov. 2002. Listed in the 1999 edition of Maureen Cairnduff, *Who's Who in Ireland.*

McCRACKEN, WILLIAM JOHN (b. 24 March 1868) eld. s. of the Revd. William John McCracken of Ballycastle, Co. Antrim, and Rachel A. Harris; B.A. (R.U.I.-Q.C.B.); M 1892. 1895/M/11 [8 items].

McCREERY, HENLEY EDWIN LEWIS (b. 26 July 1920) 3rd s. of the Revd. William John McCreery, B.D. (decd.), of 21 Sandymount Avenue, Ballsbridge, Dublin, and Anne Cullen Williams; M 1939. 1943/H/01 [7 items]. M.T., 1946 (Bencher, 1971). Recorder of Salisbury, 1969-71. Died 19 Jan. 1998. *Who's Who.*

MacCROSSAN, HENRY (b. 20 Oct. 1851) eld. s. of John MacCrossan (decd.), solicitor, of Omagh, Co. Tyrone, and Margaret Moss; [B.A.?] T.C.D.; M 1868, M.T. E 1870. 1875/E/01 [2 items].

McCULLAGH, JAMES GORDON (b. 9 Jan. 1850) 3rd surv. s. of James McCullagh (decd.), merchant, of Greenfield, Co. Dublin, and Helena Gordon; M 1870, M.T. T 1871. 1875/H/04 [2 items].

McCULLOUGH, WILLIAM HILL (b. 13 Aug. 1882) eld. s. of William McCullough (decd.), of Omagh, Co. Tyrone, and Mary Stuart Powell; M 1918. Struck off roll of solicitors at own request. 1918/M/06 [3 items].

McCUMISKEY, EDWARD FRANCIS JAMES (b. 8 Oct. 1941) only s. of James G. McCumiskey (decd.), of 13 Charleville Avenue, North Strand, Dublin, and Emily Ada Bingham; M 1960. 1964/T/03 [1 item].

McCUTCHEON, ROBERT ROSS (b. 31 Oct. 1871) 3rd s. of Gilbert McCutcheon of Ballymena, Co. Antrim, and Annie Crawford; B.A. (R.U.I.); M 1893. 1897/M/01 [4 items].

MacDERMOT, BERNARD T.J. (b. 15 Oct. 1876) 6th s. of the Rt. Hon. The MacDermot, Q.C., of 10 Fitzwilliam Place, Dublin, and Henrietta Blake; M 1896. 1900/H/05 [3 items]. Died unmarried in South Africa, 20 Sept. 1902. *Burke's Irish Family Records* (1976), 757.

MacDERMOT, CHARLES EDWARD (b. 28 Dec. 1862) eld. s. of The MacDermot, Q.C., D.L, of 10 Fitzwilliam Place, Dublin, and Mary Howley; B.A. (T.C.D.); H 1884, G.I. M 1886. 1887/M/05 [7 items]. Chairman of the Irish Prisons Board. Died 8 May 1947. Obituary, *I.L.T. & S.J.*, lxxxi (1947), 119. *Burke's Irish Family Records* (1976), 756.

MacDERMOT, EDWARD WILFRID (b. 9 Oct. 1876) eld. s. of Edward Joseph MacDermot, Resident Magistrate (retired), of 7 St. James' Terrace, Clonskeagh, Dublin, and Frances MacDermot; M 1908. 1911/T/06 [2 items].

MACDERMOT, HENRY (b. 16 Jan. 1874) 4th s. of the Rt. Hon. The Macdermot (decd.), P.C. of Coolavin, Co. Sligo, and Henrietta Blake; T 1904. 1904/M/03 [2 items]. Connaught Circuit. K.C., 27 Feb. 1918.

MacDERMOTT, JOHN CLARKE (b. 12 April 1896) 3rd s. of the Revd. J. MacDermott, M.A., DD, of Belmont Manse, Strandtown, Belfast, and Lydia A. Wilson; LL.B. (Q.U.B.); M 1919; [late Lieut. in Machine Gun Corps; awarded M.C.] 1921/M/02 [2 items]. K.C. (N.I.), E 1936. Honorary Bencher of King's Inns. Unionist M.P. for Queen's University in N.I. Parliament, 1938-44. Attorney-General (N.I.), 1941-4; Judge of the King's Bench Division in N.I., 2 Nov. 1944 - 23 April 1947; Lord of Appeal in Ordinary, 23 April 1947 - 1951; Lord Chief Justice of Northern Ireland, 6 April 1951 - 31 July 1971. Died 13 July 1979. Author of *Protection from power under English law* (1957) and *An Enriching Life* (Belfast: privately printed, 1980). See *D.N.B. 1971-80* (entry by Lord Lowry); Lord Lowry, 'The Irish lords of appeal in ordinary' [with which a photograph of Lord Mac Dermott is reproduced] in D.S. Greer and N.M. Dawson (eds.), *Mysteries and Solutions in Irish Legal History* (Dublin, 2001), 193-216; *Who's Who*; Louis McRedmond (ed.), *Modern Irish Lives;* and Kate Newmann, *Dictionary of Ulster Biography* (Belfast, 1993).

McDERMOTT, LAURENCE SYLVESTER (b. 26 Sept. 1904) 5th s. of Michael McDermott (decd.), of Manorhamilton, Co. Leitrim, and Ellen Rooney; M 1933. 1937/M/10 [2 items]. Called to English Bar, M 1945.

MacDEVITT, EDWARD O'DONNELL (b. 11 April 1841) 6th s. of Daniel MacDevitt of Glenties, Co. Donegal, and Mary O'Donnell; M 1875. 1875/M/04 [1 item].

McDEVITT, HENRY ALOYSIUS (b. 9 Jan. 1904) 3rd s. of Henry McDevitt, of Cloughfin, Castlefin, Co. Donegal, and Margaret Quinn; M 1933. 1937/M/02 [2 items]. Fianna Fáil T.D. for East Donegal, 1938-43. Secretary of the County Councils General Council. See *Thom's Directory* (Biographies).

MacDOMHNAILL, SÉAMUS CAOIMHGHIN (b. 24 June 1917) only s. of Patrick McDonnell, farmer, of Cappagh, Finglas, Co. Dublin, and Mary Kenny; M 1959. Awarded 2nd Victoria Prize. 1959/T/01 [2 items].

MacDONAGH, DONAGH (b. 22 Nov. 1912) only s. of Thomas MacDonagh (decd.), of Dublin, and Muriel Gifford; B.A. (U.C.D.); M 1933. 1936/M/08 [3 items]. Son of the executed 1916 leader and poet, Thomas MacDonagh; and nephew of the cartoonist, Grace Plunkett. Himself a poet, playwright (author of 'Happy as Larry' and other successful plays), and broadcaster, he practised at the Bar 1935-41. Aft. served as a

District Justice (Dublin Metropolitan District) until his death. Died 1 Jan. 1968. Obituary, *I.L.T. & S.J.*, cii (1968), 38. See Louis McRedmond (ed.), *Modern Irish Lives*.

MacDONAGH, DONAGH MARY (b. 17 Aug. 1931) young. s. of Michael Aloysius MacDonagh, of National Bank House, Waterford, and Loretto Oliver; M 1951. 1955/M/06 [1 item].

MacDONAGH, NIALL JOSEPH (b. 4 Aug. 1944) 2nd s. of Donagh MacDonagh (decd.), District Justice, of 141 Strand Road, Dublin 4, and Nuala Catherine Smyth; M 1962. 1968/M/16 [1 item].

MacDONAGH, OLIVER ORMOND GERARD MICHAEL (b. 23 Aug 1924) eld. s. of Michael Aloysius MacDonagh, of National Bank House, Waterford, and Loretto Oliver; M 1942. 1946/M/02 [2 items]. Contributor to James Meenan (ed.), *Centenary History of Lit. and Hist. Soc. of U.C.D.* U.C.D.-educated historian, who later taught at Cambridge and in Australia. Author of works on Daniel O'Connell, and on the history of emigration to Australia. Died in Sydney, 22 May 2002. Obituary, *The Times*, 27 June 2002.

McDONALD, ALLAN (b. 21 Aug. 1857) eld. s. of Alexander McDonald, J.P., of Glenarm, Co. Antrim, and Elizabeth Fawkner; B.A., LL.B. (T.C.D.); H 1886. 1889/M/04 [7 items].

McDONALD, BRIAN PAUL (b. 23 Sept. 1945) only s. of Denis R. McDonald, Irish Ambassador to Italy, of Irish Embassy, 3 Via Valledelle, Camene, Rome, and Una Frances Sheehan; B.C.L. (N.U.I.); M 1964. 1968/T/08 [1 item]. European civil servant.

MACDONALD, NOEL KENNAN (b. 8 Jan. 1909) eld. s. of Arthur K. Macdonald, M.A., L.D.S., RCSI, of 20 Merrion Square, Dublin, and Eithne Healy; B.A. (Oxon); M 1930, I.T. M 1928. 1933/M/02 [2 items]. S.C., 1 Nov. 1963. Died 1988. Mentioned in Patrick MacKenzie, *Lawful Occasions*, 50-52.

MacDONNELL, ANTONIA ELIZABETH (b. 12 June 1899) 2nd d. of Matthew MacDonnell (decd.), of Cross Street, Kells, Co. Meath, and Anna Maria Farrelly; H 1923. 1925/M/20 [2 items].

MacDONNELL, CHARLES RANDAL ARMSTRONG (b. 24 March 1862) eld. s. of William Edward Armstrong MacDonnell (decd.), J.P., Colonel, of New Hall, Co. Clare, and the Hon. Juliana O'Brien; H 1893. 1895/M/16 [7 items].

McDONNELL, FRANCIS JAMES (b. 1 Nov. 1893) 2nd s. of Farrell McDonnell, of Dunmore, Co. Galway, and Ina McDonogh; M 1914. 1917/M/09 [2 items]. Died 20 June 1948.

McDONNELL, FRANCIS PATRICK (b. 13 March 1914) 3rd s. of Supt. Thomas J. McDonnell (decd.), of Vartry Lodge, Roundwood, Co. Wicklow, and Cecilia Maloney; B.A. (N.U.I.); M 1938. 1941/M/10 [2 items].

McDONNELL, GEORGE PATRICK (b. 27 Oct. 1930) eld. s. of George Patrick McDonnell (decd.), BE (Civil), of Mullinahone, Co. Tipperary, and Mrs. McNamara; M 1954. 1958/M/10 [2 items].

McDONNELL, PATRICK JOSEPH (b. 15 March 1914) eld. s. of John McDonnell, of 113 Vernon Avenue, Clontarf, Dublin, and Delia Naughten; B.A. (N.U.I.); H 1934. 1937/M/11 [3 items].

McDONNELL, WILLIAM DOBBS (b. 23 May 1845) 5th s. of John McDonnell of 32 Upper Fitzwilliam Street, Dublin, and Charity Dobbs; B.A. (T.C.D.); H 1868; M.T. H 1869. 1873/H/4 [2 items].

McDONNELL, WILLIAM PATRICK (b. 28 April 1899) 2nd s. of Richard McDonnell (decd.), of 107 Lower Dorset Street, Dublin, and Bridget Ryan; M 1926. 1936/T/11 [2 items]. Senior Parliamentary Draftsman, Dublin.

McDOWELL, ANTONY GERARD (b. 1 Oct. 1912) 4th s. of John Moran McDowell (decd.), of 61 Northumberland Road, Dublin, and Maude Lynne; M 1930. 1935/M/07 [2 items]. S.C., 1 March 1977. Special Commissioner for Income Tax. Father of Michael McDowell, S.C., Minister for Justice. Died *c*. 1977/8.

McDOWELL, ROBERT (b. 28 Oct. 1852) eld. s. of George McDowell (decd.), F.T.C.D., of Herbert Street, Dublin, and Rebecca Browning; B.A. (T.C.D.); E 1880, I.T. H 1882. [Officer of High Court of Justice] 1883/T/05 [5 items].

McDUNPHY, MICHAEL (b. 3 Dec. 1890) 2nd s. of Michael P. McDunphy, of 53 Bolton Street, Dublin, and Kathleen Conlon; M 1925. 1928/E/03 [2 items]. Assistant-Secretary to the Government of the Irish Free State; later Secretary to the President (1937-54). Director of the Bureau of Military History, 1947-57. Author of *The President of Ireland. His Powers, Functions and Duties* (Dublin, 1945). See *Thom's Directory* (Biographies).

McELLIGOTT, EDWARD JOHN (b. 17 June 1874) 6th s. of Gerald McElligott, J.P., of Mount Rivers, Listowel, Co. Kerry, and Elizabeth Molony; E 1893. 1896/T/03 [4 items]. K.C., 28 Oct. 1911. Member of the committee which produced Henry Hanna's book, *The Pals at Suvla Bay* (1917) (see p. 152). One of the eight original judges of the Circuit Court, 1924, appointed to the South-Western Circuit. Died 15 Aug. 1946. Obituary, *I.L.T. & S.J.*, lxxx (1946), 211. Mentioned in Maurice Healy, *The Old Munster Circuit*, 106-7, 111-3; and in Gerard A. Lee, *A Memoir of the South-Western Circuit* (Dublin, 1990), 9.

McELROY, GEORGE (b. 21 April 1870) 3rd s. of George McElory, C.E., of Eskermore, Co. Tyrone, and Eliza Smythe; E 1917. 1917/M/02 [2 items]. Retired Resident Magistrate. Died 9 Feb. 1942. Obituary, *I.L.T. & S.J.*, lxxvi (1942), 55.

McELROY, PATRICK JOSEPH (b. 15 April 1861) only s. of James McElroy, merchant, of Glasgow, Scotland, and Rose Doyle; M 1878, M.T. M 1880. 1882/E/01 [7 items].

McELWAINE, PERCY ALEXANDER (b. 21 Sept. 1884) eld. s. of Adam John McElwaine, M.A., of Portarlington, Queen's Co., and Edith Mary Leech; B.A., LL.B. (T.C.D.); M 1905. 1908/T/04 [3 items]. Member of the Alberta Bar, 1913. K.C. (N.I.), H. 1929. Served in the 1st World War as Lieutenant in the Royal Irish Rifles. Magistrate, St. Lucia, 1920; Crown Counsel, Kenya, 1923; Attorney-General, Fiji, 1927; Attorney-General of the Straits Settlement, 1933, and Chief Justice, 1936-46 (interned by the Japanese, Feb. 1942-Aug. 1945). Commissioner, Income Tax Department, Sierra Leone, 1948. Knighted 1939. Died 24 Oct. 1969. Author of a revised edition of the laws of the Straits Settlement (1936); ibid., of the Gold Coast (1954). Retired to Teignmouth, Devon. Obituary, *I.L.T. & S.J.*, civ (1970), 235; *Who's Who*.

McENERY, PATRICK JOSEPH (b. 17 July 1904) 7th s. of John McEnery, of Ballyhale, Knocktopher, Co. Kilkenny, and Kate McCarthy; M 1922. 1925/M/13 [2 items]. Victim of an assault: see *I.L.T. & S.J.*, lxviii (1934), 341. S.C., 12 Jan. 1940. Temporary Judge of the Circuit Court. A colourful personality, mentioned (as Paddy McHenry) in Patrick MacKenzie, *Lawful Occasions*, 48. Called to the English Bar, E 1940, and practised in Liverpool. Died 1970s.

MacENROE, JOHN PATRICK (b. 2 October 1909) eld. s. of Philip MacEnroe, of 'Woodworth', Virginia, Co. Cavan, and Julia M. Finnegan; B.A., H.D.E. (N.U.I.); M 1938. 1941/T/01 [3 items].

MacENTEE, PATRICK (b. 5 Nov. 1936) eld. s. of Patrick James MacEntee, dental surgeon, of Drummully in the Barony of Truagh, Co. Monaghan, and Mary Leanor Harker; B.C.L.; M 1955. 1960/T/04 [2 items]. S.C., 6 Oct. 1975. Q.C. (N.I.). Sometime Chairman of the Bar Council. Bencher. Profile in *The Irish Times*, 30 April 2005.

MacENTEE (Mhac an tSaoi), MÁIRE CAITRÍONA (b. 4 April 1922) eld. d. of Seán MacEntee, of 9 Leeson Park, Dublin, and Margaret Browne; B.A. (N.U.I.); M 1941. 1944/T/08 [2 items]. Gaelic poetess, and wife of Conor Cruise O'Brien. Author of a memoir, *The same age as the State* (Dublin, 2003), which, at 159-160, recalls the 'numbing boredom' of King's Inns lectures, the want of lavatory facilities for women students, and the 'bare-bottomed children' who played in the mud of Henrietta Street. See Louis McRedmond (ed.), *Modern Irish Lives*.

McENTIRE, ALEXANDER KNOX (b. 8 June 1849) only surv. s. of James McEntire of Eary House, Co. Tyrone, and Elizabeth McEntire; M 1890. 1893/T/07 [10 items]. Official Assignee, Court of Bankruptcy.

MAC EOIN, GEARÓID (b. 12 June 1909). See: JOHNSON, GARRET ANTHONY.

MacERLEAN, BRIAN P. (b. 7 Feb. 1876) 4th s. of Andrew MacErlean (decd.) of Antrim Road, Belfast, and Elizabeth Campbell; T 1910. 1910/M/08 [2 items].

MacERLEAN, DONOGH ALOYSIUS (b. 30 Aug. 1882) 6th s. of Andrew MacErlean, solicitor, of 58 Donegall Street, Belfast, and Elizabeth Campbell; M 1900. 1903/M/07 [3 items].

McFEELY, WILLIAM NORMAN CRAIG (b. 6 July 1896) 5th s. of Joseph Daniel McFeely, of Holly House, Woolton, Lancashire, and Sarah Craig; B.A. (T.C.D.); M 1920. 1922/M/08 [2 items].

McGAHON, HUGH BRADBURY (b. 10 May 1942) 4th s. of Dr. N.J. McGahon, of 15 Francis Street, Dundalk, Co. Louth, and Anne Agnes Cawley; B.C.L. (N.U.I.); M 1959. 1968/M/26 [1 item]. S.C., 1 Oct. 1984.

McGILLIGAN, DENIS BRIAN (b. 26 June 1921) 2nd s. of Michael McGilligan, Barrister-at-Law, of 3 Whiteshed Road, Greystones, Co. Wicklow, and Mary Georgina Musgrave; B.A. (T.C.D.); M 1941. 1945/T/12 [2 items]. Magistrate in Sarawak, 1958.

McGILLIGAN, MICHAEL (b. 29 Sept. 1887) eld. s. of Patrick McGilligan (decd.), of Castlerock, Co. Derry, and Catherine O'Farrell; B.A. (R.U.I.). File includes personal letter. 1926/M/02 [3 items]. S.C., 30 June 1948. Employed in India before returning to practise in Ireland. Died 15 Feb. 1964. Obituary, *I.L.T. & S.J.*, xcviii (1964), 100. Contributor to James Meenan (ed.), *Centenary History of Lit. and Hist. Soc. of U.C.D.*

McGILLIGAN, PATRICK (b. 12 April 1889) 2nd s. of Patrick McGilligan (decd.), of Castlerock, Co. Londonderry, and Catherine O'Farrell; M.A.; M 1918. 1921/M/09 [2 items]. T.D. (Cumann na nGaedheal/Fine Gael) 1923-65; Minister for Industry and Commerce 1924-32 (and also for External Affairs, 1927-32); Minister for Finance, 1948-51. S.C., 3 July 1946. Attorney-General, 1954-7. Established the Electricity Supply Board, 1927. Co-author of the Statute of Westminster, 1931. Professor of Constitutional, International and Criminal Law at U.C.D., 1934-59. Volume I of the *Irish Jurist* (n.s.), (1966) is dedicated to him. Died 1979. See Louis McRedmond (ed.), *Modern Irish Lives*; and Kate Newmann, *Dictionary of Ulster Biography* (Belfast, 1993).

MacGILLYCUDDY, JOHN (b. 20 March 1855) 2nd s. of Richard MacGillycuddy of the Reeks, Co. Kerry, and Anna MacGillycuddy; M 1875, M.T. E 1880. 1882/M/15 [11 items]. High Sheriff of Kerry, 1892. 4th Battalion, Royal Munster Fusiliers. Died 1930.

MacGIOLLARNATH, PROINNSIAS (b. 4 June 1927) eld. s. of Seán Mac Giollarnath, solicitor, of Galway, and Triona Feeran, medical doctor; M.A., LL.B; M 1948. 1954/M/14 [2 items].

McGIVERN, JAMES SMITH (b. 23 Jan. 1904) 5th s. of John McGivern, of 69 Jones' Road, Dublin, and Margaret McCormick; M 1926. 1929/M/04 [2 items]. S.C., 3 March 1955. Judge of the Circuit Court (Dublin) [temporary from 1959, permanent from Oct. 1963].

McGLADERY, HERBERT (b. 27 April 1883) 5th s. of Samuel McGladery (decd.) of Woodbank, Belfast, and Jane McCully; B.A. (R.U.I.); M 1904, G.I. T 1906. 1907/M/04 [2 items].

McGONAGLE, IRIS MARY (b. 16 Sept. 1935) only d. of Joseph McGonagle, of 40 Cowper Road, Rathmines, Dublin, and Ann Gormley; B.A. (N.U.I.); M 1954. 1957/M/11 [2 items].

McGONIGAL, JOHN (b. 20 Jan. 1870) 9th s. of Michael McGonigal, merchant, of Strandtown, Co. Down, and Catherine Mack; H 1889. 1892/H/02 [7 items]. N.E. Circuit. K.C., 28 Oct. 1911. Professor at King's Inns, 1911-14. Bencher 1923. Bencher (N.I.) 1926. Crown prosecutor for Belfast, 1917. Aft. 'Father of the Ulster Bar'. County Court Judge for Tyrone, 1939. Author of 'The Bar as a profession', in *The Collegian: The Magazine of St. Malachy's College, Belfast, Centenary Number* (Belfast, 1933), 122-4. Died 24 July 1943. Obituary, *I.L.T. & S.J.*, lxxvii (1943), 190; *Who's Who*. Mentioned in Maurice Healy, *The Old Munster Circuit*, 248; and in J.C. MacDermott, *An Enriching Life*, 170.

McGONIGAL, RICHARD (b. 14 Feb. 1902) eld. s. of John McGonigal, K.C., of 6 Windsor Gardens, Belfast, and Margaret Davoren; B.Sc. (N.U.I.); M 1922. Awarded John Brooke Scholarship. 1925/M/01 [2 items]. S.C., 12 Jan. 1940. Judge of the European Court of Human Rights, 1959. Died 24 Jan. 1964. Obituary, *I.L.T. & S.J.*, xcviii (1964), 67.

MacGORIS, JAMES PATRICK (b. 14 June 1930) eld. s. of James John MacGoris, company director, of 29 Fitzwilliam Square, Dublin, and Julia Mary Murray; B.A. (N.U.I.); M 1950. 1953/M/05 [2 items].

McGOUGH, Captain JOSEPH CHRISTOPHER (b. 23 Dec. 1920) eld. s. of John McGough, of St. Bridget's, Rathfarnham, Dublin, and Ann Brennan (decd.); M 1947. 1951/T/07 [2 items]. S.C., 4 Oct. 1982. Lieutenant-Colonel, Army Legal Service. Aft. of Bord Bainne. Died 8 Nov. 2003. Obituary, *The Irish Times*, 21 Nov. 2003. Listed in the 1984 edition of Maureen Cairnduff, *Who's Who in Ireland*.

McGOVERN, JAMES NIALL (b. 4 Aug. 1922) only s. of John Paul McGovern, of Enniskillen, Co. Fermanagh, and Helena Josephine Kiernan; M 1944. 1948/T/10 [2 items]. Legal adviser, Irish Shipping, Ltd.

MacGOWAN, MAURICE JOHN LYSAGHT (b. 16 Feb. 1893) eld. s. of William Henry I. MacGowan (decd.), of Ranelagh, Dublin, and Jane White; M 1915. 1953/T/01 [11 items].

MacGOWAN, ROBERT MICHAEL (b. 8 Feb. 1873) only s. of Michael Harte MacGowan, late of Castle Road, Dundalk, Co. Louth, and Elizabeth O'Connell; B.A. (R.U.I.); M 1899. 1905/M/05 [3 items]. Died 15 Dec. 1911: *I.L.T. & S.J.*, xlv (1911), 324.

McGRATH, HENRY GARRETT (b. 3 Nov. 1896) eld. s. of William McGrath, K.C., of 129 North Circular Road, Dublin, and Gertrude Fitzpatrick; B.A. (N.U.I.); M 1916. Awarded Society's Exhibition. 1919/H/01 [2 items]. Died 1919: James Meenan (ed.), *Centenary History of Lit. and Hist. Soc. of U.C.D.*

McGRATH, JOHN (b. 13 Jan. 1901) eld. s. of John McGrath, farmer (decd.), of Lauragh, Cappoquin, Co. Waterford, and Maria Teresa Murphy; M 1930. 1933/T/02 [3 items].

McGRATH, JOSEPH (b. 25 Aug. 1859) eld. surv. s. of Pierce McGrath (decd.) of Bagnalstown, Co. Carlow, and Alicia Hughes; B.A. (London); H 1882, G.I. H 1884. 1892/T/01 [6 items]. One of the secretaries of the Royal University, and Registrar of the National University of Ireland, 1908. Chairman of the National Society for the Prevention of Cruelty to Children, and honorary secretary of the Clongowes Union. LL. D. Knighted 1911. Died 15 March 1923. *Who's Who*.

McGRATH, MURRAY MATTHEW PIUS (b. 10 Feb. 1939) eld. s. of Joseph Leo McGrath, merchant, of 30 Herbert Park, Ballsbridge, Dublin, and Ita Murray; B.A. (N.U.I.); M 1957. Awarded Brooke Scholarship. 1960/M/01 [2 items]. S.C., 28 Feb. 1974. Bencher.

McGRATH, WILLIAM (b. 17 Sept. 1866) 4th s. of Henry McGrath (decd.) of Portaferry, Co. Down, and Mary Maguire; M 1891. 1895/H/05 [6 items]. North-East Circuit. K.C., 27 Feb. 1918. Fatally wounded by armed raiders at his home on the North Circular Road, 14 Jan. 1921: *I.L.T. & S.J.*, lv (1921), 17, 27, 32, 71. James Meenan (ed.), *Centenary History of Lit. and Hist. Soc. of U.C.D.*

McGRATH, WILLIAM MARTIN (b. 9 July 1863) 2nd s. of William McGrath, merchant, of Belfast, and Margaret Martin; B.A. (R.U.I.); H 1884. 1887/H/07x [7 items]. North-East Circuit. K.C., March 1904. Died 16 Nov. 1912. Obituary, *I.L.T. & S.J.*, xlvi (1912), 297-8.

McGRENAHAN, MICHAEL FEELY (b. 8 Sept. 1851) young. s. of William McGrenahan of Barr, Omagh, Co. Tyrone, and Eileen Feely; H 1878, M.T. M 1880. 1882/H/01 [8 items]. Journalist. Died 12 Aug. 1935. Obituary, *I.L.T. & S.J.*, lxix (1935), 236.

McGUCKIN, BASIL (b. 5 July 1894) 3rd s. of Robert McGuckin (decd.), of Millbrook, Magherafelt, Co. Londonderry, and Sarah MacLaughlin; M 1913. 1916/H/01 [2 items]. S.C. , 24 April 1933. Died 10 Sept. 1944. Obituary, *I.L.T. & S.J.*, lxxviii (1944), 238.

MacGUIGAN, BRIAN JAMES (b. 5 Aug. 1942) 4th s. of Henry Joseph MacGuigan, civil servant, of 22 Nutley Park, Ballsbridge, Dublin, and Margaret Byrne, B.Comm. (N.U.I.); M 1963. 1966/M/08 [1 item].

McGUINN, PATRICK VINCENT (b. 23 June 1928) 3rd s. of Patrick McGuinn, farmer, of Bellaghy, Charlestown, Co. Sligo, and Katherine Gilligan; M 1955. 1959/T/04 [2 items].

McGUIRE, JAMES IVAN (b. 24 July 1903) 2nd s. of John Francis McGuire, of Cambridge House, Rathmines, Dublin, and Mary Molony; M 1926. 1929/M/03 [2 items]. S.C., 4 July 1947.

McGUSTY, GEORGE ALFRED (b. 31 March 1865) eld. s. of Alexander Delap McGusty, Barrister-at-Law, of Langholm House, Wiltshire, and Emily Hayes; B.A. (T.C.D.); M 1885. 1889/H/02 [7 items]. K.C., 27 Feb. 1918. Died 21 June 1930.

McHUGH, ALFRED (b. 20 Nov. 1857) 3rd s. of Arthur McHugh of 56 Northumberland Road, Dublin, and Anna Francis Duffy; B.A. (T.C.D.); T 1877, M.T. M 1880. 1881/M/05 [8 items]. ex-Scholar (T.C.D.) Died at Johannesburg of heart disease, 10 Jan. 1906. Obituary, *I.L.T. & S.J.*, xl (1906), 45.

McHUGH, JOHN BAPTIST (b. 16 April 1847) 4th s. of Edward McHugh, merchant, of Belfast, Co. Antrim, and Mary Treanor; B.A. (Queen's College Belfast); M 1868, M.T. E 1870. 1872/H/6 [7 items].

McHUGH, MUIREANN CAITRÍONA (b. 12 March 1944) eld. d. of Roger McHugh, M.A., Ph.D., of Blackrock, Co. Dublin, and Patricia Kelly; M 1964. 1967/M/03 [2 items]. Aft. Mrs. Ó Briain. S.C., 25 Feb. 1994.

McILDOWIE, JAMES MANTELL (b. 15 Aug. 1861) 2nd s. of George McIldowie, solicitor, of Belmont, Co. Down, and Charlotte Mantell; M 1879, M.T. M 1882. 1883/M/06 [7 items].

McILROY, ROBERT (b. 6 Oct. 1848) 4th s. of Hugh McIlroy, gentleman, of Belfast, and Mary Jane Black; E 1885. 1887/M/01 [5 items]. K.C., 26 Feb. 1907. Appt. Recorder of Belfast, 20 May 1910. Died (as Hugh McIlroy) 6 Sept. 1911. Obituary, *I.L.T. & S.J.*, xlv (1911), 223; *Who's Who*.

MACINERNEY, EDWIN (b. 5 Jan. 1881) 3rd s. of M.C. Macinerney, K.C., of 22 Mountjoy Square, Dublin, and Mary Lynam; M 1899. 1906/E/01 [3 items]. Sometime Dublin Police Magistrate. Died in New York, 4 Feb. 1937. Obituary, *I.L.T. & S.J.*, lxxi (1937), 69, 76.

MACINERNEY, MICHAEL CHARTRES (b. 13 Jan. 1847) 2nd s. of John Macinerney (decd.), of Bleakmount House, Co. Clare, and Mary O'Conor; M 1876, G.I. M 1878. 1879/M/17 [6 items]. Called to the New York Bar, M 1874, and to the English Bar, T 1899. North-East Circuit. Q.C., 30 June 1894. Contested Widnes as a Liberal in 1890. Revising Barrister for City of Dublin, 1907-10. Dublin Metropolitan Magistrate 1910-17. Published a volume of verse (New York, 1872) and a work on the Irish Land Act of 1881. Died 25 Dec. 1929. Obituary, *I.L.T. & S.J.*, lxiii (1929), 311; *Who's Who*. Mentioned in James Meenan (ed.), *Centenary History of Lit. and Hist. Soc. of U.C.D*, 81.

MacIVOR, JAMES (b. 13 April 1844), of Newtownstewart, Co. Tyrone eld. s. of the Revd. James MacIvor, D.D., of Ardstraw, Co. Tyrone, and Pleasant Stewart; B.A. (T.C.D.); M 1868; M.T. 1865. 1871/H/4 [2 items]. Librarian of King's Inns, 18 Jan. 1882 to 1900.

McKANE, ROBERT WILLIAM (b. 13 Nov. 1883) only s. of John McKane (decd.), M.P., LL.D., Barrister-at-Law, of 64 Lower Leeson Street, Dublin, and Anna Elizabeth Cordukes; B.A. (T.C.D.); H 1909. 1911/M/09 [4 items].

McKAY, MICHAEL VINCENT (b. 15 June 1892) young. s. of John McKay (decd.), of Richmond Avenue, Dublin, and Catherine O'Connell; M 1923. 1927/M/12 [2 items]. Died 1959.

McKEAN, EDWARD JOHN (b. 28 March 1880) eld. s. of Edward McKean, of Rosaville, Fortwilliam Park, Belfast, and Mary Houston; B.A. (Oxford); M 1903; I.T.M 1901. 1905/M/03 [3 items]. K.C. (N.I.), H 1929. Died 1942. Obituary, *I.L.T. & S.J.*, lxxvi (13 June 1942), 152.

McKEAN, JOHN (b. 6 Jan. 1869) 3rd s. of Patrick McKean (decd.), of Castleblayney, Co. Monaghan, and Mary Hanratty; M 1897. 1900/T/02 [3 items]. M.P. for South Monaghan, 1902-18. Died 1942. Obituary, *I.L.T. & S.J.*, lxxvi (23 May 1942), 134.

McKEEVER, GERARD AUGUSTINE (b. 15 April 1925) eld. s. of Patrick McKeever, of 2 Phoenix Terrace, Blackrock, Co. Dublin, and Annie Christina Lawless; M 1946. 1950/T/07 [2 items].

MACKEN, FRANCIS JOSEPH (b. 2 April 1888) 4th s. of Hugh Michael Macken, gentleman, of 2 North Great Georges Street, Dublin, and Mary Josephine Macken; M 1919. 1923/M/04 [2 items].

MACKEN, JAMES JOSEPH (b. 15 Aug. 1872) eld. s. of James Macken of 44 Mountjoy Square, Dublin, and Elizabeth Dirham; B.A.; M 1898. 1904/M/04 [4 items]. Died 31 May 1924. Obituary, *I.L.T. & S.J.*, lviii (1924), 144.

McKENNA, CHARLES BEUNO (b. 3 Sept. 1904) eld. s. of Charles McKenna, of Ballrigh, Robinstown, Navan, Co. Meath, and Marion O'Reilly (decd.); M 1928. 1931/M/02 [2 items]. Auditor of the College Historical Society, 1929-30. S.C., 29 Oct. 1951. Regius Professor of Laws, T.C.D., 1 Oct. 1966. Died 1973.

McKENNA, SÉAMUS THOMAS (b. 25 April 1929) young. s. of Patrick McKenna, teacher, of Hy Brasail, Scotstown, Co. Monaghan, and Maura Hughes; M 1948. 1951/M/13 [2 items]. S.C., 1 March 1968.

MacKENZIE, JOHN JAMES PATRICK (b. 16 March 1919) eld. s. of Stephen MacKenzie, shipbroker, of 22 Ailesbury Road, Co. Dublin, and Dorothea Clark; B.A. (N.U.I.); M 1938. Awarded certificate of Honour. 1941/M/05 [2 items]. S.C., 11 Jan. 1972. Judge of the High Court, 10 February 1986. Retired 15 March 1991. Died 2003. Author, as Patrick MacKenzie, of *Lawful Occasions: The Old Eastern Circuit* (Cork and Dublin, 1991).

MacKENZIE, VIVIAN St. CLAIR (b. 23 Nov. 1872) eld. s. of John Baker MacKenzie of Bellevue Terrace, Cork, and Grace St. Clair McOstrich; B.A. (T.C.D.); H 1895, G.I. M 1896. 1898/H/05 [3 items]. Journalist on staff of *The Times*, London. Died 1926. Obituary, *I.L.T. & S.J.*, lx (21 Aug. 1926), 210.

McKEON, JOHN (b. 1 July 1917) eld. s. of John Joseph McKeon, of Aughagreagh, Ballinalee, Co. Longford, and Mary Duffy; M 1938. 1942/M/04 [2 items]. Draftsman in Lusaka, N. Rhodesia; in Hong Kong; and to Law Reform Commission. Died 2003.

MacKEOWN, MICHAEL JOHN JOSEPH (b. 2 Sept. 1890) only s. of Thomas MacKeown (decd.), of Newry, Co. Down, and Kate Agnes Heaney Cawley; B.A.; M 1935. 1938/T/01 [2 items].

MacKEOWN, Captain ROBERT FRANCIS (b. 29 Sept. 1893) 3rd s. of Wilson MacKeown (decd.), of Ballymena, Co. Antrim, and Susan Gray Cooney. M.C. M 1924. File includes personal letter. 1926/M/14 [3 items].

MacKEOWN, WILLIAM WILSON (b. 15 Sept. 1885) eld. s. of Wilson MacKeown, solicitor, of Ballymena, Co. Antrim, and Susan Cooney; M 1905. 1908/M/06 [2 items].

MACKEY, ARTHUR JOSEPH CONNELL (b. 7 Dec. 1911) eld. s. of Joseph Mackey, of Liosnamara, Bray, Co. Wicklow, and Gertrude Elizabeth Gallagher; M 1934. 1938/M/06 [2 items]. S.C., 23 March 1973. Author (as Rex Mackey) of *The Walk of the Oysters* (a history of Bridge) and of *Windward of the Law* (London, 1965; 2nd edition, Dublin 1991). Died November 1999. Obituary [with photograph], *The Irish Times*, 20 Nov. 1999.

MacLAINE, GEORGE LANGTRY (b. 28 June 1865) eld. s. of George Langtry MacLaine, solicitor, Clerk of the Crown and Peace for Co. Down, of Wandsworth House, Co. Down, and Margaret Porter; H 1888. 1895/H/03x [10 items]. Died 24 March 1928. Obituary, *I.L.T. & S.J.*, lxii (1928), 78.

McLAUGHLIN, JAMES WILLIAM (b. 22 Aug. 1859) eld. s. of William McLaughlin Q.C., of Gardiner's Place, Dublin, and Margaret Campbell; H 1877, M.T. M 1879. 1880/M/07 [6 items].

McLEAN, JOHN (b. 19 Sept 1849) 2nd s. of James McLean, of Plasmerdyn, Co. Down, Attorney-at-Law, and Elizabeth Bryson; B.A. (T.C.D.); M 1870, M.T. M 1868. 1873/H/13 [2 items].

McLOGHLIN, BRIAN FRANCIS (b. 11 April 1946) only s. of Joseph McLoghlin, civil servant, of 3 Annaville Park, Dundrum, Co. Dublin, and Sheila Feeney; B.A. (N.U.I.); M 1965. 1968/T/06 [1 item].

McLOONE, JAMES (b. 27 Oct. 1862) eld. s. of Joseph McLoone, J.P., of Donegal, Co. Donegal, and Anne Mulreany; M 1890. 1893/T/02 [6 items]. K.C., 28 Oct. 1911. Revising Barrister for City of Belfast, 1908-13; for County of Dublin, 1914. Died 27 May 1934. Obituary, *I.L.T. & S.J.*, lxviii (1934), 154, 174.

McLOUGHLIN, RICHARD FRANCIS XAVIER JOSEPH (b. 12 March 1902) 2nd s. of James H. McLoughlin, solicitor, of 42 Pembroke Road, Dublin, and Annie Corcoran (decd.); M 1919. 1923/E/01 [2 items]. S.C., 21 Dec. 1938. Judge of the High Court,

1952-69; of the Supreme Court, May 1969-72. Died 9 Sept. 1972. Obituary, *I.L.T. & S.J.*, cvi (1972), 263.

McLOUGHLIN, THOMAS JOSEPH (b. 1 June 1927) eld. s. of Thomas A. McLoughlin, Ph.D., D.Sc., director of Electricity Supply Board, of 19 Ailesbury Road, Dublin, and Olwen O'Malley; B.A. (N.U.I.); M 1947. 1950/M/15 [2 items]. S.C., 2 Oct. 1967.

MacLYSAGHT, JAMES (b. 5 April 1886) 5th s. of Thomas MacLysaght (decd.), of Ballingarry, Co. Limerick, and Mary Sheehan; E 1924. 1928/T/06 [2 items]. Department of Local Government.

McMAHON, JAMES GERARD (b. 6 Jan. 1914) eld. s. of Morgan McMahon, timber merchant, of Moyarta, N.C. Road, Limerick, Co. Limerick, and Josephine Ryan; M 1933. Awarded John Brooke Scholarship and Certificate of Honour. 1936/M/01 [2 items]. S.C., 4 July 1952. Judge of the High Court, 21 Oct. 1975 - 5 Jan. 1986. Listed in the 1984 edition of Maureen Cairnduff, *Who's Who in Ireland*.

MacMAHON, JOHN (b. 9 July 1869) 5th s. of James MacMahon (decd.), of Armagh, Co. Armagh, and Mary McConnell; M 1911. 1914/T/14 [2 items]. Purchase Department, Land Commission., -1930. Died 25 August 1942. Obituary, *I.L.T. & S.J.*, lxxvi (1942), 223.

MacMAHON, JOHN (b. 23 July 1865) only s. of the Revd. J.H. MacMahon, LL.D., of 10 Winton Road, Dublin, and Frances Snagge; B.A., ex-Scholar (T.C.D.); M 1888. 1891/M/14 [6 items]. Died by poisoning, 30 Dec. 1909. Inquest reported, *I.L.T. & S.J.*, xliv (1910), 10.

MacMAHON, JOHN ROCHFORD (b. 27 Aug. 1893) only s. of James MacMahon of Mount Varona, Kingstown, Co. Dublin, and Mary Rochford; M 1913. 1916/T/11 [2 items]. Son of the last Under-Secretary for Ireland, and a nephew of the John MacMahon (1869-1942) called in 1914. Entered the Society of Jesus, of which Order he was the Irish Provincial from 1941 to 1947. Professor of Canon Law, and twice Rector of Milltown Park. Until his late 80s he punctiliously attended (and concelebrated) the Mass for the opening of the legal year at St. Michan's, Halston Street.

McMASTER, JOHN BOYLE (b. 16 July 1853) only s. of George McMaster, M.A., J.P., of Brookville, Co. Dublin, and Eleanor Boyle; B.A. (T.C.D.); M 1875, M.T. M 1877. 1879/T/02 [6 items].

McMENAMIN, DANIEL (b. 30 March 1882) 3rd s. of John McMenamin, of Mooneen, Cloghan, Co. Donegal, and Bridget McNamee; Undergraduate (T.C.D.); M 1914. 1917/T/21 [2 items]. Cumann na nGaedheal T.D. for Donegal, June-Sept. 1927; 1932-7; Fine Gael T.D. for Donegal East, 1937-61. See *Thom's Directory* (Biographies).

McMENAMIN, JOHN ANTHONY BENEDICT (b. 1 Nov. 1925) eld. s. of William Thomas McMenamin, solicitor, of Ballybofey, Co. Donegal, and Mary Monica Sweeney; B.A., LL.B. (T.C.D.); M 1948. 1951/M/16 [3 items].

McMORDIE, HANS (b. 30 Aug. 1842) eld. s. of the Revd. John Henry McMordie (decd.), Presbyterian Minister, of Seaforde, Co. Down, and Margaret Kirkpatrick; M.A., LL.D; M 1884, I.T. M 1884. 1885/M/13 [3 items].

McMORROW, SEÁN CHRISTOPHER (b. 13 June 1927) young. s. of James J. McMorrow (decd.), of Tallaght, Mohill, Co. Leitrim, and Catherine Moran; B.A., LL.B; M 1954. Awarded 2nd Victoria Prize. 1957/T/01 [2 items].

MACMULLEN, GEORGE READE (b. 27 May 1858) 3rd s. of John Franklin Macmullen, of Melbourne, Australia, and Beatrice Carnegie; B.A., LL.B. (T.C.D.); H 1882, M.T. M 1883. 1885/E/03 [6 items].

McMULLIN, ARTHUR MICHAEL (b. 11 Nov. 1922) 2nd s. of Joseph Columba McMullin, surgeon, of 'Inisfail', Cavan, Co. Cavan, and Frances Byrne; B.A. (N.U.I.); M 1942. 1945/T/07 [2 items]. Known as Art McMullin. Formerly a Judge of the High Court in Hong Kong.

MACNAMARA, MICHAEL AUGUSTUS (b. 8 March 1857) only s. of James Macnamara (decd.), farmer, of Leimnaleha, Co. Clare, and Anne O'Dea; M 1890. 1896/H/01 [5 items]. Mentioned in Maurice Healy, *The Old Munster Circuit*, 151-3; and in Joachim Fischer and John Dillon (eds.), *The Correspondence of Myles Dillon 1922-1925* (Dublin, 1999), 181.

MacNEILL, JOHN GORDON SWIFT (b. 11 March 1849) only s. of the Revd. John Gordon Swift MacNeill, M.A., of Blackhall Street, Dublin and Susan Tweedy; M.A. (Oxford); E 1873, I.T. M 1873. 1876/H/01 [4 items]. Munster Circuit. Q.C., 1 July 1893. Professor of Constitutional and Criminal Law at King's Inns, 1882-8. Professor of Constitutional Law at U.C.D., 1909. Nationalist M.P. for South Donegal, 1887-1918. Died 24 August 1926. Obituary, *I.L.T. & S.J.*, lx (1926), 221-2; *Who's Who*. Author of *The Irish Parliament* (1885), *How the Union was Carried* (1887), *Criminal Law in England and in Ireland* (London, 1888), *Titled Corruption* (1894), *Constitutional and Parliamentary History of Ireland* (1917), *Studies in the Constitution of the Irish Free State* (1925), and *What I have seen and heard* (1925). Mentioned in James Meenan (ed.), *Centenary History of Lit. and Hist. Soc. of U.C.D.* See Henry Boylan, *A Dictionary of Irish Biography* (1978); *Oxford DNB* (2004).

McNEILL, JOHN HILL TREVOR (b. 10 Sept. 1871) 2nd s. of John McNeill, of Hillmount, Larne, Co. Antrim, and Mary Jane Hodges; B.A. (T.C.D.); H 1891. 1894/H/08 [7 items]. Died of pneumonia at Nenagh, 12 Aug. 1915: *I.L.T. & S.J.*, xlix (1915), 206.

McNEILL, ROBERT NORMAN (b. 19 March 1886) 7th s. of the Revd. James McNeill of Drumbo Manse, Lisburn, Co. Down, and Annie McKinstry; M 1909. 1913/M/03 [3 items].

MacNEILL, TURLOUGH (b. 25 April 1903) 3rd s. of Eoin MacNeill, of 3 South Hill Avenue, Blackrock, Dublin, and Agnes Moore; M 1924. 1927/M/24 [2 items]. Superintendant, Garda Síochána. Died 1955.

McNULTY, DERMOT JOSEPH (b. 22 June 1935) 3rd s. of Peter McNulty, auctioneer, of 16 Royse Road, Phibsboro, Dublin, and Aileen Collins; M 1963. 1967/T/08 [1 item]. Joined Irish Shipping Limited, 1951, serving as Company Secretary in 1984 when the company was liquidated.

McNULTY, THOMAS (b. 1 Sept. 1863) only s. of Charles McNulty, decd., late of Great James' Street, Derry, Co. Londonderry, and Maria McColgan; B.A. (T.C.D.); M 1885. 1889/T/03 [7 items].

Mac PHARTALAIN, GEARÓID (Gerald Bartley) (b. 12 June 1898) 4th s. of Seán Mac Pharthalain (decd.), of An Faithche Mhóir, Gaillimh, and Áine Ní Choisdealbha; M 1940. 1944/M/12 [2 items]. 'Took part in numerous engagements ... with the West Connemara Brigade, I.R.A.' [Thom]. Member of Galway County Council, 1925-31. As Gerald Bartley, Fianna Fáil T.D. for Galway, 1932-7; and for Galway West, 1937-65. Parliamentary Secretary to the Minister for Agriculture, 1951-54; to the Minister for Industry and Commerce, 1957-.

MacQUAID, BRIAN EAMON JAMES (b. 22 April 1918) only s. of Philip J. MacQuaid (decd.), solicitor, sheriff, of Clarecastle, Co. Clare, and Violet Healy; M 1936. 1940/M/06 [2 items]. Mentioned in Patrick MacKenzie, *Lawful Occasions*, 60.

McQUAID, FRANCIS JOSEPH (b. 10 March 1906) only s. of Francis McQuaid (decd.), of Naas, Co. Kildare, and Kathleen Dunne (decd.); M 1927. 1930/M/04 [2 items].

McQUAID, PARAIC (b. 22 Nov. 1918) only s. of William James McQuaid, of 36 Mount Argus Road, Dublin, and Minnie McGee; B. Comm (N.U.I.); M 1944. 1947/M/07 [2 items].

McQUOID, NORMAN SCOTT (b. 28 Aug. 1886) eld. s. of James McQuoid, J.P., of The Mount, Mountpottinger, Belfast, and Mary Rebecca Scott; B.A. (T.C.D.); M 1906. 1909/T/06 [2 items].

McREDMOND, LUKE JOHN (b. 23 May 1932) only s. of John McRedmond, Athlone, Co. Westmeath, and Anne Kirby; B.A. (N.U.I.); M 1951. 1954/T/03 [2 items].

MACRORY, ROBERT HENRY (b. 4 Feb. 1868) eld. s. of Robert Augustus Macrory, solicitor, of Antrim Road, Belfast, and Kate Robert Crawford; B.A. (T.C.D.); M 1890. 1893/M/02 [6 items]. Died 10 Nov. 1929. Obituary, *I.L.T. & S.J.*, lxiii (1929), 275.

McSPARRAN, JAMES (b. 1 May 1892) 3rd s. of James McSparran of Knocknacarry, Co. Antrim, and Ann McDonnell; B.A. (Q.U.B.); LL.B. (N.U.I.); M 1913. 1916/M/02 [2 items]. K.C. (N.I.), H 1945. Bencher of the Inn of Court of N.I. Nationalist M.P. for Mourne (N.I. Parl.), 1945-58. Chairman of the Anti-Partition League. Died 15 April 1970. Obituary, *I.L.T. & S.J.*, civ (1970), 195; *Who's Who*. Mentioned in Basil McIvor, *Hope Deferred: Experiences of an Irish Unionist* (Belfast, 1998), 36.

McSTAY, MICHAEL (b. 26 April 1918) 5th s. of John Joseph McStay, of 7 Palace Field, Kildare, Co. Kildare, and Mary Ellen Daly; A.I.A.C., D.P.A; M 1949. 1953/T/03 [2 items]. Chairman of Unidare Limited.

McSWEENEY, GEORGE (b. 4 Feb. 1865) young. s. of George McSweeney (decd.) of Macroom, Co. Cork, and Mary O'Driscoll; cand. bachelor (R.U.I.); M 1893. 1896/T/04 [6 items]. Journalist. K.C., 28 Oct. 1911. Crown Counsel for Co. Cork. 3rd Serjeant, 5 July 1913. 2nd Serjeant, 29 Oct. 1919. Died 14 Nov. 1923. Obituary, *I.L.T. & S.J.*, lvii (1923), 284; *Who's Who*. James Meenan (ed.), *Centenary History of Lit. and Hist. Soc. of U.C.D.* Caricature (by C. Norman Kough [q.v.]), as 'Belly McSweeney', in A.R. Hart, *A History of the King's Serjeants at Law in Ireland* (Dublin, 2000), Plate 23.

McSWINEY, MYLES (b. 1 May 1936) eld. s. of Myles McSwiney (decd.), M.D., of Fermoy, Co. Cork, and Aideen Magher (decd.); M 1954. 1959/E/02 [2 items]. General secretary of the Royal Institute of the Architects of Ireland, 1964-72; employed by the European Commission since 1973. Contributor to Frank Callanan, *The Literary and Historical Society 1955-2005* (Dublin, 2005), 150, 392.

MacSWINEY, OWEN CHARLES VALENTINE ALEXANDER EVELYN DIEGO de AVILA (b. 30 July 1916) only s. of the Marquess Mac Swiney of Mashanaglas, K.M., M.R.I.A., of 39 Upper Fitzwilliam Street, Dublin, and Anna Grajen von Schultz [?]; M 1935. 1940/H/03 [2 items]. Dress designer in London. Author of books on Westphalia mute swans, *Six came flying* (1971), and on horses, *Training from the Ground: a special approach* (1987). Died 1986.

McTERNAN, HUGH (b. 9 July 1837) only s. of James McTernan (decd.) of Heapstown, Co. Sligo, and Marion Loughnane; M 1857; M.T. (n.d.). 1868/H/2 [6 items].

McVEY, JAMES EDWARD (b. 2 July 1931) eld. s. of James Cyril McVey, of Glencroe, Knocksinna Road, Foxrock, Co. Dublin, and Lucy McCluskey; M 1950. 1954/M/05 [2 items].

McWALTER, JAMES CHARLES (b. 25 May 1868) eld. s. of James Joseph McWalter of Dublin, and Mary O'Donnell; M 1904. 1907/T/12 [2 items].

McWILLIAM, HERBERT RUSSELL (b. 13 Feb. 1913) 2nd s. of Russell McWilliam, of Holly Lodge, Monaghan, Co. Monaghan, and Elizabeth Henry; B.A. (T.C.D.); M 1932. 1935/T/05 [2 items]. Judge of the High Court. Retired 12 Feb. 1985. Listed in the 1984 edition of Maureen Cairnduff, *Who's Who in Ireland*.

McWILLIAM, WILLIAM (b. 10 Dec. 1880) 2nd s. of William McWilliam, Clerk of Crown and Peace, of Corlatt House, Monaghan, and Hessie Morell; M 1900. 1904/M/05 [3 items].

MADDEN, JOHN CLEMENTS WATERHOUSE (b. 8 Feb. 1870) eld. s. of John Madden, J.P., D.L., of Hilton Park, Co. Monaghan, and Lady Caroline Clements; B.A. (Cambridge); M 1893, called to the Bar by I.T. E 1895. 1897/M/06 [2 items]. Educated at Eton. High Sheriff of Co. Monaghan (1906) and of Co. Fermanagh (1909). Lieutenant-Colonel, 4th Battalion, Royal Irish Fusiliers. Director of the Great Northern Railway. Member of the General Synod. Died 22 Dec. 1935. Obituary, *I.L.T. & S.J.*, lxx (11 Jan. 1936), 12; *Who's Who*; *Burke's Irish Family Records*, 768.

MADIGAN, JAMES BRENDAN (b. 16 May 1929) eld. s. of James Madigan, farmer, of Ballincollig, Co. Cork, and Eileen O'Keeffe (decd.); B.A. (N.U.I.); H.D.E. (T.C.D.); M 1961. 1967/M/02* [1 item].

MAGEE, FRANCIS (b. 23 April 1902) 2nd s. of Francis Magee, of Drumsough, Randalstown, Co. Antrim, and Matilda Alice McNally; B.A. (T.C.D.); M 1944. 1948/T/11 [2 items]. Under-Treasurer at King's Inns. Died 25 Feb. 1984.

MAGEE, HUGH JOSEPH HOGAN (b. 19 March 1938) 3rd s. of Francis A. Magee, Barrister-at-Law, Under-Treasurer, King's Inns, of King's Inns House, 11 Henrietta Street, Dublin, and Eileen A. Magee; M 1956. 1961/M/04 [2 items].

MAGENNIS, WILLIAM (b. 18 May 1867) 2nd s. of Hugh Magennis of Belfast, and Catherine Magill; M.A., Fellow of R.U.I.; M 1890. 1893/T/05 [4 items]. Professor of Philosophy (1889-1909) and Metaphysics (1909-41) at U.C.D. T.D. for the National University of Ireland, 1922-7; Senator 1938-46. Died 1946. Mentioned (with photograph) in James Meenan (ed.), *Centenary History of Lit. and Hist. Soc. of U.C.D.*

MAGINESS, BRIAN (b. 10 July 1901) 2nd s. of William George Maginess, of Avonmore Lodge, Lisburn, Co. Antrim, and Mary Boyd; B.A., Sen. Mod., LL.B. (T.C.D.); M 1919. Awarded Society's Exhibition. 1922/M/01 [2 items]. K.C. (N.I.), M 1946. Unionist M.P. for Iveagh in N.I. Parliament, 1938-64. Privy Counsellor (N.I.) and Minister of Labour, 1945; of Home Affairs, 1945-53; of Finance, 1953-6. County Court Judge for Down, 1964. Died 18 April 1967. See *Who's Who*; and Kate Newmann, *Dictionary of Ulster Biography* (Belfast, 1993).

MAGUIRE, CONOR ALEXANDER (b. 16 Dec. 1889) 2nd s. of Conor J.O'L. Maguire, M.A., of Claremorris, Co. Mayo, and Florence O'Neill; M.A., LL.B. (U.C.D.); [struck off roll of solicitors at own request, 1922] 1922/M/06 [5 items]. S.C., 11 March 1932. Bencher, T 1932. Attorney-General 1932-6. Appt. a judge of the High Court, 2 Nov. 1936; President of the High Court, 17 Dec. 1936; Chief Justice, June 1946. Retired Dec. 1961. Died 26 Sept. 1971. Obituary, *I.L.T. & S.J.*, cv (1971), 320. Author of an article on 'The Republican Courts' in the *Capuchin Annual*, 1969. Portrait by David Hone in King's Inns: see Wanda Ryan-Smolin, *King's Inns Portraits* (1992), 44

MAGUIRE, CONOR PATRICK JOSEPH (b. 16 March 1922) eld. s. of the Hon. Conor Alexander Maguire, President of the High Court, of Ashurst, Mount Merrion Avenue, Blackrock, Co. Dublin, and Nora Whelan; M 1941. 1945/T/08 [2 items]. S.C., 27 Feb. 1959.

MAGUIRE, HENRY JOSEPH (b. 24 May 1859) 2nd s. of John Francis Maguire (decd.), M.P., of Ardmanagh, Co. Cork, and Margaret Baily; M 1881, M.T. M 1883. 1884/M/09 [5 items]. Clerk of Judgments, Records and Writs. Retired 1929. *I.L.T. & S.J.*, lxiii (1929), 119.

MAGUIRE, JOHN (b. 7 Jan. 1897) 5th s. of Frank Maguire, J.P., of Bullock Castle, Dalkey, Dublin, and Mary McHenry; M 1923. 1926/M/12 [2 items].

MAGUIRE, JOSEPH (b. 8 Jan. 1851) eld. s. of James Maguire of Banbridge, Co. Down, and Sarah Ann Morgan; H 1881. 1886/H/04 [6 items]. Chief Clerk, Registry of Deeds. Author of *A Compendium of the Law and Practice relating to Registration of Deeds, Wills and Judgment Mortgages* (Dublin, 1912). Died 10 Nov. 1928. Obituary, *I.L.T. & S.J.*, lxii (1928), 277.

MAGUIRE, MARTIN CYRIL (b. 9 Feb. 1889) young. s. of John Maguire, J.P., of Drumharvey House, Irvinestown, Co. Fermanagh; B.A., LL.B. (T.C.D.); M 1908. 1911/H/02 [3 items]. S.C., 6 May 1925. Appt. a judge of the High Court, 3 Feb. 1940; advanced to the Supreme Court, 1954. Retired Feb. 1961. Died 20 Oct. 1962. Obituary, *I.L.T. & S.J.*, xcvi (1962), 279.

MAGUIRE, MARTIN CYRIL (b. 2 March 1922) 2nd s. of the Hon. Mr. Justice Martin C. Maguire, of Lonsdale, Temple Road, Rathmines, Dublin, and Philomena Beatty; M 1941. 1945/T/09 [2 items].

MAGUIRE, PETER DONOGH (b. 21 July 1926) 3rd s. of the Hon. Conor Alexander Maguire, Chief Justice, of Ashurst, Merrion Ave, Blackrock, Co. Dublin, and Norah Whelan; M 1944. 1949/T/03 [2 items]. S.C., 1 March 1968.

MAGUIRE, WILLIAM (b. 28 Jan. 1888) eld. s. of Thomas Joseph Maguire, civil servant, of Clara Villa, 31 Claremont Road, Sandymount, Dublin, and Louisa Agnes O'Hart; M 1913. 1916/T/14 [2 items].

MAGUIRE, WILLIAM JOSEPH (b. 1890) eld. s. of James Maguire (decd.), farmer, of Tomgar, Ballycanew, Gorey, Co. Wexford, and Dora Gahan; LL.D. (T.C.D.); M 1923. 1925/M/22 [2 items]. Peace] Commissioner. Died 25 July 1956.

MAHANT, JAGMOHAN NATH (b. 6 Dec. 1895) 4th s. of Mahant Janki Nath Sahib, of Gurdaspur, Punjab, India; M 1914. Includes correspondence re unpaid accounts from traders opposing call [called Hilary Term, 1920]. 1918/T/15 [10 items].

MAHENDRA, TRIBHUVAN LAL (b. 6 Feb. 1904) eld. s. of Anirudh Lal Mahendra, B.A., P.C.S., of Lucknow, India, and Mrs. D. Mahendra; M 1928. 1932/M/12 [2 items].

MAHER, JOHN HERBERT (b. 9 Dec. 1882) eld. s. of John Maher of 32 Lansdowne Road, Dublin, and Ellie Cahill; B.A. (T.C.D.); M 1905. 1908/T/09 [3 items].

MAHER-LOUGHNAN, JOHN (b. 5 Oct. 1878) eld. s. of John Maher-Loughnan (decd.), of Killarney, Co. Kerry, and Elizabeth Gertrude O'Leary; M 1911. 1914/T/07 [3 items]. Died 4 Sept. 1940. Obituary, *I.L.T. & S.J.*, lxxiv (1940), 229.

MAHONY, DANIEL SULLIVAN (b. 21 Oct. 1856) 2nd s. of Daniel Mahony of Kenmare, Co. Kerry, and Mary Sullivan; B.A. (T.C.D.); M 1877, M.T. M 1879. 1880/T/04 [7 items]. Dublin metropolitan magistrate. Died at Grand Hotel, Malahide, 16 Aug. 1915. Obituary, *I.L.T. & S.J.*, xlix (1915), 238.

MAHONY, EDMOND RONAYNE (b. 25 Nov. 1872) young. s. of Martin F. Mahony (decd.) of Lotamore, Co. Cork, and Mary Copinger; M 1904. 1907/T/03 [2 items]. Justice of the Peace. Captain on the General Staff, 1st World War. Died 10 May 1949. *Burke's Irish Family Records* (1976), 778.

MAHONY, JOHN McCARTHY *junior* (b. 7 Aug. 1854) 2nd s. of Denis McCarthy Mahony, merchant, of The Island, Rochestown, Co. Cork, and Katherine Waters; B.A. (T.C.D.); M 1874, M.T. H 1877. 1878/M/04 [5 items].

MAHONY, PIERCE CHARLES de LACY (b. 9 June 1850) 2nd surv. s. of Pierce Mahony (decd.) of Kilmorna, Co. Kerry, and Jane Cunninghame (decd.); M 1893. 1898/M/06 [3 items]. 'The O'Mahony' M.P. for Meath North 1886-1892. Died 31 Oct. 1930. Obituary, *I.L.T. & S.J.*, lxiv (1930), 269.

MAHONY, PIERCE GUN (b. 30 March 1878) eld. s. of Pierce Charles de Lacy O'Mahony, Barrister-at-Law, one of H.M. Deputy Lieutenants for the County of Wicklow, of Grange, Co. Wicklow, and Helen L. Collis; M 1901. 1910/M/03 [2 items]. Cork Herald, 1905-10. Died from a shotgun wound, 26 July 1914: Kevin Hannafin and John Cafferky, *Scandal and Betrayal: Shackleton and the Irish Crown Jewels* (Cork, 2002), 194-6.

MAHONY, THOMAS ADRIAN (b. 1 Dec. 1916) young. s. of Martin Francis Mahony, banker, of 12 Ailesbury Road, Dublin, and Teresa Mecthilde Breen; M 1935 [*in absentia*]. 1943/T/08 [2 items]. Captain in the Royal Scots Greys: M.C. (1944) and Bar (1945). Call delayed by war service until M 1946. Originally intended for call at the end of the list for T 1943. Crown Counsel in Singapore. Died Sept. 1958. *Burke's Irish Family Records* (1976), 778.

MALCOLMSON, WILLIAM HENRY (b. 18 April 1865) eld. s. of William Malcolmson, M.D., F.R.C.S.I. and surgeon, Lieut.-Colonel 4th Batt. Royal Irish Fusiliers, of Cavan, Co. Cavan, and Elizabeth Bryce; B.A. (T.C.D.); M 1889. 1892/T/10 [6 items]. Died 9 April 1905. *I.L.T. & S.J.*, xxxix (1905), 118.

MALCOMSON, CLAUDE JOHN (b. 13 June 1868) 2nd s. of John Malcomson, solicitor, of 47 Pembroke Road, Dublin, and Sarah C. [Boake]; H 1892. 1895/H/08 [5 items].

MALONE, JOHN HERBERT (b. 9 April 1890) eld. s. of John Malone, solicitor, of Cookstown, Co. Tyrone, and Minnie McCarthy; M 1907. 1911/E/02 [2 items]. Police magistrate, London.

MALONE, MARY ITA (b. 10 Dec. 1900) only d. of Laurence P. Malone, of Main Street, Trim, Co. Meath, and Mary E. Rochfort; M.A.; M 1924. Awarded 2nd Class Certificate of Honour. 1927/M/04 [2 items].

MALKA, EDMUND. S. (b.) 2nd s. of Solomon Malka, late of Khartoum, Sudan, Chief Rabbi of the Sudan, deceased. Colonial advocate. H 1962. 1962/M/04. [Memorial missing. Reference supplied from the Call Ledger and from the *I.L.T. & S.J.*, 8 Dec. 1962, 329.]

MANDERS, RICHARD (b. 3 May 1854) eld. s. of Richard Manders, J.P., of Brackenstown, Co. Dublin, and Caroline Roe; B.A. (T.C.D.); M 1877, M.T. M 1879. 1880/M/12 [6 items]. K.C., 23 Oct. 1903. Sometime parliamentary draftsman at the Irish Office. Registrar of Titles and Deeds, 1908-22. C.B. Lieutenant, R.N.V.R., 1915. Died at sea 27 Feb. 1931. Obituary, *I.L.T. & S.J.*, lxv (1931), 60; *Who's Who*.

MANDY, WALTER JAMES KIMBER (b. 12 March 1908) 2nd s. of James Kimber Mandy, of Seremban, Negri Sembilan, Federated Malay States, and Alice Euphemia Healey; H 1927. 1930/M/11 [2 items].

MANGAN, KEVIN PATRICK JOSEPH (b. 13 March 1906) 2nd s. of Henry Connell Mangan, of 'Graigue', Richmond Avenue, Milltown, Dublin, and Mary Elizabeth De Loughrey; B.A., LL.B. (N.U.I.); M 1926. 1929/M/17 [2 items]. Assistant to the Attorney-General. Member of the European Commission of Human Rights.

MANGAN, PATRICK (b. 29 April 1928) 2nd s. of Thomas Mangan (decd.), farmer, of Foynes, Co. Limerick, and Ellen Madigan; MRCPI, D.Ph., D.Ch; M 1959. 1962/M/08 [1 item].

MANN, WILLIAM HENRY (b. 11 July 1856) only s. of Thomas Mann, J.P. of Stormhill House, Aughnacloy, Co. Tyrone, and Maria Mann; B.A., LL.B. (T.C.D.); E 1879, M.T. M 1881. 1885/E/01 [3 items].

MANSFIELD, EDMUND (b. 21 May 1899) eld. s. of Charles Mansfield, of Cappoquin, Co. Waterford, and Nano Stafford; M 1927. 1930/M/03x [3 items].

MARCUS, DAVID (b. 21 Aug. 1924) 3rd s. of Solomon Marcus, of 1 Mardyke Villas, Cork, and Fanny Rebecca Goldberg; H 1942. 1945/M/06 [2 items]. Editor of *Irish Writing* 1946-54, and literary editor of *The Irish Press*, 1968-85. See his *Oughtobiography: Leaves from the diary of a hyphenated Jew* (Dublin, 2001). Listed in the 1984 edition of Maureen Cairnduff, *Who's Who in Ireland;* and in Louis McRedmond (ed.), *Modern Irish Lives*.

MARNAN, THOMAS GERALD (b. 2 Jan. 1871) eld. s. of William Henry Marnan of Palmerston Road, Dublin, and Mary Theresa Murphy; B.A. (R.U.I.); M 1894. 1897/T/13 [3 items]. Died 20 May 1950. Obituary, *I.L.T. & S.J.*, lxxxiv (1950), 139. Mentioned by V.T.H. Delany [q.v.], in his article 'The Bench and Bar in Ireland', as one prominent among those who never took silk.

MARRABLE, ARTHUR (b. 8 May 1854) eld. s. of the Revd. William Marrable D.D., Incumbent of St Andrew's Church, and Canon of Christ Church Cathedral, of 49 Waterloo Road, Dublin, and Susan Harriet Tilly; M.A. (T.C.D.); M 1876, M.T. H 1878. 1880/H/03 [6 items]. Died 13 May 1944.

MARRINAN, PATRICK ALOYSIUS (b. 17 March 1877) 3rd s. of Patrick Marrinan (decd.), of Armagh, Co. Armagh, and Sarah McGrath (decd.); M 1923. Awarded Society's Prize. 1925/M/02 [2 items]. Also called in N.I., 1925. Sometime County Inspector R.I.C. at Limerick. C.B.E. J.P. Resided in retirement in Belfast. Died 8 Oct. 1940. Obituary, *I.L.T. & S.J.*, lxxiv (1940), 275; *Who's Who*.

MARRON, PETER DESMOND (b. 29 April 1913) s. of John Marron, of Newry, Co. Down, and Evelyn MacKinney; B.A. (T.C.D.); M 1946. 1950/H/02 [6 items].

MARTIN, CATHERINE MARY (b. 24 Nov. 1908) only d. of William Martin, J.P. (decd.), of Ongenstown, Navan, Co. Meath, and Mary Jane Kelly; B.A. (N.U.I.); M 1929. 1933/M/05 [2 items].

MARTIN, FRANCIS JOSEPH CHRISTOPHER (b. 23 Dec. 1923) only s. of Francis Martin (decd.), merchant, of 4 Kincora Park, Clontarf, Dublin, and Cecilia Mary O'Reilly; T1952. 1952/M/03 [3 items]. S.C., 3 March 1973. Judge of the Circuit Court, 1975-93.

MARTIN, MALACHI THOMAS JOSEPH (b. 10 March 1883) 2nd s. of James Martin (decd.), of 2 Ely Place, Galway, and Anne Tully; M 1925. 1928/M/04 [2 items].

MARTLEY, JOHN (b. 15 May 1844) 2nd s. of Henry Martley, Judge of the Landed Estates Court, late of Sherrington, Co. Dublin, and Harcourt Street, Dublin, and Marianne McNaghten; B.A. (T.C.D.); H 1866, M.T. T 1867. 1875/H/01 [5 items].

MASON, GEORGE CUFF (b. 30 July 1925) 2nd s. of Henry William Mason, F.R.C.S. (decd.), of 61 Lower Baggot Street, Dublin, and Jane Gertrude Collins; B.A. (N.U.I.); M 1936. 1948/T/20 [2 items].

MASON, WILLIAM HENRY CUFF (b. 1 Nov. 1913) eld. s. of Dr. Henry W. Mason, of 61 Lower Baggot Street, Dublin, and Jane Gertrude Collins; M 1934. 1937/T/04 [2 items].

MATHESON, ARTHUR VICTOR (b. 27 June 1878) eld. s. of Charles Louis Matheson of 20 Fitzwilliam Square, Dublin, and Elinor Tuthill; B.A. (T.C.D.); M 1900. 1903/M/08 [3 items]. S.C., 21 Dec. 1938. First parliamentary draftsman of the Irish Free State. Died 26 Dec. 1948. Portrait photograph reproduced (No. 5, between pp 148-9) in Mary Kotsonouris, *The Winding-up of the Dáil Courts, 1922-1925: an obvious duty* (Dublin, 2004); biographical note in ibid., p. 251.

MATHESON, CHARLES FREDERICK (b. 9 Aug. 1892) 2nd s. of Charles Louis Matheson, of 20 Fitzwilliam Square, Dublin, and Elinor Tuthill (decd.); B.A., LL.B. (Cantab.); M 1912. 1918/T/01 [2 items]. S.C., 3 July 1946.

MATHESON, CHARLES LOUIS (b. 3 Feb. 1851) 2nd s. of Robert Nathaniel Matheson of Rathmines, Dublin, Clerk of the Privy Council, and Victorine Jossevel; B.A. (T.C.D.); H 1871, M.T. E 1871. 1874/H/9 [2 items]. Auditor of the College Historical Society, 1874-5. Q.C., 1 July 1892. 3rd Serjeant, 9 Dec. 1911. 2nd Serjeant, 20 July 1912. 1st serjeant, 5 July 1913. Appt. Recorder of Belfast, 17 Sept. 1919. Died 20 May 1921.

Obituary, *I.L.T. & S.J.*, lv (1921), 135-6; *Who's Who*. Mentioned by V.T.H. Delany [q.v.], in his article 'The Bench and Bar in Ireland', as one of 'those who were at the forefront of their profession during the period'. Caricature (by C. Norman Kough [q.v.]), as 'Brains Matheson', in A.R. Hart, *A History of the King's Serjeants at Law in Ireland* (Dublin, 2000), Plate 23.

MATHESON, ROBERT EDWIN (b. 6 May 1845) eld. s. of Robert Nathaniel Matheson, Clerk of the Privy Council, of 42 Upper Rathmines, Dublin, and Victorine Jossevel; [B.A.?] (Queen's College, Galway); E 1870, M.T. M 1871. 1875/E/03 [6 items].

MATHEWS, JAMES STANLEY (b. 11 Feb. 1885) eld. s. of Patrick Mathews (decd.) of Mount Hanover, Co. Meath, and Elizabeth Thompson; M 1907. 1911/H/05 [2 items].

MATHEWS, PATRICK DUFF (b. 19 Dec. 1886) 2nd s. of Patrick Mathews (decd.), of Mount Hanover, Co. Meath, and Elizabeth Thompson; B.A. (New College Oxford); M 1909. 1914/H/03 [2 items].

MATHIESON, JOHN GERARD BRUCE (b. 20 July 1912) only s. of James Clark Mathieson (decd.), of Shanganagh Cottage, Ballybrack, Co. Dublin, and Georgina Kennedy; B.A. (T.C.D.); M 1932. 1939/M/12 [1 item].

MATTIMOE, BRENDAN JOSEPH (b. 15 Feb. 1918) 4th s. of Patrick Mattimoe, of Boyle, Co. Roscommon, and Harriett Molloy; M 1952. 1957/T/03 [2 items]. S.C., 4 Oct. 1976.

MATURIN, CHARLES (b. 12 July 1860) only surv. s. of Charles Maturin (decd.) of Leeson Street, Dublin, and Margaret Clarke; B.A. (T.C.D.); M 1885, G.I. M 1889. 1892/E/01 [7 items]. Professor of Civil Law and General Jurisprudence, T.C.D., 1909-15. R.B. McDowell and David Webb observe, in their *Trinity College Dublin 1592-1952: An academic history* (Cambridge, 1982), 414, that he was 'esteemed for his good conversation and his great knowledge of international law. But he had apparently no desire to put this knowledge to any use, either in the courts or in publications'. Died 1915. Obituary, *I.L.T. & S.J.*, xlix (28 Aug. 1915), 210.

MAUGHAN, DAVID MATTHEW (b. 13 Nov. 1939) 3rd s. of Kevin Matthew Maughan, consultant surgeon, of 11 Pembroke Park, Dublin, and Avice Hearn; B.C.L. (N.U.I.); M 1964. 1968/M/10 [1 item]. District Judge, Area No. 5 [Cavan].

MAUNDER, STEPHEN THEODORE LAYTON (b. 26 Sept. 1885) 4th s. of George William Maunder of Rathgar, Dublin, and Bertha Layton; M 1904. 1907/M/02 [2 items].

MAUNSELL, DUDLEY PHILIP WINTHROP (b. 22 Aug. 1883) 3rd s. of Robert George Maunsell of 36 Ulverton Road, Dalkey, Co. Dublin, and Dorothea Jane White; B.A. (T.C.D.); M 1907. 1910/T/01 [2 items]. Died Jan. 1948.

MAUNSELL, EDMUND ROBERT LLOYD (b. 18 Oct. 1852) eld. s. of John Maunsell, solicitor, of Edenmore, Raheny, Dublin, and Catherine Lloyd; LL.B. (T.C.D.); M 1873, I.T. H 1877. 1878/E/04 [6 items].

MAUNSELL, RICHARD JOHN CASWELL (b. 2 May 1878) only s. of Captain Mark Maunsell, late 1st Dragoons, of Oakly Park, Co. Kildare, and Mary Eliza Caswell (decd.); Cand. Bach. (T.C.D.); M 1901. 1905/H/08 [3 items]. Died 27 Sept. 1955.

MAXWELL, JAMES PATRICK (b. 12 Sept. 1864) 3rd s. of Patrick Maxwell, solicitor, of North Great George's Street, Dublin, and Annie Quill; B.A. (T.C.D.); M 1883, M.T. E 1884. 1886/T/08 [items]. Died 8 June 1947.

MAXWELL, THOMAS HENRY (b. 15 Sept. 1860) eld. s. of Joseph Archibald Maxwell of Upper Sackville Street, Dublin, and Elizabeth Pim; B.A. (T.C.D.); M 1883, M.T. T 1884. 1886/T/02 [6 items]. North-West Circuit. K.C., 27 Feb. 1918. Editor of the *Irish Reports* and of *The Irish Digest 1894-1918*. First editor of *The Northern Ireland Reports*, 1925-9. Author of a revision of C. Miller's *Irish Probate Practice* (Dublin, 1900) and of *An Outline of the Law of Landlord and Tenant and of Land Purchase in Ireland, for Students* (Dublin, 1909). Died 19 Sept. 1928. Obituaries, *I.L.T. & S.J.*, lxii (1928), 228-9, 234; and [1930] N.I.

MAY, GEORGE CHICHESTER (b. 25 May 1857) 2nd s. of George Augustus Chichester May, Lord Chief Justice of Ireland, of Fitzwilliam Square, Dublin, and Olivia Barrington (decd.); B.A. (T.C.D.); M 1879, I.T. M 1881. 1882/M/07 [5 items]. Land Judge's Court. Served in the Veterans' Corps. Died 2 Nov. 1924. Obituary, *I.L.T. & S.J.*, lviii (1924), 283.

MAYNE, DESMOND FRANCIS O'REILLY (b. 30 March 1922) only s. of Vincent Fawne Mayne, of 4 Herbert Park, Ballsbridge, Dublin, and Nina O'Reilly; B.A.; M 1939. 1943/M/08 [2 items]. Died (as a result of a road accident) 15 April 1939. Obituary, *I.L.T. & S.J.*, lxxiii (1939), 118.

MAYNE, HERBERT PELHAM (b. 1 Feb. 1877) s. of Pelham Joseph Mayne (decd.), solicitor, of 33 Merrion Square, Dublin, and Emma M. Foot; B.A. (T.C.D.); M 1896. 1899/T/05 [3 items]. Assistant Registrar of the Supreme Court. Died 20 Nov. 1945. Obituary, *I.L.T. & S.J.*, lxxix (1945), 291.

MAYNE, JOSEPH St CLAIR (b. 23 June 1846) eld. s. of James Arthur Mayne, solicitor, of Aughnamallagh House, Co. Monaghan, and Anna Bradley; T 1873, G.I. M 1873. 1877/M/05 [5 items].

MAYSTON, WILLIAM HUME (b. 22 July 1872) eld. s. of the Revd. W. Hume Mayston, M.A., of Kilbehenny Rectory, Co. Limerick, and Mary Jane Bolton; undergrad. (T.C.D.); M 1900. 1903/T/08 [3 items]. Died 8 Dec. 1951.

MEADE, BRIAN EDWARD FRANCIS (b. 11 Feb. 1946) young. s. of Thomas Meade, civil servant, of 13 Sunbury Gardens, Dartry Road, Dublin, and Alicia Enda Scallan; B.C.L. (N.U.I.); M 1964. 1967/M/08 [1 item].

MEADE, CHRISTOPHER HENRY B. (b. 8 Feb. 1858) only s. of Francis Meade (decd.), Q.C., of 22 Mountjoy Square, Dublin, and Caroline Greer; M.A. (Cambridge); M 1894. 1897/T/07 [6 items]. Died 13 Oct. 1927. Obituary, *I.L.T. & S.J.*, lx (1926), 259.

MEADE, JOSEPH MICHAEL (b. 28 Aug. 1889) 4th s. of the Rt. Hon. Joseph M. Meade (decd.), of St. Michael's, Merrion, Dublin, and Ada Willis; B.A., ex-Scholar, Mod. (T.C.D.); M 1913. 1920/T/06 [2 items].

MEAGHER, DOMINICK EDWARD (b. 13 Dec. 1879) eld. s. of Philip Meagher of Moyville, Clontarf, Dublin, and Brigid Donnelly; B.A. (N.U.I.); M 1908. 1911/T/03 [2 items]. Died 9 Aug. 1944. Obituary, *I.L.T. & S.J.*, lxxviii (1944), 213.

MEAGHER, JAMES FRANCIS (b. 24 April 1892) only s. of John Francis Meagher, J.P., of Kingston Square, Mitchelstown, Co. Cork, and Julia Leonard; Sen. Mod. B.A., LL.B. (T.C.D.); M 1911. 1914/M/01 [2 items]. Died 1 March 1944. Obituary, *I.L.T. & S.J.*, lxxviii (1944), 73. Mentioned in Gerard A Lee, *A Memoir of the South-Western Circuit* (Dublin, 1990), 54-5.

MEAGHER, LAURENCE (b. 21 Nov. 1904) 2nd s. of Laurence Meagher, of Clonmeon, Banteer, Co. Cork, and Mary Fitzgerald; M 1938. 1942/T/06 [2 items].

MEARES, KEITH MUNRO (b. 9 July 1902) eld. s. of George Munro Meares, of Rozelle, Shrewsbury Road, Dublin, and Minnie Foddy; T 1924. 1924/T/02 [2 items].

MECREDY, MERVYN HUGH (b. 21 Nov. 1880) 2nd s. of Thomas Tighe Mecredy, solicitor, Local Government Board Ireland, of 91 Merrion Square West, Dublin, and Isabella Greer Purdon; B.A., LL.B. (T.C.D.); M 1900. 1905/H/06 [2 items]. Died 30 Dec. 1916.

MEEHAN, JAMES AUGUSTINE (b. 27 Aug. 1898) 2nd s. of Charles Meehan (decd.), of Prussia Street, Dublin, and Mary Leetch (decd.); M 1953. 1957/T/06 [2 items].

MEEHAN, JOSEPH PATRICK (b. 9 May 1920) younger s. of Thomas Meehan, of 105 Shandon Park, Phibsboro, Dublin, and Brigid Bergin; M 1944. 1948/M/06 [2 items].

MEEK, SAMUEL REA (b. 8 Aug. 1864) eld. s.of M. Meek of Belfast, and Anna Rea; B.A. (R.U.I.); M 1893. 1906/T/03 [2 items].

MEENAN, JAMES FRANCIS (b. 18 Oct. 1910) eld. s. of Professor James Nahor Meenan, M.D., of 28 Fitzwilliam Square, Dublin, and Mary Elizabeth Cleary; M 1929. 1935/M/04 [2 items]. Professor of Political Economy at U.C.D. Author, *inter alia*, of: *The Italian Corporative System* (Cork, 1944); *Centenary History of the Literary and Historical Society of University College, Dublin, 1855-1955* (Tralee, [1956]); *The Irish economy since 1922* (Liverpool. 1970); and *George O'Brien: a biographical memoir* (1980). Died 25 May 1987. See biographical essay by Charles Lysaght, and photograph, in the 2005 reprint of Meenan's *Centenary History of the Literary and Historical Society*, ix-xxiii.

MEENAN, PATRICK NAHOR (b. 30 June 1917) 2nd s. of James Nahor Meenan, M.D., of 28 Fitzwilliam Square, Dublin, and Mary Elizabeth Cleary; MB, B.Ch, B.A.O. (N.U.I.); M 1941. 1944/T/06 [2 items]. M.D. (U.C.D.) Author, *inter alia*, of *The Essentials of Virus Diseases* (1951); *Guidelines for preparing information and advice to the general public on healthy eating* (Dublin, 1984); *St Patrick's Blue & Saffron: A Miscellany of U.C.D. Sport since 1895* (Dublin, 1997).

MEGAW, ROBERT DICK (b. 26 Oct. 1867) eld. s. of John Megaw, J.P., farmer, of Ballyboyland, Co. Antrim, and Ellen Dick; M.A., LL.B. (R.U.I.); H 1891, M.T. M 1892. 1893/M/01 [9 items]. North-East Circuit. K.C., 25 Feb. 1921. M.P. for Co. Antrim in Parliament of N.I., and Parliamentary Secretary to the Minister of Home Affairs, 1921-25. Commissioner to inquire into the administration of the Housing Acts by Belfast Corporation, 1925-6. Judicial Commissioner, Land Purchase Commission (N.I.), 1927-37; judge of the Chancery Division (N.I.), 12 Nov. 1932 - 6 Nov. 1943. Died 2 May 1947. Obituary, *I.L.T. & S.J.*, lxxxi (10 May 1947), 113; *Who's Who*.

MEHRA, NANAH CHAND (b. 8 Dec. 1888) 2nd s. of Ishar Dass Mehra, of Peshawar City, India; M 1914. 1917/T/16 [2 items].

MEHTA, MADAN GOPAL (b. 22 April 1895) 3rd s. of Mehta Ganpat Rai, of Abbottabad, North-West Frontier, India; M 1915. 1918/T/05 [2 items].

MELDON, ALBERT GREGORY (b. 25 May 1845) 5th s. of James Dillon Meldon, solicitor, of Casino, Co. Dublin, and Bedilia Myhan [?]; M 1862, M.T. H 1864. 1868/M/6 [6 items]. Resident Magistrate, 1883-1910. Died 27 Nov. 1924. Obituary, *I.L.T. & S.J.*, lviii (1924), 295.

MELDON, Lieut.-Colonel JAMES AUSTIN (b. 13 July 1870) eld. s. of Austin Meldon, D.L. (decd.), of 15 Merrion Square, Dublin, and Margaret Ryan; C.B.E.; 1920. 1920/M/10 [2 items]. Mentioned in Maurice Healy's *Stay me with Flagons* (1939).

MELDON, WALTER DOMINICK (b. 4 Aug. 1872) 2nd s. of John J. Meldon (solicitor) of 60 Northumberland Road, Dublin, and Kate Blackney; cand. bachelor (R.U.I.); M 1890. 1894/H/07 [6 items]. Died 15 April 1932. Obituary, *I.L.T. & S.J.*, lxvi (1932), 103.

MENARY, WILLIAM JAMES (b. 16 June 1926) eld. s. of James Menary (decd.), of 1 Earlsfort Mansions, Dublin, and Winifred Mary Corr; B.A., LL.B. (T.C.D.); M 1944. 1949/H/02 [3 items].

MENON, KRISHNA Barrister-at-Law, Middle Temple. Admitted to degree *honoris causa*. 1952/T/06 [2 items]. The award of the degree *honoris causa* is unique for the period, and its peculiarity is reinforced by the circumstance that details of this Indian politician's date of birth and parentage are not held at King's Inns. Krishna Menon, described by *The Times* obituarist as 'this remarkable yet unlikeable man', was born at Calicut on 3 May 1897. Having come to England in 1924 as a member of Mrs. Annie Besant's circle, he studied at the London School of Economics, and was called to the Bar at the Middle Temple. In London he came to prominence as General Secretary of the India League, as a member of the Labour Party (sitting on the St. Pancras Borough Council), and as the first editor of Pelican Books. After Indian Independence he served, 1947-52, as his country's first High Commissioner in London. In 1953 he become a member of the Upper House of the Indian Parliament, and served as Nehru's Defence Minister, 1957-62, an office he held at the time of the war with Pakistan. Died 5 Oct. 1974. Obituary, *The Times*, 7 Oct. 1974.

MEREDITH, ARTHUR FRANCIS CAREW (b. 11 Oct. 1861) 6th s. of William Rice Meredith, solicitor, of 42 Kenilworth Square, Dublin, and Isabella A. Standish; cand. bachelor (T.C.D.); T 1883, M.T. H 1884. 1886/T/01 [8 items]. K.C., 7 July 1906. Died 16 May 1938. Obituary, *I.L.T. & S.J.*, lxxii (1938), 157-8, 255.

MEREDITH, JAMES CREED (b. 28 Nov. 1875) 2nd s. of Sir James Creed Meredith, LL.D., of Cloneevin, Co. Dublin, and Nellie Graves Meredith; M.A. (R.U.I.); M 1898. 1901/M/08 [3 items]. North-East Circuit. K.C., 27 Feb. 1918. Protestant Nationalist, involved in the Howth gun-running. President of the Dáil's Supreme Court, 1920-22: see Mary Kotsonouris, *Retreat from Revolution: The Dáil Courts, 1920-24* (Dublin, 1994), *passim*. Judge of the High Court, 1924-37; of the Supreme Court, 1937-42. Vice-President of the Supreme Saar Plebiscite Tribunal, 1934-5. Died 14 August 1942. Obituary, *I.L.T. & S.J.*, lxxvi (1942), 211, 233, 240, 259; *Who's Who*. Author of commentaries on Kant's *Critique of Aesthetic Judgment* (1912) and Kant's *Critique of Teleological Judgment* (1919); of a treatise on *Proportional Representation*; and of a novel *The Rainbow in the Valley* (1939). Portrait by Norman French McLachlan in King's Inns: see Wanda Ryan-Smolin, *King's Inns Portraits* (1992), 47. Profile in bronze reproduced (No. 1 between pp 148-9) in Mary Kotsonouris, *The Winding-up of the Dáil Courts, 1922-1925*: an obvious duty (Dublin, 2004); which see *passim*, incl. biographical note on p. 252.

MEREDITH, RICHARD EDMUND (b. 18 Nov. 1855) 4th s. of Wiliam Rice Meredith, solicitor, of 3 Kenilworth Terrace, Dublin, and Isabella Standish; M 1874, M.T. E 1876. 1879/H/02 [6 items]. Q.C., 1 July 1892. Judge of the Land Commission 1898-1906. Master of the Rolls 1906-12. Retired 1912. Died 28 Jan. 1916. Obituary, *I.L.T. & S.J.*, l (1916), 37; *Who's Who*. See Ball, *Judges*, ii, 382.

MEREDITH, RICHARD EDMUND (b. 5 March 1884) 2nd s. of the Rt. Hon. R.E. Meredith M.R. of 31 Fitzwilliam Square, Dublin, and Annie Pollock; B.A. (T.C.D.); M 1904. 1907/T/09 [1 item]. Served with the British Red Cross; died of dysentery in Italy, 20 Aug. 1917. [Name on the Bar War Memorial].

METUH, JOSEPH CHUKWUNONYELU (b. 12 Dec. 1933) eld. s. of A.E. Metuh, proprietor of St. Augustine's College, Onitsha, of 79 Nenn Road, South Onitsha, Nigeria, and Teresa Ojiakor; B.C.L. (U.C.D.); M 1956. 1961/M/09 [2 items].

MICHAEL, EDMOND LABIB (b. 7 Dec. 1938) eld. s. of Michael Michael, motor engineer, of Bo, Sierra Leone, West Africa, and Juliette [?]; B.C.L. (N.U.I.); M 1959. 1964/M/02 [1 item].

MICKS, EDWARD CHRISTOPHER (b. 30 Dec. 1900) young. s. of William Lawson Micks, M.A., of 3 Palmerston Villas, Rathmines, Dublin, and Isabel Meyrick; Sen. Mod., B.A., LL.B. (T.C.D.); M 1922. 1925/M/19 [2 items]. S.C., 2 March 1948. Died 1973. Obituary, *I.L.T. & S.J.*, cvii (15 Dec. 1973), 311.

MILEY, JOHN FELIX (b. 10 Aug. 1886) eld. s. of Daniel O'Connell Miley of The Chalet, Foxrock, Dublin, and Eleanor Rosenthal; B.A. (Oxford); M 1908. 1911/T/04 [2 items]. S.C., 11 Dec. 1952. Legal adviser to the Department of Local Government, -1946, and authority on town planning. Died 1967. Obituary, *I.L.T. & S.J.*, ci (21 Jan. 1967), 28.

MILL-ARDEN, ERWAN JOSEPH (b. 19 March 1943) only s. of Leo Victor Mill-Arden (decd.), property owner, of 3 Redesdale Road, Mount Merrion, Co. Dublin, and Bridget McMahon; B.C.L. (N.U.I.); M 1962. 1965/M/04 [1 item]. S.C., 3 Oct. 1994.

MILLAR, LIONEL (b. 4 May 1925) eld. s. of Stanley Millar, engineer, of Christ Church Island, Barbados, and Rita Porter; B.C.L., LL.B. (N.U.I.); M 1958. 1964/E/01 [3 items]. At the Benchers' meeting on 27 May 1964 [Minute Book 1957 to 1964, pp 338-9]:

> 'The Under-Treasurer informed the meeting that Mr. Millar had requested that the report of his admission to Degree & Call to the Bar be not given to the Press for publication. [339] This request was rejected as contrary to established custom.'

MILLER, Sir ALEXANDER EDWARD, C.S.I. (n.d.) only s. of Alexander Miller, late of Ballycastle, Co. Antrim, and Jane McNeill; L.I. H 1852, called to the Bar, L.I. [1854] 1897/M/14 [2 items]. T.C.D. Gold Medallist. Editor of the English *Solicitors' Journal*, 1863-9. Appt. a Master in Lunacy and knighted, 1889. Legal member of the Council of the Governor General of India, 1891-6. Practised at the Irish Bar following his retirement to Ireland. Died 13 Sept. 1903. Obituary, *I.L.T. & S.J.*, xxxvii (1903), 404, 422.

MILLIN, SAMUEL SHANNON (b. 8 Sept. 1864) young. s. of John Millin (decd.), gentleman, of Belfast, and Jane Shannon; B.A. (R.U.I. / Q.C.B.); M 1891. 1894/T/08 [7 items]. Author of *Sidelights on Belfast History* (Belfast and London, 1932) [also *Additional Sidelights* ... (1936)], of several shorter works on local historical themes, and of a memoir of G.F. Savage-Armstrong (Belfast, 1906), and an introduction to the latter's *Poems* (1917). Died at Harpenden, Herts., c. 1947.

MILLS, HENRY McGILDOWNEY (b. 4 Sept. 1850) 2nd s. of Henry Mills, solicitor, of 12 Upper Temple St, Dublin, and of Inver, Co. Antrim, and Mary Casement; B.A. (T.C.D.); E 1868, M.T. T 1871. 1876/M/02 [4 items].

MILLS, RICHARD LOUIS [KENNETH] (b. 21 Aug. 1924) 3rd s. of William Mills, farmer, of Drumlarney, Derrylane, Co. Cavan, and Francis Annie Wood; B.A. (T.C.D.); M 1958. Awarded Society's Prize. 1961/M/01 [2 items]. President of the University Philosophical Society, T.C.D., 1949-50. Known as 'Kenneth' Mills. S.C., 27 Feb. 1975.

MITCHELL, REGINALD ALFRED (b. 2 June 1869) 4th s. of Robert John Mitchell, M.A., D.Litt., Inspector of Registration, Lld, of Lever House, Clonskea, Dublin, and Marianne Fry; LL.D. (T.C.D.); M 1891. 1895/M/05 [5 items]. Death noted, without date, in T.C.D. *Register of Alumni*, 5th ed., 1950.

MITCHELL, ROBERT ARMSTRONG (b. 15 Aug. 1868) eld. s. of William Charles Mitchell (decd.), J.P., of Marmont, Strandtown, Belfast, and Robertina Jane Mitchell; M 1898, M.T. H 1890. 1899/E/03 [3 items].

MOANE, MICHAEL (b. 1 Nov. 1853) 2nd s. of James Moane (decd.), gentleman, of Crumlin, Co. Monaghan, and Mary Duffy; M 1881, G.I. M 1883. 1884/M/02 [6 items].

MOCKLER, JAMES SWAYNE (b. 6 May 1883) eld. s. of Thomas Mockler, of Ardeen, Blackrock, Co. Cork, and Caroline Leahy; M 1910. 1913/T/09 [3 items].

MOFFAT, CHARLES BETHUNE (b. 16 Jan. 1859) eld. s. of James Moffat J.P., of Ballyhyland, Co. Wexford, and Anne Harrison; B.A. (T.C.D.); M 1878, M.T. M 1880. 1881/M/11 [7 items].

MOFSOVITZ, LIONEL JOSEPH (b. 8 Sept. 1906) eld. s. of Simon Mofsovitz, of 60 Grosvenor Road, Rathgar, Dublin, and Mary Goldberg; B.A., LL.B. (T.C.D.). Includes letter re alleged breach of the Rules, by 'Lionel Morris', April 1932. 1927/M/21 [3 items].

MOLES, JAMES (b. 29 Aug. 1872) eld. s. of Edward Moles of Bellevue, Ballymena, Co. Antrim, and Margaret Jane Carson; M 1899. 1902/M/06 [3 items]. Died 1 Oct. 1943. Obituary, *I.L.T. & S.J.*, lxxvii (1943), 249.

MOLLOY, MARTIN JOSEPH (b. 17 Dec. 1896) 2nd s. of William Molloy, of Rose Inn Street, Kilkenny City, and Honoria Crotty; E 1927. 1927/M/25 [2 items]. Died 24 Oct. 1948. Obituary, *I.L.T. & S.J.*, lxxxii (1948), 262.

MOLONEY, HENRY JOHN (b. 19 Aug. 1887) eld. s. of John Moloney, solicitor, of Midleton, Co. Cork, and Kate Duggan; undergraduate (Q.C.C.); M 1906. 1909/M/01 [3 items]. S.C., 6 May 1927. Bencher of King's Inns, E 1939.

MOLONY, HENRY PATRICK (b. 10 March 1884) 2nd eld. s. of Thomas W. Molony, J.P., of 10 Castlewood Park, Rathmines, Dublin, and Mary Shanks; M.A. (N.U.I.); M 1910. 1916/T/01 [3 items].

MOLONY, JOHN (b. 17 Dec. 1854) 2nd s. of James Molony, F.R.C.S.I., of Clonmore, Tulla, Co. Clare, and Rebecca Greene; B.A. (Q.C.G.); E 1875, M.T. T 1877. 1879/E/02 [6 items].

MOLONY, THOMAS FRANCIS (b. 31 Jan. 1865) young. s. of James Molony of Bolton Street, Dublin, and Jane Sweetman; B.A., LL.B. and Senior Moderator (T.C.D.); M 1884. 1887/M/02 [6 items]. Q.C., 22 April 1899. 2nd Serjeant, 9 Dec. 1911, and Bencher, 1911. Contested West Toxteth Division of Liverpool, Dec. 1910. Solicitor-General, 1912-13; Attorney-General, 1913. Judge of the King's Bench Division, 1913-15; Lord Justice of Appeal, 1915-18; Honorary Officer of the Dublin Veterans' Corps; Lord Chief Justice, 1918-24. Baronet 1925. Visitor of Trinity College, 1918-31. As Vice-Chancellor of Dublin University, 1931-49, made a donation to Trinity College for the erection in the 1937 Reading Room of a tablet to the memory of the Revd. Michael Moore, D.D. (1640-1726). Bencher of the Inn of Court of N.I., 1926, and of the Middle Temple, 1933. Died 3 Sept. 1949. Obituary, *I.L.T. & S.J.*, lxxxiii (1949), 231; *Who's Who*; *Debrett's Illustrated Baronetage*. See Ball, *Judges*, ii, 383-4; W.N. Osborough, *Irish Jurist*, ix (1974), 87; *Oxford DNB* (2004) [article by Daire Hogan]. Portrait by Sir William Orpen in King's Inns: see Wanda Ryan-Smolin, *King's Inns Portraits* (1992), 648

MOLONY, WALTER HUGH (b. 8 June 1899) 3rd s. of Dr. Patrick Bernard Molony, of Dunna-nDroichead, Cappamore, Co. Limerick, and Ellen Mary Condon (decd.); M 1922. 1925/T/03 [2 items]. District Justice, Dublin Metropolitan District. Died 18 Sept. 1971. Obituary, *I.L.T. & S.J.*, cv (1971), 310.

MONAHAN, HENRY JAMES (b. 18 Oct. 1871) eld. s. of Henry James Monahan, Registrar of the late consolidated Nisi Prius Court, of Stillorgan Park, Dublin, and Mary O'Brien; H 1893. 1895/M/02 [7 items]. Q.C. Legal adviser, Irish Land Commission. Died at Oxford 11 May 1950. Obituary, *I.L.T. & S.J.*, lxxxiv (1950), 123.

MONCK, WILLIAM HENRY STANLEY (b. 21 April 1839) 3rd s. of the Revd. Thomas Stanley Monck (decd.) of Inistoge, Co. Kilkenny, and Lydia Elinor Kennedy; M.A. (T.C.D.); E 1869, M.T. E 1870. 1873/T/2 [2 items].

MONGEY, EDWARD GABRIEL (b. 30 July 1925) young. s. of William Paul Mongey (decd.), of Newport Road, Castlebar, Co. Mayo, and Cecilia Philbin; M 1949. 1955/H/01 [2 items]. Probate Officer, and Registrar of the Supreme Court. Author of *Probate Practice in a Nutshell* (Dublin, 1980; revised edition, 1993)

MONKS, GERALD CHRISTOPHER (b. 30 Dec. 1919) 3rd s. of Richard Monks, of 22 Park Street, Inchicore, Co. Dublin, and Mary Anne Flynn; B.A., LL.B.(Hons); M 1952. 1955/M/12 [2 items].

MONKS, Captain THOMAS FRANCIS (b. 22 Aug. 1889) eld. s. of Thomas Francis Monks, LL.D., of 2 Waterloo Road, Dublin, and Madge O'Brien; E 1919. 1919/E/04 [2 items]. Called to English Bar, M 1923. S.C., 12 April 1937. Bencher 1943. Died 1961. Obituary, *I.L.T. & S.J.*, xcv (25 Feb. 1961), 50.

MONROE, JAMES HARVEY (b. 7 April 1884) only s. of Samuel Holmes Monroe, M.A., solicitor, of Armagh, Co. Armagh, and Mary Elizabeth Fullerton; B.A., LL.B. (T.C.D.); M 1906. 1909/T/08 [2 items]. K.C., 27 July 1920. Bencher (N.I. Inn), 1926. Knighted. Puisne Judge of Lahore. Died 21 May 1944. Obituary, *I.L.T. & S.J.*, lxxviii (1944), 148.

MONTGOMERY, DAVID LOUIS (b. 25 Aug. 1938) eld. s. of William B. Montgomery, solicitor, of 52 St. Lawrence Road, Clontarf, Dublin, and Kathleen Durkan, solicitor; M 1958. 1962/M/10 [1 item]. S.C., 6 Oct. 1980.

MOONAN, GEORGE ALOYSIUS (b. 3 Nov. 1872) 2nd s. of Richard Moonan (decd.) of Drogheda, Co. Louth, and Mary Anne Tiernan; M 1908. 1911/M/08 [2 items]. S.C., 25 June 1930. Early member of the Gaelic League. Author (with Mary Hayden) of *A Short History of the Irish People* (Dublin, 1921; London, 1924; and later editions for schools). Judge of the Circuit Court, 1932-44. Died 15 Dec. 1945. Obituary, *I.L.T. & S.J.*, lxxix (1945), 308.

MOONEY, EDMUND WILLIAM BENJAMIN (b. 2 Sept. 1887) eld. s. of Edmund Mooney, J.P., of Elm Green, Castleknock, Co. Dublin, and Gretta McCartan; B.A. (Oxford); M 1909. 1912/T/15 [2 items].

MOONEY, FREDERICK MICHAEL (b. 23 June 1876) 4th s. of William Mooney of Leixlip Castle, Co. Kildare, and Catharine [Merlehan]; M 1896. 1901/T/07 [3 items].

MOONEY, GERALD KINGSTON (b. 1 Dec. 1892) eld. s. of Gerald Mooney, J.P., of Vartry Lodge, Killiney, Co. Dublin, and Louise Crolly; M 1909. 1914/H/04 [2 items].

MOONEY, JOHN JOSEPH (b. 10 Aug. 1874) 5th s. of James G. Mooney (decd.) of 26 Mountjoy Square, Dublin, and Maria Teresa Doran; M 1892. 1895/M/10 [5 items]. Nationalist M.P. for Dublin South, 1900-1906; for Newry, 1906-18. Knighted (K.B.E.) 1920. Died 12 April 1934. Obituary, *I.L.T. & S.J.*, lxviii (1934), 103.

MOONEY, JOSEPH JOHN (b. 24 June 1894) eld. s. of Joseph Mooney, of Cabra Lodge, Dublin, and Mary Aloysius Donnelly; M 1914.1917/M/05 [2 items]. Leinster Circuit. Judge Advocate General. Died 1952. Mentioned (by Dermot F. Gleeson) in James Meenan (ed.), *Centenary History of Lit. and Hist. Soc. of U.C.D.*, 161.

MOONEY, NIALL (b. 16 Dec. 1929) eld. s. of William Mooney, Chief Superintendent C.G., of Heath House, Abbeyleix, Co. Leix, and Johanna Ward; B.A. (N.U.I.); M 1949. 1952/M/04 [2 items].

MOONEY, PHILIP (b. 19 July 1908) eld. s. of Philip Mooney (decd.), of Moonvale, Marlyn Road, Ballsbridge, Dublin, and Mary Rose Hudson; M 1940. 1944/T/10 [2 items]. Hotelier. Died *c.* 1955.

MOORE, ARTHUR ROBERT (b. 22 July 1883) 2nd s. of John William Moore, Knight, M.D., of 40 Fitzwilliam Square, Dublin, and Dame Louisa Emma Armstrong; B.A. (T.C.D.); H 1904. 1906/M/08 [2 items]. Captain, Royal Fusiliers, M.C. Died on the Somme, 1 July 1916. [Name on the Bar War Memorial, and at Thiepval].

MOORE, CHARLES TYRELL (b. 9 Dec. 1892) eld. s. of Charles Edward Moore of Calcutta, India, and Jenny Seth; M 1912. 1915/T/07 [2 items].

MOORE, EDMUND JOHN (b. 10 March 1842) 7th s. of James Moore (decd.) of Northampton, and Sarah Harday (decd.); B.A., LL.B. (London); M 1903. 1906/H/03 [3 items]. Died 1911: *I.L.T. & S.J.*, xlv (5 August 1911), 193.

MOORE, HELEN THERESE (b. 10 March 1945) eld. d. of Patrick C. Moore, solicitor, of 17 Leeson Park, Dublin, and Nell McGovern; M 1965. 1968/M/14 [1 item].

MOORE, HUGH HAMILTON (b. 24 Sept. 1847) eld. s. of Cecil Moore of Gilford Lodge, Co. Dublin, and Emily Catherine Battye; T 1889. 1890/T/10 [2 items]. Appt. County Court Judge for Tipperary, 29 Nov. 1898. Died 21 Feb. 1933. Obituary, *I.L.T. & S.J.*, lxvii (1933), 69, 74, 129, 142, 293.

MOORE, JOHN WILLIAM (b. 22 March 1892) only s. of Edward Moore, of 6 Albert Terrace, Ashfield Road, Ranelagh, Dublin, and Nora Collins; M 1923. 1926/T/02 [2 items].

MOORE, JOSEPH HENRY HAMILTON (b. 24 May 1852) 2nd s. of James Hamilton Moore, solicitor, of 42 Mountjoy Sq, Dublin, and Anne C. Abbott; M 1872, M.T. E 1874. 1879/E/03 [2 items]. County Court judge in England. Died 21 Feb. 1933.

MOORE, SAMUEL (b. 24 Jan. 1868) 3rd s. of John Moore (decd.) of Sallow Park, Ferry Bank, Co. Waterford, and Mary Moore; LL.B. (T.C.D.), ex-auditor and Plunkett Gold Medallist, Law Stud. Deb. Soc. K.I; M 1898. 1901/E/02 [3 items]. Leinster Circuit. K.C., 25 Feb. 1921. Died 1924. Obituary, *I.L.T. & S.J.*, lviii (13 Dec. 1924), 307.

MOORE, THEODORE CONYNGHAM KINGSMILL (b. 16 March 1893) only s. of Henry Kingsmill Moore, D.D., Canon of St. Patrick's, of Cedar Mount, Dundrum, Dublin, and Constance Turpin; M 1914. 1918/M/02 [2 items]. Auditor of the College Historical Society, 1918-9. S.C., 12 April 1935. Senator (Dublin University), 1943-7. Appt. Judge of the High Court 10 June 1947; of the Supreme Court, 1951-65. Died 21 Jan. 1979. Joint author (with T.U. Odell [q.v.] of *The Landlord and Tenant Act, 1931, fully annotated: with historical and explanatory introduction. and appendix of statutes and forms* (1932). Author of *A man may fish* (London: Herbert Jenkins, 1960; and later editions). See Louis McRedmond (ed.), *Modern Irish Lives*.

MOORE, THOMAS LEVINS (b. 10 April 1871) only s. of Andrew Thomas Moore (decd.), J.P., of Ashton, Co. Dublin, and Anna Levins; B.A. (T.C.D.); M 1889. 1896/E/01 [3 items]. Died 25 Nov. 1937.

MOORE, WILLIAM (b. 22 Nov. 1864) eld. s. of William Moore, M.D., Physician in Ordinary to H.M. the Queen in Ireland, of 56 Fitzwilliam Square, Dublin and Moore Lodge, Co. Antrim, and Sidney B. Fuller; B.A. (T.C.D.); H 1885, L.I. T 1886. 1887/M/14 [9 items]. President of the University Philosophical Society, T.C.D., 1886-7. Q.C., 22 April 1899. Unionist M.P., 1899-1917 [N. Antrim, 1899-1906; N. Armagh, Nov. 1907-1917]. Parliamentary private secretary to George Wyndham as Chief Secretary, 1902-4. Senior Crown Prosecutor, Belfast, 1915-17. Treasurer of King's Inns, 1918-20. Judge of the King's Bench Division of the High Court, 1917-21. Privy Councillor 1921. Lord Justice of Appeal in N.I., 17 Oct. 1921-2 Nov. 1925. Lord Chief Justice of Northern Ireland, 2 Nov. 1925 – 30 Nov. 1937. Created a Baronet 3 June 1932. Died 28 Nov. 1944. Obituaries, *I.L.T. & S.J.*, lxxviii (1944), 304, 315-6; [1945] N.I. Mentioned in Maurice Healy, *The Old Munster Circuit*, 266. See: *Who's Who*; *Debrett's Illustrated Baronetage*; Ball, *Judges*, ii, 386; and Kate Newmann, *Dictionary of Ulster Biography* (Belfast, 1993).

MOORHEAD, FREDERICK WILLIAM (b. 27 Sept. 1864) 7th s. of M. J. Moorhead (decd.), M.D., F.R.C.S.I., of Tullamore, King's Co., and Julia Humphreys; B.A., LL.B. (T.C.D.); M 1884. 1887/T/08 [6 items]. Emigrated to Western Australia, 1889. Attorney-General, Western Australia, 1901. Judge of the Supreme Court of Western Australia, 1902. Died 1903. Obituary, *I.L.T. & S.J.*, xxxvii (1903), 42.

MOOSA, SAIT ESHAQ (b. 1 Jan. 1897) only s. of Sait Bacchu Moosa (decd.), of Phoolgach, Amretalla Street, Calcutta, Bengal, India; M 1914. 1918/H/03 [2 items].

MORAN, EILEEN MARY (b. 10 June 1922) eld. d. of John Moran, civil servant, of 'Somerton', Donabate, Dublin, and Eileen McAlister; B.A. (N.U.I.); M 1940. Awarded Society's Exhibition prize. 1943/M/03 [2 items].

MORAN, FRANCES ELIZABETH (b. 6 Dec. 1892) 2nd d. of Senator James Moran, of St. James', Clontarf, Dublin, and Elizabeth Faulkiner; B.A., Sen. Mod., LL.D; M 1922.

1924/M/01 [2 items]. Professor of property law at King's Inns, 1932-1968. First woman to become Senior Counsel, 9 May 1941. Reid Professor, T.C.D., 1925-30. Professor of Laws, T.C.D., 1934-44; Regius Professor of Laws, T.C.D., 1944-63 (first woman professor in T.C.D.). Died 1977. Obituaries in *The Times*; *Trinity Trust News* (R.F.V. Heuston), vol. iii, No. 2 (March 1978), 13; and see also R.F.V. Heuston, in *Dublin University Law Journal*, xi (1989), 1-9. Benefaction to T.C.D. Law School. Portraits in T.C.D.: see Anne Crookshank and David Webb, *Paintings and Sculptures in Trinity College Dublin* (Dublin, 1990), 99. *Who's Who*; Louis McRedmond (ed.), *Modern Irish Lives*.

MORAN, LIAM BRIAN (b. 25 Jan. 1911) 2nd s. of John Moran, solicitor, of Minnowbrook House, Terenure, Dublin, and Elizabeth Richardson; M 1929. 1932/M/07 [2 items]. As 'William' Brian Moran., S.C., 28 Feb. 1964.

MORAN, NORBERT LOUIS (b. 7 Oct. 1855) 3rd surv. s. of William Moran of St. Edmondsbury, Lucan, Co. Dublin, and Elizabeth E. Moran; M.A. (T.C.D.); M 1879, M.T. H 1881. 1883/E/04 [5 items].

MORAN, PATRICK JOSEPH (b. 13 Aug. 1943) only s. of Joseph Moran, merchant, of Avondale House, Mulranny, Co. Mayo, and Florence Mullen; B.C.L. (N.U.I.); M 1968. 1966/M/04 [1 item].

MORAN, THOMAS ALOYSIUS (b. 28 June 1919) eld. s. of Patrick J. Moran, of 77 Whitworth Road, Glasnevin, Co. Dublin, and Anne Lowe; M 1952. 1956/T/04 [2 items].

MORELL, WILFRID LAWSON (b. 20 Oct. 1866) young. s. of James Morell, Commissioner of National Education, of Lennoxvale, Belfast, and Mary Brown; B.A. (R.U.I. / Q.C.B.); M 1895. 1899/E/04 [5 items]. Died 13 Jan. 1909: *I.L.T. & S.J.*, xliii (1909), 28.

MORGAN, JOHN HENRY SPREAD (b. 28 Sept.1858) only s. of Edmund Moore Mulcahy (decd.), J.P., of Garranlea, Co. Tipperary, and Susan Westropp Morgan; B.A., LL.B. (T.C.D.); E 1882, M.T. H 1884. 1885/E/04 [6 items]. Editor of *The New Irish Constitution. An Exposition and some Arguments* (London: The Eighty Club, 1912)

MORGAN, THOMAS LAMSDEN (b. 13 March 1922) only s. of Major Thomas Poole Morgan (retd.), R.A., of Kilnagleary, Carrigaline, Co. Cork, and Muriel Lumsden; B.A. (T.C.D.); M 1942. 1951/H/04 [2 items].

MORGAN-BYRNE, HENRY ALEXANDER (b. 16 April 1859) only s. of James P. Byrne (decd.), solicitor, of Brooklaw, Chapelizod, Dublin, and M. Morgan; H 1891 [solicitor, Larne, Co. Antrim]. 1891/M/16 [5 items]. Formerly a land agent. Remembered by Garrett Gill (q.v.) Died 9 May 1938. Obituary, *I.L.T. & S.J.*, lxxii (1938), 145.

MORIARTY, JOHN F. (b. 26 March 1870) 4th s. of Oliver Moriarty (decd.), Resident Magistrate, of Killarney, Co. Kerry, and Helena Morrogh; T 1907. 1907/M/09 [2 items]. Died 18 Nov. 1941. Obituary, *I.L.T. & S.J.*, lxxv (1941), 304, 309.

MORIARTY, JOHN FRANCIS (b. 17 Dec. 1854) 2nd s. of John Moriarty, solicitor, of Mallow, Co. Cork, and Ellen O'Connell; B.A. (T.C.D.); M 1873, M.T. M 1875. 1877/H/01 [6 items]. Munster Circuit. Q.C, March 1904. 3rd Serjeant, 5 June 1908. 1st Serjeant, 14 Jan. 1910. In one year (1913) successively Solicitor-General, Attorney-General, and Lord Justice of Appeal. Died 1915. See *Who's Who*; Ball, *Judges*, ii, 384. Mentioned in Maurice Healy, *The Old Munster Circuit*, 80-88; and by V.T.H. Delany [q.v.], who speaks of his 'robust advocacy', in 'The Bench and Bar in Ireland', xxxii. Caricature (by C. Norman Kough [q.v.]), in A.R. Hart, *A History of the King's Serjeants at Law in Ireland* (Dublin, 2000), Plate 20.

MORIARTY, MICHAEL (b. 10 Aug. 1946) only s. of James Moriarty, surgeon, of 38 Mount Merrion Avenue, Blackrock, Co. Dublin, and Nora Diamond; B.C.L. (N.U.I.); M 1965. 1968/M/19 [1 item]. S.C., 5 March 1982. Judge of the Circuit Court. Advanced to be a Judge of the High Court, 15 April 1996. Listed in the 1999 edition of Maureen Cairnduff, *Who's Who in Ireland*.

MORIARTY, OLIVER L. (b. 12 March 1890) only s. of David M. Moriarty of Sunday's Well, Killarney, Co. Kerry, and Mary Frances Griffin; M 1911. 1914/T/06 [3 items]. S.C., 2 April 1941. Died 26 Feb. 1953. Obituary, *I.L.T. & S.J.*, lxxxvii (1953), 87.

MORPHY, EDWARD (b. 1 June 1847) eld. s. of Edward Morphy, solicitor, of Tralee, Co. Kerry, and Arabella McGillycuddy; B.A. (T.C.D.); H 1870, M.T. H 1871. 1873/H/9 [4 items]. County Court Judge for Mayo, 7 April 1903-1910.

MORRIN, FRANCIS DERMOT (b. 27 Feb. 1936) 2nd s. of Joseph Morrin, doctor, of 14 Fitzwilliam Place, Dublin, and Eileen Dowling (decd.); B.A.; M 1954. Awarded 2nd Victoria Prize. 1958/M/02 [2 items]. Lecturer in Economics, U.C.D.

MORRIS, DENNIS GERARD (b. 10 April 1930) elder s. of Martin Robert Morris, of 14 Idrone Terrace, Blackrock, Co. Dublin, medical practitioner, and Catherine Gavin; M. 1949. Awarded Society's Prize of £21. 1953/H/01 [2 items]. Formerly a parliamentary draftsman in Dublin and Hong Kong; now resident in Portugal.

MORRIS, ERNEST ADOLPHUS MONTMORENCY (b. 29 Nov. 1874) eld. s. of Joseph William Charles Morris of Winton House, Cabra, Dublin, and Elizabeth Louise Rudge; M.A. (R.U.I.); M 1906. 1909/T/07 [3 items]. Died 8 Nov. 1933. Obituary, *I.L.T. & S.J.*, lxvii (1933), 307.

MORRIS, FREDERICK REGINALD (b. 1 Dec. 1929) 4th s. of Michael Archdale Morris, of Clonmore House, Piltown, Co. Kilkenny; M 1948 1952/M/09 [2 items]. S.C., 1 Oct. 1973. Judge of the High Court, 22 Dec. 1990; President of the High Court, 14 Jan. 1998. Retired 30 Nov. 2001. Listed (with photographs) in the 1991 and 1999 editions of Maureen Cairnduff, *Who's Who in Ireland*. *Burke's Irish Family Records* (1976), 863.

MORRIS, MARTIN HENRY FITZPATRICK (b. 22 July 1867) eld. s. of the Rt. Hon. Lord Morris of Spiddal, Co. Galway, and Anna Hughes; B.A.; M 1887, L.I. M 1889. 1890/M/06 [8 items]. Private secretary and registrar to his father when Lord Chief Justice, 1887-89. Unionist M.P. for Galway, 1900-1. Succeeded his father as 2nd Lord Killanin, 1901. Privy Councillor. Member of Galway County Council, 1899-1920. Member of the Senate of the Royal University of Ireland, 1904-9, and a Governor of University College, Galway, 1909-22. Author of an essay on Spiritual Realism (1892) and of *Transatlantic Traits* (1897). Contributor to the *Nineteenth Century* and other journals. Died *sine prole* 11 Aug. 1927. *Burke's Peerage*; *Who's Who*.

MORRIS, MAURICE LINDSAY O'CONNOR: see O'CONNOR MORRIS, MAURICE LINDSAY

MORRIS, Hon. MICHAEL REDMOND (b. 11 Oct. 1878) 3rd s. of the Rt. Hon. Lord Morris and Killanin, of Spiddal, Co. Galway, and Anna Hughes; B.A. (T.C.D.); M 1898, L.I. M 1900. 1901/M/06 [2 items]. Died 8 Dec. 1902: *I.L.T. & S.J.*, xxxvi (1902), 486.

MORRISON, Captain DAWSON (b. 14 Sept. 1893) only s. of James Morrison, of Regent Street, Newtownards, Co. Down, and Mary Dawson; H 1924. 1926/M/16 [2 items].

MORRISSEY, JOHN EUCHANIA WILLIAM (b. 22 June 1916) first s. of Thomas F. Morrissey (decd.), of Tipperary, Co. Tipperary, and Kathleen Cullinan; M.A., LL.B (N.U.I.); M 1937. 1940/M/07 [2 items]. S.C., 1 Nov. 1963. As *Seán* Morrissey, legal adviser in the Departments of Local Government and External Affairs; ambassador to Switzerland and the Netherlands.

MORRISSEY, THOMAS JOSEPH (b. 25 Aug. 1877) 2nd s. of William Morrissey of St. Nicholas' Glebe, Oldbridge, Clonmel, Co. Tipperary, and Mary Gleeson; B.A. (London), LL.B. (N.U.I.); M 1909. 1912/M/04 [2 items]. Assistant Keeper of the Records, -1922; thereafter Assistant Commissioner of Secondary Education. Died 31 Jan. 1942. Obituary, *I.L.T. & S.J.*, lxxvi (1942), 43.

MORROGH, ROBERT B. (b. 22 Jan. 1863) 3rd s. of Walter Morrogh (decd.), solicitor, of Belgrave Place, Cork, and Maria Harrington; B.A. (T.C.D.); M 1883, M.T. T 1884. 1887/E/05 [7 items]. Died 5 March 1945. Obituary, *I.L.T. & S.J.*, lxxix (1945), 65.

MORTON, JOHN DESMOND (b. 3 Feb. 1929) eld. s. of John Morton, J.P., of Lurgan, Co. Armagh, and Louie McHood; B.A., LL.B. (T.C.D.); M 1947. 1952/H/01 [2 items]. Q.C. Regius Professor of Laws, T.C.D., 1 Jan. 1965. Appt. Professor in Toronto, 1966.

MOSTYN, JAMES NEWCOMEN (b. 17 Feb. 1851) 7th s. of Thomas Mostyn (decd.), Crown and Treasury Solicitor for Ireland, of 19 Merrion Square South, Dublin, and Elizabeth Alger; LL.B. (T.C.D.); E 1872, I.T. H 1879; 1879/M/01 [7 items].

MOUTRAY, WHITNEY JOHN UPTON (b. 5 Jan 1849) elder s. of Whitney Moutray J.P. of Fort-Singleton, Co. Monaghan, and Annabella Crawford; AB (T.C.D.); M 1868; I.T. H 1869. 1873/E/1 [4 items].

MOYLAN, EDWARD KYRAN (b. 14 March 1841) eld. s. of Denis Moylan of Leeson Street, Dublin and Elizabeth Fitzgerald; B.A. (T.C.D.); M 1860, M.T. E 1862. 1872/M/1 [4 items].

MOYLAN, THOMAS JOSEPH (b. 7 Dec. 1928) 2nd s. of Peter Joseph Moylan, hotelier, of Main Street, Loughrea, Co. Galway, and Anne Teresa Callanan; B.A. (N.U.I.); M 1949. 1952/T/01 [2 items].

MOYNAGH, FRANK A. (b. 10 Oct. 1885) young. s. of Michael C. Moynagh, LL.D., Crown Solicitor, of Dundalk, Co. Louth, and Angela Constance Carroll; M 1902. 1906/M/04 [2 items].

MULDOON, JOHN (b. 11 July 1865) 3rd s. of of James Muldoon (decd.), gentleman, of Dromore, Co. Tyrone, and Catherine Gahan; E 1891. 1894/E/03 [7 items]. K.C., 26 April 1913. Nationalist M.P. for Donegal North, 1905-6; Wicklow East, 1907-11; Cork East 1911-18. Registrar in Lunacy, 1921. Registrar in the Office of the Chief Justice, 1926-35. Died 20 Nov. 1938. Obituary, *I.L.T. & S.J.*, lxxiii (6 Jan. 1939), 6; *Who's Who*. Mentioned in Maurice Healy, *The Old Munster Circuit*, 147.

MULDOON, JOSEPH MALACHI (b. 6 March 1890) young. s. of John Muldoon (decd.) of O'Maoldubhian House, Dungannon, Co. Tyrone, and Margaret Sheerin; M 1910. 1913/T/20 [2 items].

MULDOON, WILLIAM BERNARD (b. 7 Nov. 1935) 2nd s. of Paul Muldoon, licensed vintner and grocer, of Ardee, Co. Louth, and Margaret Carolan; M 1959. 1963/M/04 [1 item].

MULHALL, JOHN JOSEPH (b. 22 Sept. 1856) eld. s. of Joseph Mulhall of Termon Boyle, Co. Roscommon, and Anna Mulhall; H 1879, M.T. M 1880. 1881/M/19 [8 items].

MULLEN, EDWARD JOSEPH (b. 25 May 1927) only s. of Edward J. Mullen (decd.), of Shrule House, Shrule, Co. Galway, and Margaret Igoe; M 1953. 1958/H/02 [6 items].

MULLETT, HUGH ALOYSIUS (b. 19 May 1882) only s. of James Mullett (decd.), of 'Brookside', Merrion, Dublin, and Elizabeth Jane Brownrigg; M 1912. 1915/M/05 [2 items].

MULLIGAN, GEORGE ANGUS (b. 31 Jan. 1870) only s. of Angus James Mulligan (decd.), of Holywood, Co. Down, and Harriet Isabella Stringer (decd.); T 1914. 1914/M/07 [2 items].

MULLIGAN, WILLIAM GEORGE (b. 18 July 1864) eld. s. of William J. Mulligan (decd.), M.A., of Lurganville, Moira, Co. Down, and Harriett Scott; B.A., LL.B. (T.C.D.); M 1884. 1887/T/07 [6 items].

MULRINE, DANIEL JOHN CHRYSOSTOM (b. 27 Jan. 1927) 2nd s. of Peter Mulrine, of Rosemount, Ballybofey, Co. Donegal, and Margaret McGranaghan (decd.); M 1943. 1954/T/05 [2 items].

MULVIN, NOEL GEAROID SOUTHWELL (b. 26 Dec. 1922) only s. of William Gearoid Southwell Mulvin, of 'Selma', Nashville Park, Howth, Co. Dublin, and Harrietta Maude Ryan; B. Comm; M 1951. 1954/T/06 [2 items].

MUNN, LIONEL OULTON MOORE (b. 4 May 1887) 3rd s. of Alfred Moore Munn of Lisleen, Londonderry, Co. Londonderry, and Blanche Brady; M 1909. 1912/M/09 [3 items]. Died 25 Oct. 1958.

MURDOCH, HENRY JAMES PASCAL (b. 14 April 1938) 2nd s. of Archibald John Murdoch, bank manager, of Provincial Bank House, Abbeyfeale, Co. Limerick, and Margaret Mary Lyons; B.E. (U.C.D.); M 1963. Awarded 1st Victoria Prize. 1966/T/01 [1 item]. Career in business and administration. Author of *Invention and the Irish Patent System* (Dublin, 1971); *A Dictionary of Irish Law* (Dublin, 1988; 2nd ed., 1993; 3rd ed. 2000); and *Building Society Law in Ireland. A Guide* (Dublin, 1989). Listed in the 1984 edition of Maureen Cairnduff, *Who's Who in Ireland*.

MURLAND, WILLIAM (b. 5 May 1855) eld. s. of James William Murland, Barrister-at-Law, of Nutley, Booterstown, Dublin, and Priscilla Hutton; B.A. (T.C.D.); H 1878, I.T. T 1880. 1881/T/02 [8 items].

MURNAGHAN, GEORGE DANIEL (b. 5 July 1907) eld. s. of George Murnaghan, of Lionamallard, Omagh, Co. Tyrone, and Rosa Hackett (decd.); M 1927. 1930/M/03 [2 items]. S.C., 14 Oct. 1942. Judge of the High Court, 1953-79. Died 1990. Portrait by Thomas Ryan in King's Inns: see Wanda Ryan-Smolin, *King's Inns Portraits* (1992), 50.

MURNAGHAN, JAMES AUGUSTINE (b. 6 July 1881) 2nd s. of George Murnaghan, M.P., of Omagh, Co. Tyrone, and Angela Mooney; M.A., LL.B.; M 1900. 1903/M/01 [3 items]. LL. D. Went the Northern and Midland Circuits. Professor of Jurisprudence, Roman Law and International Law at the National University of Ireland, 1910-24. Judge of the High Court, 1924-5; of the Supreme Court, 1925-53. Hon. Bencher of King's Inns, 1953. Member (1925-) of the Board of Governors (and Chairman, 1962) of the National Gallery of Ireland. Died 13 Nov. 1973. *Who's Who*. The Murnaghan Prize at King's Inns is awarded in his memory.

MURNANE, JAMES PETER 3rd s. of David Murnane, of 5 Warrenpoint, Clontarf, Dublin 1925/M/14. Memorial missing; receipt only. Sometime District Inspector, R.I.C. Died 14 Nov. 1939. Obituary, *I.L.T. & S.J.*, lxxiii (1939), 328.

MURPHY, ANGELO JEROME (b. 30 June 1932) only s. of Angelo Murphy, Registrar, High Court of Justice, of 84 Grace Park Road, Co. Dublin, and Mary Evelyn Brennan (decd.); M 1951. 1954/T/16 [2 items].

MURPHY, ANTHONY G. (b. 1 Sept. 1931) 2nd s. of Jeremiah Joseph Murphy, of Endsleigh, Douglas Road, Cork, and Irene Crosbie; M 1950. 1954/M/16 [2 items]. Judge of the Circuit Court in Cork, 1985-2001.

MURPHY, CHARLES (b. 7 June 1857) eld. s. of Isaac James Murphy of Armagh, and Caroline Haughton; M.A. (T.C.D.); M 1884. 1887/M/07 [5 items]. Died 23 Dec. 1928. Obituary, *I.L.T. & S.J.*, lxii (1928), 314.

MURPHY, CHARLES O'BRIEN (b. 9 Jan. 1853) s. of Richard Murphy (decd.) of Castletown House, Co. Louth, and Matilda Lowe; B.A., LL.B., H 1886. 1890/H/03 [11 items]. Died 17 March 1941. Obituary, *I.L.T. & S.J.*, lxxv (1941), 77.

MURPHY, CHARLES WILLIAM (b. 4 Dec. 1873) 4th s. of Edmund Murphy, Government Arbitrator and Chief Receiver, High Court of Chancery, Ireland, of 81 Pembroke Road, Dublin, and Elizabeth Pemberton; B.A. (T.C.D.); M 1894. 1898/H/02 [4 items]. Provincial Commissioner, Gold Coast Colony. Died at Kwitta, 1905. Obituary, *I.L.T. & S.J.*, xxxix (25 Nov. 1905), 402.

MURPHY, DESMOND THOMAS CARMEL St. PAUL (b. 16 July 1900) 2nd s. of Henry M.A. Murphy, of 57 Grosvenor Road, Rathgar, Dublin, and Elizabeth Semple; B.A. (N.U.I.); T 1918. 1921/M/08 [2 items].

MURPHY, EDWARD (b. 27 Dec. 1857) 4th s. of Daniel Murphy (decd.), of Belfast, and Margaret McTear; M 1876, M.T. M 1878. 1880/H/04 [6 items].

MURPHY, EDWARD JOSEPH (b. 3 June 1888) young. s. of Thomas Murphy (decd.), of Coppenagh, Graig-na-managh, Co. Kilkenny, and Johanna White; M 1915. 1919/E/01x [2 items]. S.C., 9 July 1953. Registrar of the Supreme Court.

MURPHY, EDWARD SULLIVAN (b. 3 Feb. 1880) 4th s. of Mr. Justice Murphy (decd.) of Glencairn, Co. Dublin, and Mary Josephine Keogh; B.A.; M 1899. 1903/M/02 [3 items]. North-West Circuit. K.C., 27 Feb. 1918. M.P. for Londonderry City, 1929-39. Attorney-General (N.I.), 3 Dec. 1936-13 April 1939; Lord Justice of Appeal (N.I.), 13 April 1939. Died 3 Dec. 1945. Obituary, *I.L.T. & S.J.*, lxxix (1945), 297.

MURPHY, FRANCIS DOMINICK (b. 4 Oct. 1931) 3rd s. of Henry Magennis Murphy, of 16 Temple Villas, Rathmines, Dublin, and Mary Scott; B.A. (N.U.I.); M 1950. 1953/M/09 [2 items]. Professor at King's Inns, 1962-70. S.C., 6 Oct. 1969. Judge of the High Court, 5 March 1982; of the Supreme Court, 15 April 1996-17 Oct. 2002. Listed in the 1984 and 1991 editions of Maureen Cairnduff, *Who's Who in Ireland*.

MURPHY, GERALD EDGAR (b. 19 Aug. 1884) 4th s. of the Revd. Hugh Davis Murphy, M.A., D.D., of 39 Wellington Park, Belfast, and Francesca Burgess; cand. bachelor (T.C.D.); M 1907. 1910/M/06 [2 items]. Died 14 Aug. 1944.

MURPHY, HAROLD JOHN DICKINSON (b. 10 February 1915) only s. of Arthur Neville Murphy, merchant, of Station House, Bray, Co. Wicklow, and Elizabeth Humphries; B.A. (N.U.I.); M 1936. 1939/M/13 [1 item].

MURPHY, HAROLD LAWSON (b. 12 Dec. 1882) 5th s. of the Rt. Hon. James Murphy (decd.) of Glencairn, Sandyford, Co. Dublin, and Mary Josephine Keogh; B.A. (T.C.D.); M 1903. 1906/T/05 [2 items]. Auditor of the College Historical Society, 1905-6. Held the first non-professorial appointment in history in T.C.D., 1905-8, as asssistant to J.H. Wardell, Professor of Modern History (1904-10). Barrington Lecturer in Political Economy, 1910. In 1904 he won the Helen Blake National History Scholarship for a study of the early years of Trinity College, a work published posthumously as *A History of Trinity College Dublin from its foundation to 1702* (Dublin, 1951): see R.B. McDowell and David Webb, *Trinity College Dublin 1592-1952: An academic history* (Cambridge, 1982), 412. Called to the English Bar in 1910, he entered the chambers of Sir John Simon, going in England the Western Circuit. Served in the Royal Navy during the 1st World War. K.C. (in England) 1936. Chairman of the Croydon Typhus Enquiry, 1937. Died in London, 7 Jan. 1942. Obituary, *I.L.T. & S.J.*, lxxvi (1942), 19, 24-5, 42. For further biographical information see the foreword by T.S.C. Dagg [q.v.] to Harold Murphy's *History of Trinity College* (1951), which has as its frontispiece a youthful photograph of the author.

From the obituary of Harold Lawson Murphy in the *Law Journal*

He came from that professional class, I might almost say from that professional caste, in Ireland which for many generations has served the State and sent to the Church, the Bar, and the Army and Navy men whose names will ever be honoured. Wellington and Roberts, de Robeck, McGee and Boyd-Carpenter, come at once to mind. Harold Murphy had a judicial father, one may say a judicial mother, for she was the daughter of Judge Keogh, and he married the charming daughter of Lord Justice Holmes. He had the law in his blood, and though his greatest academic honour was the gold medal in history at T.C.D., he was always a lawyer at heart …

I.L.T. & S.J., lxxvi (1942), 42-3.

MURPHY, JAMES FITZGERALD (b. 7 June 1873) 2nd s. of William Martin Murphy, J.P., of Dartry, Co. Dublin, and Mary Lombard; M 1891. 1894/T/03 [7 items]. Munster Circuit. Died 30 Nov. 1903. Obituary, *I.L.T. & S.J.*, xxxvii (1903), 514.

MURPHY, JOHN PELLY (b. 19 March 1909) eld. s. of John Joseph Lawrence Murphy, solicitor, of Laxton, Bray, Co. Wicklow, and Anne Pelly; E 1946. 1946/M/07 [2 items].

MURPHY, JOSEPH PATRICK (b. 10 May 1904) 2nd s. of William Murphy, engineer, of 5 Royal Terrace, Fairview, Dublin, and Elizabeth Anne O'Connor; M 1934. 1938/T/05 [2 items].

MURPHY, LAURENCE WILLIAM RAYMOND (b. 30 Dec. 1888) lawful s. of Michael McDonnell Murphy, of 1 Ellerslie, Bray, Co. Wicklow, and Ellinor Mary Josephine Corcoran (decd.); M 1920. 1923/H/07 [2 items]. Registrar of the Central Office. Died 25 July 1961.

MURPHY, LINDSAY P. (b. 16 March 1893) eld. s. of Henry M.A. Murphy, Local Government inspector, of 57 Grosvenor Road, Rathgar, Dublin, and Elizabeth Semple; B.A., LL.B. (R.U.I.). Awarded First Class Certificate of Honour. 1920/H/03 [2 items].

MURPHY, MICHAEL (b. 20 Feb. 1865) 3rd s. of Michael Murphy, wine merchant, of 63 South Mall, Cork, and Elizabeth O'Callaghan; M 1883, G.I. E 1885. 1886/T/06 [7 items].

MURPHY, MICHAEL J. (b. 31 March 1924) 4th s. of Edward Michael Murphy, B.E., MICEI, of 51 Northumberland Road, Dublin, and Margaret O'Sullivan; B.A. (N.U.I.); M 1942. 1945/T/04 [2 items].

MURPHY, MICHAEL JOSEPH (b. 10 Feb. 1864) young. s. of Edward Murphy, merchant, of Balbriggan, Co. Dublin, and Mary Butler; E 1884. 1887/H/08 [7 items].

MURPHY, MICHAEL KEVIN (b. 24 July 1937) 2nd s. of Dr. Christopher Murphy, of Castlerea, Co. Roscommon, and Bridget Devine; M 1956. 1962/M/09 [1 item].

MURPHY, NICHOLAS DANIEL (b. 19 March 1853) 3rd s. of Nicholas Daniel Murphy, M.P., merchant, of Sidney Place, Cork, and Johanna Waldron; B.A. (T.C.D.); E 1873, M.T. H 1876. 1877/M/01 [6 items].

MURPHY, NICHOLAS PHILIP (b. 13 April 1879) eld. s. of Nicholas Murphy (decd.) of Carrigmore, Co. Cork, and Mary Murphy. 1912/T/14 [2 items].

MURPHY, OLIVER (b. 29 April 1872) 3rd s. of Isaac James Murphy, of Armagh, Co. Armagh, and Caroline Haughton; M 1900. 1903/H/01 [2 items].

MURPHY, STANISLAUS P. (b. 4 April 1868) young. s. of Patrick Murphy (decd.) of Athy, Co. Kildare, and Catherine Hearne (decd.); LL.B; M 1898. 1901/T/06 [3 items].

MURPHY, WILLIAM AGNEW (b. 23 July 1869) 2nd s. of John Christopher Murphy, J.P., of Oberstown, Co. Kildare, and Margaret Connell; B.A. (T.C.D.); M 1891. 1894/M/03 [6 items].

MURPHY, WILLIAM QUINLAN (b. 17 Sept. 1873) 2nd s. of the Rt. Hon. James Murphy, Judge, Exchequer Division, of Glencairn, Stillorgan, Co. Dublin, and Mary Keogh; B.A. (T.C.D.); M 1892, I.T. M 1894. 1895/M/14 [6 items]. Died 10 Feb. 1933. Obituary, *I.L.T. & S.J.*, lxvii (1933), 54, 160.

MURRAY, ARTHUR WILLIAM (b. 24 June 1847) 2nd s. of Arthur George Murray of Ashfield, Co. Meath and Elizabeth Knight-Boswell; B.A. (T.C.D.); H 1868, M.T. T 1869. 1871/H/3 [4 items].

MURRAY, JAMES WILLIAM BRADY (21 Dec. 1859) eld. s. of Patrick Brady (decd.), solicitor, of Danby House, Ballyshannon, Co. Donegal, and Mary Brady; B.A. (T.C.D.); M 1881, G.I. M 1883. 1884/M/10 [4 items].

MURRAY, JOHN (b. 25 Feb. 1840) 3rd s. of Gervas Murray (decd.) of Clontarf, Co. Dublin, merchant, and Margaret Collins; B.A. (T.C.D.); H 1865; M.T. T 1865. 1868/H/6 [4 items]. In early life 'a successful grinder in T.C.D.'. Retired from practice, 1895. Died 14 July 1914. Obituary, *I.L.T. & S.J.*, xlviii (1914), 198, 203.

MURRAY, JOHN (b. 6 Nov. 1869) 2nd s. of Patrick Murray of Inchicore House, Dublin, and Ellen Ahearne; T 1905. 1905/M/04 [2 items].

MURRAY, JOHN LOYOLA (b. 27 June 1943) eld. s. of John Cecil Murray, company director, of Carraigerra House, Limerick, and Catherine Casey; M 1962. 1967/M/06 [1 item]. S.C., 12 March 1981. Attorney-General, Aug.-Dec. 1982, 11 March 1987-Oct. 1991; Judge of the European Court of Justice, 1994; Judge of the Supreme Court, 10 Sept. 1999. Appt. Chief Justice, 21 July 2004. Listed in the 1984, 1991 and 1999 editions of Maureen Cairnduff, *Who's Who in Ireland*.

MURRAY, PATRICK JOSEPH (b. 11 Oct. 1943) only s. of Joseph Murray, motor company representative, of 88 Haddington Road, Ballsbridge, Dublin, and Mary Doyle; M 1965. 1968/M/23 [1 item].

MURRAY, ROBERT DOUGLAS (b. 28 May 1851) eld. s. of John Murray, of Longford Terrace, Monkstown, Co. Dublin, solicitor, and Helen Lindsay; B.A. (T.C.D.); M 1868, M.T. E 1870. 1872/T/3 [1 item]. Bencher 1928. Died 14 Oct. 1934. Obituary, *I.L.T. & S.J.*, lxviii (1934), 297.

MURTAGH, JOHN JOSEPH (b. 28 Feb. 1905) only s. of James Murtagh, of Willanestadt, Ailesbury Road, Co. Dublin, and Sara White; M 1923. 1926/M/09 [2 items]. Died 15 Feb. 1947.

MYLES, JOHN (b. 22 May 1853) eld. s. of Thomas Myles (decd.), of 10 Crescent, Limerick, and Sarah Goggin; E 1873, M.T. M 1874. 1876/E/03 [4 items].

NAGLE, GARRETT THOMAS (b. 5 Feb. 1853) only s. of Garrett Nagle (decd.), J.P., of Clogher House, Co. Cork, and Margaret Neligan; M 1874, M.T. T 1876. 1879/E/05 [5 items]. Died 4 March 1932. Obituary, *I.L.T. & S.J.*, lxvi (1932), 68.

NAGPAL, GIRDHARI LAL (b. 1887?) 2nd s. of Tikkan Lal Nagpal, of Multan, Punjab, India; M 1914. 1917/T/18 [2 items].

NAISH, REDMOND JOSEPH (b. 3 November 1886) only s. of Redmond Peter Naish of 2 Proby Square, Blackrock, Co. Dublin, and Mary MacDermott; undergraduate (R.U.I.); M 1906. 1909/T/13 [2 items].

NAQI, SYED KHURSHED (b. 22 Feb. 1894) eld. s. of [Moulni?] Syed Ali Hussan (decd.), of Hussanpura, Behar, India; M 1915. 1918/T/21x [2 items].

NARAYANA, BRAHMADESAM CIDAMBI SANKARA (b. 25 Nov. 1893) eld. s. of Rao Bahadur Brahmadesam Cidambi Raghavayya, of 'Sitasadan', Chittoor, Madras, India, and Thripura Sundari Ammal; M 1914. 1917/T/10 [2 items].

NASH, GEORGE BRABAZON HERBERT (b. 3 April 1852) eld. surv. s. of Francis Herbert Nash late of Clonbur, Co. Galway and now of 9 Synnotts Place, Dublin, and Leonora Ann Brabazon; B.A. (University of France); H 1872; M.T. T 1873. 1874/M/6 [2 items].

NATH, MAHANT BAIJ (n.d.) eld. s. of Mahant Janki Nath Sahib of [?], Punjab, India; M 1914. 1917/T/13 [2 items].

NEILL, JAMES SCOTT (b. 19 Nov. 1889) eld. s. of James Neill, of 27 Eglantine Avenue, Belfast, and Jane Allen Moore; late Sch., Sen. Mod. B.A. (T.C.D.); M 1920. 1921/M/20 [2 items]. C.M.G. Died Oct. 1958.

NEILSON, WILLIAM HORNER (b. 11 March 1857) only s. of James H. Neilson, solicitor, of 5 Upper Mount Street, Dublin, and Mary Corban; LL.B (T.C.D.); H 1875, L.I. H 1875. 1879/E/08 [6 items].

NELIGAN, WILLIAM NOEL (b. 8 Jan. 1869) eld. s. of Major John Redmond Neligan (decd.), of Dingle, Co. Kerry, and Anastatia Gallwey; M 1892. 1896/H/02 [6 items].

NELSON, HOWARD ARTHUR (b. 12 Sept. 1874) 3rd s. of Arthur Nelson, J.P., of Ardmore, Armagh, Co. Armagh, District Registrar of the Probate Court, and Anna Elizabeth Mills; sophister (T.C.D.); M 1894. 1897/T/12 [4 items]. Chief Registrar of King's Bench Division (Probate and Matrimonial) Belfast. Author of *The Probate Law and Practice of the Principal and District Registries of the High Courts of Justice in Northern Ireland and Irish Free State* (3rd edition. Belfast: Allen, 1937). Died 25 April 1944. Obituary, *I.L.T. & S.J.*, lxxviii (1944), 123.

NEVILLE, FRANCIS MICHAEL (b. 31 Oct. 1914) eld. s. of Edward Francis Neville, solicitor, of Roseleigh, Western Road, Cork, and Katherine O'Sullivan; M 1933. 1937/M/16 [2 items].

NEVILLE, RICHARD MAXIMILIAN (b. 5 Sept. 1938) eld. s. of Thomas Anthony Neville, medical practitioner, of Weston Lodge, Clonakilty, Co. Cork, and Nora Mary Sheehy; M 1958. 1959/T/03 [2 items]. Died c. 1970.

NEWCOMEN, GEORGE ARNOLD (b. 8 May 1855) only s. of Captain George Newcomen (decd.), 59th Regt., of [Camla], Co. Roscommon, and Harriet O'Donnell; LL.B.; E 1883, M.T. M 1884. 1886/E/03 [7 items]. Died at Vichy, 19 Sept. 1932. Obituary, *I.L.T. & S.J.*, lxvi (1932), 241. Contributor to *Kottabos*.

NEWELL, PETER (b. 25 Nov. 1860) 4th s. of John Newell (decd.), of Kilroe House, Headford, Co. Galway, and Catherine Garvey; M 1911. 1914/T/10 [3 items].

NEWELL, ROBERT JOHN (b. 12 June 1858) eld. s. of Robert Newell (decd.) of 1 Wilmount Avenue, Kingstown, Co. Dublin, and Susan Porter; E 1879, M.T. E 1881. 1882/E/02 [7 items]. Died 10 Sept. 1936. Obituary, *I.L.T. & S.J.*, lxx (1936), 243.

NEWETT, ARTHUR CONYNGHAM (b. 20 Jan. 1877) 3rd s. of Brereton John Newett (decd.), stockbroker, of Mount Lyons, Belfast, and Frances Lyons; Sen. Mod. B.A. (T.C.D.); M 1897. 1900/M/06 [4 items]. Bencher 1945. Died 18 Jan. 1955. Obituary, *I.L.T. & S.J.*, lxxxix (1955), 32. Mentioned by V.T.H. Delany [q.v.], in his article 'The Bench and Bar in Ireland', as one of 'those who were at the forefront of their profession during the period'.

NEWTON, ANDREW WILLOUGHBY (b. 14 Jan 1849) only s. of Joseph Courtenay Newton, J.P., of Dungannon, Co. Tyrone, and Ann Howard; B.A. (T.C.D.); H 1869, M.T. E 1870. 1872/T/6 [2 items].

NEYLON, MARY JOSEPHINE (b. 9 March 1916) eld. d. of Edward Neylon, of Co. Cork, and Norah Culligan; B.A. (N.U.I.); M 1946. 1949/M/08 [3 items]. Librarian of King's Inns, 1 January 1970 to 31 July 1984. Died 19 May 1995. Author of an article on the King's Inns Library published in *The Law Librarian*, vol. 4, No. 1 (April-July 1973).

NEYLON, THOMAS JOSEPH (b. 1 February 1916) only s. of Thomas Neylon, County Inspector, Royal Irish Constabulary (disbanded), of Seamount, Sligo, Co. Sligo, and Catherine Sheedy; M 1937. 1940/M/02 [1 item]. S.C., 1 July 1955. Judge of the Circuit Court (Cork Circuit); aft. President of the Court, 1977-86, sitting in Dublin. Retired 31 Jan. 1986.

NIC CHURTAIN, SÍOBHÁN ÍTE (b. 28 April 1911) eld. d. of Brigade Commandant Tomás Mac Churtain, of Cork City, and Eilis Walsh; M 1929. 1937/M/09 [2 items]. For notice of her welcome to the Bar, see *I.L.T. & S.J.*, lxxii (1938), 46.

NICHOLSON, CYRIL ANTHONY de LACY (b. 2 Feb. 1902) eld. s. of Major Thomas Francis Nicholson (decd.), of Beech Hill, Co. Londonderry, and Frances Byrne; M 1924. 1926/M/15 [2 items]. Q.C. (N.I.), H 1945. Mentioned in Basil McIvor, *Hope Deferred: Experiences of an Irish Unionist* (Belfast, 1998), 37. Father of Sir Michael Nicholson (M 1975; N.I. 1956), Lord Justice of Appeal in N.I.

NICOLLS, ARCHIBALD JOHN (b. 12 July 1844) eld. s. of Simon Nicolls, doctor of medicine, of Longford, Co. Longford, and Delia McCann; B.A., LL.B (T.C.D.); T 1863, M.T. E 1865. 1868/E/03 [4 items].

NIGHTINGALE, GEORGE OSWALD (b. 9 Nov. 1896) 2nd s. of Henry Nightingale, of 3 Upper Clanbrassil Street, Dublin, and Lavinia Ellison; E 1929. 1932/M/09 [2 items]. Died 10 March 1962. Obituary, *I.L.T. & S.J.*, xcvi (1962), 76.

NIXON, CHRISTOPHER WILLIAM (b. 19 Nov. 1877) eld. s. of Sir Christopher John Nixon, M.D., of 2 Merrion Square, Dublin, and Mary Agnes Blake; M 1896. 1900/E/01 [2 items]. Baronet. Major. D.S.O. Died 21 April 1945.

NOLAN, EAMONN PATRICK (b. 27 March 1920) 3rd s. of Thomas Nolan (decd.), company director, of 35 Upper Castle Street, Tralee, Co. Kerry, and Mary Knightly; B.A. (N.U.I.); M 1938. 1941/M/13 [2 items].

NOLAN, PATRICK JAMES (b. 17 March 1862) 3rd s. of James Nolan, merchant, of Barrington Street, Limerick, and Mary O'Rourke; candidate bachelor (T.C.D.); E 1882, G.I. M 1883. 1885/H/05 [7 items]. K.C. 1907. Died at Calgary, Alberta, 11 Feb. 1913. Obituary, *I.L.T. & S.J.*, xlvii (1913), 67.

NOLAN, PIERCE LAURENCE (b. 10 Aug. 1865) 2nd s. of Edward Nolan (decd.), J.P., of Killeen House, Dublin, and Mary Crosbie; B.A. (R.U.I.); E 1889. 1892/T/04 [7 items]. One of the Registrars in Chancery. Died at Rosapenna, 15 Sept. 1917, having become unconscious after diving into the sea. Obituary, *I.L.T. & S.J.*, li (1917), 230, 260.

NOLAN-WHELAN, JAMES V. (b. 22 Oct. 1880) eld. s. of James V. Nolan (decd.), solicitor, of Queen's Park, Monkstown, Dublin, and Maria Kelly; M 1898. 1904/H/08 [2 items]. S.C., 12 April 1937. Died 29 April 1950. Obituary, *I.L.T. & S.J.*, lxxxiv (1950), 117.

NORTON, DAVID RICHMOND (b. 27 April 1875) eld. s. of the Hon. David Norton C.S.I.I.C.S., Financial Commissioner of Burma, and Alice Kathleen Browne; M 1897, L.I. M 1899. 1902/E/05 [4 items].

NORWOOD, WILLIAM STUART (b. 3 May 1869) only s. of William Norwood, J.P., of Ballyhalwick, Co. Cork, and Letitia Stuart; B.A. (T.C.D.); H 1893. 1896/H/04 [6 items]. Munster Circuit. Called to English Bar. K.C., 26 April 1913. J.P. for County Cork. Resigned as Bencher of K.I. Died 11 March 1944. Obituary, *I.L.T. & S.J.*, lxxviii (1944), 98; *Who's Who*.

NOWLAN, KEVIN BARRY (b. 2 Nov. 1921) only s. of John Joseph Nowlan, of 40, Crannagh Road, Rathfarnham, Co. Dublin, and Barbara O'Neill; B.A. (N.U.I.); M 1941. 1945/T/10 [2 items]. Formerly Professor of Modern History at U.C.D. Said in the 1984 edition of Maureen Cairnduff's *Who's Who in Ireland* to be 'a great favourite with Dublin hostesses'.

NOWLAN, KEVIN INGRAM (b. 2 Nov. 1910) 2nd s. of J.B.W. Nowlan, of 7 Chestnut Road, Mount Merrion, Co. Dublin, and Kathleen Winifred Browning; B.Sc., B.E. (N.U.I.); M 1948. 1951/T/04 [2 items]. Author of *A Guide to the Planning Acts* (Dublin, 1978; 3rd ed., 1998). Died 5 Jan. 2003. Appreciation (by D. McC.), with photograph, *The Irish Times*, Friday 14 Feb. 2003, 19.

NUGENT, PETER BERNARD (b. 20 Aug. 1937) 2nd s. of Peter John Nugent, Senior Counsel, of Modeshill, The Grove, Stillorgan, Co. Dublin, and Mary Neilan (decd.); B.C.L.; M 1955. Awarded Society's Exhibition Prize. 1959/M/02 [2 items]. Left the Bar to enter the Benedictine Order at Glenstal Abbey, where he became headmaster of the school and is known as Dom Andrew Nugent, O.S.B.

NUGENT, PETER JOHN (b. 7 Jan. 1910) 4th s. of John Dillon Nugent, of 272 North Circular Road, Dublin, and Mary Nolan; M 1928. 1931/M/11 [2 items]. S.C., 3 March 1950. Died 1969.

NUNAN, JOSEPH JOHN (b. 26 April 1873) eld. s. of Patrick Nunan of Limerick, Co. Limerick, and Mary Frances Nunan; B.A., LL.B; M 1896, G.I. T 1898. 1898/M/03 [3 items]. Helen Blake Scholar in National History, 1896. K.C., 1913. Colonial Service, 1900-25 (Central and East Africa, 1900-6; British Guiana, 1906-). Austrian and Hungarian Reparation Committee, 1920-3. Hon. LL.D. (T.C.D.), 1913. Knighted 1924. Retired to practise at the English Bar, 1925. Editor of *Timehri*, a West Indian magazine, 1911-20. Author of *Islam before the Turk* [also *Islam and European Civilization* (Demerara, 1907)] and *Ireland from Cromwell to Anne*. Died 19 Dec. 1934. Obituary, *I.L.T. & S.J.*, lxviii (1934), 355-6; *Who's Who*.

NUNAN, MANUS (b. 1 Oct. 1891) 4th s. of Patrick Nunan (decd.), of Limerick, and Mary Ann Doran; B.A. (T.C.D.); M 1921. 1923/T/08 [2 items]. District Justice. Mentioned in Patrick MacKenzie, *Lawful Occasions*, 55-7.

NUNAN, MANUS (b. 26 March 1926) only s. of Manus Nunan, District Justice, of 19 Castlewood Avenue, Rathmines, Dublin, and Nan FitzGerald; B.A. (T.C.D.); M 1944. 1950/M/04 [2 items]. Solicitor-General, Nigeria; acting Recorder, England.

NUNN, JOHN HENRY Jun. (b. 28 Nov. 1856) only s. of John Henry Nunn, solicitor, of Wellington Place, Dublin, and Catherine Elizabeth [?]; LL.B. (T.C.D.); H 1875, L.I. E 1877. 1879/T/05 [6 items]. Sometime Registrar to Mr. Justice Pim. 'Mr Nunn was an able lawyer, but his practice was never very large'. Died 30 Sept. 1920. Obituary, *I.L.T. & S.J.*, liv (1920), 248.

O'BEIRNE, DONNCHADH PIARAS REGIS (b. 15 May 1920) eld. s. of John Regis O'Beirne, civil servant (decd.), of Rathdown, Dartry Road, Dublin, and M. Power; B.A.; H 1940. 1943/M/07 [2 items].

OBONNA, LINUS (b. 25 Dec. 1928) 3rd s. of Chief Nwehoma Obonna, of Obizi-Nbaise Owerri, Nigeria, in the county of Nbaise Owerri, and Enagu Ada Nwekagwu; B.C.L. (U.C.D.); M 1957. 1961/M/06 [2 items].

Ó BRIAIN, Major BARRA (b. 19 Sept. 1901) eld. s. of Christopher Michael O'Brien, M.D., L.R.C.P.I., of 29 Merrion Square North, Dublin, and Mary Theresa Rooney; B.A., LL.B; M 1924. 1926/M/11 [2 items]. S.C., 2 April 1940. Appt. Judge of the Circuit Court (South-Western) Circuit, 1943. President of the Circuit Court, 1959-1973. Mentioned in Gerard A. Lee, *A Memoir of the South-Western Circuit* (Dublin, 1990), 12, 23.

Ó BRIAIN, COLM CRISTÓIR (b. 22 Feb. 1931) eld. s. of Judge Barra O Briain, S.C., of Ard Mor, Killiney, Co. Dublin, and Anna Flood; B.A. (N.U.I.); M 1950. 1953/M/13 [2 items]. Aft. President of the Dublin Stock Exchange.

O'BRIEN, ALFRED (b. 15 April 1850) 2nd s. of John Stackpool O'Brien, J.P., of Tanderagee, Co. Armagh, and Frances Hardinge; M 1870, M.T. M 1871. 1875/H/05 [4 items].

O'BRIEN, ANTHONY NORBERT (b. 6 June 1925) eld. s. of Daniel O'Brien, of 121 North Circular Road, Dublin, and Annie Rathborne; M 1944. 1947/M/03 [2 items].

O'BRIEN, CHARLES ANDREW (b. 18 Jan. 1866) 4th s. of William O'Brien of Charlemont, Cork, and Anne Byrne; B.A. (R.U.I.); M 1885, M.T. M 1887. 1888/T/05 [9 items].

O'BRIEN, CONAL (b. 17 Oct. 1937) only s. of Eric K. O'Brien, commercial representative, of Eastmount Cottage, Knoc-na-Cree Road, Co. Dublin, and Louise Coghlan; B.C.L.; M 1955. 1958/M/11 [2 items].

O'BRIEN, DANIEL J. (b. 31 Jan. 1866) eld. s. of Michael O'Brien, merchant, of Kingstown, Co. Dublin, and Anne Quaid; M 1896, G.I. M 1897. 1898/T/10 [3 items]. K.C., 27 June 1914. Crown Prosecutor for Carlow, 1912; for Kilkenny, 1917. Standing Counsel to the General Post Office, 1918. Appt. County Court Judge for Queen's Co., Kilkenny and Waterford, 18 Jan. 1920. Chairman of the Railway Tribunal, 1924-44. Died 30 Nov. 1949. Obituary, *I.L.T. & S.J.*, lxxxiii (1949), 310; *Who's Who*.

O'BRIEN, DONOUGH CONOR JOSEPH (b. 31 Jan. 1928) eld. s. of Patrick Joseph O'Brien, dentist, of 3 Parnell Square East, Dublin, and Hilda White; B.A. (N.U.I.); M 1947. 1950/M/16 [2 items].

O'BRIEN, GEORGE THOMAS (b. 29 Jan. 1892) 3rd s. of Richard O'Brien (decd.) of 8 Marine Terrace, Kingstown, Co. Dublin, and Mary Dowse; B.A. (N.U.I.); M 1910.

1913/M/01 [2 items]. Professor of the National Economics of Ireland at U.C.D., 1926-61. Author of a 3-volume *Economic History of Ireland* (1918-21). Senator (N.U.I.) 1948-65. Died 31 Dec. 1973. Contributor to James Meenan (ed.), *Centenary History of Lit. and Hist. Soc. of U.C.D.*, and subject of the latter's *George O'Brien: a biographical memoir* (1980). See *Who's Who*; Henry Boylan, *A Dictionary of Irish Biography* (1978), and Louis McRedmond (ed.), *Modern Irish Lives*.

O'BRIEN, IGNATIUS JOHN (b. 30 July 1857) young. s. of Mark Joseph O'Brien (decd.), of 47 King Street, Cork, and Jane Dunne; H 1877, M.T. T 1879. 1881/E/01 [6 items]. Q.C., 22 April 1899. Bencher 1907. 3rd Serjeant, 14 Jan. 1910. 2nd Serjeant, 18 May 1911. Solicitor-General, 1911. Attorney-General, 1912. Lord Chancellor, 1913. Stood aside in 1918 in favour of Sir James Campbell, and was in compensation created a peer as Baron Shandon. Died in London, 10 Sept. 1930. See *D.N.B.* (article by T.C. Kingsmill Moore) and Ball, *Judges*, ii, 383. The King's Inns has a framed photograph of Ignatius O'Brien C. dated 3 Nov. 1916.

O'BRIEN, JAMES (b. 13 Aug. 1876) 2nd s. of Jerome O'Brien (decd.), 77th Regt., of 77 'B' Marlboro Road, Dublin, and Elizabeth Clarke; Sen. Mod. B.A. (T.C.D.); H 1896. 1899/T/02 [3 items]. Registrar of the Supreme Court. Died 10 Dec. 1947. Obituary, *I.L.T. & S.J.*, lxxxi (1947), 297.

O'BRIEN, JOHN JOSEPH (b. 31 January 1910) 2nd s. of Henry Joseph O'Brien (decd.), hotel proprietor, of Claremount, Waterloo Road, Dublin, and Mary Josephine Byrne; B.A.; M 1938. 1941/M/14 [2 items].

O'BRIEN, KEVIN (b. 18 Feb. 1921) 3rd s. of Martin O'Brien (decd.), of 8 St. Aidan's Park Road, Marino, Dublin, and Julia Linehan; M 1941. 1947/T/06 [2 items].

O'BRIEN, MICHAEL (b. 5 Sept. 1901) young. s. of Patrick O'Brien, of Curragh, Skibbereen, Co. Cork, and Kate Fitzgerald; B.A. (N.U.I.); M 1921. 1925/M/09 [2 items].

O'BRIEN, PATRICK FRANCIS (b. 24 March 1863) young. s. of Cornelius O'Brien of Banquet Hill Cottage, Kilcommon, Hollyford, Co. Tipperary, and Kate Ryan; B.A., LL.B. (T.C.D.); E 1883. 1887/E/01 [6 items]. Ordained a priest in 1891; Professor of Classics at Carlow College and in various Roman Catholic universities in the United States. Died Sept. 1927. Memorial in Kilcommon church.

O'BRIEN, RICHARD BARRY (b. 7 March 1847) 3rd s. of Patrick Barry O'Brien of Kilrush, Co. Clare, and Sarah Hannan; M 1870; M.T. M 1871. 1874/M/03 [2 items]. Historian and biographer. Called to the English Bar, 1875. One of the founders of the Irish Literary Society, London (and its President 1906-11). Biographer of Thomas Drummond, Parnell, Lord Russell of Killowen and John Bright. Died 17 March 1918. See *Who's Who;* Henry Boylan, *A Dictionary of Irish Biography* (1978).

O'BRIEN, RICHARD P. only s. of Patrick O'Brien, merchant, of Clonmel, Co. Tipperary, and Bridget Fitzpatrick; M 1876, M.T. M 1878. 1879/M/14 [6 items].

O'BRIEN, STEPHEN (b. 21 April 1884) 3rd surv. s. of Stephen Patrick O'Brien of Lady Lane, Waterford, and Mary Anne Kelly; B.A.; M 1906. 1910/E/02 [4 items].

O'BRIEN KELLY, MICHAEL JOHN (b. 23 Oct. 1938) only s. of John O'Brien Kelly, solicitor, of Clonmackin House, Co. Limerick, and Anne MacNamara; B.A. (T.C.D.); M 1957.1961/T/07 [2 items].

O'BRIEN-TWOHIG, JOSEPH PATRICK: see TWOHIG, JOSEPH PATRICK.

Ó BROIN, LEÓN (b. 10 Nov. 1902) 2nd eld. s. of Séamus P. Ó Broin, of 21 Aungier Street, Dublin, and Máire Ní Chillín; M 1922. 1924/M/10 [2 items]. Aft. Secretary of the Department of Posts and Telegraphs, 1946-67. Author of several historical and biographical works, *inter alia* on Emmet, Parnell, Augustine Birrell, Michael Collins, Frank Duff, and W.E. Wylie (q.v.); and of an autobiography, *Just like yesterday* (Dublin, 1986). Died 26 Feb. 1990. See Louis McRedmond (ed.), *Modern Irish Lives*. Papers in the National Library of Ireland.

Ó BUACHALLA, DOMHNALL C.: see BUCKLEY, DANIEL CHRISTOPHER JOSEPH.

O'BYRNE, BRENDAN PETER (b. 19 June 1919) eld. s. of Joseph Michael O'Byrne, Senior Counsel, of 55 Dartmouth Square, Leeson Park, Dublin, and Margaret Mary Doran; E 1954. 1954/E/01 [3 items]. Northern Rhodesia.

O'BYRNE, EDWARD ALEXANDER (b. 7 Feb. 1865) eld. s. of John O'Byrne, J.P., of Corville, Roscrea, Co. Tipperary, and Eleanora de Hubner; H 1887. 1890/T/04 [8 items]. Papal Count.

O'BYRNE, JOHN (b. 24 April 1884) 4th s. of Patrick Byrne, of Killabeg, Coolkenno, Co. Wicklow, and Mary Tallon; M.A., 'student' of the N.U.I.; M 1908. 1911/H/01 [3 items]. K.C., 11 June 1924. Attorney-General, 1924-6. Judge of the High Court, 9 Jan. 1926; of the Supreme Court, 18 Jan. 1940. Died 14 Jan. 1954. Obituary, *I.L.T. & S.J.*, lxxxviii (1954), 26. Inspired the 'O'Byrne letter' (precedent in Julian Deale, *Circuit Court Practice and Procedure*, 21). See Louis McRedmond (ed.), *Modern Irish Lives*.

O'BYRNE, JOSEPH MICHAEL (b. 14 Dec. 1888) young. s. of Peter O'Byrne (decd.), of 7 Barrow Street, Pembroke, Dublin, and Rosa Cox; M 1923. 1926/H/01 [2 items]. S.C., 7 April 1954. Author of *Prisoners of War* (1919). Registrar of Titles and Deeds. Died 11 Aug. 1966. Obituary, *I.L.T. & S.J.*, vol. c (1966), 328.

O'BYRNE, PATRICK (b. 8 Dec. 1929) eld. s. of the Hon. Mr. Justice John O'Byrne, of St Catherine's, Ballyboden, Rathfarnham, Dublin, and Marjorie McGuire; B.A. (N.U.I.); M 1948. 1952/M/17 [2 items].

O'BYRNE, PATRICK JOSEPH (b. 30 Aug. 1870) 2nd s. of John Count O'Byrne of Corville, Roscrea, Co. Tipperary, and Eleanore de Hubner; M 1888. 1893/T/01 [7 items]. Died 20 Jan. 1944. Obituary, *I.L.T. & S.J.*, lxxviii (1944), 30.

O'CALLAGHAN, AUBREY BRYAN (b. 17 May 1929) only s. of Aubrey E. O'Callaghan, of 'Burnsley', Templeogue, Dublin, and Kathleen Rezin; M 1949. 1957/H/04 [2 items].

O'CALLAGHAN, EDWARD JOHN (b. 25 May 1876) 3rd s. of Edward Hackett O'Callaghan (decd.) of George Street, Limerick, and Ellen Smithwick; M 1897. 1900/M/11 [3 items].

O'CALLAGHAN, JOHN (b. 6 Jan. 1893) 3rd s. of John O'Callaghan, of Bantry, Co. Cork, and Susan Berry; B.A. (N.U.I.); M 1917. 1927/M/27 [2 items].

O'CALLAGHAN, MICHAEL (b. 19 March 1897) 5th s. of John O'Callaghan, of Bantry, Co. Cork, and Susan Berry; M 1928. 1931/T/08 [2 items]. District Justice.

O'CALLAGHAN, THOMAS (b. 3 Aug. 1923) 3rd s. of Michael O'Callaghan (decd.), civil engineer, of Letterkenny, Co. Donegal, and Margaret Molloy; M.A., F.R.G.S., B.E., D.Sc; M 1944. 1958/T/08 [2 items].

O'CALLAGHAN DUNN, JOHN (b. 27 May 1904) only s. of Joseph Alphonsus Dunn, of 124 Lindsay Road, Dublin, and Mary Josephine O'Callaghan; M 1940. 1943/T/07 [2 items].

Ó CAOIMH, MÍCEÁL: see O'KEEFFE, MICHAEL.

O'CARROLL, FREDERIC JOHN (b. 27 Jan 1843) only s. of Frederick Francis O'Carroll of Avondale, Blackrock, Co. Dublin, Inspector of National Schools, and Catherine McCarthy; B.A. (T.C.D.); H 1865, L.I. E 1865. 1868/T/05 [4 items].

O'CARROLL, JAMES (b. 15 Nov. 1930) only s. of James F. O'Carroll, of Tullyroe, Ballingar, Co. Galway, and Agatha O'Sullivan; M 1949. 1955/M/03 [2 items].

O'CARROLL, LOUIS ELY (b. 27 March 1863) young. s. of Peter Francis O'Carroll, C.E., of 77 Harcourt Street, Dublin, and Kate Josephine Garvie; B.A. (R.U.I.); H 1885. 1887/M/16 [7 items].

O'CARROLL, RICHARD PATRICK (b. 26 May 1879) only s. of Patrick O'Carroll of Ballyclough, Bruree, Co. Limerick, and Margaret O'Mahony; M 1902. 1905/T/10 [3 items].

Ó CILLÍN, PROINNSIAS PÁDRAIG (b. 7 March 1943) 3rd s. of Francis Killeen, retired Garda Síochána, of 64 Norfolk Road, Dublin 7, and Sheila Hickey; M 1962. 1966/T/03 [1 item].

Ó CONCHUBHAIR, DONNCHADH AODHACH (b. 19 June 1903) 3rd s. of Denis Hayes O'Conor (decd.), of Rathluirc, Co. Cork, and Bridget Nolan; T 1942. 1946/M/03 [2 items]. Father of Stella Mildred O'Conor [q.v.].

Ó CONCHUBHAIR, MICHEÁL PÁDRAIG SEOSAMH (b. 8 March 1925) eld. s. of Philip O'Connor, of 333 Griffith Avenue, Dublin, and Kathleen McDermott; M 1944. 1948/T/05 [2 items].

O'CONNELL, CHARLES (b. 2 June 1842) young. s. of John O'Connell (decd.) of Glanmire Road, Cork and Margaret Punch; M 1863, M.T. H 1865. 1868/M/03 [6 items].

O'CONNELL, DANIEL CHRISTOPHER (b. 27 Sept. 1907) 2nd s. of William O'Connell (decd.), of Summerville, Winters Hill, Cork, and Frances Mary Buckley; M 1926. 1931/M/16 [2 items].

O'CONNELL, MICHAEL FLANNAN (b. 17 Dec. 1926) 2nd s. of William Joseph O'Connell, M.E., FSI, of Monkstown, Co. Cork, and Rosaleen Hanrahan; M 1942. 1947/T/10 [2 items].

O'CONNELL, PETER (b. 16 Jan. 1910) only s. of Thomas O'Connell, of Boher, Co. Limerick, and Mary Reilly; M 1961. 1965/T/04 [1 item].

O'CONNELL, PETER IVAN (b. 18 April 1944) 2nd s. of Peter O'Connell, civil servant, of 58 Waterloo Road, Dublin, and Rita Harvey; M 1962. 1966/M/02 [1 item].

O'CONNELL, WILLIAM ARTHUR (b. 15 Dec. 1855) 3rd s. of Maurice O'Connell (decd.), J.P., of Kilgory, Co. Clare, and Emily McCarthy O'Leary; E 1885. 1888/E/09 [6 items].

O'CONNOR, ART (b. 18 May 1888) 2nd s. of Art O'Connor (decd.), of Elm Hall, Celbridge, Co. Kildare, and Elizabeth Saul; B.A., BAI, LL.B. (T.C.D.); M 1924. Awarded 3rd Class Certificate of Honour. 1927/M/06 [2 items]. Interned as a republican during the civil war. S.C., 26 June 1944. Judge of the Circuit Court. Died 10 May 1950. Obituary, *I.L.T. & S.J.*, lxxxiv (1950), 127.

O'CONNOR, BERNARD (b. 2 Aug. 1849) 4th s. of William O'Connor, M.D. (decd.), of Dingle, Co. Kerry, and Charlotte Frances Day; B.A. (R.U.I.); M 1922, G.I. M 1887. Called to English Bar, Gray's Inn, M 1890. 1923/T/01 [2 items]. Died 1937 at Allahabad, whither he had gone from Ireland 45 years before. Obituary, *I.L.T. & S.J.*, lxxi (7 Aug. 1937), 212.

O'CONNOR, BRENDAN (b. 2 Feb. 1930) 4th s. of Thomas O'Connor (decd.), railway executive, of The Station House, Tralee, Co. Kerry, and Nora Maher; M 1961. 1965/T/03 [1 item].

O'CONNOR, CHARLES ANDREW (b. 31 Dec. 1854) 3rd s. of Charles Andrew O'Connor (decd.) of Acres, Co. Roscommon, and Kate Smyth; B.A. (T.C.D.); M 1874, M.T. T 1876. 1878/M/03 [5 items]. Auditor of the College Historical Society, 1877-8. Connaught Circuit. Q.C., 30 June 1894. 3rd Serjeant, 23 March 1907; 1st Serjeant, 5 Dec. 1907. Solicitor-General, 1909-11; Attorney-General, 1911-12. Master of the Rolls, 1912-24. Heard the Childers *Habeas Corpus* application. Judge of the Supreme Court of the Irish Free State, 1924-5. Died 8 Oct. 1928. Mentioned in Maurice Healy, *The Old Munster Circuit*, 269-70. See Louis McRedmond (ed.), *Modern Irish Lives*.

O'CONNOR, FERGUS LAURENCE (b. 1 May 1898) eld. s. of the Rt. Hon. James O'Connor, Lord Justice of Appeal in Ireland, of St. Aidan's, Merrion, Dublin, and Mary Josephine Kehoe; M 1915. 1919/T/06 [3 items]. Died 1 Aug. 1965. Obituary, *I.L.T. & S.J.*, xcix (1965), 266. Mentioned in Patrick MacKenzie, *Lawful Occasions*, 31-3.

O'CONNOR, GEORGE RICHARD (b. 8 June 1863) eld. s. of Meredith Ferrall O'Connor of Kiltimagh, Co. Mayo, and Mary Blackhall; E 1891. 1894/E/04 [6 items]. Died 22 March 1944. Obituary, *I.L.T. & S.J.*, lxxviii (1944), 91.

O'CONNOR, GERALD (b. 5 June 1916) 3rd s. of John O'Connor (decd.), solicitor, of Crossmaglen, Co. Armagh, and Ellie J. O'Hanlon; B.A., LL.B. Mod. (T.C.D.); H 1939. 1941/M/09 [2 items].

O'CONNOR, HUBERT MICHAEL (b. 22 Jan. 1887) eld. s. of Charles Joseph O'Connor, F.R.C.S.I, of The Grove, Celbridge, Co. Kildare, and Marion Lynch; M 1905. 1910/H/03 [3 items]. Captain, King's Shropshire Light Infantry, M.C. Died of wounds, 17 Aug. 1917. Obituary, *I.L.T. & S.J.*, li (1917), 206. [Name on the Bar War Memorial].

O'CONNOR, JAMES (b. 1 April 1872) 3rd s.of Michael Joseph O'Connor, of Weston Wexford, Co. Wexford, and Johanna Murphy; T 1900. 1900/M/03 [2 items]. Leinster Circuit. K.C., 24 June 1908; Solicitor-General 1914; Attorney-General 1917; Judge of the Chancey Division, 1918; Lord Justice of Appeal, 1918-24. Knighted 1925. Author of *The Irish Justice of the Peace* (Dublin, 1911; 2nd edition, 1915), *The Licensing Laws of Ireland*, *The Motor-Car Acts*, and *History of Ireland, 1798-1924* (2 vols., 1926). Died 29 Dec. 1931. Obituary, *I.L.T. & S.J.*, lxvi (1932), 5-6. See: *Who's Who*; Ball,

Judges, ii, 386;. and G.W. Hogan, 'Chief Justice Kennedy and Sir James O'Connor's application', in *The Irish Jurist*, new series, xxiii (1988), 144-58.

O'CONNOR, JAMES JOHN MARY (b. 2 July 1873) eld. s. of John O'Connor of Ashton Lawn, Co. Cork, and Mary Gertrude Evans; M 1897. 1900/M/12 [3 items].

O'CONNOR, JAMES JOSEPH (b. 31 March 1931) 3rd s. of James J. O'Connor, solicitor, of 74 Merrion Square, Dublin, and Mabel Fitzgerald; M 1949. 1954/T/10. Disbarred at his own request, 1 Aug. 1959. [6 items]. Aft. a solicitor in Wexford,

O'CONNOR, JOHN WILLIAM (b. 24 August 1918) 2nd s. of Patrick O'Connor, solicitor, of Swinford, Co. Mayo, and Ellen Mulligan; M 1937. 1940/M/03 [2 items]. Judge of the Circuit Court, Oct. 1971. Died 6 June 1978. Obituary, *I.L.T. & S.J.*, cxii (1978), 148.

O'CONNOR, JOSEPH (b. 7 May 1875) 4th s. of Terence O'Connor of Ashford, Co. Limerick, and Mary Reidy; M 1902. 1906/T/04 [3 items]. S.C., 14 July 1924. Judge of the Circuit Court, Cork, 1932-47.

O'CONNOR, KIERAN JOHN (b. 2 Nov. 1931) 3rd s. of John S. O'Connor, of Iona, 130 Howth Road, Dublin, and Mary Patricia Willis; M 1950. 1954/T/09 [2 items]. S.C., 28 Feb. 1974. Judge of the Circuit Court.

O'CONNOR, MICHAEL GABRIEL (b. 2 July 1929) only s. of Patrick Joseph O'Connor, of 'Shamrock Hill', Stillorgan Road, Dublin, and Bridget O'Brien; B. Arch. (N.U.I.); M 1953. 1956/T/05 [2 items].

O'CONNOR, MICHAEL KEVIN (b. 17 May 1915) 2nd s. of William Joseph O'Connor, of The Cottage, Ballitor, Co. Kildare, and Catherine C. Aylmer; M 1933. 1937/M/13 [2 items].

O'CONNOR, PETER EDMUND (b. 3 Dec. 1940) eld. s. of Lieut.-Colonel Edmund A. O'Connor, of Belfast, and Helen Mary Doran; B.A. (Mod.) (T.C.D.); M 1960. 1966/M/18 [1 item]. Banker

O'CONNOR, RORY (b. 26 Nov. 1925) 2nd s. of James E. O'Connor, of Holywood, Co. Down, and Mary Savage; B. Comm. (N.U.I.); M 1945. 1949/T/02 [2 items].

O'CONNOR, RORY BRENDAN (b. 28 Jan. 1928) eld. s. of James J. O'Connor, national teacher, of Knocknagoshel, Co. Kerry, and Ann Keane; M 1955. 1959/M/06 [2 items].

O'CONNOR, ULICK HARRIS (b. 12 Oct. 1928) eld. s. of Matthew Harris O'Connor, Professor of Medicine, R.C.S.I., of 15 Fairfield Park, Highfield Road, Rathgar, Dublin, and Eileen Murphy; B.A. (N.U.I.); M 1947. 1951/M/05 [2 items]. Biographer (of Brendan Behan and Oliver St. John Gogarty) and literary man. Contributor to James Meenan (ed.), *Centenary History of Lit. and Hist. Soc. of U.C.D.* See his *Diaries 1970-1981* (2001). Listed in the 1984 and 1991 editions of Maureen Cairnduff, *Who's Who in Ireland*, and in Louis McRedmond (ed.), *Modern Irish Lives*.

O'CONNOR, WILLIAM BERCHMANS (b. 28 July 1877) eld. s. of Hugh O'Connor of Limerick, Co. Limerick, and Sarah Fennelly; M 1909. 1911/M/04 [2 items].

O'CONNOR MORRIS, MAURICE LINDSAY (b. 23 March 1865) only s. of Judge O'Connor Morris of Gurtnamona, King's Co., and Georgina Lindsay; B.A. (T.C.D.); H 1888. 1891/H/04 [7 items].

O'CONOR, BRIAN E. (b. 7 Feb. 1869) only s. of James E. O'Conor, Assistant Financial Secretary to the Government of India, of Simla, India, and Marian Ahern; B.A. (R.U.I.); M 1888. 1892/M/05 [6 items].

O'CONOR, DENIS CHARLES JOSEPH (b. 26 Oct. 1869) eld. s. of the Rt. Hon. O'Conor Don, of Clonalis, Castlerea, Co. Roscommon, and Georgina Mary Perry (decd.); M 1904; M.T. E 1891. 1905/T/12 [3 items]. H.M.'s Lieutenant, High Sheriff, and Justice of the Peace for County Roscommon. Died unmarried 22 Feb. 1917. *Burke's Irish Family Records* (1976), 903.

O'CONOR, STELLA MILDRED (b. 18 Feb. 1934) only child of Denis Hayes O'Conor, Barrister-at-Law, of 24 Ashdale Road, Terenure, Dublin, and Josephine Lawless; M 1955. 1959/M/08 [2 items]. Her father was called, M 1946, as Donnchadh Aodhach Ó Conchubhair [q.v.].

Ó CUIRC, LIAM (b. 12 Oct. 1917) young. s. of Patrick Quirke (decd.), baker, of 3 William O'Brien Street, Clonmel, Co. Tipperary, and Ellen O'Mara (decd.); M 1951. 1961/T/08 [2 items].

Ó CUIV, AYINDRIES (b. 4 Oct. 1912) 2nd s. of Shan O Cuiv, of 6 Harcourt Terrace, Dublin, and Hanna O'Keeffe; M 1931. 1935/M/01 [2 items]. [Name also rendered Aindrias Ó Caoimh and Andreas O'Keeffe] S.C., 5 July 1951. Attorney-General. 1954, and 1957. Judge of the High Court, 1957-65; of the Supreme Court, 1965-6; President of the High Court, 1966-74; Judge of the European Court of Justice, 1974-84. Listed in the 1984 edition of Maureen Cairnduff, *Who's Who in Ireland.*

O'DALY, CARROLL [Cearbhall Ua Dálaigh] (b. 12 Feb. 1911) 2nd s. of Richard O'Daly (decd.), of Vevay, Bray, Co. Wicklow, and Una Thornton; M 1931. 1934/M/07 [2 items]. S.C., 12 Feb. 1945. Bencher, 1946. Attorney-General, 1946-8, 1951-3. Judge of the Supreme Court, 1953-61; Chief Justice, 1961-72; Judge of the European Court of Justice, 1973-4; President of Ireland, Dec. 1974 – Oct. 1976. Died 21 March 1978. Portrait by Thomas Ryan, and bronze by Garry Trimble, in King's Inns: see Wanda Ryan-Smolin, *King's Inns Portraits* (1992), 54, 82. Assessment by Hugh O'Flaherty in *The Irish Times*, 26 Sept. 1997. See *Who's Who*; Louis McRedmond (ed.), *Modern Irish Lives.*

ODELL, THOMAS URQUHART (b. 1898) only s. of Lieut.-Colonel L.S. Odell, of Kilcheagh Park, Moate, Co. Westmeath, and Henrietta Cecilia Urquhart; M 1927. Awarded Society's Prize. 1930/H/01 [2 items]. S.C., 30 June 1948. In April 1932 published with T.C. Kingsmill Moore *The Landlord and Tenant Act, 1931, fully annotated: with historical and explanatory introduction and appendix of statutes and forms.*

O'DOHERTY, JOSEPH (b. 24 Dec. 1891) 6th s. of Michael O'Doherty (decd.), of 23 Creggan Street, Derry, and Rose McLoughlin; M 1930. 1936/T/08 [2 items].

O'DOHERTY, LOUIS CASIMIR (b. 5 Sept. 1892) 5th s. of Hugh C. O'Doherty, solicitor, of Bay View Terrace, Londonderry, and Lucy C. Sinnott; M 1911. 1916/T/02 [2 items]. Died at Sidcup, Kent, 19 Oct. 1949.

O'DONNELL, DANIEL (b. 24 Jan. 1872) 4th s. of Daniel O'Donnell, farmer, of Kilraine, Glenties, Co. Donegal, and Mary Breslin; B.A. (R.U.I.); H 1893. 1896/H/03 [6 items].

O'DONNELL, MAURICE F. (b. 11 Nov. 1899) eld. s. of Michael O'Donnell, of Loughill, Newcastle West, Co. Limerick, and Elizabeth Flanagan; M 1924. Awarded 2nd Class Certificate of Honour. 1927/M/05 [2 items].

O'DONNELL, THOMAS (b. 29 Nov. 1872) eld. s. of Michael O'Donnell of Liscarney, Co. Kerry, and Eileen Rohan; M 1902. 1905/T/08 [3 items]. Nationalist M.P. for West Kerry, 1900-1918. S.C., 24 April 1933. Appt. Judge of the Circuit Court (Clare, Kerry, Limerick), 29 Sept. 1941. Died 11 June 1943. Obituary, *I.L.T. & S.J.*, lxxvii (1943), 153. Biography by J. Anthony Gaughan, *A Political Odyssey: Thomas O'Donnell, M.P. for West Kerry 1910-1918* (Mount Merrion, 1983), which contains photographs taken on his call to the Bar, his taking of silk, and his appointment as a judge; a portrait (1935) by Seán O'Sullivan is reproduced as the frontispiece. Mentioned in Gerard A. Lee, *A Memoir of the South-Western Circuit* (Dublin, 1990), 5, 12.

O'DONOGHUE, AUSTIN (b. 24 May 1890) 4th s. of Thomas O'Donoghue (decd.), of Dingle, Co. Kerry, and Sara Curry; M 1917. 1920/T/05 [2 items]. District Justice. Died 4 July 1955. Obituary, *I.L.T. & S.J.*, lxxxix (1955), 176, 183-4.

O'DONOGHUE, EUGENE (b. 30 Aug. 1911) 2nd s. of Thomas O'Donoghue, of Abbeyfeale, Co. Limerick, and Mary Doody (decd.); M 1950. 1954/T/08 [2 items].

O'DONOGHUE, JOHN (b. 23 Jan. 1872) 5th s. of Daniel O'Donoghue (The O'Donoghue of the Glens) (decd.), formerly M.P. for Co. Tipperary and for Tralee, and Mary Ennis; M 1899. 1902/M/12 [3 items]. Died unmarried 25 Dec. 1958. *Burke's Irish Family Records* (1976), 905.

O'DONOGHUE, PADRAIG (b. 2 Dec. 1921) 2nd s. of Patrick Joseph O'Donoghue, of 36 Herbert Park, Ballsbridge, Dublin, and Elizabeth Violet Gore; B.A. (N.U.I.); M 1941. 1944/M/03 [2 items]. Solicitor-General of Somaliland, 1960.

O'DONOGHUE, PATRICK (b. 11 March 1872) 2nd s. of Owen O'Donoghue of 25 Alexandra Avenue, Belfast, Co. Antrim, and Elizabeth McGahan; M 1904. 1907/M/05 [2 items].

O'DONOGHUE, PATRICK PHILIP (b. 15 Oct. 1896) only s. of Patrick O'Donoghue, M.D., J.P., of Masseytown House, Macroom, Co. Cork, and Julia MacCarthy; B.A. (N.U.I.); M 1916. 1919/M/07 [2 items]. Appt. District Justice, Oct. 1924. S.C., 20 June 1939.

Aft. Head of the Office of the Attorney-General, and a Judge of the European Court of Human Rights.

O'DONOVAN, DAVID VINCENT (b. 8 Oct. 1932) only s. of Brendan O'Donovan, of Provincial Bank House, Carrick-on-Suir, Co. Tipperary, and Margaret Knight; M 1951. 1956/M/10 [2 items]. G.I. Died in London, *c.* 1975.

O'DONOVAN, DENIS ANTHONY (b. 26 May 1945) eld. s. of Timothy M. O'Donovan, chartered accountant, of 'St. Anthony's', 90 Lower Churchtown Road, Co. Dublin, and Alice Stokes; B.A. (N.U.I.); M 1964. 1967/T/06 [1 item].

O'DONOVAN, DENIS PATRICK (b. 5 April 1914) 2nd s. of Cornelius O'Donovan, civil servant, of 37 Mespil Road, Dublin, and Hannah Twomey; M.A., LL.B. (N.U.I.); M 1934. Awarded Special Prize. 1939/M/04 [1 item].

O'DONOVAN, DIARMUID BRIAN DOMINIC (b. 4 Aug. 1937) eld. s. of Donough O'Donovan, Chief State Solicitor, of 6 Greenmount Road, Terenure, Dublin, and Florence Kenny; B.C.L.; M 1956. 1959/M/09 [2 items]. S.C., 7 Oct. 1974. Judge of the High Court, 23 July 1996.

O'DRISCOLL, DESMOND JOHN (b. 16 Feb. 1918) eld. s. of James Joseph O'Driscoll, engineer, of Cahir, Co. Tipperary, and Josephine O'Loughnan; M 1947. 1956/M/14 [2 items].

O'DRISCOLL, FACHTNA MICHAEL (b. 8 Oct. 1902) eld. s. of Patrick O'Driscoll, of 147 North Circular Road, Dublin, and Margaret Collins; M 1924. 1927/M/20 [2 items]. Died 26 July 1938. Obituary, *I.L.T. & S.J.*, lxxii (1938), 228.

O'DRISCOLL, JAMES (b. 27 Aug. 1940) 2nd s. of John O'Driscoll, farmer, of Kilcrea, Ovens, Co. Cork, and Annie O'Keeffe (decd.); B.C.L. (N.U.I.); M 1961. 1964/M/04 [1 item]. S.C., 4 Oct. 1976.

O'DRISCOLL, MICHAEL (b. 1 March 1905) 2nd s. of John O'Driscoll, of Kilcrea, Farran, Co. Cork, and Catherine O'Sullivan; M 1924. Awarded John Brooke Scholarship and 1st Class Certificate. 1927/M/01 [2 items]. S.C., 1 March 1945. Died 6 Jan. 1951. Obituary, *I.L.T. & S.J.*, lxxxv (1951), 16-17.

Ó DROIGHNEÁIN, MÁIRTÍN PIARAS (b. 17 Oct. 1918) eld. s. of Micheál Ó Droighneáin, of Furbough, Galway, and Máire de Búrca; B.A.; M 1939. 1942/M/05 [2 items].

Ó DUIBHIR, TOMÁS DIARMUID (b. 13 January 1903) eld. s. of John O'Dwyer, of 28 Sandycove Road, Dún Laoghaire, Co. Dublin, and Margaret M. D'Arcy. Official of the Revenue Commissioners, Customs and Excise. 1940/T/01 [2 items].

ODUMOSU, FRANKLIN OLATUNBOSUN (b. 30 Oct. 1933) 4th s. of Frank Oladipo Odumosu, of Ijebu-Ode, Ijebu Province, Nigeria, and Adeola Ogunade; B.A. (Mod.) (T.C.D.); M 1956. 1962/T/05 [2 items].

O'DWYER, ALFRED JAMES (b. 4 Nov. 1912) 4th s. of Denis O'Dwyer, of Limerick, Co. Limerick, and Teresa O'Connor; B.A.; M 1931. 1934/M/09 [2 items]. Registrar of Titles, 1975.

O'DWYER, JOHN (b. 27 May 1915) 2nd s. of James O'Dwyer, of Carrowkeal, Kilshanny, Co. Clare, and Katherine Harkins; B.A., B. Comm., LL.B.; M 1948, L.I. M 1950. 1951/H/03 [2 items].

O'DWYER, TOMÁS: see Ó DUIBHIR, TOMÁS DIARMUID.

O'FARRELL, EDWARD (b. 6 Dec. 1856) 3rd s. of Michael Richard O'Farrell, Barrister-at-Law, of 9 Pembroke Road, Dublin, and Ellen Thunder; B.A. (T.C.D.), M 1878, M.T. T 1880.1882/H/02 [6 items]. Successively Registrar of the Land Commission, Secretary to the Estates Commissioners, and (September 1908) Assistant Under Secretary to the Lord Lieutenant. Knighted. Died 13 Aug. 1926. Obituary, *I.L.T. & S.J.*, lxi (1927), 210.

Ó FATHAIGH, PROINNSEAS (b. 23 May 1880). See: FAHY, FRANCIS PATRICK.

O'FLAHERTY, HUGH JAMES (b. 20 Jan. 1938) only s. of James F. O'Flaherty, electrician, of Killarney, Co. Kerry, and Catherine McSweeney; B.C.L., LL.B; M 1956. Awarded Society's Prize. 1959/M/03 [2 items]. S.C., 13 May 1976. Judge of the Supreme Court, 26 March 1990. Author of *Justice, Liberty and the Courts: Talks and Reflections of Hugh O'Flaherty* (Dublin, 1998). Resigned 17 April 1999: for the circumstances see Dublin newspapers of the period; for his pension arrangements, see Courts (Supplemental Provisions) (Amendment) Act, 1999 [No. 25]. Listed in the 1991 edition of Maureen Cairnduff, *Who's Who in Ireland*.

O'FLYNN, ALPHONSUS MARIA (b. 28 May 1869) 3rd s. of John O'Flynn, J.P., of Passage West, Co. Cork, and Mary O'Brien; H 1892 [includes personal letters seeking exemption due to injury to hands in gas explosion]. 1895/H/09 [9 items].

OGILVY, JOHN FREDERICK (b. 9 Nov. 1868) 2nd eld. s. of Alexander Ogilvy, J.P. (decd.), of 26 Rathgar Road, Dublin, and Fanny Barklie; B.A., LL.B. (T.C.D.); T 1914. 1914/M/08 [2 items]. Served in the Boer War with Lord Longford's Horse (Imperial Yeomanry). Died 13 Feb. 1941. Obituary, *I.L.T. & S.J.*, lxxv (1941), 51.

O'GORMAN, MARTINA LOUIE (b. 30 Jan. 1937) young. d. of James W. O'Gorman (decd.), pharm. chemist, of 1 St. James's Terrace, Sandymount, Co. Dublin, and Sara Fitzpatrick; M 1961. 1965/M/09 [1 item].

O'GRADY, GUILLAMORE (b. 18 Nov. 1878) 2nd s. of Edward O'Grady (decd.), of Merrion Square, Dublin, and of Clenagh, Co. Clare, and Minnie Bishop; B.A. (T.C.D.); M 1899. 1903/T/03 [3 items]. Auditor of the College Historical Society, 1901-2. Major, South Irish Horse. Dublin Herald in the Office of Arms, 1908. Shown in a painting by H. Harris Brown (reproduced in Susan Hood, *Royal Roots - Republican Inheritance*: *The survival of the Office of Arms* (Dublin, 2002), 87) participating in the formal proclamation of King George V. Died 4 Sept. 1952. *Who's Who*. Mentioned in Maurice Healy, *The Old Munster Circuit*, 155-6.

O'GRADY, JAMES JOHN (b. 18 Jan. 1935) 2nd s. of William J. O'Grady, of National Bank House, Tralee, Co. Kerry, and Mary K. McEllin; B.A.; M 1953. 1957/M/05 [2 items].

O'GRADY, STANDISH (b. 18 Sept 1846) 2nd s. of the Revd. Thomas O'Grady (decd.) of Magourney Glebe, Coachford, Co. Cork, and Susan Dowe; B.A. (T.C.D.); T 1869, M.T. T 1870. 1872/T/07a [2 items]. Relinquished the Bar first for journalism, then for literature. Historian and novelist: 'Father of the Irish literary revival'. Died 18 May 1928. See *Who's Who*; and Henry Boylan, *A Dictionary of Irish Biography* (1978).

O'GRADY, WILLIAM MICHAEL (b. 25 Sept. 1885) 2nd s. of Bernard Michael O'Grady, solicitor, of Corbally, Grosvenor Road, Rathmines, Dublin, and Annie Bond; 1920. Removed from roll of solicitors at own request, 5 Nov. 1920. 1920/M/11 [3 items].

O'HANLON, ORIEL JOHN (b. 2 Aug. 1860) only s. of John D. O'Hanlon, Barrister-at-Law, of 11 Henrietta Street, Dublin, and Maria Keogh; H 1888. 1892/H/04 [7 items].

O'HANLON, RODERICK JOSEPH (b. 11 April 1923) 3rd s. of Terence O'Hanlon, of 14 Royse Road, Phibsboro, Dublin, and Mary Hally; M 1943. 1946/M/01 [2 items]. S.C., 2 Oct. 1967. Professor at U.C.D. Judge of the High Court, 20 March 1981. Retired 11 April 1995. President of the Law Reform Commission, 1992. Died 24 March 2002. Obituaries, with photographs, *The Times*, 28 March 2002; *The Irish Times*, 30 March 2002; and *Courts Service News* (Joseph Finnegan), vol. 4 (2), May 2002, page 7. Listed in the 1984 and 1991 editions of Maureen Cairnduff, *Who's Who in Ireland*.

O'HANRAHAN (Ó hAnnracháin) , FACHTNA (b. 2 Sept. 1920) eld. s. of Peadar Ó hAnnracháin, of Cuan Dor, Strand Road, Baldoyle, Co. Dublin, and Máire Ní Dheasúna; B.A., H. Dip. Ed; M 1949. Awarded Society's Exhibition Prize. 1952/M/02 [2 items].

O'HANRAHAN (Ó hAnnracháin), FIACHRA (b. 14 Feb. 1930) 4th s. of Peadar Ó hAnnracháin, of Cuan Dor, Strand Road, Baldoyle, Co. Dublin, and Máire Ní Dheasúna; B.A. (N.U.I.); M 1949. Awarded John Brooke Scholarship. 1952/M/01 [2 items].

O'HANRAHAN, ROGER CHARLES (b. 23 May 1907) 3rd s. of David O'Hanrahan, of Altamount, Kilkenny, and Margaret Bowl; M.A., LL.B. (N.U.I.); M 1926. 1929/M/02 [2 items]. S.C., 3 March 1955. Died 19 April 1971. Obituary, *I.L.T. & S.J.*, cv (1971), 138.

O'HANRAHAN, SEÁN DESMOND MARY (b. 25 Mar. 1922) eld. s. of Seán O'Hanrahan, of 'Inisfail', Ballyshannon, Co. Donegal, and Josephine Owens; B.A. (N.U.I.); M 1941. 1944/T/04 [2 items]. S.C., 16 March 1962. Judge of the Circuit Court.

O'HARA, LIAM (b. 18 Aug. 1915) eld. s. of James O'Hara (decd.), of Kiltimagh, Co. Mayo, and Alice Maher; M 1951. 1954/T/12 [2 items].

O'HARA, ROBERT FRANCIS (b. 13 June 1851) only s. of John Michael O'Hara, Clerk of the Crown, of 33 Mountjoy Square, Dublin and Derryhoyle, Co. Galway, and Elizabeth

Burke; B.A. (Queen's University); E 1872, L.I. H 1874. 1875/T/06 [2 items]. Died 13 April 1911: *I.L.T. & S.J.*, xlv (1911), 104.

O'HIGGINS, KEVIN CHRISTOPHER (b. 7 June 1892) 4th s. of Thomas Francis Higgins, F.R.C.S.I. (decd.), of 'Woodlands', Stradbally, Queen's Co., and Annie Josephine Sullivan; H 1925 [note from Att.-Gen; Mem. signed by J.A. Costello] 1925/H/03 [3 items]. Minister for Justice (and Vice President of the Executive Council) of the Irish Free State, 1922-7. Assassinated 10 July 1927. See Terence de Vere White, *Kevin O'Higgins* (1949); *Who's Who*; *D.N.B.*; and Louis McRedmond (ed.), *Modern Irish Lives*.

O'HIGGINS, KEVIN CHRISTOPHER (b. 23 March 1946) 4th s. of Niall B. O'Higgins, medical doctor, psychiatrist, of Elmhurst, Mulgrave Street, Limerick City, and Joan O'Shea; B.A. (N.U.I.); M 1965. 1968/M/25 [1 item]. S.C., 5 March 1982. Judge of the Circuit Court, 1986. Advanced to be a Judge of the High Court, 15 May 1997.

O'HIGGINS, PAUL (b. 4 Oct. 1927) eld. s. of Richard Leo O'Higgins, M.C., M.R.C.V.S., of Rochester House, Uxbridge, Middlesex, and Elizabeth Deane; MA; M 1953; L.I. M 1954. 1957/M/04 [2 items]. Fellow of Christ's College, Cambridge. Regius Professor of Laws, T.C.D. Author, *inter alia*, of *A bibliography of periodical literature relating to Irish Law* (Belfast: 1966); *ibid. First Supplement* (Belfast, 1973); *ibid. Second Supplement* (Belfast, 1986), and of *A bibliography of Irish trials and other legal proceedings* (Abingdon, Oxon, 1986). Joint editor (with John McEldowney) of *The Common Law Tradition: Essays in Irish Legal History* (Dublin, 1990).

O'HIGGINS, THOMAS FRANCIS KEVIN PETER (b. 23 July 1916) eld. s. of Thomas Francis O'Higgins, T.D., of 26 Kenilworth Road, Rathgar, Dublin, and Agnes McCarthy; M 1935. 1938/M/02 [2 items]. S.C., 7 April 1954. Bencher, 1967. T.D. 1948-73. Judge of the High Court, 1973, Chief Justice, 1974-84; Judge of the European Court of Justice, 1985-91. Died 25 February 2003. Obituary in *The Times*, 27 Feb. 2003; news coverage and obituary in *The Irish Times*, and 26 Feb-1 March 2003. Obituary (by T.A. Finlay) in *The Bar Review*, vol. 8 (No. 2; April 2003), 50. See his autobiography *A Double Life* (Dublin, 1996). Portrait by James Le Jeune in King's Inns: see Wanda Ryan-Smolin, *King's Inns Portraits* (1992), 56. Listed in the 1984 edition of Maureen Cairnduff, *Who's Who in Ireland.*

Ó hINNSE, SÉAMUS (b. 6 Dec. 1917) 2nd s. of Padraig Ó hInnse (merchant), of Corofin, Co. Clare, and Margaret O'Grady; M.A., LL.B., M 1939. 1942/M/06 [2 items]. S.C., 2 July 1959. Ph.D. Professor of Roman History, Jurisprudence and Legal History at U.C.D., 1948-62. Judge of the High Court, 1962-72; of the Supreme Court, 2 Oct. 1972. Retired 16 Oct. 1988. Listed [under Henchy] in the 1984 edition of Maureen Cairnduff, *Who's Who in Ireland*, and likewise in Louis McRedmond (ed.), *Modern Irish Lives.*

Ó hUADHAIGH, ROBERT JOSEPH (b. 24 April 1914) eld. s. of Seán O hUadhaigh, solicitor, of Glencairn, Harbour Road, Dalkey, Co. Dublin, and Mary Dinon; M 1933. 1937/T/05 [2 items]. District Justice.

OKECHUKWU, ARTHUR EZEAKORNOBI (b. 21 July 1927) 2nd s. of Mark Dike Okechukwu, merchant, of No. 1 Bishop Johnson Street, Port Harcourt, Nigeria, and Grace Agwagha Ezeanochie; M 1956. 1959/T/07 [2 items].

O'KEEFFE, DANIEL (b. 24 Jan. 1943) eld. s. of Dr. William O'Keeffe, of Abbey House, Ennis, Co. Clare, and Maureen Treacy; B.C.L. (N.U.I.); M 1960. Awarded Brooke Scholarship. 1964/H/01 [1 item]. S.C., 7 Oct. 1985.

O'KEEFFE, EUGENE (b. 4 Sept. 1913) eld. s. of Eugene O'Keeffe, of 37 Whitehall Road, Terenure, Dublin, formerly [New] Street, Killarney, Co. Kerry, and Mary Anne Cooper; B.A. (N.U.I.); H. Dip., LL.B; M 1944.1948/T/18 [2 items].

O'KEEFFE, MICHAEL (b. 15 July 1898) 2nd s. of Joseph O'Keeffe, of Tralee, Co. Kerry, and Katherine Fitzgerald; M 1923. 1926/T/05? [*recte* 1926/E/01] [2 items].

O'KEEFFE, MICHAEL P. (Micheál Pádraig Ó Caoimh) (b. 5 April 1930) eld. s. of William O'Keeffe (decd.), engineer, of 67 Croydon Park Avenue, Marino, Dublin, and Anne Byrne; M 1949. 1953/M/08 [2 items]. Aft. a solicitor, specialising in tax.

O'KELLY DE GALWAY, GUY MARIE-JOSEPH PHILIPPE GHISLAIN (b. 4 Aug. 1917) 2nd s. of Philippe O'Kelly de Galway (decd.), of Jambes (Namur), Belgium, and Marie Le Clement du Saint Marcq; M 1953. 1954/M/09 [4 items]. Characterised in Patrick

MacKenzie, *Lawful Occasions*, 131 as 'a most eccentric Belgian and Irish country gentleman'.

O'KENNEDY, JOHN JOSEPH KARBRY (b. 20 May 1860) young. s. of Jeremiah Maurice O'Kennedy of Bantry, Co. Cork, and Hanna O'Crowley; M.A., LL.B. (R.U.I.); M 1884. 1887/T/06 [6 items].

O'KENNEDY, MICHAEL EAMONN (b. 21 Feb. 1936) eld. s. of Eamonn O'Kennedy (decd.), merchant, of Bank Place, Nenagh, Co. Tipperary, and Helena Slattery; M.A. (N.U.I.); M 1957. 1961/M/02 [2 items]. S.C., 1 June 1973. Fianna Fáil Senator, T.D. and Minister for various Departments, including Foreign Affairs and Finance. European Commissioner, 1981-2. Listed in Maureen Cairnduff, *Who's Who in Ireland* (1984 and 1999 editions).

OKOLO, JEROME HERBERT CHUKWULOZIE (b. 21 Aug. 1935) eld. s. of Herbert Okole, M.B.E., supervisor of schools, of 10 Okolo Street, Onitsha, in the Province of Onitsha, Nigeria, and Margaret Ikeagu; M 1956. Awarded 2nd Victoria Prize. 1960/T/02 [2 items].

OLDHAM, CHARLES HUBERT (b. 4 March 1859) 4th s. of Eldred Oldham (decd.) of Pembroke Road, Dublin, and Anne Alker; B.A. (T.C.D.); H 1888. 1890/M/02 [9 items]. Professor of Economics at U.C.D. Mentioned in James Meenan, *George O'Brien: a biographical memoir* (1980).

O'LEARY, DANIEL (b. 25 May 1878) 5th s. of Florence O'Leary of Glandore, Bantry, Co. Cork, and Mary Hurley; Sch. (Law Faculty, Q.C.C., T.C.D.); T 1898. 1902/H/01 [3 items].

O'LEARY, JOHN (b. 4 Jan. 1902) eld. s. of [Simon?] O'Leary, of Limestone Road, Belfast, and Mary Kane; H 1927. 1929/M/14 [2 items]. S.C., 27 April 1949. Master of the High Court.

O'LEARY, MAURICE CHARLES MCCARTHY (b. 6 March 1854) 4th s. of MacCarthy O'Leary D.L., of Cromlagane, Co. Cork, and Jane O'Connell; M 1877, M.T. M 1880. 1881/M/07 [7 items].

O'LEARY, SIMON PETER (b. 18 Feb. 1944) eld. s. of John O'Leary, Senior Counsel, of 17 Temple Villas, Palmerston Road, Dublin, and Mary Eva Montgomery; B.A. (N.U.I.); M 1962. 1965/M/03 [1 item]. Deputy D.P.P. Law Reform Commission.

Ó LOINGSIGH [Lynch], FIONÁN (b. 17 March 1889) 4th s. of Finian Lynch (decd.), of Kilmakerin, Cahirciveen, Co. Kerry, and Ellie M. Lynch; M 1931. 1931/M/12 [2 items]. M.P. for Kerry South 1918-22, T.D. for various constituencies 1921-44. Minister for Lands, -1932. Judge of the Circuit Court (North-Western Circuit). Retired 1959. Mentioned in T.F. O'Higgins, *A Double Life*, 76-7.

OLPHERT, ROBERT FANNIN (b. 2 April 1851) 3rd s. of Wybrants Olphert of Ballyconnell, Co. Donegal, and Marianne Fannin; B.A. (T.C.D.); M 1871, M.T. E 1872. 1874/M/04 [2 items].

O'MAHONY, DAVID (b. 21 Oct. 1926) only s. of Timothy O'Mahony, company director, of Carrigfern, College Road, Co. Cork, and Anna Canton; M.A. (N.U.I.); M 1948. 1951/T/03 [2 items]. Lecturer in Economics at U.C.C. Author, *inter alia*, of *Industrial Relations in Ireland: the background* (Dublin, 1964) and *The Irish Economy: an introductory description* (Cork, 1964).

O'MAHONY, Revd. DERMOT PATRICK LEO (b. 18 Feb. 1935) 2nd s. of Gerald William O'Mahony, retired bank official, of 14 Corbawn Avenue, Shankill, Co. Dublin, and Elizabeth McGuinness; D.C.L., B.A.; M 1964. Awarded 1st Victoria Prize. 1967/M/01 [1 item]. Ordained 1960. Auxiliary Bishop of Dublin, 1975. Listed in Maureen Cairnduff, *Who's Who in Ireland* (1984, 1991 and 1999 editions).

O'MAHONY, EOIN SEOSAMH (b. 22 March 1904) only s. of Daniel John O'Mahony, City Analyst, of Dunmahon, Douglas Road, Cork, and Julia Mary O'Keeffe, B.A.; M 1926, I.T. H 1928. 1930/M/06 [2 items]. Auditor of the College Historical Society, 1930-1. Called to English Bar, M 1933. Panel of Defence Counsel (English Bar) at Nuremberg Trials, 1946. Knight of Malta. Gentleman scholar and raconteur, known as 'the Pope'. Mentioned in Gerard A. Lee, *A Memoir of the South-Western Circuit* (Dublin, 1990), 18, 28, 35; T.F. O'Higgins, *A Double Life* (Dublin, 1996), 85-6; Hubert Butler, *Escape from the Anthill* (Mullingar, 1985) 193-7. Died 15 Feb. 1970. Obituary in *The Times*,

19 Feb. 1970. See Henry Boylan, *A Dictionary of Irish Biography*; Louis McRedmond (ed.), *Modern Irish Lives*; and *Burke's Landed Gentry of Ireland* (1958), 549-550.

O'MAHONY, JOHN (b. 28 Jan. 1871) 2nd s. of John Francis Mahony of Sheares Street, Cork, and Mary Sheehan; M 1894. 1899/H/01 [3 items]. Died 1904. *Burke's Landed Gentry of Ireland* (1958), 550.

O'MAHONY, JOHN FINBARR MICHAEL (b. 23 July 1901) 2nd s. of John Francis O'Mahony (decd.), Barrister-at-Law, of Suile-na-Tire, Clondalkin, Dublin, and Nora Tynan; M 1923. 1926/T/03 [2 items]. Died 19 June 1946 [?]: *cf.* the obituary of 'Barry Tynan O'Mahony' (called 1926), in *I.L.T. & S.J.*, lxxx (1946), 157.

O'MALLEY, BRENDAN GEORGE (b. 11 May 1926) 1st s. of Patrick E. O'Malley, Ardmochree, Co. Limerick, and Kathleen Bonass; B.A.; M 1944. 1947/M/06 [2 items].

O'MALLEY, PETER (b. 10 June 1922) 2nd s. of Michael George O'Malley, surgeon, of Barna House, Barna, Galway, and Christina Mary Ryan; B.A. (N.U.I.); M 1941. 1944/T/03 [2 items]. S.C., 19 July 1963. Judge-Advocate General, 1966. Appt. President of the Circuit Court, 21 May 1990. Retired 10 June 1992. Died 4 March 2002.

O'MEARA, ARTHUR JOSEPH (b. 20 July 1893) only s. of John O'Meara (decd.), of Garville Avenue, Rathgar, Dublin, and Anne L. Markin; Undergrad. (N.U.I.); M 1912. 1915/T/02 [2 items].

OMO, MICHAEL AMUZIAM (b. 17 July 1934) eld. s. of Felix Edozie Omo, manager of textile factory, of AsaB.A., Mid-Western State of Nigeria, West Africa, and Catherine Anuchi Halim; M 1963. 1968/M/18 [1 item].

Ó MODHRÁIN, DOMHNALL FIONÁN (b. 6 Sept. 1923) eld. s. of Michael Moran, of Murriagh, Waterville, Co. Kerry, and Eileen Lynch (decd.); M 1943. 1946/T/07 [2 items]. Chief Executive of Gael-Linn. Died 11 Jan. 2000. Obituary, *The Irish Times*, 13 Jan. 2000. See Louis McRedmond (ed.), *Modern Irish Lives*.

O'MULLANE, MICHAEL JOSEPH (b. 12 Jan. 1889) eld. s. of James O'Mullane, of Sligo, Co. Sligo, and Brigid MacCaffrey; M.A.; M 1925. 1928/M/07 [2 items].

O'NEILL, DENIS JOSEPH (b. 28 April 1880) 8th s. of John Henry O'Neill (decd.) of Summerville House, Upper Rathmines, Dublin, and Maria Hearn (decd.); M 1904. 1907/E/01 [3 items].

O'NEILL, HENRY (b. 9 Sept. 1853) 5th s. of Henry O'Neill (decd.), farmer, of Castlereagh, Co. Down, and Mary Jane McDowell; H 1893. 1902/T/02 [2 items].

O'NEILL, HUGH (b. 12 December 1917) 2nd s. of Henry O'Neill, civil servant, of 1 Mountain View Road, Ranelagh, Co. Dublin, and Josephine McInerney; B.A. (N.U.I.); M 1936. Awarded Certificate of Honour. 1939/M/05 [1 item]. Died 1970. Obituary, *I.L.T. & S.J.*, civ (1970), 497.

O'NEILL, HUGH O'HAGAN (b. 14 Feb. 1875) 2nd s. of Constantine O'Neill (decd.) of Hy-Niall, Belfast, and Sarah Hagan; H 1897. 1900/T/01 [3 items].

O'NEILL, JOHN BRENDAN (b. 24 May 1909) 2nd s. of James O'Neill (decd.), of Dunnamanagh, Strabane, Co. Tyrone, and Ellen Fitzgerald; M 1940. Awarded Brooke Scholarship. 1943/M/01 [2 items]. Called to N.I. Bar, M 1948.

O'NEILL, JOHN PATRICK (b. 27 May 1937) eld. s. of Thomas Joseph O'Neill (decd.), company director, of Uplands, Delgany, Co. Wicklow, and Moira Murphy; B.A. (N.U.I.); M 1956. 1960/M/04 [2 items].

O'NEILL, PATRICK JOSEPH (b. 5 Nov. 1921) 5th s. of John O'Neill (decd.), of Uplands, Delgany, Co. Wicklow, and Kathleen Elliott; M 1941. 1944/T/05 [2 items].

O'NEILL, PETER JOHN (b. 9 Aug. 1847) 4th s. of John O'Neill, farmer, of Deroran House, Co. Tyrone, and Ellen Montague; B.A. (QUI); E 1871, G.I. M 1878. 1880/H/01 [5 items].

O'NEILL, RAYMOND JOSEPH (b. 27 June 1912) eld. s. of Laurence Joseph O'Neill, solicitor, of 33 Ailesbury Road, Dublin, and Flora Fitzgerald; B.A., LL.B. (T.C.D.); M 1933. Awarded Society's Exhibition and Certificate of Honour. 1936/M/02 [2 items]. S.C., 1 July 1955. Appreciation (by Frank Murphy) in *The Irish Times*.

O'NEILL, VINCENT JOSEPH (b. 19 March 1875) young. s. of Anthony O'Neill (decd.) of Ard Brugh, Co. Dublin, and Elizabeth Purcell; cand. B.A.; M 1895. 1898/T/09 [3 items].

O'PHELAN, EILEEN MARY de RIVA (b. 31 May 1918) daughter of Michael Joseph de Riva O'Phelan, The O'Phelan (decd.), of Glenbower, and the Mall, Waterford, and Aine O'Kenlan; M 1937. 1941/M/15 [2 items].

O'QUIGLEY, JOHN BENIGNUS (b. 27 Aug. 1925) 4th s. of James O'Quigley, teacher (retd.), of Blackfort, Castlebar, Co. Mayo, and Mary Margaret McGrath (decd.); M 1946. 1950/M/10 [2 items]. Active, while at the Bar, as a member of the Senate. Died 1969.

O RAHILLY, THE (b. 3 July 1903) eld. s. of The O Rahilly, of 40 Herbert Park, Dublin, and Nannie Brown; M 1925. 1932/M/03 [2 items].

O'REGAN, TIMOTHY PATRICK (b. 12 Nov. 1918) eld. s. of Daniel O'Regan, national teacher, of Glenview, Ballinhassig, Co. Cork, and Mary Twomey; M 1944. 1948/T/08 [2 items]. Registrar.

O'REILLY, ANDREW EVARISTUS (b. 20 Oct. 1897) 3rd s. of Terence O'Reilly, of Valentia House, Kinawley, Enniskillen, Co. Fermanagh, and Frances Lanner; M 1929. 1934/T/02 [3 items].

O'REILLY, GERARD JOSEPH MARY (b. 1 Sept. 1920) eld. s. of Joseph O'Reilly, rate collector (retd.), of 58 St. Patrick's Road, Drumcondra, Dublin, and Mary Margaret McGann; M 1945. 1949/M/10 [2 items].

O'REILLY, JAMES PATRICK (b. 13 April 1900) eld. s. of John O'Reilly, of 314 Banbury Road, Oxford, England, and Anne Agatha Cleburne (decd.); H 1923. 1925/T/05 [2 items]. B.A. (Oxon.). Professor of Common Law at King's Inns.

O'REILLY, JAMES PATRICK (b. 3 Sept. 1931) eld. s. of Owen O'Reilly (decd.), of The Green, Westport, Co. Mayo, and Frances Keane; M 1951. 1955/M/13 [2 items].

O'REILLY, JOHN PATRICK JOSEPH (b. 14 March 1906) 3rd s. of John O'Reilly, of North Quay, Drogheda, Co. Louth, and Margaret McKeever; M 1928. 1932/M/13 [2 items]. Aft. Inspector General in the Customs Service. Died 1976. Father of Dr. Sir Anthony O'Reilly. Bronze bust in T.C.D.: see Anne Crookshank and David Webb, *Paintings and Sculptures in Trinity College Dublin* (Dublin, 1990), 106.

O'REILLY, JOSEPH RICHARD (b. 4 July 1843) eld. s. of Richard Pearce O'Reilly of 21 Rutland Squar Nth, Dublin, and Olivia Kenny; B.A. (T.C.D.); M 1865, M.T. T 1867. 1870/E/02 [2 items].

O'REILLY, PEADAR MADHMHUIRE (b. 15 Aug. 1922) only s. of Peter A. O'Reilly, civil servant, of 'Baufac', Fortfield Road, Terenure, Dublin, and Mary G. Murphy; M 1945. 1949/M/17 [2 items].

Ó RIAIN, EOIN (b. 12 June 1920) eld. s. of James Ryan, Minister of State, of Kendlestown House, Delgany, Co. Wicklow, and Mairin Cregan; B.A. (N.U.I.); M 1941. 1945/T/11 [2 items]. S.C., 19 July 1963. Better known as Eoin Ryan. Fianna Fáil Senator 1957-87. Died 14 Dec. 2001. Obituary, *The Irish Times*, 15 Dec. 2001. Listed (under Ryan) in the 1984 edition of Maureen Cairnduff, *Who's Who in Ireland*.

O'RIORDAN, JOSEPH DANIEL (b. 3 Feb. 1926) 2nd s. of Christopher J. O'Riordan, of 21 Edenvale Road, Ranelagh, Dublin, and Stella Josephine Hall; M 1945. 1948/T/19 [2 items].

ORME, ROBERT (b. 20 Oct. 1865) only s. of Robert Orme (decd.) of Vallombrosa, Co. Wicklow, and Henrietta O'Driscoll; M 1889. 1892/M/09 [7 items].

ORMSBY, ALFRED HAMILTON (b. 14 May 1852) 5th s. of the Rt. Hon. Henry Ormsby, Judge of the High Court of Justice, of Fitzwilliam Sq, Dublin, and Julia Hamilton; B.A. (T.C.D.); M 1876, L.I. M 1878. 1879/M/15 [6 items]. Called to English Bar, T 1899. J.P., D.L., Co. Dublin. Listed in *Thom's Directory*, under Hamilton, as A.H. Ormsby-Hamilton.

ORMSBY, FRANCIS BALFOUR (b. 26 June 1849) 3rd s. of the Revd. William Edwin Ormsby (decd.), Vicar of St Peter's, Drogheda, Co. Louth, and Ellen Price; M 1877, L.I. T 1879. 1880/M/11 [6 items].

O'RORKE, WILLIAM EDWARD (b. 23 Feb. 1863) 2nd s. of Daniel O'Rorke, J.P., solicitor, of Ballybollan, Co. Antrim, and Carrickfergus, and Susan Murphy; B.A. (T.C.D.); H 1883. 1886/M/07 [6 items].

ORPEN, JOHN RICHARDS (b. 23 April 1844) eld. s. of John Herbert Orpen, LL.D., Barrister-at-Law, of 58 St Stephen's Green, Dublin, and Ellen Richards; B.A. (T.C.D.);

E 1875, M.T. E 1865. 1877/E/09 [6 items]. Died 21 July 1920. *Burke's Landed Gentry of Ireland* (1958), 558.

ORPEN, RICHARD THEODORE (b. 13 Oct. 1869) eld. s. of Ven. Raymond d'A. Orpen, Archdeacon of Ardfert, of Tralee, Co. Kerry, and Sarah Lucinde MacGillycuddy; Sch. Mod. B.A. (T.C.D.); H 1895. 1898/H/07 [5 items]. Police Magistrate, aft. a Law Officer, Southern Nigeria, Aug. 1903-; Resident Magistrate, aft. acting Puisne Judge, Jamaica, June 1910-; Chief Justice of Barbados, 1925-6. Died 15 Aug. 1926. *Who's Who*; *Burke's Landed Gentry of Ireland* (1958), 559.

ORR, JAMES WILLIAM (b. 9 Jan. 1879) 2nd s. of Judge Orr, K.C., of 37 Upper Mount Street, Dublin, and Annie Davison; B.A. (Oxon); M 1903. 1906/T/01 [3 items].

ORR, JOHN WILLIAM (b. 4 March 1838) only s. of William Orr of Liverpool, Lancaster, and Ann Maria Sausse; M.A. (T.C.D.); E 1871, I.T. M 1859. 1871/M/11 [3 items].

ORR, ROBERT DAVISON (b. 9 Jan. 1879) 3rd s. of James Orr, K.C. County Court Judge of Down, of 37 Upper Mount Street, Dublin, and Anne Davison; B.A. (T.C.D.); M 1899. 1902/M/07 [2 items].

ORR, WILLIAM (b. 9 Feb. 1856) 2nd s. of the Revd. John Henry Orr of Antrim, and Matilda Harper; M 1881, M.T. E 1882. 1884/T/04 [9 items].

OSBORNE, ROBERT ERNEST (b. 6 June 1861) eld. s. of John Osborne, J.P., merchant, of Londonderry, and Mary Callender; M.A. (Edinburgh); M 1883, L.I. E 1885. 1886/M/01 [7 items]. K.C., 27 June 1914. Author of *The Jurisdiction and Practice of County Courts in Ireland in Equity and Probate Matters* (Dublin, 1890; 2nd edition 1910). County Court Judge and Recorder of Londonderry, 10 Aug. 1919. Died 29 July 1939. Obituary, *I.L.T. & S.J.*, lxxiii (1939), 223; *Who's Who*.

O'SHANAHAN, JAMES (b. 29 April 1839) 2nd s. of Edmund O'Shanahan, gentleman, of Listowel, Co. Kerry, and Margaret Stack; M 1877, M.T. M 1879. 1882/T/01 [8 items].

O'SHAUGHNESSY, KEVIN (b. 25 June 1914) only s. of Vincent Kevin O'Shaughnessy, of 4 St. Ita's Road, Glasnevin, Co. Dublin, and Mary Molloy; Mod. B.A. (T.C.D.); M 1942. 1945/M/04 [2 items]. S.C., 18 March 1976.

O'SHAUGHNESSY, THOMAS (b. 22 Dec 1850) eld. s. of Thomas O'Shaughnessy, solicitor, of 112 Lower Gardiner Street, Dublin, and Maryannie Lopdell; T 1870; M.T. H 1871. 1874/H/06 [2 items]. Called to the English Bar, 1894. Q.C., June 1889. Bencher, 1895. Appt. Recorder of Dublin, 26 June 1905. Appt., aged 73, a Judge of the High Court of the Irish Free State, June 1924, being the beneficiary of section 100 of the Courts of Justice Act, 1924 [No. 10], which extended the age of retirement by 3 years. Retired 1925: see appreciation in *I.L.T. & S.J.*, lx (1926), 14. Died 7 March 1933. Obituary, *I.L.T. & S.J.*, lxvii (1933), 76, 83-4, 93, 204; *Who's Who*. Mentioned in Maurice Healy, *The Old Munster Circuit*, 239. See 'Sir Thomas O'Shaughnessy', in J.B. Hall, *Random Records of a Reporter* (Dublin, n.d.), 99-101, with J.B. Hall's sketched portrait, 'The last of the Recorders', done in 1923. O'Shaughnessy was mentioned by V.T.H. Delany [q.v.], in his article 'The Bench and Bar in Ireland', as one of 'those who were at the forefront of their profession during the period'.

O'SHAUGHNESSY, THOMAS LOPDELL (b. 29 Aug. 1881) eld. s. of Thomas Lopdell O'Shaughnessy, K.C., of 64 Fitzwilliam Square, Dublin, and Catherine Jane Truman; B.A. (T.C.D.); M 1898. 1904/H/03 [4 items]. Died 29 Feb. 1928. Obituary, *I.L.T. & S.J.*, lxii (1928), 19.

O'SHEA, TIMOTHY JOSEPH (b. 9 Feb. 1918) eld. s. of Timothy O'Shea (decd.), District Justice, of Mount Sion, Kilkenny, Co. Kilkenny, and Sheila [?]; M 1939. 1959/E/01 [2 items].

O'SHIEL, KEVIN ROANTREE (b. 23 Sept. 1891) eld. s of Francis Shields of Highfield, Omagh, Co. Tyrone, and Elizabeth Roantree; M 1910. 1913/M/07 [2 items]. Judge of the Dáil's Land Commission, 1920. S.C., 4 July 1947. Involvement with Dáil courts. Adviser to Michael Collins. Assistant Legal Adviser to the Provisional Government, 1922-3; Director of the Norther-Eastern Boundary Bureau, 1922-5: see Ronan Keating, Michael Kennedy, Dermot Keogh and Eunan O'Halpin (eds.), *Documents on Irish Foreign Policy. Volume II. 1923-1926* (Dublin: 2000). Author of *The Making of a Republic* (1922) and of a series of twelve articles, 'Memories of my Lifetime', in *The Irish Times*, November 1966. Father of Professor Eda Sagarra. Died 1970. Obituary,

I.L.T. & S.J., civ (1970), 344. See Mary Kotsonouris, *Retreat from Revolution: The Dáil Courts, 1920-24* (Dublin, 1994), 24-5, 32, 85, 93, 131; and ibid., *The Winding-up of the Dáil Courts, 1922-1925: an obvious duty* (Dublin, 2004), 253.

Ó SÚILLEABHÁIN, PRONNSIAS EOGHAN (b. 13 Oct. 1889) 2nd s. of Eoghan Ó Súilleabháin, of Adrigale, Bantry, Co. Cork, and Nano Ní Dhuinn; M 1944. 1948/M/08 [2 items]. B. Comm.; LL.B.; M.A.; Ph. D. (Freiburg). Died 27 Feb. 1956.

O'SULLIVAN, DANIEL (b. 27 June 1857) eld. s. of Patrick Daniel O'Sullivan (decd.) of Tralee, Co. Kerry, and Margaret Roche; student (T.C.D.); M 1884. 1888/H/06 [6 items].

O'SULLIVAN, DONAL JOSEPH (b. 24 Dec. 1893) only s. of James O'Sullivan, of 33 Wyatt Road, Forest Gate, Essex, and Mary Hudson; M 1920. 1922/M/05 [2 items]. LL.D.

O'SULLIVAN, FINBARR JOSEPH ANTHONY (b. 18 Sept. 1945) 2nd s. of Dr. John Vincent O'Sullivan, opthalmic surgeon, of 'Maymount', Sunday's Well, Cork, and Doris Joan Walsh; B.A. (N.U.I.); M 1964. 1968/M/08 [1 item].

O'SULLIVAN, Lieut.-General GEARÓID (b. 28 Jan. 1891) 4th s. of Michael O'Sullivan (decd.), of Coolnagrave, Skibbereen, Co. Cork, and Margaret McCarthy; M 1924. 1926/M/10 [2 items]. Died 26 March 1948. Obituary, *I.L.T. & S.J.*, lxxxii (1948), 80.

O'SULLIVAN, GERALD THOMAS (b. 27 Nov. 1929) s. of Thaddeus Gerald O'Sullivan, District Justice, of 24 Castle Park Road, Dún Laoghaire, Co. Dublin, and Mary O'Higgins; M 1948. 1952/M/10 [2 items].

O'SULLIVAN, JAMES (b. 11 Jan. 1918) eld. s. of Daniel O'Sullivan, civil servant (retd.), of 12 Kenilworth Square, Rathgar, Dublin, and Anne Mary O'Mahony (decd.); M 1946. 1950/M/11 [2 items].

O'SULLIVAN, JAMES RAYMOND (b. 29 Aug. 1946) eld. s. of Patrick Joseph O'Sullivan, legal executive officer, of Maryland, Cahir, Co. Tipperary, and Noreen Morrissey; B.C.L. (N.U.I.); M 1965. 1968/M/11 [1 item].

O'SULLIVAN, JOHN CHRISTOPHER (b. 6 Dec. 1898) 2nd s. of Michael W. O'Sullivan, of Kenmare, Co. Kerry, and Johana Coffey; H 1928. 1931/M/10 [2 items].

O'SULLIVAN, JOHN MICHAEL (b. 22 April 1903) young. s. of John Clifford O'Sullivan, of 246 North Circular Road, Dublin, and Marianne O'Shaughnessy; B.A., LL.B. (N.U.I.); M 1925. 1928/M/03 [2 items].

O'SULLIVAN, JOSEPH P. (b. 19 March 1872) 4th s. of Laurence O'Sullivan of Sunview, Western Road, Cork, and Alice Grace; B.A. (R.U.I.); M 1902. 1905/T/07 [3 items]. A registrar of the High Court. Died 20 May 1943. Obituary, *I.L.T. & S.J.*, lxxvii (1943), 141.

O'SULLIVAN, PATRICK (b. 19 Aug. 1876) 3rd s. of Michael O'Sullivan of Graigue, Shanballymore, Mallow, Co. Cork, and Elizabeth O'Toole; M 1909. 1915/M/02 [2 items].

O'SULLIVAN, PAUL (b. 3 May 1922) eld. s. of Martin O'Sullivan, of 'Kilmanaheem', Sutton Cross, Co. Dublin, and Mary Hughes; ME, B.Sc., A.M.I. Struct. E., A.M.I.C.E.I.; M 1952. Awarded 1st Victoria Prize. 1955/T/01 [2 items].

O'SULLIVAN, ROGER JOHN (b. 4 Dec. 1867) eld. s. of Roger O'Sullivan (decd.) of Rathkeale, Co. Limerick, and Anne Naish; M 1885. 1892/E/02 [7 items].

O'TOOLE, CONAL (b. 8 July 1938) 3rd s. of Christopher O'Toole, of Coolawinnia House, Ashford, Co. Wicklow, and Edna Florence Hartley; B.A. (T.C.D.); M 1958.1961/M/03 [2 items]. In practice in Australia.

O'TOOLE, FRANCIS JOSEPH (b. 24 March 1947) 2nd s. of Henry E. O'Toole, building contractor, of 'Glenesk House', Church Street, Skerries, Co. Dublin, and Maureen Murphy; B.C.L. (N.U.I.); M 1965. 1968/T/05 [1 item].

O'TOOLE, MARGARET MARY BERMINGHAM (b. 25 May 1917) 2nd d. of John O'Toole, Assistant Commissioner of Police, Shanghai (retd), of Ballykett, Kilrush, Co. Clare, and Ellen Bermingham; B.A., B. Comm, LL.B. (N.U.I.); H 1940. 1942/M/02 [2 items]. Mentioned in T.F. O'Higgins, *A Double Life* (Dublin, 1996), 65.

O'TOOLE, PATRICK ALBERT (b. 13 July 1883) 6th s. of John O'Toole of 18 Cabra Road, Dublin, and Margaret Caffrey; M.A., LL.B. (N.U.I.); M 1910. 1913/T/16 [3 items].

OULTON, GEORGE NUGENT (b. 9 Feb. 1848) 2nd s. of the Revd. Richard Oulton, Rector of Keady, Co. Armagh, and Anne Oulton; B.A. (T.C.D.); M 1869, M.T. M 1870.

1873/H/07 [2 items]. North-East Circuit. K.C., March 1904. Conveyancing counsel to the Rolls Court. Died 30 Dec. 1928. Obituary, *I.L.T. & S.J.*, lxiii (1929), 4-5; *Who's Who*.

OVEREND, ANDREW KINGSBURY (b. 30 July 1877) eld. s. of Judge Thomas George Overend, K.C., Recorder of Londonderry, of Sorrento House, Dalkey, Co. Dublin, and Hannah Kingsbury; B.A. (Oxford); H 1900. 1902/T/09 [2 items]. K.C., 20 Feb. 1920. Judge of the High Court, 1943-7. Died 16 April 1947. Obituary, *I.L.T. & S.J.*, lxxxi (1947), 91 and 118. Mentioned in T.F. O'Higgins, *A Double Life* (Dublin, 1996), 269-70.

OVEREND, HENRY BURLEIGH LETHEM (b. 6 July 1852) 4th s. of John Overend, gentleman, of 57 Rutland Square West, Dublin, and Anne Lethem; B.A. (T.C.D.); M 1877, I.T. T 1879. 1881/M/08 [8 items]. Assistant Registrar of the Court of Chancery. Died 12 May 1904. Obituary, *I.L.T. & S.J.*, xxxviii (1904), 170.

OVEREND, OLIVE NANCY (b. 2 May 1909) elder daughter of Andrew Kingsbury Overend, of 1 Wilton Terrace, Dublin, and Olive Rosaleen Whitton; M 1928. 1940/M/04 [2 items]. Actually called H 1941.

OVEREND, THOMAS GEORGE (b. 24 Oct 1846) 5th s. of James Overend (decd.), architect, of Tandragee, Co. Armagh, and Martha Best (decd.); B.A. (Oxford); H 1873, L.I. M 1870. 1874/E/01 [6 items]. North-East Circuit. Q.C. 1885. Recorder of Londonderry, 23 July 1892-1912. Died 9 Feb. 1915. Obituary, *I.L.T. & S.J.*, xlix (1915), 23.

OWENS, OWEN PAUL (b. 25 Jan. 1942) 2nd s. of Leopold C. Owens, insurance official, of 126 Collins Avenue, Whitehall, Dublin, and Marie Anderson; M 1963. 1967/M/10 [1 item].

PAL, SITA NATH (b. 1 March 1897) 2nd s. of Hon. Radha Charan Pal, Rai Bahadwa, Hon. Member of Legislative Council of Bengal, Hon. Magistrate, of 108 Baranoshi Ghosis Street, Calcutta, India; M 1915. 1918/T/08 [2 items].

PARK, ROBERT SPENCER (b. 12 July 1873) eld. s. of John Park, M.A., D. Litt, Professor of Logic and Metaphysics, Queen's College, Belfast, and Margaret Lyons; B.A. (R.U.I. / Q.C.B.); M 1894, G.I. M 1896. 1898/M/01 [8 items]. Brooke Scholar, 1898. Mentioned in J.W. Henderson, *Methodist College Belfast 1868-1938* (2 vols.; Belfast, 1939), 181.

PARKE, WELDON ROYCRAFT CECIL (b. 25 November 1912) only s. of Patrick William Parke, of 'Glenart', Dartry Road, Rathgar, Co. Dublin, and Nora Aske; B.A., LL.B. (T.C.D.); M 1936. 1939/M/11 [1 item]. S.C., 19 July 1963. Judge of the High Court, 29 Oct. 1974; of the Supreme Court, 16 Jan. 1976. Died 18 Feb. 1981.

PARKER, WILLIAM NASSAU (b. 15 Jan. 1866) eld. s. of the Revd. Canon John Frederic Parker, M.A., of Kilmacthomas, Co. Waterford, and Edith S. Carroll; B.A. (T.C.D.); M 1887. 1892/M/03 [6 items].

PASSAU, OWEN (b. 19 April 1885) 4th s. of James Passau (decd.), of 5 Kerry Park Terrace, Waterford, and Mary Murphy; M 1924. 1927/T/04 [2 items].

PATCHELL, JOHN ROBERT (b. 13 June 1854) eld. s. of John Patchell of Dungannon, Co. Tyrone, and Frances Minchin; M.A. (T.C.D.); H 1876, M.T. E 1878. 1884/H/02 [6 items]. North-West Circuit. K.C., March 1904. Died 9 August 1911: *I.L.T. & S.J.*, xlv (1911), 206.

PATTERSON, WILLIAM REGINALD LAMBERT (b. 4 March 1893) 2nd s. of George Barnes Patterson (decd.), of 13 Kenilworth Road, Rathgar, Dublin, and Mary Elizabeth Meeke; M 1919. Captain. 1921/M/14 [2 items].

PATTON, ARTHUR ST GEORGE (b. 23 April 1853) eld. s. of the Revd. George A.F. Patton (decd.) of Rathmines, Dublin, and Kate Magill; B.A. (T.C.D.); M 1877, G.I. M 1883. 1884/M/04 [6 items].

PATTON, THOMAS (b. 7 March 1874) eld. s. of the Revd. Samuel Patton, M.A., Reformed Presbyterian Minister of the Manse, Waterside, Londonderry, and Esther Dunn; B.A., Sch., Sen.-Mod. (T.C.D.), B.A. (R.U.I.); M 1899. 1902/H/03 [2 items]. President of the University Philosophical Society, T.C.D., 1900-1; and Helen Blake Scholar in National History, 1900.

PATTON, WILLIAM FRANCIS (b. 12 Nov. 1897) 2nd s. of John Patton, of 27 Wellington Park, Belfast, and Anna Martin Orr; M 1919. 1921/M/04 [2 items]. K.C. (N.I.), H 1945.

PAUL, SAMUEL WENTWORTH (b. 18 June 1857) 4th s. of William John Paul, J.P., of Portadown, Co. Armagh, and Eliza Graham; B.A. (T.C.D.); M 1883. 1887/T/04 [7 items].

PAYNE, SOMERS HENRY (b. 27 June 1853) 3rd s. of John Warren Payne, J.P., of Beach House, Bantry, Co. Cork, and Sarah Warren; E 1872, M.T. E 1874. 1875/T/04 [2 items].

PEARSE, PATRICK HENRY (b. 10 Nov. 1879) 2nd s. of James Pearse (decd.), sculptor, of Sandymount, Dublin, and Great Brunswick Street, Dublin, and Margaret Brady; M 1898. 1901/T/09 [3 items]. Leader of the 1916 rebellion. Shot 4 May 1916. See Hedley McCay, *Patrick Pearse: A new biography* (Cork, 1966), 41-6; Ruth Dudley Edwards, *Patrick Pearse: The Triumph of Failure* (1977; paperback edition, 1979), 23-5, 47-8, 79-81; *D.N.B. Missing Persons* (1993) [notice by Ruth Dudley Edwards]; and Louis McRedmond (ed.), *Modern Irish Lives*. For Pearse's name in the Law Reports, see: McBride v. McGovern [1906] 2 I.R. 181 and 5 *New Irish Jurist Rep.*, 242; and Buckley v. Finnegan 40 ILTR 76. Busts in Leinster House (by Oliver Sheppard) and in Tralee (by Yann Renard Goulet).

PEART, JOHN NOEL LUBE (b. 1 Jan. 1917) 2nd s. of John Redmond Peart, solicitor, of 5 Ailesbury Road, Dublin, and Matilda Mary Macnamara; M 1935. 1939/M/07 [1 item]. S.C., 5 July 1954. President of the Irish Association of the Sovereign Military Order of Malta. Mentioned in Patrick MacKenzie, *Lawful Occasions*, 39.

PEART, JOHN R. (b. 20 Nov. 1875) 2nd s. of Colonel George Richard Peart, of St. Andrew's, Ballsbridge, Dublin, and Madeline Naish; H 1895. 1898/H/10 [3 items].

PENNEFATHER, FREDERICK WILLIAM (b. 29 April 1852) young. s. of Edward Pennefather, Q.C., of 6 Fitzwilliam Place, Dublin, and Harriet Hall; LL.M. (Cambridge); M 1874, L.I. H 1875. 1878/T/02 [6 items]. Judge of the Supreme Court of New Zealand. Died unmarried 1921. *Burke's Landed Gentry of Ireland* (1958), 571.

PENTLAND, GEORGE HENRY (b. 29 May 1849) eld. s. of George Henry Pentland J.P. of Black Hall, Co. Louth, and Sophia Montgomery; B.A. (T.C.D.); E 1870, M.T. H 1872. 1874/E/3 [2 items].

PERRY, HENRY (b. 18 Feb. 1852) young. s. of John Perry, iron merchant, of 89 Patrick Street, Cork, and Elizabeth Walsh; H 1872, M.T. E 1873. 1876/M/04 [2 items].

PERRY, JEREMIAH GEORGE (b. 3 Nov. 1871) only s. of George Joseph Perry, B.L. (decd.), of 38 Rutland Square, Dublin, and Fanny Dunne; T 1915. 1915/M/07 [2 items]. Died 30 June 1953.

PETTIT, THOMAS ALPHONSUS (b. 7 April 1942) young. s. of James Pettit (decd.), creamery manager, of Croghan, Boyle, Co. Roscommon, and Catherine Kenny; B.C.L. (N.U.I.); M 1965. 1968/M/15 [1 item].

PHELAN, ANDREW JAMES (b. 26 July 1923) eld. s. of Cornelius Phelan, merchant farmer, of Kilganey House, Clonmel, Co. Tipperary, and Bridget Walsh; M.A. (N.U.I.); M 1941. 1945/T/05 [2 items]. Died 5 Aug. 1941. Obituary, *I.L.T. & S.J.*, lxxv (1941), 205.

PHELAN, CECIL BERNARD SWINHOE (b. 15 Nov. 1879) young. s. of Alfred Bernard Phelan of Cricklewood, Middlesex, late of the Indian civil service, and Ada Caroline Swinhoe; B.A. (T.C.D.); M 1901; G.I. M 1903. 1906/T/06 [5 items].

PHELAN, KATHLEEN (b. 20 April 1890) eld. d. of Robert Francis Phelan (decd.), of Whitfield, Butlerstown, Co. Waterford, and Annie Power; B.A., M.Sc. (N.U.I.); M 1924. 1927/T/06 [2 items].

PHELPS, ERNEST JAMES (b. 5 Aug. 1867) 2nd s. of John Lecky Phelps of Waterpark, Co. Clare, and Rosetta Anne Vandeleur; M 1897, I.T. M 1889. 1898/H/09 [3 items]. S.C., 14 July 1924. Judge of the Court of the General Synod of the Church of Ireland. Died 20 March 1944. Obituary, *I.L.T. & S.J.*, lxxviii (1944), 85. Mentioned in Maurice Healy, *The Old Munster Circuit*, 153-5.

PHILLIPS-CONN, THOMAS HARRY MEREDITH (b. 28 April 1881) only s. of Henry H. Phillips-Conn, M.D., of Mount Ida, Co. Kilkenny, and Fanny Meredith; B.A., LL.B. (Cambridge); M 1902. 1905/M/06 [2 items].

PHILP, RICHARD (b. 26 Feb. 1832) young. s. of Andrew Philp (decd.) of Kirkaldy, Fife, and Magdalene Haig; B.A. (T.C.D.); H 1865, M.T. E 1866. 1868/H/7 [5 items].

PHINAINITISATRA, PINYO (b. 19 Oct. 1934) 3rd s. of Lung (Pinai) Phinainitisatra, of 37 Saladang Road, Bangkok, Thailand, and Lady Soomthavin Soom Boontham; M 1956. 1963/T/06 [1 item].

PICKEN, ANDREW (b. 19 Feb. 1886) eld. s. of James Picken (decd.), of Hazelbank, Randalstown, Co. Antrim, and Anna Gray; B.A. (Univ. of London); M 1911. 1914/T/19 [2 items]. Died 22 Sept. 1938. Obituary, *I.L.T. & S.J.*, lxxii (1938), 294, 382.

PIERSE, GERARD RICHARD (b. 8 July 1907) 2nd s. of John Hodgins Pierse, of Patrick Street, Listowel, Co. Kerry, and Ellen Cussen; M 1928. 1931/M/15 [2 items].

PIGOT, JOHN HENRY (b. 4 Nov. 1863) 5th s. of David Richard Pigot, M.A., Master of the Exchequer, of Dundrum, Dublin, and Christina Murray; B.A., LL.B. (T.C.D.); M 1887, L.I. M 1889. 1890/M/05 [9 items]. K.C., 16 Dec. 1909. Professor at King's Inns. Appt. County Court Judge for Limerick, 1920 (retired 1924). Candidate in the election for the Senate of the Irish Free State, 1925 [photograph in *Who's Who in the Seanad Election 1925* (Dublin: Cahill & Co. Ltd., 1925)]. Temporary Assistant Circuit Court Judge (attached to Dublin Circuit), 1925-8. One of the founders of the Forestry Society of Ireland. Died 1928. Obituary, *I.L.T. & S.J.*, lxii (21 April 1928), 96; *Who's Who*.

PIGOT, THOMAS EDWARD (b. 30 Nov. 1908) 4th s. of Judge John Henry Pigot, K.C. (decd.), of Avondale, Avoca Road, Blackrock, Co. Dublin, and Alice Maud Knox; M 1928. 1933/T/01 [3 items]. Joined Red Cross, 1948. Died of a heart attack in Saigon, Nov. 1966. Obituary, *I.L.T. & S.J.*, c, 10 Dec. 1966, 448. Mentioned in Gerard A. Lee, *A Memoir of the South-Western Circuit* (Dublin, 1990), 15.

PILLAI, MOOZHIYIL RAGHAVAN NARAYANA [called *in absentia* – no biographical details] 1930/H/07 [2 items]. Name does not appear on the Supreme Court Roll.

PILLAY, NARAYANA PILLAY PADMANABHA (b. 7 Feb. 1881) 2nd s. of Kesava Pillay (decd.), of Pullavelil, Kunnattoor, Travancore State, Madras, India. Awarded first class certificate of honour, Oct. 1917. M 1915. 1918/H/02 [2 items].

PIM, JONATHAN ERNEST (b. 2 May 1858) eld. s. of Thomas Pim, Junior, J.P., merchant, of Rathleigh, Ballybrack, Co. Dublin [Windsor House, Monkstown, Co. Dublin], and Susan Evans; B.A. (T.C.D.); M 1880, G.I. E 1882. 1886/H/03 [7 items]. President of the University Philosophical Society, T.C.D., 1883-4. K.C., 16 Dec. 1909. Solicitor-General 1913. Attorney-General 1914. Judge of the King's Bench Division 1915-24. Retired 1924. Died 22 April 1949. See: *Who's Who*; Ball, *Judges*, ii, 384-5. Mentioned in Maurice Healy, *The Old Munster Circuit*, 267.

PIM, WILLIAM HARVEY (b. 23 July 1881) 6th s. of James Pim of 2 Belgrave Square, Monkstown, Dublin, and Elizabeth Fayle Evans; B.A.; M 1901. 1904/T/04 [2 items].

PLACE, CHARLES GODFREY MORRIS (b. 2 Nov. 1886) only s. of George William Place, Barrister-at-Law, of 9 Ailesbury Road, Merrion, Co. Dublin, and Henrietta Ussher; B.A., LL.B. (T.C.D.); M 1906. 1909/T/10 [2 items]. Sometime of the Land Registry. Later Solicitor-General of Northern Rhodesia. Died 1931. Obituary, *I.L.T. & S.J.*, lxv (19 Dec. 1931), 305.

PLACE, GEORGE WILLIAM (b. 4 July 1852) eld. s. of Charles Godfrey Place (decd.), of Maryborough, Queen's Co., and Eleanor Whitaker (decd.); B.A. (T.C.D.); Barrister-at-Law (M.T.) 1885; H 1902. 1902/T/11 [5 items].

PLUNKETT, ARTHUR FRANCIS (b. 24 Sept. 1942) eld. s. of Eric A. Plunkett, solicitor, of 6 Whitebeam Road, Clonskeagh, Dublin, and Stella McDonald; B.A. (N.U.I.); M 1961. Awarded Society's Exhibition Prize. 1965/M/01 [1 item]. Leinster Circuit. Attorney-General's Office. Counsellor with the Law Reform Commission. Died March 2001. Appreciation (by Charles Lysaght) in *The Irish Times*, 27 March 2001.

PLUNKETT, GEORGE NOBLE (b. 3 Dec. 1851) eld. surv. s. of Patrick Joseph Plunkett, of Palmerston Road, Rathmines, Dublin, and Elizabeth Noble; M 1870, M.T. M 1874. 1886/M/02 [9 items]. Director of the National Museum of Science and Art, and member of the RDS Committee of Fine Arts. Father of Joseph Mary Plunkett (executed 1916). Forced to resign from the RDS: see Terence de Vere White, *The Story of the Royal Dublin Society* (Tralee, 1955), 178. Minister for Foreign Affairs (later for Fine

Arts) in the Dáil Government. Sinn Féin T.D. for Roscommon, 1922-7. Author, *inter alia*, of *Sandro Botticelli* (1900); co-editor with J. Hogan of *The Jacobite War in Ireland* (1894); editor of *Hibernia*, 1882-3, and contributor to numerous journals. Died 12 March 1948. *Who's Who.*

PLUNKETT, GERALD (b. 11 Aug. 1887) young. s. of Patrick Joseph Plunkett of 14 Palmerston Road, Dublin, and Helena O'Sullivan; B.A. (Oxford); M 1907; I.T. M 1907. 1910/T/07 [3 items]. Sub-Lieutenant, Royal Naval Volunteer Reserve. Died 4 June 1915. [Name on the Bar War Memorial; also on the Helles Memorial, Gallipoli].

PLUNKETT, OLIVER (b. 4 Jan. 1884) eld. s. of Patrick Joseph Plunkett of 14 Palmerston Road, Dublin, and Helen O'Sullivan; undergraduate (Pembroke College, Oxford); M 1906. 1909/T/05 [2 items]. Judge of the Mixed Courts, Egypt.

PLUNKETT, THOMAS JOHN (b. 3 April 1850) eld. s. of John William Plunkett (decd.), J.P., of Portmarnock House, Co. Dublin, and Caroline White; M 1869, M.T. E 1873. 1876/E/02 [8 items].

POLLOCK, HUGH (b. 12 March 1851) eld. s. of John Pollock (decd.), solicitor, of Grosvenor Square, Rathmines, Dublin, and Elizabeth Stoute; B.A. (T.C.D.); E 1875, M.T. H 1877. 1880/T/01 [5 items].

POOLE, HEWITT ROBERT (b. 19 Dec. 1866) 2nd s. of the Revd. Hewitt Robert Poole, D.D., of 15 Lower Fitzwilliam Street, Dublin, and Harriet Dorothea Jellett; M 1887. 1891/M/01 [6 items]. Died 5 March 1943. Obituary, *I.L.T. & S.J.*, lxxvii (1943), 56, 69. Mentioned by V.T.H. Delany [q.v.], in his article 'The Bench and Bar in Ireland', as one prominent among those who never took silk.

PORTER, ANDREW MARSHALL (b. 6 Jan. 1874) 3rd s. of the Rt. Hon. Andrew Marshall Porter, Master of the Rolls in Ireland, of 42 Merrion Square, Dublin, and Agnes H[orsbrugh]; B.A. (T.C.D.); M 1894. 1898/M/07 [3 items].

PORTER, CLASSON (b. 7 April 1858) 3rd s. of the Revd. Classon Porter of Larne, Co. Antrim, and E. Wallace; B.A. (T.C.D.); M 1879, G.I. H 1882. 1882/M/12 [7 items]. Died 11 May 1944. Obituary, *I.L.T. & S.J.*, lxxviii (1944), 135.

PORTER, HORACE DESMOND (b. 2 July 1916) first s. of Ernest Lees Porter, M.R.C.V.S., of Dunkitt House, Dunkitt, Co. Kilkenny, and Edith Alice Boulger; M 1935. Includes correspondence from Porter. 1940/M/05 [7 items]. Died Oct. 2001.

PORTER, SAMUEL CLARKE (b. 14 June 1875) 3rd s. of William John Porter (decd.) of Portrush, Co. Antrim, and Catherine Clarke; M 1900. 1903/H/02 [2 items]. K.C. (N.I.), H 1933. Scholar in Classics of the Royal University, 1886. Contested the Belfast (Pottinger) Division for the Labour Representative Committee in 1918. Wrote on Workmen's Compensation. Mentioned (with photograph) in J.W. Henderson, *Methodist College Belfast 1868-1938* (2 vols.; Belfast, 1939), 180-1. 'A North Antrim man who supported the Labour Party': see J.C. MacDermott, *An Enriching Life*, 173-4. Lord Justice in Northern Ireland, 15 March 1946 – 10 July 1957. Died 10 July 1957. *Who's Who.*

PORTER, WILLIAM HENRY (b. 23 Aug. 1862) only s. of Sir George H. Porter, D.L., surgeon in ordinary to the Queen in Ireland, of 3 Merrion Square, Dublin, and Julia Bond; B.A. (T.C.D.); M 1884, L.I. T 1886. 1888/M/05 [7 items]. 2nd Baronet. Captain, 3rd Battalion, Royal Irish Regiment. Alderman, London County Council, 1899-1901. Died 27 June 1935. *Who's Who; Debrett's Illustrated Baronetage.*

PORTER, WILLIAM McMEEKIN (b. 28 March 1886) 2nd s. of George Francis Lambert Porter, of Vernon Parade, Clontarf, Dublin, and Sarah Alice McMeekin; M 1920. 1923/H/01 [2 items]. Died 17 July 1935. Obituary, *I.L.T. & S.J.*, lxix (1935), 204.

POSNETT, HUTCHESON MACAULAY (b. 26 Feb. 1855) 3rd s. of the Revd. Robert Posnett (decd.), late Rector of Laracor, Co. Meath, and Julia Henrietta Macaulay; M.A., LL.D. (T.C.D.); H 1878. 1886/H/02 [5 items].

POWELL, ARTHUR PATRICK JOSEPH (b. 18 March 1895) only s. of Robert Arthur Powell, B.L. (decd.), of 19 South Terrace, Cork, and Rose Mary Hegarty; M 1913. 1916/E/01 [2 items].

POWELL, ASHLEY (b. 7 October 1885) 4th s. of Dacre Hamilton Powell, DD., (decd.), Archdeacon of Cork, of St. Mary Shandon, Cork, and Edith Louisa Cummins; Scholar, B.A. (T.C.D.); M 1908. Cert. of Honour. Min. of Finance, Egypt. 1913/T/01 [4 items].

Order of the Nahda (Hedjaz), 1919. Judge of the native courts, Egypt, 1919-23. Reid Professor, T.C.D., 1930-5. S.C., 2 March 1948. Joint author of *A Manual of Egyptian Arabic* (Cairo, 1926). Died 5 May 1967. Obituary, *I.L.T. & S.J.*, ci (1967), 199-200. Mentioned affectionately in Patrick MacKenzie, *Lawful Occasions*, 146.

POWELL, EYRE BURTON (b. 30 Nov 1846) eld. s. of Eyre Burton Powell of Madras, East Indies, Director of Public Instruction, and Hamilton Langley; B.A. (T.C.D.); E 1866, M.T. E 1868. 1870/H/2 [4 items].

POWELL, JOHN BLAKE (b. 8 Nov. 1861) eld. s. of John Powell (decd.) of Ballytiernan House, Co. Sligo, and Mary Kernan; T 1894 [solicitor]. 1894/M/05 [3 items]. K.C., 25 Feb. 1905. Representative of the Southern Unionists at the Irish Convention, 1917. Solicitor-General 1918. Judge of the High Court (Chancery Division) 1918. Privy Councillor 1920. See Ball, *Judges*, ii, 386; J.F. Larkin, *Irish Jurist*, xx (1985), 403-24; R.B. McDowell, *The Irish Convention 1917-18* (1970). Died 13 Sept. 1923. Obituary, *I.L.T. & S.J.*, lviii (1923), 236-7.

POWELL, ROBERT ARTHUR (b. 1 Feb. 1862) only s. of Arthur Powell (decd.) of Macroom, Co. Cork, and Mary Hallissy; M 1883. 1886/T/07 [6 items].

POWER, CHARLES STEWART (b. 29 March 1892) eld. s. of John Wyse Power of 21 Henry Street, Dublin, and Jennie O'Toole; cand. bach. (T.C.D.); M 1910. 1913/M/06 [2 items]. Judicial Commissioner under the Dáil Éireann Courts (Winding-Up) Act, 1923. One of the eight original judges of the Circuit Court, 1924, appointed to the Western Circuit. Died 17 June 1950. See Mary Kotsonouris, *Retreat from Revolution: The Dáil Courts, 1920-24* (Dublin, 1994), 107; and ibid., *The Winding-up of the Dáil Courts, 1922-1925: an obvious duty* (Dublin, 2004), p. 254 (biographical note). Photograph in Patrick Lindsay, *Memories* (1992). See also Gerard Hogan, 'The Sinn Féin Funds judgment fifty years on', in *The Bar Review*, vol. 2 (9: July 1997), 375-81.

POWER, VIRGIL (b. 2 Aug 1849) 2nd s. of Michael Power (decd.) of Gayndah, Colony of Queensland, and Anne Conolly; B.A. (T.C.D.); H 1869, M.T. M 1870. 1873/T/4 [2 items].

PRATT, GEORGE CHARLES NIGEL WYNCH (b. 17 Feb. 1928) eld. s. of Charles Young Pratt, of Frankville, Athboy, Co. Meath, and Stella Maud McVeagh; (Mod.) B.A. (T.C.D.); M 1948. 1951/T/08 [2 items].

PRESTON, CHRISTOPHER ALEXANDER (b. 2 Oct. 1913) only s. of Lieut.-Colonel W.I. Preston, D.S.O., O.B.E., late Indian Army, of 9 Longford Terrace, Dublin, and Christina Nixon; (Mod.) B.A. (T.C.D.); M 1934. 1937/M/14 [2 items]. Judge Advocate General, and Office for Statute Law Revision. Died Dec. 1983. Appreciation (by Declan Costello) in the *Irish Law Times*, new series, ii (April 1984), 74; and (by Gerard Lee) in *The Irish Times*.

PRICE, FREDERICK WILLIAM (b. 17 Dec. 1870) 8th s. of James Price (decd.), Member of the Institute of Civil Engineers, of Greystones, Co. Wicklow, and Frances Alicia Peebles; Sch. B.A. (T.C.D.); M 1892. 1895/M/07 [6 items]. Connaught Circuit. K.C., 27 Feb. 1918. Hereditary Freeman of the City of Dublin. Administrator of the Law Library in the 1940s. Died 25 Oct. 1946. Obituary, *I.L.T. & S.J.*, lxxx (1946), 282. Mentioned in Patrick MacKenzie, *Lawful Occasions*, 14

PRICE, WILLIAM GEORGE (b. 23 Feb. 1891) only surv. s. of George Roberts Price (decd.), of 84 Lower Leeson Street, Dublin, and Kate Askin; B.A. (T.C.D.); M 1912. 1919/T/05 [3 items]. Appt. District Justice, Oct. 1924. Protestant supporter of Sinn Féin, and placenames scholar. Husband of Elinor Dorothy (*née* Stopford), tuberculosis expert. As *Liam* Price, author of *The Place-names of Co. Wicklow* (Dublin: 1945-1967). Mentioned unfavourably in Patrick MacKenzie, *Lawful Occasions*, 34-5. Died 23 Jan. 1967. For his career see the introduction to Christiaan Corlett and Mairéad Weaver (eds.), *The Price Notebooks* (2 vols.; Dublin, 2002), which publishes several photographs of Price, including one of him in uniform in 1918 with the cap of the Pay Corps]; and León Ó Broin, *Protestant Nationalists in Revolutionary Ireland: The Stopford Connection* (Dublin, 1985), 197-201.

PRINGLE, ALFRED DENIS (b. 16 May 1902) eld. s. of Robert W. Pringle (decd.), Barrister-at-Law, of St. Philip's, Milltown, Dublin, and Alberta Henshaw; Sch. Sen. Mod., B.A., LL.B. (T.C.D.); M 1922. Awarded 2nd Class Cert. of Honour. 1925/M/04 [2 items].

S.C., 26 June 1944. Bencher, 1948. Judge of the High Court, 30 April 1969. Retired 15 May 1974. Served subsequently in the Special Criminal Court, and as chairman of An Bórd Pleanála. Died 22 Aug. 1998. Obituary, *The Times*, 4 Sept. 1998. Appreciation (by D.N.O. Budd), *The Irish Times*, 16 Sept. 1998.

PRINGLE, JAMES ALEXANDER (b. 18 Aug. 1874) 3rd s. of Henry Pringle of Clonbay House, Clonboy, Co. Monaghan, and Matilda King; [n.d.] 1912/M/10 [2 items]. K.C. , E 1922. M.P. for Fermanagh and Tyrone, 1924-9: see *I.L.T. & S.J.*, lix (1925), 89. Died 7 July 1935. Obituary, *I.L.T. & S.J.*, lxix (1935), 192, 198; *Who's Who*.

PRINGLE, MICHAEL HENRY (b. 25 Nov. 1909) eld. s. of Harold Pringle, of Trinity College, Dublin, and Enid Pringle; M 1930. Awarded John Brooke Scholarship. 1933/M/01 [2 items]. Died 6 Dec. 1933. Obituary, *I.L.T. & S.J.*, lxvii (1933), 336.

PRINGLE, ROBERT WILLIAM (b. 18 Jan. 1871) 2nd s. of Henry Pringle of Clonboy House, Co. Monaghan, and Matilda King; B.A., LL.B. (T.C.D.); M 1890. 1894/H/06 [6 items]. Died 22 Oct. 1919. Obituary, *I.L.T. & S.J.*, liii (1919), 258.

PROCTOR, JAMES CLAUDE BEAUCHAMP (b. 21 June 1885) eld. s. of James Edwin Proctor of Tullydoey, Moy, Co. Tyrone, and Frances Jenkinson Orr; [n.d.] 1913/M/09 [2 items]. Captain, Royal Inniskilling Fusiliers. Died on the Somme, 1 July 1916. [Name on the Bar War Memorial].

PROUD, FRANCIS HARVEY (n.d.) eld. s. of Nicholas Proud of 77 Pembroke Road, Dublin, and Marion [?]; M 1905, L.I. M 1891; Barrister-at-Law of Lincoln's Inn. 1906/T/09 [2 items].

PURCELL, HERBERT KEVIN (b. 4 June 1885) eld. s. of Daniel Purcell of 45 Lower Leeson Street, Dublin, and Mary Clare Hoey; M.A. (R.U.I.); M 1908. 1911/T/10 [2 items]. Died 19 May 1950.

PURCELL, JAMES PATRICK (b. 13 March 1912) 2nd s. of Laurence Michael Purcell, of 92 South Circular Road, Dublin, and Catherine Smith; M 1942. 1946/T/11 [2 items].

PURCELL, MARMADUKE FRANCIS (b. 1 Feb. 1854) 9th s. of Theobald Andrew Purcell, Q.C., County Court Judge, Limerick, of 71 Harcourt Street, Dublin, and Anna Jane Morris; T 1878, M.T. M 1879. 1881/E/02 [7 items].

PURVIS, WILLIAM JOHNSTON (b. 2 April 1874) only s. of David Purvis, tea merchant, of Altamount, Bangor, Co. Down, and Frances Johnston; B.A. (R.U.I.); M 1895, G.I. M 1896. 1899/M/01 [9 items]. Brooke Scholar, 1899. N.E. Circuit. Died May 1907. Mentioned (with photograph) in J.W. Henderson, *Methodist College Belfast 1868-1938* (2 vols.; Belfast, 1939), 180-1; and in *I.L.T. & S.J.*, 14 July 1917, 171.

QUEKETT, ARTHUR SCOTT (b. 27 Aug. 1881) eld. s. of Arthur Edwin Quekett, M.A., of Usan, Orwell Park, Rathgar, Dublin, and Marian Adams; B.A., LL.B. (T.C.D.); M 1906. 1909/T/11 [2 items]. K.C. (N.I.), M 1923. Knighted. Legal Assistant to the Local Government Board for Ireland, 1912-21; Parliamentary Counsel to the Government of Northern Ireland, 1921-45. Author of *Constitution of Northern Ireland* (2 vols., 1928). Died 2 Oct. 1945. *Who's Who*.

QUIGLEY, PETER PAUL DECLAN (b. 29 June 1923) 3rd s. of James Edward Quigley, of Ballycrissane, Ballinasloe, Co. Galway, and Margaret Kelly; M 1944. 1947/T/09 [2 items]. Senior Legal Assistant in the Office of the Attorney-General. Member of the Law Enforcement Commission set up under the Sunningdale Agreement. Retirement noted in the *Irish Law Times*, new series, ii (no. 10: October 1984), 186.

QUILL, ALBERT WILLIAM (b. 13 Sept 1843) eld. s. of Thomas Quill of Kingstown, Co. Dublin, and Ellen O'Sullivan; B.A. (T.C.D.); M 1865, M.T. M 1867. 1870/H/1 [2 items]. Auditor of the College Historical Society, 1871-2. Claimed desacent from O Cuil, the chief poet of Munster, and (through his mother) from O'Sullivan Bere. Joint author (with F.P. Hamilton) of the 8th edition of De Moleyns' *Land Owner's Guide*; and (with Hamilton and E.V. Longworth) of *The Irish Land Acts of 1903, 4, with Appendix of Rules and Forms and a Commentary* (Dublin, 1904) and *The Town Tenants (Ireland) Act, 1906, with Commentary, Rules and Forms* (Dublin, 1907). Translator of Tacitus (1892), and a poet. Afflicted by deafness. Died 1 Feb. 1908. Obituary, *I.L.T. & S.J.*, xlii (1908), 42; *Who's Who*.

QUIN, HERBERT (b. 6 July 1890) eld. s. of Stewart Blacker Quin, of Innisfallen, Annadale, Belfast; and Emma Cornelia Sands; M 1913. 1916/H/05 [2 items].

QUINLAN, JOHN FRANCIS (b. 23 June 1926) 3rd s. of John F. Quinlan, of 3 Magdala Terrace, Gardiner's Hill, Cork, and Mary Horgan; M 1945. 1949/T/05 [2 items].

QUINN, GERARD PHILOMENA (b. 18 Dec. 1931) eld. s. of Thomas Quinn, Milltown House, Donegal, Co. Donegal, and Margaret Gildea; B.A. (N.U.I.); M 1951. 1954/T/04 [2 items]. Associate Professor of Economics, University College, Dublin.

QUINN, JAMES AIDEN (b. 3 Jan. 1922) 2nd s. of William Patrick Quinn, of Lordello House, Sidmontown Road, Bray, Co. Wicklow, and Helen Mary Walshe; B.A., LL.B. (N.U.I.); M 1954. 1957/M/07 [2 items].

QUINN, MICHAEL JOSEPH KELLEHER (b. 16 May 1896) eld. s. of Thomas Quinn, of Violet Ville, College Road, Cork, and Mary A. Kelleher; M 1921. 1924/T/05 [2 items].

RAFTERY, PATRICK (b. 25 Aug. 1920) eld. s. of Patrick Joseph Raftery, civil engineer, of 64 Upper Leeson Street, Dublin, and Margaret Halligan; M.A., M.C.I.; M 1952. 1961/M/08 [2 items]. Engineer, Department of Local Government. Died c. 1987.

RAI, AFTAB (b. 25 Oct. 1893) only s. of Rai Khushwakt Rai, Barrister-at-Law, of Murub, India; M 1914. 1917/T/22 [2 items].

RAINSFORD, EDWIN GROME (b. 20 March 1874) 7th s. of the Revd. Joseph Godman Rainsford, D.D., Rector of Dundalk, Co. Louth, and Maria Carthy; sen. Mod. and gold medallist, B.A., LL.B. (T.C.D.); M 1894, G.I. H 1896. 1897/T/09 [5 items]. LL. D. Took Holy Orders. Died, as the Revd. Edwin Grome Rainsford, Dec. 1954.

RAJ, SITARAM RAJU BHUPATI (b. 15 Sept. 1892) eld. s. of the Hon. Venkatapati Raju Bhupati Raj, of the Madras Legislative Council, Vizagapatam, Northern Circars, Madras, India; M 1914. 1917/T/27 [2 items].

RAJAGOPALAN, NARAYANA (b. 1896) 2nd s. of Narayana Swami Aiyar, of Kumbakonam, Tanjore; M 1914. 1917/T/07 [2 items].

RAJAH, SUBRAMANIAM DHARMA (b. 28 March 1906) 2nd s. of the Hon. M.M. Subramaniam, M.L.C., Crown Proctor, Notary Public, and J.P.V.P.M., of Trincomalee, Ceylon; M 1928. 1933/E/01 [5 items].

RAMASWAMY, TRIPURANENI (b. July 1886) 5th s. of Tripuraneni Chalamayya, of Angalur, Kristna, Madras, India; M 1914. 1917/T/24 [2 items].

RAMAYYA, NADIMPALLI DASARATHA (b. 15 Feb. 1893) 2nd s. of Nadimpalli Pattabhi Ramayya Garw, of Guntur, Madras, India; M 1913. 1917/T/02 [2 items].

RAMDAS, JAYSEN (b. 25 Nov. 1891) 2nd s. of Ramdas Chabildas, Barrister-at-Law, of the Inner Temple, of Nagpore, India; M 1914. 1918/T/03 [2 items].

RAPHAEL, JOHN ROWAN (b. 2 July 1858) eld. s. of John Raphael, J.P., of Cookstown, Co. Tyrone, and Emily Rowan; B.A., LL.B. (T.C.D.); M 1879, M.T. M1881. 1883/T/03 [6 items]. Died 4 Oct. 1935. Obituary, *I.L.T. & S.J.*, lxix (1935), 286.

RATTIGAN, PATRICK MICHAEL (b. 11 Nov. 1930) only s. of Michael Rattigan (decd.), of Main Street, Ballymahon, Co. Longford, and Margaret Mulroy; M 1957. 1962/M/12 [1 item].

RAYMOND, JAMES WILLIAM (b. 26 April 1858) only s. of James Raymond (decd.), of Dromin House, Listowel, Co. Kerry, and Kate Mason; B.A. (T.C.D.); M 1880, I.T. E 1883. 1885/M/03 [6 items].

RAZZAQ, ABDUR (b. July 1888) 2nd s. of Moulvi Abdul Jabbar, sub-Judge, of Bankura, Bengal, India; M 1913. 1916/M/04 [2 items].

REA, DERMOT NEIL EGERTON (b. 24 July 1927) only s. of Colonel John Egerton Rea (retd.), care of Glyn Mills & Co., Whitehall, London, and Nora Corrigan; B.A. (Mod.), LL.B. (T.C.D.); M 1946. 1951/H/02 [2 items]. Senior Crown Counsel in Hong Kong. Died Feb. 1969.

REARDEN, JAMES AMBROSE (b. 31 May 1882) 2nd s. of John Rearden of Monkstown, Cork, and Mary Murphy; M 1902. 1905/H/01 [4 items]. K.C. (N.I.), 2 Dec. 1922; S.C., 21 Nov. 1927. Died 4 May 1933. Obituary, *I.L.T. & S.J.*, lxvii (1933), 138. Mentioned in Maurice Healy, *The Old Munster Circuit*, 77-80.

REARDEN, THOMAS DAVID (b. 7 Nov 1849) 4th s. of John Rearden of Cork, and Katherine Roche; M.A. (Queen's College Cork); M 1868, M.T. M 1870. 1873/H/5 [2 items].

REAY, JAMES McCABE (b. 8 June 1875) eld. s. of Henry Reay (decd.) of Ardee, Co. Louth, and Margaret Armstrong (decd.); ex-Scholar, Sen. Mod. (T.C.D.); M 1906. 1913/M/02 [2 items].

REDDI, BYREDDI LUKSHMI (b. 3 April 1896) eld. s. of Byreddi Chinna Rami Reddi, of Reddamudium, Cuddapah, South India; M 1914. 1917/T/19 [2 items].

REDDY, JOSEPH ALPHONSUS (b. 6 Dec. 1885) 6th s. of John Reddy (decd.), of 10 Great Denmark Street, Dublin, and Catherine Plunkett; Undergraduate (T.C.D.); M 1911. 1914/T/20 [2 items]. Died 16 Sept. 1929. Obituary, *I.L.T. & S.J.*, lxiii (1929), 227.

REDMOND, FREDERICK (b. 16 July 1861) 4th surv. s. of Philip Redmond of Kilmore Cottage, Co. Armagh, and Mary Hamilton; B.A., First Senior Moderator in History (T.C.D.); M 1883, G.I. E 1886. 1887/H/07 [8 items]. Death noted, without date, in T.C.D. *Register of Alumni*, 6th ed., 1955.

REDMOND, GERARD ANTHONY (b. 14 June 1923) only s. of Christopher Edward Redmond, of 70 Lower Beechwood Avenue, Ranelagh, Dublin, and Christina Everett; M 1945. 1949/T/04 [2 items].

REDMOND, JOHN EDWARD, M.P. (b. 1 Sept. 1856) eld. s. of William Archer Redmond (decd.), MP, J.P., of Ballytrent, Co. Mayo, and Mary Hoey; E 1886, G.I. M 1880. 1887/M/18 [5 items]. M.P. 1881-1918. Leader of the Irish Party, 1900-1918. Died 6 March 1918. Funeral noted: *I.L.T. & S.J.*, lii (1918), 63. See: *Who's Who*; *D.N.B.* [article by Stephen Gwynn]; *Oxford DNB* (2004) [article by Alan O'Day]; Louis McRedmond (ed.), *Modern Irish Lives*. Biographies by Warre B. Wells (New York, c. 1919), Denis Gwynn (London, 1932), and Paul Bew (Dundalk, 1996).

REDMOND, WILLIAM ARCHER (b. 16 Oct. 1886) only s. of J.E. Redmond, M.P., B.L., of 8 Leeson Park, Dublin, and Johanna Dalton; B.A. (R.U.I.); M 1907. 1910/T/06 [3 items]. Captain. Nationalist M.P. for Tyrone East, Dec. 1910-1918, and for Waterford City, March 1918-1922. At successive elections an Independent, National League and Cumann na nGaedheal T.D. for Waterford, 1923-32. Died 17 April 1932. Obituary, *I.L.T. & S.J.*, lxvi (1932), 103-4.

REDMOND, WILLIAM HOEY KEARNEY, M.P. (b. 13 April 1861) 2nd s. of William Archer Redmond, M.P., of Balllytrent, Co. Wexford, and Mary Hoey; T 1887, M.T. E 1887. 1891/H/07 [10 items]. M.P. 1883-1917. Major, Royal Irish Regiment. Killed in action on 7 June 1917. See: *Who's Who*; *D.N.B.*; Terence Denman, *A Lonely Grave*: *The life and death of William Redmond* (Dublin, 1995); and Louis McRedmond (ed.), *Modern Irish Lives*. Bust (Oliver Sheppard, 1931) in Wexford. [Grave at Locre in West-Vlaanderen; name on the Bar War Memorial].

REED, ANDREW (b. 1 Oct 1837) eld. s. of John Reed (decd.) of Galway, and Mary Adamson; B.A. (Queen's Univ.); M 1869, M.T. T 1870. 1873/H/2 [2 items]. Joined R.I.C. as an officer cadet, 1859. Author of the *Irish Constable's Guide* (1873) and *The Liquor Licensing Laws of Ireland* (1874). Inspector General of the R.I.C., 1885-1900. Knighted, K.C.B. Died 7 Nov. 1914. *Oxford D.N.B.* (2004) [article by Elizabeth Malcolm]. Photograph (1900), reproduced in R.J.K. Sinclair and F.J.M. Scully (eds.), *Arresting Memories*: *Captured Moments in Constabulary Life* (Belfast, 1982), plate 26.

REED, SAMUEL PERCY (b. 30 Oct. 1855) 1st s. of the Revd. Samuel Reed, Rector of Donegal, and Anne Brown; B.A. (T.C.D.); M 1878, M.T. M 1880; prize at Honor Examination. 1881/M/03 [6 items].

REGAN, GERARD PHILIP (b. 22 Aug. 1905) 5th s. of Thomas Joseph Regan, of Mervue, Monkstown, Dublin, and Euphemia Conlon; M 1928. 1931/T/05 [2 items]. Died 7 Dec. 1944. Obituary, *I.L.T. & S.J.*, lxxviii (1944), 316.

REID, ALEXANDER JOHN (b. 19 July 1853) eld. s. of Andrew William Reid, of 66 Pembroke Road, Dublin, and Helena Labertouche; LL.B (T.C.D.); H 1875, L.I. 1875. 1878/E/05 [6 items].

REID, JAMES (b. 25 Jan. 1878) 2nd s. of John Reid (decd.) of 101 Agincourt Avenue, Belfast, gentleman, and Marion Reynolds; M 1905. 1909/H/04 [3 items]. Died 1936. Obituary, *I.L.T. & S.J.*, lxx (30 May 1936), 139.

REID, JOHN HAMILTON (b. 20 Nov. 1856) only s. of John Hamilton Reid of Orwell Park, Rathgar, Co. Dublin, and Margaret M. Reid (decd.); M.A. (T.C.D.); M 1893. 1905/E/01 [2 items].

REIDY, JOSEPH (b. 3 March 1892) 3rd s. of John Reidy, of Beaufort, Killarney, Co. Kerry, and Mary McGillicuddy; M 1919. 1921/M/13 [2 items].

REZA, SALAH JEHANGIR ALI (b. 21 July 1940) only s. of Ali R. Reza, merchant, of Bahrain, Persian Gulf, and Fatima Reza; B.C.L. (N.U.I.); M 1963. 1968/H/03 [1 item].

RICE, EDMOND ZITA (b. 24 April 1920) only s. of John Herman Rice, Barrister-at-Law, District Justice (retired), of 8 Templemore Avenue, Rathgar, Co. Dublin, and Mary Cooney; M 1937. 1941/T/02 [2 items].

RICE, JAMES PATRICK (b. 6 July 1868) only s. of Patrick M. Rice, J.P., physician and surgeon, of Millbrook House, Galway, and Julia Davis; cand. bachelor (R.U.I.); M 1891. 1894/T/06 [7 items]. Died 1921. Obituary, *I.L.T. & S.J.*, lv (10 Sept. 1921), 225.

RICE, JOHN HERMAN (b. 28 April 1876) only s. of Edmund S. Rice, Crown Solicitor (decd.), of Tipperary, Co. Tipperary, and Mary Josephine Coghlan; M 1913. 1916/T/03 [2 items]. District Justice for Tipperary; later for Leitrim-Roscommon. Died 25 Feb. 1943. Obituary, *I.L.T. & S.J.*, lxxvii (1943), 64.

RICE, JOHN JOSEPH (b. 13 June 1887) 3rd s. of James Rice (decd.), of Linden, Dublin Road, Lisdrumliskey, Co. Armagh, and Rose McEvoy [?]; M 1920. 1941/T/04 [2 items].

RICE, JOSEPH A. (b. 8 Oct. 1872) eld. s. of Michael Rice (decd.), of Dundalk, Co. Louth, and Anne Gormley; M 1910. 1913/H/01 [2 items]. Died 1936. Obituary, *I.L.T. & S.J.*, lxx (8 Aug. 1936), 202.

RICE, ROBERT (b. 21 Feb. 1867) 3rd s. of the Revd. James Rice, B.D., De Vesci Lodge, Monkstown, Dublin, and Harriette Richardson; B.A. (T.C.D.); H 1894. 1897/T/02 [4 items]. Died 3 Feb.1939. Obituary, *I.L.T. & S.J.*, lxxiii (1939), 45.

RICE, SAMUEL (b. 28 Sept. 1868) young. s. of Samuel Rice (decd.), of Crediton, Devon, and Harriet Farr (decd.); M 1910. 1913/T/17 [3 items].

RICE, VINCENT (b. 21 April 1875) 2nd s. of Michael Rice of Dundalk, Co. Louth, and Anna Gormley; B.A. (R.U.I.); M 1900.1904/H/06 [3 items]. S.C., 14 July 1924. National League T.D. for Dublin South, June-Sept. 1927; Cumann na nGaedheal T.D. for Dublin North, 1933-7. Bencher (and Treasurer) of King's Inns.

RICHARDS, HENRY (b. 22 Sept. 1861) 2nd s. of John Henry Richards, County Court Judge, Mayo, of Treholford, Brecon, Wales; B.A. (T.C.D.); M 1880, L.I. M 1882. 1883/M/09 [6 items]. Connaught Circuit. K.C., March 1904. Aft. judge of the High Court of the North-West Provinces of India, 1905; Chief Justice, 1911. Knighted, 1911. Retired 1919. Died in Durban, 10 March 1928. Obituary, *I.L.T. & S.J.*, lxii (1928), 66; *Who's Who*.

RICHARDS, JOHN WILLIAM (9 April 1857) only s. of Captain A. Oswald Richards, late 9th Regt. of Foot, of Albemarle Street, Middlesex, and Marie McMahon Reeves; B.A. (T.C.D.); M 1877, M.T. E 1879. 1880/M/13 [8 items].

RICHARDSON, GEORGE CLEMENTS KIRKWOOD (b. 25 Sept 1844) 2nd s. of John Richardson (decd.) of Poplar Vale, Co. Monaghan and Frances Jackson; B.A. (T.C.D.); M 1865; M.T. M 1866. 1868/M/5 [4 items].

RICHARDSON, HENRY ERNEST (b. 6 April 1867) 5th s. of Joseph Richardson of Springfield, Lisburn, Co. Antrim, and Eliza Jane Fennell; B.A. (T.C.D.); M 1888. 1891/M/04 [5 items]. Died 21 Feb. 1949.

RICHARDSON, JOHN JOSEPH (b. 31 Dec. 1879) eld. s. of Edward Richardson (decd.) of Lamagh, Newtownforbes, Co. Longford, and Susan Moore; B.A., LL.B. (N.U.I.); M 1909. 1911/M/02 [2 items].

RICHARDSON, NICHOLAS GOSSELIN (b. 20 Nov. 1844) 2nd s. of Thomas Richardson, of Tyaquin, Co. Galway, J.P., and Catherine Alicia Gosselin; B.A. (T.C.D.); M 1864; I.T. E 1866. 1871/M/4 [4 items].

RICHARDSON, SAMUEL THOMAS STANISLAUS (b. 25 Nov. 1844) only s. of Thomas Samuel Richardson of Clonmel, Co. Tipperary and Marianne Mulcahy; B.A. (T.C.D.); E 1864, M.T. H 1866. 1868/T/3 [4 items].

RICHEY, HENRY ALEXANDER (b. 13 Oct. 1862) eld. s. of Alexander George Richey, Q.C., LL.D., late of Upper Pembroke Street, Dublin, and Jane Smith; B.A. (T.C.D.); M 1884. 1887/M/08 [6 items]. Died 29 July 1932. Obituary, *I.L.T. & S.J.*, lxvi (1932), 193.

RIGG, RICHARD, M.P. (b. 22 Aug. 1877) only s. of Alderman John Rigg of Windermere, Westmorland, and Sarah Anne Sutton; B.A. (Cantab.), M.P. (North Westmoreland), J.P.; E 1899; I.T. H 1896 (called to English Bar, 26 Jan. 1899). 1902/M/09 [3 items]. Major, 4th Border Regiment. Radical M.P. for North (Appleby) Division of Westmoreland, 1900-05. Mayor of the City of Westminster, 1939-40. Died 29 Aug. 1942. *Who's Who*.

RINGWOOD, HARRY PERRY (b. 3 April 1854) 2nd s. of the Revd. Frederic Howe Ringwood of Dungannon, Co. Tyrone, and Henrietta Perry; B.A. (T.C.D.); E 1876, M.T. H 1879. 1880/M/04 [6 items].

RINGWOOD, RICHARD FREDERIC (b. 19 May 1863) 5th s. of the Revd. Frederic Howe Ringwood, D.Litt., Headmaster of the Royal School, Dungannon, Co. Tyrone, and of Dean's Grange, Foxrock, Co. Dublin, and Henrietta Perry; LL.B. (T.C.D.); M 1884. 1888/E/04 [6 items]. Died at Worthing, 17 March 1921. Obituary, *I.L.T. & S.J.*, lv (1921), 83.

RIYAMI, Mrs. ABDULLAH *née* SOAD MOHAMMAD NASSER LAMKI (b. 26 Nov. 1938) 4th d. of Sheikh Mohammad Nasser Lamki, landowner, of Minaramiwilli, Shangani, Zanzibar, and Asia Said Kharusu; M 1958. 1963/M/07 [1 item].

ROBB, FREDERICK JOSEPH (b. 22 Sept. 1869) 3rd s. of John Robb, J.P., of Lisnabreeny House, Belfast, and Rachel M'Credy; LL.B. (R.U.I. / Q.C.B.); M 1890, M.T. M 1893. 1894/M/01 [8 items].

ROBB, JOHN HANNA (b. 4 Nov. 1873) 2nd s. of the Revd. James Gardner Robb (decd.), D.D., LL.D., of Nun's Island, Galway, and Martha Hanna Robb; B.A. (R.U.I.); M 1895, G.I. M 1896.1898/M/09 [9 items]. K.C., 16 June 1921. Author of *The Law of Bankruptcy and Arrangements in Ireland* (1907). M.P. (Stormont) for Queen's University, 1921-37, and Minister of Education (N.I.), 1925-37. Leader of the Senate, 1937-43. P.C., 1937. County Court Judge for Armagh and Fermanagh, 1943-54. Died 21 June 1956. See *Who's Who*.

ROBERTS, NOEL SAWYER (b. 28 Dec. 1937) 3rd s. of Sir George William Kelly Roberts, C.B.E., J.P., of Nassau, Bahamas, and Lady Freda Genevieve Sawyer; M 1959. 1963/M/06 [1 item].

ROBINS, RONALD ARTHUR MAYNE (b. 2 July 1939) eld. s. of Victor Douglas Robins, company director, of 97 Kimmage Road West, Dublin, and Noelle Pickett; M 1958. 1962/T/02 [2 items]. S.C., 24 Feb. 1978.

ROBINSON, ADRIAN (b. 13 April 1892) 3rd s. of the Right Hon. H.A. Robinson, K.C.B., of Lisnacarrig, Foxrock, Dublin, and Harriet Blosse; B.A. (T.C.D.); M 1912. 1915/T/09 [2 items].

ROBINSON, CHRISTOPHER HENRY (b. 18 Oct. 1884) eld. s. of the Rt. Hon. Sir H.A. Robinson, Bart., K.C.B., of Lisnacarrig, Foxrock, Co. Dublin, and Harriet Lynch-Blosse; M 1919. 1920/M/06 [2 items]. Descended on both sides from Irish judges: viz., Christopher Robinson (1712-87), whose books were the nucleus of the King's Inns Library, and Sir Henry Lynch (d. 1691), a Baron of the Exchequer under King James. Early career as a soldier (3rd Battalion, Royal Fusiliers). Private secretary to the Governor of Jamaica, 1909-11. Resident Magistrate in Counties Donegal and Louth, 1912-22. Author of *The Last of the Irish R.M.s* (1951), a book with a photograph of the author as frontispiece. Succeeded as 2nd Baronet on death of his father (the Vice-President of the Local Government Board for Ireland, 1898-1920) in 1927. Assumed the name Lynch-Robinson in 1947. Died 22 Nov. 1958. *Burke's Peerage* (107th ed., 2003), 2439.

ROBINSON, ERNEST St. CLAIR (b. 4 Feb. 1882) 3rd s. of William Woolridge Robinson, of Glenageary Hill, Kingstown, Co. Dublin, and Margaret Donaldson Brunton; M 1919. 1921/T/02 [1 item]. Died 22 Oct. 1947. Obituary, *I.L.T. & S.J.*, lxxxi (1947), 255.

ROBINSON, HENRY LIGHTON (b. 3 March 1854) 2nd s. of John Robinson of 3 Wilton Place, Dublin, and Isabella Rebecca Boyd; B.A. (T.C.D.); E 1873, M.T. M 1874. 1877/M/04 [9 items].

ROBINSON, JOHN (Seán) JOSEPH (b. 1 June 1899) 3rd s. of James Robinson (decd.), of Main Street, Letterkenny, Co. Donegal, and Mary O'Donnell; B.A. (N.U.I.); M 1930. 1933/M/09 [2 items]. Died 25 Jan. 1942. Obituary, *I.L.T. & S.J.*, lxxvi (1942), 43.

ROBINSON, PHILIP (b. 15 Jan. 1885) 2nd s. of Abram Rabinowiz, of Pretoria, South Africa, and Leah Lebin; E 1924. 1924/M/09 [2 items].

ROBINSON, WILIAM HENRY (b. 28 Nov. 1850) 2nd s. of William Henry Robinson (decd.) of Aughenarget, Co. Westmeath, and Grace Caroline; M.A., LL.B. (T.C.D.); E 189[7] [special exemption from examination]. 1897/T/15 [2 items]. Knighted. Died 11 June 1940. Obituary, *I.L.T. & S.J.*, lxxiv (1940), 157-8.

ROCHE, BERNARD (b. 15 Nov. 1872) 2nd s. of Redmond Roche (decd.) of Maglass, Co. Kerry, and Mary Purcell; B.A. (T.C.D.); H 1892. 1895/H/06 [6 items]. Additional Judge of the Circuit Court (Midland Circuit), 1925-31. Died 4 Jan. 1932. Obituary, *I.L.T. & S.J.*, lxvi (1932), 11. Mentioned in Maurice Healy, *The Old Munster Circuit*, 131.

ROCHE, CECIL ROBERT (b. 21 May 1849) only s. of William Roche J.P. of 9 De Vesci Terrace, Kingstown, Co. Dublin, and Emily Borrowes; B.A. (T.C.D.); M 1869; M.T. M 1870, 1873/H/8 [2 items]. Auditor of the College Historical Society, 1873-4. Munster Circuit. Edited a standard work on Irish fishery laws. Appt R.M., 1886; Inspector of Fisheries, 1892. Adopted the surname Borrowes on succeeding to the estates of his uncle. Died 6 May 1902. Obituary, *I.L.T. & S.J.*, xxxvi (1902), 206.

ROCHE, CHARLES REDINGTON (b. 16 Sept. 1867) 4th s. of Thomas Redington Roche, J.P., D.L., of Ryehill, Co. Galway, and June Elizabeth Cliffe; M 1888, I.T. M 1890. 1891/M/11 [8 items].

ROCHE, CHRISTOPHER (b. 31 Aug. 1877) 2nd s. of George Roche, solicitor, of 76 Merrion Square South, Dublin, and Pauline Chevers; B.A. (T.C.D.); M 1895. 1899/M/06 [3 items]. Called to the English Bar, L.I., 1935. Identified [see Bruce Bradley, *Joyce's Schooldays*, p. 146, r. 11] as the 'Nasty Roche' who features in the early pages of James Joyce's *A Portrait of the Artist as a Young Man*. Still a member of the Law Library in the 1960s. Died Nov. 1966.

ROCHE, FREDERICK JOHN (b. 25 August 1915) eld. s. of James Roche, resident magistrate, of Belfast, and Janet C. Wallace; B.A. (N.U.I.); M 1936. File includes petition from Roche explaining late payment of fees – 'owing to the unsettled conditions'. 1939/M/14 [2 items]. S.C., 5 Oct. 1970.

ROCHE, JOHN (b. 29 April 1841) eld. s. of John Roche of Glanworth, Fermoy, Co. Cork and Elizabeth Sisk; M 1870, I.T. H 1868. 1872/T/1 [2 items]. Munster Circuit. Q.C., 5 July 1884. County Court Judge (Down), 1894-6. Died 1896: James Meenan (ed.), *Centenary History of Lit. and Hist. Soc. of U.C.D.*

ROCHE, WILLIAM FREDERICK (b. 25 May 1912) 2nd s. of Bernard Roche, Circuit Court Judge (decd.), of 74 Upper Leeson Street, Dublin, and Constance Clemesha; M 1930. 1933/M/03 [7 items]. Mentioned in Gerard A. Lee, *A Memoir of the South-Western Circuit* (Dublin, 1990), 37.

ROCHFORD, JAMES FAGAN (b. 3 Oct 1843) 2nd s. of Thomas Rochford (decd.) of Cork City, Merchant, and Stephanie Fagan; B.A. (University of London); M 1864, M.T. M 1865. 1868/H/1 [2 items].

ROE, PATRICK JOSEPH (b. 11 April 1893) 3rd s. of Thomas Roe (decd.), of Dundalk, Co. Louth, and Catherine Flood; T 1925. 1925/M/27 [2 items]. S.C., 12 April 1935. Bencher 1948. Judge of the Circuit Court, 1948. Died 17 Oct. 1957. Obituary, *I.L.T. & S.J.*, xci, 264.

ROE, THOMAS FRANCIS (b. 18 May 1920) eld. s. of Patrick Joseph Roe, S.C., of Palmerston Lodge, Dartry Road, Dublin, and Josephine Coffey; B.A. (U.C.D.); M 1938. 1942/T/03 [2 items]. I.T., T 1972. S.C., 1 June 1973. Appt. judge of the Circuit

Court, 1974; President of the Circuit Court, 4 Feb. 1986. Retired 18 May 1990. Died 7 Oct. 2003. Obituaries, *The Irish Times*, 11 Oct. 2003; *The Times*, 24 Oct. 2003.

RONAN, STEPHEN (b. 13 April 1848) eld. s. of Walter Ronan of Cork City, Solicitor, and Sarah McNamara; B.A. (Queen's University); M 1867, I.T. M 1868. 1870/M/6 [2 items]. Q.C., June 1889. Queen's Advocate 1892. Lord Justice of Appeal 1915. Privy Councillor 1915. Died 3 Oct. 1925. Obituary, *I.L.T. & S.J.*, lix (1925), 244-6; *Who's Who*. See *D.N.B.* (article by T.C. Kingsmill Moore); and Ball, *Judges*, ii, 384. Mentioned in Maurice Healy, *The Old Munster Circuit*, 34, 117-27, 128-9. V.T.H. Delany [q.v.], in 'The Bench and Bar in Ireland', xxxii, mentions Ronan's 'matchless erudition', and says that judicial preferment came too late, 'his great legal talents' going 'unperceived in the Court of Appeal'.

RONAYNE, EDWARD CAMILLUS (b. 15 July 1876) young. s. of Charles O'Lomasney Ronayne, physician, of South Abbey, Youghal, Co. Cork, and Helen FitzGerald; B.A. (T.C.D.); M 1896. 1900/H/04 [3 items]. Commisioned in the Royal Navy. Aft. Justice in Kenya. Died 7 Jan. 1927. Obituary, *I.L.T. & S.J.*, lxi (1927), 16. Remembered affectionately in Maurice Healy, *The Old Munster Circuit*, 73-4.

RONAYNE, JOHN ALOYSIUS (b. 2 May 1886) 2nd s. of Thomas Ronayne, of 73 South Circular Road, Dublin, and Anne Southwell; undergraduate (R.U.I.); M 1907. 1909/M/02 [2 items]. Went Munster Circuit. Died of influenza, 4 Nov. 1918. Obituary, *I.L.T. & S.J.*, lii (1918), 274. Mentioned (with photograph) in James Meenan (ed.), *Centenary History of Lit. and Hist. Soc. of U.C.D.*

RONAYNE, LAURENCE MICHAEL (b. 6 March 1928) 2nd s. of James Ronayne (decd.), commercial traveller, of Panorama Terrace, Sunday's Well, Cork, and Anna Heffernan; B.E. (U.C.C.); M 1957. 1960/T/09 [2 items].

RONAYNE, MICHAEL PAUL (b. 29 June 1925) eld. s. of Michael John Ronayne, of 8 Prince of Wales Terrace, Queensboro Road, Bray, Co. Wicklow, and Mary Lacey; M 1945. 1949/T/07 [2 items].

ROONEY, FRANCIS XAVIER MARY (b. 20 Jan. 1927) only s. of Patrick Joseph Rooney (decd.), of 1 Mayfield Road, Terenure, Dublin, and Mary Dempsey; M 1944. 1948/T/16 [2 items]. Advocate in the High Court of Tanganyika, 1952, and Pleader in the High Court of Nyasaland, 1956, and Notary Public. Aft. a judge, residing in retirement in South Africa. Contributor to James Meenan (ed.), *Centenary History of Lit. and Hist. Soc. of U.C.D.*

ROPER, CHARLES EDWARD ALEXANDER (b. 21 Jan. 1858) eld. s. of Alexander Roper of Rathgar, Dublin, and Geraldine Fitzgerald; M 1885. 1889/H/01 [7 items]. Died (as Roper-Fitzgerald) 12 Feb. 1926. Obituary, *I.L.T. & S.J.*, lx (1926), 50.

ROSENTHAL, LIONEL HENRY (b. 4 Aug. 1856) eld. s. of John D. Rosenthal, solicitor, of 88 Harcourt Street, Dublin, and M. Solomon; B.A. (T.C.D.); E 1877, M.T. M 1875. 1893/H/03 [2 items]. Leinster Circuit. K.C., 26 April 1913. Died 14 July 1932. Obituary, *I.L.T. & S.J.*, lxvi (1932), 181-2.

ROSS, ANGUS COLEMAN (b. 7 June 1884) only s. of William Philip Ross, Barrister-at-Law, of 24 Synnott Place, Dublin, and Jane Mary Brown; M 1902. 1905/T/06 [3 items].

ROSS, ARTHUR PATRICK (b. 21 Jan. 1872) 2nd s. of Patrick Joseph Ross of 24 Brookfield Terrace, Dublin, and Elizabeth Asken; E 1898. 1902/H/05 [2 items].

ROSS, ERNEST ALEXANDER (b. 20 Dec. 1873) eld. s. of Alexander Ross of 24 Victoria Road, Rathgar, Dublin, and Abigail Ingram; M 1905. 1908/T/06 [3 items].

ROSS, JOHN (b. 18 Dec. 1853) eld. s. of the Revd. Robert Ross of Ardfoyle, Co. Londonderry, and Margaret Christie; LL.B. (T.C.D.); M 1876, G.I. T 1878. 1879/M/18 [6 items]. President of the University Philosophical Society, T.C.D., 1877-8, and Auditor of the College Historical Society, 1878-9. Q.C., Jan 1891. M.P. for Londonderry, 1892-5. Judge of the High Court (Chancery Division), 1896-21. Lord Chancellor, 1921-2. Sworn of the Privy Council and created a baronet, 1919 [baronetcy extinct with the death of the 2nd Baronet in 1958]. Died 17 Aug. 1935. Obituary, *I.L.T. & S.J.*, lxix (1935), 235, 250, 265; *Who's Who*. Author of *The Days of my Pilgrimage* (1924) and of *Pilgrim Scrip: More random reminiscences by the Rt. Hon. Sir John Ross, Bart. Last Lord Chancellor of Ireland* (1927). Mentioned appreciatively in

Maurice Healy, *The Old Munster Circuit*, 263-6. See Ball, *Judges*, ii, 380; and Kate Newmann, *Dictionary of Ulster Biography* (Belfast, 1993).

ROSS, WILLIAM AUGUSTUS (b. 21 Feb. 1853) 2nd s. of James Ross of Cliftonville, Belfast, and Ellen McQuillan; B.A. (T.C.D.); E 1880, M.T. E 1881. 1883/E/07 [5 items].

ROSS, WILLIAM PHILIP (b. 12 Feb. 1859) eld. s. of John Ross (decd.), contractor, of Belfast, and Mary [Corland]; M 1877, M.T. M 1881. 1882/M/04 [5 items].

ROUNDTREE, ISAAC (b. 15 Aug. 1889) eld. s. of Edward Roundtree, J.P., of Cancestown House, Stackallen, Navan, Co. Meath, and Sarah Jane Cochrane; Mod. B.A., LL.B. (T.C.D.); [n.d.] 1914/T/08 [3 items]. Died 28 Jan. 1959.

ROUX, JOHN ALBERT (b. 24 July 1869) eld. s. of Jacobus Isaac Roux of Rustenburg, Stellenbosch, Cape Colony, South Africa, and Catherine Roux; M 1903. 1907/H/05 [2 items].

ROY, KANAK SINGH (b. 14 March 1892) eld. s. of Ex. Justice Harinath Roy, of the Calcutta High Court, Bengal, India; M 1914. 1917/T/25 [2 items].

ROYCHOWDHURI, HEMENDRAVARAYAN (b. 1893?) 5th s. of [Jogendrananayan] Roychowdhuri, of Calcutta, India, and Saradasundari, late of Delhi; M 1913. 1916/T/12 [2 items].

RUDD, GEOFFREY BURKITT WHITCOMB (b. 29 May 1908) eld. s. of Thomas Alexander Rudd, of Oriel Temple, Collon, Co. Louth, and Esther Mabel McEntaggart; M 1929. 1932/M/08 [2 items].

RUSE, ARTHUR JOHN (n.d.) only s. of John Ruse, of Ballincarrig House, Co. Cork, and Katherine Duffy; M 1911. 1918/M/07 [2 items].

RUSSELL, CHARLES VERNER WALLACE (b. 7 Jan. 1878) 2nd s. of Bartholomew Campbell Russell of Rhaniskey, Hazlehatch, Co. Kildare, and Cornelia Murphy; T 1901. 1905/T/04 [3 items].

RUSSELL, JOHN HENRY SINCLAIR (b. 10 Oct. 1865) 2nd surv. s. of John Russell (decd.), solicitor, of 39 Mountjoy Square, Dublin, and Amanda Emily Hughes; E 1884. 1887/T/05 [7 items]. Sometime secretary to the Bar Council. Died 29 Jan. 1939. Obituary, *I.L.T. & S.J.*, lxxiii (1939), 39.

RUSSELL, MATTHEW (b. 18 Aug. 1933) 2nd s. of Matthew John Russell (decd.), F.R.C.S.I., medical officer of health, of 85 Pembroke Road, Ballsbridge, Dublin, and Dr. Angela Coyne; B.A. (Mod.), LL.B; M 1953. Awarded Society's Prize. 1957/H/01 [2 items]. Reid Professor, T.C.D., 1 July 1960; aft. Lecturer in Law, T.C.D., 1 Oct. 1965. Later career in the Office of the Attorney-General.

RUTHERFORD, ANDREW ADAMS (b. 19 March 1878) eld. s. of Wm. Rutherford of 6 College Green, Belfast, and Lily Watt Rutherford; B.A., LL.B. (R.U.I.); M 1901; M.T. M 1903. 1904/M/10 [7 items].

RYAN, EDWARD ARTHUR (b. 2 Nov. 1882) eld. surv. s. of James Fitzgerald Ryan (decd.), of Dungarvan, Co. Waterford, and Annie Hayes; T 1914. 1914/M/06 [2 items].

RYAN, EDWARD FRANCIS (b. 23 Jan. 1914) eld. s. of Sir Andrew Ryan, late H.B.M.'s ambassador to Albania and Saudi Arabia, of Short Avenue, East Bergholt, Suffolk, and Ruth Marguerite [van] Millingen; H 1946, M.T. E 1936. 1946/M/08 [5 items]. Degree awarded *in absentia* – serving in British Army. Shown on S.C. Roll as called H 1947. Professor of Common Law, University College, Cork. Compiler of *Notes of Irish Cases 1949-58* (Cork, 1969); *ibid. 1959-68* (Cork, 1970) and *ibid. 1969-78* (Cork, 1982). Editor of *The Irish Digest 1959-70*; and joint editor (with Julitta Clancy) of *The Irish Digest 1984-88*. Author (with Philip P. Magee) of *The Irish Criminal Process* (Dublin and Cork, 1983).

RYAN, FRANCIS (b. 12 Oct. 1926) 3rd s. of James Raphael Ryan, of 53 Garville Avenue, Rathgar, Dublin, and Irene Rose Boyle; M 1945. 1949/M/15 [2 items].

RYAN, FREDERICK WILLIAM (b. 6 Dec. 1883) only s. of William Leeson Ryan (decd.) of 13 Clyde Road, Dublin, and Mary Tagliaferro; M 1903. 1908/T/02 [3 items]. Died 18 June 1956.

RYAN, JAMES GERRARD (b. 1 April 1917) 3rd s. of Thomas Ryan, merchant, of 51 Haddington Road, Dublin, and Mary Troy; B.A. (N.U.I.); M 1936. 1939/M/10 [1 item]. Resident Magistrate in Northern Rhodesia, 1958.

RYAN, JOHN PATRICK (b. 25 Aug. 1917) 2nd s. of Thomas Ryan, engineer, of Farranshone, Limerick, and Marian Mullane; M 1945. 1949/M/19 [2 items].

RYAN, JOHN VINCENT (b. 23 Sept. 1872) eld. s. of William Francis Ryan of Mitchelstown, Co. Cork, and Sophia Friendship Rutter; B.A., LL.B. (T.C.D.); M 1902; District Superintendent of Police, Bengal. 1904/T/12 [3 items]. Death noted, without date, in T.C.D. *Register of Alumni*, 5th ed., 1950.

RYAN, LEONARD MORROGH (b. 27 Feb. 1876) eld. s. of Leonard Morrogh (decd.) of Sleedagh, Co. Wexford, and Mina Ryan of 7 Fitzwilliam Place, Dublin; B.A. (T.C.D.); M 1896.1901/H/04 [3 items].

RYAN, MICHAEL (b. 18 Oct. 1870) only s. of James Ryan of Crogue, Tipperary, Co. Tipperary, and Joanna Quin; M 1905. 1908/H/01x [3 items].

RYAN, MICHAEL JOHN (b. 4 Dec. 1882) only s. of John Ryan (decd.), of 19 Rathmines Road, Dublin, and Margaret Mary Dunne; T 1920. 1920/M/07 [2 items].

RYAN, MICHAEL JOSEPH (b. 13 Dec. 1890) eld. s. of John Ryan, of 2 St. John's Villas, Limerick, and Bridget Fitzgibbon; B.A., B.E., B.Sc., LL.B. (N.U.I.); M 1917. Awarded John Brooke Scholarship. 1919/M/01 [3 items]. S.C. 29 May 1929. Reid Professor, T.C.D., 1921-5. Senator for the National University, 1944. Professor of Constitutional Law, U.C.D., 1927-34; aft. Professor of the Law of Property, Common law and Equity, U.C.D. Died 24 Oct. 1952. Obituary, *I.L.T. & S.J.*, lxxxvi (1952), 275. See James Meenan (ed.), *Centenary History of Lit. and Hist. Soc. of U.C.D.*

RYAN, PATRICK CYRIL (b. 5 July 1930) eld. s. of Superintendent James Ryan (Garda Síochána), of Trim, Co. Meath, and Johanna Mary Robinson; M 1951. 1955/M/07 [2 items].

RYAN, PATRICK JOSEPH (b. 27 July 1916) 3rd s. of Thomas Ryan, of Donohill, Co. Tipperary, and Mary O'Brien; M 1937. 1941/T/03 [2 items].

RYAN, PATRICK NOEL (b. 13 December 1915) 3rd s. of Patrick Joseph Ryan, merchant, of 6 Dufferin Avenue, South Circular Road, Dublin, and Deborah Altman; (N.U.I.); M 1936. 1939/M/09 [1 item]. Judge of the Circuit Court, 1959-84. Died 30 March 2003. Obituary, *The Irish Times*, 19 April 2003.

RYAN, THOMAS ALOYSIUS (b. 5 May 1923) 1st s. of Edward James Ryan, of The Square, Stewartstown, Co. Tyrone, and Kathleen Crilly; M 1942. 1946/T/10 [1 item].

RYAN, WILLIAM ALBERT (b. 9 Sept. 1866) eld. s. of Valentine Ryan, J.P., of Belleville, Mountrath, Queen's Co., and Helena Kenny; B.A. (T.C.D.); H 1886. 1889/M/06 [7 items]. Died 8 Jan. 1951. Obituary, *I.L.T. & S.J.*, lxxxv (1951), 16.

RYAN, WILLIAM EWER (b. 20 July 1845) eld. s. of John Ryan, solicitor, of Nenagh, Co. Tipperary, and Louisa Pennefather; B.A. (T.C.D.); M 1869, M.T. T 1871. 1873/H/6 [4 items].

RYLAND, RICHARD THEODORE HUGHES (b. 12 Feb. 1871) eld. s. of Theodore Ryland, Barrister-at-Law, of 26 Herbert Place, Dublin, and Mary Anne Hughes; M 1892. 1895/M/13 [6 items]. Editor of *The Irish Digest 1919-28*, and *ibid. 1929-38*. Died 3 Dec. 1958.

RYND, JAMES ALEXANDER (b. 6 April 1846) eld. s. of James Goodlatte Rynd, solicitor, of Serpentine Avenue, Dublin, and Isabella Stephens; E 1869, I.T. H 1872. 1874/H/2 [2 items]. Died 17 March 1917. Obituary, *I.L.T. & S.J.*, li (1917), 74.

RYND, WILLIAM HENRY (b. 29 July 1851) 3rd s. of James Goodlatte Rynd (decd.), solicitor, of 1 Lower Ormond Quay, Dublin, and Isabella Stephens; B.A. (Q.C.G.); H 1875, I.T. H 1876. 1877/M/10 [5 items].

RYNNE, MICHAEL ANDREW LYSAGHT (b. 12 Sept. 1899) eld. s. of Michael Andrew Rynne, M.D., B.A., of Springfield House, Ennis, Co. Clare, and Mary O'Mara; B.A. (N.U.I.); M 1918. 1924/M/02 [2 items]. Legal adviser, Department of External Affairs; ambassador to Spain.

RYNNE, MICHAEL LEON (b. 11 Sept. 1932) eld. s. of Dr Michael Rynne, B.L., of St John's, Kimmage Road East, Terenure, Co. Dublin, and Nathalie Fournier; M 1951. Awarded Society's prize. 1954/M/03 [2 items].

SADLEIR, THOMAS ULICK (b. 15 Sept. 1882) 3rd s. of Franc Sadleir, Clerk in Holy Orders, of Newcastle, Hazlehatch, Co. Dublin, and Philippa Burke; B.A. (T.C.D.); M 1901. 1906/H/04 [3 items]. Leinster Circuit, -1916. Member of the Royal Irish Academy, 1910. Joint author (with G.D. Burtchaell [q.v.]) of *Alumni Dublinenses* (Dublin, 1924; 2nd edition, 1935). Deputy to the Ulster King of Arms, administering that office 1940-43. Assistant Librarian at King's Inns, 1943-57. Original compiler of *King's Inns Admission Papers 1607-1867* (Dublin, 1982), a project the genesis of which is marked by a letter from the Under-Treasurer (Richard Armstrong [q.v.]) dated 10 June 1907, communicating the Benchers' assent to his request to index the records. A Vice-President of the Irish Genealogical Research Society. Died 21 Dec. 1957. See *Thomas Ulick Sadleir 1882-1957. A memoir by Randal Sadleir* (Dublin: National Library of Ireland Society, 2004); Susan Hood, *Royal Roots - Republican Inheritance: The survival of the Office of Arms* (Dublin, 2002) [including (on p. 91), the photograph reproduced in this work]; *Burke's Landed Gentry of Ireland*, 4th ed (1958), 624.

SAINSBURY, RICHARD CLAUDE (b. 11 Jan. 1900) young. s. of William Draper Sainsbury, solicitor, of Sans Souci, Sydney Parade, Dublin, and Gertrude Harvey; M 1925. 1928/T/05 [2 items].

SAINSBURY, WILLIAM LEOPOLD (b. 14 May 1888) eld. s. of William Draper Sainsbury of 14 Dawson Street, Dublin, and Gertrude Harvey; M 1908. 1911/T/01 [2 items]. Died 22 Sept. 1950. Obituary, *I.L.T. & S.J.*, lxxxiv (1950), 234-5.

SALAFIA, JAMES PATRICK (b. 21 June 1940) only s. of Vincent James Salafia, engineer, of Sheepwalk House, Avoca, Co. Wicklow, and Bridget Frances McGee; B.C.L. (N.U.I.); M 1960. 1963/M/02 [1 item]. S.C., 7 Oct. 1985.

SALARIYA, GURDIAL SINGH (b. 23 Dec. 1893) eld. s. of Piara Singh Salariya, of Amritsar, Punjab, India. 1918/T/19 [2 items].

SALMON, GEORGE (b. 1 June 1881) only s. of Edward William Salmon of Summerville, Dundrum, Co. Dublin, and Henrietta Maria Braddell; B.A. (T.C.D.); M 1903. 1906/M/06 [3 items]. Died Sept. 1968.

SAMUELS, ARTHUR PUREFOY IRWIN (b. 14 Feb. 1887) only s. of Arthur Warren Samuels, K.C., of 80 Merrion Square, Dublin, and Emma Margaret Irwin; B.A. (T.C.D.); M 1907. 1910/T/14 [2 items]. Captain, Royal Irish Rifles. Died in Flanders, 24 Sept. 1916. Author of *The Early Life Correspondence and Writings of the Rt. Hon. Edmund Burke LL.D.* (Cambridge, 1923) [prefaced by a memoir of the author by his father and photograph]. Portrait as a child in T.C.D.: see Anne Crookshank and David Webb, *Paintings and Sculptures in Trinity College Dublin* (Dublin, 1990), 119. [Name on the Bar War Memorial].

SAMUELS, ARTHUR WARREN (b. 19 May 1852) 2nd s. of Arthur Samuels, M.A., solicitor and proctor, of Langara, Glenageary, Kingstown, Co. Dublin, and Kate Daly; B.A. (T.C.D.); M 1874, G.I. E 1876. 1877/M/02 [6 items]. Leinster Circuit. Q.C., 30 June 1894. M.P. (Dublin University), 1916-19. Solicitor-General, 1917. Attorney-General, 1918. Judge of the King's Bench Division, 1919: retired 1924. Died at La Croix in France, 11 May 1925. Obituary, *I.L.T. & S.J.*, lix (1925), 119; *Who's Who*. Ball, *Judges*, ii, 386-7. Mentioned in Maurice Healy, *The Old Munster Circuit*, 267.

SANDES, JOHN (b. 25 Sept. 1868) only s. of George Sandes of Greenville, Co. Kerry, and Anna Whyte; M 1888. 1893/H/05 [5 items]. Author of *The New Death Duties: an address delivered ... at the inaugural meeting of the 65th Session* [of the Law Students' Debating Society] (Dublin: Ponsonby and Weldrick, 1894).

SANDFORD, JOHN BEACH (b. 14 Sept. 1843) eld. s. of the Revd. William Sandford (decd.), Rector of Clonmel, Co. Tipperary, and Susan Lyster; B.A. (T.C.D.); M 1882, M.T. M 1877. 1884/T/05 [6 items]. Died 28 Aug. 1902: *I.L.T. & S.J.*, xxxvi (1902), 338.

SANDS, ROBERT RADCLIFFE LINDSAY (b. 24 June 1877) 2nd s. of Thomas Sands of Kenilworth Park, Dublin, and Annie Lindsay; T 1907. 1907/M/12 [2 items]. Called to the English Bar, 1919. Advocate of the Supreme Court of South Africa (Roman Dutch Law).

SARSFIELD-HALL, EDWIN GEOFFREY (b. 24 April 1886) eld. s. of Edwin Hall, of 31 Auriol Road, West Kensington, London W14, and Ada Georgina Shekleton; M 1905.

Called *in absentia* – file includes personal letter. 1925/M/28 [3 items]. Sudan Political Service, 1908. Governor of Khartoum Province, 1929-36. Retired to Keswick, Cumbria, where he held company directorships. Died 30 March 1975. *Who's Who*.

SASTRI, GOLLAPUDI ANJANEYA (n.d.) 3rd s. of Gollapudi Venkata Subbayya, of Repalle, Guntur, Madras, India; M 1914. 1917/T/28 [2 items].

SCANLAN, THOMAS (b. 21 May 1872) 2nd s. of Matthew Scanlan (decd.), of Drumcliffe, Co. Sligo, and Catherine Scanlan; H 1916, G.I. H 1912. 1916/M/05 [2 items].

SCANLAN, THOMAS HENRY (b. 10 June 1894) eld. s. of John Joseph Scanlan, of 29 Ailesbury Road. Dublin, and Margaret McEvoy; M 1919. 1921/H/05 [2 items].

SCANLON, JOHN WILLIAM (b. 2 March 1904) 2nd s. of William Scanlon, of Carnaugh, Collooney, Co. Sligo, and Ellen Foley; M 1924. 1927/M/16 [2 items]. Examiner of the High Court. Author of *Practice and Procedure in Administration and Mortgage Suits in Ireland* (Dublin, 1963).

SCOTT, JAMES EMERSON (b. 12 Aug. 1855) eld. s. of James Anderson Scott, journalist, of 4 Salem Place, Dublin, and Letitia Wilson; B.A. (T.C.D.); M 1880, G.I. H 1885. 1886/E/01 [8 items].

SCOTT, PERCY CECIL (b. 24 Feb. 1910) eld. s. of Thomas Cecil Scott, of Altona House, Harold's Cross Road, Dublin, and Kathleen May Deakin; M 1927. 1931/E/02 [2 items].

SCOTT, SÉAMUS OLIVER (b. 5 Jan. 1944) eld. s. of James Joseph Scott, civil servant, of 164 Collins Avenue, Whitehall, Dublin, and Esther Josephine Smyth; M 1964. 1968/T/12 [1 item].

SCULLY, DARBY (b. 30 Oct. 1851) elder s. of Jerome James Scully, J.P., decd., late of Silverfort, Co. Tipperary, and Ellen Kennefick; M.A. (T.C.D.); E 1875, I.T. E 1877. 1889/T/01 [9 items].

SCULLY, JOHN (b. 3 May 1854) 2nd s. of James Scully, J.P., of 25 Mountjoy Sq, Dublin and Shanballymore, Co. Tipperary, and Catherine Gallwey; M 1875, M.T. E 1877. 1878/M/11 [5 items].

SEALE, EDWARD GILBERT (b. 3 Sept. 1870) eld. s. of Richard Stoker Seale (decd.), gentleman, of Airfield, Dundrum, Dublin, and Alice Mary Haskins; ex-Scholar, M.A. (T.C.D.); M 1897. 1901/M/03 [3 items].

SEALES, PETER CLINTON (b. 1 Nov. 1929) eld. s. of James M. Seales, solicitor, of 7 Clyde Road, Ballsbridge, Dublin, and Angela O'Doherty; M 1949. 1954/T/13 [2 items].

SEALY, JAMES (b. 19 March 1876) 4th s. of John Sealy of Arborfield, Dundrum, Co. Dublin, and Margaret Shaw; ex-Scholar, Sen. Mod., B.A. (T.C.D.); M 1899. 1902/H/02 [3 items]. Leinster Circuit. K.C., 27 Feb. 1918. Member of the Irish Selection Board of the Inns of Court Officers' Training Corps. One of the eight original judges of the Circuit Court, 1924, appointed to the Southern Circuit (afterwards renamed the South-Eastern Circuit). Son-in-law of Douglas Hyde. Died 4 Feb. 1949. Obituary, *I.L.T. & S.J.*, lxxxiii (1949), 45. *Burke's Irish Family Records* (1976), 619.

SEEDS, JAMES THOMPSON (b. 26 Oct. 1870) eld. s. of William Seeds (decd.), of Ballymote, Downpatrick, Co. Down, and Elizabeth Atkinson; cand. bachelor (T.C.D.); H 1892. 1895/H/07 [5 items].

SEKYI, KWEKU ANU (b. 16 Jan. 1924) 2nd s. of William Esuman-Gwira Sekyi, Barrister-at-Law, of Bentsi, Cape Coast, Gold Coast, and Lily Anna Cleanand (decd.); B.A. (N.U.I.); M 1948. 1952/T/04 [2 items].

SELIGMAN, DONALD LIONEL (b. 19 July 1928) 2nd s. of Ephraim Seligman, company director, of 175 Upper Rathmines Road, Dublin, and Esther Malka Wigoder; B.A., LL.B. (T.C.D.); M 1945. 1949/M/05 [2 items].

SELLORS, EDWARD MARMADUKE (b. 9 July 1860) eld. s. of Michael Sellors, solicitor, of 47 George Street, Limerick, and Louisa Clarke; B.A. (T.C.D.); M 1882, L.I. T 1884. 1885/T/03 [7 items].

SETHI, CHUNI LAUL (b. 28 April 1891) eld. s. of Rai Sahib Din[e]anchand, M.A., LL.B., judge, of Lahore, Punjab, India; M 1914. 1917/M/10 [2 items].

SETHI, RAM LAL (b. 17 March 1894) eld. s. of Mangal Sain Sethi, of Sargodha, Punjab, India; M 1915. 1918/T/18 [2 items].

SHAH, SYED NAZEERULLAH (b. 25 March 1890) only s. of Syed Maseehullah Shah, of Jullundur City, Punjab, India; M 1914. 1917/T/26 [2 items].

SHANAHAN, ARTHUR DESMOND (b. 11 Sept. 1925) eld. s. of Jerome Shanahan, of 8 Mulgrave Street, Dún Laoghaire, Co. Dublin, and Lilian Parker; B.A. (N.U.I.); M 1946.1950/H/01. Disbarred on 11 Jan. 1961. [6 items]. A Director of Shanahans Stamp Auctions Limited. See the judgment of Budd J. in *Shanahans Stamp Auctions Limited v. Farrelly and Dawson*, [1962] I.R. 386.

SHANLEY, PETER THOMAS (b. 2 Aug. 1946) 2nd s. of Dermot Francis Shanley, director of planning, Bank of Ireland Group, of St. John's, Sandycove, Co. Dublin, and Rosaleen O'Higgins; B.C.L., LL.B. (N.U.I.); M 1964. 1968/T/03 [1 item]. S.C., 4 Oct. 1982. Judge of the High Court, 15 April 1996. Died 7 Sept. 1998. Obituary, *The Irish Times*, 9 Sept. 1999. Appreciation in *The Bar Review*, vol. iv, no. 1 (Oct. 1998), 54.

SHANNON, GEORGE HENRY (b. 25 Feb. 1855) 2nd s. of George William Shannon, solicitor, of Dublin, and Emily Goodman; B.A. (T.C.D.); District Inspector, R.I.C.; T 1883, M.T. H 1885. 1886/T/04 [7 items].

SHANNON, GEORGE WILLIAM (b. 9 Dec. 1881) eld. s. of James Shannon (decd.) of Dublin, and Nannie Brabazon; B.A. (T.C.D.); M 1901. 1904/M/07 [3 items]. President of the University Philosophical Society, T.C.D., 1904-5. S.C., 21 Dec. 1948. Died Dec. 1959. Obituary, *I.L.T. & S.J.*, xciv (1960), 17, 22.

SHANNON, GEORGE WILLIAM (b. 3 Aug. 1887) 2nd s. of George Henry Shannon, R.M., of Birr, King's Co., and Mary Nolan; B.A. (T.C.D.); M 1906. 1910/H/04 [2 items]. S.C., 14 July 1924. Judge (1928) and first President (1947) of the Circuit Court: *I.L.T. & S.J.*, lxxxi (2 Aug. 1947), 183. Retired 1 Aug. 1959. Died 1968. Obituary, *I.L.T. & S.J.*, cii (13 Apr. 1968), 149. Mentioned in Patrick MacKenzie, *Lawful Occasions*, 86-7.

SHANNON, JAMES (b. 31 Dec 1851) eld. s. of George William Shannon of Leeson Park, Dublin, and Emily Goodman; B.A. (T.C.D.); T 1871, M.T. M 1872. 1874/T/2 [2 items].

SHAPER, HARRIS AUGUSTUS (b. 7 April 1945) youngest s. of Hyman Shaper (decd.), company director, of 94 Bushy Park Road, Terenure, Co. Dublin, and Frieda Cherrick (decd.); B.A., LL.B. (T.C.D.); M 1964. Awarded 3rd Victoria Prize. 1968/M/03 [2 items].

SHARMA, KHRAITI RAM (b. 26 April 1895) 2nd s. of Missar [Dhigt] Ram, of Nakodar, Jullundur, Punjab, India. 1917/T/15 [2 items].

SHARPE, SAMUEL HOWARD (b. 7 May 1873) 3rd s. of Henry Sharpe (decd.) of 12 Ailesbury Road, Dublin, and Isabella Hill; M.A., M.D., LL.D. (T.C.D.); M 1910. 1913/T/07 [2 items]. Medical doctor, sometime senior resident surgeon at Jervis Street Hospital. Died 1942. Obituary, *I.L.T. & S.J.*, lxxvi (7 March 1942), 67.

SHAW, EDWARD (b. 8 June 1848) eld. s. of James Shaw (decd.) of Ballyoram, Co. Down, and Letitia Lambe; B.A. (Cambridge); T 1870, I.T. H 1867 [M 1868]. 1873/M/7 [7 items].

SHAW, JAMES HERBERT (b. 17 May 1860) 3rd s. of James Shaw of Ballyoran, Co. Down, and Letitia Mary Tombe; Candidate Bachelor T.C.D.; M 1880, I.T. E 1882. 1883/T/08 [5 items].

SHAW, JAMES JOHNSTON (b. 4 Jan. 1845) 2nd s. of John Maxwell Shaw (decd.), farmer, of Kirkcubbin, Co. Down, and Anne Johnston; M.A. (Q.C.B.); M 1876, L.I. M 1873. 1878/E/01 [7 items]. Q.C., June 1889. Whately Professor of Political Economy, T.C.D., 1877-82. County Court Judge of Kerry, 1891; of Antrim, 1909; Recorder of Belfast, 1909-10. Chairman of the viceregal inquiry into the disappearance of the crown jewels, 1908. Died 27 April 1910. Obituary, *I.L.T. & S.J.*, xliv (1910), 114. Portrait and memorial brass unveiled on 13 May 1911 in Q.U.B. (the statutes of which he framed in 1908): *I.L.T. & S.J.*, xlv (1911), 132-4. See *Who's Who* and *D.N.B.*

SHAW, JAMES ROWAN (b. 20 May 1880) eld. s. of James J. Shaw, K.C., County Court Judge of Kerry, of 69 Pembroke Road, Dublin, and Mary Elizabeth Maxwell; B.A. (T.C.D.); M 1901. 1904/M/09 [3 items]. Member of D.U.O.T.C. 2nd Lieutenant, 9th Cheshire Regiment; killed in France, 22 Feb. 1916. [Name on the Bar War Memorial].

SHAW, JOHN HENRY de BURGH (b. 6 Sept. 1887) 2nd s. of John Shaw (decd.), ex-Acting Governor, Lagos, W.A., of Cloncallow House, Ballymahon, Co. Longford, and Alice de Burgh Sidley; Cand. Bach. (T.C.D.); M 1911. 1914/T/12 [3 items]. Member of the 'Pals' Battalion. Photograph (right) in Henry Hanna, *The Pals at Suvla Bay* (1917), 233. Died Aug. 1969.

SHAW, RICHARD JAMES HERBERT (b. 7 March 1885) only s. of James Herbert Shaw of 36 Upper Fitzwilliam Street, Dublin, and Mary Herbert Armstrong; B.A. (T.C.D.); M 1905. 1908/M/02 [2 items]. London representative of the Irish Unionist Alliance, 1911-13. Commissioned, 1914; Captain, 5th Battalion, Connaught Rangers, 1915. Assistant Press Censor, Ireland, 1916-18. Assistant-Secretary, Irish Convention, 1917-18; Assistant to the Lord Lieutenant, 1918-19. Editorial Stall of *The Times*, 1919-. Died 12 July 1946. Obituary, *I.L.T. & S.J.*, lxxx (27 July 1946), 190; *Who's Who*.

SHEAHAN, THOMAS HELSHAM (b. 26 March 1847) only s. of Timothy Sheahan (decd.) of Passage West, Co. Cork, Head Inspector of National Schools, and Frances Ryan; A.B. (T.C.D.); T 1870, M.T. H 1872. 1873/T/8 [2 items].

SHEEHAN, DANIEL D. (b. 29 May 1874) 2nd s. of Daniel Sheehan (decd.) of Percival Street, Kanturk, Co. Cork, and Ellen Fitzgerald; M 1908. 1911/T/12 [2 items]. M.P. for Mid-Cork, 1901-18. Author of *Ireland since Parnell* (1921). Died 1948. Obituary, *I.L.T. & S.J.*, lxxxii (4 Dec. 1948), 296.

SHEEHAN, EDWARD (b. 26 April 1872) eld. s. of William J. Sheehan (decd.), of 15 Grattan Hill, Cork, and Norah O'Connor; MA; M 1897. 1919/T/02 [2 items].

SHEEHAN, JAMES JOSEPH (b. 13 Jan. 1864) 2nd s. of Daniel Sheehan (decd.) of Rushbrooke, Co. Cork, and Ellen Danckert; LL.B; M 1881, M.T. M 1885. 1886/M/03 [7 items]. Died 14 Nov. 1906. Obituary, *I.L.T. & S.J.*, xl (1906), 359.

SHEEHAN, PATRICK AUGUSTINE (b. 26 May 1905) 4th s. of Captain Daniel Desmond Sheehan, Barrister-at-Law, of 67 Merrion Square, Dublin (formerly of Cork City), and Mary O'Connor (decd.); M 1927. 1936/M/09 [2 items]. S.C, 2 March 1948. Author, as P. A. Ó Síocháin, of *The Criminal Law of Ireland* (6th ed., Dublin, 1977)

SHEEHAN, ROSE CONSTANCE (b. 24 Feb. 1904) eld. d. of Jeremiah Sheehan (decd.), 120 Tritonville Road, Sandymount, Dublin, and Catherine Mooney (decd.); M 1947. 1953/M/11 [2 items].

SHEEHY, DAVID B. (b. 30 April 1924) only s. of Eugene Francis Sheehy, of Belmont, Palmerston Road, Dublin, and Carmel Neary; B.A. (N.U.I.); M 1943. 1946/T/05 [2 items]. Judge of the Circuit Court, 1975. The Sheehys are identified as one of Ireland's 'legal dynasties' in *Burke's Irish Family Records* (1976), xxii, 1019-20.

SHEEHY, EUGENE (b. 26 March 1883) 2nd s. of David Sheehy, M.P., of 2 Belvedere Place, Dublin, and Elizabeth McCoy; M 1905. 1910/M/04 [3 items]. Judicial Commissioner under the Dáil Éireann Courts (Winding-Up) Act, 1923. Judge of the Circuit Court. Died 23 Oct. 1958. *Burke's Irish Family Records* (1976), 1020. See Mary Kotsonouris, *Retreat from Revolution: The Dáil Courts, 1920-24* (Dublin, 1994), 107. Author of *May it Please the Court* (Dublin, 1951), to which a photograph of the author forms the frontispiece.

SHEEHY, Revd. JOHN GERARD (b. 16 Oct. 1924) eld. s. of Professor Edmond J. Sheehy, of 'Cuilin', Hampstead Avenue, Glasnevin, Dublin, and Bridget E. McPhillips; B.A., D.C.L; M 1955. 1958/M/07 [2 items]. Marriage Tribunal, R.C. Archdiocese of Dublin. Died 19 March 2003.

SHEEHY, RICHARD JOSEPH (b. 1 Jan. 1882) eld. s. of David Sheehy, of 2 Belvedere Place, Dublin, and Elizabeth McCoy; B.A., LL.B. (R.U.I.); M 1904. 1907/M/01 [3 items]. Went Munster Circuit. Died 12 Oct. 1923. *Burke's Irish Family Records* (1976), 1020; James Meenan (ed.), *Centenary History of Lit. and Hist. Soc. of U.C.D.*

SHEEHY, RUTH MARY, R.S.C.J. (b. 8 May 1926) only d. of Eugene Sheehy (decd.), Circuit Court Judge, of Belmont, Palmerston Road, Dublin, and Carmel Neary; M 1946. 1960/M/09 [2 items]. Identified in *Burke's Irish Family Records* (1976), xxiii and 1020, as 'the first nun to be called to the Irish Bar', serving the Sacred Heart Order in Tokyo.

SHEIL, CHARLES LEO (b. 11 April 1897) young. s. of Peter Joseph Sheil, of Ulster House, Portadown, Co. Armagh, J.P., and Mary Jane Henry; LL.B., M 1918. 1921/E/01 [1 item]. K.C. (N.I.), T 1943. Crown Counsel for Co. Antrim, 1926-43. County Court Judge of Co. Tyrone, 1943-5 (resigned). Senior Crown Counsel, City of Belfast, 1946. Judge of the King's Bench Division (N.I.), 3 March 1949. Died 5 Sept. 1968. See *Who's Who*; Kate Newmann, *Dictionary of Ulster Biography* (Belfast, 1993). Mentioned in Basil McIvor, *Hope Deferred: Experiences of an Irish Unionist* (Belfast, 1998), 32, 34, 37. Father of Sir John Sheil (M. 1976), Judge of the N.I. High Court.

SHEIL, RICHARD HENRY (b. 24 Sept. 1856) eld. s. of Richard Henry Sheil (decd.) of Liverpool, Lancaster, and Teresa Leonard; B.A. (University of London); H 1877, M.T. H 1879. 1880/M/19 [5 items]. Land Registry. Died 11 May 1935. Obituary, *I.L.T. & S.J.*, lxix (1935), 142, 248.

SHERIDAN, ALFRED PATRICK STANISLAUS (b. 5 Dec. 1926) 7th s. of John Sheridan (decd.), of 2 Park Grove, Barnsley, Yorkshire, and Eva Moran; M 1947. 1955/T/02 [2 items].

SHERIDAN, DIARMUID PATRICK (b. 12 March 1928) eld. s. of John Gabriel Sheridan, of 9 Hampstead Park, Glasnevin, Dublin, and Nora O'Connor; B.A. (N.U.I.); M 1949. 1952/M/06 [2 items]. S.C., 2 Oct. 1967. Judge of the Circuit Court. President of that Court, 19 Jan. 1998; retired 11 March 1998.

SHERIDAN, FRANCIS STEPHEN (b. 27 Dec. 1864) eld. s. of Francis P. Sheridan (decd.) of Moyne Arva, Co. Longford, and Marie A. O'Byrne; M 1910. 1913/T/08 [2 items]. Died 13 March 1935. Obituary, *I.L.T. & S.J.*, lxix (1935), 84.

SHERIDAN, JOSEPH ALFRED (b. 12 Nov. 1882) 3rd s. of Joseph Sheridan of Spencer Park, Castlebar, Co. Mayo, and Margaret Murphy; M 1904. 1907/M/07 [2 items]. Connaught Circuit. Judicial Clerk, Nyasaland Protectorate, 1908-13; Resident Magistrate, Kenya, 1913-20; Puisne judge, Kenya, 1920-8; Acting Chief Justice of Kenya, 1928-9; Chief Justice of Tanganyika Territory, 1929-34; and of Kenya, 1934-46. Knighted, 1932. LL.D. (*h.c.*, conferred *in absentia*), T.C.D., 1938. See note on his career in *I.L.T. & S.J.*, lxxii (1938), 256. Died 26 Dec. 1964. *Who's Who.*

SHERIDAN, THOMAS BRINSLEY (b. 21 Sept. 1844) young. s. of John Sheridan (decd.) of Tonagh, Co. Cavan, and Margaret Lowndes; M 1867, I.T. E 1869. Evergreen Lodge, Ballybrack, Co. Dublin. 1871/M/2 [2 items].

SHERLOCK, DAVID (b. 27 March 1850) 2nd s. of David, Q.C., M.P., Sergeant-at-Law, of Stillorgan Castle, Co. Dublin and Elizabeth Therry; M 1868; M.T. E 1870. 1872/M/3 [2 items].

SHERLOCK, DAVID THOMAS JOSEPH (b. 6 Sept. 1881) only s. of Thomas Therri Sherlock of 20 Upper Mount Street, Dublin, and Letitia Mary Nugent; M 1899. 1904/H/04 [3 items]. K.C. (N.I.), M 1922 [2 Dec. 1922]. Colonial Service (Borneo and Jamaica). Died 12 Oct. 1964. Obituary, *I.L.T. & S.J.*, xcviii (1964), 388; *Who's Who.*

SHERRY, FELIX HUGH (b. 6 Dec. 1892) 4th s. of Hugh Sherry (decd.), of Dublin Street, Monaghan, and Margaret Begley; M 1915. 1918/M/03 [2 items]. A prime mover of the petition to the Benchers for the disbarring of Serjeant Sullivan [q.v.], 13 April 1956. Died 31 Aug. 1956. Obituary, *I.L.T. & S.J.*, xc (1956), 217. Mentioned in Patrick MacKenzie, *Lawful Occasions*, 61-3

SHIEL, JOHN (b. 25 Jan. 1895) eld. s. of James Shiel, of Cecil Street, Manchester, England, and Elizabeth Jackson; M 1928. 1932/M/11 [2 items].

SHIELDS, JAMES FRANCIS (b. 12 Oct. 1925) eld. s. of Vincent Peter Shields, of Knockanina, Loughrea, Co. Galway, and Dorothy Eleanor Tighe; M 1944. 1949/M/13 [2 items].

SHIELDS, KEVIN ROANTREE: see O'SHIEL, KEVIN ROANTREE.

SHILLMAN, BERNARD (b. 19 Dec. 1892) s. of Julius M. Shillman (decd.), of 33 Victoria Street, South Circular Road, Dublin, and Ada Shillman; M 1923. 1926/M/05 [2 items]. Called to the English Bar, E 1946. S.C., 2 March 1948. Author of *The Licensing Laws of Ireland* (Dublin: Dollard, 1941). *Trade Unionism and Trade Disputes in Ireland* (Dublin, n.d. [1960]); four works on Workmen's Compensation and the Factories Acts; and *A Short History of the Jews in Ireland* (Dublin, n.d.) Died 22 Oct. 1965: *I.L.T. & S.J.*, xcix (1965), 329. Mentioned in Patrick MacKenzie, *Lawful Occasions*, 45-6.

SHINKWIN, JAMES (b. 15 July 1846) 8th s. of John Shinkwin (decd.) of Main Street, Cork, and Mary Dunlea; M 1869, M.T. M 1867. 1872/H/11 [2 items].

SHORT, WILLIAM (b. 24 Feb. 1832) eldest s of Joseph Short (decd.) of Harcourt Street, Dublin and Catherine Kiernan; M 1863, M.T. T 1866. 1868/M/2 [5 items].

SHORTT, FRANCIS HELY (b. 21 Oct. 1864) 5th s. of John Shortt, Barrister-at-Law, of 17 Belgrave Square, Dublin, and Charlotte Owen; B.A. (T.C.D.); M 1889. 1892/M/02 [6 items].

SHORTT, JOSEPH BARTHOLOMEW (b. 9 March 1884) eld. s. of John Shortt, of Ballydan, Co. Kilkenny, and Mary Anne Leonard; M 1914. 1917/T/09 [2 items].

SIDDIKI, KHALILUZZAMAN M. (b. 15 Dec. 1895) only s. of Mohd Mumiruzzamau, of Hyderabad, Dacca, India, and Masood Fatima; M 1914. 1917/T/06 [2 items].

SIEV, RAPHAEL VICTOR (b. 13 March 1935) 2nd s. of Nathan Albert Siev, property owner, of 7 Emorville Avenue, Dublin, and Edith Fanny Arnovitch; M 1955. 1960/T/11 [2 items]. Deputy legal adviser, Department of Foreign Affairs.

SILKE, WILLIAM JAMES (b. 21 Sept. 1929) only s. of William Joseph Silke (decd.), of Stanley, Kill O'Grange, Co. Dublin, and Gertrude Mary Delaney; M 1949. 1955/M/09 [2 items]. Judge in Hong Kong.

SINCLAIR, WILLIAM HUGH MONTGOMERY (b. 24 Dec. 1868) eld. s. of James Montgomery Sinclair, J.P., of Bonnyglin, Co. Donegal, and Mary B[arton]; B.A. (Oxford); H 1894. 1897/T/03 [4 items].

SINGH, GEORGE (b. 12 July 1937) eld. s. of George Singh, attorney-at-law, of Durban, South Africa, and Elizabeth Andrews; M 1963. 1968/H/04 [3 items].

SINGH, GURDIT (b. 27 May 1884) 3rd s. of S. Budh Singh, of Rawalpindi, Punjab, India; M 1915. 1918/T/12 [2 items].

SKINNER, GERALDINE MARY (b. 10 Aug. 1935) only d. of Leo B. Skinner, District Justice, of Mitchelstown, Co. Cork, and Sheila FitzGerald; B.A.; M 1953. Awarded 2nd Victoria Prize. 1958/M/03 [2 items]. Legal adviser, Department of Foreign Affairs; ambassador to Luxembourg.

SKINNER, JAMES JOHN (b. 24 July 1923) only s. of Luke William J. Skinner, of Mountain Villa, Clonmel, Co. Tipperary, and Kathleen O'Donnell; M 1941. 1946/M/06 [2 items]. Called to the English Bar (G.I.), M 1950, and to the Bar of Northern Rhodesia, T 1951 (Q.C. there, 1964). M.P. for Lusaka East, 1964-8; Minister of Justice, 1964-5, and Attorney-General, 1965-9. Chief Justice of Zambia, March-Sept. 1969. Chief Justice of Malawi, 1970-85. Grand Commander of the Order of Menelik II of Ethiopia, 1965. Mentioned in Patrick MacKenzie, *Lawful Occasions*, 81-2. *Who's Who*.

SLOSS, FRANCIS ALEXANDER (b. 30 Oct. 1865) 2nd s. of Joseph Sloss, M.D., Staff-Surgeon, Royal Navy, of Belfast, and Eliza M'Gahey; B.A.; M 1889. 1894/H/03 [9 items].

SLYNE, DENIS (b. 7 June 1855) 2nd surv. s. of Patrick Slyne (decd.), Clerk of Petty Sessions, of Cappawhite, Dundrum, Co. Tipperary, and Catherine Harding; M 1895. 1898/T/06 [4 items].

SMITH, GEORGE HILL (b. 7 July 1833) 2nd s. of George Smith, late of the Paymaster's Office, Dublin Castle, of Cullenwood, Co. Dublin, and Elizabeth Lee; B.A. (Q.U.B.); M 1874, I.T. M 1874. 1877/M/08 [9 items]. K.C., 28 Nov. 1914. Father of the Northern Bar. Author of *Rambling Reminiscences (Notes of a political speaker)* (Newry, 1896); *The North East Bar. A sketch historical and reminiscent* (Belfast, 1910); and *Sketch of the Supreme Court of Judicature of Northern Ireland* (Belfast, 1926). A photograph of the author forms the frontispiece to *The North East Bar*. Died 1 April 1926. Obituary, *I.L.T. & S.J.*, lx (1926), 93; *Who's Who*.

SMITH, JOHN HOWARD (b. 16 March 1900) eld. s. of Arthur Howard Smith, M.A., B.Sc., of Presteigue, Polters Lane, Worthing, Sussex, and Louisa Frances Smee; M 1927. 1930/M/10 [2 items].

SMITH, JOHN IRVINE (b. 29 Sept. 1850) 2nd s. of the Revd. Samuel Johnson Smith of Smithborough, Co. Monaghan, and Fanny Irvine; H 1879. 1887/H/03 [7 items].

SMITH, MATTHEW PATRICK (b. 22 March 1936) 2nd s. of Matthew Smith, of Kells, Co. Meath, and M.A. Duffy; B.A., LL.B; M 1957. 1957/M/02 [2 items]. S.C., 4 Oct. 1982. Judge of the Circuit Court, 1985; of the High Court, 23 Jan. 1998; ret. 31 Dec. 2004.

SMITH, PATRICK (b. 16 June 1886) 5th s. of Mathew Smith, of Crosskeys, Co. Cavan, and Anne McInerney[?]; M.A., LL.B; M 1917. 1920/M/05 [2 items]. Retired sergeant of the Dublin Metropolitan Police. Died 1932. Obituary, *I.L.T. & S.J.*, lxvi (16 Jan. 1932), 18.

SMITH, PATTEN (b. 24 May 1852) eld. s. of John Sidney Smith, of Westport, Co. Mayo, and Anne Allen; B.A. (T.C.D.); M 1871, M.T. E 1873. 1875/T/01 [2 items].

SMITH, PHILIP HENRY LAW (b. 26 July 1863) 2nd s. of Philip Smith, J.P., of Kevitt Castle, Co. Cavan, and Delia Mary Banahan; M.A., LL.D. (T.C.D.); M 1883, M.T. M 1884. 1887/H/02 [7 items]. K.C., 22 Jan. 1906. Appt. County Court Judge for Limerick, 11 May 1908. Author, jointly with Judge Drummond, of a work on High Court procedure. Died at Bath, 1920. Obituary, *I.L.T. & S.J.*, liv (1920), 10-11; *Who's Who*.

SMITH, PHILIP NORBERT (b. 4 June 1896) eld. s. of Louis C.P. Smith, of Arranmore, Cavan, Co. Cavan, and Hettie Fay; sen. Mod. B.A. (T.C.D.); M 1915. 1921/H/02 [2 items].

SMITH, RAYMOND WALTER AQUILLA (b. 14 March 1877) eld. s. of Walter George Smith, M.D., of 25 Merrion Square, Dublin, and Anna Cathcart (decd.); Sch. B.A. (T.C.D.); Prizeman (T.C.D. and King's Inns); E 1899. 1901/M/02 [3 items]. Land Registry. Died 16 March 1927. Obituary, *I.L.T. & S.J.*, lxi (1927), 71. Joint author (with F.H. Browning) of the 2nd edition of *Local Registration of Title in Ireland* (Dublin, 1912).

SMITH, ROBERT JOHN CRAWFORD CHATTERTON (b. 7 Jan. 1847) eld. s. of William Peters Smith, of Belmount, Raheny, Co. Dublin, Assistant Registrar of the Court of Chancery, and F. Dickson; B.A. (T.C.D.); M 1868, I.T. H 1870. 1871/M/10 [4 items].

SMITH, STEPHEN CATTERSON (b. 16 March 1875) only s. of Stephen Catterson Smith of 42 Stephen's Green, Dublin, and Henrietta Frazer Aitken; H 1896. 1899/H/03 [3 items].

SMITH, WILLIAM (b. 11 April 1840) eld. surv. s. of Brabazon Pearson Smith (decd.), solicitor, of Kildare Street, Dublin, and Margaret Walsh; M 1867, M.T. E 1868. 1872/H/01 [2 items].

SMITH-CHATTERTON, WILLIAM ALLEYNE (b. 19 April 1888) eld. s. of Robert Smith-Chatterton, Barrister-at-Law, of Belmont, Raheny, Dublin, and Margaret Isabella Young; B.A. (T.C.D.); M 1909. 1912/T/09 [3 items].

SMITHSON, SAMUEL RAYNER (b. 27 June 1845) 2nd s. of John Smithson of Cloraugh, Dublin, Merchant, and Anne Rayner; B.A. (T.C.D.); H 1866, M.T. T 1867. 1869/E/01 [2 items].

SMITHWICK, MICHAEL (b. 20 April 1878) only s. of Thomas Smithwick (decd.) of Golden, Co. Tipperary, and Catherine Guilfoyle (decd.); B.A. (R.U.I.); M 1904. 1908/T/03 [3 items]. Died 22 Jan. 1939. Obituary, *I.L.T. & S.J.*, lxxiii (1939), 39.

SMYLIE, ARCHIBALD (b. 29 June 1841) 2nd s. of James Smylie, farmer, of Magheramore, Co. Antrim, and Elizabeth Hunter; M.A., LL.B (Queen's College Belfast); T 1870, M.T. E 1872. 1876/T/02 [2 items].

SMYLIE, ROBERT ROMILLY (b. 14 April 1875) 2nd s. of John Dryden Smylie, Rector of St. Nicholas Without and St. Luke's, Dublin, of St. Luke's Rectory, South Circular Road, Dublin, and Charlotte Elizabeth Pigott; B.A. (T.C.D.); M 1897. 1900/T/03 [3 items]. Called to the English Bar, H 1912. Died Aug. 1968.

SMYLY, PHILIP CRAMPTON (b. 28 March 1866) eld. s. of Philip Crampton Smyly, M.D., of 4 Merrion Square, Dublin, and Selina Plunkett; B.A. (T.C.D.); H 1885. 1888/M/06 [7 items]. Called to the English Bar, G.I., 1902. Queen's Advocate, Sierra Leone, 1895; Attorney-General, 1896-1901; Chief Justice, 1910-11. Chief Justice of Gold Coast Colony, 1911-29. Knighted, 1905. Died 29 May 1953; *Who's Who*.

SMYTH, EDWARD JAMES (b. 22 Sept. 1883) eld. s. of John P. Smyth, J.P. (decd.), of Alexander Terrace, Novaro Road, Bray, Co. Wicklow and Guilford Road, Dublin, and R. M. Smyth; B.A. (R.U.I.); M 1911. 1914/T/02 [3 items]. Department of Industry and Commerce. Author of *The Seashores of Ireland: Foreshore Act, 1933 with commentaries and a chapter on coastal erosion* [Privately printed. Dublin, 1935]. Died 29 March 1941. Obituary, *I.L.T. & S.J.*, lxxv (1941), 87.

SMYTH, ESMOND (b. 16 Dec. 1944) eld. s. of Patrick J. Smyth, Barrister-at-Law, of The Slopes, Knapton Road, Dún Laoghaire, Co. Dublin, and Anne Devlin; B.C.L. (N.U.I.); M 1964. 1968/H/02 [1 item]. President of the Circuit Court, 3 April 1998-2005.

SMYTH, GEORGE BESTALL JENKINSON (b. 23 July 1890) 2nd s. of James Davis Smyth (decd.) of Milltown House, Banbridge, Co. Down, and Charlotte Jenkinson; M 1909. 1913/T/04 [2 items]. Captain, Royal Irish Rifles. Died in Flanders, 22 Oct. 1918. [Name on the Bar War Memorial].

SMYTH, JAMES LAWRENCE (b. 14 April 1891) eld. s. of James Smyth, of 128 Lower George's Street, Dún Laoghaire, Co. Dublin, and Elizabeth O'Driscoll; M 1918. 1925/M/12 [2 items].

SMYTH, JOHN CHRISTOPHER (b. 12 Dec. 1920) 2nd s. of William Lawrence Smyth, of 95 Kincora Road, Clontarf, Co. Dublin, and Nora Kenny; B.Comm; M 1954. 1957/M/15 [2 items].

SMYTH, JOHN LOWE BLOOD. See: BLOOD-SMYTH, JOHN LOWE.

SMYTH, JOHN MARTIN FARRELL (b. 3 Aug. 1931) 3rd s. of John Farrell Smyth (decd.), solicitor, of Laurence Street, Drogheda, Co. Louth, and Kathleen Meade; B.A. (N.U.I.); M 1950. 1954/M/08 [2 items]. Council of Europe; Deputy Registrar of the European Court of Human Rights.

SMYTH, PATRICK JOSEPH (b. 6 Oct. 1915) 2nd s. of William Joseph Smyth, of 53 Lower Baggot Street, Dublin, and Claire Cahill; M 1940. 1944/T/02 [2 items].

SMYTH, THOMAS CLEMENT (b. 29 Dec. 1937) eld. s. of Joseph A. Smyth (decd.), F.C.I.S., of 'Ardglass', St. Mary's Road, Dundalk, Co. Louth, and Eileen O'Gorman (decd.); M 1962. 1968/M/17 [17 items]. S.C., 3 Oct. 1977. Judge of the High Court, 11 July 1996.

SMYTH, THOMAS JONES (b. 15 April 1866) 2nd s. of Thomas Jones Smyth, printer, of Cavan, Co. Cavan, and Anne Kellett; LL.B. (T.C.D.); M 1888, G.I. M 1890. 1891/M/02 [8 items]. President of the University Philosophical Society, T.C.D., 1891-2. Died 4 March 1944. Obituary, *I.L.T. & S.J.*, lxxviii (1944), 72-3. Mentioned by V.T.H. Delany [q.v.], in his article 'The Bench and Bar in Ireland', as one prominent among those who never took silk.

SMYTH, WILLIAM (b. 13 Nov. 1887) eld. s. of William Smyth, of 7 Palmerston Park, Upper Rathmines, Dublin, and Jane Fagan; Dip. Economics (T.C.D.); M 1925. 1928/E/01 [2 items].

SORAHAN, SÉAMUS (b. 29 Sept. 1924) only s. of James Sorahan, of 77 Lower Seán MacDermott Street, Dublin, and Bridget Hunt; M 1945. 1952/M/13 [2 items]. S.C., 4 Oct. 1971. Bencher.

SPAIN, FRANCIS ROBERT MARY (b. 2 Nov. 1943) young. s. of Thomas Joseph Spain, detective sergeant, Garda Síochána, of 24 Patrician Avenue, Naas, Co. Kildare, and Mary Bridget Morgan; B.C.L. (N.U.I.); M 1963. 1968/T/11 [1 item]. S.C., 6 Oct. 1980. Appt. a Judge of the Circuit Court, July 1987; President of the Circuit Court, 1 July 1991. Died 21 December 1997. Obituary (by N.J. Kearns), *The Irish Times*, 18 Feb. 1998. Listed [with photograph] in the 1991 edition of Maureen Cairnduff, *Who's Who in Ireland*.

SPAIN, PATRICK JOHN (b. 25 Dec. 1895) eld. s. of Alexander Patrick Spain, Senior Inspector, National Bank Ltd., of 3 Raglan Road, Dublin, and Ellen Mullins; M 1919. 1923/H/05 [2 items]. Revenue Commissioners, Dublin.

SPIRO, CHARLES (b. 22 June 1884) 2nd s. of Leon Spiro of 12 Fade Street, Dublin, and Olga Kopelanski; LL.B. (T.C.D.); H 1908 1910/E/01 [2 items].

SPRATT, HORNER DEVEREUX (b. 23 Feb. 1867) 2nd s. of Richard Spratt (decd.) of Pencil Hill, Co. Cork, and Elizabeth Louise Loott; M 1889. 1892/M/08 [6 items].

STACK, GEORGE HALL (b. 2 March 1850) 3rd s. of George Hall Stack, J.P., of Mullaghmore, Omagh, Co. Tyrone, and Mary Orpen; M.A. (T.C.D.); M 1870, I.T. E 1872. 1876/H/04 [2 items].

STACK, LIAM (b. 1 Dec. 1896) only s. of Maurice Stack, of Courthouse Road, Listowel, Co. Kerry, and Brigid Collins; M 1927. 1930/M/05 [1 item]. Chief Superintendent W.J. Stack. Died 28 Jan. 1935. Obituary, *I.L.T. & S.J.*, lxix (1935), 47.

STACK, ROBERT EDWARD HILLIARD (b. 1 May 1890) only s. of Gerald Leahy Stack, J.P. (decd.), of Market Street, Listowel, Co. Kerry, and Sarah Anne Hilliard; T 1927. 1927/M/26 [2 items].

STACK-MURPHY, JEROME O'DONOGHUE (b. 22 Aug. 1872) eld. s. of Jeremiah Stack-Murphy (decd.), County Inspector R.I.C., and Lucy Elizabeth Ludlow; M 1898. 1901/T/05 [3 items].

STANLEY, JOHN (b. 22 Nov 1846) 2nd s. of John Stanley of Armagh, solicitor, and Catherine Bell; B.A. (T.C.D.); H 1869; I.T. E 1870. 1872/T/5 [2 items]. Q.C., 1 July 1892. Honorary Bencher, 1898. Chief Justice of the North-West Provinces of India. Knighted: K.C.I.E., C.B.E. Died in London 7 Dec. 1931. Obituary, *I.L.T. & S.J.*, lxv (1931), 300; *Who's Who*.

STANLEY, JOHN (b. 3 May 1860) only surv. s. of Edward Stanley, Colonel coommanding 3rd Batt. 87th Royal Irish Fusiliers, of Summer Hill, Co. Armagh, and Anna Mayne; B.A. (T.C.D.); M 1882, M.T. H 1884. 1885/M/02 [7 items]. Resident in Worcestershire.

STANLEY, ROBERT HENRY (b. 28 Sept 1848) 3rd s. of the Revd. Robert Henry Stanley (decd.) of Edirmine Rectory, Co. Wexford and Charlotte Stanley; B.A. (T.C.D.); M 1868, I.T. H 1870. 1872/M/4 [4 items].

STAPLES, JAMES HEAD (b. 13 Oct. 1849) 2nd s. of Sir Nathaniel Alexander Staples, Bt., of Lissan, Co. Tyrone, and Elizabeth Lindsay Head; M 1876, L.I. M 1873. 1880/H/07 [7 items].

STAUNTON, PETER MAURICE (b. 20 March 1859) only surv. s. of Michael John Staunton (decd.), of Ballysimon, Co. Limerick, and Mary Luigard; E 1882, M.T. M 1884. 1885/T/02 [6 items].

STAVELEY, JONES HODDER (b. 17 April 1851) 2nd surv. s. of John Hodder Staveley, Clerk of Records and Affidavits, Landed Estates Court, of 6 Hardwicke Place, Dublin, and Ellen Knight; B.A. (T.C.D.); H 1873, M.T. M 1874. 1876/H/07 [4 items].

STEADMAN, DAVID ADDIE (b. 29 Nov. 1865) 3rd s. of David Williamson Steadman (decd.), of Newington, Edinburgh, Scotland, and Mary Simpson Hardie; M 1888. 1905/E/01* [3 items].

STEELE, LAWRENCE EDWARD (b. 13 March 1855) 2nd s. of William Edward Steele (decd.), M.D., Director-General, Science & Art Department, Dublin, late of Hatch Street, Dublin, and Susan Parkinson; B.A. (T.C.D.); E 1885. 1888/H/05 [7 items]. Died 9 Oct. 1944.

STEEN, AMBROSE GERARD (b. 4 Sept. 1920) 3rd s. of Ambrose Steen, of Johnstown House, Navan, Co. Meath, and Mary Barry; B.A. (N.U.I.); M 1942. 1946/T/08 [2 items]. Subsequently ordained a priest: see News in *I.L.T. & S.J.*, lxxxxiii (1959), 203.

STEEN, DAVID MILLER (b. 26 Dec. 1864) 2nd s. of Robert Steen (decd.), Ph.D., Headmaster, Royal Academical Institution, Belfast, and Anne Carmichael; B.A. (R.U.I.); M 1894, L.I. H 1894. 1898/T/04 [6 items]. Ceylon Civil Service. Died 12 Feb. 1949.

STEEN, WILLIAM (b. 8 June 1850) 2nd s. of William Steen (decd.) of Owen O'Cork, Co. Down, and Susanna Boyd; AB (Queen's College Belfast); M 1870; M.T. H 1873. 1874/M/5 [3 items].

STEPHENS, DENIS SYNGE (b. 28 June 1916) eld. s. of Edward Willington Stephens, of No. 2, Harcourt Terrace, Dublin, and Lilian Mary Day; B.A. (T.C.D.); M 1935. 1938/M/07 [2 items]. Crown Counsel in Nigeria, 1958.

STEPHENS, EDWARD MILLINGTON (b. 8 Nov. 1888) 2nd s. of Henry Francis Stephens of Silchester House, Glenageary, Co. Dublin, and Annie Isabella Synge; B.A.; M 1909. 1912/T/04 [3 items]. Joint Secretary of the Irish Free State Constitution Committee (1922) and Secretary to the North-Eastern Boundary Bureau, Dublin, 1922-6. Died March 1955. See Ronan Keating, Michael Kennedy, Dermot Keogh and Eunan O'Halpin (eds.), *Documents on Irish Foreign Policy. Volumes II 1923-1926* and *III 1926-32* (Dublin: 2000, 2002).

STEPHENSON, VENETIA JOSEPHINE MARY (b. [?]) d. of Charles Arthur Stephenson (decd.), and Constance Venetia Tillotson (decd.); H 1948, G.I., M 1924. 1949/H/01 [2 items]. Called to the English Bar, G.I., M 1924.

STEWART, ROBERT RODGERS (b. 10 Oct. 1870) 2nd s. of John Stewart (decd.), of Breda Park, Newtownbreda, Belfast, and Sarah Dickson Rodgers; M 1909. 1912/T/12 [3 items].

STEWART, THOMAS (b. 27 Jan. 1863) 2nd s. of Thomas Stewart of Portrush, Co. Antrim, and Mary Stafford; M 1886. 1890/M/01 [5 items].

STOKES, HENRY JOHN (b. 29 May 1842) 3rd s. of William Stokes, M.D., late of Merrion Square, Dublin, and Mary Black; E 1881, M.T. T 1882. India Civil Service. 1889/M/03 [7 items]. He appears to have been admitted while an Indian civil servant. After his Call to the Irish Bar, he became a judge in Madras. Retired from India 1889. Died 1920. See the memoir by his grandson, Michael Purser, *Jellett, O'Brien, Purser and Stokes: Seven Generations, Four Families* (Dublin: Prejmer Verlag, 2004), 124-9.

STOKES, NOEL NICHOLAS JOHN (b. 24 November 1909) only surviving s. of Nicholas Joseph Stokes, of Hollywood, Rathangan, Co. Kildare, and Josephine Leary; M.A. (Cantab); B.A. (N.U.I.); M 1932, I.T. M 1931. 1941/T/05 [5 items].

STONE, HERBERT KENWYN (b. 29 March 1886) eld. s. of Herbert Cockerton Stone (decd.), of Trinidad, British West Indies, and Eliza Gibbon; B.A., LL.B. (T.C.D.); M 1905, L.I. M 1905. 1908/T/12 [3 items].

STONES, LIAM LAURENCE JOHN (b. 9 June 1946) 2nd s. of Dr. Laurence Stones, LDS, of 102 Westbourne Road, Sheffield, Yorkshire, and Patricia C.H. Ennis; B.C.L. (N.U.I.); M 1965. 1968/M/24 [1 item].

STREET, JAMES HOWARD ALGERNON (b. 25 Oct. 1881) only s. of James Henry Street (decd.), of Stoneleigh, Exmouth, Devon, and Mary Street; M 1930; I.T. T 1922; [previously called to English Bar, M 1924] 1931/E/01 [3 items]. S.C., 20 June 1939. Author of *The Law relating to Local Government* (Dublin: Stationery Office, 1955). Author also of 'Street on Ultra Vires', i.e. *A Treatise on the Doctrine of Ultra Vires, based on the work of Seward Brice* (London, 1930); of *The Law of Gaming* [with Notes] (London, 1937); and of the contract section in Odgers' *Laws of England.*

STRITCH, ANDREW O'QUAELLEY RUSSELL (b. 29 April 1869) eld. s. of John Russell Stritch of 17 North Great Georges Street, Dublin, and E.L. Seymour; M 1887. 1890/T/07 [7 items].

STRITCH, JOHN RUSSELL (b. 20 Oct 1843) eld. s. of Andrew John Russell Stritch, R.M., of Castlebar Co. Mayo, and Margaret Gray; B.A. (T.C.D.); M 1867; M.T. H 1869. 1870/M/7 [2 items]. Went Connaught Circuit. Q.C., 30 June 1894. In his youth 'the very counterpart of a Greek athlete – the perfect type of compact and graceful masculinity'. Chair of Law at King's Inns. J.P. Died 1903. Obituary, *I.L.T. & S.J.*, xxxvii (1903), 134.

STRONGE, HERBERT CECIL (b. 3 Jan. 1875) eld. s. of S.E. Stronge, M.A., Head Inspector of National Schools, of Dundrum, Co. Dublin, and M.L. Moorhead; B.A. (T.C.D.); M 1897. 1900/M/08 [3 items]. K.C. (N.I.), H. 1929. Knighted, 1930. Chief Justice of Tonga, 1917-25; of the Leeward Islands, 1925-31; and of Cyprus, 1931-8. Retired to South Africa, where he died, 22 Aug. 1963; *Who's Who.*

STUART, ALAN LENOX CONYNGHAM (b. 18 July 1863) young. s. of Robert Arthur Walter Charles Stuart (decd.), Lieut.-Colonel, Madras Army, of Kingstown, Co. Dublin, and Louisa Frances Burton; B.A., LL.B. (R.U.I.); E 1886. 1890/H/01 [7 items].

STUART, ARCHIBALD (b. 17 June 1894) only s. of William Stuart, J.P., of Ballymoney, Co. Antrim, and Mary McMaster. 1924/M/06 [2 items]. Died Jan. 1969.

STUBBS, WILLIAM COTTER (b. 19 Feb. 1862) only s. of the Revd. John William Stubbs, D.D., Senior Fellow, T.C.D., of Fortwilliam, Dublin, and 39 Upper Fitzwilliam Street, Dublin, and Catherine Louisa Cotter; B.A. (T.C.D.); M 1882, M.T. M 1883. 1885/T/06 [6 items]. Land Commission. Author (with James Sinclair Baxter) of *Irish Forms and Precedents being a Supplementary Volume to 'Encyclopedia of Forms and Precedents'* (London: Butterworth, 1910). Died 4 Oct. 1926. Obituary, *I.L.T. & S.J.*, lx (1926), 253.

STUDDERT, JONAS WALLER (B. 18 Aug. 1857) eld. s. of Major Charles Washington Studdert, J.P., of Crag Moher, Co. Clare, and Kate Waller; B.A. (T.C.D.); H 1880, G.I. H 1882. 1883/H/02* [5 items]. Died unmarried 18 Jan. 1889. *Burke's Irish Family Records* (1976), 1070.

SUBBAROW, PANGULURI VENKATA (b. 28 Nov. 1892) 2nd s. of Panguluri Ankamma of Zammulapalem, Madras, India; M 1913. 1916/T/13 [2 items].

SUFFERN, WILLIAM (b. 17 March 1854) only s. of John Suffern of Windsor, Belfast, and Emily McBride; LL.B. (T.C.D.); M 1875, M.T. M 1877. 1879/E/09 [6 items]. Author of *The Law relating to the Compulsory Purchase and Sale of Lands in Ireland, under the provisions of the Irish Railways and Land Clauses Acts* (Dublin: 1882).

SUGARS, JOHN CHARLES (b. 1 March 1875) 2nd s. of John Colvan Sugars, M.D., of Dungannon, Co.Tyrone, and Mary Morrison; B.A. (T.C.D.); M 1909. 1910/M/02 [3 items].

SUGRUE, Captain TIMOTHY (b. 28 Jan. 1884) young. s. of Michael Sugrue (decd.), of Camp, Tralee, Co. Kerry, and Anne Browne; M 1925. 1928/T/09 [2 items].

SULLIVAN, ALEXANDER MARTIN (b. 15 May 1830) 2nd s. of Daniel Sullivan of Amiens Street, Dublin, and Catherine Baylor; E 1873, I.T. E 1874. 1876/M/09 [7 items]. Journalist; editor of *The Nation*. Special call to the English Bar at the Inner Temple, Nov. 1877. Died 17 Oct. 1884. *Burke's Irish Family Records* (1976), 1079. See *D.N.B.* and Henry Boylan, *Dictionary of Irish Biography*.

SULLIVAN, ALEXANDER M. (b. 14 Jan. 1871) 2nd s. of Alexander Martin Sullivan (decd.), B.L., M.P., of Clapham, Surrey, and Francis Donovan; M 1889. 1892/T/07 [6 items]. Munster Circuit. K.C., 24 June 1908. 3rd Serjeant, 20 July 1912. 1st Serjeant, 29 Oct. 1919. Called to the English Bar in 1899, Sullivan practised in both countries until 1922, and thereafter in England until 1949. Attacked at Tralee, and near Millstreet, 9 and 27 Jan. 1920: see *I.L.T. & S.J.*, liv (1920), 17, 32. Resigned (July 1956) as an Honorary Bencher of King's Inns, following censure by the Benchers, after 34 members of the Bar (including Seán Hooper and Felix H. Sherry, who had also agitated the matter in letters to *The Irish Times*) had signed a Petition (see panel opposite) calling for him to be removed as a Bencher and disbarred because he had disclosed to René MacColl, author of *Roger Casement: A New Judgment* (1956), a conversation with Casement tending to establish that the latter was a homosexual: see Benchers' Minute Book, 1939-57, 414-46, at pp 445-6. Died 9 Jan. 1959. Obituary, *I.L.T. & S.J.*, xciii (1959), 31-2. Author of three volumes of reminiscences, *Old Ireland: Reminiscences of an Irish K.C.* (1927), *Practice at the Irish Bar* (1936) and *The Last Serjeant* (1952), the last title reflecting his status as the last First Serjeant at the Irish Bar; also an article, 'The last forty years of the Irish Bar', in *Cambridge Law Journal*, iii (1929), 365-75. See: *Who's Who*; *D.N.B.*; *Burke's Irish Family Records* (1976), 1079; Henry Boylan, *Dictionary of Irish Biography*; and Louis McRedmond (ed.), *Modern Irish Lives*. Tall and neatly bearded, Sullivan appears in Sir John Lavery's painting of the Casement trial, a painting which Sullivan was instrumental in procuring for King's Inns, where it now hangs: see Wanda Ryan-Smolin, *King's Inns Portraits* (1992), 12-13. He appears as 'Bones Sullivan' in the caricature of 'The King's Serjeants' by C. Norman Kough [q.v.], in A.R. Hart, *A History of the King's Serjeants at Law in Ireland* (Dublin, 2000), Plate 23. V.T.H. Delany [q.v.], in his article 'The Bench and Bar in Ireland', names Sullivan first in a list of eight of 'those who were at the forefront of their profession during the period'. Ronan Keane has revised the entry for Serjeant Sullivan in the *Oxford DNB* (2004).

SULLIVAN, DANIEL FINBARR FRANCIS (b. 25 Jan. 1941) 3rd s. of John J. Sullivan, farmer, of Kealkill, Bantry, Co. Cork, and Catherine Donovan; B.A. (N.U.I.); M 1964. 1967/T/04 [1 item].

SULLIVAN, DENIS BAYLOR (b. 5 April 1843) young. s. of Daniel Sullivan of Bantry, Co. Cork, and Catherine Baylor; T 1867, I.T. M 1869. 1873/T/3 [2 items]. Q.C., June 1889. Grand-uncle of Maurice Healy, mentioned in *The Old Munster Circuit*.

SULLIVAN, DENIS BRENDAN (b. 5 Sept. 1883) 3rd s. of Denis B. Sullivan (decd.), of 56 Mountjoy Square, Dublin, and Harriett Cullinane; T 1912. 1913/H/03 [2 items]. Appt. District Justice, Nov. 1922: *I.L.T. & S.J.*, lvi (4 Nov. 1922), 266.

SULLIVAN, EDWARD (b. 27 Sept. 1852) eld. s. of the Rt. Hon. Edward Sullivan, Master of the Rolls in Ireland, of Dublin, and Bessie Josephine Bailey; T 1875, M.T. T 1877. 1879/M/04 [6 items]. Uncle of Edward Sullivan Murphy [q.v.]. See Fergal McGrath, *Father John Sullivan S.J.* (1941).

SULLIVAN, JOSEPH (b. 19 Sept. 1877) eld. s. of D.B. Sullivan, Q.C., of 56 Mountjoy Square, Dublin, and Harriet Cullinane; M 1896. 1899/T/09 [2 items]. Author of a commentary on *The Irish Land Acts, 1903 and 1904* (Dublin, 1906).

SULLIVAN, MICHAEL PATRICK (b. 26 May 1912) 2nd s. of Thomas Sullivan, of Grouse Lodge, Cornamona, Co. Galway, and Mary Dunne (decd.); M 1950. 1954/T/11 [2 items].

SULLIVAN, MICHAEL PAUL (b. 6 July 1885) eld. s. of James Sullivan, of College Road, Cork, and Margaret Ahearn; B.A., LL.B. (N.U.I.); M 1924. 1927/E/01 [2 items].

SULLIVAN, PATRICK DONALD (b. 13 Oct. 1862) eld. s. of W.K. Sullivan, LL.D., President, Queen's College, Cork, and Frances Hennessy; M.A. (R.U.I.); M 1884. 1888/E/03 [5 items].

SULLIVAN, TIMOTHY (b. 25 Aug. 1874) 3rd s. of Timothy Daniel Sullivan, MP, of 1 Belvedere Place, Dublin, and Catherine Healy; M 1892. 1895/M/03 [6 items]. Munster Circuit. K.C., 27 Feb. 1918. Bencher 1921. Appt. first President of the High Court, 5 June 1924; Chief Justice of the Irish Free State, 12 Dec. 1936. Retired 1946. Died 1949. *Who's Who*. Mentioned by Maurice Healy (his cousin) in *The Old Munster Circuit*, 230-1. Portraits by Maev Sullivan (his wife, a daughter of Tim Healy) and Seán O'Sullivan in King's Inns: see Wanda Ryan-Smolin, *King's Inns Portraits* (1992), 65- 6. Portrait photograph in *I.L.T. & S.J.*, lxii (1938).

The detractors of Serjeant Sullivan

To the Benchers of the Honourable Society of the Kings Inns

13th April 1956

The Memorial of the undersigned members of the Bar Sheweth:-

1. That your Memorialists respectfully submit to the Benchers of the Honourable Society of the Kings Inns a copy of the Irish Times dated the 11th April, 1956 containing a letter signed A.M. Sullivan who is known to us and to the public to be Alexander M. Sullivan Serjeant a member of the Bar of Ireland and an Honorary Bencher of your Honourable Society.

2. That it is the opinion of us your Memorialists that the publication of this letter which is portion of a course of conduct by him involving the disclosure of matters of a confidential nature purporting to have been obtained by him as Counsel from his client constitutes gross and dishonourable professional misconduct.

We respectfully pray that the name of the said Alexander M. Sullivan be removed from the Roll of Benchers of your Honourable Society and that he be disbarred from the Bar of Ireland.

Desmond Bell	Noel Hartnett	Patrick Bourke	James Henry
Edward Fahy	Felix H. Sherry	Thomas J. Conolly	T.F. Donnelly
Ua Raig[h]uille	Seán Butler	James S. McGivern	John Kenny
James P. O'Reilly	Samuel V. Kirwan	E.T. Sweetman	P.A. Ó Síocháin
J.S. Geraghty	Patrick Connolly	Kevin M. Kenny	T.A. Doyle
Seán Hooper	John V. Coleman	Seán MacD. Fawsitt	James R. Heavey
Brian Walsh	Errnest M. Wood	Oliver D. Gogarty	K O'Shaughnessy
Dermot J. Hanly		James I. McGuire	Eoin Ryan
H.A. McDevitt			P. Noel Ryan
Noel A. Macdonald			

SULLIVAN, WILLIAM (b. 21 Feb. 1860) 2nd s. of the Rt. Hon. Sir Edward Sullivan, Bart., late Lord Chancellor of Ireland, of Dublin, and Bessie Josephine Baily; M 1882, M.T. M. 1884. 1885/T/05 [5 items]. 3rd (and last) Baronet. Lieutenant, 4th Battalion, Royal Inniskilling Fusiliers. Died 7 July 1937. *Who's Who*.

SUTHERLAND, JOHN JOSEPH (b. 26 Nov. 1868) 4th s. of William Sutherland (decd.), of Rosemount, Co. Cork, and Sarah Cooke; H 1895. 1898/H/08 [4 items]. Died 1 April 1952.

SUTHERLAND, PETER DENIS WILLIAM (b. 25 April 1946) eld. s. of William George Sutherland, insurance broker, of Hillmount, The Hill, Monkstown, Co. Dublin, and Barbara Nealon; B.C.L. (N.U.I.); M 1964. 1968/T/14 [1 item]. S.C., 6 Oct. 1980. Attorney-General 1981-2, 1982-4. Irish member of the European Commission, 1985-9. Appt. Director-General of GATT, June 1993. Has served as head of the World Trade Organisation; and chairman, *inter alia*, of AIB, British Petroleum, and Goldman Sachs International. Hon. K.C.M.G. (Dec. 2003). Listed in the 1984, 1991 and 1999 editions of Maureen Cairnduff, *Who's Who in Ireland* [in 1991 and 1999 with photographs]. See also: *Who's Who*; and Louis McRedmond (ed.), *Modern Irish Lives*.

SUTTON, RALPH GERARD (b. 9 May 1924) 2nd s. of Francis Harding Sutton (decd.), merchant, of Cork, and Una Dorgan; B.A. (U.C.C.); M 1944. 1948/T/14 [2 items]. S.C. 1 March 1968. Lecturer at University College Cork. In 1967 'took fur' (rather than silk) as a Fine Gael member of Cork Corporation: for anecodes and a photograph, see 'Ralph Sutton S.C., called to the Bar, July 1948, reminisces on 50 years at the Irish Bar', in *The Bar Review*, vol. 4 (3: December 1998), 152-4. Died 24 Nov. 1999. Obituary [with photograph], *The Irish Times*, 4 Dec. 1999.

SWAYNE, EDMUND AUGUSTINE (b. 31 Oct. 1880) 4th s. of John Broderick Swayne of Glenbervie, Bray, Co. Wicklow, and Mary Fitzgerald; T 1908. 1908/M/01 [2 items]. Leinster Circuit. K.C., 27 Feb. 1918. Died 5 July 1925. Obituary, *I.L.T. & S.J.*, lix (1925), 166-7.

SWEENEY, DERMOT (b. 27 July 1932) 2nd s. of William Sweeney, engineer, of 26 Philipsburgh Avenue, Dublin, and Margaret Cregan; B.A., B. Comm. (N.U.I.); M 1957. 1960/T/05 [2 items].

SWEENEY, JAMES AUGUSTINE (b. 25 March 1883) 3rd s. of James Sweeney (decd.), of Dungloe, Co. Donegal, and Sarah Gallagher; B.A. (T.C.D. and R.U.I.), 1927. 1927/M/26x [2 items]. Indian Civil Service. Died 6 Nov. 1945. Obituary, *I.L.T. & S.J.*, lxxix (1945), 279.

SWEENEY, JAMES PETER (b. 2 March 1913) 2nd s. of Maurice Sweeney, of Rockbarton, Salthill, Galway, and Kathleen Moran; M 1940. 1944/T/09 [2 items].

SWEENEY, JOHN (b. 5 Oct. 1916) 2nd s. of Edward Sweeney, farmer, of Achonry, Ballymote, Co. Sligo, and Catherine Brennan; M.A. (Hons.); M 1954. 1960/M/10 [3 items].

SWEENEY, MICHAEL JOHN (b. 13 May 1896) eld. s. of James Sweeney (decd.), of Magdalene Road, Kells, Co. Meath, and Julia Nolan; M.Sc. (N.U.I.); M 1930. 1933/M/04 [2 items]. Judge of the Circuit Court (North-East Circuit, 1956-9; Midland, 1959-66).

SWEENY, FRANCIS T. (b. 26 Feb. 1868) young. s. of Denis Sweeny, of 3 Hayes Terrace, Kilkenny, and Elizabeth Dollard; B.A.; T 1902. 1905/E/02 [3 items].

SWEETMAN, EDMUND THOMAS (b. 15 May 1912) 3rd s. of R.M. Sweetman, of Derrybawn, Glendalough, Co. Wicklow, and Kathleen Aliaga Kelly; M 1931. 1934/M/08 [2 items]. Member of the Bar Council. Senator, April 1948-51. Member of the Irish Land Commission. Died Dec. 1968. *Burke's Irish Family Records* (1976), 1081.

SWEETMAN, JAMES MICHAEL (b. 5 Nov. 1872) 3rd s. of Hugh Sweetman (decd.) of Roebuck Hall, Co. Dublin, and Gertrude Blackney; M.A., LL.B.; M 1896. 1899/E/02 [3 items]. K.C., 28 Nov. 1914. High Sheriff of Co. Kildare, Jan. 1916. Died 31 July 1939. Obituary, *I.L.T. & S.J.*, lxxiii (1939), 229, 344.

SWEETMAN, JOHN OLIVER JOSEPH (b. 16 Jan. 1936) eld. s. of John Walter Sweetman, of Desmond, Killiney, Co. Dublin, and Olivia Dudley; M 1955. 1959/T/05 [2 items]. S.C., 2 Oct. 1978. Died 27 Jan. 2005.

SWEETMAN, ROGER (b. 15 Aug. 1874) 4th s. of Hugh Sweetman of 45 Raglan Road, Dublin, and Gertrude Black[ney]; H 1895. 1898/H/06 [4 items]. Sinn Féin M.P. for North Wexford, 1918-21. Died 20 May 1954. *Burke's Irish Family Records* (1976), 1080.

SWEETMAN, WILLIAM (b. 6 Dec. 1903) 4th s. of John Sweetman (decd.), of Kells, Co. Meath, and Agnes Hanly (decd.); B. Comm.; M 1934. 1937/M/15 [2 items]. Editor of *The Irish Press*. District Justice.

SWIFTE, ERNEST GODWIN MEADE (b. 14 Aug. 1870) eld. s. of Ernest Godwin Swifte, Metropolitan Police Magistrate, of 18 Fitzwilliam Square, Dublin, and Frances Coddington; B.A. (Oxon); M 1893. 1896/M/09 [4 items]. His like-named father was the Dublin Police magistrate, K.C. 1911, and knighted in 1921. The son, a country gentleman resident at Foulksrath Castle (which in 1947 he presented to the Irish Government for use as a youth hostel) and Swifte's Heath, both in Co. Kilkenny, was educated at Shrewsbury and University College, Oxford, In 1903 his address in *Thom's Directory* was The Palace, Ispahan, Persia. Major, Royal Artillery and Royal Tank Corps. Died unmarried 17 Aug. 1957. *Burke's Irish Family Records*, 1083.

SYMES, ROBERT WARREN (b. 19 July 1841) eld. s. of Robert Symes of Wingfield, Co. Wexford and Ellen Dowse; B.A. (T.C.D.); H 1865, M.T. E 1866. 1868/E/5 [4 items].

SYNNOTT, WALTER JOSEPH (b. 23 Jan. 1861) 4th s. of Thomas Synnott, J.P., of Innismore, Glenageary, Co. Dublin, and Catherine Dunne; H 1882, M.T. M 1883. 1884/M/13 [6 items]. Disbarred on bankruptcy, 1894. Married Frances, formerly the wife of Charles Peter Danby, music hall comedian. Later a solicitor in London. Died 18 Oct. 1924. *Burke's Irish Family Records* (1976), 1095.

TALBOT, BERTRAM HENRY (b. 22 March 1849) eld. s. of Marcus Talbot (decd.) of Strasburg [?], Co. Clare and Elizabeth Lardner; B.A. (Queen's College, Galway); H 1870, G.I. E 1871. 1872/M/8 [5 items].

TARLETON, FRANCIS ALEXANDER (b. 28 April 1842) 4th s. of the Revd. John Tarleton, Rector of Tyholland in Co. Monaghan and Judith Catherine Falkiner; B.A. (T.C.D.); T 1862, M.T. M 1866. 1868/T/2 [4 items].

TARPEY, WILLIAM B. (b. 18 Dec. 1857) eld. s. of Hugh Tarpey, alderman, J.P., of 51 Upper Mount Street, Dublin, and Jane Brennan; E 1878, M.T. T 1878. 1881/M/09 [6 items].

TAYLOR, HENRY (b. 19 June 1849) 2nd s. of Thomas H. Taylor of 36 Wellington Road, Dublin, and Mary Terry; B.A. (T.C.D.); E 1872, M.T. M 1873. 1876/H/06 [2 items].

TAYLOR, HUGH STOWELL BROWN (b. 21 June 1883) 2nd s. of the Revd. David Alexander Taylor of Bertha House, Belfast, and Dora Brown; B.A. (T.C.D.); M 1904. 1908/H/03 [2 items].

TAYLOR, JOHN FRANCIS (b. 13 Feb. 1853) 3rd s. of John Taylor (decd.), gentleman, of Riverstown, Co. Sligo, and Maria Feely; M 1879, M.T. T 1880. 1882/M/11 [7 items]. Connaught Circuit. Q.C., 1 July 1893. Liberal Home Ruler. Contributor to the *Manchester Guardian*. Died 7 Nov. 1902. Obituary, *I.L.T. & S.J.*, xxxvi (1902), 455. Mentioned in James Meenan (ed.), *Centenary History of Lit. and Hist. Soc. of U.C.D.*

TAYLOR, WILLIAM CHARLES (b. 7 April 1850) 3rd s. of George Taylor, engineer and mine owner, of Cadiz, Spain, and Glenbrook, Co. Cork, and Mary Anne Scannell; M.A., LL.B (Queen's College Cork); T 1874, M.T. E 1873. 1877/E/02 [5 items].

TEELING, CHARLES HAMILTON (b. 19 April 1841) eld. s. of John Francis Teeling, solicitor, Assistant Registrar, Court of Bankruptcy, Local Inspector of the Courts Marshalsea, of Mountjoy Place, Dublin and Eliza O'Callaghan; M 1863, M.T. M 1865. 1868/E/4 [2 items]. Munster Circuit. Q.C., 30 June 1894. Died 4 Sept. 1921. Obituary, *I.L.T. & S.J.*, lv (1921), 225.

TEELING, LUKE ALEXANDER (b. 9 Feb. 1856) young. s. of Charles George Teeling (decd.) of 1 Upper Sherrard Street, Dublin, and Anna McCarthy; B.A. (T.C.D.); M 1878, M.T. T 1880. 1881/M/14 [7 items]. Accountant-General of the Supreme Court of Judicature, 1896-1921. Died 2 Nov. 1943. Portrait in the Kildare Street and University Club. *Burke's Landed Gentry of Ireland* (1958), 684.

TEELING, SAMUEL GEORGE (b. 14 Oct. 1875) only s. of Samuel James Teeling, agent, Bank of Ireland, of Drogheda, Co. Louth, and Marie Louise Foley; cand. bach. (T.C.D.); M 1894. 1898/H/03 [5 items].

TEELING, THEODORE FRANCIS (b. 1 July 1889) 3rd s. of Captain Bartholomew John Teeling of Hotel d'Allemagne, Via Condotti, Rome, Italy, and Theodora Louisa Lane [Clarke] (decd.); M 1909. 1912/T/08 [2 items]. Prisoner-of-war in Germany, 1915: *I.L.T. & S.J.*, xlix (1915), 115.

TEEVAN, THOMAS (b. 29 Nov. 1902) eld. s. of Dr. Francis James Teevan (decd.), of Sunbury Gardens, Dartry Road, Dublin, and Anne Teresa O'Brien; E 1936. 1936/T/09 [3 items]. S.C., 7 March 1946. Attorney-General, July 1953-Jan. 1954. Judge of the High Court, 1954-71. Died 1976. See *The Irish Times*, 1 Feb. 1954, 20 Feb. 1976.

TERRY, PATRICK AUGUSTINE (b. 10 March 1920) youngest s. of Augustine P. Terry, of Abbeyside, Dungarvan, Co. Waterford, and Mary Rose O'Grady; B.A., B.Comm., LL.B; M 1952. 1955/T/04 [2 items].

THALPASAYE, PANGULURY SESHA (b. 15 May 1895) 3rd s. of Pangulury Venkata Narasimham of Vetapalem, Guntur District, Madras, India; M 1913. 1916/T/05 [2 items].

THOMAS, IAN DAVID (b. 16 March 1932) 2nd s. of Evan Morgan Thomas, civil servant, of 305 Western Avenue, Llandaff, Cardiff, Glamorgan, Wales and Nancy Watkin; B.A. (T.C.D.); M 1951. 1961/M/07 [2 items].

THOMAS, RICHARD WILLIAM (b. 26 March 1888) eld. s. of Stephen Sylvester Thomas of Delhi, India, Clerk in Holy Orders, and Sarah Purser Biggs; Mod. B.A. (T.C.D.); M 1909. 1912/T/06 [2 items].

THOMPSON, HERBERT MARSHALL (b. 6 Aug. 1873) 4th s. of the Revd. William Thompson, M.A., of Cushendall, Co. Antrim, and Sarah Margaret Sprott; B.A. (T.C.D.); M 1899. 1902/M/04 [3 items]. North-East Circuit. K.C., 20 Feb. 1920. Recorder of Belfast and County Court Judge for Antrim, 1921-1941. Mentioned in J.C. MacDermott, *An Enriching Life*, 167. Died 11 Feb. 1945. Obituary, *I.L.T. & S.J.*, lxxix (1945), 40; *Who's Who*.

THOMPSON, ISAAC (b. 10 Jan. 1848) 4th s. of Isaac Thompson (decd.) of Knockduff, Co. Armagh, and Mary Henry; M.A., LL.D. (R.U.I. / Q.C.B.); M 1887. 1891/H/03 [8 items].

THOMPSON, JOHN GAMBLE (b. 26 Feb. 1857) only s. of William Thompson, J.P., of 87 Kenilworth Square, Rathgar, Dublin, and Isabella Wood; LL.B. (T.C.D.); M 1876, L.I. T 1879. 1880/M/01 [5 items]. Reid Professor, T.C.D., 1894-9. Died 1932. Obituary, *I.L.T. & S.J.*, lxvi (28 May 1932), 133. Author of *The Law of Criminal Procedure in Ireland* (Dublin, 1899)

THOMPSON, ROBERT WADE (b. 22 April 1845) eld. surv. s. of Thomas Thompson of 95 Leeson Street, Dublin, and Martha Wallace; B.A. (T.C.D.); T 1871, I.T. M 1868. 1873/T/11* [4 items].

THORNHILL, THOMAS (b. 12 Dec. 1867) 2nd s. of the Revd. Jonathan Thornhill (decd.), M.A., of Barr Parsonage, Co. Tyrone, and Christina Leech; LL.B.; M 1891. 1894/T/07 [7 items]. Photographed as President of the Irish Rugby Football Union in the *Tatler* (1903). Died 1939. Obituary, *I.L.T. & S.J.*, lxxiii (11 March 1939), 77, 116.

THORNTON, EDWARD (b. 24 Dec. 1899) 4th s. of Patrick Thornton, of Toomore, Foxford, Co. Mayo, and Mary O'Brien; M 1928. 1931/T/02 [2 items].

THOUNG, MAUNG KYAW (b. 14 Aug. 1908) young. s. of U. Ngwe Laing, A.T.M., of Churchill Road, Rangoon, Burma, and Mah Hla Ohn; H 1929. 1931/M/01 [2 items].

TIAH, EUGENE (b. 11 June 1929) 2nd s. of Sultan Kariman Tiah, of Freeport Village, CalapichaiM.A., Caroni, Trinidad, British West Indies, and Jasocha Tiah; M 1956. 1960/M/07 [2 items].

TIERNEY, HERBERT JOSEPH STANISLAUS (b. 13 Nov. 1888) 2nd s. of Christopher Tierney of 14 Rostrevor Terrace, Rathgar, Co. Dublin, and Frances Healy; B.A. (R.U.I.); M 1907. 1910/H/02 [3 items]. Member successively of the 'Pals' Battalion and of the Cheshire Regiment. Died in Mesopotamia, 9 April 1916. Photograph (right) in Henry Hanna, *The Pals at Suvla Bay* (1917), 235. A.P. Quinn's forthcoming volume, *Wigs and Guns*, which deals with the 25 Irish barristers who fell in the Great War, includes some of Herbert Tierney's letters. [Name on the Bar War Memorial; also on the Memorial at Basra].

TIERNEY, MARTIN JOHN (b. 27 Dec. 1933) 3rd s. of Dr. Michael Tierney, of University Lodge, Donnybrook, Co. Dublin, and Eibhlin MacNeill; M 1952. 1957/M/08 [2 items].

TIGHE, MACARTAN HUBERT (b. 24 May 1880) 5th s. of John M. Tighe, J.P., of 8 Belvedere Place, Dublin, and Honoria Burke; B.A. (R.U.I.); M 1907. 1910/T/09 [3 items]. Captain, Royal Dublin Fusiliers. Crown prosecutor in Dar-es-Salaam. Died 13 Aug. 1929. Obituary, *I.L.T. & S.J.*, lxiii (1929), 197.

TIGHE, ROBERT DOLPHIN (b. 20 Sept. 1877) 2nd s. of Thomas Tighe, D.L., J.P., of The Heath, Co. Mayo, and Marie Antoinette Dolphin; M 1897. 1900/T/04 [3 items]. K.C. Emigrated to Canada. Member of the Bars of Nova Scotia and Alberta. Died 2 Feb. 1942. Obituary, *I.L.T. & S.J.*, lxxvi (1942), 55.

TIMLIN, JOHN WILLIAM (b. 20 May 1918) only s. of Dominick Timlin, of Rehins, Ballina, Co. Mayo, and Nora Finnerty; B.A. (N.U.I.); M 1937. File includes letter from Timlin. 1941/M/16 [3 items].

TISDALL, GEORGE ARCHIBALD (b. 12 March 1860) only s. of William Tisdall, of Ballyray, Navan, Co. Meath, and Frances O'Connor; B.A. (T.C.D.); M 1879, M.T. M 1881. 1882/M/09 [6 items].

TOBIAS, THEODORE CRONHELM (b. 7 April 1876) eld. surv. s. of Matthew Tobias, solicitor, of 7 Eustace Street, Dublin, and Elizabeth Cronhelm; Sch. B.A. (T.C.D.); M1898. 1901/M/09 [3 items]. Under-Treasurer at King's Inns. Died 28 Aug. 1959. Obituary, *I.L.T. & S.J.*, xciii (12 Sept. 1959), 217.

TODD, ANDREW (b. 22 Sept. 1852) 4th s. of William Todd of Fyfin, Co. Tyrone, and Margaret Henderson; LL.B (Q.C.G.); H 1877, G.I. T 1878. 1880/M/02 [5 items]. North-West Circuit. K.C., March 1904. Appt. County Court Judge for Tyrone, 4 Sept. 1909; Recorder of Londonderry, 1912. Died 16 June 1920. Obituary, *I.L.T. & S.J.*, liv (1920), 148.

TODD, ROBERT (b. 30 March 1856) 2nd s. of the Revd. Andrew Todd of Finvoy, Ballymoney, Co. Antrim, and Elizabeth McRay; M.A. (Q.C.B.); H 1881, I.T. E 1882. 1884/T/02x [6 items]. North-East Circuit. Died 5 Aug. 1905. Obituary, *I.L.T. & S.J.*, xxxix (1905), 243.

TODD, WILLIAM FRANCIS (b. 27 Sept. 1869) eld. s. of John Todd, late of Tankardstown, Queen's Co., and Mary Morton; B.A. (T.C.D.); H 1894. 1898/H/01 [4 items].

TOMBE, GEORGE GORDON (b. 12 March 1855) eld. s. of Gordon Evelyn Tombe, J.P., of Bromley, Greystones, Co. Wicklow, and Grace Joy; B.A. (Oxford); M 1879, I.T. M 1881. 1883/M/07 [6 items].

TOOMEY, WILLIAM (b. 25 Oct. 1877) 2nd s. of William Gosselin Toomey (decd.), LL.D., of Ardmore, Bray, Co. Wicklow, and Edith Harte; E 1897. 1900/M/07 [3 items]. Died 28 Oct. 1944. Obituary, *I.L.T. & S.J.*, lxxviii (1944), 279.

TOOMEY, WILLIAM CHRISTOPHER (b. 27 Nov. 1906) eld. s. of Denis Toomey, of 42 Iona Crescent, Glasnevin, Dublin, and Hannah Roche; M 1944. 1948/M/07 [2 items].

TOOMEY, WILLIAM GOSSELIN (b. 27 Feb. 1846) 3rd s. of Frank Toomey (decd.), solicitor, of 75 Herbert Street, Dublin, and Jane Kelly; LL.D. (T.C.D.); H 1891. [solicitor]. 1891/M/15 [4 items].

TORMEY, ANTOINETTE CATHERINE (b. 3 Jan. 1946) only d. of Thomas Tormey, book maker, of Auburn, Stillorgan Road, Blackrock, Co. Dublin, and Catherine Banks; B.C.L. (N.U.I.); M 1964. 1967/M/05 [2 items].

TORRENS, JOHN (b. 20 Oct. 1849) eld. s. of James Torrens, solicitor, of Edenmore, Co. Antrim, and Sarah Gelston; B.A. (Oxford); M 1874, M.T. M 1876. 1877/M/09 [5 items].

TOWNSEND, WILLIAM RICHARD (b. 8 Dec. 1869) 3rd s. of Edward Townsend, Professor of Engineering at Queen's College, Galway, and Judith Townsend; B.A. (T.C.D.); M 1890. 1894/M/02 [5 items]. Attorney-General of the Gambia, 1902-6; Chief Minister there, 1906-12; Attorney-General of the Gold Coast, 1912-17. Lost at sea, 28 Nov. 1917. Obituary, *I.L.T. & S.J.*, li (1917), 296.

TOWNSHEND, GEORGE (b. 14 June 1876) eld. s. of Charles Uniacke Townshend, of 10 Burlington Road, Dublin, and Anna M. Roberts; B.A. (Oxford); M 1899. 1903/M/05 [3 items]. Archdeacon of Clonfert. Died 25 March 1957. *Burke's Irish Family Records* (1976), 1118.

TRACY, HENRY (B. 18 Aug 1844) 3rd s. of William Samuel Tracy, R.M., of Bray, Co. Wicklow, and Margaret Simpson; B.A. (T.C.D.); H 1867; M.T. M 1868. 1870/M/1 [2 items].

TRAILL, JAMES ANTHONY (b. 7 Aug. 1870) 2nd s. of Anthony Traill, F.T.C.D., L.L.D, of Ballybough, Co. Antrim, and Catharine Moore; B.A. (T.C.D.); M 1889. 1892/T/08 [7 items]. Died 11 Nov. 1901. *Burke's Irish Family Records* (1976), 1127.

TRAILL, Major ROBERT GAYER (b. 21 Nov. 1839) 2nd s. of William Traill (decd.) of Ballylough House, Co. Antrim, and Louisa French; H 1893. 1895/T/07 [3 items]. Major, Yorkshire Regiment. Died 4 March 1908. *Burke's Irish Family Records* (1976), 1127.

TRAINOR, JAMES PATRICK (b. 14 Oct. 1914) eld. s. of Owen Trainor, wine merchant, of 39 Ailesbury Road, Dublin, and Mary McArdle; B.A. (N.U.I.); T 1950. 1950/M/09 [2 items]. Justice of the Special Court, Cyprus. Judicial Commissioner, New Hebrides, 1960.

TRAVERS, CHARLES (b. 22 May 1883) 7th s. of Charles Travers, of Rossinver, Co. Leitrim, and Mary Clancy; M 1926. 1929/E/01 [2 items]. Died 26 May 1932. Obituary, *I.L.T. & S.J.*, lxvi (1932), 140.

TRAVERS, ROBERT (b. 19 May 1855) eld. s. of Robert Augustus Travers, J.P., of Timoleague, Co. Cork, and Alice Stewart; M 1876, M.T. E 1878. 1879/T/04 [6 items]. Registrar of the Probate Court. Died 2 April 1935. Obituary, *I.L.T. & S.J.*, lxix (13 April 1935), 102. *Burke's Irish Family Records* (1976), 1136-7.

TREACY, JOHN JOSEPH (b. 20 July 1879) only s. of Daniel J. Treacy, solicitor, of Belle-Vue, Mountrath, Queen's Co., and Mary J. Keon; M 1900. 1905/T/02 [2 items]. Died 7 Dec. 1947.

TRENCH, FREDERICK NETTERVILLE le POER (b. 12 Aug 1845) only s. of Admiral William Le Poer Trench of Ballinasloe, Co. Galway and Margaret Downing; B.A. (T.C.D.); M 1865, I.T. E 1867. 1868/M/4 [4 items]. Connaught Circuit. Q.C., 1885. Died 24 Nov. 1893. *Burke's Peerage* (107th ed., 2003), 792.

TRODDYN, PATRICK JAMES (b. 5 Aug. 1877) eld. s. of Patrick Troddyn (decd.), of Maghera, Co. Londonderry, and Sarah Murnin; M 1925. 1928/H/02 [2 items]. Died 25 Jan. 1933. Obituary, *I.L.T. & S.J.*, lxvii (1933), 37.

TUCKEY, DAVYS (b. 10 Oct. 1847) 2nd s. of Charles Henry Tuckey, of Borlem, Co. Carlow, and Ellen Tuckey; B.A. (T.C.D.); M 1868, M.T. H 1870. 1871/M/1 [2 items].

TUITE, ROBERT HENRY S. (b. ?), only son of Captain Mark Hardress S. Tuite, M.C., J.P., of 1 Trimleston Gardens, Booterstown, County Dublin. B.A., T.C.D. [0 items]. Papers not located at King's Inns. Called T 1946 (the last name of seventeen in the Call List of 24 June 1946): see S.C. Roll and *I.L.T. & S.J.*, lxxx (1946), 164.

TULLY, FARRELL JOSEPH (b. 9 Nov. 1895) 2nd s. of Nicholas Tully, of Bective Street, Kells, Co. Meath, and Honorah Curran; M 1927. Awarded Certificate of Honour. 1930/H/06 [2 items].

TUOHY, PATRICK JOHN (b. 21 June 1845) eld. s. of Patrick Tuohy (decd.) of Sundays Well, Cork, and Mary Anne O'Donoghue; H 1873, M.T. T 1875. Office of Board of Works, Dublin. 1883/T/01 [5 items].

TURBETT, IVAN JOLIFFE TUFNELL (b. 18 Dec. 1890) 3rd s. of Thomas Turbett of 2 Crosthwaite Park South, Kingstown, Dublin, and Florence Tufnell; M 1909. 1913/T/03 [2 items].

TUTHILL, ARTHUR HENDLEY (b. 12 April 1851) 4th s. of Charles Tuthill, Barrister-at-Law, of Newstead Abbey, Roebuck, Co. Dublin, and Sarah Taylor; T 1872, M.T. T 1872. 1875/E/07 [2 items].

TWEEDY, RICHARD THOMAS (b. 17 April 1856) 2nd s. of John Johnston Tweedy, M.A., solicitor, of 71 Lower Baggot Street, Dublin, and Amelia Griffin; H 1891. 1894/E/02 [6 items].

TWOHIG, JOSEPH PATRICK O'BRIEN (b. 31 May 1905) 4th s. of John Patrick Twohig, of 'Craigmillar', Clontarf, Dublin, and Ellen O'Brien; B.A. (T.C.D.); M 1921. 1926/T/04 [2 items]. Brigadier, Royal Inniskilling Fusiliers. Died 17 Aug. 1973. See *Who's Who*.

TWOHIG, MICHAEL JOSEPH O'BRIEN (b. 6 Aug. 1892) eld. s. of John Patrick Twohig, of 'Craigmillar', Clontarf, Dublin, and Ellen Moray O'Brien; T 1924. 1924/M/07 [2 items]. Colonel. King's Messenger, Foreign Office. Author of *Diplomatic Courier* (!960). Died 9 April 1971. See *Who's Who*.

TYNAN, GERALD MICHAEL JOSEPH (b. 11 June 1944) only s. of Dr. Gerald Tynan, medical doctor, of 9 The Crescent, Limerick, and Dr. Angela McMahon; B.C.L. (N.U.I.); M 1965. 1968/M/05 [1 item]. S.C., 13 March 1987.

TYNAN, PATRICK (b. 23 March 1912) 2nd s. of Michael Tynan, solicitor, of 41 William Street, Limerick, and Johanna Colbert; M 1931. 1935/T/06 [2 items].

TYRRELL, ROBERT LESLIE (b. 7 Feb. 1880) 2nd s. of Robert Yelverton Tyrrell, of 4 Sandford Terrace, Ranelagh, Co. Dublin, and Ada Shaw; B.A. (T.C.D.); M 1906. 1909/E/02 [2 items]. Professor at King's Inns. Examiner of Title, Land Commission. Died March 1961.

Ua DÁLAIGH, CEARBHALL: see O'DALY, CARROLL.

Ua DONNCHADHA, DAITHÍ GEARÓID (b. 20 Aug. 1938) eld. s. of Donnchadh L. Ua Donnchadha, District Justice, of St. Bernard's, Athlone, Co. Westmeath, and Sylvia Mary Woods; B.C.L. (N.U.I.); M 1959. 1963/M/01 [1 item].

UDENZWE, CHUKWUEMEKA (b. 1 Jan. 1924) 4th s. of Ogbuefi Edenwanu Udenzwe, farmer, of Enugwu-Ukwu, Nigeria, and Nwokana; B.A.; LLB; M 1955. 1959/M/11 [6 items].

UFFORD, GERARD JOMBO (b. 16 April 1930) eld. s. of Jombo Ufford, of Edem Ekpat, county of Uyo, Nigeria, and Cecilia News Inyang Udo; B.A. (U.C.C.); M 1957. 1961/M/11 [2 items].

UILEAS [Willis], OSCAR DIARMUID Mac CARTHA (b. 28 April 1903) only s. of R.H.A. Willis (decd.), of Killarney, Co. Kerry, and Jane M. Willis; M 1925. 1931/M/04 [2 items]. Died Feb. 1969.

UPINGTON, ARTHUR (b. 6 Jan. 1875) 2nd s. of Sir Thomas Upington (decd.), Attorney-General of Cape Colony, and Mary Guerin; H 1895. 1899/M/12 [3 items].

UPINGTON, BEAUCLERK (b. 12 Oct. 1872) eld. s. of Sir Thomas Upington, K.C.M.G., Attorney-General, Cape Town, and Mary Guerin; H 1895. 1898/E/04 [3 items]. Auditor of the College Historical Society, 1896-7. Advocate in the Cape Supreme Court. Died 1938. Obituary, *I.L.T. & S.J.*, lxxii (3 Sept. 1938), 261. Listed in Eric Rosenthal, *Southern African Dictionary of National Biography* (1966), 385.

UPWARD, GEORGE ALLEN (b. 20 Sept. 1863) only s. of George Upward of Monmouth, Monmouthshire, and Mary Allen; M 1884, M.T. T 1885. 1887/H/01 [7 items].

VANSTON, GEORGE THOMAS BARRETT (b. 31 May 1853) 2nd s. of John Davis Vanston, solicitor, of Hildon Park, Terenure, Dublin, and Catherine Biggs; LL.B. (T.C.D.); H 1876, G.I. T 1876. 1878/M/01 [6 items]. K.C., 24 June 1908. Legal adviser to the Local Government Board, Knighted 1917. Author of *The Grand Jury Laws of Ireland* (1883); *The Law of Public Health in Ireland* (1892, 1895; 2nd ed. 1913); *The Law relating to Local Government in Ireland* (2 vols.; 1899, 1905; 2nd ed. 1916, 1919); and *The Law relating to Municipal Boroughs in Ireland* (1905). Died 6 July 1923. Obituary, *I.L.T. & S.J.*, lvii (1923), 171. See *Who's Who*.

VARMA, BEPIN B. (b. 16 Dec. 1891) 4th s. of Dewan B. Adeyaprasad Saheb of Shikanpore, India; M 1912. 1915/T/06 [2 items].

VAUGHAN, HENRY (b. 3 May 1862) eld. s. of Hugh Vaughan, J.P., of 42 Northumberland Road, Dublin, and Kate Taaffe; B.A. (T.C.D.); H 1888. 1891/H/06 [6 items].

VAUGHAN BUCKLEY, DENIS JOSEPH: see BUCKLEY, DENIS JOSEPH VAUGHAN.

VENKATARAMAN, ADDEPALLI (b. 25 Aug. 1893) 2nd s. of Addepalli Gopalem, of Chintalapalli, Godavari District, Madras, India; M 1914. 1918/H/04x [2 items].

VENKATESWARA RAO, TURLAPATY (b. 22 Jan. 1894) eld. s. of M.R.Ry Turlapaty Sundarasiva Rao, of Adiviravulapadu Nandigama Taluq, Kistna, Madras, India; M 1913. 1918/T/02 [2 items].

VERNON, JOHN FANE (b. 5 July 1849) eldest s. of John Edward Vernon of Erne Hill, Co. Cavan, and Harriet Leslie; B.A. (Cambridge); H 1873, L.I. E 1871. 1874/T/8 [4 items].

VERSCHOYLE, HAMILTON FREDERICK STUART GOOLD (b. 6 Oct. 1874) only s. of the Revd. Hamilton Stuart Verschoyle of Cashelshanaghan, Co. Donegal, and Frances Frederika Dorothea Goold; B.A. (Oxford); M 1901, M.T. M 1899. 1904/T/08 [2 items]. Justice of the Peace for Counties Donegal and Limerick. Father-in-law of the historian J.G. Simms, and great-grandfather of Daniel Paul Simms (M 2003). Died 31 Aug. 1942. *Burke's Irish Family Records* (1976), 1165. This was the grandson of the like-named 'picturesque Hamilton Verschoyle, Bishop of Kilmore' [1803-1870; called H 1828], 'who had forsaken a career at the Bar when he felt a Call to the Church'. In *So long to wait: an Irish childhood* (London, 1960), 27-8, Moira Verschoyle recorded of the grandfather: 'He had great physical beauty besides being a fine rider, and Queen Victoria, seeing him in Rotten Row … expressed the opinion that he was the handsomest creature she had ever seen on horseback — except, of course, for her dear Albert'.

VINCENT, ARTHUR ROSE (b. 9 June 1876) 2nd s. of Colonel Arthur H. Vincent of Summerhill, Co. Clare, and Rose Tor Lumison; B.A. (T.C.D.); M 1898. 1901/T/04 [2 items]. Died Sept. 1956.

WACHUKU, JAJA ANUCHA (b. ? April 1916) 3rd s. of Chief Justice Ndubisi Wachuku, of Orange House, Nbawsi, in the district of AB.A., Owerri Province, Eastern Nigeria, and Ngwanchuiva; B.A., LL.B. (T.C.D.); E 1941. 1944/M/09 [3 items]. Elected to parliament in Nigeria, 1952; Speaker of the Federal parliament, 1960; Minister for Economic Development, 1960; Foreign Minister of Nigeria, 1962-5. During the period of military rule a successful lawyer and businessman. See John A. Wiseman, *Political Leaders in Black Africa* (1991), 226. Mentioned as a contemporary in Máire Cruise O'Brien, *The same age as the State* (Dublin, 2003), 160.

WACHUKU, NHANNA NWA (b. 20 May 1933) eld. s. of Chief J.N. Wachuku, of Nbawsi-AB.A., Nigeria, county of Aba-Ngwa, Umurhia Province, and Hannah Arungwa; B.A. (T.C.D.); M 1956. 1962/M/14 [2 items].

WADDELL, JOHN JOSEPH HARRISON KINSEY (b. 7 Dec. 1871) only s. of Alexander Waddell (decd.), L.K.Q.C.P. Ireland, of Trevor Hill, Co. Down, and Sarah Harrison; B.A., LL.B. (T.C.D.); M 1894. 1897/M/10 [4 items]. Died 31 May 1945.

WADE, EDWARD ROBERT (b. 19 Dec. 1861) eld. s. of the Revd. Edward John Wade of London, and Elizabeth Katherine Waller; B.A., Scholar, Senior moderator (T.C.D.); M 1884. 1888/H/02 [8 items]. President of the University Philosophical Society, T.C.D., 1887-8. Assistant Legal Land Commissioner. Died 25 Nov. 1943.

WADE, Mrs. FLAVIA MARGARET (b. 26 Nov. 1928) only d. of John Adolphus Davis, solicitor, of 2 Upper Belmont Valley Road, Port of Spain, Trinidad, West Indies, and Anna Bertha Kernahan; H 1966, G.I. T 1956. 1967/T/13 [1 item].

WAKELY, ION GEORGE (b. 4 May 1892) only s. of William George Wakely, solicitor, Secretary of the Incorporated Law Society, of Rosario, Temple Gardens, Dublin, and Elinor Ann Thomson; Mod. B.A. (T.C.D.); M 1911. 1914/T/09 [3 items]. M.C., LL.B., M.A. County Court judge in England. Died 31 July 1943.

WAKELY, JOHN (b. 30 Sept. 1861) eld. s. of John Wakely, J.P., of Ballyburly, Edenderry, Kings Co., and Mary C. George; B.A. (T.C.D.); E 1882, M.T. M 1882. 1885/H/06 [7 items]. Q.C., 22 April 1899. Bencher, 1902. Joint author (with R.R. Cherry) of the first edition of Cherry's *Irish Land Law and Land Purchase Acts* (Dublin 1888). Appt. County Court Judge for Roscommon and Sligo, 13 Sept. 1904. One of the eight original judges of the Circuit Court, 1924, appointed to the Midland Circuit. Retired 31 Dec. 1931. Lord of the Manor of Ballyburly. Died 15 July 1942. Obituary, *I.L.T. & S.J.*, lxxvi (1942), 186, 190; *Who's Who*.

WALDRON, DERMOT PATRICK (b. 5 Dec. 1926) only s. of Timothy Joseph Waldron, of Tuam, Co. Galway, and Kathleen Mary Cunningham; B.A. (N.U.I.); T 1948. 1948/T/12 [2 items]. Legal adviser, Department of Foreign Affairs; ambassador.

WALDRON, JAMES KEVIN (b. 4 April 1921) eld. s. of James Waldron, of 1 Rosmeen Gardens, Dún Laoghaire, Co. Dublin, and Ellen Kearney; M 1943. Awarded 1st

Victoria Prize. 1948/T/01 [1 item]. Registrar of the Supreme Court; later Director of Education at King's Inns.

WALDRON, PATRICK HENRY PEARSE (b. 5 Feb. 1917) young. s. of John Waldron, of 58 Merrion Drive, Dublin, and Mary McNamara; M 1944. 1948/T/13 [2 items]. Registrar.

WALKER, GARRETT WILLIAM eld. s. of John Francis Walker Q.C., of 9 Gardiner's Place, Dublin, and Priscilla Wall; B.A. (T.C.D.); Scholar (T.C.D.); H 1880, M.T. T 1881. 1882/M/14 [6 items]. K.C., 30 June 1906. Died 1 Feb. 1932. Obituary, *I.L.T. & S.J.*, lxvi (1932), 37.

WALKER, HERBERT JAMES (b. 1 Aug. 1905) 3rd s. of William C. Walker, of Ballybrennan, Killinick, Co. Wexford, and Caroline Morris; M 1926. 1929/M/16 [2 items].

WALKER, JOHN (b. 3 June 1858) 2nd s. of Robert Walker (decd.), of Aughnacloy, Co. Tyrone, and Margaret Fullerton; T 1923; [Memorial endorsed 'not admitted; not called': see p. 34 *supra*, where this case is discussed by W.N. Osborough]. 1923/M/05 [2 items].

WALKER, MAURICE CECIL (b. 28 Nov. 1896) 3rd s. of Garrett Wm Walker, K.C., of 38 Fitzwilliam Square, Dublin, and Katherine Leeper; B.A. (T.C.D.); M 1920. File includes record of war services. Awarded Military Cross, June 1918. 1921/H/03 [3 items]. S.C., 28 Oct. 1941. Died 16 June 1946. Obituary, *I.L.T. & S.J.*, lxxx (1946), 157.

WALKER, ROBERT (b. 25 Dec. 1881) only s. of William Walker of Charleville, Dundrum, Co. Dublin, and Jane Norton; B.A. (T.C.D.); M 1902. 1905/H/04 [3 items].

WALL, JOHN RICHARD (b. 16 Sept. 1886) only s. of Michael Wall of Egerton Villas, Cork, and Ellen Crean (decd.); M 1908. 1911/M/03 [2 items].

WALL, THOMAS PATRICK (b. 25 May 1875) eld. s. of Patrick Wall (decd.) of Seville Lodge, Kilkenny, and Kate Murphy (decd.); M 1904. 1907/T/06 [3 items]. Died 9 Nov. 1936. Obituary, *I.L.T. & S.J.*, lxx (1936), 301, 308.

WALLACE, JAMES (b. 1 Nov. 1876) 3rd s. of John Wallace of Belfield, King's Co., and Margaret Mooney; B.A. (T.C.D.); M 1898. 1901/M/07 [3 items]. Died 14 Jan. 1960.

WALLACE, JOHN (b. 31 Aug. 1839) 3rd s. of the Revd. Henry Wallace, late Professor of Christian Ethics in the Presbyterian Theological College, Belfast, of Belfast, and Mary Simpson; B.A. (T.C.D.); M 1874, M.T. M 1884. 1887/T/10 [9 items].

WALLACE, NORRIS EDMUND (b. 28 Jan 1852) 2nd surviving s. of the Revd. Thomas Wallace of Belfield, Co. Dublin, and Sophia Roberts; B.A. (T.C.D.); H 1872, M.T. E 1873. 1874/M/8 [2 items].

WALLACE, OCTAVIUS (b. 19 Sept. 1848) 6th surv. s. of Richard Wallace, merchant, of George Street, Limerick, and Bridget Bunton; M.A. (T.C.D.); M 1869; M.T. T 1871. 1875/T/03 [4 items]. Chairman of the Limerick Clothing Factory, Ltd. High Sheriff of the City of Limerick for 53 years. Died 24 Feb. 1934. Obituary, *I.L.T. & S.J.*, lxviii (1934), 64.

WALLACE, THEODORE DAVID (b. 4 Nov. 1906) 4th s. of Octavius Wallace, B.L., of Rathmore, Palmerston Road, Rathmines, Dublin, and Helena O'Sullivan; B.A. (Cambridge, a*d eundem* T.C.D.); LL.B. (T.C.D.); M 1927. Awarded Cert. of Honour. 1930/H/04 [2 items]. Crown Counsel, Kenya 1934; Kuala Lumpur 1939. Prisoner in Changi Jail. Attorney-General, Borneo 1947; Tanganyika 1951. Died at Daar-es-Salaam, 1 Jan. 1952. Obituary, *I.L.T. & S.J.*, lxxxvi (1952), 17.

WALSH, ARTHUR HEPBURN (b. 31 July 1867) eld. s. of Arthur Francis Walsh, J.P., of Canterbury, Kent, and Helen Hepburn; T 1894, M.T. T 1896. 1897/T/05 [6 items].

WALSH, BRIAN CATHAL PATRICK (b. 23 March 1918) first s. of Patrick Walsh, civil servant, of 47 Beaumont Road, Dublin, N.E. 4, and Elsie O'Brien (decd.); M.A. (N.U.I.); M 1938. Awarded Society's Prize. 1941/M/03 [2 items]. Lecturer in French at Maynooth, 1940-50; in Roman Law and Civil Law, 1947-58. Lecturer in Social Legislation and Industrial Law at U.C.D., 1945-56. S.C., 29 Jan. 1954. Judge of the High Court, 1959-1961; of the Supreme Court, 1961-90. President of the Law Students' Debating Society of Ireland, 1973-1990. First President of the Law Reform Commission, 1975-85. Retired 23 March 1990. Appreciations on retirement, *Irish Law Times*, new series, viii (1990), 100-101. Recipient of a festschift: James O'Reilly (ed.),

Human Rights and Constitutional Law (Dublin, 1992). Died 9 March 1998. Obituaries, *The Irish Times* [by Richard Balls], 10 March 1998; *The Times*, 11 March 1998; and *Irish Law Times*, new series, xvii (1999), 30-32 [by Hugh O'Flaherty]. Listed in the 1984 and 1991 editions of Maureen Cairnduff, *Who's Who in Ireland*; and in Louis McRedmond (ed.), *Modern Irish Lives*. See also: Gerard Hogan, *Dublin University Law Journal*, xiii (1990), 106-14. Bronze by Garry Trimble in King's Inns: see Wanda Ryan-Smolin, *King's Inns Portraits* (1992), 85.

WALSH, BRIDGET (b. 30 Dec. 1904) d. of Thomas Walsh (decd.), of Ballybrusa, Grange, Co. Waterford, and Ellen O'Byrne; B. Comm. (N.U.I.); M 1942. 1945/M/07 [2 items]. Mrs. McMenamin. Assistant-Librarian of King's Inns, 1938-44; Librarian of King's Inns, 1 June 1944 to 31 Dec. 1969. Died 20 Nov. 2000.

WALSH, EDWARD MICHAEL (b. 14 Sept. 1923) eld. s. of Thomas Walsh, civil servant, of 130 Cabra Road, Dublin, and Delia Patterson; B.A. (N.U.I.); M 1943. 1946/T/12 [2 items]. S.C., 6 Oct. 1969. Judge of the High Court, 18 Dec. 1981. Died 2 Nov. 1982. Author of *Planning and Development Law* (Dublin, 1979; 2nd edition, 1984)

WALSH, JAMES F. (b. 10 Jan. 1884) 2nd s. of John Walsh, of Shannon Lodge, Bandon, Co. Cork, and Minnie O'Keeffe; M 1904. 1907/T/07 [3 items].

WALSH, JAMES JOSEPH (b. 20 Sept. 1895) 2nd s. of Thomas Walsh, of Lewistown House, Duncannon, Co. Wexford, and E. M. Walsh; 1922. 1922/M/07 [2 items]. Died 19 June 1938. Obituary, *I.L.T. & S.J.*, lxxii (1938), 191, 210.

WALSH, JOHN EDWARD (b. 20 July 1845) 3rd s. of John Edward Walsh of 14 Merrion Square South, Dublin, Master of the Rolls (decd.) and Blair Belinda McNeill; B.A. (T.C.D.); H 1866, M.T. H 1867. 1869/M/3 [4 items]. Chief Clerk, Consolidated Accounting Office. Died 1931. Obituary, *I.L.T. & S.J.*, lxv (4 April 1931), 84.

WALSH, JOHN EDWARD (b. 29 Oct. 1875) eld. s. of the Revd. Robert Walsh, D.D., Rector of Donnybrook, Co. Dublin, and Elizabeth Sophia Carson; B.A. (T.C.D.); M 1895. 1898/M/11 [3 items]. Auditor of the College Historical Society, 1900-1. Sometime Secretary of the Irish Unionist Alliance. Died 3 June 1941. Obituary, *I.L.T. & S.J.*, lxxv (1941), 148.

WALSH, JOHN FITZ (b. 16 May 1853) 2nd s. of John Henry Walsh of 45 Richmond Square, Dublin, and Joanna Fitzmaurice; H 1871, M.T. E 1874. 1883/H/01 [2 items].

WALSH, MARGARET MARY PATRICIA (b. 25 Mar. 1920) eld. d. of Patrick Joseph Walsh, M.D., of Carrick Hill, Malahide, Co. Dublin, and Kathleen Nealon; M 1938. 1942/T/09 [2 items].

WALSH, MICHAEL JOHN (b. 17 Sept. 1884) 2nd s. of Michael J. Walsh (decd.), of 8 Waterloo Road, Dublin, and Belinda A. Mullarkey; M 1915. 1932/E/01 [3 items].

WALSH, PATRICK JOSEPH (b. 1 July 1912) 2nd s. of Michael Joseph Walsh, of Main Street, Kiltimagh, Co. Mayo, and Mary Jane Malone; M.A., H. Dip. in Ed. (N.U.I.); M 1942. 1945/M/05 [2 items].

WALSH, PATRICK STANISLAUS (b. 27 Oct. 1857) eld. s. of Richard Walsh (decd.) of Manor Cunningham, Co. Donegal, and Sarah Jordan; Ph.D.; M 1895. 1898/T/05 [4 items]. Appeared on two occasions with Patrick Pearse (q.v.) in Irish language cases. K.C., 28 Feb. 1910. Ph. D. President of the District Court of Cyprus, and (1931) Chief Justice of the Seychelles. Died 16 May 1943. Obituary, *I.L.T. & S.J.*, lxxvii (1943), 135.

WALSH, WILLIAM JOSEPH (b. 30 Dec. 1928) young. s. of William Walsh, of 9 Killarney Street, North Strand, Dublin, and Julia Brady; M 1951. 1955/T/03 [2 items].

WALSHE, MICHAEL JOSEPH (b. 14 Jan. 1942) only s. of Colman Walshe, civic guard, of 23 Galtymore Road, Drimnagh, Co. Dublin, and Barbara Quinn; M 1960. 1966/M/15 [1 item].

WARD, THOMAS FRANCIS (b. 3 Sept. 1879) only s. of Thomas Francis Ward (decd.) of Merrion Lodge, Salthill, Galway, and Nannie Louisa O'Flaherty; B.A. (Cambridge); M 1905. 1908/T/01 [3 items].

WARNOCK, JOHN EDMOND (b. 8 May 1887) young. s. of John Warnock (decd.) of Dunarno, Annadale, Belfast and Mary McDowell; M 1908. 1911/M/07 [2 items]. K.C. (N.I.), H 1933. M.P. (N.I. Parl) for Belfast (St. Anne's), 1938-69. Parliamentary Secretary, 1939-40; Minister of Home Affairs, 1944-9; Attorney-General, 9 Nov. 1949

- 10 April 1956. Photograph (on call to the Inner Bar) in J.W. Henderson, *Methodist College Belfast 1868-1938* (2 vols.; Belfast, 1939), 182. Died 19 Dec. 1971. See *Who's Who*.

WARREN, HENRY CHARLES JACKSON (b. 23 Jan 1852) only s. of the Rt. Hon. Robert Richard Warren of Fitzwilliam Square, Dublin, Judge of the Court of Probate, and Mary Perry; AB (T.C.D.); M 1870, M.T. T 1871. 1874/T/9 [2 items].

WATERS, CHARLES TEELING (b. 28 Feb. 1857) 2nd s. of George Waters Q.C., of 10 Upper Temple Street, Dublin and Rocklands, Co. Waterford, and Adelaide Teeling; B.A. (T.C.D.); H 1878, M.T. H 1879. 1880/M/15 [5 items]. Admiralty Registrar.

WATERS, GEORGE FRANCIS (b. 3 Oct. 1853) eld. s. of George Waters Q.C., of 10 Upper Temple Street, Dublin, and Adelaide Teeling; B.A. (T.C.D.); H 1873, G.I. M 1875. 1877/H/02 [6 items].

WATERS, JAMES ARTHUR HILL (b. 6 Oct. 1886) 2nd s. of Samuel Abraham Walker-Waters, J.P., Ex-Assistant-Inspector-General, R.I.C., of Woodview, Stillorgan, Dublin, and Margaret Helen McNab; M 1911. 1914/T/16 [2 items].

WATSON, FREDRICK STANLEY (b. 1 April 1914) 2nd s. of Gerrett Watson, merchant, of Cappoquin, Co. Waterford, and Margaret Cullinan-Roche; Ph.C.; M 1954. 1961/M/12 [2 items].

WATSON, HUGH (b. 6 March 1848) 2nd s. of Hugh Watson (decd.) of Stramore House, Gilford, Co. Down, and Marianne Armstrong; B.A. (T.C.D.); H 1870; M.T. T 1871. 1874/H/5 [2 items].

WATSON, MAELISSA ROSE MARY (b. 19 June 1943) eld. d. of Patrick Watson (decd.), army officer, of Cootehall, Boyle, Co. Roscommon, and Kathleen O'Gara; H 1964. 1966/T/09 [3 items].

WATTS, WILLIAM NEWELL (b. 17 April 1863) 2nd s. of the Revd. Professor Robert Watts, D.D., LL.D., of Belfast, and Margaret Newell; B.A., LL.D. and Prizeman (R.U.I.); M 1885, M.T. T 1886. 1888/M/02 [9 items].

WEATHERUP, WILLIAM (b. 28 July 1890) young. s. of William J. Weatherup of 'The Dairy', Ballyclare, Co. Antrim, and Mary E. Hall; M 1913. 1916/H/03 [2 items]. Practised in N.I.

WEBB, AMBROSE HENRY (b. 13 Aug. 1882) 2nd s. of Charles Webb of Park Place, Tashinny, Co. Longford, and Louisa Maria Bole; B.A. (Oxford); M 1906. 1909/H/01 [2 items]. K.C., 30 July 1920. Member of the General Council of the Bar of Ireland, 1916-21. President of the District Court of Samaria, Palestine, 1921-33; Puisne judge of the Supreme Court of Kenya, 1933-7; Chief Justice of Sierra Leone, 1938-9, and of Tanganyika, 1940-5. Knighted: known as Sir *Henry*. Died 19 May 1964. See *Who's Who*.

WEBB, GERALD CAIRNS (b. 10 Aug. 1860) eld. surv. s. of Thomas Webb Q.C., LL.D., Regius Professor of Law in the University of Dublin, of 5 Mount Street Crescent, Dublin, and Susan Gilbert; B.A. (T.C.D.); H 1881, G.I. E 1883. 1885/H/02 [5 items]. Died 21 Sept. 1944. Obituary, *I.L.T. & S.J.*, lxxviii (1944), 255.

WEBB, JOHN JOSEPH (b. 7 March 1886) 2nd s. of Peter Webb of Carmel House, Drumcondra, Co. Dublin, and Elizabeth Gallagher; M.A., LL.B. (N.U.I.); M 1910. 1913/M/05 [2 items]. S.C., 9 July 1953. Registrar of Wards of Court.

WEBB, SEYMOUR HOFFE MITCHELL (b. 22 May 1906) 2nd s. of James Henry Webb, of Tinoran, Glenageary, Co. Dublin, and Laura Gertrude Mitchell; B.A. (T.C.D.); M 1925. 1928/T/04 [2 items]. Resident Magistrate in Tanganyika. Died 22 Nov. 1953. Obituary, *I.L.T. & S.J.*, lxxxvii (1953), 309.

WEEKES, CHARLES ALEXANDER (b. 11 June 1867) 2nd s. of Francis Weekes (decd.) of Alexandra House, Rock Road, Co. Dublin, and Sarah Charlotte Johnston; M 1889. 1904/E/01 [3 items].

WEIR, JOHN CHARLES (b. 14 March 1872) eld. s. of the Revd. Edmund Malone Weir (decd.) of Kilmanon Rectory, Co. Monaghan, and Isabella Anne Murray (decd.); Mod. B.A. (T.C.D.); M 1894. 1898/T/03 [4 items]. Auditor of the College Historical Society, 1895. K.C. (N.I.), 1927. Knighted 1935. Professor of Law, Allahabad University, 1911-36. Acting puisne judge, High Court, Allahabad, March-August 1928. Died 17 Feb. 1936. *Who's Who*.

WELLS, MARY WILHELMINA (b. 9 Feb. 1912) 2nd d. of Andrew A. Wells, solicitor, of Carrickmacross. Co. Monaghan, and Mary Moore; B.A., LL.B. (T.C.D.); M 1930. 1935/H/01 [6 items].

WELLWOOD, HERBERT EDWIN (b. 7 April 1908) only s. of Richard Nicholls Wellwood, of Springmill, Cavan, Co. Cavan, and Harriet Emily Wellwood; M 1928. 1931/M/09 [2 items]. S.C., 4 July 1957. Judge of the Circuit Court, 1966. Mentioned in Gerard A. Lee, *A Memoir of the South-Western Circuit* (Dublin, 1990), 13.

WEST, ERSKINE EYRE (b. 19 May 1868) eld. s. of Augustus George West, late H.M. 76th Regiment, of Whitepark, Co. Fermanagh, and Sara Eyre; E 1891. 1895/M/08 [6 items]. Died 24 Feb. 1950. Obituary, *I.L.T. & S.J.*, lxxxiv (1950), 63.

WEST, HENRY AUGUSTUS (b. 9 Jan. 1857) eld. s. of Henry J.P. West, solicitor, of 33 North Great Georges Street, Dublin, and Mary Fitzsimons; T 1875, L.I. M 1877. 1879/E/14 [6 items].

WEST, RAYMOND (b. 18 Sept. 1832) only s. of Frederick West (decd.), of Shanklin, Isle of Wight, and Frances Raymond; B.A., M.A. (Queen's University, Dublin); M 1869; L.I. E 1870; member of H.M. Bombay Civil Service. 1871/E/1 [3 items].

WHEELER, ARTHUR WILLIAM EDGE (b. 1 Aug. 1930) eldest son of Arthur William Wheeler, of Danesfield, Dollymount, Co. Dublin, insurance broker, and Rowena Anne Yardley; B.A. (Mod.), LL.B. (T.C.D.); M. 1949. 1953/H/02 [2 items].

WHEELER, HENRY ELIARDO (b. 17 March 1872) 2nd s. of William Ireland Wheeler, M.D, of 32 Merrion Square, Dublin, and Frances Victoria Shaw; B.A. (T.C.D.); M 1893. 1896/T/08 [4 items]. Landowner (of Robertstown House, Co. Kildare) and soldier (8th King's Royal Rifle Corps [*quondam* the Carlow Militia]), who never practised. Features, under the name Harry de Courcy-Wheeler [the family name was changed to de Courcy-Wheeler in 1897], in the story of the 1916 rebellion. As Staff Captain to General Lowe, he stood beside Pearse when the latter surrendered: see panel opposite, and Alex. Findlater, *Findlaters: The Story of a Dublin Merchant Family 1774-2001* (Dublin, 2001), 271-288 [including several photographs] and 298-300. Died 13 Dec. 1956. *Burke's Irish Family Records* (1976), 1204.

WHELAN, Lieutenant CLAUDE BLAKE (b. 19 Dec. 1893) 2nd s. of Joseph Percival Whelan, of 'Barna', Osborne Park, Belfast, and Ellis Letitia Greene; M 1912. 1919/M/04 [4 items]. Died 28 Nov. 1953.

WHELAN, LAURENCE (b. 7 July 1932) only s. of Cornelius Whelan, of 11 Thorncliffe Park, Orwell Road, Rathgar, Co. Dublin, and Kathleen McCreery; M 1950. 1954/M/13 [2 items].

WHELAN, MICHAEL JOSEPH (b. 1 May 1932) eld. s. of Michael Whelan, of Athenry, Co. Galway, and Mary Therese Hynes; B.A. (N.U.I.); M 1951. 1954/M/04 [2 items]. Oil executive. Listed in the 1984 edition of Maureen Cairnduff, *Who's Who in Ireland*.

WHELAN, SEÁN CHRISTOPHER (b. 21 Jan. 1944) eld. s. of Patrick Whelan, merchant, of Nenagh, Co. Tipperary, and Sarah Devaney; M 1963. 1966/T/08 [1 item]. Ambassador to Turkey. Died 2004.

WHELEHAN, HAROLD ANTHONY (b. 17 Feb. 1944) 2nd s. of John Kevin Whelehan, company director, of Claremont Road, Howth, Co. Dublin, and Maureen Spollen; B.C.L. (N.U.I.); M 1962. 1966/M/13 [1 item]. S.C., 29 Feb. 1980. Attorney-General, Oct. 1991-Nov. 1994. Appointed President of the High Court, 15 Nov. 1994; resigned, 17 Nov. 1994. Returned to practise at the Bar pursuant to resolution of the Bar in general meeting. Listed in the 1991 and 1999 editions of Maureen Cairnduff, *Who's Who in Ireland*.

WHITAKER, JOHN MARTIN (b. 7 Oct. 1872) 3rd s. of Henry Whitaker, M.D., Medical Superintendent Officer of Health for the City of Belfast, of Belfast, and Elizabeth Martin; LL.B. (R.U.I.); M 1893. 1896/M/01 [6 items]. Brooke Scholar, 1896. Professor at King's Inns. K.C., 27 Feb. 1918. Died 1943. Obituary, *I.L.T. & S.J.*, lxxvii (25 Dec.

1943), 315. Photograph in J.W. Henderson, *Methodist College Belfast 1868-1938* (2 vols.; Belfast, 1939), 71; and see ibid., 73, 181.

WHITAKER, WILLIAM BAILEY MARTIN (b. 12 May 1859) eld. s. of Henry Whitaker, M.D., of Belfast, and Elizabeth Martin; B.A. (T.C.D.); M 1877, M.T. M 1878. 1881/M/06 [7 items]. North-East Circuit. K.C., 26 Feb. 1907. Land Purchase Commission (N.I.). Bencher of the Inn of Court of N.I. Mentioned in J.C. MacDermott, *An Enriching Life*, 169; and by V.T.H. Delany [q.v.], in 'The Bench and Bar in Ireland', xxxiii. Died 12/13 Sept 1930. Obituary, *I.L.T. & S.J.*, lxiv (1930), 228.

WHITE, DUDLEY (b. 2 March 1873) 2nd s. of William Dudley White (decd.), physician and surgeon, of Rutland Square, Dublin, and Emily Noble; Scholar, B.A. (T.C.D.); M 1893, M.T. M 1896. 1897/M/05x [5 items]. President of the University Philosophical Society, T.C.D., 1897-8. K.C., 16 Dec. 1909. Crown counsel for Wicklow, 1909; aft. at Green Street. Died 3 July 1930. Obituary, *I.L.T. & S.J.*, lxiv (1930), 167-8.

OF THE ARREST OF BARRISTERS LEADING IRISH REBELLIONS

Harry De Courcy-Wheeler [T 1896] recalled his part in the arrest of Patrick Pearse [T 1901] as follows:

At 2.30 p.m. [on 29 April 1916] Commandant-General Pearse surrendered to General Lowe accompanied by myself and Lieutenant Lowe at the junction of Moore Street and Great Britain Street. He handed over his arms and military equipment. His sword and automatic repeating pistol in holster, with pouch of ammunition, and his canteen, which contained two large onions, were handed to me by Commandant General Pearse. Onions were carried by the insurgent troops as iron rations. They were believed to be high in nutriment value.

The fate of the onions is not recorded, but Harry De Courcy-Wheeler presented Pearse's pistol, pouch and canteen to the State in 1949. [Alex. Findlater, *Findlaters*, 272, 277].

While it is unlikely that either Pearse or De Courcy-Wheeler was conscious at the time that the other was a fellow graduate of the King's Inns, their meeting has a resonance with an earlier incident in Irish history. On 3 November 1798, when Wolfe Tone (T 1789) was brought ashore at Buncrana, after the capture of the *Hoche*, it was reported that he was 'immediately recognised by *many* of his College and Bar acquaintances'. One of these was Sir George Hill (T 1786), who mentions, in a letter describing the arrival of the French prisoners, that 'the first man who stepped out of the boat habited as an officer was T.W. Tone', and that he 'recognised and addressed me instantly with as much *sang-froid* as you might expect from his character'. Captain John Boyd of the Letterkenny Cavalry, the officer who arrested Tone, is thought to have been the barrister of that name called in Hilary Term 1790. Boyd took custody of Tone's possessions, which included his copy [now in the National Library of Ireland] of *Belmont Castle*, a novel which Tone and others had written while Bar students. [Kenneth Ferguson, 'The Irish Bar in December 1798', in *Dublin Historical Record*, lii (No. 1: Spring 1999), 32-60, at p. 46].

WHITE, JASPER THOMAS (b. 16 June 1868) 2nd s. of John P. White, D.L., J.P., of Nantenan, Co. Limerick, and Emily McMahon; M 1888. 1891/T/01 [7 items]. Died 1934. *Burke's Irish Family Records* (1976), 1205.

WHITE, MICHAEL BARRY (b. 13 Sept. 1944) only s. of Kevin Thomas White, legal accountant, of 'Chimes', Mount Anville Road, Dundrum, Co. Dublin, and Emily Gertrude Kenneally; B.C.L. (N.U.I.); M 1964. 1967/M/07 [1 item]. S.C., 5 March 1982. Appt. Judge of the High Court, 5 July 2002.

WHITE, PHILIP AUGUSTINE O'CONNELL (b. 31 Jan. 1851) 2nd s. of Matthew James White, solicitor, of 14 Belgrave Square, Dublin, and Helena O'Connell; H 1874, M.T. H 1876. 1878/T/01 [3 items]. Died 27 Oct. 1927. Obituary, *I.L.T. & S.J.*, lxi (1927), 262.

WHITE, ROBERT GROVE (b. 9 Sept. 1881) 2nd surv. s. of James Grove White of 18 Elgin Road, Dublin, and Emily Wilson; B.A. (T.C.D.); M 1903. 1906/H/02 [2 items]. Died 23 Jan. 1960. *Burke's Irish Family Records* (1976), 1209.

WHITE, WILLIAM JEFFREY (b. 17 June 1871) eld. s. of Dr. William Dudley White of Rutland Square, Dublin, and Emily Noble; M.A. and holder of studentship (R.U.I.); M 1892. 1895/M/06 [6 items].

WHITFIELD, GEORGE (b. 19 Oct. 1870) eld. surv. s. of George Whitfield (decd.) of Modreeny, Co. Tipperary, and Jane Whitfield; B.A. (Oxford); H 1895. 1898/E/02 [5 items].

WHITTON, HENRY McMANUS (b. 4 Nov. 1869) 5th s. of William Whitton of Springfield, Stradbally, Queen's Co., and Marjorie Robertson; M.A., LL.B. (R.U.I.); M 1903. 1906/M/01 [2 items].

WIJEMANNE, HUBERT ASHLEY (b. 10 Dec. 1906) 2nd s. of Simon Richard Wijemanne (decd.), of Kalatara South, Ceylon, and Adeline Wijemanne; M 1928. 1931/M/13 [2 items].

WILDE, WILLIAM CHARLES KINGSBURY (b. 26 Sept. 1852) eld. s. of Sir William Robert Wills Wilde, M.D., F.R.C.S.I., of 1 Merrion Square North, Dublin, and Jane F. Agnes Elgee; T.C.D.; H 1872, M.T. M 1872. 1875/E/06 [2 items]. Journalist who wrote much for the *World* and the *Daily Telegraph*. Pianist. Died in London in March 1899. Mentioned in the *D.N.B.* under the entry for Oscar Wilde, who was his younger brother, and in *Burke's Irish Family Records* (1976), 1217.

WILLIAMS, MAURICE SWIFT (b. 4 Aug. 1884) eld. s. of Arthur Griffith Williams of Pernambuco, Brazil, and Edith Anne Boxwell; H 1902. 1905/T/03 [3 items].

WILLIAMS, THOMAS FRANCIS DESMOND (b. 26 May 1921) only s. of William J. Williams, M.A., lecturer in education, U.C.D., of 79 Wellington Road, Ballsbridge, Dublin, and Angela Murnaghan; M 1939. 1942/M/01 [2 items]. Professor of Modern History at U.C.D., 1949-83. Died 18 Jan. 1987. See Louis McRedmond (ed.), *Modern Irish Lives*.

WILLIAMSON, JAMES (b. 22 March 1861) only s. of Richard Williamson (decd.), merchant, of Hartford Place, Armagh, and Matilda Cooper; M 1892, solicitor. 1893/M/07 [3 items]. North-East Circuit. 26 April 1913. Died 1935. Obituary, *I.L.T. & S.J.*, lxix (12 Oct. 1935), 286.

WILLIAMSON, RICHARD (Captain) (b. 14 April 1886) eld. s. of James Williamson, K.C., of 18 Northumberland Road, Dublin, and Margaret Elizabeth [?]; M 1918. 1919/H/04 [2 items].

WILLIAMSON, ROBERT CECIL (b. 16 Aug. 1891) young. s. of Robert Williamson of 42 Brighton Road, Rathgar, Dublin, and Anna Francis Sharpe; Cand. Bach. (T.C.D.); M 1910. 1913/T/13 [2 items].

WILLINGTON, JAMES THOMAS CAMBIE (b. 18 March 1863) eld. s. of Frederick Willington of St. Kieran's, Parsonstown, Co. Tipperary, and Margaret Cambie; E 1883, M.T. M 1886. 1888/H/01 [7 items]. Died 9 May 1951.

WILLIS, GILBERT de LAVAL (b. 17 Dec. 1844) eld. s. of the Revd. William Newcombe Willis (decd.), sometime Rector of Kilpeacon and Prebendary of St. Mary's Cathedral, Limerick, and Emily Evans Dartnell (decd.); M 1896. 1899/M/09 [5 items]. Died 26 Sept. 1926. Obituary, *I.L.T. & S.J.*, lx (1926), 247.

WILLIS, OSCAR. See: UILEAS, OSCAR DIARMUID MAC CARTHA.

WILMOT, SAMUEL CUSACK (6 Aug. 1851) 1st s. of Samuel George Wilmot, M.D., surgeon and physician, of Merrion Square, Dublin and Vesey Place, Kingstown, and Elizabeth Cusack; B.A. (T.C.D.); E 1873, L.I. T 1871. 1875/T/07 [5 items].

WILSON, CHARLES (b. 26 April 1889) eld. s. of Samuel Wilson, of 2 Rock Villas, Londonderry, and Mary Greer; Ex. Sch., Sen. Mod., B.A. (T.C.D.) 1923/M/06 [2 items]. Registrar of High Court, Singapore. Member of N.I. Bar.

WILSON, CHARLES JOHN (b. 6 July 1852) only surv. s. of Thomas Wilson (decd.) of Sallymount, Dalkey, Co. Dublin, and Louisa Dalton; B.A. (T.C.D.); M 1889. 1892/T/06 [7 items].

WILSON, CYRIL HERBERT (b. 25 Feb. 1899) 2nd s. of Herbert Charles Wilson, K.C. (decd.), of 12 Hatch Street, Dublin, and Emily Dunne; M 1924. 1927/T/02 [2 items].

WILSON, DANIEL JAMES (b. 16 Jan. 1861) eld. s. of the Revd. Mervyn Wilson, B.A., of Camus Rectory, Strabane, Co. Tyrone, and Maria Hunter; B.A. (T.C.D.); M 1882, I.T. M 1884. 1885/M/06 [7 items]. North-West Circuit. Aft. stockbroker. Unionist parliamentary candidate. Died (by suicide) 13 Oct. 1902. Obituary, *I.L.T. & S.J.*, xxxvi (1902), 409.

WILSON, DANIEL MARTIN (b. 4 Feb. 1862) 5th s. of the Revd. David Wilson D.D., of 14 Barrington Street, Limerick, and Jessie Bannatyne; B.A., Sen. Mod. (T.C.D.); M 1882, M.T. M 1883. 1885/M/08 [6 items]. K.C., 26 Feb. 1907. Unionist M.P. for West Down, 1918-21. Solicitor-General, 1919. Briefly Recorder of Belfast, 1921. Appt. Judge of the Chancery Division of the N.I. High Court, 17 Oct. 1921. Died 5 Jan. 1932. Obituary, *I.L.T. & S.J.*, lxvi (1932), 11. See Kate Newmann, *Dictionary of Ulster Biography* (Belfast, 1993).

WILSON, HENRY BERTRAM (b. 7 Feb. 1879) 2nd s. of John Wilson, of Dunboyne, Co. Meath, and Mary Dawson Pilkington; T 1919. Removed from roll of solicitors at own request. 1919/T/04 [3 items].

WILSON, HERBERT (b. 8 July 1862) only s. of Robert Wilson (decd.), Barrister-at-Law, of Milltown, Co. Dublin, and Caroline Anderson; B.A., scholar (T.C.D.); M 1883, M.T. H 1886. 1887/H/06 [8 items]. K.C., 13. Feb. 1902. Died 22 Jan. 1927. Obituary, *I.L.T. & S.J.*, lxi (1927), 29.

WILSON, Captain HERBERT VAUGHAN (b. 19 Dec. 1894) eld. s. of Herbert Wilson, K.C., of 12 Hatch Street, Dublin, and Emily Dunne; M 1914. 1919/M/02 [2 items]. S.C., 14 Oct. 1942. Professor at King's Inns. Mentioned by V.T.H. Delany [q.v.], in 'The Bench and Bar in Ireland', xxxiv. Died 4 May 1956.

WILSON, HUGH RAMSEY (b. 16 Nov. 1894) eld. s. of Robert James Wilson, of Knowehead, Ballyclare, Co. Antrim, and Anna Ferguson; LL.B. (Q.U.B.); M 1916. Awarded Society's Prize. 1919/H/02 [2 items].

WILSON, MARK (b. 22 Oct. 1896) young. s. of William Wilson (decd.), of Cloneen, Castlecomer, Co. Kilkenny, and Catherine Smyth; Sch., Sen. Mod. B.A., LL.B. (T.C.D.); M 1921. 1924/E/02 [2 items]. Auditor of the College Historical Society, 1922-3, and captain of Wanderers R.F.C. Colonial Administrative Service, Tanganyika, 1924; District Magistrate, Uganda, 1926-36; Puisne Judge, Tanganyika, 1936-48. Chief Justice of the Gold Coast, 1948-56. Knighted 1950. Author of *International Peace and the League of Nations* (1922). Died 10 April 1956. *Who's Who*.

WILSON, ROBERT MACKAY WILLIAM (b. 10 Feb. 1864) only s. of Robert Mackay Wilson, J.P., of Coolcarrigan, Co. Kildare, and Elizabeth Jackson [Suffern]; B.A., LL.B. (T.C.D.); M 1883. 1886/M/11 [7 items]. Died unmarried 18 Dec. 1887. *Burke's Irish Family Records* (1976), 1218.

WILSON, ROBERT CHRISTOPHER KIDD (b. 23 April 1868) eld. s. of Christopher Wilson, merchant, decd., late of Belfast, Co. Antrim, and Mary Jane Kidd; B.A., LL.B. (T.C.D.); M 1886. 1889/T/06 [7 items].

WILSON, WILLIAM HENRY (b. 25 Nov. 1852) young. s. of William Wilson, insurance agent, of 69 Pembroke Road, Dublin, and Jane Newland; B.A. (T.C.D.); H 1876, G.I. H 1878. 1879/M/07 [6 items].

WINDER, LIONEL JAMES (b. 18 February 1916) younger s. of James Winder, of Langara, Alma Road, Monkstown, Co. Dublin, and Mary Emily Lipscombe; M 1935. 1940/H/02 [2 items]. S.C., 18 March 1976. Last editor of the *Irish Law Times and Solicitors' Journal Reports*. Died 29 July 2001.

WINDLE, HENRY (b. 10 April 1900) eld. s. of Nicholas Windle, of Aughrim, Newtownards, Co. Kerry, and Mary Hanrahan; M 1929. 1934/M/03 [2 items]. Superintendent in the Garda Síochána. Died by drowning 16 Oct. 1938. Obituary, *I.L.T. & S.J.*, lxxii (1938), 321.

WOOD, BENJAMIN USSHER (b. 16 Oct. 1878) young. s. of John C. Wood, J.P., of Lota, Glanmire, Co. Cork, and Helena Ussher; B.A. (Oxford); M 1900. 1903/M/09 [3 items].

WOOD, ERNEST MOUNTENEY (b. 12 July 1909) 3rd s. of Albert Ernest Wood, of 86 Northumberland Road, Dublin, and Edyth Gillespie; M 1929. 1932/M/01 [2 items]. President of the University Philosophical Society, T.C.D., 1932-3. S.C., 4 July 1947. Known as an orator, and skilful in cross-examination; an expert in bankruptcy and defamation. Died 25 April 1991. Mentioned in Patrick MacKenzie, *Lawful Occasions*, 88-90; and listed in Louis McRedmond (ed.), *Modern Irish Lives*.

WOOD, ROBERT ALBERT ERNEST (b. 10 March 1874) 2nd s. of James Wood (decd.), of Norwich, Norfolk, and Minnie Corbett; M 1899. 1902/T/06 [3 items]. K.C., 25 Feb. 1919. Known by colleagues as the Thunderer. Member of (and parliamentary candidate in England for) the Independent Labour Party. Died 9 April 1941. Obituary, *I.L.T. & S.J.*, lxxv (1941), 100. Mentioned by Sir Christopher Lynch-Robinson [q.v.] in *The Last of the Irish R.M.s* (1951), 149-51, 165, and by V.T.H. Delany [q.v.], in 'The Bench and Bar in Ireland', xxxiii.

WOOD, WILFRID DAVID (b. 5 Sept. 1904) 2nd s. of Albert Ernest Wood, of 14 Herbert Street, Dublin, and Edythe Gillespie; M 1928. 1931/T/09 [2 items]. Died 28 March 1932. Obituary, *I.L.T. & S.J.*, lxvi (1932), 85.

WOODCOCK, THOMAS CHARLES (b. 30 May 1911) 2nd s. of Albert Woodcock, solicitor, of Shanid, 47 Brighton Road, Rathgar, Dublin, and Mary Elizabeth Goodwin; M 1928. 1936/T/10 [2 items].

WOODS, JOHN LOWE (b. 24 Jan. 1899) eld. s. of Sir Robert Henry Woods, Knight Bachelor, of 39 Merrion Square East, Dublin, and Margaret Shaw; B.A., Sen. Mod. (T.C.D.); M 1923. 1925/M/23 [2 items]. Law practice in Malaya. Died March 1956. Obituary, *I.L.T. & S.J.*, xc (14 April 1956), 93.

WOODS, ROBERT HEWITT (b. 30 May 1852) eld. s. of James Woods (decd.) of Dromore, Co. Down, and Mary Hewitt; M 1881, M.T. E 1883. 1884/T/03 [7 items].

WOOLFSON, SOLOMON SEFTON (b. 10 May 1932) 3rd s. of William Louis Woolfson, of 122 St. Catherine's Terrace, S.C.R., Dolphin's Barn, Dublin, and Sarah Bella Clein; M 1950. 1954/M/15 [2 items]. Aft. an industrialist.

WOOLLCOMBE, ROBERT LLOYD (b. 11 March 1852) eld. s. of Robert William Woollcombe, surgeon, of Stoke Damarel, Devonshire, and Jane Mary Kilkelly; B.A. (T.C.D.); H 1874, I.T. M 1875. 1876/M/08 [8 items]. Chief Clerk of the King's Bench Division. Died 13 Sept. 1919. Obituary, *I.L.T. & S.J.*, liii (1919), 222.

WRIGHT, DAVID ANDREW LESLIE (b. 4 Feb. 1918) eld. s. of Ernest Albert Paul Wright, of Mount Eden, Waterville, Co. Kerry, and Mary Keane; M 1937. 1943/T/02 [2 items].

WRIGHT, GEORGE (b. 8 June 1847) 2nd s. of Thomas Richard Wright, of Fern Hill, Clonakilty, Co. Cork, and Eliza Turner; B.A. (T.C.D.); E 1868, M.T. M 1869. 1871/M/8 [2 items]. Munster Circuit. QC, 5 July 1884. Opponent of Lecky in the 1895 election for the Dublin University constituency. Solicitor-General 1900. Judge of the King's Bench Division, 1901. Died 15 May 1913. Obituary, *I.L.T. & S.J.*, xlvii (1913), 143-5, 248. See Ball, *Judges*, ii, 381. Mentioned in Maurice Healy, *The Old Munster Circuit*, 39-40.

WRIGHT, RICHARD (b. 4 Oct. 1842) eld. s. of Thomas Richard Wright (decd.), solicitor, of Fern Hill, Co. Cork, and Eliza Turner; B.A. (T.C.D.); M 1883, M.T. H 1884. 1884/M/03 [2 items]. Formerly a solicitor, he was called to the Bar after his younger brother George (q.v) had taken silk. Died 1908. Obituary, *I.L.T. & S.J.*, xlii (29 August 1908), 211.

WYER, MATTHEW DALY (b. 4 March 1855) 2nd s. of John Wyer (decd.), gentleman, of Castletown-Geoghegan, Co. Westmeath, and Catherine Daly; H 1885. 1887/M/13 [8 items].

WYLIE, JAMES OWENS (b. 28 Nov 1845) [Coleraine] 5th s. of William Andrew Wylie of Rushvale, Ballyclare, Co. Antrim and Jane Beatty; M.A., LL.B (Queen's University); M 1867, M.T. E 1868. 1872/H/2 [2 items]. North-West Circuit. Q.C., 30 June 1894. Judge of the High Court (Irish Land Commission), 1906-20. Served as a Lord Justice during the absences of the Lord Lieutenant, 1909-19, notably between June-August 1916. Retired 1920, yielding the office to his nephew, W.E. Wylie. Author of a commentary on the Judicature Acts (1895). Died 13 Dec. 1935. Obituary, *I.L.T. & S.J.*, lxix (1935), 354. *Who's Who*. Mentioned, but inaccurately, in Kate Newmann, *Dictionary of Ulster Biography* (Belfast, 1993).

WYLIE, WILLIAM EVELYN (b. 26 June 1881) 1st s. of the Revd. R.B. Wylie, LL.D., of Coleraine, Co. Londonderry, and Marian Drury; B.A.; M 1902. 1905/H/02 [2 items]. K.C., 27 June 1914. As Lieutenant Wylie, K.C., prosecutor in the 1916 courts martial. Judge of the Irish Land Commission 1920-36. Judge of the High Court of the Irish Free State 1924-36. For Chief Justice Kennedy's view (in a diary entry dated 29 Dec. 1929) of Willie Wylie's attention to his judicial duties, viz. 'That he should sit only once a week and disport himself for the rest of the week at horse shows, hunts and races is a quite intolerable situation, especially with the volume of work thrown upon the other five [High Court judges] who cannot keep up with it', see G.W. Hogan, 'Chief Justice Kennedy and Sir James O'Connor application', in *Ir. Jurist*, xxiii (1988), 144-158, at p. 158. Retired 1936 and devoted himself thereafter to the service of the Royal Dublin Society, of which he was President, 1939-41. Died 12 Oct. 1964. Obituary, *I.L.T. & S.J.*, xcviii (1964), 407-8. See Terence de Vere White, *The Story of the Royal Dublin Society* (Tralee, 1955) [where (opp. p. 209) Leo Whelan's portrait of Judge Wylie in riding pink is reproduced in colour]; Leon Ó Broin, *W.E. Wylie and the Irish Revolution 1916-1921* (Dublin, 1989) [supplemented by Brian Barton, *From Behind a Closed Door: Secret Court Martial Records of the 1916 Easter Rising* (Belfast, 2002)]; *Who's Who*; and Kate Newmann, *Dictionary of Ulster Biography* (Belfast, 1993).

WYMES, ENDA JOHN (b. 21 March 1944) 3rd s. of Michael J. Wymes, Assistant Commissioner, Garda Síochána, of 58 Iona Road, Glasnevin, Co. Dublin, and Anne Josephine Devlin; B.C.L. (N.U.I.); M 1962. 1966/M/11 [1 item].

WYNDHAM, TEDDY OMOLADE BENJAMIN (b. 14 March 1929) 2nd s. of Obadiah Agibabi Wyndham, of 10 Little East Street, Freetown, Sierra Leone, West Africa, and Henrietta Benjamin; M 1953. 1957/M/10 [2 items].

YATES, CHARLES (b. 12 Dec. 1860) 2nd s. of William Yates (decd.) of Blackhall Place, Dublin, and Elizabeth Diffin; B.A. (T.C.D.); M 1884. 1888/H/03 [6 items]. Died 27 March 1953.

YEATES, RICHARD BEVERLY (b. 19 Sept. 1890) 2nd s. of George W. Yeates, M.B., of 25 Lower Baggot Street, Dublin and Alma Ussher; M 1909. 1912/T/05 [2 items]. Cairo.

YEATS, MICHAEL BUTLER (b. 22 Aug. 1921) only s. of William Butler Yeats, of 46 Palmerston Road, Dublin, and Georgie Bertha Hyde-Lees; B.A. (T.C.D.); M 1945. 1948/T/06 [2 items]. Auditor of the College Historical Society, 1944-5. Son of the poet, and nephew of the painter; sometime member of the European Parliament and Senator. Author of an autobiography, *Cast a cold eye: Memoirs of a poet's son and politician* (Dublin: Blackwater Press,[1988]). Listed in the 1984 and 1999 editions of Maureen Cairnduff, *Who's Who in Ireland*.

YEO, HENRY VIVIAN (b. 2 June 1843) eld. s. of Henry Yeo of Howth, Co. Dublin, and Jane Ferns; B.A. (T.C.D.); H 1866, M.T. E 1867. 1870/E/3 [4 items]. Registrar in the King's Bench Division for close on 60 years. Clerk to Chief Baron Palles, 1879-1916 [V.T.H. Delany, *Christopher Palles*, 96]. Died 16 Oct. 1925. Obituary, *I.L.T. & S.J.*, lix (1925), 256.

YOUNG, GOODWIN (b. 18 Jan. 1850) eld. s. of Henry Lindsay Young J.P., of Lee Mount, Co. Cork, and Margaret Thornhill Sloan; M.A. (Cambridge); H 1882, I.T. E 1871. 1883/T/10 [5 items].

YOUNG, ROBERT CHICHESTER (b. 4 July 1887) eld. s. of George Lawrence Young of Millmount, Randalstown, Co. Antrim, and Annie Harvey; B.A. (T.C.D.); M 1907. 1910/T/13 [2 items]. Died 25 Dec. 1941. Obituary, *I.L.T. & S.J.*, lxxvi (1942), 12.

THE ROLLS

1868-2004

Roll of the Outer Bar
1868-2004

Hilary 1868

(Saturday 18th January 1868)
Rochford, James Fagan
McTernan, Hugh
Doyle, Laurence
Green, William
Barrett, John Samuel
Murray, John
Philp, Richard

Easter 1868

(Wednesday 22nd April 1868)
Lane, James Clarke
Cahill, Edward Francis
Nicolls, Archibald John
Teeling, Charles Hamilton
Symes, Robert Warren
Carr, George Whitmore
Byrne, John Ouseley

Trinity 1868

(Friday 29th May 1868)
Farrelly, Philip
Tarleton, Francis Alexander
Richardson, Samuel Thomas
    Stanislaus
Kenny, William
O'Carroll, Frederic John
Atkins, George

Michaelmas 1868

(Monday 9th November 1868)
Gerrard, John Netterville
Short, William
O'Connell, Charles
Trench, Frederick Netterville le Poer
Richardson, George Clements
    Kirkwood
Meldon, Albert Gregory

Hilary 1869

(Monday 18th January 1869)
Cogan, Owen
McCorkell, David Browne
Casey, Thomas Julian Smith
Boughey, Charles

Easter 1869

(Thursday 22nd April 1869)
Smithson, Samuel Rayner
Killen, James Bryce
Brady, Robert Samuel
Hitchcock, Henry Edward

Trinity 1869

(Saturday 29th May 1869)
Brew, Thomas Studdert
Hamilton, Edward Blayney
Huband, William George
Kirkpatrick, Henry Clare

Michaelmas 1869

(Tuesday 9th November 1869)
Allen, Samuel
Andrews, John Thomas
Walsh, John Edward
Greene, Benjamin
Forde, Henry
Davison, Arthur Bolden

Hilary 1870

(Tuesday 18th January 1870)
Quill, Albert William
Powell, Eyre Burton
Lentaigne, Joseph Hussey Nugent
Bourke, John Ulick

Easter 1870

(Friday 22nd April 1870)
Boyle, Alexander
O'Reilly, Joseph Richard
Yeo, Henry Vivian
Beatty, Edward Frederick

Trinity 1870

(Friday 3rd June 1870)
Gibson, John George
Gyles, William Thomas McGwire

Michaelmas 1870

(Wednesday 9th November 1870)
Tracy, Henry
Fitzgerald, Richard Valentine
La Touche, John James Digges

Evans, Francis Nicholas
Gartlan, George Henry
Bird, William Seymour
Ronan, Stephen
Stritch, John Russell
Brady, Horace Newman

Hilary 1871
(Wednesday 18th January 1871)
Louden, John James
Murray, Arthur William
MacIvor, James
Johnston, William

Easter 1871
(Wednesday 19th April 1871)
West, Raymond
(Saturday 22nd April 1871)
Barry, Michael Francis
Kelly, George Alexander Patrick

Trinity 1871
(Wednesday 31st May 1871)
Hodder, Francis George
Doyle, Charles
Keogh, Henry
Barron, Eustace John FitzGerald
Allen, Robert
Johnston, James Graydon
Craig, John Walker

Michaelmas 1871
(Thursday 9h November 1871)
Tuckey, Davys
Sheridan, Thomas Brinsley
Keogh, William
Richardson, Nicholas Gosselin
Counihan, Francis
FitzGerald, James John Foster Vesey
Leech, Henry Brougham
Wright, George
FitzGerald, Gerald
Smith, Robert John Crawford
   Chatterton
Orr, John William

Hilary 1872
(Thursday 18th January 1872)
Smith, William
Wylie, James Owens
Ffrench, Daniel O'Connell
Gartlan, James
McHugh, John Baptist
Carter, Samuel Richard
De Burgh, Hubert John
Hewson, Thomas
Le Fanu, William Joseph Henry
Shinkwin, James

Trinity 1872
(Wednesday 29th May 1872)
Roche, John
Burke, Martin John
Falconer, John Boursiquot
Murray, Robert Douglas
Blake, John Hubert
Stanley, John
Newton, Andrew Willoughby
Collum, Rupert Francis
O'Grady, Standish
Conroy, James Gerve
Armstrong, William
Henderson, James
Fitzgerald, David
Graves, Arnold Felix

Michaelmas 1872
(Thursday 14th November 1872)
Moylan, Edward Kyran
Sherlock, David
Stanley, Robert Henry
Kelly, Thomas
Drummond, Michael
Berry, Henry Fitzpatrick
Talbot, Bertram Henry
De Butts, George

Hilary 1873
(Saturday 18th January 1873)
Geoghegan, Jacob Thomas
Reed, Andrew
Kehoe, Miles Vincent
McDonnell, William Dobbs
Rearden, Thomas David
Adams, Richard
Ryan, William Ewer
Oulton, George Nugent
Roche, Cecil Robert
Morphy, Edward
Kelly, Richard
Dodd, William Huston
Eames, Robert
McLean, John

Easter 1873
(Wednesday 23rd April 1873)
Moutray, Whitney John Upton
Browne, Matthew Barry Charles

Trinity 1873
(Friday 30th May 1873)
Eiffe, Luke Sweetman
Monck, William Henry Stanley
Sullivan, Denis Baylor
Power, Virgil
MacCartie, Gerald Falkiner
McCammon, Thomas Andrew

Sheahan, Thomas Helsham
Johnston, Henry Augustus
Harris, Francis William Fitzgerald
Thompson, Robert Wade

Michaelmas 1873
(Monday 10th November 1873)
Lawson, Samuel Arnold
Hawkins, Alexander Bruce
Cross, William Pennell
Blake, Thomas Joseph
Hamill, Arthur John
Flemyng, William Westropp
Shaw, Edward

Hilary 1874
(Monday 19th January 1874)
Barton, Molyneux
Rynd, James Alexander
De Versan, John Richard Raoul
  Couturier
Hickey, John M.
Watson, Hugh
O'Shaughnessy, Thomas
Kelly, Bernard Dowell
Lynch, Michael Palles
Matheson, Charles Louis
Browne, John Henry

Easter 1874
(Wednesday 22nd April 1874)
Overend, Thomas George
Lawrence, George
Pentland, George Henry
Lawless, Edmund Constantine

Trinity 1874
(Friday 29th May 1874)
Bourke, Matthew John
Shannon, James
Beveridge, John Francis Barry
Kyle, William
Birch, Michael
Greer, George
Day, Joseph Michael
Vernon, John Fane
Warren, Henry Charles Jackson

Michaelmas 1874
(Monday 9th November 1874)
Howley, Edward
Dunne, Francis William Bradney
O'Brien, Richard Barry
Olphert, Robert Fannin
Steen, William
Nash, George Brabazon Herbert
Hackett, John Winthrup

Wallace, Norris Edmund
Bagenal, Philip Henry

Hilary 1875
(Monday 18th January 1875)
Martley, John
Dillon, William
Henn, Francis Blackburne
McCullagh, James Gordon
O'Brien, Alfred
McComas, Richard Henry Archibald
Dillon, Luke Plunkett

Easter 1875
(Thursday 22nd April 1875)
MacCrossan, Henry
Holt, Henry
Counsel, Edward Patrick Sarsfield
Matheson, Robert Edwin
Dunn, Michael Joseph
Bernard, William Leigh
Wilde, William Charles Kingsbury
Tuthill, Arthur Hendley

Trinity 1875
(Saturday 29th May 1875)
Smith, Patten
Colthurst, Herbert Baldwin
Wallace, Octavius
Payne, Somers Henry
Barrington, Richard Manliffe
O'Hara, Robert Francis
Wilmot, Samuel Cusack

Michaelmas 1875
(Tuesday 9th November 1875)
Kennedy, Edward Thomas
Gordon, Richard Mayberry
Leslie, William Moutray
MacDevitt, Edward O'Donnell

Hilary 1876
(Tuesday 18th January 1876)
MacNeill, John Gordon Swift
Dooner, Lawrence
Adair, Henry Ross William
Stack, George Hall
Copinger, Richard Henry
Taylor, Henry
Staveley, Jones Hodder

Easter 1876
(Saturday 22nd April 1876)
Macbeth, James Daxelhoffer
Plunkett, Thomas John
Myles, John

Trinity 1876
(Thursday 1st June 1876)
Holmes, Robert William Arbuthnot
Smylie, Archibald
Lane, Hugh Dillon

Michaelmas 1876
(Thursday 9th November 1876)
Cuming, Edward
Mills, Henry McGildowney
Geoghegan, Gerald
Perry, Henry
Johnson, Edward Philip
Barrington, Croker
Brady, Charles William Rawson
Woollcombe, Robert Lloyd
Sullivan, Alexander Martin, M.P.

Hilary 1877
(Thursday 18th January 1877)
Moriarty, John Francis
George Francis
Kennedy, Joseph Mary
Cronhelm, Edward William
Anderson, Samuel Lee

Easter 1877
(Monday 23rd April 1877)
Fleming, Frederick
Taylor, William Charles
Ingham, Richard Patrick
Dane, Richard Martin
Blood, Alexander Findlater
Delmege, Arthur James
Carson, Edward Henry
Ferguson, George Joseph Napier
Gordon, John
Orpen, John Richards

Trinity 1877
(Tuesday 29th May 1877)
Joyce, John

Michaelmas 1877
(Friday 9th November 1877)
Murphy, Nicholas Daniel
Samuels, Arthur Warren
Bodkin, Matthias McDonnell George
Robinson, Henry Lighton
Mayne, Joseph St Clair
Hennessy, Richard Martin
Fitzgerald, William
Smith, George Hill
Torrens, John
Rynd, William Henry
Hamilton, Frederick Alexander
  Pollock

Hilary 1878
(Friday 18th January 1878)
Brady, Andrew Newton
Long, Walter Edward

Easter 1878
(Wednesday 24th April 1878)
Shaw, James Johnston
Campbell, James Henry Mussen
Calwell, John Torrens
Maunsell, Edmund Robert Lloyd
Reid, Alexander John

Trinity 1878
(Saturday 8th June 1878)
White, Philip Augustine O'Connell
Pennefather, Frederick William
Atkinson, Edward Dupré

Michaelmas 1878
(Saturday 9th November 1878)
Vanston, George Thomas Barrett
Johnston, Robert
O'Connor, Charles Andrew
Bagge-Hearn, John William
Mahony, John McCarthy, Jun.
Kernan, John George
Carmichael-Ferrall, John
Cooke, John
Hannigan, Denis Francis
Hemphill, Stanhope Charles John
Scully, John

Hilary 1879
(Saturday 18th January 1879)
Bates, Arthur Henry
Meredith, Richard Edmund
Crotty, Richard Demsy
Black, William

Easter 1879
(Tuesday 22nd April 1879)
Kane, William Vincent
Molony, John
Moore, Joseph Henry Hamilton
Herrick, John Henry Beamish
Nagle, Garrett Thomas
Holmes, Alexander
Jones, Francis John
Neilson, William Horner
Suffern, William
Hickson, Edward Fitzgerald
Glynn, Patrick McMahon
Joynt, William Russell
Macalister, Robert
West, Henry Augustus
Bushe, Seymour Coghill

Trinity 1879

(Wednesday 11th June 1879)
Lynch, Francis
McMaster, John Boyle
Bourke, William Campbell
Travers, Robert
Nunn, John Henry *junior*

Michaelmas 1879

(Monday 10th November 1879)
Mostyn, James Newcome
Collins, Charles MacCarthy
Burtchaell, George Dames
Sullivan, Edward
Kenny, James David
Alcorn, James G.
Wilson, William Henry
Hassard, William
Bourke, Arthur Edward Desborough
Kenny, William Frederick
Jackson, Henry William
Battersby, Thomas
Stephenson Francis
Campbell, Harper
O'Brien, Richard P.
Ormsby, Alfred Hamilton
Brett, Joseph Patrick
Macinerney, Michael Chartres
Ross, John
Flood, Benjamin Thomas Bradley
FitzGibbon, Henry Macaulay

Hilary 1880

(Monday 19th January 1880)
O'Neill, Peter John
Armstrong, Richard
Marrable, Arthur
Murphy, Edward
Bustard, George
Barton, Dunbar Plunket
Staples, James Head
Atwool, Henry Richard Herbert
Corley, Henry Hagarty
Keating, Michael

Easter 1880

(Thursday 22nd April 1880)
Bolton, John Frederick
Boyd, Adolphus James
Allingham, John

Trinity 1880

(Tuesday 8th June 1880)
Pollock, Hugh
Lawless, Henry Hamilton
Feely, Edward Maurice
Mahony, Daniel Sullivan

Michaelmas 1880

(Tuesday 9th November 1880)
Thompson, John Gamble
Todd, Andrew
Gilliland, William Louis
Ringwood, Harry Perry
Barry, Ralph Westropp Brereton
Aylmer, Hans Hendrick
McLaughlin, James William
Ledwich, Frederick Francis
Adair, John Olphert
Dixon, George Yeates
Ormsby, Francis Balfour
Manders, Richard
Richards, John William
Colles, John Dawson Mayne
Waters, Charles Teeling
Digby, Everard
Courtenay, Arthur Henry
Andrews, Thomas John
Sheil, Richard Henry

Hilary 1881

(Tuesday 18th January 1881)
Lowry, John
Cramsie, Robert
Brown, Samuel Lombard
Ellis, William Edward
Alexander, George
Humphreys, John Thomas Conolly

Easter 1881

(Wednesday 27th April 1881)
O'Brien, Ignatius John
Purcell, Marmaduke Francis

Trinity 1881

(Wednesday 8th June 1881)
Edge, Joseph Saw
Murland, William

Michaelmas 1881

(Wednesday 9th November 1881)
Cherry, Richard Robert
Hume, George Alexander
Reed, Samuel Percy
Lawson, William
McHugh, Alfred
Whitaker, William Bailey Martin
O'Leary, Maurice Charles McCarthy
Overend, Henry Burleigh Lethem
Tarpey, William B.
Browne, Daniel Francis
Moffat, Charles Bethune
Kenny, Michael Edward
Bailey, William Frederick
Teeling, Luke Alexander
Blood-Smyth, John Lowe

Fleming, Patrick David
Leech, John
Bird, James William
Mulhall, John Joseph
Kehoe, Daniel

Hilary 1882
(Wednesday 18th January 1882)
McGrenahan, Michael Feely
O'Farrell, Edward
Hennessy, William Charles
Austin, Henry Evans

Easter 1882
(Saturday 22nd April 1882)
McElroy, Patrick Joseph
Newell, Robert John

Trinity 1882
(Thursday 8th June 1882)
O'Shanahan, James

Michaelmas 1882
(Thursday 9th November 1882)
Harrison, Robert Francis
Bastable, Charles Francis
Kilpatrick, William Archibald
Ross, William Philip
Jellett, William Morgan
Conner, Henry Daniel
May, George Chichester
Lucas, Robert William
Tisdall, George Archibald
Jefferson, Wood Gibson
Taylor, John Francis
Porter, Classon
Carroll, Redmond Francis
Walker, Garrett William
MacGillycuddy, John

Hilary 1883
(Thursday 18th January 1883)
Walsh, John Fitz
Studdert, Jones Waller
Brown, Hugh Dunlop
Connolly, Edward

Easter 1883
(Monday 23rd April 1883)
Alcock, George
Eason, Charles
Crookshank, Charles Henry
Moran, Norbert Louis
Drury, Thomas Chalmers
Keightley, Samuel Robert
Ross, William Augustus
Kearney, Edward Henry

Trinity 1883
(Friday 8th June 1883)
Tuohy, Patrick John
Ball, William Paumier
Raphael, John Rowan
Coffey, George
McDowell, Robert
Casey, Henry Edward Macmahon
Dowse, Richard
Shaw, James Herbert
Bourne, Thomas Morgan Richard
Young, Goodwin

Michaelmas 1883
(Friday 9th November 1883)
Fetherstonhaugh, Godfrey
Creed, John Percy
Hunt, Henry
Dillon, Henry Joseph
Lynam, William
McIldowie, James Mantell
Tombe, George Gordon
Gilmore, John Edward
Richards, Henry
Foot, Albert Revell
Grant, James
Leech, Hunt Walsh Chambre

Hilary 1884
(Friday 18th January 1894)
Hime, Maurice Charles
Patchell, John Robert
Bagwell, Frèderick Taylor
Denning, Frederick Ffolliott
Bernard, James Symes

Easter 1884
(Wednesday 23rd April 1884)
Keogh, George Darrell

Trinity 1884
(Wednesday 11th June 1884)
Johnstone, Eustace Meredyth Martin
Christie, David Wilson
Todd, Robert
Woods, Robert Hewitt
Orr, William
Sandford, John Beach

Michaelmas 1884
(Monday 10th November 1884)
Le Fanu, William Richard
Moane, Michael
Wright, Richard
Patton, Arthur St. George
Barry, Charles David
Figgis, Herbert Benjamin
Lynch, Henry Charles

Healy, Timothy Michael, M.P.
Maguire, Henry Joseph
Murray, James William Brady
Kelly, Henry Greene
Griffin, Gerald
Synnott, Walter Joseph
Houston, Frederick Henry

Hilary 1885
(Monday 19th January 1885)
Cooper, Mark Bloxham
Webb, Gerald Cairns
England, William George
Gaynor, Joseph Edward
Nolan, Patrick James
Wakely, John
Conlan, William
Lowry, James Moody

Easter 1885
(Wednesday 22nd April 1885)
Mann, William Henry
Henry, Denis Stanislaus
Macmullen, George Reade
Morgan, John Henry Spread

Trinity 1885
(Monday 8th June 1885)
Leamy, Edmund, M.P.
Staunton, Peter Maurice
Sellors, Edward Marmaduke
Harris, Reginald Thomas
Sullivan, William
Stubbs, William Cotter
Hamilton, Andrew Breakey
Dickson, John MacGeagh

Michaelmas 1885
(Monday 9th November 1885)
Donaldson, John
Stanley, John
Raymond, James William
Adair, John Frederick
Byrne, James Benjamin
Wilson, Daniel James
Campbell-Gaussen, Perceval David
    William
Wilson, Daniel Martin
Anderson, Barcroft
Eccles, William
Baker, Ronald Hepburn
Dames-Longworth, Edward Travers
McMordie, Hans

Hilary 1886
(Monday 18th January 1886)
Gray, John
Posnett, Hutcheson Macaulay
Pim, Jonathan Ernest
Maguire, Joseph
Christian, Jonathan
Gamble, Richard Keene

Easter 1886
(Thursday 22nd April 1886)
Scott, James Emerson
Kelly, Richard J.
Newcomen, George Arnold
Godley, John

Trinity 1886
(Tuesday 8th June 1886)
Meredith, Arthur Francis Carew
Maxwell, Thomas Henry
Byrne, Coleman Michael
Shannon, George Henry
Clarke, Matthew John
Murphy, Michael
Powell, Robert Arthur
Maxwell, James Patrick

Michaelmas 1886
(Tuesday 9th November 1886)
Osborne, Robert Ernest
Plunkett, George Noble
Harrison, Thomas
Sheehan, James Joseph
Gardner, William Charles
Greene, George Comerford
Ennis, Edward Armstrong, *junior*
O'Rorke, William Edward
Dobbin, James Sheridan Knowles
Dillon, Charles
Gallagher, John
Wilson, Robert Mackay Wiliam
Barlow, Francis Faris
Chambers, James
Austen, Henry
Kelly, Patrick Joseph
Ennis, Edward Henry

Hilary 1887
(Tuesday 18th January 1887)
Upward, George Allen
Smith, Philip Henry Law
Smith, John Irvine
Greene, Ernest Henry

Falkiner, Caesar Litton
Wilson, Herbert
Redmond, Frederick
McGrath, William Martin
Murphy, Michael Joseph
Lloyd, Humphrey Wilmot
Harrington, Timothy, M.P.
Johnstone, Robert Stewart

Easter 1887
(Friday 22nd April 1887)
O'Brien, Patrick Francis
Hughes, Henry Charles
Corvan, Clarence William
Cronin, Dominic
Morrogh, Robert B.
Bowen, Henry Charles Cole
Clancy, John Joseph, M.P.

Trinity 1887
(Wednesday 8th June 1887)
Brown, William H.
Dunne, Charles William Henry
Greene, Arthur Alexander
Paul, Samuel Wentworth
Russell, John Henry Sinclair
O'Kennedy, John Joseph Karbry
Mulligan, William George
Moorhead, Frederick William
Hamilton, Edwin
Wallace, John

Michaelmas 1887
(Wednesday 9th November 1887)
McIlroy, Robert
Molony, Thomas Francis
Gorham, Alfred
Abraham Richard
MacDermot, Charles E.
Barrington, Manliff
Murphy, Charles
Richey, Henry Alexander
Horner, Andrew Long
Johnson, John Daniel Andrew
Herdman, John Octavius
Hamilton, Edmund Hardy
Wyer, Matthew Daly
Moore, William
Littlevale, Richard William Whaley
O'Carroll, Louis Ely
Cuming, Francis Edward
Redmond, John Edward, M.P.

Hilary 1888
(Wednesday 18th January 1888)
Willington, James Thomas Cambie
Wade, Edward Robert
Yates, Charles
Condon, James Edmund Smith
Steele, Lawrence Edward
O'Sullivan, Daniel

Easter 1888
(Monday 23rd April 1888)
Kilbride, Joseph
Hynes, John William
Sullivan, Patrick Donald
Ringwood, Richard Frederic
Dalton, James Joseph
Deasy, John, M.P.
Campbell, William Bernard
Hickie, Charles Valentine
O'Connell, William Arthur

Trinity 1888
(Friday 8th June 1888)
Brunskill, Gerald Fitzgibbon
Cathcart, Robert
Ewart, Frederick William
Lynch, Patrick Gregory
O'Brien, Charles Andrew
Barry, Redmond John
Johns, Edward Henry

Michaelmas 1888
(Friday 9th November 1888)
King, Robert MacFarland
Watts, William Newell
Litton, Edward de l'Establire
Doyle, Charles Francis
Porter, William Henry
Smyly, Philip Crampton
Burke, Matthew Alexander
Longfield, Mountifort George
Henry, Wesley Pettigrew

Hilary 1889
(Friday 18th January 1889)
Roper, Charles Edward Alexander
McGusty, George Alfred
Crawford, Alexander Ross
Kenny, Matthew Joseph, M.P.

Easter 1889
(Wednesday 24th April 1889)
Jordan, Augustus Christopher
McCance, John Stouppe Finlay

Trinity 1889
(Wednesday 12th June 1889)
Scully, Darby
Hill, Richard Cotton Walker
McNulty, Thomas
McAuley, Joseph
Crosbie, George
Wilson, Robert Christopher Kidd
Hoare, Thomas Edward

Michaelmas 1889
(Saturday 9th November 1889)
Joynt, Albert Edward Russell
Doyle, Robert Joseph
Stokes, Henry John
McDonald, Allan
Little, Isaac
Ryan, William Albert
McCarthy, Michael John
Fawcett, Jasper Evelyn
Bartley, John
Hall, William Clarke
Gowan, James Robert

Hilary 1890
(Saturday 18th January 1890)
Stuart, Alan Lenox Conyngham
Henry, George Hewitt
Murphy, Charles O'Brien

Easter 1890
(Tuesday 22nd April 1890)
Keenan, Norbert Michael
Lockhart, Henry

Trinity 1890
(Monday 9th June 1890)
Esmonde, Laurence Grattan
Hackett, Arthur Frederick
Chaytor, David Grainger
O'Byrne, Edward Alexander
Burke, Joseph Bermingham
Crawford, Alfred Douglas
Stritch, Andrew O'Quaelley Russell
MacCarthy, John Henry
Cullinan, Henry Cooke
Moore, Hugh Hamilton
Kelleher, James
Macartney-Filgate, Edward

Michaelmas 1890
(Monday 10th November 1890)
Stewart, Thomas
Oldham, Charles Hubert
Burke, William Anthony
Faulkner, Thomas Patrick
Pigot, John Henry

Morris, Martin Henry Fitzpatrick
Flanagan, James Woulfe
Breakey, William Alexander

Hilary 1891
(Monday 19th January 1891)
Joly, Jaspar John
Carton, Joseph John
Thompson, Isaac
O'Connor Morris, Maurice Lindsay
Harris, Edwin
Vaughan, Henry
Redmond, William Hoey Kearney,
   M.P.
Farrelly, Michael James

Easter 1891
(Wednesday 22nd April 1891)
Linehan, John
Jones, Herbert William
Hardy, William Johnston
Doherty, Patrick Edward

Trinity 1891
(Monday 8th June 1891)
White, Jasper Thomas
Browning, Francis Henry
Healy, John J.C
Barnhill, William Wilson

Michaelmas 1891
(Monday 2nd November 1891)
Poole, Hewitt Robert
Smyth, Thomas Jones
FitzGibbon, Gerald
Richardson, Henry Ernest
Batty, Espine Fitzherbert
Byrne, John P.
McCotter, Frank
Boyd, Walter Herbert
Keily, John Townsend
Butler, John Piers
Roche, Charles Redington
Longfield, Henry Foster
Harrel, Alfred Gisborne Wharton
MacMahon, John
Toomey, William Gosselin
Morgan-Byrne, Henry Alexander

Hilary 1892
(Monday 18th January 1892)
Gibson, Thomas Henry
McGonigal, John
Kelly, Joseph Francis
O'Hanlon, Oriel John
Harvey, Ernest Louis

Easter 1892
(Wednesday 27th April 1892)
Maturin, Charles
O'Sullivan, Roger John
Howley, John Gerard

Trinity 1892
(Wednesday 8th June 1892)
McGrath, Joseph
McCann, Thomas S.
Collum, Arthur Percival Tod
Nolan, Pierce Laurence
Browne, Harvey
Wilson, Charles John
Sullivan, Alexander M.
Traill, James Anthony
Crowe, Henry
Malcolmson, William Henry
Harvey, Edward Augustine

Michaelmas 1892
(Tuesday 1st November 1892)
Johnston, William John
Shortt, Francis Hely
Parker, William Nassau
Luke, Edward Harris
O'Conor, Brian E
Collins, Edward Tenison
Johnston, Henry Thomas Gerrard
   Stuart
Spratt, Horner Devereux
Orme, Robert

Hilary 1893
(Wednesday 18th January 1893)
Dickie, Alexander Alfred
Cusack, John
Rosenthal, Lionel Henry
Dobbin, Francis Knowles
Sandes, John
Harrison, James Whitelaw Stronge

Easter 1893
(Saturday 22nd April 1893)
Healy, Francis Jerome Burke
Colclough, John George

Trinity 1893
(Thursday 8th June 1893)
O'Byrne, Patrick Joseph
McLoone, James
De Renzy, Annesley St. George
Greer, Frank Nugent
Magennis, William
Ball, John William
McEntire, Alexander Knox

Michaelmas 1893
(Wednesday 1st November 1893)
Megaw, Robert Dick
Macrory, Robert Henry
Ennis, John Joseph
Barry, Jas. J. McCarthy
Buckley, Jeremiah
Greene, George Courtenay Ball
Williamson, James
Carbery, William Joseph

Hilary 1894
(Thursday 18th January 1894)
Kerr, James Patrick
Brennan, Thomas Joseph
Sloss, Francis Alexander
Dromgoole, Charles
Leahy, Daniel Vincent
Pringle, Robert William
Meldon, Walter Dominick
McNeill, John Hill Trevor

Easter 1894
(Monday 23rd April 1894)
Briscoe, Henry Whitby
Tweedy, Richard Thomas
Muldoon, John
O'Connor, George Richard

Trinity 1894
(Friday 8th June 1894)
Byrne, William J.
McAuliffe, Michael Joseph
Jones, Bolton C.
Murphy, James Fitzgerald
Henry, Alexander Patterson
Brayden, William Henry
Rice, James Patrick
Thornhill, Thomas
Millin, Samuel Shannon
De la Cour, Robert William

Michaelmas 1894
(Thursday 1st November 1894)
Robb, Frederick Joseph
Townsend, William Richard
Murphy, William Agnew
Campbell, Robert Seymour
Powell, John Blake

Hilary 1895
(Friday 18th January 1895)
Kelly, Patrick
Kelly, Lawrence John O'Brien
MacLaine, George Langtry
Coll, Edmond Christopher

McGrath, William
Roche, Bernard
Seeds, James Thompson
Malcomson, Claude John
O'Flynn, Alphonsus Maria

Easter 1895
(Wednesday 24th April 1895)
Kennedy, Thomas
Allison, Edwin George

Trinity 1895
(Saturday 18th June 1895)
Little, Edward Joseph
Chadwick, Robert St. James
Chute, Charles George Falkiner
Best, Richard
Jefferson, James Fulton
Harley, Thomas Turner
Traill, Robert Gayer [Major]

Michaelmas 1895
(Friday 1st November 1895)
Baxter, James Sinclair
Monahan, Henry James
Sullivan, Timothy
Glover, William Erskine
Mitchell, Reginald Alfred
White, William Jeffrey
Price, Frederick William
West, Erskine Eyre
Gaussen, Stewart Macnaghten
    Pennefather Ash
Mooney, John Joseph
McCracken, William John
Holmes, William
Ryland, Richard Theodore Hughes
Murphy, William Quinlan
Coyne, William Patrick
MacDonnell, Charles Randal
    Armstrong

Hilary 1896
(Saturday 18th January 1896)
Macnamara, Michael Augustus
Neligan, William Noel
O'Donnell, Daniel
Norwood, William Stuart
Browne, Keppel Glenny Dodwell

Easter 1896
(Wednesday 22nd April 1896)
Moore, Thomas Levins

Trinity 1896
(Monday 8th June 1896)
Barcroft, Richard Cecil
Gilbert, Henry
McEligott, Edward John
McSweeney, George
Lavan, Michael Gibson
Caruth, Alexander
Bridgeman, Joseph Kirwan
Wheeler, Henry Eliardo
Little, James

Michaelmas 1896
(Monday 2nd November 1896)
Whitaker, John Martin
Healy, Richard
Hanna, Henry
Leet, Ernest Fleetwood
Coyle, James Vincent
Brady, John Cochrane
Dunlop, Robert Alexander
Gaynor, John Patrick
Swifte, Ernest Godwin Meade

Hilary 1897
(Monday 18th January 1897)
Dolmage, Cecil Goodrich Julius

Easter 1897
(Thursday 22nd April 1897)
Ellison, Martin Gore
Keogh, Edward Joseph Lorean

Trinity 1897
(Tuesday 8th June 1897)
Delaney, Patrick
Rice, Robert
Sinclair, William Hugh Montgomery
Hunt, Frederick John Robert
Walsh, Arthur Hepburn
Bushe, Arthur Plunket
Meade, Christopher Henry Barry
Gibson, William George
Rainsford, Edwin Grome
Daly, James Dermot
Bourke, Geoffrey Theobald Joseph
Nelson, Howard Arthur
Marnan, Thomas Gerald
Devenish-Meares, John Frederick
Robinson, Wiliam Henry

Michaelmas 1897
(Monday 1ˢᵗ November 1897)
Miller, Sir Alexander Edward, C.S.I.
  [i.e., Companion of the Order of the
  Star of India]
McCutcheon, Robert Ross
Hogan, Patrick Joseph
Collins, Edward Alphonsus
Carrigan, William
Condon, John Patrick
White, Dudley
Madden, John Clements Waterhouse
Kenny, Edward Henry
Doherty, James Walker
Crawley, William Stoker Chetwode
Waddell, John Joseph Harrison Kinsey
Daniell, Robert George
Cowl, Richard Pape
Connor, Arthur Ernest
Greer, Edward

Hilary 1898
(Tuesday 18ᵗʰ January 1898)
Todd, William Francis
Murphy, Charles William
Teeling, Samuel George
Downing, Daniel McCarthy
MacKenzie, Vivian St. Clair
Sweetman, Roger
Orpen, Richard Theodore
Sutherland, John Joseph
Phelps, Ernest James
Peart, John R.

Easter 1898
(Friday 22ⁿᵈ April 1898)
Jones, Hume Riversdale
Whitfield, George
Kemmis, Edward Bernhard
Upington, Beauclerk

Trinity 1898
(Wednesday 8ᵗʰ June 1898)
Burke, Thomas
Griffin, Charles James
Weir, John Charles
Steen, David Miller
Walsh, Patrick Stanislaus
Slyne, Denis
Brett, George Henry
Harvey, Albert William
O'Neill, Vincent Joseph
O'Brien, Daniel J.

Michaelmas 1898
(Thursday 1ˢᵗ November 1898)
Park, Robert Spencer
Davison, John Clarke
Nunan, Joseph John
Houston, Arthur Henry
Comyn, Michael
Mahony, Pierce Charles de Lacy
Porter, Andrew Marshall
Crozier, William Magee
Robb, John Hanna
Drennan, John Thomas
Walsh, John Edward
Butler, Edward Gerald
Dickinson, Cyril Henry

Hilary 1899
(Wednesday 18ᵗʰ January 1899)
O'Mahony, John
Crean, John Berchmans
Smith, Stephen Catterson

Easter 1899
(Saturday 22ⁿᵈ April 1899)
Calvert, Robert Henry
Sweetman, James Michael
Mitchell, Robert Armstrong
Morell, Wilfrid Lawson

Trinity 1899
(Thursday 8ᵗʰ June 1899)
Lyhane, Cornelius
O'Brien, James
Kennedy, Francis Charles
Gibson, *Hon.* Victor
Mayne, Herbert Pelham
Little, Joseph Christopher
Davidson, John Craig Nelson
FitzSimon, Robert Louis Patrick
Sullivan, Joseph

Michaelmas 1899
(Wednesday 1ˢᵗ November 1899)
Purvis, William Johnston
Henry, James
Leonard, Robert Galloway Louis
Garland, Richard Charles
FitzGerald-Kenney, James C.
Roche, Christopher
Louden, Thomas
Dodd, William Huston
Willis, Gilbert de Laval
Hayes, Samuel
Julian, James Edward John
Upington, Arthur
Lidwill, Robert Arthur

JOHN M. WHITAKER.   WILLIAM JOHNSTON PURVIS.

THE BROOKE SCHOLARS OF 1896 AND 1899.

Whitaker (1872-1943) was afterwards a Professor at King's Inns; Purvis (1874-1907), who practised on the N.E. Circuit, died young.

SAMUEL C. PORTER.   JOHN EDMOND WARNOCK.

POLITICIANS IN NORTHERN IRELAND

In 1918 Samuel Porter (H 1903) contested the Belfast (Pottinger) Division for the Labour Representative Committee. J.E. Warnock (M 1911) was M.P. (N.I. Parl.) for Belfast (St. Anne's), 1938-69, and successively Minister of Home Affairs and Attorney General.

All four of these portrait photographs show past pupils of the Methodist College, Belfast, and are taken from J.W. Henderson's admirable record volume, *Methodist College Belfast 1868-1938* (2 vols.; Belfast, 1939). William Black and J.S.R. Cole (photographs, p. 122, *supra*) and William Johnston (whose studio portrait appears on p. 418 *infra*) were other barrister-Old Boys of the largest grammar school in Ireland, as were the unphotographed Charles Bartley, John Octavius Herdman, Walter Clarence Huggard and Robert Spencer Park.

Hilary 1900
(Thursday 18th January 1900)
Armstrong, William Reginald
Atkinson, Thomas Joyce
Dunlop, James Marcus Muntz
Bulloch, Alexander Miller
Ronayne, Edward Camillus
MacDermot, Bernard T.J.
Carter, Jasper James

Easter 1900
(Wednesday 25th April 1900)
Nixon, Christopher William
Gerrard, John Denison Wardell

Trinity 1900
(Thursday 14th June 1900)
O'Neill, Hugh O'Hagan
McKean, John
Smylie, Robert Romilly
Tighe, Robert Dolphin
Duncan, Samuel Joseph

Michaelmas 1900
(Thursday 1st November 1900)
Burke, James Michael
Campbell, Thomas Joseph
O'Connor, James
Evans, Roberts Walter
Andrews, James
Newett, Arthur Conyngham
Toomey, William
Stronge, Herbert Cecil
Hewson, John Gilbert
Finny, William Watson
O'Callaghan, Edward John
O'Connor, James John Mary
Babington, Anthony Brutus

Hilary 1901
(Friday 18th January 1901)
Devitt, St. Lawrence Ernest Joseph
Brunskill, Gerald FitzGibbon
Black, William Bullick
Ryan, Leonard Morrogh
Leech, Arthur Graves

Easter 1901
(Monday 22nd April 1901)
Gibson, Edward Graves Mayne
Moore, Samuel
Atkinson, William Herbert

Trinity 1901
(Saturday 8th June 1901)
Browne, James Swan
Hart, George Vaughan
Atkinson, Cecil Thomas
Vincent, Arthur Rose
Stack-Murphy, Jerome O'Donoghue
Murphy, Stanislaus P.
Mooney, Frederick Michael
Dobbin, William Tertius
Pearse, Patrick Henry

Michaelmas 1901
(Friday 1st November 1901)
Macafee, William
Smith, Raymond Walter Aquilla
Seale, Edward Gilbert
Figgis, Edward Allen Keene
Horan, Gerald
Morris, Hon. Michael Redmond
Wallace, James
Tobias, Theodore Cronhelm

(Tuesday 3rd December 1901)
Meredith, James Creed

Hilary 1902
(Saturday 18th January 1902)
O'Leary, Daniel
Sealy, James
Patton, Thomas
Law, Arthur Gerald Sidney
Ross, Arthur Patrick

Easter 1902
(Tuesday 22nd April 1902)
Hague, William Vesey
Cosgrave, Maurice
Bolton, Albert Denne
Corley, Harry Cecil
Norton, David Richmond

Trinity 1902
(Monday 9th June 1902)
Dick, William
O'Neill, Henry
Lowry, Henry Edgar
Lewin, Frederick Henry
Campbell, William
Wood, Robert Albert Ernest
Lehane, Cornelius
Barrett, William
Overend, Andrew Kingsbury
Bewley, Edward Dawson
Place, George William

Two Northern Ireland judges, both called in Michaelmas Term 1900: (left) Sir James Andrews [1877-1951], 3rd Lord Chief Justice of Northern Ireland; and (right) Anthony Brutus Babington [1877-1972], a Lord Justice of Appeal, who received as a wedding present the copyright of R.E. Osborne's *The Jurisdiction and Practice of County Courts in Ireland in Equity and Probate Matters*.

King's Inns Barristers, 1868-2004, page 339

A REMINISCENCE OF THE KING'S INNS

In *Hamlet* Ophelia says 'we know what we are but know not what we may be'. Hamlet himself tells Horatio –

> There's a divinity that shapes our ends
> Rough hew them how we will.

The prophetic truth of these words struck me the other day on glancing down the list of students in the Continuous Course Examination of the Junior Class at the King's Inns in the year 1899 — nigh twenty golden years ago. The list was the last to bear the signature of that friend of a long succession of law students, John David O'Hanlon, whose individuality was so Celtic and whose memory is still kept green. He was the Under Treasurer from the year 1865, and had been called to the Bar in 1845, when Queen Victoria was only eight years on the throne, and eight years before the call of Christopher Palles, Lord Chief Baron of the Exchequer — the last in time and the first in his great wealth of jurisprudence of a right royal line of Barons of the Exchequer — *clarum et venerabile nomen*. The class had a roll-call of 48. Name No. 8 on the list is that of P.H. Pearse, President of the insurrectionary Irish Republic of Easter Week, 1916 and Commander-in-Chief of its forces, who fell in front of a firing squad at Kilmainham on May 4, 1916. In those days, in the eyes of his class-fellows, Pearse's 'life was gentle', his ways studious, and his manner retiring. His name follows in the list that of a student [Daniel L. O'Leary, M.P. for West Cork, 1916-18] now M.P. for a division of Cork County. Nearby is printed the name of the present Clerk of the Crown and Hanaper — Gerald Horan, K.C. H.C. Stronge exercises jurisdiction in the far-off tropical Bahamas. C.T. Atkinson is a Judge of the High Court in Assam. One is in practice in a new town in the farthest Canadian West. Another enforces the *lex Britannica* among the uplands of Nigeria. One whom I would particularly select from that long throng — T.J. Atkinson (†) — fell fighting as a Major of the Royal Irish Fusiliers leading his men in the Ulster Division's superb advance on the Somme on July 1, 1916. It was a day of glory on a stricken field. Among the brave men who fell there to free these islands from the constant threat of war none was more quietly steadfast than T.J. Atkinson. Another name on this list — that of W.J. Purvis — should be rescued from the dust of oblivion. The awards of the Victoria Prizes were to — (1) W.S. Purvis (94.9), (2) T.J. Campbell (94.6), and (3) J.M. Burke (90.0). Purvis had won the Inns of Court Studentship in Hilary 1899, and his death soon after his call at the dawn of what promised to be a career of rare distinction took from the Irish Bar a scientific jurist and 'a scholar, and a ripe and good one'. Of others in that goodly band I say with Praed—

> And some compose a tragedy,
> And some compose a rondo,
> And some draw swords for liberty,
> And some draw pleas for John Doe.

[An anonymous contribution to the *Irish Law Times* of 14 July 1917, p. 171.]

† T.J. Atkinson (called H 1900) became a solicitor, and his name appears on the Solicitors' Memorial at the Four Courts.

Michaelmas 1902
(Saturday 1st November 1902)
Holmes, Robert Francis
Fitz-Henry, William Albert
Clery, Arthur Edward
Thompson, Herbert Marshall
Geoghegan, Hanbury Clements
Moles, James
Orr, Robert Davison
Kennedy, Frederick Alexander
Rigg, Richard, M.P.
Atkinson, Joseph Albert Nelson
McConnell, James
O'Donoghue, John
Evans, Samuel William
Kennedy, Hugh

Hilary 1903
(Monday 19th January 1903)
Murphy, Oliver
Porter, Samuel Clarke
Johnston, John Alexander Weir
Darley, Cecil Hastings
Longworth, Ernest Victor

Easter 1903
[No Call: *vide supra*, page 77]

Trinity 1903
(Tuesday 9th June 1903)
Lepper, John Heron
Kelly, Louis O'Sullivan
O'Grady, Guillamore
Hughes, James Lawrence Joseph
Burrowes, Paul
Callan, Walter Ernest Everard
Allen, Robert Lougheed
Mayston, William Hume
Jones, Percy James Colvill

Michaelmas 1903
(Monday 2nd November 1903)
Murnaghan, James Augustine
Murphy, Edward Sullivan
Cowdy, Henry Lloyd
Atkinson, George Glanville
Townshend, George
Fforde, Cecil Robert
MacErlean, Donogh Aloysius
Matheson, Arthur Victor
Wood, Benjamin Ussher
Julian, Ernest Lawrence
Allen, David
Kough, Charles Norman

Hilary 1904
(Monday 18th January 1904)
Lowry, Frederick James Sharples
Farran, Edmond Chomley
O'Shaughnessy, Thomas Lopdell
Sherlock, David Thomas Joseph
Daly, Oscar Bedford
Rice, Vincent
Lynch, Michael Breen
Nolan-Whelan, James V.

Easter 1904
(Friday 22nd April 1904)
Weekes, Charles Alexander

Trinity 1904
(Wednesday 8th June 1904)
Cullinan, Robert Hornidge
FitzGerald, John Mary
Clarke, Edward Stanley
Pim, William Harvey
Lillis, Richard Joseph
Kennedy, Henry Edward
Higgins, Thomas Alfred
Verschoyle, Hamilton Frederick Stuart Goold
Hamilton, John Miller
Kinahan, Henry
Butler, William James
Ryan, John Vincent

Michaelmas 1904
(Tuesday 1st November 1904)
Edgar, John Hammond
Fitzgibbon, Frank
MacDermot, Henry
Macken, James Joseph
McWilliam, William
McCann, Hugh Joseph Lawrence
Shannon, George William
Dawson, William
Shaw, James Rowan
Rutherford, Andrew Adams
Colquhoun, David William Sproule
Atkinson, Thomas John Day

Hilary 1905
(Wednesday 18th January 1905)
Rearden, James Ambrose
Wylie, William Evelyn
Begley, Marcus Dill
Walker, Robert
Harbinson, William Dawson
Mecredy, Mervyn Hugh
Gogarty, Henry Hamill Devereux
Maunsell, Richard John Caswell

Easter 1905
(Wednesday 26th April 1905)
Reid, John Hamilton
Steadman, David Addie
Sweeny, Francis T.

Trinity 1905
(Thursday 8th June 1905)
Coffey, Alfred
Treacy, John Joseph
Williams, Maurice Swift
Russell, Charles Verner Wallace
Carson, William Henry Webster
Ross, Angus Coleman
O'Sullivan, Joseph P.
O'Donnell, Thomas
Goligher, William Alexander
O'Carroll, Richard Patrick
Dorgan, Joseph
O'Conor, Denis Charles Joseph

Michaelmas 1905
(Wednesday 1st November 1905)
Kingan, Thomas Davison
Hamilton, Gustavus Everard
McKean, Edward John
Murray, John
MacGowan, Robert Michael
Phillips-Conn, Thomas Harry
  Meredith
Fahy, Edward

Hilary 1906
(Thursday 18th January 1906)
Cullinan, Charles Bartholomew
White, Robert Grove
Moore, Edmund John
Sadleir, Thomas Ulick
Davey, William Hamilton
Kinahan, Robert Joseph Ignatius

Easter 1906
(Wednesday 25th April 1906)
Macinerney, Edwin
Kettle, Thomas Michael

Trinity 1906
(Friday 8th June 1906)
Orr, James William
Findlater, Adam Seaton
Meek, Samuel Rea
O'Connor, Joseph
Murphy, Harold Lawson
Phelan, Cecil Bernard Swinhoe
Barton, Cecil Molyneux
Condon, Denis FitzGerald
Proud, Francis Harvey
Healy, John Crichton

Ginnell, Lawrence

Michaelmas 1906
(Thursday 1st November 1906)
Whitton, Henry McManus
Black, Arthur Edward
McConnell, James Adams
Moynagh, Frank A.
Healy, John Edward
Salmon, George
Glennon, Christopher Patrick
Moore, Arthur Robert
Gleeson, Paul
Arnold, John Corry

Hilary 1907
(Friday 18th January 1907)
Lowry, William
Kavanagh, Eugene Rupert
Linehan, Matthew Francis
Comyn, James Joseph
Roux, John Albert

Easter 1907
(Monday 22nd April 1907)
O'Neill, Denis Joseph
Houston, Ross
Burke, William

Trinity 1907
(Saturday 8th June 1907)
Copinger, William Frederick
Connolly, Cyril
Mahony, Edmond Ronayne
Huggard, Walter Clarence
Lipsett, William Alfred
Wall, Thomas Patrick
Walsh, James F.
Daly, George Joseph
Meredith, Richard Edmund
Brown, Thomas Watters
Donnelly, Henry Grattan
McWalter, James Charles
Allen, William Kennedy Abbott
Bury, Ambrose Upton Gledstane
Dougherty, John Gerald
Duffy, Bernard Joseph

Michaelmas 1907
(Friday 1st November 1907)
Sheehy, Richard Joseph
Maunder, Stephen Theodore Layton
Anderson, James
McGladery, Herbert
O'Donoghue, Patrick
Kenny, Vincent Raymond
Sheridan, Joseph Alfred
FitzGerald, Edward Martin

Moriarty, John F.
Lupton, Edmond
Campbell, Henry
Sands, Robert Radcliffe Lindsay

Hilary 1908
(Saturday 18th January 1908)
Ryan, Michael
Burke, Michael Canty
Taylor, Hugh Stowell Brown

Easter 1908
(Wednesday 22nd April 1910)
MacCormack, Francis Joseph

Trinity 1908
(Tuesday 9th June 1908)
Ward, Thomas Francis
Ryan, Frederick William
Smithwick, Michael
McElwaine, Percy Alexander
Bacon, Thomas Francis
Ross, Ernest Alexander
Corbett, Arthur Edward
Hamilton, Hubert Charles
Maher, John Herbert
Grubb, Richard
Gill, Roy Anthony Furlong
Stone, Herbert Kenwyn
Flood, Joseph Mary
Bonass, George Joseph

Michaelmas 1908
(Monday 2nd November 1908)
Swayne, Edmund Augustine
Shaw, Richard James Herbert
Gleeson, William Joseph
Crawley, Herbert Capel
MacKeown, William Wilson
Cummins, William Ashley
Macan, Arthur Vernon

Hilary 1909
(Monday 18th January 1909)
Webb, Ambrose Henry
Kenny, Joseph Patrick
Cruise, Henry Ernest Raleigh
Reid, James

Easter 1909
(Thursday 22nd April 1909)
Hickman, Poole Henry
Tyrrell, Robert Leslie

Trinity 1909
(Tuesday 8th June 1909)
Casey, William Francis
Benner, John
Dickinson, Harold Evory
Lee, Joseph Bagnal
Plunkett, Oliver
McQuoid, Norman Scott
Morris, Ernest Adolphus
  Montmorency
Monroe, James Harvey
Hungerford, Winspeare Campbell
  Augustus
Place, Charles Godfrey Morris
Quekett, Arthur Scott
Cotter, Francis MacCarthy
Naish, Redmond Joseph

Michaelmas 1909
(Monday 1st November 1909)
Moloney, Henry John
Ronayne, John Aloysius
Hughes, Thomas
Dickie, Thomas Wallace
Dagg, Thomas Sidney Charles
Joynt, William Lane
Macaulay, Arthur Harold

Hilary 1910
(Tuesday 18th January 1910)
McCarthy, Gerald Florence
Tierney, Herbert Joseph
O'Connor, Hubert Michael
Shannon, George William
Dockrell, Kenneth Brooks

Easter 1910
(Friday 22nd April 1910)
Spiro, Charles
O'Brien, Stephen

Trinity 1910
(Wednesday 8th June 1910)
Maunsell, Dudley Philip Winthrop
Donegan, Cornelius O'Kane
Kennedy, Alfred St. J.
Curran, Constantine Peter
Burke, Fitzstephen
Redmond, William Archer
Plunkett, Gerald
Early, James
Tighe, Macartan Hubert
Hunter, Robert John
Carey, Cecil William Victor
Healy, Maurice Francis
Young, Robert Chichester
Samuels, Arthur Purefoy Irwin

Michaelmas 1910
(Tuesday 1ˢᵗ November 1910)
Holmes, Hugh Oliver
Sugars, John Charles
Mahony, Pierce Gun
Sheehy, Eugene
Hughes, Bernard Edward
Murphy, Gerald Edgar
Hughes, George Spencer
MacErlean, Brian P.

Hilary 1911
(Wednesday 18ᵗʰ January 1911)
O'Byrne, John
Maguire, Martin Cyril
Ford, John Fowler
Cox, Vincent Aedan
Mathews, James Stanley
Cox, William Humphreys

Easter 1911
(Wednesday 26ᵗʰ April 1911)
Leland, John Henry Frederick
Malone, John Herbert

Trinity 1911
(Thursday 8ᵗʰ June 1911)
Sainsbury, William Leopold
Henderson, James
Meagher, Dominick Edward
Miley, John Felix
Ellis, Arthur Charles
MacDermot, Edward Wilfrid
Herrick, John Theodore Francis
Hegarty, Thomas Laurence Oswald
Lentaigne, Joseph Ignatius Nugent
Purcell, Herbert Kevin
(Monday 26ᵗʰ June 1911)
Duggan, James Stephen
(Tuesday 3ʳᵈ July 1911)
Sheehan, Daniel D.

Michaelmas 1911
(Wednesday 1ˢᵗ November 1911)
Duncan, John Colley
Richardson, John Joseph
Wall, John Richard
O'Connor, William Berchmans
Beatty, Cyril Joseph
Kenny, Charles Stewart
Warnock, John Edmond
Moonan, George Aloysius
McKane, Robert William
Callaghan, Alfred John
Coughlan, Arthur

Hilary 1912
(Thursday 18ᵗʰ January 1912)
Fitzgerald-Lombard, Roger Edward
McCorry, Patrick Leo

Easter 1912
(Saturday 8ᵗʰ June 1912)
Doig, Henry Stuart

Trinity 1912
(Saturday 8ᵗʰ June 1912)
Keeley, James Robert
Bodkin, Thomas
Campbell, Charles Stewart Parnell
Stephens, Edward Millington
Yeates, Richard Beverley
Thomas, Richard William
Forsayeth, Gordon William
Teeling, Theodore Francis
Smith-Chatterton, William Alleyne
Healy, Joseph
Crean, Bernard A.
Gordon, Alan Samuel
Stewart, Robert Rodgers
Henderson, Joseph Dunlop
Murphy, Nicholas Philip
Mooney, Edmund William Benjamin

Michaelmas 1912
(Friday 1ˢᵗ November 1912)
Blackall, Henry William Butler
Farrell, Gerald Patrick
Lemass, Edwin Stephen
Morrissey, Thomas Joseph
Coffey, Hugh Diarmid James
Kenny, Cecil Stackpoole
Gahagan, James Henry
Hanbury, Hubert [Thornburgh]
Munn, Lionel Oulton Moore
Pringle, James Alexander
Lipsett, Lewis Richard

Hilary 1913
(18ᵗʰ and 20ᵗʰ January 1913)
Rice, Joseph A.
Kelly, Arthur Burke
Sullivan, Denis Brendan

['Messrs. Rice and Sullivan were called on Saturday 18ᵗʰ inst. Mr. A.B. Kelly, who did not attain 21 years of age until the 19ᵗʰ, was called on the 20ᵗʰ inst.': *I.L.T. & S.J.*, 1913, p. 29].

Trinity 1913
(Monday 9th June 1913)
Powell, Ashley
Crawford, Alfred
Turbett, Ivan Joliffe Tufnell
Smyth, George Bestall Jenkinson
McCormick, Hilgrove
Jameson, James Algerna Durand
Sharpe, Samuel Howard
Sheridan, Francis Stephen
Mockler, James Swayne
Cullinan, George Critchley
Hand, William Joseph
Jackson, James Alfred
Williamson, Robert Cecil
Doran, Charles Frederick Garfield
MacCarthy, Cornelius Aloysius
O'Toole, Patrick Albert
Rice, Samuel
Lane, Richard Donal
Gentleman, John Wesley
Muldoon, Joseph Malachi

Michaelmas 1913
(Saturday 1st November 1913)
O'Brien, George Thomas
Reay, James McCabe
McNeill, Robert Norman
Dixon, Joseph Henry
Webb, John Joseph
Power, Charles Stewart
O'Shiel, Kevin Roantree
Beattie, William
Proctor, James Claude Beauchamp
Lardner, James C.R.

Hilary 1914
(Monday 12th January 1914)
Bewley, Charles Henry
Hoy, Edward Mark
Mathews, Patrick Duff
Mooney, Gerald Kingston
Burgess, Robert Balderston

Easter 1914
(Thursday 23rd April 1914)
Donovan, John Thomas

Trinity 1914
(Wednesday 10th June 1914)
Dempsey, Frederick Jerome
Smyth, Edward James
John, Samuel Spedding
Hughes, Thomas William Gillilan
   Johnson
Kelly, Denis Bernard
Moriarty, Oliver L.

Maher Loughnan, John
Roundtree, Isaac
Wakely, Ian George
Newell, Peter
Fox, Bernard Joshua
Shaw, John Henry de Burgh
Callaghan, Frederick William
MacMahon, John
McCarron, Edward Patrick
Waters, James Arthur Hill
Hume, Walter Oakman
Lillis, Martin Arthur
Picken, Andrew
Reddy, Joseph Alphonsus
Carvill, John Henry

Michaelmas 1914
(Monday 2nd November 1914)
Meagher, James Francis
Costello, John Aloysius
Byrne, Gerald
Conner, Henry Longfield
FitzGerald, Albert Victor Stewart
Ryan, Edward Arthur
Mulligan, George Angus
Ogilvy, John Frederick

Hilary 1915
(Monday 18th January 1915)
Black, Arthur

Easter 1915
(Wednesday 21st April 1915)
Grant, Charles William

Trinity 1915
(Wednesday 9th June 1915)
Cassedy, James
O'Meara, Arthur Joseph
Hughes, Hector Samuel James
Hussain, Javad
Haq, Mohammed Abdul
Varma, Bepin B.
Moore, Charles Tyrrell
Carney, John Francis
Robinson, Adrian
Coghlan, Joseph Patrick

Michaelmas 1915
(Monday 1st November 1915)
Lavery, Cecil Patrick Linton
O'Sullivan, Patrick
Finlay, Thomas Aloysius
Hannan, Matthew Joseph
Mullett, Hugh Aloysius
Geoghegan, James
Perry, Jeremiah George

Hilary 1916
(Tuesday 18th January 1916)
McGuckin, Basil
Davitt, Cathar
Weatherup, William
Lakshminarayana, Vunnava
Quin, Herbert

Easter 1916
(Friday 26th May 1916)
Powell, Arthur Patrick Joseph

Trinity 1916
(Wednesday 21st June 1916)
Molony, Henry Patrick
O'Doherty, Louis Casimir
Rice, John Herman
Giri, Varahagiri Venkata
Thalpasaye, Pangulury Sesha
Crowley, Jeremiah
Burke, James A.
Gharpuray, Parshuram Vyankatrao
McCarthy, Henry Augustine
Chowdhury, Rajendatal
Mac Mahon, John Rochford
Roychowdhuri, Hemendravarayan
Subbarow, Panguluri Venkata
Maguire, William
Kinnear, Thomas John
Husain, Sheikh Ajmal

Michaelmas 1916
(Wednesday 1st November 1916)
Binchy, Michael
McSparran, James
Bourke, John Francis
Razzaq, Abdur
Scanlan, Thomas

Hilary 1917
(Thursday 18th January 1917)
Avergal, M.R. Ry. T. Adinavayana
   Chettiar [called in absentia?]
Kelly, Edward Joseph
Gupta, Polisetty Hanumayya

Easter 1917
(Thursday 19th April 1917)
Butler, William Bilbie
Kalia, Daulat Ram

Trinity 1917
(Wednesday 6th June 1917)
Hasan, Sayed Nazir
Ramayya, Nadimpalli Dasaratha
Burke, Daniel
Bhatia, Autar Singh
Ghantamraju, Kapally

Siddiki, Khaliluzzaman M.
Rajagopalan, Narayana
Hand, Joseph Antony
Shortt, Joseph Bartholomew
Narayana, Brahmadesam Cidambi
   Sankara
Faruqi, Sheikh Mohammad Mumtaz
Kohli, Gokal Chand
Nath, Mahant Baij
   [called in absentia?]
Bedi, Hari Dass
Sharma, Khraiti Ram
Mehra, Nanah Chand
Gaharwar, Thakur Ram Lal Singh
Nagpal, Girdhari Lal
Reddi, Byreddi Lukshmi
McMenamin, Daniel
Rai, Aftab
Kapur, Vaishna Dass
Ramaswamy, Tripuraneni
Roy, Kanak Singh
Shah, Syed Nazeerullah
Raj, Sitaram Raju Bhupati
Sastri, Gollapudi Anjaneya
Agasti, Bijay Naraijan
McCarthy, Joseph Andrew

Michaelmas 1917
(Thursday 1st November 1917)
Fitz Gerald, Herbert Gerald
McElroy, George
Duffy, George Gavan
Kennedy, Kenneth Arthur
Mooney, Joseph John
Lambah, Diwan Chand
Cannon, John Hugh Gerald Tandy
McDonnell, Francis James
Sethi, Chuni Laul
Campbell, John Hugh Hamilton
Hadoke, William Clark

Hilary 1918
(Friday 18th January 1918)
Basudev, Bansi Lall
Pillay, Narayana Pillay Padmanabha
Moosa, Sait Eshaq

(Friday 8th February 1918)
Venkataraman, Addepalli

Easter 1918
(Wednesday 17th April 1918)
Flanagan, Martin Joseph

Trinity 1918
(Wednesday 5th June 1918)
Matheson, Charles Frederick
Venkateswara Rao, Turlapaty

Ramdas, Jaysen
Bhan, Frederick James
Mehta, Madan Gopal
Kothare, Khanderas Gajanan
Burke, Arthur Ulick
Pal, Sita Nath
Dempsey, Patrick Joseph
Chopra, Iqbalchand
Bhatia, Jagdish Singh
Singh, Gurdit
Kavanagh, Patrick Gladstone
Kenny, Patrick Berchmans
Mahant, Jagmohan Nath
Behl, Bhawani Das
Lokko, Christian Charles
Sethi, Ram Lal
Salariya, Gurdial Singh
Dhall, Achrajram
Naqi, Syed Khurshed

Michaelmas 1918
(Friday 1st November 1918)
Farrell, Henry William
Kingsmill Moore, Theodore
  Conyngham
Sherry, Felix Hugh
Aggarwala, Dwarka Nath
Connolly, Martin Joseph
McCullough, William Hill
Ruse, Arthur John

Hilary 1919
(Monday 20th January 1919)
McGrath, Henry Garrett
Wilson, Hugh Ramsey
Hearn, Thomas Edmund [Lieutenant]
Williamson, Richard [Captain]

Easter 1919
(Thursday 1st May 1919)
Gwira, Daniel Essuon
Baily, Francis
Monks, Thomas Francis [Captain]

Trinity 1919
(Wednesday 18th June 1919)
Murphy, Edward Joseph
Sheehan, Edward
Cheeke, William Alexander
  [Major, Royal Engineers]
Law, Hugh Alexander
Price, William George
O'Connor, Fergus Laurence

Wilson, Henry Bertram
Flanagan, Stanislaus

Michaelmas 1919
(Monday 3rd November 1919)
Ryan, Michael Joseph
Wilson, Herbert Vaughan
Hearne, John Joseph
Whelan, Claude Blake [Lieutenant]
Cawley, James Joseph
Devlin, John Joseph Lee
O'Donoghue, Patrick Philip
Beaumont, John Nelson
Healy, John
Greene, Maurice Cherry

Hilary 1920
(Monday 19th January 1920)
Dardis, Patrick Gregory
Copeland, Isaac
Murphy, Lindsay P.
Lanktree, Charles Joseph [Captain]
Doyle, John Patrick
Burne, Arthur Henry [*in absentia*]

Easter 1920
(Wednesday 21st April 1920)
Kisseadoo, William Assah Asare
Campbell, Charles Henry Gordon
Bell, Philip Sydney [Captain]

Trinity 1920
(Wednesday 9th June 1920)
Fallon, William
Christie, Michael
Fernando, W.S.C.
Gray, David
O'Donoghue, Austin
Meade, Joseph Michael

Michaelmas 1920
(Monday 1st November 1920)
Humphreys, Richard
Holmes, William John Longford
  Curran
Binchy, Daniel Anthony
 Smith, Patrick
Robinson, Christopher Henry
Ryan, Michael John
McCoy, William Frederick
Hanna, George Boyle
Meldon, James Austin
  [Lieutenant-Colonel]
O'Grady, William Michael
Blood, Lancelot Ivan Lloyd

Hilary 1921
(Tuesday 18th January 1921)
Cherry, Richard Theodore
Smith, Philip Norbert

Walker, Maurice Cecil
Duns, William
Scanlan, Thomas Henry
Davis, Charles Stewart Parnell
Kennedy, Charles Michael

Easter 1921
(Wednesday 13th April 1921)
Sheil, Charles Leo
Esmonde, John Lymbrick
Donnelly, Joseph Aloysius

Trinity 1921
(Wednesday 1st June 1921)
McCauley, Leo Thomas
Robinson, Ernest St. Clair
Kaul, Pandit Parmeshur Nath
Gillespie, John [Captain]

Michaelmas 1921
(Tuesday 1st November 1921)
Kyle, Frances Christian
MacDermott, John Clarke
Brown, Herbert Macaulay
Patton, William Francis
Deverell, William Berenger Statter
Kenny, George Gordon
Finn, Denis
Murphy, Desmond Thomas Carmel
   St. Paul
McGilligan, Patrick
Lynn, Alexander
Cunniam, Patrick Thomas
Farrell, John Joseph
Reidy, Joseph
Patterson, William Reginald Lambert
Deverell, Averil Katherine Statter
Chowdhury, Kahan Singh
King, Frederick Charles
Hyland, Arthur C
McCoy, Richard Patrick Joseph
   [Major]
Neill, James Scott

Hilary 1922
(Wednesday 18th January 1922)
Hastings, Samuel Henry
Lennon, Michael John
Fitzpatrick, Fintan

Easter 1922
(Thursday 27th April 1922)
Coyne, Thomas Joseph
Kelly, Ignatius Joseph

Trinity 1922
(Wednesday 14th June 1922)
Anderson, Alfred Hastings

McCarthy, Thomas Paul
Daly, Michael Bernard
Dillon, Theobald Augustus

Michaelmas 1922
(Wednesday 1st November 1922)
Kavanagh, Joseph [Captain]
Maginess, Brian
Barry, Ralph Brereton
Burke, Thomas Gerard Anthony
Hare, Herbert Hamilton
O'Sullivan, Donal Joseph
Maguire, Conor Alexander
Walsh, James Joseph
McFeely, William Norman Craig
   [called *in absentia*?]

Hilary 1923
(Thursday 18th January 1923)
Porter, William McMeekin
Hogan, Gabriel Patrick Sarsfield
Harbinson, James Magoffin
Guise-Brown, Gerald Edward
Spain, Patrick John
Carson, William Roland
Murphy, Laurence William Raymond
Fitzgerald, William James [called *in absentia*?]

Easter 1923
(Wednesday 18th April 1923)
McLoughlin, Richard Francis Xavier
   Joseph
Hodnett, George Pope

Trinity 1923
(Wednesday 6th June 1923)
O'Connor, Bernard
Howe, Gerard Lewis
Clampett, George Joseph Travis
Kirwan, Samuel Valentine
Dillon-Leetch, Mary
Kelly, Robert James
King, Leo Aloysius [Captain]
Nunan, Manus
Gregg, James Reali
Blackmore, Thomas Maitland
Curran, Lancelot Ernest
Duff, John Edwin

Michaelmas 1923
(Thursday 1st November 1924)
Cromie, Alfred Albert
Little, Esmonde William
Crawford, William Ernest
Macken, Francis Joseph
~~Walker, John~~ [call refused; *vide supra*, page 34]

Wilson, Charles
Casey, Charles Francis
Chambers, John Desmond
Hogan, Robert Simon
Henry, Herbert George [Captain]
Forde, Daniel Peter
Macaulay, Andrew Alfred
Kane, Akba Bailey Alexander

Hilary 1924
(Friday 18th January 1924)
Alexander, John George
Hallinan, Eric

Easter 1924
(Thursday 1st May 1924)
Johnson, William
Wilson, Mark
Dixon, Martin Joseph [*in absentia*]

Trinity 1924
(Thursday 1st May 1924)
Cawley, Francis Joseph
Meares, Keith Munro
Dutt, Dhan Raj
Long, John Oliver Horner
Quinn, Michael Joseph Kelleher
McCarthy, Andrew Joseph [Captain]

Michaelmas 1924
(Saturday 1st November 1924)
Moran, Frances Elizabeth
Rynne, Michael Andrew Lysaght
Diffin, John
Clancy, Herbert Edgar
Kirwan, Patrick Joseph
Stuart, Archibald
Twohig, Michael Joseph O'Brien
Bartley, Charles
Robinson, Philip
Ó Broin, Leon
Geraghty, Joseph Sebastian
  [called *in absentia*?]

Hilary 1925
(Monday 19th January 1925)
Kirkwood, Andrew Torton
Crosbie, James
O'Higgins, Kevin Christopher

Trinity 1925
(Thursday 11th June 1925)
Duggan, Marion Elizabeth
Macauley, Maurice Scott
Molony, Walter Hugh
Cassidy, John Price
O'Reilly, James Patrick

Michaelmas 1925
(Monday 2nd November 1925)
McGonigal, Richard
Marrinan, Patrick Aloysius
Danaher, Maurice
Pringle, Alfred Denis
Johnston, William Denis
Cleary, Edward A.
Boles, William
Cooper, Joseph James
O'Brien, Michael
Lamb, Benjamin
Houston, John James
Smyth, James Lawrence
McEnery, Patrick Joseph
Murnane, James Peter
Johnston, Frederick William
Condy, John Devenish
Caldwell, John Foster
Joyce, Patrick Simon
Micks, Edward Christopher
MacDonnell, Antonia Elizabeth
Conway, John Edward
Maguire, William Joseph
Woods, John Lowe
Gallagher, Dermot Charles Arthur
Dougan, James Hamilton
Haugh, Kevin O'Hanrahan
Roe, Patrick Joseph
Sarsfield-Hall, Edwin Geoffrey
Donovan, John Thomas
Lewis, Francis William
  [called *in absentia*?]

Hilary 1926
(Monday 18th January 1926)
O'Byrne, Joseph Michael
Holland, Robert Smith
Donovan, Philip Joseph
Flood, Gretta Una

Easter 1926
(Wednesday 21st April 1926)
O'Keeffe, Michael
Byrne, Edward Le Cesne

Trinity 1926
(Wednesday 9th June 1926)
Henrion, Peter William
Moore, John William
O'Mahony, John Finbarr Michael
Twohig, Joseph Patrick O'Brien

Michaelmas 1926
(Monday 1st November 1926)
Dixon, Kevin Joseph
McGilligan, Michael

Long, John Gerard
Feely, Richard J.
Shillman, Bernard
Bell, Stephen Joseph
FitzGerald, Maurice V.
Battley, John D'Oyly
Murtagh, John Joseph
O'Sullivan, Gearóid [Lieut.-General]
Ó Briain, Barra [Major]
Maguire, John
FitzSimon, Samuel Ernest Sydney
    [Major]
MacKeown, Robert Francis [Captain]
Nicholson, Cyril Anthony de Lacy
Morrison, Dawson [Captain]
Hayden, James Joseph
Duffy, Frederick Myles
Belford, Alfred James

[*The Roll of the Outer Bar kept in the Supreme Court commences here.*]

Hilary 1927
(18th January 1927)
Dillon, Brian Francis
Budd, Frederick Gardner Orford
Kangley, John
Little, Edward Gerald [Captain]

Easter 1927
(2nd May 1927)
Sullivan, Michael Paul

Trinity 1927
(22nd June 1927)
Keely, James Patrick
Wilson, Cyril Herbert
Harris, Leslie Gerald Eyre
Passau, Owen
Keating, Michael Joseph
Phelan, Kathleen
Husein, Choudhri Zafar
Leahy, Michael
Byrne, John Joseph

Michaelmas 1927
(1st November 1927)
O'Driscoll, Michael
Joyce, Patrick Weston
Conolly, Thomas James
Malone, Mary Ita
O'Donnell, Maurice F.
O'Connor, Art
FitzGerald, William O'Brien
MacCarthy-Morrogh, Francis Denis
    M.A.J.
Galvin, Thomas Eustace
Cobbe, William Arthur Thompson

McKay, Michael Vincent
Belton, John
Campbell, David Robb
Adamson, Robert St. Claire
Scanlon, John William
Killeen, Timothy [Major]
Coghlan, John Richard Charles
Dobbyn, George Lancelot
O'Driscoll, Fachtna Michael
Mofsovitz, Lionel Joseph
Hooper, John Joseph
Bonnar, Hugh
MacNeill, Turlough
Molloy, Martin Joseph
Stack, Robert Edward Hilliard
Sweeney, James Augustine
O'Callaghan, John

Hilary 1928
(Wednesday 18th January 1928)
Herlihy, John
Troddyn, Patrick James

Easter 1928
(Monday 23rd April 1928)
Smyth, William
Duffy, Patrick
McDunphy, Michael

Trinity 1928
(Wednesday 13th June 1928)
Branigan, Patrick Francis
Crump, Patrick Joseph
Webb, Seymour Hoffe Mitchell
Sainsbury, Richard Claude
MacLysaght, James
Fawsitt, Diarmaid
Hall, Reginald
Sugrue, Timothy [Captain]

Michaelmas 1928
(Thursday 1st November 1928)
Liston, Terence Kevin
Bowen, Bartholomew Patrick
O'Sullivan, John Michael
Martin, Malachi Thomas Joseph
Bourke, Paget John
Barnard, Francis Joseph
O'Mullane, Michael Joseph

Hilary 1929
(Tuesday 18th January 1929)
Law, Robert Kenneth

Easter 1929
(Monday 15th April 1929)
Travers, Charles
Adefolu, Omasanya

Trinity 1929
(Wednesday 5th June 1929)
Buckhalter, Simon William
Kimpton, Violet
Hogan, Connor

Michaelmas 1929
(Friday 1st November 1929)
Bourke, Patrick
O'Hanrahan, Roger Charles
McGivern, James Smith
Hughes, Vincent Philip
Bryan, John Donough Owen
Harrison, Reginald Alfred
Corbet, John Dermot Mulhall
Fraher, Patrick
Jeffares, Alfred Shaun
Carter, William Seymour Jessop
Griffin, Patrick
Conniffe, Patrick
O'Leary, John
Coghlan, Daniel
Walker, Herbert James
Mangan, Kevin Patrick Joseph
Macaulay, Roderick Muredach
Davy, Thomas Vincent
Hayes, Michael

(Wednesday 13th November 1929)
McGuire, James Ivan

Hilary 1930
(Monday 20th January 1930)
Odell, Thomas Urquhart
Hamill, William Ingram
Hemphill, Hon. Martyn
Wallace, Theodore David
Mhac Fhionnlaoich, Dubhglas Colm
Tully, Farrell Joseph
*Pillai, Moozhiyil Raghavan
   Narayana [* not called]

[Easter 1930]
Gyaw, Maung Hla [not called]

Trinity 1930
(Wednesday 25th June 1930)
Garrett, Kathleen Butler

Michaelmas 1930
(Monday 3rd November 1930)
De Búrca, Pádraig [Patrick Bourke]
Conroy, John Charles
Murnaghan, George Daniel
Gallagher, Edward Stanislaus
Mansfield, Edmund
McQuaid, Francis Joseph

Smith, John Howard
O'Mahony, Eoin Seosamh [in Irish]
Caulfield, Anne [in Irish]
Mandy, Walter James Kimber
Staic, Liam [Stack, William J.]

Easter 1931
(Monday 20th April 1931)
Street, James Howard Algernon
Scott, Percy Cecil
Dennison, Thomas Andrews
Barry, Ivor Henry Harte

Trinity1931
(Wednesday 10th June 1931)
Crivon, Samuel
Gogarty, Oliver Duane
Evans, Robert Brendan
Thornton, Edward
Regan, Gerard Philip
Wood, Wilfrid David
O'Callaghan, Michael
Han, Maung Ba
Dillon, James Mathew

Michaelmas 1931
(Monday 2nd November 1931)
Fay, William Patrick
McKenna, Charles Beuno
Binchy, William Francis
Uileas [Willis], Oscar Diarmuid Mac
   Cartha
Fahy, Francis Patrick
   [Proinnsias Ó Fathaigh]
Buckley, Francis Bernard Vaughan
Cronin, Thomas Eugene
Greene, Ian Rawdon
Wellwood, Herbert Edwin
O'Sullivan, John Christopher
Nugent, Peter John
Ó Loingsigh [Lynch], Fionan
Donovan, Timothy
Pierse, Gerard Richard
O'Connell, Daniel Christopher
Donovan, Thomas Joseph Anthony
Callanan, Denis Joseph

(Friday 6th November 1931)
Wijemanne, Hubert Ashley

(Tuesday 15th December 1931)
Thoung, Maung Kyaw

Hilary 1932
(Monday 18th January 1932)
O'Reilly, John Patrick Joseph

Easter 1932
(Monday 11th April 1932)
Walsh, Michael John

Michaelmas 1932
(Tuesday 1st November 1932)
Wood, Ernest Mounteney
Carroll, Patrick Joseph
Ua Rathghaille, Risteárd
  [The O'Rahilly]
Baker, Joshua
Heron, Charles Bernard
Hannin, Thomas John Berchmans
  Steen
Moran, Liam Brian
Rudd, Geoffrey Burkitt Whitcomb
Nightingale, George Oswald
Mac Firbhisigh [Forbes], Tadhg
Shiel, John
Mahendra, Tribhuvan Lal
Doyle, Brian André James

Hilary 1933
(Wednesday 18th January 1933)
Gill, Garrett Edward
Ellis, Malcolm Henry Graeme

Easter 1933
(Monday 1st May 1933)
Rajah, Subramaniam Dharma

Trinity 1933
(Wednesday 5th July 1933)
Pigot, Thomas Edward
McGrath, John
Byrne, Patrick

Michaelmas 1933
(Wednesday 1st November 1933) 'called by
  Mr Justice FitzGibbon'
Pringle, Michael Henry
Macdonald, Noel Kennan
Roche, William Fredrick
Sweeney, Michael John
Martin, Catherine Mary
Dunne, Richard Patrick
Griffin, Martin
Keane, John Joseph
Robinson, John [Seán] Joseph
Lowry, George Trevor

Trinity 1934
(Wednesday 27th June 1934)
Lysaght-MacGowan, Muriel
O'Reilly, Andrew Evaristus
Hughes, John
Coffey, Donough Joseph
FitzGibbon, Edward M.

Michaelmas 1934
(Thursday 1st November 1934)
Keogh-Nolan, Alfred Arthur Myles
Fleming, Patrick David
Windle, Henry
McCann, Dermot Paul
Kenny, Kevin Michael
Keane, Charles Owen
O'Daly, Carroll
  [Cearbhall Ua Dálaigh]
Sweetman, Edmund Thomas
O'Dwyer, Alfred James
Convery, John Gerard Plunket

Hilary 1935
(Friday 18th January 1935)
Wells, Mary Wilhelmina

Trinity 1935
(Wednesday 3rd July 1935)
Cole, John Sydney Richard
Deale, Kenneth Edwin Lee
Ferriss, Alfred
Griffith, Naomhan Michael
McWilliam, Herbert Russell
Tynan, Patrick

Michaelmas 1935
(Friday 1st November 1935)
Ó Cuiv, Ayindries
Good, Donal Bernard Waters
Hurley, Wilfrid Hugh
Meenan, James Francis
Byrne, James Patrick
Doyle, Thomas Aloysius
McDowell, Antony Gerard

Trinity 1936
(Wednesday 24th June 1936)
Garland, James Noel
Carty, Frank
Cole, John Copeland
Dillon, Sir Robert William Charlier,
  Bart.
Durcan, John James
Hogan, Patrick
Hogan, Michael Joseph Patrick
O'Doherty, Joseph
Teevan, Thomas
Woodcock, Thomas Charles
McDonnell, William Patrick

Michaelmas 1936
(Monday 2nd November 1936)
McMahon, James Gerard
O'Neill, Raymond Joseph
Kiernan, Brendan Joseph
Crockett, Robert William McDowell

Fahy, Edward
Henry, James Joseph Eric
Kent, John
MacDonagh, Donagh
Sheehan, Patrick Augustine
Hurley, John Gordon

Trinity 1937
(Wednesday 9th June 1937)
Boyle, Charles Vesey
de Valera, Vivion
Jennings, Brendan Joseph
Mason, William Henry Cuff
Ó hUadhaigh, Robert Joseph

Michaelmas 1937
(Monday 1st November 1937)
Grogan, Vincent Benedict
McDevitt, Henry Aloysius
Bell, Desmond Edward
Barry-Walsh, James Owen
Donnelly, John Andrew
Doyle, John Gerrard
Heavey, James Richard
Mac Bride, Seán
Nic Churtain, Síobhán Ite
McDermott, Laurence Sylvester
McDonnell, Patrick Joseph
Mac Grianna, Domhnall [Donal Greene]
O'Connor, Michael Kevin
Preston, Christopher Alexander
Sweetman, William
Neville, Francis Michael
Fitzgerald, Thomas Edward

Easter 1938
(Monday 2nd May 1938)
Dockrell, Anne Dorothy

Trinity 1938
(Wednesday 29th June 1938)
MacKeown, Michael John Joseph
Kirkpatrick, Stanley Victor
Fitzgerald, Pierce
Keady, Dermot
Murphy, Joseph Patrick
Kissane, Edward [Eamon]

Michaelmas 1938
(Tuesday 1st November 1938)
Burke, John Alphonsus
O'Higgins, Thomas Francis Kevin Peter
Cooke, Richard Noel
D'Arcy, James Augustine
Cannon, Patrick Francis Garrett

Mackey, Arthur Joseph Connell
Stephens, Denis Synge

Hilary 1939
(Wednesday 18th January 1939)
Clements, Robert Nathaniel
Concannon, James Patrick McDonnell

Michaelmas 1939
(Wednesday 1st November 1939)
Lynch, Joseph Edward
Fawsitt, Seán MacDiarmaid
Bradfield-England, Austen St. James
O'Donovan, Denis Patrick
O'Neill, Hugh
Green, James Maxwell Dalton
Peart, John Noel Lubé
Burke, Anthony
Ryan, Patrick Noel
Ryan, James Gerrard
Parke, Weldon Roycroft Cecil
Mathieson, John Gerard Bruce
Murphy, Harold John Dickinson
Roche, Frederick John

Hilary 1940
(Thursday 18th January 1940)
Cassidy, Agnes Beatrice
Winder, Lionel James
MacSwiney, Owen Charles Valentine Alexander Evelyn Diego de Avila

Easter 1940
(Monday 8th April 1940)
Carey, Patrick Joseph [Padhraic Ó Ciardha]

Trinity 1940
(Wednesday 12th June 1940)
Ó Duibhir, Tomás Diarmuid
Collins, Sean
Carey, Patrick Paul
Desmond, Timothy Noel

Michaelmas 1940
(Friday 1st November 1940)
Kenny, John Joseph
Neylon, Thomas Joseph
O'Connor, John William
Porter, Horace Desmond
MacQuaid, Brian Eamon James
Morrissey, John Euchania William
Igoe, Francis Gerard
Hayes, Roger

Hilary 1941
(Monday 20th January 1941)
Overend, Olive Nancy

Trinity 1941
(Wednesday 2nd July 1941)
MacEnroe, John Patrick
Rice, Edmond Zita
Ryan, Patrick Joseph
Rice, John Joseph
Stokes, Noel Nicholas John

Michaelmas 1941
(Monday 3rd November 1941)
Leonard, Patrick Francis Xavier
Gleeson, John
Walsh, Brian Cathal Patrick
Gannon, John Mary Joseph
MacKenzie, John James Patrick
Clarke, Gerard Anthony
Coogan, Edward James
Coleman, John Vincent
O'Connor, Gerald
McDonnell, Francis Patrick
Conlan, Peter
Cresswell, John Victor Peacock
Nolan, Eamonn Patrick
O'Brien, John Joseph
O'Phelan, Eileen Mary de Riva
Timlin, John William

Trinity 1942
(Wednesday 17th June 1942)
Harrison, Anthony Clephane
Kennedy, Joseph Patrick
Roe, Thomas Francis
Barron, Nicholas
Lee, Gerard Anthony
Meagher, Laurence
Gargan, John Gilbert
Curley, Thomas Joseph
Walsh, Margaret Mary Patricia

Michaelmas 1942
(Monday 2nd November 1942)
Williams, Thomas Francis Desmond
O'Toole, Margaret Mary Bermingham
Finlay, William Denis
McKeon, John
Ó Droighneáin, Máirtín Piaras
Ó hInnse, Séamus

Hilary 1943
(Thursday 21st January 1943)
McCreery, Henley Edwin Lewis

Trinity 1943
(Monday 21st June 1943)
Ahern, Patrick Sylvester
Wright, David Andrew Leslie
Cosgrave, Liam Michael Gobbin
Higgins, Patrick Robert
Creedon, Timothy
McCarthy, John Eugene
O'Callaghan Dunn, John

Michaelmas 1943
(Monday 1st November 1943)
O'Neill, John Brendan
Johnson, Garret Anthony
   [Gearóid Mac Eoin]
Moran, Eileen Mary
Hartnett, Maurice Noel
Costello, Grace Mary
O'Beirne, Donnchadh Piaras Regis
Mayne, Desmond Francis O'Reilly

(Thursday 18th November 1943)
Lardner, Gerard Joseph William

Trinity 1944
(Thursday 22nd June 1944)
Finlay, Thomas Aloysius
Smyth, Patrick Joseph
O'Malley, Peter
O'Hanrahan, Seán Desmond Mary
O'Neill, Patrick Joseph
Meenan, Patrick Nahor
Ellis, William Roche Denny
*Mhac an tSaoi (MacEntee), Máire
   Caitríona*
Sweeney, James Peter
Mooney, Philip

Michaelmas 1944
(Wednesday 1st November 1944)
Donnelly, Thomas Feidhlim
Fahy, Brian Vincent de Paul
O'Donoghue, Padraig
Johnston, George Edward Patrick
Condon, Columba
McArdle, Eamon Augustine
Hederman, Anthony James Joseph
Linehan, Una McAuliffe
Wachuku, Jaja Anucha
Hinkson, Alexander Lionel
Cooke, Frederick George
Mac Phartalain, Gearóid
   [Gerald Bartley]
Lanigan-O'Keeffe, Arthur John

(Friday 23rd November 1944)
Das, Ram Krishna

Trinity 1945
(Friday 22nd June 1945)
Fitzsimons, Charles Bernard
Flynn, William
Collins, Eamonn Flannery
Murphy, Michael Joseph
Phelan, Andrew James
Brennan, Peter James
McMullin, Arthur Michael
Maguire, Conor Patrick Joseph
Maguire, Martin Cyril
Nowlan, Kevin Barry
Ó Riain, Eoin
McGilligan, Denis Brian
Donovan, Terence Desmond
Humphries, Robert Percy
Lynch, John Mary

Michaelmas 1945
(Friday 1st November 1945)
Bacon, Edward William Delany
Egan, James Francis
MacCabe, Niall Francis
O'Shaughnessy, Kevin
Walsh, Patrick Joseph
Marcus, David
Walsh, Bridget
Byrne, Alfred Patrick
Hanly, Dermot Joseph
Heron, Seamus Connolly

Easter 1946
(Wednesday 8th May 1946)
Healy, Rowland Henry Savage

Trinity 1946
(Monday 24th June 1946)
Griffin, Michael Francis
Blayney, Alice Elizabeth
McCarthy, Niall St John
Holland, Patrick Columba
Sheehy, David B.
Kelly, Patrick
Ó Modhráin, Domhnall Fionan
Steen, Ambrose Gerard
McCarthy, Dermot Joseph Thaddeus
Ryan, Thomas Aloysius
Purcell, James Patrick
Walsh, Edward Michael
Casey, Patrick Joseph
Barrett, Stephen Declan
Harnett, Michael Joseph
Buckley, John Mary
*Tuite, Robert Henry S.

Michaelmas 1946
(Friday 1st November 1946)
O'Hanlon, Roderick Joseph
MacDonagh, Oliver Ormond
Ó Conchubhair, Donnchadh Aodhach
Lindsay, Patrick James
Boden, Ivar McGrath
Skinner, James John
Murphy, John Pelly
Mahony, Thomas Adrian

Hilary 1947
[Friday 1st January 1947]
Ryan, Edward Francis

Trinity 1947
(Monday 23rd June 1947)
Heuston, Robert Francis Vere
Kelly, Michael Joseph
Browne, Dillon Augustus
Ellis, Henry
Duff, Liam Brendan
O'Brien, Kevin
Breathnach, Seán
Quigley, Peter Paul Declan
O'Connell, Michael Flannan

(Thursday 31st July 1947)
Comyn, James Gerard Peter

Michaelmas 1947
(Monday 3rd November 1947)
Landy, Andrew Vincent
Kepple, Simon
O'Brien, Anthony Norbert
Beatty, Francis Christopher
FitzGerald, Garret Michael Desmond
O'Malley, Brendan George
McQuaid, Paraic
Coyle, Geoffrey David
Brennan, Charles Joseph
Liddy, Patrick Joseph

Hilary 1948
(Thursday 5th February 1948)
Donnelly, John Desmond Mary

Trinity 1948
(Friday 2nd July 1948)
Waldron, James Kevin
Durkan, Nora
Gray, Edward Joseph
Blayney, John Joseph Patrick
Ó Conchubhair, Micheál Pádraig
  Seosamh
Yeats, Michael Butler
McAuley, Denis Robert

O'Regan, Timothy Patrick
Conway, Joseph Augustine Michael
McGovern, James Niall
Magee, Francis
Waldron, Dermot Patrick
Waldron, Patrick Henry Pearse
Sutton, Ralph Gerard
Guiney, Thomas Jarlath
Rooney, Francis Xavier Mary
Flynn, Andrew Ignatius
O'Keeffe, Eugene
O'Riordan, Joseph Daniel
Mason, George Cuff

Michaelmas 1948
(Monday 1st November 1948)
Campbell, Michael Mussen
Cronin, Anthony Gerard Richard
Costello, David Declan
Corduff, Philip Edward Joseph
Horgan, John Christopher
Meehan, Joseph Patrick
Toomey, William Christopher
Ó Súilleabháin, Pronnseas Eoghan

Hilary 1949
(Tuesday 25th January 1949)
Stephenson, Venetia Josephine Mary
Menary, William James

Trinity 1949
(Wednesday 15th June 1949)
Elyan, Isidore Victor

(Thursday 23rd June 1949)
De Blaghd, Earnán Pádraig
O'Connor, Rory
Maguire, Peter Donogh
Redmond, Gerard Anthony
Quinlan, John Francis
Geoghegan, James Joseph
Ronayne, Michael Paul
Bennett, Francis Patrick

Michaelmas 1949
(Tuesday 1st November 1949)
Lynch, Kevin
De Búrca, Marcus
Boyd, Patrick George Cardwell
Abrahamson, Maurice
Seligman, Donald Lionel
Lovatt-Dolan, John Henry Geoffrey
Neylon, Mary Josephine
Donnellan, Mary Josephine Britta
Cooper, Thomas Kennan
O'Reilly, Gerard Joseph Mary
Haughey, Charles James
Giblin, Bartholomew Augustine

Shields, James Franci
Flood, Fergus Michael
Ryan, Francis
Buchanan, John Gerard
O'Reilly, Peadar Madhmhuire
Connolly, Patrick Joseph
Ryan, John Patrick
Esmonde, John Henry Grattan

Hilary 1950
(Wednesday 25th January 1950)
Shanahan, Arthur Desmond
Marron, Peter Desmond
Burke, Cormac Patrick
Geary, Colm Eamonn

Trinity 1950
(Tuesday 27th June 1950)
Crosbie, Donal Philomena
Lynch, Vincent James
McCay, John Hedley Douglas
Brennan, Gabriel Joseph
Delany, Vincent Thomas Hyginas
Brady, George Edward
McKeever, Gerard Augustine
Harrington, Michael John
Dixon, Benjamin Joseph
McCarthy, Jeremiah Gerald

Michaelmas 1950
(Wednesday 1st December 1950)
Beatty, Ethel Ursula
Fitzpatrick, Richard Anthony
Kearns, James Desmond
Nunan, Manus
Cassidy, John Bernard
Hanly, John Barry
Fennell, Michael John
Trainor, James Patrick
Quigley, John Benigimus
O'Sullivan, James
Loughrey, Martin Charles
Lloyd-Blood, Nevil
Hogan, Patrick Joseph
McLoughlin, Thomas Joseph
O'Brien, Donough Conor Joseph

(Wednesday 20th December 1950)
Connolly, James Matthew

Hilary 1951
(Wednesday 15th February 1951)
Barron, Henry Denis
Rea, Dermot Neil Egerton
O'Dwyer, John
Morgan, Thomas Lamsden
Everard, James Patrick

Trinity 1951

(Friday 6th July 1951)
Heslin, Ita Brigid
Geraghty, Patrick Joseph
O'Mahony, David
Nowlan, Kevin Ingram
Daly, George Francis Alexander
Counihan, Roger Ambrose
McGough, Joseph Christopher
  [Captain]
Pratt, George Charles Nigel Wynch

Michaelmas 1951

(Monday 5th November 1951)
Diggin, Christopher Valentine
  Bernadette
Goodbody, Alys Mary Osterberg
Bluett, Maud Cherry
Boylan, Gerald John
O'Connor, Ulick Harris
Coleman, James Gerard
Callinan, Brian Patrick Christopher
Early, Daniel Patrick
Forde, Patrick Bernard
Barrington, Donald P.M.
Enright, Daniel Dominic
Butler, Seán
McKenna, Seamus Thomas
Lynch, Henry Raphael
Dwyer, Matthew Joseph Francis
McMenamin, John Anthony Benedict

Hilary 1952

(Monday 25th February 1952)
Morton, John Desmond   [John Brooke
  Scholarship of £50 per annum for 3 years]
Doyle, Arthur Joseph Peter
Campbell, James Alexander
Caruana, Robert Joseph

Easter 1952

(23rd April 1952)
Cuddon, Bernard Eric Doughby
  [Engl. Barr.]

Trinity 1952

(Monday 30th June 1952)
Moylan, Thomas Joseph
De Courcy, John Aloysius Francis
Botting, John George Grinstead
  [Engl. Barr.]
Sekyi, Kweku Anu
Kilfedder, James Alexander
*Menon, Krishna

Michaelmas 1952

(10th November 1952)
O'Hanrahan [Ó hAnnracháin], Fiachra
  [John Brooke Scholarship of £50 per
  annum for 3 years]
O'Hanrahan [Ó hAnnracháin],
  Fachtna [Society's Exhibition of £21 per
  annum for 3 years]
Martin, Francis Joseph Christopher
Mooney, Niall
Kinlen, Dermot Patrick
Sheridan, Diarmuid Patrick
Judge, John Francis Willis
Comyn, Edward Frederick
Morris, Frederick Reginald
O'Sullivan, Gerald Thomas
Hayes, Francis Mahon
Hughes, Brian M.
Sorahan, Seamus
Doyle, Charles Gerard
Adye-Curran, Oliver George
  Valentine
Lenihan, Brian Joseph
O'Byrne, Patrick

Hilary 1953

(Thursday 19th February 1953)
Morris, Dennis Gerard
Wheeler, Arthur William Edge

Trinity 1953

(30th June 1953)
MacGowan, Maurice John Lysaght
Brennan, Patrick James
McStay, Michael
De Courcy, Cyril Noel
Doyle, Maurice Francis
Lehane, Leonie Mary

Michaelmas 1953

(2nd November 1953)
Exshaw, Eldon Young
Callan, Paul
Byrne, John Myles
Feehan, Michael A.
MacGoris, James Patrick
Flanagan, Desmond David
Hill, William Harry
O'Keeffe, Michael Patrick
  [Micheál Pádraig Ó Caoimh]
Murphy, Francis Dominick
Lewis-Heath, Frederick Ronald
Sheehan, Rose Constance
Carolan, Thomas James Rupert
Ó Briain, Colm Cristóir
Gwira, Kobina Daniel

Hilary 1954
(19th February 1954)
Gaffney, Maurice Patrick
Corcoran, Owen Francis
Barror, Cecil John

Easter 1954
(16th June 1954)
O'Byrne, Brendan Peter [ex-Solr. (N. Rhodesia); admitted to the degree *in absentia.*]

Trinity 1954
(Monday 26th July 1954)
McCormack, Liam Caoimgein [Captain]
Kennedy, Martin Joseph Alexander
McRedmond, Luke John
Quinn, Gerard Philomena
Mulrine, Daniel John Chrysostom
Mulvin, Noel Gearoid Southwell
Harty, Donal Joachim
O'Donoghue, Eugene
O'Connor, Kieran John
O'Connor, James Joseph
Sullivan, Michael Patrick
O'Hara, Liam
Seales, Peter Clinton
Gleeson, Edward
Gleeson, Donough Patrick
Murphy, Angelo Jerome

Michaelmas 1954
(1st November 1954)
Keane, Ronan Colman [John Brooke Scholarship of £75 per annum for 3 years]
Callan, Sylvia Florence [Society's Exhibition of £21 per annum for 3 years]
Rynne, Michael Leon [Society's Prize of £21]
Whelan, Michael Joseph
McVey, James Edward
Casey, John Charles
Knipe, Joan Clare
Smyth, John Martin Farrell
O'Kelly de Galway, Guy Marie-Joseph Philippe Ghislain
Culligan, Michael Patrick Joseph
Hederman, Miriam
MacCarthy, Gerard Brian
Whelan, Laurence
MacGiollarnath, Proinnsias
Woolfson, Solomon Sefton
Murphy, Anthony Gabriel

Hilary 1955
(7th March 1955)
Conteh, Ansumana Philip

Mongey, Edward Gabriel
Jackson, David

Trinity 1955
(28th July 1955)
O'Sullivan, Paul
Sheridan, Alfred Patrick Stanislaus
Walsh, William Joseph
Terry, Patrick Augustine

Michaelmas 1955
(2nd November 1955)
Kennedy, Desmond
Callery, Mary Patricia
O'Carroll, James
Hickey, Henry Maurice
Comber, Thomas
MacDonagh, Donagh Mary
Ryan, Patrick Cyril
Foy, Henry Bertram
Silke, William James
Ambrose, Romuald M.
Brosnan, John Anthony
Monks, Gerald Christopher
O'Reilly, James Patrick
Hodnett, William George

Hilary 1956
(11th January 1956)
Donoghue, Florence

(6th February 1956)
Hamilton, William Joseph Lyons [Brooke Scholarship of £75 per annum for 3 years]
Bolger, Mary Aingelda Catherine
Gay, Kevin Patrick

Trinity 1956
(25th June 1956)
Barry, Kevin
Baylor, Richard Patrick
Cronin, David Watkins
Moran, Thomas Aloysius
O'Connor, Michael Gabriel

Michaelmas 1956
(6th November 1956)
Hurley, William Michael Mary
Liddy, James Daniel Reeves
Bastable, Bartholomew John
Kuma, Alexander Cuthbert
Flynn, Ann Mary Gabriel Philomena
Fitzpatrick, John Ignatius
Keaney, Irene Mary Cecilia
Clery, Gerald Francis Hogan
McArdle, Joseph Ardle Francis
O'Donovan, David Vincent

Firtear [Ferriter], Michael Patrick
Hussey, Paul Anthony
Keegan, Bernard James
O'Driscoll, Desmond John
McCarthy, Charles

Hilary 1957
(7th February 1957)
Russell, Matthew
Buckley, Daniel Christopher Joseph
[Domhnall C. Ó Buachalla]
Frewen, Gerard L.
O'Callaghan, Aubrey Bryan

Easter 1957
(29th April 1957)
Kelly, John Maurice Dominic

Trinity 1957
(22nd July 1957)
McMorrow, Sean Christopher
Barr, Robert Paul
Mattimoe, Brendan Joseph
Cruess Callaghan, Crosadella
Ledwith, James
Meehan, James Augustine

Michaelmas 1957
(11th November 1957)
Carroll, Mella Elizabeth Laurie
Smith, Matthew Patrick
Donnelly, Therese Anne
O'Higgins, Paul
O'Grady, James John
McCracken, Brian Moore
Quinn, James Aiden
Tierney, Martin John
Hickey, Denis John Borromeo Gideon
Wyndham, Teddy Omolade Benjamin
McGonagle, Iris Mary
FitzGerald, John Southwell
Jordan, Patrick [Captain]
Adesanya, Charles Olayinka
Smyth, John Christopher

Hilary 1958
(27th March 1958)
McCarthy, Timothy Joseph
Mullen, Edward Joseph

Trinity 1958
(22nd July 1958)
Curtin, [Revd] Jerome Kevin
[1st Victoria Prize of £25]
McCarthy, Jeremiah Christopher
[3rd Victoria Prize of £10 *ex aequo*]
Dillon, James

King, George Gordon
Butler, Paschal Baylon Brendan
Fitzsimon, Bartholomew Kevin
Barragry, Richard M.
O'Callaghan, Thomas

Michaelmas 1958
(11th November 1958)
Conroy, Patrick Dominic [John Brooke
Scholarship of £75 per annum for 3 years]
Morrin, Francis Dermot [2nd Victoria Prize
of £15]
Skinner, Geraldine Mary
Bourke, John Oliver Paget [3rd Victoria
Prize of £10 *ex aequo*]
FitzGerald, James Dermot Joseph
Aylmer, Francis
Sheehy, [Revd] John Gerard
Loftus, John Daniel
Corboy, Denis
McDonnell, George Patrick
O'Brien, Conal
Barnes, Eamonn Mary

Easter 1959
(20th April 1959)
O'Shea, Timothy Joseph
McSwiney, Myles
Joyce, John Anthony

Trinity 1959
(Monday 13th July 1959)
MacDomhnaill, Séamus Caoimhghín
[2nd Victoria Prize of £15]
Coffey, Patrick Joseph
Neville, Richard Maximilian
McGuinn, Patrick Vincent
Sweetman, John Oliver Joseph
Carroll, James
Okechukwu, Arthur Ezeakornobi

Michaelmas 1959
(16th November 1959)
Kinlen, Aideen Patricia [John Brooke
Scholarship of £75 per annum for 3 years]
Nugent, Peter Bernard [Society's
Exhibition of £21 per annum for 3 years]
O'Flaherty, Hugh James
[Society's Prize of £21]
Daly, Marcus James Albert
Donohue, Frederick Joseph
O'Connor, Rory Brendan
Carroll, Adrian Francis
O'Conor, Stella Mildred
O'Donovan, Diarmuid Brian Dominic
Ekwerekwu, Isaac Ifeanyi
*Udenzwe, Chukwuemeka [not called]

Trinity 1960

(Thursday 21st July 1960)
Linehan, Daniel Cornelius [3rd Victoria Prize of £10]
Okolo, Jerome Herbert Chukwulozie [2nd Victoria Prize of £15]
Lowey, Michael James Anthony
MacEntee, Patrick
Sweeney, Dermot
Christle, Joseph Patrick
Kearney, Francis Joseph
Egan, Donal Brian
Ronayne, Laurence Michael
Kowa, Abraham Joseph
Siev, Raphael Victor
Butler, Anne Kathleen
Grealy, Michael Eucharia
Christle, Colmcille Paschal

Michaelmas 1960

(Monday 7th November 1960)
McGrath, Murray Matthew Pius [John Brooke Scholarship of £75 per annum for 3 years]
Farrell, John Michael
Johnson, Richard Parnell Fitzgibbon
O'Neill, John Patrick
Cooney, Garrett Francis
Duffy, Francis Joseph
Tiah, Eugene
Kirwan, James St. Lawrence
Sheehy, Ruth Mary, R.S.C.J.
Sweeney, John

Trinity 1961

(Wednesday 26th July 1961)
Cukwurah, Anthony Oye
Heelan, Louis Joseph
   [1st Victoria Prize of £25]
Hanley, Eamonn [2nd Victoria Prize of £15]
Hannan, John James
Burke, Seán Oilibhéar
Hand, Geoffrey Joseph
O'Brien Kelly, Michael John
Ó Cuirc, Liam
Costello, Cornelius

Michaelmas 1961

(Tuesday 7th November 1961)
Mills, Richard Louis Kenneth
   [Society's Prize of £21]
O'Kennedy, Michael Eamonn
O'Toole, Conal Patrick
Magee, Hugh Joseph Hogan
Browne, Aidan Francis
Obonna, Linus
Thomas, Ian David
Raftery, Patrick

Metuh, Chukwunonyelu Joseph
Andrews, David Patrick
Ufford, Gerard Jombo
Watson, Fredrick Stanley

Trinity 1962

(Friday 27th July 1962)
Carberry, John Hugh
Robins, Ronald Arthur Mayne
Amasian, Charles Igboanugo
Malka, Edmond S.
*Odumosu, Franklin Olatunbosun [not called]

Michaelmas 1962

(Friday 9th November 1962)
McCann, Thomas Stanislaus [John Brooke Scholarship of £75 per ann. for 3 years]
Geoghegan, Hugh [Society's Exhibition of £21 per annum for 3 years]
Liston, Jeremiah Louis Vincent
   [Society's Prize of £21]
Haugh, Joseph D. [1st Victoria Prize of £25]
Lysaght, Charles Edward
Keely, John Joseph Mary
Cronin, Edmond Matthew Jude
Mangan, Patrick
Murphy, Michael Kevin
Montgomery, David Louis
Crawford, Thomas Henry
Rattigan, Patrick Michael
*Darko, Joseph Anthony [not called]
*Wachuku, Nhanna Nwa [not called]

Trinity 1963

(Friday 26th July 1963)
Doherty, James Columba
   [1st Victoria Prize of £25]
Dunne, Francis
Butler, David Arthur Seton
Cullinan, Brendan Peter [Captain]
Lowe, John
Phinainitisatra, Pinyo
Hill, Hugh
Graham, Henry George Dunne

Michaelmas 1963

(Tuesday 29th October 1963)
Ua Donnchadha, Daithí Gearóid
Salafia, James Patrick
Daramy, Lahai Evans Kapindi
Muldoon, William Bernard
Little, Edward David
Roberts, Noel Sawyer
Riyami, Mrs. *Abdullah* née *Soad Mohammad Nasser Lamki*

Hilary 1964

(29th January 1964)

O'Keeffe, Daniel [John Brooke Scholarship
of £75 per annum for 3 years]
Fennelly, Michael Patrick [Society's
Exhibition of £21 per annum for 3 years]
MacCarthy, Dermot F.
McCollum, William Paschal

Easter 1964

(6th April 1964)

Millar, Lionel Darrel Arthur

Trinity 1964

(3rd July 1964)

Langan, Peter St. John Hevey
    [1st Victoria Prize of £25]
Hamilton, David Paul Ignatius
McCumiskey, Edward Francis James
Kehoe, Patrick Thomas
Farrell, Niall Christopher

Michaelmas 1964

(Friday 6th November 1964)

Gaynor, Liam Anthony
Michael, Edmond Labib
Cotay, Alexander Bajulaiye
O'Driscoll, James
Lynch, James Dominic

Trinity 1965

(Wednesday 21st July 1965)

Fitzsimons, Eoghan
Doolin, Eugene Joseph
O'Connor, Brendan
O'Connell, Peter
England, William Henry Philip

Michaelmas 1965

(Friday 12th November 1965)

Plunkett, Arthur Francis [Society's
Exhibition of £21 per annum for 3 years]
Egan, Patrick Joseph
O'Leary, Simon Peter
Mill-Arden, Erwan Joseph
McCarthy, Nodlaig Mary Patricia
Gilroy, Seán Laurence
Buckley, Denis Joseph Vaughan
Dalton, John
O'Gorman, Martina Louie
Bohan, Brian
Kiritta, Jesse Willibald
Corrigan, John Francis Anthony

Hilary 1966

(Thursday 10th February 1966)

Carney, Paul James Patrick
Fanning, Arnold F.
Coffey, Timothy Joseph
Anyanwu, Hyacinth Ihezie

Easter 1966

(Monday 16th May 1966)

Donnelly, Arthur Joseph [who had been
awarded the 1st Victoria Prize of £25 at the
Final Examination in May 1918]
Dunboyne, Rt. Hon. Lord [Patrick
Theobald Tower Butler]

Trinity 1966

(Wednesday 20th July 1966)

Murdoch, Henry James Pascal
    [1st Victoria Prize of £25]
Johnson, Josephine Mary Philomena
    [3rd Victoria Prize of £10]
Ó Cillín, Proinnsias Pádraig
Clancy, Noel Aubrey
Gallagher, Patrick
Hogan, Christopher
Convery, Denis Brendan
Whelan, Seán Christopher
Watson, Maelissa Rose Mary
Haugh, Kevin John
Kelly, Frances Declan
Carroll, Justin Edward Emmanuel

Michaelmas 1966

(Wednesday 9th November 1966)

Galvin, Barry St. John
    [Society's Prize of £21]
O'Connell, Peter Ivan
Cooke, John Donal
Moran, Patrick Joseph
Hogan, Esther Anne
Kelly, Jane Frances
Cunningham, Adrian Anthony
    Bernard
MacGuigan, Brian James
Carney, Thomas Patrick
Lalor, Edward Finbarr John
Wymes, Enda John
Kilduff, Constance Margaret
Whelehan, Harold Anthony
Humphreys, Dermot Sigerson
Walshe, Michael Joseph
Jones, Wordsworth Filomeno
Keogh, Desmond Joseph Bernard
O'Connor, Peter Edmund
Collins, John Joseph Mary

Trinity 1967

(Wednesday 26th July 1967)

Kehily, Cornelius Francis
[2nd Victoria Prize of £15]
Brady, George Anthony
[2nd Victoria Prize of £15]
Bourke, Marie Teresa Winifred
Sullivan, Daniel Finbarr Francis
Kenny, Caroline Elizabeth
O'Donovan, Denis Anthony
Hegarty, Patrick Hubert
McNulty, Dermot Joseph
Herbert, Daniel Nicholas
Donnelly, John
Buckley, Cornelius Thomas Vaughan
Boland, John Anthony
Wade (née Davis), Flavia Margaret
Arora, Vijay Kumar

Michaelmas 1967

(7th November 1967)

O'Mahony, [Revd Dr.] Dermot
Patrick Leo [1st Victoria Prize of £25]
Breen, Gerald Vincent Breen
McHugh, Muireann Caitríona
Goldberg, David Simon
Tormey, Antoinette Catherine
Murray, John Loyola
White, Michael Barry
Meade, Brian Edward Francis
Kilroy, Michael Gerard
Dempsey, David Brian Paul
Kenny, Bernard Harvey
Liston, Kevin Denis Mary
Guiney, Cornelius

(14th December 1967)

Owens, Owen Paul [conferred *in absentia* on 7th November 1967]
Hickey, Clodagh Margaret
Madigan, James Brendan

Hilary 1968

(Monday 1st April 1968)

Dempsey, Paul Ronan
Smyth, Esmond
Reza, Salah Jehangir Ali
Singh, George

Trinity 1968

(Monday 29th July 1968)

Bracken, John Francis
[2nd Victoria Prize *ex aequo*]
Diamond, David
Shanley, Peter Thomas Harman
Kennedy, Anthony
O'Toole, Francis Joseph
McLoghlin, Brian Francis

Glynn, David Kevin
McDonald, Brian Paul
Kearns, Nicholas James
Hurley, John Anthony
Spain, Francis Robert Mary
Scott, Seamus Oliver
McCourt, John Declan Kevin
Sutherland, Peter Denis William
Bradley, Michael Kieran
McAleer, Peter
Lysaght, Margaret Ann
Brennan, Ian Gerard Mary
Liddy, Michael Christopher
Conan, Alaistair Stewart

Michaelmas 1968

(Tuesday 12th November 1968)

Binchy, William Thomas [John Brooke
Scholarship of £75 per annum for 3 years]
McCarthy, Donal Timothy
[1st Victoria Prize of £25]
Shaper, Harris Augustus
[3rd Victoria Prize of £10]
Doyle, Donald F.P.
Tynan, Gerald Michael Joseph
Budd, Declan Nicholas Orford
Doyle, Denis Conor
O'Sullivan, Finbarr Joseph Anthony
Hastings, Patrick Anthony
Maughan, David Matthew
O'Sullivan, James Raymond
Heavey, Aidan
Karim, Nishar Ahmed
Moore, Helen Therese
Pettit, Thomas Alphonsus
MacDonagh, Niall Joseph
Smyth, Thomas Clement
Omo, Michael Amuziam
Moriarty, Michael Anthony Richard
Kinsella, Gerald Stephen
Charleton, Aengus Joseph Pius
Grogan, Brendan Joseph
Murray, Patrick Joseph
Stones, Liam Laurence John
O'Higgins, Kevin Christopher
McGahon, Hugh Bradbury
Doran, Michael Joseph

(20th December 1968)

Gilbert, Mrs. Jennie Zelda

Easter 1969

(Tuesday 13th May 1969)

Rochford, Odran James Mary
O'Hagan, Fergus McKenna
Harty, John Patrick Joseph
Lindsay, Ronald Blennerhassett
Kisch, Augustus Kennedy

Trinity 1969

(Monday 28th July 1969)

Merrins, Hugh Conleth
Sheehan, Hugh Noel
Rayel, Edward Joseph
Nugent, James Anthony
Burke, Robert Herbert
Egan, Daniel Anthony
O'Flynn, Mary Catherine
Mellett, Michael John
O'Reilly, Una Rose
O'Hagan, John Desmond
O'Kennedy, Carol Ann
O'Sullivan, Philip John Roger
Bradley, Andrew Shaun
Lavan, Vivian Herbert
Dargan, Peter
Reid, John Stanislaus
Collins, Edward Anthony Denis
Murray, Diarmuid Pádraig
O'Dea, John
Haccius, Charles Henry Albert

Michaelmas 1969

(Wednesday 12th November 1969)

Bourke, Henry Orme
Toal, Thomas Brendan
Bradley, Liam
Keane, Patrick Edward Thomas
Candy, Ian St. Clair Mary
Kierans, Thomas Noel
Nott, William Anthony
Tierney, Patrick Oliver
McCartan, Pádraig Thomas
McCarthy, Fergus
Lynch, James Peter
Foley, Fergal Patrick Scott
Chisengalumbwe, Edward
Fitzsimons, Bernard Kenny
Moores, Derek Charles

Easter 1970

(Wednesday 13th May 1970)

Owen-Flood, Dermod Dmitri
Magourty, Catherine Gabrielle
McDowell, Thomas Bleakley

Trinity 1970

(Tuesday 21st July 1970)

Went, David [John Brooke Scholarship of
    £120 per annum for 3 years]
Gleeson, Dermot [Society's Exhibition of
    £60 per annum for 3 years]
O'Sullivan, Carmel Mary
O'Leary, Daniel Vincent
FitzGerald, John M.
Reedy, Brendan John

Duggan, Francis Anthony
O'Dwyer, James Patrick
Ó Maoláin, Seán Traolach
Cotter, Jacqueline Eva
Murphy, Antoin E.
de Valera, Éamon

Michaelmas 1970

(Thursday 12th November 1970)

Holohan, John Redmond Joseph
Byrne, David Mary
Fitzpatrick, Dermot Francis Mary
Stewart, Ercus Gregory
Donnelly, Patrick Joseph
Moore, Catherine Ann
O'Neill, Desmond Michael
Murnaghan, Eoin Michael
Govender, Oothamaseelan Candasamy
Doolan, Brian Anthony
Ó Brolcháin, Aongus
Byrne, Patrick Anthony
(Wednesday 9th December 1970)
Duffy, Brendan George
Sher, Louis Oscar
Nealon, Leo Patrick
Appleby, Charles Mark
Maharaj, Sirinarian
Henry, Leo C.

Trinity 1971

(Tuesday 27th July 1971)

Laffoy, Mary [John Brooke Scholarship of
    £120 per annum for 3 years]
Condon, John Francis [Society's
    Exhibition of £60 per annum for 3 years]
Morrissey, Patricia Josephine
Buckley, Roderick Bryan
Wright, John Francis Patrick
Murphy, Henry Russell
Kelleher, John Patrick
Ghent, Patrick John
Mathews, Joseph Gerard
O'Donoghue, John Anthony
Reynolds, Thomas Ignatius
*[1] Stanley, Cyril Francis
Murtagh, Richard
Murphy, Roderick Henry
Kathrada, Ebrahim Mahomed
Denham (née *Gageby*), *Susan Jane*

[1] Stanley did not sign the Roll, a space in which was left for his signature; but a note in ink on the Registrar's copy of the Call List reads: 'No. 12 (*in absentia*) was called, the formula being varied accordingly'.

Butler, Paul
Govender, Sivalingum
    Purushothamam
Bresnihan, Brian Joseph
Mandal, Paritosh
Margai, Charles Francis

Michaelmas 1971
(Thursday 18th November 1971)
McCullough, Denis John
Murphy, Yvonne
Hearns, Patrick Joseph Desmond
Reilly, Peter Thomas
Mullins, John Kevin
Maguire, Conor John
Keegan, Hugh Donagh O'Donnell
[Dourado], Ricardo Levindo Silverio
    Xavier Falcao e Dourado
Wymes, Michael James
Gilligan, Paul Frederick William
Phelan, John Joseph
Durnin, Niall Plunkett
Farry, Michael John
Costigan, John Anthony
Teehan, Thomas Francis Martin
Mall, Idris †
McGonigal, Eoin Patrick
Walsh, Anthony Joseph
Olu, Julius Ayodele
Sheils, Owen O'Rourke
Moore, Jacinta Mary
Connell, Patrick John

Trinity 1972
(Wednesday 26th July 1972)
Ní Shúilleabháin, Onóra Bernardine
    [Brooke Scholarship of £120 per annum for 3
    years]
Gunne, Colum Michael [Society's
    Exhibition of £60 per annum for 3 years]
McKechnie, William
Tracey, Patrick George
Kilcullen, Máire Emer
Murphy, Mary
Deery, Matthew Francis
Gallagher, Martin John
Jordan, John Francis
O'Connor, Brendan Dominic
    Roderick
Mooney, Seán Mary
Harrington, Francis Patrick
O'Rourke, Bernard Clinton
Gawley, James
Kenny, Michael Joseph Anthony
O'Mahony, Edward Finbarr
Carroll, Blaise Augustine
McHale, William Patrick
Abbott, Henry James Joseph

Conneely, Michael Joseph
Ryan, Seán
McGovern, Brian J.
Fox, Noel Louis
O'Neill, David Joseph Patrick
Alkin, Edwin Randolph
Pillay, Nehru Morgan
Cafferty, Martin Charles
O'Donnell, John Christopher
Hayes, Joseph Mary James
Cahill, Michael Joseph
Ijomah, Kenneth Boniface Chinedu
Molloy, Kevin James
Crotty, Martin Gerard
Keating, Barbara Monica
Greene, Michael Christopher

Michaelmas 1972
(Monday 13th November 1972)
McGovern, Declan Constantine
Flood, Jane
O'Riordan, John Francis
McGarr, Edward Patrick
Coughlan, John Christopher
Forkin, Michael Patrick
O'Loughlin, Ciaran John
Bowman, Thomas Raymond Mary
O'Toole, John Jerome
Ó Cuiv, Aindrias
Cotter, Brigid Mary
Peart, John Basil David Lube
Nono, Bernard Francis
Derham, Kieran Mary Joseph
Bruton, John G.

Trinity 1973
(Monday 30th July 1973)
Gormley, Mary Philomena [John Brooke
    Scholarship of £120 per annum for 3 years]
Kelly, Peter Augustine [Society's
    Exhibition of £60 per annum for 3 years]
Dillon, Justin
Clarke, George Bernard Francis
Macken (née *O'Kelly*), *Fidelma M.*
Miller (née *Rice*), *Mary Geraldine
    Therese*
Morgan, Thomas Michael
Skelly, William Augustine
Smyth, Peter Edward
McGrath, Seán Anthony
McMahon, Michael Joseph Mary
Heffernan, Thomas Paul
Groarke, Raymond Gerard Thomas
McStay, Margaret Mary
Hamilton, James Henry
Keys, Gerald Brendan Francis
Conroy, Martin A.
Campion, Michael A. J.

McDonnell, James Paul
Allen, Colm Michael

Michaelmas 1973
(Tuesday 13th November 1973)
Gordon, John Joseph
Feeney, Kevin Timothy Bernard
Koorn, Johanna Cornelia
McArdle, James Martin
McGough, John Joseph
Kelly, Florence Frances
Durack, Michael Patrick
Connolly, Peter James
Kelly, Henry Anthony Joseph Paul
*Murphy, Mary Iseult Averil
MacMurrough*
Counihan, Michael John
Karim, Rashid Ahmed
Murphy, Gregory Paul
O'Farrell, Francis Joseph Michael
McCarthy, Peter Paul
Brennan, Flannan Vincent
Foley, Ciaran Peter
Donaghy, Mary Rose
Carroll, Michael John Gerard
Farquharson, Elizabeth
Burke, Richard Sylvester
McSwiney, Edward Brian
*[1] MacCana, Liam
Kenny, John Roger

(Monday 10th December 1973)
Scannell, Honora JosephineYvonne
Rogers, John
Watson, Philippa Mary Louise
Lanigan-O'Keeffe, Reginald Stephen

Trinity 1974
(Thursday 30th July 1974)
Cannon, Patricia Susan [John Brooke
  Scholarship of £120 per annum for 3 years]
McElroy, Patrick
Fitzgerald, Francis Christopher
Reidy, Liam Gerard
Dowling, Joseph Colum
McDowell, Michael Alexander
Cruess Callaghan, Anne
Downes, Patrick Thomas
Quirke, John Michael Thornton

*[1] MacCana did not sign the Roll, a space in which was left for his signature. Kenny's name, last in the Roll, appears between Henry A.J.P. Kelly and *Mary I.A. MacM. Murphy* in the published version of the list.

Mitchell, Denis Cormac
Fingleton, Michael Patrick
Ward, Paul John
Dillon (née *Deasy*), *Mary Jane*
Kenny, Colum Joseph
MacPartlin, Thomas Connolly
Aston, Anthony C.
O'Kelly, John
O'Donovan, Iris Marie Therese
Devally, Liam Gerard
O'Doherty, Katherina Margaret
MacKenzie, Mary
Doyle, Laurence
Daly, Bartholomew Donal
John (née *Rogers-Wright*), *Jamesina*
Hooper, Garrett Anson
Kiely, Denis Joseph
Hegarty, Diarmuid Arthur
Alam, Shams-ul
Boyd, Michael Patrick

Michaelmas 1974
(Friday 22nd November 1974)
Whyte (née *Condon*), *Mary Bernadette*
Sweeney, Fergal Peter
McGilligan, Roderick Joseph
O'Callaghan, James Francis
Bushe, Denis Francis Peter
Sammon, Anthony Christopher
Heron, James Connolly
O'Halloran, Kerry Joseph
Callaghan, Valentine Edward
Hardiman, Adrian Patrick
Giblin, Patrick Martin Gerard
Horan, Timothy Joseph

(Friday 20th December 1974)
Bowles, Patrick Nicholas
Roundtree (née *Tierney*), *Anne*

Trinity 1975
(30th July 1975)
Gleeson, Martin Gerard [John Brooke
  Scholarship of £120 per annum for 3 years]
Finlay, John Robert [Society's Exhibition of
  £60 per annum for 3 years]
Fahy, Conor Bernard
Wright, Arthur Blackburn
Mulholland, John Peter Patrick
Ward, Kenneth Joseph Patrick
Hurst, Eamon Patrick
King, Dympna
Beirne, Eidín
Cross, Kevin Peter
Lindsay, Kathryn Mary Alison
Nesbitt, Richard Law
Ashe, Thomas Michael

Ó Cuív, Brian
O'Leary, Nicholas
FitzGerald, Ruth Anne Moira Christine
McGlynn, Noel Anthony
Lambe, Patricia Mary
Mahony, John
Linnane, Jacqueline Catherine
Honohan, Edmund William
Devereux, Paul Andrew
Walsh, Paul Roderick Dowse
O'Neill, Nuala Geraldine Maria
Wolsey, James Stuart
O'Grianna, Michael
O'Donnell, Mary
McInerney, Doreen Mary
O'Connor, Cornelius Hugh
Cronin, Ellen Mary
O'Neill, Hugh Raymond Ralph
Groarke, Michael Vincent
O'Neill, Séamus Iarfhlaith
Keane, Desmond St. John
Fysh, Robert Michael
O'Donovan, Alice Patricia

Michaelmas 1975
(Thursday 27ᵗʰ November 1975)
Clark, Maureen Harding
Connolly, James Martin Philip
Donelan, Edward Joseph
Kane, Russell F.M.
Macken, James Joseph
McFadden, Denis James
MacMenamin, John
McQuinn, Margaret Mary
Slattery, Thomas Francis
Stark, Desmond Allen
MacLynn, Adrian Geoffrey Simon
O'Shea, Michael Martin
Bagale, Vaman Nimba
Hanratty, Patrick Francis
Keating, Albert Martin
Madigan (née Callanan), Patricia Josephine
Meghen, Patrick Joseph
O'Brien, William Francis
Devaney, Stephen John Simon
Kilcullen, Fionnuala Anne
O'Higgins, Padraic Pearse
Spring, Richard Martin
Moran, Carroll
O'Sullivan, Henry Oliver
Cush, Peter John [N.I. Barr.]
Doyle, William Patrick [N.I. Barr.]
Ferguson, Richard [N.I. Barr.]
Hill, Robert Charles [N.I. Barr.]
Kennedy, Hugh Paul [N.I. Barr.]
Lavery, Charles Michael [N.I. Barr.]

Martin, John Alfred Holmes [N.I. Barr.]
McKee, John [N.I. Barr.]
Nicholson, James Michael Anthony [N.I. Barr.]
Porter, Robert Wilson [N.I. Barr.]
Asmal, Abdul Kader [Engl. Barr.; L.I.]
Brennan, Francis Marie Joseph [Engl. Barr.; I.T.]
Stewart, Robin Milton [Engl. Barr.; M.T.]

Hilary, 1976
(19ᵗʰ January 1976)
Leonard, Brian Thomas Simon

* Trinity 1976 [1]
(29ᵗʰ July 1976)
O'Mahony, William I. [35] [John Brooke Scholarship of £120 per annum for 3 years]
Miggin, James Richard [30] [Society's Exhibition of £60 per annum for 3 years]
Taaffe, Francis Brendan [20]
Clarke, Gerard Martin [17]
Hamill, (née Moody) Margaret Eileen [8]
Carey, Eamonn J.J. [12]
Killoran, Aiden [31]
Brennan, Paul Christopher [10]
O'Riordan, Miriam Bernadette [7]
Deeney, John Bartholomew [5]
Cahill, Eamon Arthur Timothy [2]
Deegan, Patrick Martin [28]
Buckley, Lorcan Joseph [27]
MacDarby, Ralph Francis [25]
Conway, Thomas Gabriel [21]
O'Rourke, John Fergus [19]
MacGreevy, Dara Desmond [16]
Kilduff, Elizabeth [15]
Rice, Margaret Mary [14]
O'Reilly, Michael Francis [9]
McCarthy, Patrick John [4]
Roche, Gerald Francis [3]
Sheahan, David [32]
Curtin, Brian Michael [34]
Healy, John Pascal [29]
Agnew, Grainne Mary Rita [33]
O'Connor, Paul Anthony [26]

* [1] Those called on 29ᵗʰ July 1976 did not sign the Roll in the order intended by King's Inns, but haphazardly. The precedence conferred by the Roll is indicated by the numbers in square brackets.

O'Brien, *Ann Mary* [24]
Gibson, Peter Leo [36]
Malone, Margaret Mary [22]
Hartnett, Hugh John [23]
Gleeson, Elizabeth A.P. [13]
Gageby, Patrick Charles Lester [11]
Sherlock, Richard Terence [18]
Duggan, James Anthony [1]
Twomey, John Martin Anthony [6]

Michaelmas 1976

(18th November 1976)
Fitzpatrick, Maura Teresa
Feely, Matthew Patrick
O'Connor, John Francis
Birmingham, George Martin
Hanna, Michael Anthony
Moran, Patricia Catherine
Mahon, Alan Philip
McGovern, Aedan John
O'Reilly, David Gerard Joseph
McEvaddy, Desmond P.
Golden, Thomas Eoin
Hannaway, Martin Conor
Hedigan, John Edward
Hazlett, Thomas John
McKeown, Anthony Patrick
Crilly, Mary Catherine Josephine
Ferry, Neil Joseph Terence
Coffey, Eamonn Martin Joseph
Dooley, Cyril
O'Brien, Eamon
Sheil, John Joseph [N.I. Barr.]
Higgins, Malachy Joseph [N.I. Barr.]
Maloney, Mary Josephine
Murray, James Milne
Gallagher, Peter Brendan
O'Neill, Peter Joseph
O'Neill, Michael Anthony
Collins, Gerard Anthony
Dolan, Thomas M.J.
Mulligan, Malachy
Skeffington, Nuala Elizabeth
Coen, Michael Anthony Charles
Flanagan, Mary Catherine Doirbhile
Hearne, Maurice
Dennehy, Patrick Joseph
Kidney, Anthony William

Hilary 1977

(Monday 7th February 1977)
McDonagh, Donagh Joseph
Doherty, Patrick
McMorrow, Deirdre
Cafferky, Hugh Edward
Maguire, John Ronan
Byrne, William Gerard

Kelleher (née *Walley*), *Mary*
Lloyd, Raymond
Oliso-Emingoit, Francis Xavier
Downey, Michael Alexander
Margai, Samuel Milton
McMorrow, Peter Damien
de Picarda, Guy Reginald Pierre
  [Engl. Barr.; M.T.]

Trinity 1977

(28th July 1977)
O'Callaghan, Antonia Margaret [John
  Brooke Scholarship of £120 per annum for 3
  years]
Ging, Brigid Mary [James
  MurnaghanMemorial Prize of £50]
O'Reilly, James
Boyle, Michael Joseph
Barton, Bernard Joseph
McGuinness (née *Ellis*), *Catherine
  Isabel Brigid*
McGann, Gabriel Joseph
Farrelly, James Norbert
Keane, John David
Dunne, Elizabeth
Needham, Michael John
Melinn, Michael Gerard
Buttimer (née *Burgess*), *Olive
  Margaret*
O'Donnell, Una Elizabeth Frances
Maher, Rosemarie
Comyn, John Raymond Gerald
  Eugene
Quinn, Thomas Francis
McElligott, Finbarr Charles
Rochford, Francis Gerard
Laverty (née *O'Brien-Twomey*), *Mary
  Elizabeth*
Wheeler, Deborah Harriet
Taaffe, Joseph Kieran
O'Brien, Aloysius Bernard
Egan, Frances
Smyth, Robert Patrick Oliver
O'Donoghue, Donal
McLoughlin, Daniel
Mooney, Kieran Arthur
Fullam, Raymond Gerard Gentili
McCluskey, Darine
McCaffrey, Hugh Gerald
Ahern, Timothy Joseph
Noonan, Séamus T.
O'Higgins, Paul Peter M.
McDermott Roe, John Anthony
White, Michael Anthony
Sheridan, Séamus Anthony
Conroy, Marion Bernadette
Walshe, James William

Flanagan, Finola Mary
Quinn, John Eugene
Horan, Roderick
Young, Odran Patrick
McCarthy, Charles T.
Ward, Joseph V.
Hogan, Joseph Stephen
O'Connell, Justin
O'Connell, Thomas
Martin, Inez Vanessa
Riordan, David
Govender, Satchithanathan Moonsamy
Regan, Mary Philomena

Michaelmas 1977
(16th November 1977)
Mullen, Thomas Patrick
de Blacam, Mark
Curtin, Hannah Marie (Síobhán)
Ryan, Philip
McCarthy, John Richard
Roseingrave, Jerome
Chambers, Mary
McDonald, Marc Thomas
Leddy, Nastaise
Rea, Luigi Orlando Anthony
Duffy, Edward Patrick
Collins, Conor Michael John
Mullane, Christopher Eric
Cantwell, Thomas Joseph
Kennedy, Clifford Patrick Kevin
Meehan, Mary Elizabeth
Charleton, John Gregory
Nix, Brendan Christopher
Kelly, Cyril Colman
Hayden, Francis Edward
Carty, Patrick Pearse
O'Higgins, Malachy
O'Connell, Michael [Engl. Barr.; I.T.]
Wilson, Alastair James Drysdale
   [Engl. Barr.; I.T.]

Trinity 1978
(24th May 1978)
Colhoun, James Leslie Alexander

(25th July 1978)
Brosnan, Joseph Patrick [John Brooke
   Scholarship of £120 per annum for 3 years]
Irvine, Mary Cecily [Society's Exhibition]
Collins, Michael M. [Murnaghan Prize]
Whelan, John Aidan
Danaher, John Gerard
O'Sullivan, Marcus Mary
Deale, Julian Kenneth Brian
Field, [Father] Raymond William
Kiernan, Michael Thomas
Walsh, Aidan Patrick

Lydon, Eileen Marian
Hickson, Joseph Barry Patrick
Hester, Catherine Anne
Harrington, Timothy Finbarr
Delahunty, John Christopher
Kiely, Gerard Francis
O'Sullivan, Patrick Eugene John
Roche, Stephen Joseph
Kelly, Dermot Peter
Fawsitt, Alice
Walsh, [Father] Eamonn Oliver
Boyle, Bridget Mary Rosario
Fallon, Thomas Joseph
Greene, Peter Eugene
Creed, Thomas Finbarr
Healy, Eamon Brendan
Slattery, Brendan James
Deeney, Declan Francis Martin
Breathnach, Séamus Proinsiais
Kelly, Peter John Gerard
Horan, Hilary
Keigher, John Dominic
Murphy, Timothy Desmond
Sheahan, Mary
Grace, Joseph Gerard
Condon, Mary Alacoque
Dunne, Anne Marie Therese
Griffin (née O'Toole), Corinne Edna
   Lesley
Doyle, Seán M.
Smyth, Colm Anthony
McCabe, Yvonne Catherine
Barry (née Hamill), Bridget Mary
Keating, Mary Una
O'Donovan, John Joseph
MacAllister, Mary Jacinta
Kemery, Keith Anthony John
Grace, Edmond Dermod [S.J.]
O'Donoghue, Michael
O'Sullivan, Thomas James
Dunne, Joseph Brendan
Gormley, John Francis
Clissmann, Inge Fedelma
Dwyer, James John Vianny
Claveloux, Denise
Shea, Timothy Bertrand [N.I. Barr.]
O'Brien, Kathleen Jeannie Horner
   [N.I. Barr.]
Phelan, Thomas Patrick Joseph
   [Engl. Barr.; L.I.]
McAleese (née Leneghan), Mary
   Patricia [N.I. Barr.]

Michaelmas 1978
(24th November 1978)
Finnegan, Joseph Gerald
Munro, David Mary Reid
Brehony, John Patrick Anthony

Fleck, Philip K.
Hussey, Samuel Gerard
O'Dwyer, John Thomas Purcell
Brady, Gerard
Magauran, Amber Maria
Cahalane, Donal
Foley, Vincent
Groarke (née *Marnell*), *Ita Dympna*
Durcan, Mary Philomena
Nash, Pyers David
Curran, Peter Anthony
Mangan, William
Mullins, Michael Gerard
Connolly, John Henry Boyd
Kelly, Andrew Edward
Sullivan-Byrne (née *Byrne*), *Laura*
Murphy, Patrick Gerard
Hardiman, Francis Louis David
Guckian, Aengus Thomas
Nelson, Gayle Arnold Valentine
Allen, Michael Edward
Cronin, Nora Bernadette
Sooknanan, Kikaramjith
Norton, Margaret Patricia
Crean, Catherine
Long, Desmond Patrick
Dowling, Jeremiah Bernard
Mooney, Patrick Terence
Marrinan, Desmond Patrick James
    Ruane [N.I. Barr.]
Weir, Reginald E. [N.I. Barr.]
McNulty, James [N.I. Barr.]
Boyle, Christopher Kevin [N.I. Barr.]
Lavery, James Patrick [N.I. Barr.]
McLaughlin, Richard [N.I. Barr.]
Creaney, John Alexander [N.I. Barr.]

(15th December 1978)
Mills, William Jonathan
O'Brien, Patricia Ann Mary
Fagan, Mary Bernadette
MacMahon (née *Walsh*), *Mary*
    Valentine
Elkinson, Jeffrey
Schuster, Alexander William Edward

Hilary 1979
(Thursday 11th January 1979)
Rogers, Bernard V.

Trinity 1979
(Thursday 19th July 1979)
Ryan, Noel Christopher [John Brooke
    Scholarship]
O'Sullivan, Terence Mary Dominic
    Francis [Society's Exhibition]
O'Riordan, Seán

Healy, Jeremiah Joseph
O'Connell, Brian Dalton
Kane, Maeve Margaret
Antoniotti, Bruce A.
Quinn, Patrick Gerard
White, John Patrick Mary
Mooney, Patrick Stephen
Haughton, Robert Watson
Smith, Paul Gerard
Sreenan, Paul
Kenny, Shane Vincent
Crowley, William Kevin
McCann, Neil Patrick
Hannon, [Father] Patrick
Brady, Francis Rory
Minch, Matthew David
O'Byrne, John William
Quinn (née *Marrinan*), *Paulyn*
    Patricia
Watkin, Anne Maria
Gallagher, Paul Martin Joseph
Veldenz-Dunne (née *Veldenz*),
    Monika Maria
Murray, Nigel Ormiston Gauvain
    [Engl. Barr.; I.T.]

(Friday 20th July 1979)
Ryan, Patrick Moling
Mullins, Joseph Patrick
O'Donnell, Turlough Joseph
Doyle, Paul Francis
O'Donovan, David
Aherne, Michael
Dockrell, Hayes Rodney
Lovitt, Brian Richard
Dooge, Meliosa
Murphy, Deirdre Patricia
Walsh, Edward Scott
Jackson, Joseph
Callery, John Thomas
Charleton, Peter
FitzGerald, Catherine Frances
    Augusta Jacinta
Jordan, Patrick
Ó Buacháin, Seán
Bourke, John Joseph
Sweeney, Nora Patricia
Murphy, Declan Anthony
McGurk, Una Mary
O'Donoghue, James Gerard Francis
Quirke, Paul Norbert
Leahy, Eamon Ceannt
O'Mahony, James Jude Cadden
Callanan, Frank
Corrigan, Michael Gerard
Gallagher, Donal John
Nagillah, Crispin Beda

Ferguson, Kenneth Patrick

Michaelmas 1979
(8th November 1979)
Holmes, Declan Michael Cowell
McGrath, David Edward Lawrence
Barrett, Richard Joseph
Kelly, Ciaran Mary
Vandenberghe, Nadine Michele
Macken, Mary Theresa
Ronan, Johanna
Biggar, Maurice James
Nicholson, James Joseph
Downes, Mary Emily
Gilsenan, Thomas
O'Quigley, Shaymus Joseph Mary
Kelly, Suzanne
O'Dowd, Barry
Harris, Robert Iain Colquhoun Eyre
[Engl. Barr.; M.T.]

Hilary 1980
(11th January 1980)
McKendry, Felix Vincent
Finlay, Mary
O'Brien, Philip Fidelis
Magee, Philip Patrick [N.I. Barr.]

Trinity 1980
(25th July 1980)
Hussey, Dominick Patrick [John Brooke
Scholarship of £120 per annum for 3 years]
Barrett, Richard
[James Murnaghan Memorial Prize of £50]
McLoughlin, Nuala
O'Leary, Seán Anthony
Desmond, Honor Mary B.
Carson, Michael Taylor
Behan, Christopher Patrick
Hayden, Anthony Fergus
McCourt, Patrick Anthony
McDonnell, Richard Joseph John
Gogan, Robert Patrick
Sheehan, Timothy Francis
Havel, Brian Francis
Cathcart, Philip Francis
Hoban, Joseph Raymond
Ó Tuathail, Séamus Seosamh
Ní Fhaoláin, Síobhán Máire
Scally, William
O'Toole, Mary
Farren, Antoinette
Treacy, Francis Aloysius John
Cahill, Thomas Joseph
Keane, Richard T.
Dillon, Patricia
Fitzgibbon, Michael Patrick Gerard
Maloney, Brigid Mary Josephine

Shepherd, Katharine Mary
Kennedy, Patricia Monica
Murray, Peter Hugh M.
McGuinness, Diarmaid Thomas
Edward
Durcan, Gerard P.
Crawford, Adrian Frederick Alan
Owens, Alexander John
Trainor, John Patrick
Wallace, Francis Joseph
Gannon, Stefan Michael
[Engl. Barr. M.T.]

Michaelmas 1980
(7th November 1980)
Meenan, Charles Francis Aloysius
O'Leary, Donal John
McGuigan, Mary Patricia
Kirwan, Helen Anne Hermione
McDermott, Paul Matthew
Christle, Mel André
Byrne, Michael Gerard
Feddis, Noel
Higgins, Moira
Heffernan, Helena Mary
O'Connor, Mary Patricia
Mannering, Adrian David Paul
Roe, Catherine
Gray, Michael William
O'Connell, Michael Joseph
Gleeson, Eugene Philip
Collins, Martin Joseph
Lalor, Stephen
Conlon, Peter Joseph
Walsh, Margaret Breda
Mahon, Desmond Joseph
Glynn, Geraldine Margaret
Fitzgerald, John
Ó Cinneide, Séamus
Mullaly, Helen Francis
Shipsey, William Edward

(17th December 1980)
Kissane, Eileen
MacMahon, Seán Séamus
Haugh, Senan

Hilary 1981
(20th February 1981)
Marrinan, Patrick. A.

(12th March 1981)
Drysdale, John Gillespie
[Engl. Barr.; Gray's Inn]

Trinity 1981

(24th July 1981)
Finlay, Ian Peter
MacMahon, Noel Arthur
Gallagher, Nora
Ryan, John
Connellan (née *Burke*),
  Catherine Mary
Anderson, Noel
Browne, Helena Christina
Linnane, Howard Thomas
Coughlan, Patrick Joseph
Lamb, Randal Neal Patrick
Meehan, Christopher
Griffin, Conor J.
Moloney, Paschal Joseph
Gleeson, Michael Thomas
Corbett, James Patrick

Michaelmas 1981

(13th November 1981)
Butler, Nicholas
Malone, Francis Patrick
Egan, Brian Séamus
Reynolds, Miriam
Buckley, James
Barry, Margaret Mary Teresa
Sibeta, Kabika Mukelabai
Martin, Matthew Edward
Reilly, John Joseph
Forwood, Nicholas James

(16th November 1981)
O'Leary, Michael

Trinity 1982

(27th July 1982)
Gaynor, Michael Colm [John Brooke
  Scholarship of £120 per annum for 3 years]
O'Donnell, Donal Gerard [Society's
  Exhibition of £60 per annum for 3 years]
Nolan, John Anthony
Stokes, Thomas Christopher
Boyle, Simon
Murphy, Deirbhle
Connell, James William
Punch, John Edward
O'Donnell, John Leydon
Opdebeeck, Maria-Anna
Stynes, Margaret
Hartnett, Brian Noel
O'Donnell, John Gerard
O'Donoghue, Edward M.M.
Whyte, Gerard
Counihan, Michael Arthur
McKenna, John Gerard
Doorly, Diarmuid Francis

Byrne, Raymond Gerard
Carroll, Claude
McDonagh, Ann Sunniva
Gilhooly, James J.
O'Sullivan, John Gerard
Godfrey, Donal Charles
Whelan, Raphael A.
Kilty, Brendan
Kirrane (née *Ruane*), *Máire P.*
O'Donoghue (née *Kelly*), *Catherine*
Kelly, Gerard Francis
Sheehan, Michael Edward
  [Commandant]
Doyle, Declan Marrhew
Sullivan, Norah Mary
Gallagher, Brian Joseph
  [Engl. Barr.; I.T.]

Michaelmas 1982

(29th October 1982)
McCarthy, Patrick Joseph M.
Nerney, Margaret M.
MacKeogh, Michael Senan
Gavin, Joseph Mary
Fogarty, Paul
Lynch, Thomas Simon [Austr. Barr.]
Milte, Kerry Leon [Austr. Barr.]
Lester, Anthony Paul [Engl. Barr.]
Somerville, Thomas Clinton
  [Engl. Barr.]
Hamer, George Clemens [Engl. Barr.]

Trinity 1983

(22nd July 1983)
Griffin, Francis John [John Brooke
  Scholarship of £120 per annum for 3 years]
Egan, Adrienne Isobel [Society's
  Exhibition £60 per annum for 3 years]
McCrann, Oonah Meabh
  [Murnaghan Prize of £50]
Corrigan, Kieran Patrick
Curtin, Deirdre
Macdonald, Willis Niall T.
O'Rourke, Mona Virginia
Allen, Senan
McDonagh, Edward Feichín Thomas
Quinn, Mary Virginia
Leahy, Brendan Joseph
Conlon, Eamon Patrick
Donagh, Catherine Mary
Kehoe, John Anthony
Edwards, John A.
Hogan, Desmond Francis [Captain]
Kean, Richard Nigel
Lehane, Christopher Daniel
Madden, Bernard Joseph
Mangan, Michael Anthony

Murphy, Bartholomew
Hanly, Sinéad Elizabeth
McKeon, Dermot Thomas Patrick
McMorrow, Patrick Killian
Casey, Eithne Maria
Quinn (née *Kennedy*), *Margaret Mary*
Connolly (née *McCaughey*),
    Gerardine Denise
O'Brien (née *Condell*), *Pauline*
Godfrey, Patrick Gerard [Captain]
Newham, Pádraig Joseph
Reardon, Miriam Ann
Conlon, Michael John
Walsh, Marion J.
Whooley, James
Hill, Mary Bernadette
Farren, Brian Patrick
Nash, Carol A.
Wyer, Laurence
McKeown, Nuala Mary
Meade, Kathryn
McDonagh, John Martin
Baynes, Michael Joseph
Dobson, James Joseph
Hynes, Hugh Patrick Francis
Cullen, Thomas Michael
MacGowan, Nicholas John Lysaght
Campbell (née *Connolly*), *Mona*
Putnam, Thomas Drew
    [Engl. Barr.; G.I.]

Michaelmas 1983
(28th October 1983)
Walshe, John Joseph Mary
Barrett, Francis John
Gallagher, Nicholas Joseph
Scallan, Vincent Mary
Maguire (née *O'Connor*), *Eileen*
    O'Connor
Halton, Barry Declan
Quinn, Gerard Mary
Sweetman, Roger Louis
Dorman-O'Gowan, Christopher
    Patrick Desmond [Engl. Barr.]

(18th November 1983)
Loughran, Paul Vincent [N.I. Barr.]

(9th December 1983)
Kelly, Matthias [Engl. Barr.]

Hilary 1984
(24th January 1984)
Gadd, Ronald Patrick [Engl. Barr.]

Trinity 1984
(26th July 1984)
MacGrath, Michael Gerard Anthony
    [John Brooke Scholarship of £240 p.a for 3
    years]
O'Brien, Jacqueline Mary [Society's
    Exhibition of £120 p.a. for 3 yerars]
Hogan, Gerard William
    [Murnaghan Prize of £100]
Hussey, Léonie Carmel
O'Donoghue, Síle Aingeal Carmel
Kelly, Margaret Brigid
Pye, Stephen Anthony
Baker, Marie
Lenihan, Brian Joseph
Bilberg, Astrid
Ward, Eoin Francis
Clarke, Padraic
Cawley, Cormac T.
O'Sullivan, Lorraine Anne
MacCabe, Rory Paul
Hastings, Robert Victor
Lynch, John Francis
Coffey, Paul
McDonald, Séamus
Forde, Michael Patrick
O'Malley, William Anthony

(27th July 1984)
McGettigan, Joseph Patrick
O'Daly, Liam Mary
Murphy, Raymond Emmanuel
Murphy, John James
Morgan, John Bernard
Lenihan, Pádraig Donal
Doyle, Christopher James
O'Reilly, Ciaran John
Payne, Jennifer Susan
Kelly, Maria Jacinta
O'Moore, Brian Gerard
Ryan, Patricia
McEnroy, Felix
Stafford, Liam Tomás
Ó Muirthile, Séamus Fintan
O'Driscoll, Margaret
Dunne, Maurice Joseph
McCarthy, Patrick Noel
Dillon, John Michael

Michaelmas 1984
(1st October 1984)
Solan, Dudley Francis

(20th November 1984)
Joyce, Paul Cyril
Sheehan, June Mary
Cronin, Denis Gerard
Lynch, Michelle

Ní Chaoimh, Áine Caitríona
Ó Caoimh, Gearóid Eoin
Gillespie, Brian David
Leahy, Dermot
McBratney, Richard John
[ex-Solicitor]
Leavy, Adrienne Therese
Galligan, Eamon Michael
Morrissey, William Joseph
O'Hanlon, Roderick Francis
Geoghegan, Patrick Richard
Kennedy, Patrick
McDonagh, Bernard Joseph
Mulloy, Eanna Michael
O'Dwyer, James John
Johnston, Mark Kevin Francis
O'Mahony, Michael Aquinas
Quinn, Anthony Pascal
Smith, Ann Geraldine
O'Regan, Edmond Thomas
Taaffe, James William
O'Brien, Patrick Jeremiah
Ní Shúilleabháin, Niamh Marie
O'Driscoll, Terence Anthony
Finn, Thomas Mary Bernard
O'Connell, Annette
Segrave, Kevin Barry
Johnston, Andrew Thomson
Maguire-O'Beirne (née *Maguire*),
  Patricia Monic Therese
Gordon, Brigid
Maginnis, Alban Alphonsus
[N.I. Barr.]

Easter 1985
[Special Call for Northern Ireland Barristers]
(19th April 1985)
Kennedy, Brian Charles [N.I. Barr.]
Drennan, Neil Patrick Cecil
[N.I. Barr.]
Grant, Martin Alistair Piers
[N.I. Barr.]
Morgan, Charles Declan [N.I. Barr.]
Rodgers, Hugh Martin [N.I. Barr.]
Orr, Hugh Mark [N.I. Barr.]
Kennedy (née *Halliday*), *Denise
Margaret* [N.I. Barr.]
McDowell (née *Forsythe*), *Iris Edithe*
[N.I. Barr.]
Deeny, Donnell Justin Patrick
[N.I. Barr.]

Trinity 1985
(morning 25th July 1985)
Spierin, Brian Edward [John Brooke
Scholarship of £240 per annum for 3 years]

Byrne, Gerard Noel Jackson [Society's
Exhibition of £120 per annum for 3 years]
McCullough, Eoin Denis
[Murnaghan Prize of £100]
Fitzgerald, Colman Seán
Murray, Paul
Treacy, Sheila Mary Andrea
O'Donohoe, Maurice Martin
[Commandant]
Ronayne, Mark Vincent
Hughes, Kieran H.
Fennell, Bridget Mary Caroline
McGrath, Patrick John
Rubotham, Gerard Noel
Mohon, Hugh Ignatius
Barr, Anthony William Edward
Maguire, William Ruttledge
Horgan, Dennis Joseph
Kennedy, Richard David
Ward, Peter Ross
Woods, James Vincent
Buckley, John William
McCann, Patrick Martin
Flannery, Mary
Ó hUiginn, Caoimhín
Barr, William [N.I. Barr.]
Macdonald, Barry James [N.I. Barr.]
Grant, Eugene [N.I. Barr.]
Brady, James Oliver [N.I. Barr.]
Leviseur, Nicholas Templer
[Engl. Barr., G.I.]
Carney, Caroline Mary [Engl. Barr.]

(afternoon 25th July 1985)
Fox, Finbar Peadar Seán
Brennan, John Francis
Flynn, Delia Marie
McCormack, Gerard
Ryan (née *O'Malley*), *Catherine
Agnes*
Beirne, Niall Desmond
Confrey, Anne
O'Driscoll, Sheelagh Teresa
Bailey, Sarah Anne Rosemary
Ryan, John Gerard
Cush, Michael Christopher Peter
Lee, Patrick Anthony
Whelan, Máire R.
McCullough, Hugh Martin
Reid, John Joseph
Delahunty, Cornelius P.
McRandal (née *Mangan*),
  Pauline Mary Mangan
Martin, Francis Joseph
O'Malley, Finbarr Patrick
Spillane, Jeanne Margaret
McHugh, Damien

O'Callaghan, William
Donnan, Maeve Mary
Devitt, Noel Patrick
Walsh (née *Morgan*),
  Margaret Josephine
Cahill, Niamh Teresa
Martin (née *McCullough*),
  Patricia Marie
Keleher, Padraig Finbarr

(26th July 1985)
Nolan, David Patrick McGivney
*.1 Goh, Aik Wee
* Abdlullah, Haji Abdul Kadir Haji
O'Leary, Eileen
O'Brien, James Gerard
O'Neill, Paul Henry
Murray, Richard William
Treanor, James Gerard
Farrelly, Brendan [Captain]
Regan, Eugene
McMorrow, Gráinne
O'Grady, Dennis Gerard
Ring, Mary Ellen
Hyland, John Oliver
O'Kane, Michael Patrick
* *Selvaratnam, Rathi*
O'Toole, Michael Peter
Comerford, Francis John
Keogh, Michael John
Molloy, Mary Teresa
Larkin, Brian Joseph
Mulcahy, Neil Jarlath John
O'Connor, John Vincent
Lyons (née *Shanahan*), *Joan*
Mulcahy, Michael Edward Joseph
  Ruben
Little, Gilbert Kieran
Plunkett, Gina
Ging (née *Morrissey*), *Helen*
O'Connor, Geraldine Frances
Spollen, Mary
Fanning, Helen
Seligman (née *Levine*), *Dorothy*
  Barbara
Meagher (née *Collins*), *Olivia Carmel*
O'Connor, Séamus Patrick
  [Commandant]
Vaughan, Brian
Blighe, James
Boyce, Michael Joseph
Folan, Gerard W.
Barry, Elizabeth Mary

Mackey, Noreen P.
Corrigan, Cormac Mel
McHugh, Bernard Kevin
Rea, John Bernard
Carragher, Geraldine Mary
Flannery, Paul Joseph
O'Donnell, Owen Laurence
Lennon, Patrick Charles
Browne, Josephine Marion
Staunton, Dorothy de Lacy
* Kanagasabai, Bimalarajah
O'Reilly, Breifne
Maloney, Michael Anthony
O'Leary, Peter Joseph
Breslin, Kevin
Humphreys, Gerard Franciscus
  [Captain]

Michaelmas 1985
(8th October 1985)
Forde (née *McNicholl*), *Catherine*

(8th November 1985)
Jordan, John Gerard
O'Leary, James Francis
Fitzpatrick, Joseph
O'Leary, Daniel Joseph
Cassidy, Constance Ann
Murphy, Jane Margaret
Crosbie, John Wilde
Brennan, Fintan Gerard
Sweeney, David Robert
Deegan, John Christopher
Farrelly, Margaret Mary
Houston (née *Bowe*), *Jane Teresa*
Somers, Peter Henry
Hickey, Liam
Richardson, Peter Thomas [Captain]
Sutton, Isabelle Rose
Maguire, Nora Maria Barbara
Báiréad, Eoin Criostóir
McHugh, David James [Captain]
Ryan, Michael Patrick
Manners, Geraldine Mary
Kelly, Patrick Declan
Hughes, Marina Catherine
Bradford, Mary Teresa

Hilary 1986
(21st January 1986)
Skene, Graeme John

* [1] The four Malaysian students here indicated by an asterisk were not called.

Trinity 1986

(morning 24th July 1986)

McDonald, Denis Michael [John Brooke
Scholarship of £240 per annum for 3 years]
Butler, Nuala [Society's Exhibition (£120)
and Murnaghan Prize (£100) *ex aequo*]
McGovern, Mary Caroline [Society's
Exhibition (£120) and Murnaghan Prize (£100)
ex aequo]
Barron, Síobhán Teresa Mary
Clohessy, Gráinne Michelle Catherine
Downing, Henry Charles
Friel, Raymond John
McGowan (née *Kirk*), *Louise Bridget*
Hunt, Anthony George
Burns, Paul
Cleary, Patrick Cyril Joseph
Devally, Conor Thomas
McDonnell, Michael Paul
O'Grady, Michael
Hunt, Patrick
Browne, Dervla Frances
Jackson, Claire Oonagh
More O'Ferrall (née *Plunkett*), *Joan
Mary*
O'Kelly, Catherine Mary Michele
Brogan, James Ignatius
Silke (née *Hughes*), *Geraldine Ann
Patricia*
McMorrow, John Paul
Monti, Trevor Stanley [Austr. Barr.]
Rowe, John Jermyn
[Engl. Barr.; M.T.]
*Sharpston, Eleanor Veronica
Elizabeth* [Engl. Barr.; M.T.]
Blackburn, Alan David [N.I. Barr.]
Magee, Eamonn Anthony [N.I. Barr.]

(afternoon 24th July 1986)
Boughton, Francis Edward
Priestley, Helen
Faherty, Mary Martina
O'Meara, Anita Maria Christina
Walsh, Patrick M.
O'Neill, Ann Marie
Murphy, Ronan M.
Reid, Paula Marie Therese
Buttanshaw, Angus David
Doherty, John Noel
Finlay, Peter Edward
Bird, Timothy Collins
O'Shea, John Martin
Ford, Margaret
Corcoran, Margaret Carmel
Fahy, Andrew O.
Needham, Gerald Joseph
Banim, Edward Patrick Roughan

Mahon, John Thomas Anthony
Pilkington, Teresa Mary
Martin, Helen
Minogue, Katherine
Kavanagh, Peter David
Kearney, Miriam
McAuley, Eileen Mary
Ó Dúlacháin, Cormac Seosamh

(morning 25th July 1986)
Barry, Frederick John
Maher, Jeremy
O'Kelly, Bernard Patrick Joseph
Tynan, Thomas Gerard
McCarrick, Honora Agnes
O'Connell, Patrick Cuthbert
Murray, Shane Patrick
Murphy, Patrick Sexton
McCarthy, Noel Charles
Nicholas, Patrick
Shannon, Richard
Neylon, Teresa Frances
Collins, Michael Finbarr
Nolan, Peter Paul
Hanlon, John Gerard
Henry, James Patrick
Frayne, Edward James
Ward, Desmond Francis Joseph
Healy, James Vincent
McCourt, Ciaran Gerard
Corcoran (née *Peyton*), [Dr.] *Nuala
Peyton*
Power, Edmund Patrick
Sweeney (née *Bray*), *Catherine*
Halloran, Martin
O'Kelly (née *Dennehy*), *Sarah Anne*
Kelly, William Joseph
Hegarty, David John
McDonough, Deirdre A.
Doyle, Alice Teresa

(afternoon 25th July 1986)
Moylan, Noreen Theresa
Crawford, Ann Ita
Doran, James Noel
Halligan, Michael
Cooney (née *Carty*), *Mary Anne*
Fennelly, John William
Ryan (née *Corboy*), *Ann Mary*
Kiely, John Finbar [Captain]
Mallon, Thomas Gabriel
Ryan, Thomas Cyril
Carney, Alban Patrick
Leavy, Edward Canice
Crawford, Damien Gerard Neil
Ruane, Séamus Seosamh
Burns, John William

Hurley, Daniel Patrick
Cunnane. John Anthony Felix
Shackleton, Eamon T.
O'Sullivan, Darina Francesca
Tyrrell, Thomas Peter
Tobin, Brendan Michael
Martin, Eugene D.A.V.
Gallery, Gerard Dominic
Clancy, Cormac Mary Cahir
Spierin, John Joseph [Captain]
Barry, Michael Denis John
Garavan, Irene
Murphy, Donal Finbarr
Collins, Anthony Michael
McKone, Edward

Michaelmas 1986
(3rd October 1986)
Gibbons, John Thomas

(7th November 1986)
Carroll, Brian Gerard
Clein, Peter Gerard
Corcoran, Charles
Croke, Gabrielle Geraldine Marian
Cusack (née *Keogh*), *Dympna Mary*
Doherty, Noel Anthony
Faulkner, Mary Brigid
Fitzgerald, Patrick Joseph
Flynn, John
Foley-Friel (née *Foley*),
  Mary-Anne Majella
Horgan, Dermot John
Jacobs (née *Lynam*), *Maureen Olive*
Keane, Esmonde Benedict Stephen
Lawlor, Fiona Jane
Long, Patrick Joseph
Murray, Michael Joseph
Ní Fhlaitheartaigh, Caitlín Bernadette
O'Neill, Timothy Paschal
Reilly, Gerard Michael
Ridge, James
Sheehan, Timothy Dermot Francis
Finlay, Finbar John
Walsh, Edward Mark David
Dalton, Helen Frances
O'Connor, Ellen Marie
O'Dea, Mark Damien
Ryan, Paula Geraldine
Lang, John Temple
Osborne, David Thomas
  [Engl. Barr., G.I.]

Hilary 1987
(12th January 1987)
Colclough Walsh of Branagh, John
  Francis Patrick Cyril

(13th January 1987)
Boal, Desmond Norman Orr
  [N.I. Barr.]

Trinity 1987
(morning 17th July 1987)
Gardiner, Paul Stephen
  [Brooke Scholarship]
Grist, Berna [Society's Exhibition]
Lucey, John Joseph [Muraghan Prize]
Gleeson, Catherine
O'Brien, Julia Bernadette
Ó hOisín, Colm
Holland, David Martin Daniel
Power, Vincent John Gerard
Synnott, Aidan John
Buckley, Declan
Richardson, James Gerard
Mangan (née *Brennan*), *Ita*
Doyle, James John
Finn, Eileen
Woulfe, James (Séamus) Philip
Murphy, Shane Gerard
de Brúir, Rory
Bouchier-Hayes (née *Dungan*),
  Mary Teri
O'Dea, William Gerard
Blake, Gerard
Boudren, Christopher
Keane, Michael Brendan
Smith, Anthony Philip
Brennan, Olive T.M.
Condon, Colm Power
Farrell, Raymond Patrick
Lynch (née *McManus*), *Yvonne*
O'Callaghan, David
Sutton, David Gerard Nathaniel
Phillips, James
Marrinan, Desmond Patrick
  [N.I. Barr.]
Cowan, David [Austr. Barr.]
O'Callaghan, Peter John [Austr. Barr.]
Trew, John Labatt [Austr. Barr.]

(afternoon 17th July 1987)
Gilvarry, Evlynne
Shiels, Trevor
Sanfey,Mark Gerard
Scaife, Lucy Anne
White, Alexander Martin
Barron, Jane
Drislane, Declan Joseph
Maguire, Peter Anthony
O'Connor, John Charles
Murray, Stanislaus F.
MacFhógartaigh, Breandán Proinsias
Harewood (née *Fitzgerald*), *Maureen*
Keane, Peter Anthony

Ralston, Gavin Andrew
Brosnan, Kathleen Mary (Kate)
Mara, Damien Martin
O'Connell, Terence Mary
O'Malley, Iseult Pauline Mary
Crivon (née *Franks*), *Louise Anne*
Horgan, Patrick Timothy
White, Iris Mary
Quirke, Francis Michael
Ó Buachalla, Diarmuid
Egan, Catherine (née Donovan)
Foy, Agnes Mary
Harkin, Louis Joseph
Lyons, Peter
Ball, Mary Katherine Jessica
Hennessy, John Joseph
Dillon-Leetch, Thomas [ex- Solicitor]

(afternoon 20th July 1987)
McGeough, Celestine Declan
Nerney, Suzanne Patricia
Stewart, Carmel Teresa
Terry, Seán Augustine
Bermingham, Bridget Mary
McAllister, Martin Stewart
McLoughlin, Anna Maria
Foynes, Dara Mary
Kelly, Philip James
Maher, Mary Dolores
Flanagan, Dermot Anthony
Horan, Michael Bernard
O'Dwyer, Patrick Michael
Dully, Martin Joseph
Ennis, Thomas Patrick
O'Higgins, Irene Agnes
Bunni (née *Carroll*), *Anne*
Hayden, Martin James
Clark, Robert William
Gilmore, Brian
Golden, James Oliver
Kerr, Raymond Alexander
O'Connell, Maria Bernadette
O'Kelly (née *Staunton*), *Mary Dympna*
Richardson, Andrew Pius Marian
O'Connor, Joanna Mary

Michaelmas 1987
(Friday morning 6th November 1987)
O'Donoghue, Nicholas Gerard
Redmond, Aidan Francis
Collins, Anne Maria Claire
Aylmer, John Francis Michael
Daly, Frederick Marcus John
MacEochaidh, Colm Cyril
O'Hare, Paula
White, Noel Michael Joseph
Power, Denis Anthony

Kearney, Timothy Noel
Kavanagh, Feargal Piarais
Kearney, Kevin Timothy
Cullinane, Patrick
Dowling, Maurice Edward
Fleming, John Patrick
Ó Síothcháin, Seán
McDonough, Mark Richard Adam
O'Toole, Dolores Mary
McCarthy, Thomas John
Revington, Joseph
Ryan, James Noel
Gilvarry, David Francis
Brangam, William Alva [N.I. Barr.]
Bateson, Philomena Lucy [N.I. Barr.]

(afternoon 6th November 1987)
Costello, John Kevin
O'Connor, Edward Michael
MacDonnell, Rosemary Anne Elizabeth
Cahill, Patrick Oliver
Harney, Catherine
Burke, David Joseph
Keeley, Patrick John
Dunne, Dermot Anthony
Mack, Anne Patricia
O'Higgins, Michael Liam
Mulholland, John Duncan
Kilkenny (née *Brennan*), *Anna Rachel*
Mulhall, Brendan Patrick
O'Shea, Eoin Francis
de Brún, Deirdre Áine
Nielsen, Jacqueline Carol Patricia
Daly (née *O'Neill*), *Nuala Brigitt*
O'Kelly, Síle Proinsias
Hutton, Kathryn Anne
Garvey, William Benedict
Hickey, Eugene Noel
McKeone, Marion Martina
Tackaberry, John Antony
[Engl. Barr.]

Trinity 1988
(Tuesday 19th July 1988)
Murphy, Declan John [John Brooke Scholarship of £500 per annum for 3 years]
Corrigan, Anne [Society's Exhibition of £200 per annum for 3 years and the Murnaghan Prize of £150 *ex aequo*]
MacCann, Lyndon Jonathan Wiltshire [Society's Exhibibtion and Murnaghan Prize *ex aequo*]
Delany, Hilary Anna
Donnelly, Aileen Mary
Maher, Imelda Patricia
Murphy, Marie Therese

Turner, Sharon
Keaveny, Vincent Thomas
Walsh, Michael George
Jackson, Nuala Evelyn
O'Riordan, Cornelius Patrick
Costello, Caroline
Elworthy, Samantha Sarah-Ann
Woods (née *Kelly*), *Bernadette*
    Martina
Tunney, James Gerard
Lacey, Roisin Mary
Cooke (née *McDermott*), *Mary Louise*
Finlay, Thomas Aloysius
Cowman, Johanna Mary
Doherty, Alan Martin
Butler, Patrick Andrew
McQuillen, Anthony John
    [Austr. Barr.]
Symons, Christopher John Maurice
    [Austr. Barr.]
Meade, John Joseph

(afternoon 19th July 1988)
Kennedy, Isobel Anna-Maria
O'Riordan, Pádraig Antóin
Whelan, Darius Dominic
Burke, Senan Patrick
Neary, Annemarie
Fitzpatrick, Anthony James
Moloney, Damien Mary Patrick
Robertson, Martina
Kenneally, Derek Christopher Jude
Clarke, Thomas Joseph Kevin
Egan, Suzanne Josephine
Gordon, Joan Bernadette
O'Loghlen, Grainne
O'Reilly, Angela Frances Michele
McGovern, Damien John
Ní Mhuircheartaigh, Máire Treasa
McKenna, Conan Damien
Curtin, Edmond John
Hickey, Paul Martin
Ó Dubhghaill, Feargal
Phelan, Nuala Mary
Linehan, Paul
Minogue, Patrick Joseph
Lankford, Síobhán

(Wednesday 20th July 1988)
O'Hara, Aidan Anthony
Curran, John Patrick
Byrne, Stephen Joseph Harrington
Gilmore, Maire Niamh
Vallely, Michael Eugene Brendan
Collery, Laurence Michael
MacMenamin, Fiona
O'Neill, Patricia Aisling
Whitty, Nicholas Francis

Murphy, Brian Timothy
Glennon, John Thomas
Doyle, Katherine Rose (*Irene*)
Moriarty, [Doctor] John Francis
Murray, Isobel Margaret
MGovern, Peter Ronan
Gloster, Michael Joseph Benilde
Moore, Maureen
Fogarty, Kenneth Christopher
Donnelly, Peter Raphael
Fannon, Eoin Vincent
Kelly, James Francis
Cosgrove, Noel Patrick
Byrne, Patrick Joseph

Michaelmas 1988

(Friday 4th November 1988)
Cirillo (née *Griffin*), *Angela*
Clancy, Tomás Christopher Mary
Colbert, Norbert Ronan Murray
Cregan, Joseph Patrick
Dempsey, Peter David
Egan, Patrick Joseph
Gallagher, Brian
Hussey, Danielle Frances
Kavanagh, Michael Paul
Kerr, Robert Boyle
Kirwan, Mary Patricia
Mulligan, Sheila Ann
O'Donoghue, Michael Gerard
Ring, Julie Patricia
Sexton, Alfred John Andrew
Shortt, John Paul
Tuohy, John Peter Martin
Watchorn, Brendan Alfred
White, Catherine Antoinette
Farrell, Joanne Mary
O'Neill, Robert Denis
Kinneen, Michael Eoin
Boushel, Margaret Mary Ethna
Donnelly, Garvan
Egan, Karen Bernadette
Reynolds, Teresa Mary
Quinn (née *Brennan*), *Fionnuala Áine*
    [N.I. Barr.]
Quinn, Patrick Fintan [N.I. Barr.]
Floyd, Christopher David
    [Engl. Barr., I.T.]
O'Donovan, Morgan Teige Gerald
    [Engl. Barr., I.T.]
Gogarty, Alain Patrice [N.I. Barr.]
Jennings, Mary

Trinity 1989
(Wednesday 24th May 1989)
Ellicott, Robert James [Austr. Barr., New South Wales]

Special Call of N.I. Barristers
(Friday 2nd June 1989)
Finnegan, Kevin James, Q.C. [N.I. Barr.]
McDermott, Eilis Maire, Q.C. [N.I. Barr.]
Comerton, Edward Alan, Q.C. [N.I. Barr.]
Smyth, David William, Q.C. [N.I. Barr.]
Foote, Jeffrey Ian, Q.C. [N.I. Barr.]
Berry, Robert Marshall Michael [N.I. Barr.]
Colton, Adrian [N.I. Barr.]
Corrigan, Aidan Christopher [N.I. Barr.]
Cushinan, John Martin [N.I. Barr.]
Dunn, Campbell John Laughlin [N.I. Barr.]
Fee, Brian Francis [N.I. Barr.]
Ferrity, Patrick Joseph [N.I. Barr.]
Jenkinson, Angela Ruth [N.I. Barr.]
Keenan, Colm Joseph [N.I. Barr.]
Kerr, Gordon William [N.I. Barr.]
McCrudden, Laurence Patrick [N.I. Barr.]
McCrudden, Samuel Garry [N.I. Barr.]
McDonnell, John Martin [N.I. Barr.]
O'Neill, John Duncan [N.I. Barr.]
O'Reilly, Francis Edward Patrick [N.I. Barr.]
Simpson, Carl Alexander [N.I. Barr.]
Simpson, Gerald Eric John [N.I. Barr.]
Treacy, James Mary Eugene [N.I. Barr.]
Weatherup, Ronald Eccles [N.I. Barr.]
Weir, Richard Keenan [N.I. Barr.]

(Friday morning 21st July 1989)
Hussey, Rachel Mary [John Brooke Scholarship of £500 per annum for 3 years and Society's Exhibition of £200 for 3 years *ex aequo*]
O'Sullivan, John Michael [Brooke Scholarship and Society's Exhibition *ex aequo*]
Caffrey, Niamh Louise [Murnaghan Prize of £150]
Coughlan, Paul Ralph
Reilly (née *Sheridan*), *Bridget*
Keane, Mary Majella

Walley (née *Coyle*), *Pauline*
Whooley, Paul Joseph
Kerr, Anthony
Madden, Deirdre
Murray, Brian Raphael
Cruess Callaghan, Maria Samantha
de Búrca, Gráinne
O'Donoghue, Michael Joseph
Buckley, Margaret Frances
Collins, Maurice Gerard
Byrne, Deirdre Ann
Dwan, [Capt.] Francis Eugene
Hayden, Nicola Therese
Mahony, Kathleen Teresa
O'Hara, Clíodhna
Torrens (née *Maguire*), *Marie Patricia*
Moorhead, Sara
McGowan, Vincent Ciaran
Ryan, Richard Michael
Moriarty, Jeanne-Marie
Doyle, David Anthony [Austr. Barr.]
Crimmins, Michael Thomas [Austr. Barr.]
Gates, Margaret Veronica Gladys
Ryan, James Brendan
Ní Chúlacháin, Sinéad Áine
Cross, Gerard Mary
Lynch, Jeremiah James [Captain]
Barron, Robert
Cousins, Mel
Hickey, Marco William
Campbell, Brenda Margaret Mary
Boland, Thomas Gerard
McGettigan, Paul William
O'Hanlon, Bronagh Mary
Kehoe, Teresa Josephine
Mac Namee, Michael Anthony
Kelly (née *Curran*), *Gillian*
Maguire, Kevin
McKenna, Felix
Ó Ceallaigh, Tomás
Barron, Elizabeth Anne
Boyle, John Christopher Joseph
Cusack, Pauline
McHugh, Declan John
Galligan, Paul
Neville, James Richard
O'Dwyer, Paul John

(Monday afternoon 24th July 1989)
McCarthy, Paul Charles
O'Leary, Clare Jean Mary
Hayden, John Francis
Corry, Declan Gerard
Harty, John Flannan
Smith, Mary Bernadette

McGarry, John
Ward, Paul Anthony
Connaughton, Mark Gerard
Hughes, Oliver Gerard
O'Toole Antoniotti (née *O'Toole*),
  Mary Sabrina
Keane, Patrick Joseph
Fennell, Hilary
O'Reilly, Anne Marie
Farragher, Patrick Joseph
Gleeson, John
Manning, Patrick J.
Blanksby, Dorothy Christine
  [Austr. Barr.]
Trigar, Philip Richard [Austr. Barr.]

Michaelmas 1989
(Tuesday 24th October 1989)
Curtin, John Gerard
Linehan, Donal Conor
Michel, Niall Nicholas
Murphy, Cliona Mary Margaret
O'Riordan, Donal Gerard
Regan, Catherine Geraldine
Van Esbeck, Geraldine Louise
Lynch, Michael Conor
O'Connell, Brenda Patricia
Archbold, John Joseph
Barrett, Aileen Mary
Boland, Daniel Joseph
Cahalan, Thomas Cyril
Feehan, Daniel Mary Michael
Gavigan, Gabriel
Graham, Mark Francis
Hennigan, Michael Paul
Mulkerrins, Eileen Ellen Patricia
Ushewokunze, Herbert Sylvester
  Masiyiwa
McGuinn, Edward James
Nolan, Martin Edward
Grehan, Brendan Thomas
McKenna, Mairead Maria
Ó Sé, Mícheál Mairtín
Swift, Aine
Bridgeman, James Jude
Byrne, Brian Patrick
Cooney, Michael Patrick
Horgan, Patrick
O'Leary, Laurence Oliver
Ó Lideadha, Giollaíosa
Ward, Ann Marie
Prendergast, Thomas James
Byrne, Laurence Joseph
Dunne, Margaret Joan
Cowdroy, Dennis Antill [Austr. Barr.]
Callinan, Ian David Francis
  [Austr. Barr.]
Foley, John Joseph [Austr. Barr.]

Easter 1990
(Wednesday 30th May 1990)
Gruzman, Laurence Charles, Q.C.
  [Austr. Barr.]

Trinity 1990
(Thursday 19th July 1990)
Barniville, David Andrew [John Brooke
  Scholarship of £500 per annum for 3 years]
O'Dowd, Thomas John [Society's
  Exhibition of £200 per annum for 3 years]
Murphy, Maurice Patrick [Murnaghan
  Prize]
Conlan-Smyth, David
Penrose, William James
Tighe, Una Mary
O'Farrell, Carol Anne
Murphy, Carole Bridget
Reilly, Anne Elizabeth
Mee, John Patrick
Garavan, Eoin Gerard
Doherty, Noel David
Breen, Ciaran Joseph
Martin, James Owen
Wilkinson, Brian Thomas
Finn, James Edward
Gray, Robert Michael Ker
  [Engl. Barr.; L.I.]
Hobson, John Graham [Engl. Barr.]
Greenslade, Henry Michael
  [Engl. Barr.]
Higgs, Roland Francis [Engl. Barr.]
McCahill, Patrick Gerard [Engl. Barr.]
Jones, Timothy Arthur [Engl. Barr.]
Stimpson, Michael Edward
  [Engl. Barr.]
McCollum, Liam Gerard [N.I. Barr.]
McGuinness, Anne Marie [N.I. Barr.]
Rundle, Geoffrey Philip Farrell
  [Austr. Barr.]
Gruzman, Adrian Michael
  [Austr. Barr.]

(afternoon 19th July 1990)
O'Driscoll, Karen Margaret Helen
Barrington, Eileen Patricia
Oakes, Ciaran Peter Eamonn
Cregan, Brian James
Flahive, Michael
Zaidan, Desmond
Twomey, Patrick Martin
Long, Antoinette Mary
Lyons, John Richard
Howard, Michael Joseph
O'Callaghan, Martin Stephen Patrick
Kenny, Karen Elizabeth
Gallagher, Eugene James
Devlin, James Vincent Campion

O'Donovan, Diarmuid Patrick Arthur
Collins, Maeve Monica
Sreenan, Pearse Michael
Carroll, Edmund Patrick Pius
Orange, Garnet Joseph
Cullen, Yvonne, Marie
Drea, Edmund Patrick Pius
O'Mara, Helen Geraldine
Rowley, Shane Thomas
Dwyer, Walter Padraig Daniel

(Friday 20th July 1990)
Marray, Edward Michael
Madden, Edward Joseph
Ryan, Stephen Augustine
Pathe, Amanda
Clarke, Blanaid Julie Mary
O'Riordan, Raghnal William
Cahalane, Barbara
Williams, Caroline Mary
Brennan, Diarmuid Michael
Eaton, Sinead Josephine
Kirby, Bernadette
Foley, Anthony
O'Callaghan, Ellen Abina
O'Higgins, Michael Patrick
Kinirons, Thomas Peter
Fogarty, Kevin Joseph
Fox, Mary Patricia

Michaelmas 1990
(Thursday 18th October 1990)
Crowe, Orla Brid Mary
D'Arcy, Kevin John
Kennedy, Patrick Christopher
MacAodha, Eamonn Eoin
O'Loughlin, Michael Patrick
Collins, Fergus Patrick Joseph
Courtney, Randal John Campion
Curran, Aidan Gerard
Curran, Vincent Joseph
Stapleton, Síobhán
Hogan, Conor Patrick
Kelly, Conor Patrick
Hughes, Edward John
Moran, Dolores Ann
Nolan, Michael Francis
Manning, Thomas James
Golden, Francis Christopher Patrick
Regan, Mary
Devitt, Patrick Joseph
Hutchinson, George Brian
Marlborough, Anne Martina Mary
Moorehead, Eamon Christopher
Ó Briain, Colm Finbarr
O'Gorman, Patrick Kieran
Rice, Thomas Brendan

Roche, Séamus
Connolly, Brendan Joseph Oliver
Woolfson, Saul Justin
Dent, Peter [Austr. Barr.]
Wolf, Thomas Jules [Austr. Barr.]
Johnson, Richard Anthony
    [Austr. Barr.]
Gullotta, Samuel Peter [Austr. Barr.]
O'Brien, Paul [Engl. Barr.]
Brennan, Daniel Joseph [Engl. Barr.]
Rylands, Elizabeth [Engl. Barr.]
Abdullah, Haji Abdul Kadir Haji
    [Sabah/Malaysian Barr.]

Easter 1991
(Thursday 9th May 1991)
Toulmin, John Kelvin, Q.C.
    [Engl. Barr.; M.T.]

Trinity 1991
(Monday 10th June 1991)
Bennett, David Michael John
    [Austr. Barr.]

(Thursday 27th June 1991)
Lauterpacht, Elihu [Engl. Barr.]

(Thursday morning 18th July 1991)
Ó Raifeartaigh, Una [John Brooke
    Scholarship of £500 per annum for 3 years]
Delaney, Michael Patrick [Society's
    Exhibition of £200 per annum for 3 years]
O'Leary, Julianne Christina [Murnaghan
    Prize of £150 *ex aequo*]
Humphreys, Richard Francis
    [Murnaghan Prize of £150 *ex aequo*]
O'Gorman, Garry Anthony
Maguire, Elizabeth
Cahill, Marian Kathleen McDonnell
Smyth, Thomas Clement
Brady, Francis Joseph
Cusack, Denis Anthony
Kennedy, Deirdre Mary
Boland, John
Clancy, Agatha Eileen Rita
Ó Braonáin, Luan Paraic
Greally, Melanie
Griffin, Catherine
Harley, Timothy John
O'Rourke, Christine Hjortshoj
McGrath, Margaret Clare
Tunissen, Claire Patricia Christine
Healy, Kathleen Veronica
Kelly, Ann
Kilfeather, Jonathan
King, Maura
Nicholas, Thomas Mark

O'Leary, Eoin Finbarr
Ong, David Kim Ming
Ryan, Brendan Peter
Ahern, Anne
Kirrane, Aedamar Ann Marie
Hickey, Owen Michael
Barraclough, Anthony Roger
   [Engl. Barr.]
Breheny, Mark Patrick [Engl. Barr.]
Bueno, Antonio De Padua José Maria
   [Engl. Barr.]
Hewson, Barbara Mary [Engl. Barr.]
McDermott, Thomas Francis
   [Engl. Barr.]
McGuire, Donal Patrick [Engl. Barr.]
McGuire, Deirdre Maria [Engl. Barr.]
Sheridan, Francis Anthony
   [Engl. Barr.]

(Thursday 18th July 1991, 2 p.m.)
   [Group of 55 Australian Barristers]
Arden, Peter Ronald
Arnott, David Urlic
Atkin, John Michael
Backhouse, Cecily Elizabeth
Barker, Ian McClelland
Burn, Raymond James
Collins, Bruce Wilkie
Cook, Colin Maxwell
Costigan, Francis Xavier
Crennan, Michael Joseph
Crumpton, John Alfred
Dooley, Brian Daniel
Donovan, Brian Harrie Kevin, Q.C.
Dowd, John Robert Arthur
Dwyer, Jennifer Rose
Einstein, Clifford Roy
Garnsey, John Joseph James
Greenhill, Robert Patrick
Guest, Brian Albert John
Halligan, Howard John
Hamilton, John Perry
Hartigan, John Charles
Hastings, Peter Selby
Healey, Terence Michael
Hickey, Christopher Kevin
Hodgekiss, William George
Santamaria, Joseph Gerard
Santamaria, Paul Donal

(at 4 p.m.)
Hodgson, Thomas Lindsay Poole
Holmes, Malcolm
Hughes, Braddon Hamilton
Katzmann, Anna Judith
Kavanagh, Patricia Marie
Kennedy, Desmond Thomas
Kennedy, Keiran William

Margo, Robin Fabian
Mater, Roderick Colin Paul
MacGregor, Malcolm Alexander
   McLeod
McSpedden, Linda Margaret
Neil, Maurice James
Newton, Michael Cecil
Odgers, Stephen James
Parnell, John
Ramage, Michael Carmichael
Rochlin, John Stuart
Seery, Peter Michael
Sharpe, John Lawrence
Small, Trevor Newton
Stratton, Bruce Thomas
Thompson, Mark Norman
Tobin, Terence Kevin
Toner, Robert Stephen
Wheelahan, Dennis Anthony
Wilkins, Russell Francis
Wong, Leslie Gaye

(Friday morning 19th July 1991)
Lawlor, Monica Patricia Mary
Murphy, Eavan Cecilia
O'Connor, Bríd Goretti
O'Keeffe, Hugh Thomas
Shields, Thomas Francis
Travers, Joseph Noel Anthony
O'Leary, David Barry
Browne, Rita Anne
Carragher, Monica Christina
Connolly, Catherine Martina Ann
Conway, John Brendan
Fox, John
Henry, Paula Maria
Langwallner, David Johann
MacBride, Seán John Pius
McCormack, John Anthony G.
McLaughlin, Patricia Mary
O'Connor, Miceál Anthony
O'Leary, James Anthony
O'Leary, Timothy James
O'Reilly, Patrick Finbarr
O'Toole, Christopher John
Ó hUallacháin, Seán
Parker, Richard Leonard
Peart, Arthur James Noel
Quigley, John Redmond
Ryan, John Gregory
Territt, Martin John
Timmins, Patrick Joseph
Ward, Brigid Geraldine
McCabe, Bernard Gerard
Fergus, Karen Marie
Leahy, Dennis Gerard
Magennis, Bernard James Joseph
Smith, Padraig Liam

Stelzer, Ingrid Nora
Romeril, Agnes Ann
Greene, Paul Joseph

Michaelmas 1991

(Wednesday 16th October 1991)
Nugent, Jonathan Joseph
McCarthy, Gary Daniel Paul
Ní Fhatharta, Bríd
Clifford, Michael Thomas
Prendeville, Orla Patricia
Maher, Judith Mary
Malone, Anne Marie
Newcombe, Kenneth James Gerald
Callaly, Colm Francis
Cowley, Jeremiah Peter
Crowley, Donal Patrick
Daly, Caroline Ann
Davis, Carolyn
Fahy, John Francis
Fitzgerald, Mark John Alexander
Furlong, Una Mary
Gilsenan, Seán Declan
Gilvarry, Michael Patrick
Hannigan, Thomas Joseph Mary
Hynes, Joan Mary
Larkin, Martina Mary
Long, Sharon Jane Alice
Lucey-Neale, Catherine
McInerney, Brian Patrick
Neiland, Anthony Michael Ernest
Neville, Catherine Teresa
Ó Briain, Austin
O'Brien, Adrian Michael
O'Connell, Mary Magdalen
O'Hara, Nuala Brigid
Aylett, Kenneth George [Engl. Barr.]
Frazer, Christopher Mark
  [Engl. Barr.]
Mitchell, Andrew Robert [Engl. Barr.]
Mullally, Maureen Vincent
  [Engl. Barr.]

(at 2 o'clock)
Seligman, Arthur
Seymour, Colin Brian
Sheridan, Jacqueline Mary
Shortt, Michael Gerard
Tier, Brendan Francis
Treacy, Patrick Richard
Tuite, Michael Donald
O'Connor, Anthony [ex-Solicitor]
Coghlan, Terence Woakes
  [ex-Solicitor]
McKenna, Isolde [ex-Solicitor]
Crennan, Susan Maree [Austr. Barr.]
Crittle, Charles Peter [Austr. Barr.]

Cummins, John Daniel [Austr. Barr.]
Curran, Francis Denis Michael
  [Austr. Barr.]
Curtain, David Edmund [Austr. Barr.]
Gibson, Judith Clare [Austr. Barr.]
Inglis, Michael Benjamin
  [Austr. Barr.]
Little, Peter John [Austr. Barr.]
Middleton, John Eric [Austr. Barr.]
Murray, Brian Francis [Austr. Barr.]
Nash, Pamela Rose [Austr. Barr.]
Weinberg, Mark Samuel [Austr. Barr.]

Trinity 1992

(Thursday morning 23rd July 1992)
Whelan, Anthony Tomas [Society's
  Exhibition of £200 per annum for 3 years]
Kerins, Fiona Louise [Murnaghan Prize of
  £150]
Colbert, Maria Johanna
Boner, Ann
Gearty, Mary Rose
Coughlan, Linda Anne
Mahon, Oliver Michael Thomas
Quinn, Oisín
Berkeley, Sarah Marie
Rutherdale, Alistair Johnston
O'Doherty, Sharon Lorraine
Carmody, Ruth Catherine
Gayer, Sasha Louise
Carney, Margaret Teresa
Moore, Thomas John
Bland, Peter William
Lawlor, Thérèse Catherine
O'Donnell, Michael Vincent
Kearney, Conor Patrick
Dyke, Vandra Carolyn
Conroy, Margaret Mary
O'Hara, Gráinne Anne
Coleman, Derek
Foley, John Anthony
Ó Scanaill, Mícheál
Kelleher, Denis Patrick Albert
Kingston, James William
Whitney, Brian Michael Kevin
Quinn, Cormac Martin
Lyne, Elizabeth Anne
O'Brien, Arlene Maria
Dwyer, John Leonard [Austr. Barr.]
Towson, Peter Granvill [Austr. Barr.]
Pagone, Gaetano Tony [Austr. Barr.]
Beaumont, Frederick George Albion
  [Austr. Barr.]
Jopling, Peter John [Austr. Barr.]

(Thursday afternoon 23rd July 1992)
Dolan, Ronan Christopher

McGrath, Penelope Ann Margaret
Manning, Dermot Philip
Spellman, Jarlath Anthony
MacKenna, Laura Jean
Shivnen, Doreen Therese
Dodd, Kevin
Brophy, Michael Francis
Scully, Lorraine [ex-Solicitor]
Ruane, Blathna Linda [ex-Solicitor]
Blackburn, Thomas Dutton
    [Austr. Barr.]
Connell, Bruce Anthony Moore
    [Austr. Barr.]
de Meyrick, John Julian [Austr. Barr.]
Hogg, Alfred Christopher
    [Austr. Barr.]
Ritter, Gordon Raymond [Austr.
    Barr.]
Robinson, Wendy Louise
    [Austr. Barr.]
Zichy-Woinarski, William Brind
    [Austr. Barr.]
McMahon, Joseph Patrick Michael
    [Austr. Barr.]
Prince, Roger Graham [Austr. Barr.]
Rickard, David [Austr. Barr.]
Cahill, Patrick John [Engl. Barr.]
McGowan, Maura Patricia
    [Engl. Barr.]
Neill, Robert James MacGillivray
    [Engl. Barr.]
Dinsmore, Margaret-Ann [N.I. Barr.]

(Friday morning 24th July 1992)
Mullooly, Michael Joseph
Courtney, Fergus Michael
Ó Floinn, Séamus Benedict
Reilly, Miriam
Dockery, Desmond Patrick
Doyle, Aidan Patrick
Murnaghan, Philomena Nora
McCarthy, [Father] Patrick Anthony
Kenny, Mary Teresa
Keane, Thomas Michael
O'Connell, Donncha Séamas
Cullinane, Hilda Teresa
Hickey, John Martin
McDonald, Simon Charles
McGagh, Francis Ambrose
Waddell, David Anthony
Connell, Johannah Mary
Codd, Pauline Bernadette
Heslin, Jacinta Carmel
Nerney, Elaine Anne
O'Sullivan, Gerard Patrick
Feaheny, Teresa Mary
Walsh, Gabrielle Mary
Lowery, Aileen Christina Ann

Tuite, Richard Joseph
Walsh, John Thomas
Smith, Michael Charles Ward
Smyth, Declan John

Michaelmas 1992
(Friday 16th October 1992)
Cahill, Conor Vincent
Barnes, Joseph Mary Xavier
Baxter, Martina Mary
Bowman, Conor Vincent
Carney, [Dr.] *Marjorie May*
Crawford, Brendan Francis
Duffy, Gordon Michael
Field, Amanda-Jane
Gilleran, Peter
Halpenny, Michael Denis
Kellaghan, Peter Columba
Kiely, Joseph Marian
Donnelly, John Patrick [Engl. Barr.]
Magill, Ciaran Seosa [Engl. Barr.]
Maher, Martha Johanna Dorothy
    [Engl. Barr.]
Seaward, Martin Vincent [Engl. Barr.]
Styles, Mark Patrick [Engl. Barr.]
Walling, Philip Thomas George
    [Engl. Barr.]
Willers, Mark Lawrence George
    [Engl. Barr.]
Deakin, Peter John [Austr. Barr.]
Fleming, Justin [Austr. Barr.]
Daly, Ivan Patrick John
Levins, Tara Sadhbh
May, Joseph Gerard
McGauley, Clement Alphonsus
McGuiggan, John
McNally, Mary
O'Brien, Elizabeth Mary
O'Neill, Anne Catherine
O'Riordan, James Austin
Phelan, Mary
Reichert, Nicholas George Gerard
Taaffe, Helen Mairead Philomena
Toal, Alan Patrick
Walker, Andrew James
Ward, Patrick Joseph
Keane, Donal Francis
Diskin, Mary Anne
Bourke, Denise Mary
Gill, John Jude
Ruddy, David

Easter 1993
(Friday 14th May 1993)
Cowdery, Nicholas Richard
    [Austr. Barr.]

Trinity 1993

(Thursday 22nd July 1993)

Power, Ann Geraldine [John Brooke
   Scholarship of £500 per annum for 3 years]
Leland, Carol Ella [Society's Exhibition of
   £200 per annum for 3 years]
Faughnan, Vincent John [Murnaghan
   Prize of £150]
O'Callaghan, James Jeremiah
Craven, Ciaran Donal
Boylan, Annette Marie
O'Donnell, Rebecca Mary
O'Loughlin, Kevin Jude
Curran, Patrick David [Engl. Barr.]
Enright, Seán [Engl. Barr.]
Hickey, Eugene [Engl. Barr.]
Law, Robert [Engl. Barr.]
Morley, Iain Charles [Engl. Barr.]
Williams of Mostyn, Lord
   [Engl. Barr.]
Masters, Alan Bruce Raymond
   [Engl. Barr.]
Ryan, David Patrick [Engl. Barr.]
Cranitch, Michael James
   [Austr. Barr.]
Digby, Geoffrey John [Austr. Barr.]
Galbally, David Norman
   [Austr. Barr.]
Golombek, Peter Christopher
   [Austr. Barr.]
Gray, Peter Walter [Austr. Barr.]
Linder, William Benjamin
   [Austr. Barr.]
Manly, Richard James [Austr. Barr.]
Nicholson, Julie Ann [Austr. Barr.]
Perry, Michael James [Austr. Barr.]
Simpson, Michael Anthony
   [Austr. Barr.]
Stitt, Robert Reginald [Austr. Barr.]
Malik, Akbar Ali [Pakinstani Barr.]
Mina, Alexis Beatrice [Engl. Barr.]
Coghlin, Patrick [N.I. Barr.]

(afternoon)

Lucey, Mary Catherine
McAuliffe, Conor Dominic
Fitzpatrick, Geraldine Patricia Mary
Bolger, Marguerite Mary
Liston, Julie Claire
Muldoon, Orla Margaret
Fields, Adrianne Clare
Carroll, Paul Joseph
McSweeney, Sinéad Anne
Kelly, Paul Geoffrey Pius
Delahunt, Raymond
Power, Martin Michael
O'Dell, Eoin

Conlon, Michael James
Rogerson, Mary Teresa
Kimber, Cliona Janet Marie
Cody, Colman Patrick
Gallagher, Grace Marie Walsh
Kerins, Francis
*Heneghan, Margaret Patricia
   Josephine*
Widdis, Hugh William Patrick
McParland, David James William
Keville, Cathrina Elizabeth
Major, John Thomas
Philpott, Thomas
Walsh, Patrick
Corcoran, Ann Edel
Condon, Bernard Thomas
Twomey, Adrian Finbarr
Cagney, David Gerard Mary

(Friday 23rd July 1993)

Murray, Karen Josephine
O'Connell, John Anthony
Willcocks, Patrick Desmond
McGowan, James Christopher Finbarr
Tierney, Niall Henry
Murphy, Hunter Martin
Levey, Margaret Mary Frances
Whitney, Michael John
McManus, Mary Claire
Ging, John Francis
Keane, William Joseph
Dinneen, Kevin David
Molloy, Sarah Bernadette
O'Donoghue, Michael Ignatius
Pigott, Mary Clare
Flynn, Thomas Brendan
Fleming, Denis Anthony
Hughes, Noel Patrick Joseph
O'Halloran, Garrett Anthony
McEntaggart, Louis Dominic Martin
Brophy, Henry Niall Edward
McCoy, John Gerard
Kelly, Caroline Elizabeth
Turner, Mary Patricia
Hughes, William John
O'Sullivan, Michael Dermot
Callanan, Siobhan Marie
Redmond, Morgan James
Ó Morain, Seán Gearóid
Grealy, Clare Mary Colette
McCarthy, Alan William James

Michaelmas 1993

(Friday 15th October 1993)

Dillon-Malone, Patrick Rafael
Mara, Dermot Malachy
Sheehan, Anne Marie

Farrell, Brian Joseph
O'Connor, Patricia
Byrne, Gerald Paul
Daly, Denis John Christopher
Holt, Seán Súilleabhán
Kennedy, David William
Morgan, Eugene
O'Connor, Karen Martha
Reynolds, Leonie Brigid
*Tan, Edwin Boon Chong [not called]
Andrews, Geraldine [Engl. Barr.]
Dalby, Joseph Francis [Engl. Barr.]
Duffy, Peter Joseph Francis
   [Engl. Barr.]
Jones, Peter William Warburton
   [Engl. Barr.]
Quigley, Conor [Engl. Barr.]
Burton, Gregory Keith [Austr. Barr.]
Cameron, Robert Norman
   [Austr. Barr.]
Whelan, Simon [Austr. Barr.]

Northern Ireland Barristers
(Friday 19th November 1993)
Coyle, John Joseph [N.I. Barr.]
Lennon, Mark Joseph [N.I. Barr.]
Lunny, Patrick Anthony [N.I. Barr.]
Mallon, Kieran Anthony Joseph
   [N.I. Barr.]
McCartney, Brian Gerard [N.I. Barr.]
McCrea, Michael Edward [N.I. Barr.]
McCrory, Francis Gerald [N.I. Barr.]
McNeill, Séamus Joseph [N.I. Barr.]

Hilary 1994
(Tuesday 11th January 1994)
Maconachie, John Edwin
   [Austr. Barr.]

Easter 1994
(11th April 1994)
Banbrick, Michael Oliver
   [Engl. Barr.]

Trinity 1994
(Thursday 21st July 1994)
Heffernan, Elizabeth Maeve
   [Brooke Scholarship]
Goodman, Aoife Frances
   [Murnaghan Prize]
Egan, Emily Jane
Bradley, Conleth Michael
Roarty, Gerald Thomas
Phelan, Diarmuid Rossa
O'Neill, Philip David John Dornan
Buttimore, Jonathan William Thom
Healy, John Paul
El-Falahi, Sami David [Engl. Barr.]

Hunter, Mack Robert [Engl. Barr.]
McCreath, Jean Alexander
   [Engl. Barr.]
Nutter, Julian Andrew [Engl. Barr.]
O'Sullivan, Michael Neil [Engl. Barr.]
Winch, John [Engl. Barr.]
More-O'Ferrall, Geraldine Ann
   [Engl. Barr.]
Farnon, Patricia Rona Gabrielle
   [Engl. Barr.]
Lecointe, Elpha Mary [Engl. Barr.]
Polson, Alistair James [Engl. Barr.]
Isles, Mary Patricia Theresa
   [Engl. Barr.]
Keegan, Leslie Francis [Engl. Barr.]
McCarraher, Colin Fraser
   [Engl. Barr.]
Humphreys, Sarah Louise
   [Engl. Barr.]
Bacik, Ivana Catherine [Engl. Barr.]
Freeman, Christopher Domenic
   [Austr. Barr.]
Hickey, Gregory John [Austr. Barr.]
Lynch, Mark Gregory [Austr. Barr.]

(afternoon 21st July 1994)
O'Hanlon, Niall
Scally, Gean Frances
Byrne, Donna Mary Bernadette
Charleton, Gerard Martin
Maguire, Caitriona Ann Mary
Moffatt, Paul Anthony
Bagnall, John Brendan
Bailey, Teresa Josephine
Bracken, Gregory Patrick
Callan, Kevin Anthony
McLaughlin, Rose-Marie
Corcoran, Richard Andrew
O'Connor, Kevin Thomas
Parker, Christopher James
Dreelan, Richard Michael
Donohoe, Thomas Martin
Donnelly, Neil Michael
Hickey, Sheena Deirdre
Cunnane, Garrett Joseph
McDonough, Donough Michael
Byrne, Rory
Clesham, Philip Alan
Haugh, Amanda Jane
Culleton, Peter Francis
Brophy, Jacqueline Frances
Corbett, Thomas
McCann, Henry Stephen Patrick
Andrews, Philip Michael
Andrews, Jane Rachel [Engl. Barr.]
McCarroll, John Johnston
   [Engl. Barr.]

(Friday morning, 22nd July 1994)
O'Kelly, Aisling Justine
Cole McColgan, Violet Virginia
Daly, Maria Emily
Connolly, Kenneth John
Kelly, David Thomas
Hill, Niall Benjamin Morrison
Brennan, Lara Caoimhe
Delargy, Donal Thomas
Colgan, Damien James
Scannell, Paul Frederick
Chambers, Declan James
Leahy, Eithne Mary
McKenna, Marie-Thérèse Síobhán
Cullinane, Pádraig Joseph
Cawley, Adrienne Margaret
Purcell, Patrick Gregory
Hayes, Dara Bernard Maurice
Johnson, Richard Murray
O'Connor, Caoilte Joseph
Carway, Martin David
Healy, Paula
Harkness, Anthony
Johnson, Edmund John
Sweeney, Conor Liam
O'Connell, Elizabeth Mary

Michaelmas 1994
(Friday 14th October 1994)
Blake, Mary Teresa Lucy
Connolly, Lorcan Paul
Egan, Nuala Mary
Garavan, Charles Gerard
Gaughran, Noel
Hyland, Niamh Margaret
Kennedy, Marie Elizabeth Therese
Moran, Mary Teresa
Synnott, Deirdre Maeveen
Ward, Anastasia Margaret
Cheatle, John Francis
Dillon, Gabrielle Maria
Duggan, Susan
Fahy, James Thomas
Finneran, Lynda Frances
Gordon, Breffni Paul
Greene, Maria Bernadette Teresa
Horan-McHugh, Deirdre Marie
Houlihan, Brian
Kearns, Martin Joseph
Lynch, Geraldine Teresa
Martin, Orla Mary
MacManus, Edward Paul Anthony
O'Reilly, Paul Mary
O'Shea, John Paul
Walker, Brian John Francis
Walsh, Eamonn Thomas
Cregan, John Paul [Engl. Barr.]

Foster, Charles Andrew [Engl. Barr.]
Stewart, George Barry [Engl. Barr.]
Jones, Nest Elizabeth [Engl. Barr.]
O'Callaghan, Patrick [Engl. Barr.]
Flockton, Siobhán Mary [Engl. Barr.]
Campbell, Joan Martha [ex-Solicitor]

Trinity 1995
(Thursday morning 20th July 1995)
Burns, Tara Mary [Brooke Scholarship]
O'Leary, Anne [Murnaghan Prize]
Ryall, Áine Michele
Doherty, James Connolly
Newman, Jonathan Francis
Stack, Hannah Teresa Mary
Doherty, Barry Mathew
Gleeson, Niamh Christina
McCormack, John Michael
Fitzgibbon, Niall John
Flynn, Myra Teresa
Hanniffy, Elaine Margaret
Canniffe, Catherine Jane
Chee, Guek-San
MacCormack, Marita Joanne
Hill, Norman Leonard Alexander
[N.I. Barr.]
Irvine, Peter Charles [N.I. Barr.]
Larkin, John Francis [N.I. Barr.]
O'Hanlon, Patrick Michael [N.I. Barr.]
Benson, Peter Charles [Engl. Barr.]
Bermingham, Gerald Edward
[Engl. Barr.]
Best, Stanley Philip [Engl. Barr.]
Constable, John Martyn Chester
[Engl. Barr.]
Freeman, Lucy Mekhala Catherine
[Engl. Barr.]
Lucas, Edward Allan [Engl. Barr.]
Shannon, Áine Patricia [Engl. Barr.]
Smith, Simon Noel [Engl. Barr.]
Freeman, Christopher Domenic
[Austr. Barr.]
Sheil, Brenda Margaret Hale
[E.C. Directive]
Staunton, Kevin Francis
[E.C. Directive]
Grainger, Thomas James Gerald
[N.I. Barr.]

(Thursday afternoon)
O'Donnell, Barry Patrick
Munro, Ronan Alberic
O'Neill, Alison Jane
Power, Thomas Keane
Kearney, Elva Ann
Boland, Raymond Anthony
Loughlin, Marie

Connor, Finbar Patrick
Phelan, Mary Josephine
McGee, Henry
Fehily, Rachel Anne
Crowley, Cornelius Gerard
McCaffrey, Deirdre Helen
Moylan, Marian Frances Therese
Devlin, John Conrad
*Siew Tiong, Jacqueline Siew
   [not called]
Corrigan, Mary Bernardine
Fraser, Ursula Mary
Wood, Kieron Laurence
O'Neill, Michael John
McDonald, Neal Michael
Murphy, Elizabeth Mary
McMahon, Brendan Gerard
Ó Muirí, Michael Damien
O'Regan-Cazabon, Attracta Lena
Earley, Esther Catherine
Jones, Morgan William Barry
Slattery, Mary Margaret
McGonigal, Patrick Eoin
Hannan, John Anthony

(Friday 21st July 1995)
Fitzgerald, Paul Vincent
McAuley, Adam Noel
Molony, Phelim Anthony
Smyth, Kieran Patrick
Naidoo, Kerida Thomas Aquinas
Heneghan, Patrick Michael Vincent
Ward, James St. John
Hickey, Joseph Anthony
Horan, Anne Maria
Mullins, Elizabeth Geraldine
Ramsey, Michael Francis
Moloney, Philip Mary
O'Keeffe, James Lyons
Keane, Catherine Laboure
Kelleher, Maeve Margaret
Whitney, Catherine
*Siev, Kah-Lian [not called]

Michaelmas 1995
(Friday 13th October 1995)
Fealy, Michael
Kearney, Ann Marie
Deely, Patrick Joseph
Ward, Helen Mary
Dempsey, Timothy Finbar
Hyland, Jane
Oluwole, Frederick Oluyemi
Maguire, Kieran Ross
Connolly, Diarmuid John
Byrne, Rachel Mary
O'Reilly, Sarah Patricia
Ffrench-Davis, Stephen Luke

Christle, Joseph Louis
Carroll, Cindy Mary
Lavin, Deirdre Mary
Halpin, Anthony Joseph
Kelly, Francis Gerard
Martin, Vincent Peter
Sisk, Patricia
Lennox, Susan Victoria
McMahon, Eimear Elizabeth
Glanville, Stephen John
Walsh, Martin William
McNally, John Martin
Blishen, Eileen Mary
Sharkey, Leo Eamonn
Cleary, Kevin Patrick
Finn, John Alexander Christopher
Shearer, Aaron Daniel Joseph
Binchy, Paul Gerard [ex-Solicitor]
O'Connell, John [ex-Solicitor]
George, Charles Richard [Engl. Barr.]
Newcombe, Andrew Bennett
   [Engl. Barr.]
Wainwright, Jeremy Patrick
   [Engl. Barr.]
Fitzpatrick, Bernard Joseph Louis
   [N.I. Barr.]

Hilary 1996
Special Call for N.I. Barristers
(Friday 23rd February 1996)
McReynolds, Melody Jane [N.I. Barr.]
Miller, Geoffrey Biddall [N.I. Barr.]
Henderson, Lois Amanda Laird
   [N.I. Barr.]
Sweeney, Honoria Pauline Mary
   [N.I. Barr.]
Kearney, John Joseph [N.I. Barr.]
Hunter, David William [N.I. Barr.]
Bradley, Mary Suzanne [N.I. Barr.]
Finegan, Anne Frances [N.I. Barr.]
Matthews, Agnes-Jane [N.I. Barr.]
Duffy, Michael Gerard [N.I. Barr.]
McMahon, Kenneth Robert More
   [N.I. Barr.]
Lamont, Mary Fiona [N.I. Barr.]
O'Hara, John Ailbe [N.I. Barr.]
Dornan, William Philip [N.I. Barr.]
McKillop, Thomas Gerard [N.I. Barr.]
Connolly, Patrick James [N.I. Barr.]
Orr, John [N.I. Barr.]
McGreena, Noelle [N.I. Barr.]
Finlay, Kathleen [N.I. Barr.]
Stephens, William Benjamin Synge
   [N.I. Barr.]
Butcher, Ian Frank [Austr. Barr.]

Trinity 1996
(Thursday morning 18th July 1996)
McDermott, Paul Anthony
[Brooke Scholarship]
Byrne, Kevin Martin [Society's Exhibition]
Mooney, Kilda Maria Elliott
[Murnaghan Prize]
Bredin, Kenneth James
Curran, Anna Maria
Farrell, Sarah Eleanor
Simons, Garrett
Creighton, Dawn Marie [N.I. Barr.]
Ferran, Paul Anthony [N.I. Barr.]
Hamill, Michael Joseph Francis
[N.I. Barr.]
Hanna, Robert Nicholas Harvey
[N.I. Barr.]
Horner, Thomas Mark [N.I. Barr.]
Macartney, Brian Wilfred [N.I. Barr.]
McAlinden, Gerald Joseph
[N.I. Barr.]
O'Grady, Adele Marie [N.I. Barr.]
Smith, Christine Anne [N.I. Barr.]
Stitt, Michael William [N.I. Barr.]
Thompson, John [N.I. Barr.]
Toolan, James Celsus [N.I. Barr.]
Watt, Elizabeth Jane Lillian
[N.I. Barr.]
Watters, Rosemary [N.I. Barr.]
Maxwell, Michael Edmond
[N.I. Barr.]
Casement, David John [Engl. Barr.]
Arnheim, Michael Thomas Walter
[Engl. Barr.]
Holles, Francis Dominic [Austr. Barr.]
O'Gorman, Gary Vincent
[Austr. Barr.]
Bannon, Margaret [E.C. Directive]
Breslin, John Arthur [E.C. Directive]

(afternoon 18th July 1996)
Phelan, Sara Mary
Donnelly, Daniel Talbot
Cummings, Caroline Joan
Power, Bridget Rosario
O'Hegarty, Lia Maire
Buckley, Oonagh Mary
Daly, Ciara Maria
Faughnan, Barra Mark
Brett, Denise Catherine Mary
Corkery, Mary Geraldine
Mooney, Niall Patrick
Johnston, Nicole Elizabeth
O'Connor, Michael Columba
O'Keeffe, Siun Emer
Murray, Susan Jacinta
Coghlan, Margaret Mary

Dignam, Conor Thomas
Cordial, Margaret Elizabeth
Power, Conor
Reidy, Aisling Marie
Crosbie, Sophie
Oates, Patrick Joseph
McGinn, Paul Roper
Quinn, Patrick Gerard
Quirke, Bernard Daniel Thornton
McMahon, Laurence James
Blake, Judith Ann

(Friday morning 19th July 1996)
Boyle, Maeve Elaine Josephine
Terry, Mary Regina Bernadette
Beatty, Robert
Fleming, Gareth John
O'Connor, Fintan John
Ross, Ann
Walshe, Kathleen Geraldine
O'Connor, Mary Martine Bernadette
Egan, Sara Patricia
Territt, Catherine
Boyle, Helen Mary
Hogan, Thomas Patrick
O'Mahony, Mark
McMahon, Linda Marie
O'Raw, Eunice Ann
Davis, John Cormac
Lavelle, Kathleen Imelda
Maloney, Angela
O'Donohoe, Nuala Antoinette
Harty, Mark Kevin
Rutledge, John Francis

(afternoon 19th July 1996)
O'Driscoll, Adrian Arthur Eugene
Ross
Cousins, Brona Mary
Sheahan, Elma Regina
Fallon, Valerie Ann
O'Neill, Niall Joseph
O'Sullivan, Edward Joseph
Clarke, Cornelius Noel
Donaghy, Rory Michael
Gleeson, Neil
O'Gorman, Michelle Caroline
Rafter, Jennifer
Fitzgerald, Martin Gerard
McDonagh, Padraig Anthony
Christopher
O'Toole, Enda Conor Seamus
English, Shane James
Purtill, Michael Joseph
Rae, Stephen Francis
Corbett, Carol Mary
Smith, John Denis

Foley, Niall Thomas

(Thursday 25th July 1996)
O'Dowd, David Patrick Marius
  [Austr. Barr.]

Michaelmas 1996
(Friday 18th October 1996)
Conway, Rory Patrick
Manning, Ciaran Peter
Coffey, John Maurice
Lynch, Henry Roderick
Crowe, Mary Margaret
Dockrell, Maurice Otto
Doyle, Fergal Thomas Fitzgerald
Fawsitt, Diarmaid
Flanagan, James John
Hickey, Éanna Ruaidhrí
McGarry, Paul Anthony
Sharkey, James Joseph
Davis, Louise Agnes Mary
Rahn, Philipp Anatol
Bracken, Timothy [ex-Solicitor]
Dowd, Roger Michael [N.I. Barr.]
Elliott, Stephen [N.I. Barr.]
Murphy, Ciaran Michael [N.I. Barr.]

Trinity 1997
(Thursday morning 17th July 1997)
Kearney, Damien Gerard [Brooke
  Scholarship]
Breen, Oonagh Brigid
  [Society's Exhibition]
Browne, Mary Deirdre [Murnaghan Prize]
Ní Shuilleabhain, Máire Treasa
McGrath, Declan
Kennedy, Brian Francis
Duffy, Joanne Elva
Ní Mhurchú, Cynthia Máiréad
Barrington, Brian Peter
Leonard, Patrick Thomas
Morgan, Elaine Bridgid
Heneghan, Kieran Joseph
McQuade, Justin Paul
Hourican, Michael William
Flynn, Kirsteen Mary
McGuckian, Bernard Colmcille
Henry, Colin John William
  [N.I. Barr.]
McCombe, Nigel Jeremy Wasson
  [N.I. Barr.]
Chesney, George Cecil [N.I. Barr.]
Ritchie, Stephen Kirkwood
  [N.I. Barr.]
Beattie, Thomas James Stewart
  [N.I. Barr.]
Good, Patrick Simon [N.I. Barr.]
McGivern, Anne Frances [N.I. Barr.]

O'Kane, Paula Mary Colette
  [N.I. Barr.]
Gibson, Heather Anne [N.I. Barr.]
Stewart, John Howard [N.I. Barr.]
Houston, David Martin Russell
  [Engl. Barr.]
Counihan, Caroline [Engl. Barr.]
Jones, Gregory Percy [Engl. Barr.]
Howe, Peter St. John [Engl. Barr.]

(afternoon 17th July 1997)
Ó Cinnede, Colm Pádraig
Mulherin, Grace Ann
McGoldrick, Ciara Bridget Mary
Kelly, Kieran Thomas
Smith, Catherine
Brennan, Tara Maria
Holian, Pamela Mary Catherine
O'Leary, Elizabeth Mary
Gillane, Sean
Farrell, Remy Stephen
Lonergan, Martin Mark Gerard
O'Connell, Sarah Marie
Meagher, Rachel Judith
Biggs, Caroline Philomena
O'Connor, Michael Fergus
Bird, Pamela Constance
Egan, Michael Patrick
Foley, Annette Marie
O'Connell, Gareth
Hamilton, William Richard
Lowe, Theresa Carmel Mary
O'Sullivan-Lacy, Patricia Lacy
Phelan, Sarah Marie Christine
Considine, Rita Ann
Leddy, Corinna Anne
Dunleavy, Patrick Bernard
Martin, John Richard
Barrett, Gavin Michael

(Friday morning 18th July 1997)
McDermott, James Gerard
Browne, Vincent
Beatty, Francis
O'Doherty, Margaret Mary
Stewart, Niamh Orla
Guerin, Michael John
McGrath, Sinead Bridget
McGleenan, Sean Anthony
Pillay, Roisin Marie
Daly, Triona Antonia
Forde, Robert Aidan
de Feu, Rita Mary O'Meara
Wood, Tabitha Mary
McCoy, Orfhlaith Maria
Hayes, David Eamon
O'Carroll, James
O'Carroll, Niamh Anne

Waldron, Denise Mary
Walsh, Judy Susan
Ryan, Sinead Marie
Carty, Emmet Joseph
Quirke, John Francis Thornton
Ruddy, Karen
Brooks, Eugene Harold
O'Dwyer, Colm Francis
Vaughan, Simon Peter
Friel, Eunice Louise Maria
Burns, Michael Peter
Murphy, John Francis Xavier
Madden, Mary Christine

Michaelmas 1997

(Friday 17th October 1997)
Andrews, Barry Patrick
Cassidy, Máire Bláthnaid
Lewis, Ciaran Thomas
Altman, Fergal Eoin
Brady, James Arthur Christopher
Buckley, Alan John
Cowan, Francis Peter
Cusack, Brian Joseph Michael
Drumm, Francis
Greene, Mary Sheena
Hickey, Catherine Marcella
Jordan, Patrick Joseph
McCabe, Mairead Mary
McCarthy, Aidan Pairic
McCullough, James Gerard
McGrath, Gerard John
O'Connor, Martin Gregory
O'Flynn, Rachel Sheila
Quinn, Eileen Sean
Sheahan, Philip Gerald
Smyth, Joseph Anthony
Summers, Gary [Engl. Barr.]
*[1] Geering, Ian Walter [Engl. Barr.]
Howarth, Simon Stuart [Engl. Barr.]
Stevenson, John Melford [Engl. Barr.]
Lound ter Haar, Roger Edward
   [Engl. Barr.]
Crowley, John Desmond [Engl. Barr.]
McGinn, Dominic Stuart [Engl. Barr.]
Yaqub, Zahd [Engl. Barr.]
Shannon, Vincent [ex-Solicitor]
O'Sullivan, Joseph [ex-Solicitor]
Coughlan, Stephen [ex-Solicitor]
Foley, Geraldine [E.C. Directive]
Coleman, Sarah Jane [E.C. Directive]

Trinity 1998

(Thursday morning 16th July 1998)
Breen, Faye Anne [Brooke Scholarship]
Mullan, Ann Gráinne
   [Society's Exhibition]
Gallagher, Síobhán [Murnaghan Prize]
McIntyre, Thomas Jeremiah
Ó Comhraí, Rónán Pádraig
Ferriter, Cian John
McConville, Mary Catherine
Noctor, Cathleen Catherine
Langan, John Francis
O'Rourke, Margaret Mary
Dempsey, Paul Edward
Kitson, Raymond Andrew [N.I. Barr.]
Kitson, Theresa Bridget [N.I. Barr.]
Lavery, Ronan Ulrich [N.I. Barr.]
Shaw, Stephen James [N.I. Barr.]
Conlon, Kevin Thomas [N.I. Barr.]
Gibson, William Robert Barry
   [N.I. Barr.]
Murphy, Gráinne Mary [N.I. Barr.]
McBrien, Edward Johnston David
   [N.I. Barr.]
McCullagh, Ciara Sara Alice
   [N.I. Barr.]
O'Brien, Martin Gerald [N.I. Barr.]
Shaw, Howard [Engl. Barr.]
Lyons, Timothy [Engl. Barr.]
Butler, Rupert James [Engl. Barr.]
Reynolds, Stephen Alan [Engl. Barr.]
Hamer, Michael Howard Kenneth
   [Engl. Barr.]
Patten, Benedict Joseph [Engl. Barr.]

(afternoon 16th July 1998)
Mulcahy, Leigh-Ann Maria
   [Engl. Barr.]
Farrell, Emily Jane
Healy, Annelly Sarah Josephine
Hennessy, John Michael
Kitching, Kevin Gerard
Walley, Frances Kim
Dunne, Mark John
Mooney, Gavin Anthony
Kennan, Ethna Oonagh Mary
Rattigan, Laura Nuala
Carron, Kathleen Anne
Crowe, Richard Anthony
O'Flaherty, Bríd Anne
Hughes, Deirdre
O'Shea, James Cornelius
Fitzpatrick, Lucia Jacinta
McMullan, Sinéad Assumpta
Small, Gerardine Mary
O'Shea, Sinead Eileen
Farnon, Jane Anne

*[1]   Did not sign the Roll.

Byrne, Caroline Mary
Lowe, Nicola
Moriarty, Bríd Máire
Murphy, James
Traynor, Vincent Edwin
Dalton, Paul Stephen
Finucane, Mary Geraldine
Burke, Philip Paul
Kelly, Joan Carmel
Byrne, Sophia Catherine
Grogan, Muireann

(Friday 17th July 1998)
Le Vert, Pieter Wyckoff
Cahill, Dermot Bosco
Waters, Deirdre
O'Donnell, Kathleen Anne
Keane, Mary Nicola
McGowan, Fiona Susan
Robinson, Lucy Therese
O'Driscoll, Leesha Ann
Whelan, Nicholas Gerard
Finnegan, Karl Joseph Anthony
Walsh, Lucy
Mulcahy, Rory Michael
O'Sullivan, Donal John
Lee, Gráinne Maria
Walshe, Aislinn Clare
McCullough, Stephen Domhnall
O'Connor, Timothy Joseph Blake
Ó Coileáin, Ruairí Pádraig
O'Connor, Ann
MacCártaigh, Dáithí Pádraig
Fitzsimons, Jarlath Martin Joseph
Powell, Nevan Walter
Kerrigan, Mary Patricia
O'Dwyer, Barry Stephen
Bennett, Mary Sheila Catherine
O'Driscoll, Niall Martin
Bell, Liam Ignatius
Baker, Garret Nicholas
Kearney, Brian John
O'Donnell, Susan Maria
Davis, Elizabeth Mary
Finlay, Ursula Mary

Michaelmas 1998
(Friday 16th October 1998)
Martin, Aisling Mary
Haughey, John Joseph
Barrett, Lena Bernice
Bowman, Michael Joseph
Corcoran, Eugene Mel
Heavey, Angela Mary Josephine
Kehoe, John Patrick
Ní Riagain, Íde
Ó Cuív, Barra
Ridge, Catherine Ann

Sheikh, Asim Ahmed
Walsh, John Francis
Ward, Paul Graham
O'Connell, Maeve Bridget
Boylan, Suzanne [ex-Solicitor]
Gallagher, Ann [ex-Solicitor]
Honan, Mary [ex-Solicitor]
Keane, David [ex-Solicitor]
Mulqueen, Joseph Barry [N.I. Barr.]
McNally, Geralyn Bridget [N.I. Barr.]
Nash, Raymond [N.I. Barr.]

Trinity 1999
(Thursday morning 15th July 1999)
Fanning, Rossa Alexander
    [Brooke Scholarship]
Dowling, Marcus Joseph
    [Society's Exhibition]
Kennedy, Ronan Christopher
    [Murnaghan Prize]
MacBeilliú, Seán Míceál
Reid, Gillian Mary
Feeney, Mary Isabella
Clarke, Douglas Michael
O'Connell, Michael Diarmuid
Bateman, Aine Patricia
Cahill, Nessa Ann
Ramsay, Ciaran Oisin
Staunton, Caroline Catherine
Galvin, William Maurice
Gleeson, Orlaith Mary
O'Sullivan, Fiona Ann
Skelly, Kathleen Marie
Cannon, Mona Ruth
Bonnar, Robert Gavin [N.I. Barr.]
McAteer, Ivor Columba [N.I. Barr.]
McGaughey, Gillian Elizabeth
    [N.I. Barr.]
Robinson, Linda Mary [N.I. Barr.]
Lynn, Michael Buick Cuolahan
    [E.C. Directive]

(afternoon 15th July 1999)
Fennell, Philip Edward
Quinlivan, Shivaun Marie
Higgins, Damian Francis
Sweetman, Edmund Richard
Reid, Sinead Maura
Nolan, Vincent James
Forrest, Elaine Aoife
Gaffney, Brian Adrian Gerard
Patton, Ciaran
Alexander, Robert William
O'Driscoll, Helen Lisa
Gallagher, John Patrick
Dorris, Alice Marian
Leahy, David Joseph
Kelly, Marie Therese

Murphy, Cathal Brendan
Dalton, Emma Elizabeth
Naughton, Brendan Daniel
Nulty, Aaron Patrick Joseph
O'Rourke, Kim Mina
Finnegan, Hazel Ann
Kavanagh, Ian Joseph
Boyle, Monica Mabel
Ní Chúlacháin, Síobhán
Whelan, Patrick Thomas
  [ex- Solicitor]

(Friday morning 16th July 1999)
O'Connell, Dermot Vincent
Rogan, Ruth Mary
Bourke, Conor Peter
Brady, Paul Joseph Tiernan
Creagh, Crionna Kathleen Mary
Donnelly, Nicholas Thomas
Murphy, Brian
Trimble, Marilyn Teresa
Compton, Gareth Patrick
*How, Tze Yen [not called]
Simon, Margaret Antoinette Mary
Leonard, Deborah Nuala
O'Sullivan Stephen John
Wade, Byron Patrick
Murphy, Adele Margaret
Frayne, Sandra Edith
Gill, Caroline Mary
Mulready, Michele Teresa Mary
Doherty, Gail Fiona Keeva
McLaughlin, John Noel
Munro, Caroline Mary
*Yuen, Ting Tsuey [not called]
Quinn, Graham Joseph
Rothwell, Jane-Anne Parfrey
O'Rourke, Martin [N.I. Barr.]
Hunt, Niall Joseph [N.I. Barr.]

(afternoon 16th July 1999)
Madden, Tara Jane
Walsh, Majella Mary
Rowland, Patrick Senan
Walsh, Claire Geraldine
Harding, Francis Edward
Colllins, Oisin Richard
Dempsey, Lisa Danielle
Gormley, Vincent Paul
Menzies, Donald John
O'Donnell, Thomas Richard Gerald
Halpin, Conor Joseph
Goodwin, Anthony Thomas
Hart, Sophie Julia Gertrude
Kinsley, Anna Maria Colette
McGrath, Michael Oliver
Murphy, Rachel Mary Josephine

Craddock, Caitriona Mary
Cooney, Derek Patrick
Sherry, Elizabeth
Ó Súilleabháin, Gráinne Mary
Lynch, Colin Conrad
Hughes, Pádraig Séamus

Michaelmas 1999
(Friday 15th October 1999)
Groarke, Stephen Paul
Hogan, Jacinta
Judge, Norma Mary
Lawless, Charles
Lynott, Catherine Theresa
Neligan, Niall Anthony
O'Connell, Mark John Brendan
O'Reilly, Aillil Fingin
O'Sullivan, Denis Christopher
Sheridan, Damian Patrick
Smith, Murray Joseph Brendan
Dillon, John Padraic [ex-Solcitor]
Leech, Monika [ex-Solicitor]
MacEvilly, Conn Jeremy
  [E.C. Directive]

(Friday 29th October 1999)
Quinn, Stafford Francis
Doyle, Eileen Patricia
Fleming, James Peter
*Ling, Kuok Ek [not called]
*Loh, Yeow Khoon [not called]

Trinity 2000
(Thursday morning 20th July 2000)
Steen, Neal Vincent [Brooke Scholarship]
Doyle, Audrey Patricia
  [Society's Exhibition]
Keane, Kathryn Elizabeth
Eardly, John Joseph
Sheehy, Morgan Joseph
Burke, Michael Jarleth
Dodd, Stephen Donal
Mannion, Nicole Ann
Fitzpatrick, Andrew John
Murphy, Fiona Margaret
Mahon, Heather Mary
O'Connell, Jennifer Margaret
Clarke, James Christopher
Hamilton, Claire Edith Margaret
McEvoy, Patrick Oliver
Tierney, Louise Mary
Duggan, Catherine Mary
Mitchell, Francis Joseph Michael
Abbott, Henry Michael Owen
O'Halloran, John Mary
  Brady, Anthony Bernard Gerard
  [N.I. Barr.]

Coll, Peter Gerard Joseph [N.I. Barr.]
McArdle, Eamonn Terence
  [N.I. Barr.]
McClean, David William [N.I. Barr.]
O'Brien, William Anthony Patrick
  [E.C. Directive]
Humphries, David John
  [E.C. Directive]

(afternooon 20th July 2000)
Byrne, John Arthur
Millen, Patrick
Costelloe, Shane Desmond
Groarke, Gerard Kevin Glynn
Lynch, Lorna Elizabeth
Callanan, Helen Patricia
Hickie, Aileen Mary
Smith, Mairead Paula
McCarthy, Karen
Cody, Catherine Ann
Farrelly, Martin Joseph
Dunne, Colin
Warren, Anita Martina
Conway, Gerard Martin
Croker, Cait
McGovern, Brian Joseph
Clarke, Martin Joseph
McElholm, Ciara Majella
Lawlor, Anne-Marie
Muldowney, James Christopher
McSharry, Melissa Bernardine
Cosgrave, Catherine Siobhan
O'Shea, Marie Teresa
Ennis, Leah Kiwana
Browne, Donal Anthony
Horgan, John Ronan Christopher

(Friday 21st July 2000)
Farrell, Wesley Padre Pio
Richardson, David
Cleary, Caroline Mary
McEneaney, Elizabeth
Sheahan, Derek James
Philpott, Nora Judith
Gallagher, Imelda Margaret Walsh
Walshe, Terence William
Maloney, Damian Francis
Marmelstein, Joanne Elizabeth
Collard, Edain
Mugan, Ronan Gerard
Costigan, Emer Grainne
Christopher, Paul Alan
Conlon, Sean Christopher
Durack, Dermot Patrick
Crawford, Fiona
O'Donoghue, Stephen Michael
  Anthony
Verdon, Conor

Christle, Orla Mary
Lawlor, Ann
Keogh, Barry Michael
Keogh, Conor

(afternoon 21st July 2000)
Burke, Suzanne
MacGiolla Rí, Eoin Padraic
Flynn, Mark
Moore, Esther Anne Mary
Toal, Emma Maria
Fitzpatrick, Thomas Stephen Gerard
McGreal, Cathal
Gallagher, Conor Damien
Munro, Andrew Michael
Corcoran, William
Eiffe, Mairead Mary
Gallagher, Carmel Marie Walsh
Hogan, Padraic Oliver
Keane, Dolores Susan
Waters, Seamus Michael
Cronin, Niamh Maria
Gallagher, Gerald Anthony
Quinn, Desmond Thomas
Sweetman, John Emmanuel Richard
Ní Fhearcallaí, Aoife
Hill, Randal Olin Oisin
Rowland, Anne [ex-Solicitor]

Michaelmas 2000
(Friday 20th October 2000)
Sheeran, Ivan James
Guerin, Marc Bernard
Pearse, Thomas Anthony
Johnson, Helen
Browne, Catherine Clare
Enright, Elizabeth Marie Therese
Gallagher, Lorna
Giles, Audrey Marie
Gleeson, Clodagh Mary
Hannon, Thomas Desmond John
Keeling, Daniel William Napoleon
McGarry, Maeve
Venn, Michael
Collins, Dorothy [ex-Solicitor]
O'Donnell, James [ex-Solicitor]
McKenzie, Agnes [E.C. Directive]
Campbell, Michael Stuart [N.I. Barr.]
Fowler, Stephen Alexander
  [N.I. Barr.]
Mallon, James Joseph [N.I. Barr.]
Mulholland, Mark [N.I. Barr.]
Orbinson, William James [N.I. Barr.]
Robinson, Keith Liam Hamilton
  [N.I. Barr.]
Scuffins, Orla Eileen

Trinity 2001
(Thursday morning 19th July 2001)
Brennan, Elizabeth Ellen
  [Brooke Scholarship]
Conneely, Sinéad Máire
  [Society's Exhibition]
Hill, Patricia [Murnaghan Prize]
Bulbulia, Jennifer
Stewart, Jason Francis
O'Callaghan, Deirdre Majella
McCarthy, Donnchadh Oliver
O'Shea, Ellen Margaret
O'Brien, Niamh Elsie Jude
Hickey, Rosemary
McEvoy, Deirdre Catherine
Creighton, Deirdre Marie
Murnane, Philomena Bridget
Leonowicz, Shuan Josephine
Margaret Maria
Griffin, Marie Antoinette
Denning, Karen Anne
White, Rory Joseph
Turner, Kara Alison
Byrne, Justin Martin [N.I. Barr.]
Cleland, Conor Luke [N.I. Barr.]
Doherty, Fiona Louise [N.I. Barr.]
Farrelly, Francis Justin [N.I. Barr.]
Johnston, James Michael [N.I. Barr.]
Larkin, Mary Josephine [N.I. Barr.]
McAleer, Michael Sherrard
  [N.I. Barr.]
McCreanor, Thomas [N.I. Barr.]
McNamee, Rory Michael [N.I. Barr.]
Wilson, Rosemary [N.I. Barr.]
Cousins, Edward Francis
  [E.C. Directive]

(afternoon 19th July 2001)
Ó Maolchaláin, Proinsias Antóin
Ennis, Gillian Emily
Murtagh, Ann Katherine
Morgan, Kerry Jane Mary
Abrahamson, William Jacob
O'Malley, Martin Thomas
Lane, Jeremiah Martin
Maguire, Niamh Brenda
McFadden, Niall Colm Brian
Twomey, Áine Majella
Moloney-Dunlop, Patricia Frances
Fitzpatrick, Sarah
Connellan, Liam Fergal
Moore, Anthony Michael John
Kilgarriff, Thomas William
O'Riordan, Mark Gerard
McKeon, Paul Christopher
Dwyer, James
McQuade, Denise

Clifford, Eoin Pádraig
Nunan, James John
Gallagher, Caoilfhionn Ann
Hanahoe, Carl Anthony
Oroz, Maria-Teresa Kelly
Clancy, Áine Marie
McCabe, Caoimhe Aideen
Walsh, Josephine Elizabeth
Wall, Declan Noel
Haugh, Alan John
O'Callaghan, Sarah-Jane

(Friday morning 20th July 2001)
Kealy, Annette Maria
Berry, Marian Ann Elizabeth
O'Neill, Bairbre Eilís
Buckley, Niall Francis
Langan, John William
Lyons, Padraic Joseph
O'Dwyer, David
Beck, Andrew Donald
Noonan, Muireann
Connolly, Amanda Mary
Lenihan, Anita Mary
Keane, Deirdre Catherine
Pekaar, Fiona
O'Neill, Martina Angela
Brophy, Anne Mary
Bell, Lillian Mary Layola
Burke, Olwyn Margaret
Duggan, John Francis
Dillon, Michael Joseph
Hughes, Paul
Cogan, Elizabeth Frances
Foley, Alison Deirdre
Meeneghan, Emer Louise
Kelly, Dean Michael
Ní Ghríofa, Dearbhla Mary
Nyland, Matthew George
Donegan, Emma
O'Sullivan, Kenneth Noel
Devoy, Michael Agustine

(afternoon 20th July 2001)
McGovern, Jeananne
Gibson, Emily
Leahy, Brian David
Dwyer, Edward John
Falvey, Kieran Bernard
MacNamara, Darach Joseph John
Maguire, Tracy Jane
Fitzgerald, William John
Cummins, Deirdre Elizabeth
O'Loughlin, Joella Mary
Ryan, Daniel John
Dockry, Nuala Elizabeth
Hosey, Nicholas Edward

Bunyan, Mary Margaret
O'Riordan, Seán Herbert
Quilligan, Patrick James Peter
Freeman, Sarah Maureen
Henry, Kathleen Teresa Elizabeth
Lehane, Sheila Maria
Cronin, Eamonn Christopher
McCormack, Francis Michael
Mulvenna, Tara
Ryan, Colman

Michaelmas 2001
(Friday 19th October 2001)
Byrne, Garret
Costello, Cathryn
Howells-Roder, Joanna
Ní Liatháin, Méadhbh
Russell, Patrick
*Teo, Simon K. V.
Anyadike-Danes, Monyeazo Nnenna
   Mary
Berry, William Gregory Hamilton
Daly, Rónán John [N.I. Barr.]
Haines, Florence Olive [N.I. Barr.]
Wade, Declan Joseph [ex-Solicitor]
Wheelahan, David [ex-Solicitor]
Casey, Paul [E.C. Directive]
McEvilly, Anna Marie
   [E.C. Directive]
Walsh, Brian Joseph [E.C. Directive]
Kelly, Treasa [ex-Solicitor]

Trinity 2002
(Thursday morning 18th July 2002)
Doyle, Oran Joseph [Brooke Scholarship]
Masterson, Laurence Joseph
   [Society's Exhibition]
Maher, Bronagh Bríd [Murnaghan Prize]
McGillycuddy, Dairmuid Anthony
Smith, Kelley Mary Majella
McGrath, Barbara Anne
Butler, Mary Josephine
O'Neill, Gráinne Mary
Martin, Helen Mary
Keating, Yvonne Elizabeth Mary
Whyms, Martin Patrick
Maughan, Martin Patrick
Maughan, Peter Andrew
Skally, Elizabeth Anne
Cox, Neville Richard
O'Dwyer, Margaret Mary
Higgins, Imelda Anne
Sheehan, Charles Aquinas
McCullough, Jane Brigid
Naughton, Ciarán Martin
Shaw, Richard Alphonsus
Cremins, Denis
Gilbride, David

Forrest, Claire Louise
Kent, David Gerard
McGrath, Carol Sheila
Rojack, Barry Franklin
Nolan, Niall Peter

(afternoon 18th July 2002)
Dawson, Catherine Mary
O'Regan, Maria Denise
Denning, Angela Mary
O'Keeffe, Tracy Norma
Walsh, Sarah Catherine
Gormley, Elizabeth Anne
Dowling, Stephen James
Mallon, Rosemary
Keirse, Alison Mary
Murray, Suzanne Catherine Mary
Fay, Mary
White, Ciaran James
Burke, Joseph Patrick
Bulbulia, David [ex-Solicitor]
* [1] [   ]
Myers-Jones, Stephanie
   [E.C. Directive]
O'Shea, Eoin [E.C. Directive]
Antoniotti, Sara Beth O'Toole
   [E.C. Directive]
Simms, Alan John Gordon
   [E.C. Directive]
Dunn, Michael John [N.I. Barr.]
Lenny, Paul Matthew [N.I. Barr.]
Magill, Kevin Diarmuid [N.I. Barr.]
Moran, Lisa Maria [N.I. Barr.]
Morgan, Martin Samuel [N.I. Barr.]
Moriarty, Andrew Joseph [N.I. Barr.]
McLaughlin, Brian [N.I. Barr.]
Taggart, Patrick Joseph [N.I. Barr.]

(Friday morning 19th July 2002)
Brennan, Alexander Jack
Kiely, Deirdre Mary
Keating, Alan Jude
Duffy, Gabriel Philip
Mantero-Belard, Maria Amelia
Fennell, Sarah Jane
Buckley, Elizabeth Deirdre
Brophy, David McHugh
Donnelly, Owen
O'Brien, Paula Elizabeth
Jeffers, Joseph Peter
O'Hara, Michelle Catherine
De Brúir, Alison Orna
Mullen, Yvonne

* [1] A space in the Roll has been left
for the name of 'David Georges
Mainfroy Marks [E.C. Directive]'.

Foley, Claudine Mary
Berkery, Gráinne Bridget
Fitzgerald, Evanna
Ward, Clíona Anne Mary
Shanley, Peter St John
Forde, Fiona Siobhán Mary
*[1] Cormack, Alan Keith
* Cregan, Conor Joseph
Tottenham, Mark Robert
Block, Michael
Dowling, Dara Mary
Brennan, Richard Justin

(afternoon 19th July 2002)
McNulty, Timothy Fitzgerald
Lawlor, Eoin Fintan
Cole, Eoghan Patrick
MacDermott, Louis James
Leyden, Anita Catherine
Mansfield, Barry
Baxter, Laurence Gerard
Lett, Heidi Karen
Mills, Simon Patrick
O'Neill, Michelle Maria Denise
Costello, Sinéad Ellen
Harris, Louise Eileen
Hardiman, Eoin Patrick
Farrell, Mary Teresa
Toland, Ciarán
Byrne, Kira Mary Teresa
Dunne, Elizabeth Kathleen
Murray, Michael Anthony
Rochford, Paul
Mulvihill, Siobhán Ellen
Walsh, Ian Laurence
Sexton, Neil Lionel Perris
Brady, Damien Joseph
O'Sullivan, John Mark
McAuliffe, Mary Bridget
Maguire, Declan Noel
Macauley, Leonie Susan
*Karupiah, Siva Balan

Michaelmas 2002
(Thursday 17th October 2002)
Brennan, Aoife Maria
Brolly, Nodlaig Máire
Grant, Marie-Thérèse
Duggan, Ann Marie Jackie
Ní Mhuircheartaigh, Nuala Muireann
Deasy, Michael
Doherty, Michael Brian
O'Carroll, Desmond Gerard

*   [1]   Cregan precedes Cormack in the K.I. Call List

Fitzgerald, John Denis [ex-Solicitor]
Fitzsimons, Lana Sharon Thérèse [ex-Solicitor]
Hegarty, Eithne [ex-Solicitor]
Leader, Kathleen [ex-Solicitor]
McGuinness, Donal [ex-Solicitor]
McHugh, Niamh Magaret [ex-Solicitor]
O'Meara, Anne Mary [ex-Solicitor]
Myers, Keith [E.C. Directive]
Reynolds, Patrick J.S.
Best, Harold Alexander [N.I. Barr.]
Browne, Jonathan Paul [N.I. Barr.]
Talbot, Gordon Albert [N.I. Barr.]

Trinity 2003
(Thursday 17th July 2003 at 10.15)
Healy-Rae, Rosemary
Casey, Rachel
McKechnie, William John
Butler, Una
Tattan, Dalton
Valentine, Fintan
McKenna, Máiréad
O'Sullivan, Lynn
Brown, Eimear
Donovan, Elizabeth
Leyden, Kyle
McGrath, Imogen
Hamilton, Leigh
McGowan, Laura
Duffy, Kevin
Dunne, Derek
Howlett, Triona
Nolan, Karen
Mullen, Ronan
Boyle, Antonia
Conway, Dominic

(at 11.15)
Higgins, Catherine
Costello, Christopher
Connell, Tara
O'Sullivan, Mary
O'Driscoll, Richael
Walshe, Elizabeth Anne
Brazil, Patricia
Bradshaw, Ciara
Pope, Elizabeth
Kinsella, Gareth
Lowry, Anthony
Houlihan, Elaine
Lavan, Vivian
Donnelly, John
McBride, Anthony
Hanniffy, Raymond
Byrne, Mark

Kelleher, Elizabeth
Bearman, Justin Ian [EC Directive]
Goucher, Laurence [EC Directive]

(at 2 p.m.)
Máiréad Carey
Cassidy, Una
Davin, Maria
Cunniffe, Aideen
Breen, Patrick
Hickey, Mervyn
Gallagher, Fiona
Nohilly, Gail
Toner, Ivan
Costello, Thomas Oliver
O'Neill, Ailbhe
Keo'h, Patrick
Canny, Martin
Treacy, Kathryn
Browne, Brendan
Aldworth, Philip Joseph [N.I. Barr.]
Fitzpatrick, Thomas John [N.I. Barr.]
McLaughlin, Paul Christopher
     [N.I. Barr.]
Mallon, Terence Joseph [N.I. Barr.]
Robinson, Cathal Mark [N.I. Barr.]
Sharpe, David Robert Kitson
     [N.I. Barr.]

(Friday 18th July at 10.15)
Kennelly, Kieran John
Maguire, Roderick
Melvin, Antonia
Fullam, Desmond
Courell, Ann-Marie
Kelly, Brendan
O'Donoghue, Christine
Kirwan, Brendan
Kinsella, John
Belshaw, Sarah
Kennedy, Ronan
Miley, Ingrid
Ryan, Christina
Kelleher, Joanna
Stanley, John
Meehan, Alan
Walsh, Yvonne
Smith, Ciaran
Corkery, Paul
Finnegan, Paul

(at 11-15)
Byrne, Mariaelena
Fogarty, Louise
Millrine, Claire
Quigley, Bernadette Ann
Woodfull, Emer
Reidy, Máire

Bride, Michael
MacCarthy, Conall
Murphy, Sean
Jackson, Reginald
O'Doherty, Mark
Dockery, Liam
Neville, Tom
Hogan, John
Walsh, Maria
Cronin, Linda
Fenelon, Lynn
Kenneally, Donal
Naidoo, Jadel
Hunt, Brian

(at 2 p.m.)
O'Connor, Caroline
Sugrue, Brian
Comyn, Amanda
Grange, Michael
Coll, Derek
Gardiner, Frances
Aylmer, Rosemarie
Murphy, Gerard
Munnelly, Michael
McCarthy, Eugene
Dolan, John
Fitzpatrick, Brian
Cosgrove, Ronan
McCormack, Caitriona
O'Toole, Catherine
Jones, Barry
McCartney, Stephen

Michaelmas 2003
(Friday 17th October 2003 at 10-15)
Budd, Roland Gardner
Carroll, Cian
Hussey, Arran
Jawad, Tara
Larney, Evelyn Frances
Mylotte, Ruth
Fox, Michael [ex-Solicitor]
Haughton, Gabriel Francis
     [ex-Solicitor]
Simms, Daniel Paul [ex-Solicitor]
O'Shea, Paul [ex-Solicitor]
Ashton, Raymond Keighley
     [E.C. Directive]
Rowland, Derville [E.C. Directive]
Colmer, Adrian William Gibson
     [N.I. Barr.]
Patterson, Seán Joseph [N.I. Barr.]
Rooney, Seán [N.I. Barr.]

Trinity 2004

(Thursday 22nd July 2004 at 10-30)
Bird, Neasa B. [Brooke Scholarship, €3,000]
Foley, Brian Anthony
    [Society's Prize, €1,500]
Kiernan, Nessa M.
    [Muraghan Prize, €500]
Monahan, James Carl
Redmond, Trevor
Fallon, Sarah
Graydon, Rebecca
Brennan, Nina
Broderick, Rebecca Ann
Kinsella, Mary Ita
Meehan, Thomas Gerard
Fennell, Niamh M.
Coyle, Daniel W.
Duggan, Gráinne M.
McGloughlin, Ferga
Johnson, Kerry Florence
Maguire, Richard [N.I. Barr.]
Higgins, Adrian [N.I. Barr.]
Blackburn, Robert [N.I. Barr.]
McCann, Aoife [N.I. Barr.]
Conway, Paul [N.I. Barr.]
Melvin, James [N.I. Barr.]
Kelly, Teresa [N.I. Barr.]

(at 2 p.m.)
Murphy, Gerard Nicholas
Byrne, Hugh Brendan
O'Kane, Deirdre Elizabeth
Brick, Clodagh Maria
* Kirby, Myles Matthew
    [conferred only]
Ó Ceilleachair, Donncha
Buckley, Michael D.
Carey, Michelle Mary
Cruess Callaghan, Catherine Ita
Geraghty, Catherine
Fahey, Gráinne
Flahive, Moira A.
Andrews, Nicola-Jane
Saunders, Eamon J.
Murray, Jane M.
Meaney, Mary A.
Ní Ghráinne, Áine Caitríona
Lane, Maria Clara
Norton, Angela Mary
Browne, Damien

Murphy, Mary M.
Deevey, Bernadette

(Friday 23rd July 2004 at 10-30)
O'Leary, Aoife
O'Brien, Peter E.
Brosnan, Clare
Dowling, Fiona Teresa
Smith, Rebecca Mary Elizbeth
Carson, Stephen E.
Shortall, Edward R.
Quinn, Mary Teresa
Dodd, David T.
Donovan, Ellen Nuala
Maddox, Neil Paul
Aherne, Elizabeth Lara
Lehane, Michael Darren
Walshe, Patrick Daniel
Regan, Muiríosa-Nichola
Walsh, Elizabeth-Jane Mary
O'Meara, Colin Patrick
Gibbons, Glen T.
Fitzgerald, Eavanna
Breen, Séamus Gerard
Hourihane, David
Lynam, Mark

Friday 23rd July (at 2 p.m.)
Fitzsimons, Gerard Oliver
Gunning, Helen
MacNamara, Cormac
Gleeson, Sínéad Mary
O'Brien, Rita Josephine
Freeman, John Noel
O'Brien, Emmett John
Bradley, Erika
Walsh, Elizabeth
Keary, David P.
Crehan, Fergal
Martin, Ronan
O'Sullivan, Catherine Deirdre
de Burgh, Lefre
Madden, Orna R.
Doyle, Fiona Mary Theresa
Hourigan, Michael David
McCormack, Garreth Martin
Nix, James
Dillon, Patrick Bernard
Leonard, Peter T.

Michaelmas 2004
(Friday 15th October 2004)
Benson, James Alan
Ledwith, Alan P.
McLoughlin, Paul
Meenan, Frances M.P. [ex-Solicitor]
Ryan, Jarlath Oliver [ex-Solicitor]
Kelly, Elaine Isabella [N.I. Barr.]
Devine, Michael Buxton
   [E.U. Directive]

FORMULA USED UPON CALL TO THE OUTER BAR

The Benchers of the Honorable Society of King's Inns having been pleased to admit you to the Degree of Barrister-at-Law, I now admit you to practise in the Courts of Ireland and you will take your place accordingly.

Dá bhrí go bhfuil Binseóirí Chumann Onórach Óstaí an Rí tar éis Céim mar Abhcóide dlí a bhronnadh ort, beirimse cead anois duit cleachtadh mar abhcóide dlí i gcúirteanna na hÉireann, agus glacfaidh tú d-ionad dá réir sin.

Mr ? Do you move anything?

An tUasal ? An bhfuil aon rud le chur i dtairiscint agat?

Roll of the
Inner Bar

Roll of the Inner Bar
(i) 1880-1924*

Queen's [King's] Counsel

1880
¶ John George Gibson

5th July 1884
James Clarke Lane
John N. Gerrard
George Wright
John Roche
¶ W.H. Dodd

1885
Frederick N. Le Poer Trench
Thomas George Overend
William Kenny

29th June 1889
W.S. Bird
S. Ronan
J.W. Craig
David Fitzgerald
R. Adams
D.B. Sullivan
T.L. O'Shaughnessy
E.H. Carson
J.J. Shaw
D.P. Barton

17th January 1891
Michael Drummond
John Ross

1st July 1892
Martin Burke
John Stanley
¶ Charles Matheson
¶ Matthew J. Bourke
John Gordon
James H. Campbell
Richard A. Meredith
Seymour Bushe

1st July 1893
J.G. Swift MacNeill
John F. Taylor

30th June 1894
Charles H. Teeling
John Russell Stritch

James O. Wylie
Myles Kehoe
Arthur Warren Samuels
Mathias McDonnell Bodkin, M.P.
¶ Charles O'Connor
Michael C. Macinerney

22nd February 1896
Fred. Fleming

23rd June 1896
Denis S. Henry

30th November 1898
Godfrey Fetherstonhaugh

22nd April 1899
J.B. Falconer, LL.D.
A.F. Blood
A.H. Bates
H.W. Jackson
R.W. Brereton Barry
S.L. Browne
¶ Ignatius J. O'Brien
G.A. Hume
R.F. Harrison
W.M. Jellett
H.D. Conner
T.M. Healy, M.P.
J. Wakely
¶ T.F. Molony
W. Moore, M.P.
Redmond J. Barry

19th February 1902
Richard M. Hennessy
Daniel F. Browne
James Chambers
Herbert Wilson

17th (or 27th) February 1904
T.S. Frank Battersby
James F.V. FitzGerald
Patrick D. Fleming
Andrew L. Horner
William Frederick Kenny
William Martin McGrath

* This part of the list, which is confined to men called to the Outer Bar since 1868, has been reconstructed from secondary sources.
[¶ = afterwards a Serjeant]

¶ John Francis Moriarty
George Nugent Oulton
John R. Patchell
Henry George Richards
Andrew Todd

25th February 1905
J.B. Powell

22nd January 1906
J. Dunn
Edward Cuming
P. Law Smith
R.W. Littlevale
Charles F. Doyle
D.G. Chaytor

30th June 1906
Lord Hemphill
John J. Clancy
Wood G. Jefferson
Patrick Lynch
Garnett William Walker

7th July 1906
Arthur C. Meredith

26th February 1907
William B.M. Whitaker
Daniel M. Wilson
Robert McIlroy

24th June 1908
George T. B. Vanston
George C. Greene
Gerald FitzGibbon
Thomas S. McCann
¶ A.M. Sullivan
James O'Connor

16th December 1909
Jonathan Pim
John H. Pigot
William Carrigan
Robert J. Doyle
Percival C. Gaussen
Dudley White

28th February 1910
John Leech
Charles Drumgoole
P.S. Walsh

28th October 1911
Ernest Godwin Swifte
William Herbert Brown
John McGonigal
William John Johnston

James MacLoone
Edward John McElligott
¶ George McSweeney
¶ Henry Hanna

24th February 1912
Clarence W. Corvan
John Linehan
Annesley St. G. de Renzy
Richard Best
William G. Gibson

26th April 1913
John Donaldon
John W. Hynes
Lionel H. Rosenthal
James Williamson
John Muldoon M.P.
W.S. Norwood

27th June 1914
Frederick T. Denning
Richard J. Kelly
Robert E. Osborne
Matthew J. Kenny
A. Alfred Dickie
Daniel J. O'Brien
Michael Comyn
Hon. Cecil Atkinson
W.E. Wylie

28th November 1914
George Hill Smith
James M. Sweetman
Gerald F. Brunskill

6th March 1915
John M. Colles
Gerald Horan

* 27th February 1918
T. Henry Maxwell
G.A. McGusty
John Cusack
F.N. Greer
Wm McGrath
Timothy Sullivan
F.W. Price
J.M. Whitaker
† R.G.L. Leonard
Thomas J. Campbell
James Andrews
A.B. Babington
J.C. Meredith
James Sealy
E.S. Murphy

*   Ignatius O'Brien, Lord Shandon, says on p. 339 of his unpublished memoirs [held in the King's Inns Library], that calls to the inner bar were suspended during the war at the request of the Bar. [See Daire Hogan, *The Legal Profession in Ireland 1789-1922*, p. 144]

Henry MacDermot
T.W. Brown
E.A. Swayne

5th June 1918
Raoul C. de Verson
George Dames Burtchaell
Charles H. Crookshank
T.C. Drury

25th February 1919
George Y. Dixon
Albert E. Wood
Edmond Lupton

14th May 1919
Mark B. Cooper

July 1919
† Frank FitzGibbon

Friday 27th February 1920
A.K. Overend
Herbert M. Thompson
Hugh Kennedy
Cecil Fford

6th April 1920
Edward Keen Figgis

29th June 1920
Charles David Barry

27th July 1920
H.O. Holmes
J.H. Monroe

30th July 1920 ?
Sir Ambrose Henry Webb

* 14th December 1920
C.J. Griffin
E.V. Longworth

25th February 1921
Robert Dick Megaw

Samuel Moore

16th June 1921
Edward A. Collins
John H. Robb
Marcus D. Begley

12th July 1921
William M. Beatty
James C.R. Lardner

13th July 1921
Joseph Samuel Edge
William A. Dick
Lewis R. Lipsett

** 11th June 1924
John O'Byrne

SERJEANTS

John George Gibson [3rd Serjeant 1885]
William Huston Dodd [3rd Serjeant 1892-1907]
Charles A. O'Connor [3rd Serjeant 1907; 1st Serjeant 1907-9]
Matthew J. Bourke [3rd Serjeant 1907]
John F. Moriarty [3rd Serjeant 1908; 1st Serjeant 1909-13]
Ignatius J. O'Brien [3rd Serjeant 1909; 2nd Serjeant 1911]
Thomas F. Molony [3rd Serjeant 1911; 2nd Serjeant 1911-12]
Charles L. Matheson [3rd Serjeant 1911; 2nd, 1912; 1st, 1913-19]
A.M. Sullivan [3rd Serjeant 1912; 2nd 1912-19; 1st 1919-59]
George McSweeney [3rd Serjeant 1918; 2nd 1919-23]
Henry Hanna [3rd Serjeant 1919-25]

---

†   Robert Leonard and Frank FitzGibbon, who were still members of the Law Library in 1952, duly called themselves Q.C. on the accession of Queen Elizabeth.

*   *I.L.T. & S. J.*, liv, 306. These appointments were never noted in *Thom*.

**   John O'Byrne had the distinction of being the first and only King's Counsel to be appointed *eo nomine* by the Free State. See *I.L.T.& S.J.*, 14 June 1924, p. 152: 'The Chief Justice then addressed Mr. John O'Byrne, the newly-appointed Attorney-General, who sat in Court, wearing a full-bottom wig and gown, saying - "The Governor-General has, on the advice of the Executive Council, appointed you to be Attorney-General of Saorstát Éireann, and to be a *King's Counsel*. You will, therefore, now take your place within the Bar accordingly" '.

NOTES

Sources Compiled from Thom's *Directory* and from the following contemporary reports in the *Irish Law Times and Solicitors' Journal*:

I.L.T. & S.J. 1877, p. 74. 16 February 1877 [13 names of men called to the bar between 1840 and 1866]; *I.L.T. & S.J.* 1882, p. 86. 18 February 1882 [9 names of men called to the bar between 1838 and 1864: Walliam Harris Faloon, Constantine Molloy, John Adye Curran, David Ross, Arthur Houston, Edmund T. Bewley, Francis Nolan, George Keys, Isaac Weir]; *I.L.T. & S.J.* 1884, p. 357. 5 July 1884 [11 names, including six called before 1868: Stephen P. Curtis (E 1844), William Anderson (T 1855), Athur P. Cleary (H 1864), David Lynch (H 1865), W.H. Kisbey (T 1866), James H. Orr (M 1867)]; *I.L.T. & S.J.* 1885, p. 341 [4 called, including William Irvine (E 1846)]; *I.L.T. & S.J.* 1899, p. 345 [12 called, including G.R. Price (M 1859) and R. J. Robertson (M 1860)]; *I.L.T. & S.J.* 1891 p. 37; *I.L.T. & S.J.* 1892, p 344 [3 called including George Vaughan Hart (H 1865)]; *I.L.T. & S.J.* 1893, p. 318; *I.L.T. & S.J.* 1894, p. 338 [9 called, including John H. Edge (H 1866)]; *I.L.T. & S.J.* 1899. p. 182; *I.L.T. & S.J.* 1902, p. 73; *I.L.T. & S.J.* 1904, p. 109; *I.L.T. & S.J.* 1905, p. 79; *I.L.T. & S.J.* 1906, p. 30; *I.L.T. & S.J.* 1908, p. 158; *I.L.T. & S.J.* 1910, p. 56; *I.L.T. & S.J.* 1911, pp 270-1; *I.L.T. & S.J.* 1912, p. 57; *I.L.T. & S.J.* 1913, p. 123; *I.L.T. & S.J.* 1914, pp 185-6, 340-1; *I.L.T. & S.J.* 1915, p. 66; *I.L.T. & S.J.* 1918, pp 52, 136-7; *I.L.T. & S.J.* 1919, p. 53; *I.L.T. & S.J.* 1920, pp 51, 306; *I.L.T. & S.J.* 1921, pp 58, 153, 176.

No reports of Call to the Inner Bar found in the *I.L.T. & S.J.* volumes for 1878-81, 1886 (but note p. 343), 1887-88, 1890, 1895-1901, 1903.

Serjeants: Richard Dowse, James Robinson, Denis Caulfield Heron, John O'Hagan, Charles Hare Hemphill, Peter O'Brien, William Bennett Campion, Dodgson H. Madden and H. Poole Jellett (2nd Serjeant 1892-1911) were appointed serjeants between 1868 and 1888. They had been called to the bar at dates between E 1840 (Campion) and E 1864 (Madden). The long lived Jellett (b. 5 Jan. 1825; d. 19 March 1911) was called at H 1847.

Called within the bar in Belfast: J.S. Baxter, William Macafee, and J. Pringle [E 1922]; James A. Rearden and David T. Sherlock [M 1922]; J Weir Johnston and Sir Arthur Scott Quekett [M 1923]; Thomas J.D. Atkinson [M 1924]; John Davison and William Lowry [M 1926]; Arthur Black, Sir Percy Alexander McElwaine, Edward John McKean and Sir Herbert Cecil Stronge [H 1929]; Walter Oakman Hume, Samuel Porter and John Edmond Warnock [H 1933]; John Clarke McDermott [E 1936]; Martin Gore Ellison [E 1938]; Sir Oscar Bedford Daly [T 1938]; John H.H. Campbell, Bernard Fox and William Fred. McCoy [T 1939]; L.E. Curran, T. Wallace Dickie and Leo Sheil [T 1943]; Isaac Copeland, James McSparrran, M.P., Cyril Nicholson and W.F. Patton [H 1945]; J.F. Caldwell, George B. Hanna, M.P., Brian Maginnis [M 1946]; and Alfred J. Belford [T 1950].

Roll of the Inner Bar
(ii) 1924-2004

TRANSCRIBED FROM THE VOLUMES IN THE SUPREME COURT OFFICE

* Monday 14th July 1924 [T]
Ernest J. Phelps
Vincent Rice
John M. Fitzgerald
William Henry Webster Carson
Joseph K. O'Connor
William G. Shannon
Kenneth B. Dockrell

Wednesday 6th May 1925 [E]
Martin Cyril Maguire
John A. Costello
James Geoghegan

Tuesday 30th March 1926 [H]
Hubert Hamilton
Charles Bewley

Thursday 21st October 1926 [M]
James FitzGerald-Kenney

Friday 6th May 1927 [E]
William J. Gleeson
Henry J. Moloney

Wednesday 15th June 1927 [T]
James Henry

Monday 21st November 1927 [M]
J.A. Rearden
Hector Hughes
Cyril Lavery

Wednesday 29th May 1929 [T]
Seoirse Gabhafan Ó Dubhthaigh
  [George Gavan Duffy]
Michael J. Ryan

---

*   The *Irish Law Times* reported the events of this day as follows: 'An interesting ceremony, the first of the kind since the establishment of the Supreme and High Courts of Justice of the Irish Free State, took place in the Supreme Court, Dublin Castle, on Monday, when the Chief Justice [Hugh Kennedy] called within the Bar counsel who had been granted patents of precedence. The patent of precedence grants the right of 'precedence and pre-audience ... to rank immdiately after those who are now King's Counsel', so that while counsel are now called to the inner Bar, they are not called 'King's Counsel', but are merely called 'within the Bar', and take their places accordingly. ...

'The Chief Justice called each counsel by his name in Irish, and then addressed them in that language. In English, he said to them:- 'I have received from the Governor-General letters under his hand and seal whereby, on the advice of the Executive Council, he grants to you the right of precedence and pre-audience in the Courts of Justice of Saorstát Éireann, to rank immediately after those who are now King's Counsel. I have pleasure, therefore, in admitting you to practice within the Bar of these Courts'. He called counsel individually within the Bar, and asked each if he had anything to move. Counsel bowed their acknowledgments, and the ceremony came to an end.'

[*Irish Law Times and Solicitors' Journal*, 19 July 1924, pp 180-1]

For the innovation of 1924 there was authority in two instances in England, where patents of precedence were granted to Lord Denman (1779-1854) in 1828, and to Lord Phillimore (1845-1929) in 1883. Having acted as Solicitor-General to Queen Caroline, whom George IV had divorced, Denman could ill be appointed as counsel to the King. Phillimore's patent had to do with the fact that he was a practitioner in the ecclesiastical and admiralty courts. Since 1883 the right to grant patents of precedence has not been exercised in England.

Wednesday 25th June 1930 [T]
Robert St. James Chadwick
Albert D. Bolton [LL.D.]
Seoirse Ó Muanáin
  [George A. Moonan]
Thomas A. Finlay
Michael Binchy
E.J. Kelly

Friday 11th March 1932 [H]
Conchubhar Alasdair Macguidhir
  [Conor Maguire]

Monday 24th April 1933 [E]
Tomás Ua Dómhnaill
  [Thomas O'Donnell]
Charles S. Campbell
Basil McGuckin
Joseph A. McCarthy

Friday 12th April 1935 [H]
William B. Black
Martin J. Connolly
T.C. Kingsmill Moore
T P. McCarthy
Ralph Brereton Barry
Patrick J. Roe

Monday 12th April 1937 [E]
J.V. Nolan-Whelan
George C. Cullinan
Frank Monks
James Cawley

Wednesday 21st December 1938 [M]
William Reginald Armstrong
Arthur Victor Matheson
James Comyn
Constantine P. Curran
Richard Francis Dominick
  McLoughlin
Kevin O'Hanrahan Haugh
Diarmaid Fawsitt

Tuesday 20th June 1939 [T]
John Joseph Hearne
Patrick Philip O'Donoghue
James Howard A. Street

Friday 12th January 1940 [H]
Richard McGonigal
Patrick Joseph McEnery

Friday 2nd April 1940 [E]
Oliver L. Moriarty
Kevin Dixon
Barra Ó Briain

Friday 9th May 1941 [E]
Frances E. Moran

Friday 28th October 1941 [M]
Maurice Cecil Walker
Charles Francis Casey

Wednesday 14th October 1942 [M]
Herbert Vaughan Wilson
John Lymbrick Esmonde
George Daniel Murnaghan

Friday 5th March 1943 [H]
Frederick Gardner Orford Budd

Monday 15th March 1943 [H]
Joseph Healy

Wednesday 30th June 1943 [T]
Francis Bernard Vaughan Buckley

Monday 11th October 1943 [M]
Robert S. Hogan
Seán MacBride

Monday 6th March 1944 [H]
William O'Brien FitzGerald

Monday 26th June 1944 [T]
Alfred Denis Pringle
Art O'Connor
Terence Kevin Liston

Monday 12th February 1945 [H]
John Hooper
Cearbhall Ó Dálaigh

Thursday 1st March 1945 [H]
Michael O'Driscoll

Thursday 7th March 1946 [H]
Thomas Teevan

Wednesday 3rd July 1946 [T]
C[harles] Frederick Matheson
P[atrick] McGilligan
Thomas J[ames]. Conolly
[Martyn, *4th Baron*] Hemphill
Tadhg MacFhirbhisigh [Forbes]

Friday 4th July 1947 [T]
Kevin O'Shiel
James I. McGuire
Ernest M. Wood

DUBLIN, SATURDAY, MAY 10, 1941

WOMAN K.C.

Miss Frances E. Moran became Eire's first woman K.C. when she was called to the Inner Bar yesterday.

Cutting from *The Irish Times*, Saturday 10 May 1941.

Tuesday 2nd March 1948 [H]
Ashley Powell
E[dward] C[hristopher] Micks
Bernard Shillman
Oliver D. Gogarty
P.A. Ó Síocháin
Desmond Bell

Wednesday 30th June 1948 [T]
Michael McGilligan
Thomas U[rquart] Odell

Tuesday 21st December 1948 [M]
George W. Shannon
John Charles Conroy

Wednesday 27th April 1949 [E]
John O'Leary

Friday 3rd March 1950 [H]
Thomas Vincent Davy
Peter John Nugent
Thomas Berchmans Hannin

Monday 3rd July 1950 [T]
Pádraig de Búrca [Patrick Bourke]
Kevin M. Kenny
Kenneth E.L. Deale

Thursday 5th July 1951 [T]
Aindrias Ó Caoimh
  [Andrew O'Keeffe]
Vivion de Valera

Monday 29th October 1951 [T]
Charles B[euno] McKenna

Tuesday 4th July 1952 [T]
James G[erard] McMahon

Thursday 11th December 1952 [M]
John [Felix] Miley

Thursday 5th March 1953 [H]
Seán MacDiarmaid Fawsitt
John Gleeson

Thursday 9th July 1953 [T]
John Joseph Webb
Edward Joseph A. Murphy
James R. Heavey

Friday 29th January 1954 [H]
Thomas Aloysius Doyle
James A. D'Arcy
Brian Walsh

* Wednesday 7th April 1954 [H]
Thomas F. O'Higgins
Seosamh Ó Broin [Joseph O'Byrne]

Monday 5th July 1954 [T]
Noel Peart

Thursday 9th December 1954 [M]
Patrick J. Lindsay

Thursday 3rd March 1955 [H]
Roger [Charles] O'Hanrahan
James S[mith] McGivern
Malcolm H.G. Ellis

Friday 1st July 1955 [T]
Raymond O'Neill
Thomas J. Neylon

Thursday 1st March 1956 [H]
William D. Finlay

Thursday 4th July 1957 [T]
Herbert E. Wellwood

Thursday 6th March 1958 [H]
John Kenny

Friday 18th July 1958 [T]
Liam MacCosgair [Liam Cosgrave]

Friday 27th February 1959 [H]
Conor Patrick Maguire

Thursday 2nd July 1959 [T]
Seamus Henchy

* A memorandum dated 6 April 1954 was addressed to the Chief Justice on the occasion of this Call. It read: 'Mr Waldron is in doubt about the order in which the two men will be placed for the Call tomorrow. You did say Mr. O'Higgins should take precedence, but the Calls to the Bar are as follows: O'Byrne, Hilary 1926; O'Higgins, Michaelmas 1938. Perhaps you would be so good as to say if this will make a difference'. The Chief Justice replied: 'Yes - on the last occasion I think I placed those being called in order of their call to the bar although some of the patents were of earlier date. I think that was wrong and I shall make this call in the order of the date of the patents'.

Monday 7th December 1959 [M]
Richard Noel Cooke
Colm Condon
Niall McCarthy

Friday 4th March 1960 [H]
Gerard Clarke

Thursday 2nd March 1961 [H]
Sir Paget J. Bourke

Thursday 6th July 1961[T]
William Roche Ellis

3rd October 1961 [M]
Thomas A[loysius] Finlay

Friday 16th March 1962 [H]
Seán [Desmond] O'Hanrahan
James Francis Egan

Monday 21st January 1963 [H]
Seán de Búitléir

Friday 19th July 1963 [T]
Weldon Parke
Peadar Ó Máille
Eoin Ó Riain

Friday 1st November 1963 [M]
Samuel Crivon
Joshua Baker
Garrett Gill
Noel K. Macdonald
Seán Morrissey

Friday 28th February 1964 [H]
William B[rian] Moran
Frank Griffin

Monday 19th October 1964 [M]
William G. Fallon

Friday 5th March 1965 [H]
Gerard Lardner
John [Henry] Lovatt-Dolan

Friday 30th April 1965 [E]
Anthony J[ames] Hederman
Declan D[avid] Costello

Wednesday 28th July 1965 [T]
Reginald A[lfred] Harrison

Friday 8th July 1966 [T]
Vincent Grogan
John M.J. Gannon

Thursday 23rd February 1967 [H]
Ernest S. Fitz-Simon

Monday 2nd October 1967 [M]
Roderick J. O'Hanlon
Thomas J. McLoughlin
Diarmuid P. Sheridan

Friday 1st March 1968 [H]
Ralph G[erard] Sutton
Peter Maguire
Séamus McKenna
Liam Hamilton

10th October 1968 [M]
Padraic Boyd
Donal Barrington

7th March 1969 [H]
Vincent [Andrew] Landy

6th October 1969 [M]
Edward M. Walsh
Francis D. Murphy

6th March 1970 [H]
Henry D. Barron

Friday 3rd July 1970 [T]
Maurice P. Gaffney
Ronan Keane

Monday 5th October 1970 [M]
Frederick J[ohn] Roche
Kevin Lynch

Friday 12th March 1971 [H]
Dermot P. Kinlen

Monday 4th October 1971 [M]
Patrick Connolly
J. Grattan Esmonde
Séamus Ó Soracháin
Henry Hickey

Tuesday 11th January 1972 [H]
J[ohn] J[ames] P[atrick] MacKenzie

Friday 15th July 1972 [T]
Robert Barr

Monday 2nd October 1972 [M]
J. Gerard Buchanan

Friday 23rd March 1973 [H]
Frank Martin
Rex [Arthur J.C.] Mackey

Friday 1st June 1973 [E]
Thomas F. Roe
Martin J. Kennedy
Michael O'Kennedy

Monday 1st October 1973 [M]
John B. Cassidy
Frederick R. Morris

Thursday 28th February 1974 [H]
John Blayney
Kieran J. O'Connor
Murray McGrath

Monday 7th October 1974 [M]
John V[incent] Coleman
Feargus [Michael] Flood
Diarmuid [Brian] O'Donovan

Thursday 27th February 1975 [H]
Brian Fahy
Edward Comyn
Brian McCracken
R.L. Kenneth Mills

6th October 1975 [M]
Patrick [Joseph] Geraghty
Michael Feehan
Marcus [John Albert] Daly
Patrick McEntee

18th March 1976 [H]
Lionel J. Winder
Kevin O'Shaughnessy

13th May 1976 [E]
Hugh J. O'Flaherty

4th October 1976 [M]
Paul Callan
Brendan Mattimoe
Mella Carroll
Aidan Browne
James O'Driscoll

1st March 1977 [H]
Antony McDowell

19th May 1977 [E]
John Kelly

Monday 3rd October 1977 [M]
James Carroll
Richard Johnson

Garrett Cooney
Hugh Geoghegan
T.C. Smyth

24th February 1978 [H] *
William Henry Hill
R. Robins
Nial Fennelly

Monday 2nd October 1978 [M]
John O. Sweetman
John Farrell
Thomas S. McCann

Friday 9th March 1979
David Butler
Dermot Gleeson
Gerard A. Lee

29th February 1980 [H]
James Dominic Lynch
Harold A. Whelehan
Mary Robinson

6th October 1980 [M]
David Montgomery
Eoghan Fitzsimons
Paul [James Patrick] Carney
John D. Cooke
Frank Spain
Peter D. Sutherland

12th March 1981 [H]
John L. Murray
Declan Budd
James A. Nugent

5th October 1981 [M]
Noel Aubrey Clancy
John M. FitzGerald

5th March 1982 [H]
[Michael] Barry White
Nicholas Kearns
Michael Moriarty
Kevin C. O'Higgins
Ercus Stewart

4th October 1982 [M]
Joseph Christopher McGough
    [Seosamh C. Mac Eochaidh]
M[atthew] P[atrick] Smith
Liam Gaynor
Peter Shanley

* The list for 24th February 1978, which is out of order in the Roll, occurs between
the pages for 19th May 1977 and 3rd October 1977.

Anthony Kennedy
Philip O'Sullivan
Andrew S. Bradley
Vivian A. Lavan
Patrick E. Keane

25th February 1983 [H]
Seán Ryan

10th March 1983 [H]
Richard Ferguson

3rd October 1983 [T]
Kevin Haugh
Angus Charleton
Padraig McCartan

16th March 1984 [H]
Dermot MacCarthy
Eoin P. McGonigal
John Quirke
Denis C. Mitchell

1st October 1984 [M]
George Brady
Hugh B. McGahon
Conor J. Maguire
Paul F.W. Gilligan

13th December 1984
John Rogers

1st March 1985 [H]
David M. Byrne
John Gordon

7th October 1985 [M]
James P. Salafia
Daniel O'Keeffe
Brian P. Dempsey
Denis McCullough
Blaise A. O'Carroll
Frank Clarke

13th January 1986 [H]
Edward Gleeson
Reginald G. Weir

21st February 1986 [H]
John R. Finlay

3rd October 1986 [M]
Timothy M. Desmond
Eamon de Valera
Peter Kelly
Ciaran P. Foley
John O'Mahony

6th February 1987 [H]
R. Charles Hill
Desmond Norman Orr Boal

13th March 1987 [H]
Gerald M. Tynan
Liam G. Reidy
Michael McDowell

5th October 1987 [M]
Denis V. Buckley
Mary Laffoy
Susan Gageby Denham
William McKechnie

[Friday] 26th February 1988 [H]
Alan P. Mahon
James McNulty

[Monday] 3rd October 1988
Ian Brennan
M. Finlay Geoghegan

[Friday] 24th February 1989 [H]
Adrian Hardiman

[Monday] 2nd October 1989 [M]
Henry O. Bourke
John Gallagher
Iarfhlaith O'Neill
James O'Reilly
Catherine McGuinness

Friday 9th March 1990 [H]
David P. I. Hamilton
Joseph Finnegan

Monday 1st October 1990 [M]
John Hedigan
Fergus McK[enna] O'Hagan

Friday 22nd February 1991 [H]
Paul Butler
John C[hristopher] Coughlan
M.H. Clark
Tom Slattery
Anne M T Dunne
Paul Gallagher

Monday 7th October 1991 [M]
Brendan Grogan
Roderick H. Murphy
Brian J. McGovern
K.T. Feeney
Gregory Murphy
John McMenamin
Anthony W. Kidney
Paul Sreenan

Friday 13th March 1992 [H]
David Andrews
Henry J. Abbott
James Connolly
Hugh P. Kennedy

Monday 9th October 1992 [M]
Colm Allen
Paul O'Higgins

Friday 5th March 1993 [H]
Henry Murphy
John P. W. White

Monday 4th October 1993 [M]
Aongus O Brolacháin
R.L. Nesbitt
Hugh O'Neill

Friday 25th February 1994 [H]
Muireann O Briain
Joseph Matthews
Gerard Durcan
Ian Finlay

Monday 3rd October 1994 [M]
Erwan Mill-Arden
Aindrias O Caoimh
Patrick F. Hanratty
Michael M. Collins
Inge Clissman
Michael Carson
Bill Shipsey
Michael Fysh

Friday 10th March 1995 [H]
Daniel Herbert
Ciaran J. O'Loughlin
Paul Walsh
James Macken
Patrick Gageby
Raymond Fullam
Jeremiah Healy
Peter Charleton
Patrick McCarthy
Michael Forde

Monday 2nd October 1995 [M]
Fidelma Macken
Edmund Honohan
Brian Leonard
Michael Gleeson
Donal O'Donnell

Friday 1st March 1996 [H]
Edward Bacon
John O'Hagan
John Peart

Michael McMahon
Michael Durack
Anne Cruess Callaghan
Martin P. Giblin
Padraig O'Higgins
Gerard Clarke
Michael A Hanna
Declan McGovern
Mary Irvine
James Dwyer
Kieran Fleck
Rory Brady
David McGrath
John Trainor
Donnell Deeny

Monday 7th October 1996 [M]
Sean T. Moylan
Anthony Sammon
Diarmuid McGuinness

Friday 28th February 1997 [H]
Aidan Walsh
Eileen Lydon
Turlough O'Donnell

Friday 3rd October 1997 [M]
John J. Phelan
Tony Aston
Kevin Cross
Michael O'Donoghue
J.G. Danaher
N[ora] Bernadette Cronin
Bruce Antoniotti
Edward S. Walsh
Eamon Leahy
Michael A. Counihan
Margaret Nerney
Gerardine Connolly
Gerard Hogan
Brian Lenihan
R.J. McBratney

Friday 27th March 1998 [H]
Hugh Hartnett
Dermot P. Kelly
David Hardiman
C.J. Meenan
R[ichard] N. Kean
Miriam Reynolds

Friday 2nd October 1998 [M]
Desmond M. O'Neill
Declan McGovern
Bernard Joseph Barton
John A. Whelan
Stephen J. Roche
Frank Callanan

James J. Gilhooly
John A. Edwards
Joseph McGettigan
Felix McEnroy
Michael Cush
James F. O'Leary

Tuesday 6th October 1998 [M]
Noel A. MacMahon

Friday 5th March 1999 [H]
Miriam O'Riordan
Eamonn Cahill
Donagh J. McDonagh
Vincent Foley
Paul McDermott
Rory MacCabe

Friday 1st October 1999 [M]
David Goldberg
John O'Kelly
George M. Bermingham
Mark De Blacam
Deirdre P. Murphy
Patricia Dillon
Mel Mac Criostail [Mel Christle]
Brian O'Moore
Brian Spierin
Cormac Corrigan
Peter Finlay
Patrick Horgan
Marcus F. Daly

Tuesday 5th October 1999 [M]
Feichín MacDonough

Friday 31st March 2000 [H]
Martin C. Glesson
T[homas] Michael Ashe Q.C.
Raymond Comyn
Doirbhile Flanagan
Paulyn Marrinan Quinn
Séamus Ó Tuathail
Mary O'Toole
Patrick James McCarthy
Michael MacGrath
Bernard J. McDonagh
Hugh I. Mohan
Gráinne McMorrow

Tuesday 3rd October 2000 [M]
Thomas O'Connell
Brendan C. Nix
Thomas F. Creed
Dominick P. Hussey
Richard T. Keane
Alexander Owens
Patrick Marrinan

Nicholas Butler
John Punch
Senan Allen

Wednesday 4th October 2000 [M]
Finbarr Fox
David J. Hegarty
Denis McDonald
Patrick Long
Paul Gardiner
Shane Murphy
Michael [Liam] O'Higgins
Patrick A. Butler
Dermot Flanagan
Barry Macdonald
Séamus Treacy

Friday 30th March 2001 [H]
Patricia Moran
   [Pádraigín Ní Mhóráin]
Catherine Crean
   [Caithlín Ní Chreithin]
Eamon Galligan
Constance Cassidy
John T. Gibbons
Gavin Ralston
Martin Hayden
Kenneth Christopher Fogarty
John Gleeson

Tuesday 2nd October 2001 [M]
Joseph Hogan
Colm Smyth
Patrick Gerard Quinn
Richard McDonnell
Simon Boyle
John Leydon O'Donnell
Declan Doyle
Eoin McCullough
Caroline Carney
James Gerard O'Brien

Wednesday 3rd October 2001 [M]
Patrick Hunt
Mary Faherty
Mark Orr

Monday 7th October 2002 [M]
Niall Durnin
Lewis O'Brien
Terence O'Sullivan
Gerry Kelly
John McDonagh
Roger Sweetman
Paul Coffey
Roderick O'Hanlon
Eanna Mulloy
David Kennedy

Mary Ellen Ring
Cormac Ó Dúlacháin
Mark Connaughton
Brian Murray

Friday 21st March 2003 [H]
Philip Magee
Oonagh McCrann
Colman Fitzgerald
David Nolan
Esmonde Keane
Lyndon MacCann
Isobel Kennedy
Maurice Collins
Brendan Grehan

Wednesday 8th October 2003 [M]
Mary E. Laverty
Hugo Hynes
Jacqueline M. O'Brien
Nuala Butler
Conor Devally
Anthony Collins
David Holland
Fergal Kavanagh
Joseph Revington
James Gallagher, Q.C.

Friday 5th March 2004 [H]
Stephen Lanigan O'Keeffe
Barry Hickson

Una McGurk
Adrian Mannering
Brendan Kilty
Bernard Madden
Anthony Barr
Paul Flannery
Mark Sanfey
Sara Moorehead

Thursday 7th October 2004 [M]
Roddy Horan
Robert Haughton
Marie Baker
Paul Burns
John Francis Aylmer
Aileen Mary Donnelly
Brian James Cregan

Tuesday 15th March 2005 [H]
Justin Dillon
Eugene Gleeson
Máire Whelan
Gráinne Clohessy
Dervla Browne
Séamus Woulfe
Pauline Walley
Timothy O'Leary
Conleth Bradley

* * * * *

FORMULA USED UPON CALL TO THE INNER BAR

The Government having been pleased to grant you a Patent of Precedence admitting you within the Bar in the Courts of Ireland, I now call you within the Bar and you will take your place accordingly.

Ó tharla go bhfuil an Rialtas tar éis Paitinn Tosaíochta a dheonadh dhuit dod' ligint taobh istigh den Bharra i gCúirteanna na h-Éireann, glaoimse ort anois teacht taobh istigh den Bharra, agus glacfaidh tú d-ionad dá réir sin.

Mr ?   Do you move anything?

An tUasal ?   An bhfuil aon rud le chur i dtairiscint agat?

Judges and Law Officers

whose names are recorded in this volume

Judges and Law Officers
whose names are recorded in this volume

Judges of the Supreme Court of
Judicature in Ireland
*1878-1924

* The Supreme Court of Judicature (Ireland) Act, 1877 (40 & 41 Vict., cap. 57),
came into force on 1 January 1878.

The names of barristers called before 1868 are in italics

I: BLACK (CHANCERY) JUDGES

Lord Chancellor
John Thomas Ball,[1] 1875-1880
Hugh Law, 1881-1883
Sir *Edward Sullivan*, 1883-85
John Naish, 1885, 1886
Edward Gibson, Baron *Ashbourne*,
1885-1886, 1886-92, 1895-1905
Sir *Samuel Walker*, 1892-95 and
1905-11
Redmond John Barry, 1911-1913
Ignatius John O'Brien, afterwards
Baron Shandon, 1913-1916
James H. M. Campbell (ex-L.C.J.),
aft. Baron Glenavy, 1918-1921
Sir John Ross (ex-Chancery
Division) 1921-22

Master of the Rolls
Sir *Edward Sullivan*, 1870-1883
Sir *Andrew Marshall Porter*, 1883-
1916
Richard Edmund Meredith (ex-
Q.B.D.), 1906-1912
Charles Andrew O'Connor, 1912-24

Vice-Chancellor
Hedges Eyre Chatterton, 1867-1904

Lord Justices of Appeal[2]
Rickard Deasy, 1878-1883
Gerald FitzGibbon 1878-1909
Charles Robert Barry, 1883-1897

Hugh Holmes (ex-Q.B.D.), 1897-
1914
Richard Robert Cherry, 1909-1913
John Francis Moriarty, 1914-15
Stephen Ronan, 1915-24
Thomas Francis Molony, 1915-1918
James O'Connor, 1918-24

Fomer Lord Chancellors acting as additional Lord Justices of Appeal
John Naish, 1886-90
Sir *Samuel Walker*, 1895-1905

Chancery Division[3]

Land Judges
Stephen Woulfe Flanagan, 1878-
1885
Henry Ormsby, 1878-1885
John Monroe, 1885-1896
John Ross, 1896-1921

*Puisne judges of the Chancery
Division*
Dunbar Plunkett Barton (ex-Q.B.D.)
1904-1918
James O'Connor, 1918-1918
John Blake Powell, 1918-1923

[1] Father of Francis Elrington Ball,
author of *The Judges in Ireland*.
[2] Two ordinary judges.

[3] This Division included the Master
of the Rolls and (until 1904) the
Vice-Chancellor. There were two
Land Judges until 1885, one
thereafter. In 1904 the role of the
Vice-Chancellor was filled by the
appointment to the Division of one
other puisne judge.

King's Inns Barristers, 1868-2004, p. 419.

II: RED (COMMON LAW) JUDGES

Lord Chief Justice of Ireland
George Augustus Chichester May, 1878-1887
Sir *Michael Morris*, 1887-1889
Peter O'Brien, Baron O'Brien, 1889-1913
Richard Robert Cherry (ex-Lord Justice of Appeal), 1913-1916
James Henry Mussen Campbell, 1916-18
Thomas Francis Molony (hitherto a puisne judge), 1918-24

Queen's Bench Division[1]

At the commencement of the Judicature Act
George Augustus Christopher May, Lord Chief Justice, 1878-1887
James O'Brien, 1858-1882
John David Fitzgerald, 1860-1882
Charles Robert Barry, 1872-1883

Subsequently appointed
James Anthony Lawson (ex-Common Pleas), 1882-87
William O'Brien, (ex-Common Pleas) 1883-1899
William Moore Johnson, 1883-1909

Transferred from the Common Pleas, 8 July 1887
Michael Harrison, 1887-1895
James Murphy, 1887-1892
Hugh Holmes, 1887-1897

Subsequently appointed
John George Gibson, 1888-1921
Dodgson Hamilton Madden, 1892-1919

Transferred from the Court of Exchequer, 6 August 1897
Christopher Palles, Chief Baron, 1897-1916
William Drennan Andrews, 1897-1909
James Murphy, 1897-1901

Absorbed from the Court of Bankruptcy, 6 August 1897
Walter Boyd, 1897-1916

Subsequently appointed
William Kenny, 1897-1921
Dunbar Plunkett Barton, 1900-1904
George Wright, 1901-1913
William Huston Dodd, 1907-24
Richard Robert Cherry, 1909-1913
Thomas Francis Molony, 1913-1915
Jonathan Ernest Pim, 1915-1924
John Gordon, 1916-1922
William Moore, 1917-1922
James O'Connor, 1918-1918
Arthur Warren Samuels, 1919-1924

Common Pleas Division[2]
[absorbed into the Queen's Bench Division on 8 July 1887]

At the commencement of the Judicature Act
Michael Morris, Lord Chief Justice of the Common Pleas, 1876-87
William Nicholas Keogh, 1856-1878
James Anthony Lawson, 1868-1882

Appointed subsequently
Michael Harrison, 1878-1887
William O'Brien, 1882-3
James Murphy, 1883-87
Hugh Holmes, 1887

[1] Possessed four judges (the LCJ and three puisnes), 1878-87; seven judges (upon absorption of the Common Pleas, 1887-97; nine judges (absorption of the Exchequer, and abolition of one post), 1897-1904; eight judges (after the transfer of Barton to the Chancery Division), 1904-1922

[2] Possessed three judges until 8 July 1887, when the Common Pleas Division was amalgamated with the Queen's Bench Division.

Exchequer Division[1]

Christopher Palles, Chief Baron,
1874-1916
Francis Alexander Fitzgerald, 1859-
1882
Richard Dowse, 1872-1890

Appointed subsequently

William Drennan Andrews, 1882-97
James Murphy (ex Q.B.D.), 1892-97

Probate and Matrimonial Division[2]

Robert Richard Warren, 1878-97

[*Court of Admiralty*][3]
[*Court of Bankruptcy*][4]

**Judicial Commissioner,
Irish Land Commission**[5]

John O'Hagan, 1881-1889
Edward Falconer Litton, 1889-1890
Edmund Thomas Bewley, 1890-1898
Richard Edmund Meredith, 1898-
1906
James Owens Wylie, 1906-1920
William Evelyn Wylie, 1920-1924

Law Officers
whose names are recorded in this volume

All of those named were subsequently judges, including Carson as a Lord of Appeal,
and Henry, Brown, and Wilson in Northern Ireland.

Attorney-General

J.H.M. Campbell (appt. 1905)
Richard R. Cherry (appt. 1909)
R.J. Barry (appt. 1909)
C.A. O'Connor (appt. 1911)
Ignatius J. O'Brien (appt. 1912)
Thomas F. Molony (appt. 1913)
John F. Moriarty (appt. 1913)
Jonathan Pim (appt. 1914)
John Gordon (appt. 1915)
J.H.M. Campbell (appt. 1916)
James O'Connor (appt. 1917)
Arthur Warren Samuels (appt.
1918)
Denis S. Henry (appt. 1919)
Thomas Watters Brown (appt.
1921)

Solicitor-General

Edward Carson (appt. 1892)
Charles H. Hemphill (appt. 1892)
William Kenny (appt. 1895)
Dunbar P. Barton (appt. 1898)
George Wright (appt. 1900)
J.H.M. Campbell (appt. 1901)
Redmond J. Barry (appt. 1905)
C.A. O'Connor (appt. 1909)
Ignatius J. O'Brien (appt. 1911)
Thomas F. Molony (appt. 1912)
John F. Moriarty (appt. 1913)
Jonathan Pim (appt. 1913)
James O'Connor (appt. 1914)
Arthur Warren Samuels (appt. 1917)
John Blake Powell (appt. 1918)
Denis S. Henry (appt. 1918)
Daniel M. Wilson (appt. 1919)

[1] Three judges, until 1897.
[2] One judge. The Probate and
Matrimonial Division was absorbed
into the Queen's Bench Division on
6 August 1897; and the jurisdiction
was conferred on Mr. Justice
Andrews, 11 October 1897.

[3] Independent under its existing
judge (Townshend) until his death
on 2 February 1893; jurisdiction
thereupon conferred on Mr. Justice
Johnson, 16 February 1893.
[4] Absorbed into the Queen's Bench
Division on 6 August 1897, along
with its Judge (Boyd).
[5] Land Law (Ireland) Act, 1881 (44
& 45 Vict., cap. 49).

The Judges, 1921-24

The following list, representing the bench as it was in July 1921, appears in F.E. Ball's *The Judges in Ireland, 1221-1921*, ii, p. 325.

Chancellor: Sir John Ross, Baronet.

Lord Justices of Appeal (2): Stephen Ronan, James O'Connor.

Chancery Division
Master of the Rolls: Charles Andrew O'Connor
Justices of the Chancery Division (2): John Blake Powell [and one vacancy, caused by Sir John Ross's appointment as Chancellor in June 1921]

King's Bench Division
Chief Justice: Thomas Francis Molony
Justices of the King's Bench (7): John George Gibson, William Huston Dodd, Jonathan Ernest Pim, John Gordon, William Moore, Arthur Warren Samuels [and one vacancy caused by the death, on 4 February 1921, of William Kenny]

Irish Land Commission: William Evelyn Wylie

Prior to the enactment of the Government of Ireland Act, 1920, the Supreme Court had fifteen judges: four, including the Chancellor and Master of the Rolls, in the Chancery Division; two Lord Justices of Appeal; eight, including the Lord Chief Justice, in the King's Bench Division; and the Judicial Commissioner of the Irish Land Commission. The advancement of Sir John Ross to the chancellorship, which occurred in June 1921, and was the last appointment made by the Imperial government, and the death of William Kenny, which had occurred on 4 February 1921, accounted for two unfilled vacancies on the puisne bench. A further vacancy occurred in October 1921 when Moore (1866-1944) resigned from the Dublin bench in order to become a Lord Justice in Northern Ireland, where he was afterwards (1925-37) Lord Chief Justice. Gibson also retired in 1921; and early in the following year the office of Lord Chancellor was abolished. There were two subsequent deaths (Gordon, on 26 September 1922; and Powell in 1923). This left eight of the old judges in place at the start of 1924. Of the eight, only Charles Andrew O'Connor (1855-1928) and W.E. Wylie (1881-1964) chose to continue in judicial office in the Irish Free State after 1924, O'Connor serving for one year and Wylie for twelve. The other six — Molony, Ronan, James O'Connor, Dodd, Pim and Samuels — opted for retirement. As the Government of the Irish Free State made no judicial appointments prior to June 1924, the Bench in Dublin continued, save for the resignations and deaths which have been noted, as it had been constituted in July 1921.

The Irish Free State's judicial appointments, to a Supreme Court of 3 and a High Court of 6, were announced on 5 June 1924. The names of the nine judges — O'Connor and Wylie JJ, and seven new appointees, two of whom (O'Shaughnessy and Johnston) were formerly judges of the County Court — will be found on page 425 below.

The last red judges in Dublin: (left) Orpen's portrait of Thomas Francis Molony, the last Lord Chief Justice of Ireland, appointed in 1918; and (right) Mr. Justice William Evelyn Wylie, who in 1920 succeeded his uncle as Judge of the Land Commission. Mr. Justice Wylie wore black on the bench of the High Court of the Irish Free State, but is seen in scarlet in this portrait done (by Leo Whelan) for the Royal Dublin Society.

King's Inns Barristers, 1868-2004, page 423.

Protestants appointed to the Bench of the High Court of the Irish Free State: (left) William John Johnston, 'Civil Bill', hitherto a judge of the County Court, appt. 5.6.1924. He was the father of the playwright (and barrister) Denis Johnston. (right) Henry Hanna, K.C., appt. 1.5.1925. He was author of *The Pals at Suvla Bay*, and (in 1919) the last man to be appointed 3rd Serjeant. The long-lived Serjeant Sullivan, who wrote a book with the title *The Last Serjeant*, had been appointed 3rd Serjeant in 1912.

King's Inns Barristers, 1868-2004, page 424.

The judiciary and law officers of the Irish Free State and Ireland

(i) Judiciary, 1924-1961

Chief Justice

Hugh Kennedy (appt. 5.6.1924; died 12.12.1936)

Timothy Sullivan (appt. 17.12.1936; ret. 1946)

Conor Alexander Maguire (appt. June 1946; ret. December 1961)

Supreme Court

The Right Hon. Charles Andrew O'Connor (appt. 5.6.1924; res. 30.4.1925)

Gerald FitzGibbon (appt. 5.6.1924; ret. 8.10.1938)

James Augustine Murnaghan (appt. 1.5.1925; ret. 1953)

James Creed Meredith (appt. 22.12.1936; died 14.8.1942)

James Geoghegan (appt. 22.12.1936; ret. 1950)

William John Johnston (appt. 7.3.1939; ret. 17.1.1940)

John O'Byrne (appt. 18.1.1940; died 14.1.1954)

William Black (appt. 1942; ret. 1951)

Cecil Lavery (appt. 1950; ret. 5.10.1966)

Theodore Conyngham Kingsmill Moore (appt. 1951; ret. 1966)

Carroll O'Daly (appt. 1953; prom. to C.J., December 1961)

Martin Cyril Maguire (appt. 1954; ret. February 1961)

Kevin O'Hanrahan Haugh (appt. 9.2.1961; died 5.4.1969)

President of the High Court

Timothy Sullivan (appt. 5.6.1924; prom. C.J. 17.12.1936)

Conor Alexander Maguire (appt. 17.12.1936; prom. C.J. June 1946)

George Gavan Duffy (appt. 1946; died 10.6.1951)

Cahir Davitt (appt. 1951; ret. August 1966)

High Court

James Creed Meredith (appt. 5.6.1924; prom. 22.12.1936)

The Right Hon. Thomas Lopdell O'Shaughnessy (appt. 5.6.1924; res. 23.12.1925)

*William Evelyn Wylie (appt. 5.6.1924; res. 1.7.1936)

William John Johnston (appt. 5.6.1924; prom. to SC 7.3.1939)

James Augustine Murnaghan (appt. 5.6.1924; prom. 1.5.1925)

Henry Hanna (appt. 1.5.1925; ret. 18.12.1942)

John O'Byrne (appt. 9.1.1926; prom. 18.1.1940)

*Conor Alexander Maguire (appt. 2.11.1936; President 17.12.1936)

George Gavan Duffy (appt. 22.12.1936; prom. Pres. 1946)

William Black (appt. 7.3.1939; prom. 1942)

*Martin Cyril Maguire (appt. 3.2.1940; prom. 1954)

Kevin O'Hanrahan Haugh (appt. 1942; prom. 9.2.1961)

Andrew Kingsbury Overend (appt. 1943; died 16.4.1947)

Cahir Davitt (appt. 1945; Pres. 1951)

Kevin Joseph Dixon (appt. 1946; died 25.10.1959)

Theodore Conyngham Kingsmill Moore (appt. 1947; prom. 1951)

Charles Francis Casey (appt. 1951; died 6.11.1952)

Frederick Gardner Orford Budd (appt. 1951; prom. 1966)

Richard McLoughlin (appt. 1952; prom. 1966)

George D. Murnaghan (appt. 1954; ret. 4.7.1979)

*Thomas Teevan (appt. 1954; ret. 1971)

Brian Walsh (appt. 1959; prom. Dec. 1961)

* served as Judicial Commissioner, Irish Land Commission

(ii) Judiciary, 1961-2004

The jurisdiction of the courts established in 1924 was formally extinguished by section 7 of the Courts (Establishment and Constitution) Act, 1961, which came into force on (and by virtue of an Order of the Government dated) 29th September 1961.

Chief Justice

Conor Alexander Maguire (appt. June 1946; ret. December 1961)

Cearbhaill Ó Dálaigh (appt. December 1961; to Eur. Ct. of Jus. December 1972)

William O'Brien Fitzgerald (appt. 3.1.1973; died 17.10.1974)

Thomas Francis O'Higgins (appt. 23.10.1974; to Eur. Ct. Jus. 15.1.1985)

Thomas Aloysius Finlay (appt. 16.1.1985; ret. 16.9.1994)

Liam Hamilton (appt. 19.9.1994; ret. 28.1. 2000)

Ronan Colman Keane (appt. 31.1. 2000; ret. 22.7.2004)

John Loyola Murray (appt. 23.7.2004)

Supreme Court

Cecil Lavery (appt. 1950; ret. 5.10.1966)

Theodore Conyngham Kingsmill Moore (appt. 1951; ret. 1966)

Kevin O'Hanrahan Haugh (appt. 9.2.1961; died 5.4.1969)

Brian Walsh (appt. December 1961; ret. 23.3.1990)

Andreas O'Keeffe (appt. 1965; President of the High Court, October 1966)

Frederick Gardner Orford Budd (appt. 1966; ret. 18.12.1975)

William O'Brien FitzGerald (appt. 1966; prom. 3.1.1973)

Richard McLoughlin (appt. 30.4.1969; died 9.9.1972)

Seamus Henchy (appt. 2.10.1972; ret. 16.10.1988)

Frank Griffin (appt. 3.1.1973; ret. 11.3.1991)

John Kenny (appt. 21.10.1975; ret. 26.4.1982)

Weldon Roycroft Cecil Parke (appt. 16.1.1976; died 18.2.1981)

Anthony James Hederman (appt. 1.7.1981; ret. 31.7.1993)

Niall McCarthy (appt. 1.11.1982; died 1.10.1992)

Hugh James O'Flaherty (appt. 26.3.1990; res. 17.4.1999)

Seamus Francis Egan (appt. 22.4.1991; ret. 30.11.1995)

John Joseph Blayney (appt. 19.10.1992; ret. 12.3.1997)

Susan Gageby-Denham (appt. 14.12.1992)

Donal Peter Michael Barrington (appt. 12.1.1996; ret. 18.2. 2000)

Ronan Colman Keane (appt. 26.3.1996; appt. C.J. 31.1.2000)

Francis Dominick Murphy (appt. 26.3.1996; ret. 17.10.2002)

Kevin Lynch (appt. 26.3.1996; ret. 14.12.1999)

Henry Denis Barron (appt. 19.3.1997; ret. 24.5.2000)

John Loyola Murray (appt. 10.9.1999; prom. CJ 21.7.2004)

Catherine McGuinness (appt. 9.2. 2000)

Adrian Patrick Hardiman (appt. 9.2. 2000)

Hugh Geoghegan (appt. 13.3. 2000)

Nial Fennelly (appt. 16.10. 2000)

Brian McCracken (appt. 4.11. 2002)

Nicholas James Kearns (appt. 17.11.2004)

Fidelma Macken (appt. 27.6.2005)

President of the High Court

Cahir Davitt (appt. 1951; ret. August 1966)

Andreas O'Keeffe (appt. September 1966; to Eur. Ct. Jus. December 1974)

Thomas Aloysius Finlay (appt. 17.12.1974; became Chief Justice 16.1.1985)

Liam Hamilton (appt. 16.1.1985; became Chief Justice 19.9.1994)

Harold Anthony Whelehan (appt. 15.11.1994; res. 17.11.1994)

Declan David Costello (appt. 9.1.1995; res. 1.1.1998)

Frederick Reginald Morris (appt. 14.1.1998; ret. 1.12. 2001)

Joseph Gerald Finnegan (appt. 12.12. 2001)

The High Court

Frederick Gardner Orford Budd (appt. 1951; prom. 1966)

Richard McLoughlin (appt. 1952; prom. 30.4.1969)

George D. Murnaghan (appt. 1954; ret. 4.7.1979)

Thomas Teevan (appt. 1954; ret. 1971)

Brian Walsh (appt. 1959; prom. December 1961)

John Kenny (appt. 9.2.1961; prom. 21.10.1975)

Seamus Henchy (appt. 1962; prom. 2.10.1972)

Sean Butler (appt. October 1966; died 6.7.1980)

Denis Pringle (appt. 30.4.1969; ret. 15.5.1974)

Frank Griffin (appt. 11.10.1971; prom. 3.1.1973)

Thomas Aloysius Finlay (appt. 10.10.1972; President 17.12.1974)

John Mary Joseph Gannon (appt. 19.9.1973; ret. 4.12.1990)

Thomas Francis O'Higgins (appt. 12.12.1973; prom. CJ 23.10.1974)

Kenneth Edwin Lee Deale (appt. 8.5.1974; died 21.10.1974)

Liam Hamilton (appt. 23.10.1974; President 16.1.1985)

Weldon Roycroft Cecil Parke (appt. 29.10.1974; prom. 16.1.1976)

Thomas Aloysius Doyle (appt. 17.12.1974; ret. 13.6.1984)

James Gerrard McMahon (appt. 21.10.1975; ret. 5.1.1986)

Herbert Russell McWilliam (appt. 16.1.1976; ret. 12.2.1985)

Declan David Costello (appt. 20.5.1977; President 9.1.1995)

James Augustine D'Arcy (appt. 24.6.1977; ret. 5.1.1986)

Ronan Colman Keane (appt. 16.7.1979; prom. 26.3.1996)

William Roche Denny Ellis (appt. 1.10.1979; died 10.12.1983)

Donal Peter Michael Barrington (appt. 1.10.1979; to the European Court of Justice 31.8.1989)

Mella Elizabeth Laurie Carroll (appt. 6.10.1980)

Roderick Joseph O'Hanlon (appt. 20.3.1981; ret. 11.4.1995)

Edward Michael Walsh (appt. 18.12.1981; died 2.11.1982)

Henry Denis Barron (appt. 5.3.1982; prom. 19.3.1997)

Francis Dominick Murphy (appt. 5.3.1982; prom. 26.3.1996)

Kevin Lynch (appt. 24.1.1984; prom. 26.3.1996)

Seamus Francis Egan (appt. 13.12.1984; prom. 21.4.1991)

Robert Barr (appt. 30.1.1985; ret. 27.6.2002)

Gerard Joseph William Lardner (appt. 7.3.1985; ret. 31.7.1993)

John Joseph Blayney (appt. 20.1.1986; prom. 19.10.1992)

John James Patrick MacKenzie (appt. 10.2.1986; ret. 15.3.1991)

Richard Parnell Johnston (appt. 19.1.1987)

Vivian Lavan (appt. 20.9.1989)

Frederick Reginald Morris (appt. 22.12.1990; President 15.1.1998)

Susan Gageby-Denham (appt. 12.4.1991; prom. 14.12.1992)

Paul James Patrick Carney (appt. 30.4.1991)

Feargus Michael Flood (appt. 1.10.1991; ret. 7.7. 2000)

Declan Budd (appt. 1.10.1991)

Hugh Geoghegan (appt. 14.12. 1992; prom. 13.3.2000)

Dermot Kinlen (appt. 7.10.1993; ret. 23.4.2002)

Brian McCracken (appt. 27.1. 1995; prom. 4.11.2002)

Mary Laffoy (appt. 25.4.1995)

Michael Moriarty (appt. 26.3. 1996)

Peter Shanley (appt. 26.3.1996; died 7.9.1998)

Peter Kelly (appt. 26.3.1996)

Catherine McGuinness (appt. 9.7.1996; prom. 9.2.2000)

Thomas Clement Smyth (appt. 9.7.1996)

Diarmuid O'Donovan (appt. 19.7. 1996)

Philip O'Sullivan (appt. 22.4.1997)

Kevin Christopher O'Higgins (appt. 15.5.1997)

John Quirke (appt. 15.5.1997)

Matthew Patrick Smith (appt. 23.1.98; ret. 31.12.2004)

Cyril C. Kelly (appt. 30.11.1998; res. 20.4.1999)

Nicholas James Kearns (appt. 30.11.1998; prom. 17.11.2004)

Fidelma Macken (appt. 9.12.1998; res. (Eur. Ct.) 5.10.1999; re-appt., 18.10.2004; prom. 27.6.2005)
Séamus Iarfhlaith O'Neill (appt. 25.7.1999)
Aindrias Ó Caoimh (appt. 16.11.1999)
Joseph Gerald Finnegan (appt. 16.11.1999; President 12.12.2001)
Roderick Henry Murphy (appt. 10.2. 2000)
Daniel Nicholas Herbert (appt. 8.5. 2000)
Paul Butler (appt. 8.5. 2000)
Liam McKechnie (appt. 5.10. 2000)
Henry Abbott (appt. 28.2.2002)
[Michael Peart (a solicitor) (appt. 5.7.2002)]
Eamon de Valera (appt. 5.7.2002)
Mary Finlay Geoghegan (appt. 5.7. 2002)
Barry White (appt. 5.7.2002)
Paul Gilligan (appt. 28.1.2003)
Seán Ryan (appt. 15.12.2003)
Seán O'Leary (appt. 19.12.2003)
Fidelma Macken (re-appt. 18.10. 2004)

Elizabeth Dunne (appt. 18.11.2004)
Michael Hanna (appt. 18.11.2004)
John MacMenamin (appt. 18.11.2004)
Frank Clarke (appt. 18.11.2004)

Ex officio,
as President of the Circuit Court

George William Shannon (1947-1959)
Barra Ó Briain (1959-1973)
Charles Conroy (appt. 19.9.1973; ret. 1975)
John James Durcan (appt. 21.10.1975; ret. 1977)
Thomas Joseph Neylon (appt. 20.5.1977; ret. 31.1.1986)
Thomas Francis Roe (appt. 4.2.1986; ret. 18.5.1990)
Peter O'Malley (appt. 21.5.1990; ret. 10.6.1991)
Francis Robert Spain (appt. 1.7.1991; died 21.12.1997)
Diarmaid Sheridan (appt. 19.1.1998; ret. 11.3.1998)
Esmond Smyth (appt. 3.4.1998)
Matthew Deery (appt. 16.6.2005)

(iii) Holders of the office of Attorney-General

Hugh Kennedy, K.C. (appt. 1922; res. to become Chief Justice, 5.6.1924)
John O'Byrne, K.C. (appt. 1924; res. to become a judge, 9.1.1926)
John A. Costello, K.C. (appt. 9.1.1926; res. 1932)
Conor Alexander Maguire, K.C. (appt. 1932; res. (to be President of the High Court) 2.11.1936)
James Geoghegan, K.C. (appt. 2.11.1936; res. (to become a judge of the Supreme Court) 22.12.1936)
Patrick Lynch, K.C. (appt. 22.12.1936; res. 2.3.1940)
Kevin O'Hanrahan Haugh, S.C. (appt. 2.3.1940; judge, 1942)
Kevin Joseph Dixon, S.C. (1942-6)
Carroll O'Daly, S.C. (1946-8)
Cecil Lavery, S.C. (1948-50)
Charles Francis Casey, S.C. (1950-1)
Carroll O'Daly, S.C. (1951-3)
Thomas Teevan, S.C. (1953-4)
Andreas O'Keeffe, S.C. (1954)
Patrick McGilligan, S.C. (1955-7)
Andreas O'Keeffe, S.C., 20.3.1957-15.3.1965)
Colm Condon, S.C. (1965-19.5.1973)
Declan David Costello, S.C. (1973-77)

John Kelly, S.C. (appt. 19.5.1977; res. 5.7.1977)
Anthony J. Hederman, S.C. (appt. 5.7.1977; res. June 1981)
Peter D.W. Sutherland, S.C. (June 1981-March 1982)
Patrick J. Connolly, S.C. (March-August 1982)
John L. Murray, S.C. (August-December 1982)
Peter D.W. Sutherland, S.C (appt. December 1982; res. 12.12.1984)
John Rogers, S.C. (appt. 13.12.1984; res. 10.3.1987)
John L. Murray, S.C. (appt. 11.3.1987; res. 2.10 1991)
Harold Anthony Whelehan, S.C. (appt. October 1991; res. 11.11.1994)
Eoghan Fitzsimons, S.C. (appt. 11.11.1994; res. 15.12.1994)
Dermot Gleeson, S.C. (appt. 15.12.1994; ret. 26.6.1997)
David Byrne, S.C. (appt. 26.6. 1997; res. 16.7.1999)
Michael McDowell, S.C. (appt. 17.7.1999; res. 5.6.2002)
Rory Brady, S.C. (appt. 6.6.2002)

Recorders and County Court Judges

appointed since the coming into force on 1 January 1878 of the *County Officers and Courts (Ireland) Act, 1877* [40 & 41 Vict., c. 56]

Recorders

(being also County Court Judges for their respective counties)

I: Recorder of Dublin

County Court Judge: Hon. *Charles J. Trench* [T 1830]
Recorder: *Sir Frederick R. Falkiner* [M 1852], 8 July 1876-1905.
Thomas Lopdell O'Shaughnessy, 26 June 1905–1924

II: Recorder of Belfast and County Court Judge for Co. Antrim

John H. Otway, Q.C. [H 1832]
Henry Fitzgibbon, Q.C. [M 1848], 19 Nov. 1887
David Ross, Q.C., [M 1860], 1885
James Johnston Shaw, 1909-10
Robert McIlroy [d. 1911], 20 May 1910
J. Walker Craig, 1911-19
Charles Louis Matheson, 17 Sept. 1919-1921
Daniel Martin Wilson, 1921
Herbert Marshall Thompson, 1921-41
Arthur Black, K.C., 1942-43
John Desmond Chambers, K.C. 1943-44
Bernard Joshua Fox, K.C.,1945-

William Beattie, John Leech, and M.D. Begley sat as acting Recorders or in the Ballymena Division.

III: Recorder of Cork and County Court Judge for the East Riding of County Cork

Daniel Ryan Kane, Q.C. [H 1825]
James P. Hamilton, Q.C. [H 1844], 1885
Matthew Bourke, K.C., 18 April 1908-1924

IV: Recorder of Londonderry

James Charles Coffey, Q.C. [T 1843]
J.F. Elrington, Q.C. [M 1847], 1880-
Sir *John C. Neligan* [T 1840], 1885
Thomas George Overend, 23 July 1892
Andrew Todd, K.C., 1912
Robert Ernest Osborne, K.C., 10 Aug. 1919-
John Clarke Davison, K.C. 1938-1946
Martin G. Ellison. K.C. 1947
Isaac Copeland, K.C., 1947-

V: Recorder of Galway

Richard Dudley Persse [E 1858]
Thomas Rice Henn, Q.C. [T 1839]
William Anderson [T 1855], 29 Dec. 1898]
Robert J. Doyle, K.C., 24 Nov. 1913-1924

Italic type is here used to distinguish Recorders and County Court Judges called to the Bar prior to 1868. Elsewhere and generally in the volume italic type signifies the names of women.

A NOTE ON THE HISTORY OF THE COUNTY COURTS

In 1787 [by 27 Geo. III (Ir.), c. 40] 'Assistant Barristers' were first appointed to sit with and advise magistrates. Nine years later, by 36 Geo. III (Ir.), c. 25, Assistant Barristers were given jurisdiction, in their own right, to hear proceedings commenced by Civil Bill in suits worth less than £20. Since the reign of Queen Anne, if not earlier, small claims instituted by Civil Bill [the 'Bill' being a simplified form of pleading in *English*, distinct from the Latin writ; 'Civil' to distinguish the document from the criminal Bill of Indictment] had been heard by the judges of assize; and procedure by Civil Bill had also been authorised, at an inferior level, in municipal jurisdictions, and in County Dublin: see 2 Geo. I (Ir.), c. 11, s. 13; 19 & 20 Geo. III (Ir.) c. 26). The system of Civil Bill courts established in 1796 was novel in representing a general delegation of the jurisdiction. The arrangements made in 1796 were amplified and amended in 1836 [6 & 7 Wm. IV, c. 75], in 1851 [14 & 15 Vict., c. 57] and again in 1877 [40 & 41 Vict. c., 56].

After the passing of the 1851 Act, section 2 of which provided that an Assistant Barrister 'shall by virtue of his Office be and preside as Chairman of the Justices at General or Quarter Sessions', the term 'Assistant Barrister' gradually yielded to the title of 'Chairman', a form that had hitherto been peculiar to the barrister who presided in the Court for County Dublin which sat at Kilmainham. The form 'County Court judge', used in England since 1846, was new in Ireland when introduced by s. 3 of the Act of 1877.

Section 85 of the 1877 Act provided that 'the number of chairmen (including the recorders) shall, so soon as practicable, be reduced to twenty-one ...' . The number of such appointments had latterly been twice as great. Each of the 32 counties had a chairman; Cork, with its East and West Ridings, had two; and Recorders sat in ten ancient municipal jurisdictions (including, in addition to the five which survived the 1877 Act, Carrickfergus, Drogheda, Kilkenny, Limerick and Waterford).

When first established, the office of Assistant Barrister had not been a full-time position. Section 92 of the 1877 Act, which provided that 'no person who after the passing of this Act shall be appointed chairman of any county or of any permanent union of counties shall practise at the bar ...,' is thus a milestone in the evolution of a full-time judiciary at a level intermediate between the superior courts and the magistracy. Sections 85 and 86 prescribed the salaries for those appointed: £2,500 for the Recorder of Dublin, £2,000 for the Recorders of Cork and Belfast, and £1,500 for the Recorders of Londonderry and Galway. Other County Court judges received £1,400. The differential in favour of the municipal appointments may explain why the Recorders' posts were often filled by judges who had been serving in other counties.

THE GROUPING OF COUNTIES

The scheme for grouping the counties was set out in Schedule E of the 1877 Act, and took effect, with one variation (made by an Order in Council, for which there was provision in s. 85), when Leitrim was united, not with Fermanagh, as the draughtsman had envisaged, but with Cavan. In consequence Monaghan was united with Fermanagh rather than with Cavan.

In 1921 the Judges for Monaghan and Fermanagh (William Johnston) and Armagh and Louth (G.C. Greene), exchanged a county so that their jurisdictions would not straddle the Border. Johnston parted to Greene with Fermanagh and got Louth in exchange. After Partition Judge Greene continued to reside in Dublin, and to travel from there to dispense justice in the N.I. counties of Armagh and Fermanagh.

The grouping of counties made under the 1877 Act was a precedent for, and may be compared with, the organisation of the Circuit Court established in 1924, when the sixteen County Court jurisdictions in the territory of the Irish Free State were reduced to eight Circuits. The schemes of 1877 and 1924 both effected a halving in the number of appointments; and under both the greatest grouping of jurisdictions was in the sparsely-populated counties of the midlands and east.

County Court Judges

VI: Donegal

James Gibson, Q.C. [T 1828]
Robert Carson, Q.C. [M 1850], 1880-
Thomas E. Webb, Q.C., [H 1861], 27 Dec. 1887
John Cooke, K.C., 7 Nov. 1903

VII: Monaghan and Fermanagh
[*1921- Monaghan and Louth*]

Monaghan: *William N. Barron* [M 1830]
Fermanagh: *Patrick Joseph Blake* [T 1837]; *J. Chute Neligan*, 1885

James Orr] [M 1867], 13 June 1891
J. Walker Craig, 18 March 1897
William Johnston, 15 Nov. 1911

VIII: Armagh and Louth
[1921-, Armagh and Fermanagh]

Armagh: *Thomas Lefroy,* Q.C. [M 1831], 1878; *William O'Connor Morris,* Q.C., [H 1854],1880
Louth: *William O'Connor Morris,* Q.C.

R.W. Gamble, Q.C [M 1851], 1885
W.H. Kisbey [T 1866], 21 April 1887
George Comerford Greene, K.C., 25 Sept. 1909 - 1940
Martin G. Ellison, K.C., 1941-2
John Hanna Robb, 1943-

IX: Tyrone
Sir F.W. Brady, Bart., K.C. [M 1846], 28 Dec. 1861
Andrew Todd, 4 Sept. 1909
John Linehan, 12 Sept. 1912-35?
Edward John McKean, K.C., acting 1937?
George Boyle Hanna, 1937-8
John McGonigal, 1939-43
Charles Leo Sheil, 1943-5
Thomas Joseph Campbell, 1945-6
Isaac Copeland, K.C, 1946-7
William Johnson, 1947-

X: Cavan and Leitrim

Cavan: vacant in 1878; aft. *Samuel McCurdy Greer* [E 1835]; *William F. Darley*, Q.C [M. 1830]
Leitrim: *S.M. Greer*

George Waters [T 1849], 1885
Michael Drummond, K.C., 1904-14
William H. Brown, K.C., 20 Feb. 1914

XI: Down

Robert Johnston, Q.C. [E 1829]
Thomas Lefroy, Q.C. [M 1831], 1880-
John Roche, 1894-96
James Orr [M 1867], 1897
Arthur Henry Bates, K.C., 20 Sept. 1919-39
Marcus Dill Begley, 1939-
Brian Maginess, 1964-7

XII: Mayo

John Henry Richards [M 1839]
Richard Martin Dane, 30 Sept. 1898
Edward Morphy, 7 April 1903
Charles F. Doyle, K.C., 7 Nov. 1910-1924

XIII: Roscommon and Sligo

Roscommon: *Arthur Hamill,* Q.C. [H 1853]
Sligo: *James P. Hamilton,* Q.C. [H 1844]

Arthur Hamill Q.C., 1885
William O'Connor Morris, Q.C. 15 June 1872
John Wakely, 13 Sept. 1904

XIV: Carlow, Kildare, Wicklow, Wexford

Carlow: *William Frederick Darley,* Q.C. [M. 1830]; *James A. Wall,* Q.C. [T 1827)
Kildare: *Robert Carson,* Q.C. [M 1850]
Wicklow: *William F. Darley*, Q.C.; *James A. Wall*, Q.C.
Wexford: *Henry West*, Q.C. [H 1833]

Robert Romney Kane, LL.D. [M 1865], 5 Aug. 1892
Ralph Westropp Brereton Barry, 1 April 1902
Charles Dromgoole, 1920-1924

XV: King's County, Longford, Meath and Westmeath

King's County: *Hewitt P. Jellett,* Q.C. [H 1847], 1878
Longford: *Charles Kelly* [M 1839]
Meath: *Echlin Molyneux,* Q.C. [T 1826]
Westmeath: *J.F. Elrington,* Q.C. [M 1847]

John C. Neligan, Q.C., [T 1849], 1880
Hon. Gerald FitzGerald, 1886-90
John Adye Curran [E 1860], 22 Sept. 1883
Michael Drummond, 1914-24
Patrick David Fleming, 11 March 1918-24

XVI: Queen's County, Kilkenny, Waterford

Queen's: *Joshua Clarke,* Q.C. [E 1836]
Kilkenny: *Thomas De Moleyns,* Q.C. [H 1831]
Waterford*: George Waters,* Q.C. [T 1849]

Hon. David Fitzgerald, 5 Aug. 1892
Daniel O'Brien, 19 Jan. 1920-1924

XVII: Tipperary

Charles Rolleston-Spunner, Q.C. [T 1833], 1878
James A. Wall, Q.C. [T 1827], 1880
Hugh Hamilton Moore, 29 Nov. 1898 (d. 1921)

XVIII: Clare

John O'Hagan, Q.C. [T 1845]
Charles Kelly, Q.C., [M 1839], 1880
Richard Paul Carton, Q.C. [T 1863], 29 Dec. 1898 (d. 24 Feb. 1907)
Matthias Bodkin, 7 Nov. 1907 - 1924

XIX: Cork West Riding
Robert Ferguson, Q.C. [M 1839]
William Seymour Bird, Q.C., 27 Feb. 1892
John William Hynes, 21 Sept. 1915

XX: Limerick

Theobald Andrew Purcell, Q.C. [H 1840]
Richard Adams, 9 March 1894
Philip Henry Law Smith, 11 May 1908
John Henry Pigot, 19 Jan. 1920-1924.

XXI: Kerry

Charles H. Hemphill, Q.C. [M 1845]
George Waters, Q.C. [T 1849], 1880
John Adye Curran [E 1860], 22 Sept. 1883
William O'Connor Morris [H 1854], 1885
James Johnston Shaw, 9 Dec. 1891
Daniel Francis Browne, 2 Dec. 1909
Charles Dromgoole, 28 Feb. 1913
John Cusack, 9 April 1920-1924

Judges of the Circuit Court since 1924

1 Dublin

1924-27	Charles Dromgoole
1927-45	Cathar Davitt
1938-59	William G. Shannon (2nd judge)
1945-55	J.A. McCarthy
1955-75	John Charles Conroy
1959-63	Michael Binchy
1963-74	J.S. McGivern
1974-86	Noel Ryan
1975-77	J.J. Durcan
1977-86	T.J. Neylon
1977-89	Gerard Clarke (3rd judge)
1977-93	Frank Martin (4th judge)
1980-96	Gerard Buchanan (5th judge)
1980-86	John Gleeson (6th judge)
1982-92	Seán O'Hanrahan (7th judge)
1984-03	Dominic Lynch (8th judge)
1985-90	M. Patrick Smith
1987-97	James Carroll
1989-01	Kieran O'Connor
1990-92	Peter O'Malley
1990-97	Frank Spain
1991-96	Michael Moriarty
1991-01	Kieran O'Connor
1992-02	Liam Devally
1996	Esmond Smyth
1996	Kevin Haugh
1996	*Alison Lindsay*
1996	*Elizabeth Dunne*
1998-98	Diarmuid Sheridan
1998	Frank O'Donnell
1999-01	John Buckley
2001-	*Jacqueline Linnane*
2001-	*Yvonne Murphy*
2002-	Joseph Matthews
2002 -	*Katherine Delahunt*
2003-	Patrick John McCartan

[from 1996 10 Dublin judges]

2 Cork

1924-5	Henry Daniel Conner
1925-32	Matthew Kenny
1932-47	Joseph K. O'Connor
1947-50	Art O'Connor
1950-55	John Charles Conroy
1955-77	Thomas J. Neylon
1977-88	Seán MacD. Fawsitt
1986-01	Anthony Murphy (2nd judge)
1991-	Patrick Moran
1996-99	John Buckley (3rd judge)
1999-02	Dermot Clifford [Solr.]
2001-	Brian Curtin

2002-	Seán O'Donovan

3 Northern

1924-8	St. Lawrence Ernest Joseph Devitt
1928-37	Eugene Sheehy

North-Eastern Circuit

1938-55	Eugene Sheehy
1955-56	Kenneth Deale
1956-59	[Michael] John Sweeny

North-Western Circuit

1938-44	George A. Moonan
1944-59	Fionán Lynch

(re-united) Northern Circuit

1959-74	Patrick Noel Ryan
1974-76	Herbert McWilliam
1976-94	David Sheehy
1994-05	Matthew Deery

4 Western

1924-50	Charles S. [Wyse] Power
1950-75	John James Durcan
1975-6	Stephen Barrett
1976-7	Frank Martin
1977-87	John Grattan Esmonde
1987-95	John B. Cassidy
1995-	Harvey Kenny

5 Midland

1924-31	John Wakley
1931-50	William J. Gleeson
1950-59	Michael Binchy
1959-66	John Sweeney
1966-74	Conor Maguire
1974-88	Peter O'Malley
1988-89	Kevin O'Higgins
1989-94	Matthew Deery
1994-95	Harvey Kenny
1995-96	Seán O'Leary
1996-	Anthony Kennedy

6 Eastern

1924-28	Charles Francis Doyle
1928-36	St. Lawrence E.J. Devitt
1936-43	Michael Comyn
1943-56	Diarmaid Fawsitt
1956-73	Kenneth E.L. Deale
1973-90	Thos. Francis [Frank] Roe
1990-98	M. Patrick Smith
1999-	Raymond Groarke

THE CIRCUIT COURT, AS CONSTITUTED ON 6 AUGUST 1924

[Courts of Justice Act, 1924 (No. 10)]

County	Name of Circuit and Judge	Population
1. Dublin City and County	*Dublin* Charles Dromgoole	476,000
2. Cork City and County	*Cork* Henry Daniel Conner	392,000
3. Donegal Leitrim Cavan Monaghan	*Northern* St. Lawrence Devitt	394,000
4. Mayo Galway	*Western* Charles S. Wyse Power	374,000
5. Sligo Roscommon Westmeath Leix Offaly Longford	*Midland* John Wakley	388,000
6. Louth Meath Kildare Wicklow Wexford	*Eastern* Charles Francis Doyle	358,000
7. Kerry Limerick Clare	*South-Western* Edward J. McElligott	406,000
8. Tipperary Kilkenny Waterford Carlow	*Southern* (1938-: *South Eastern*) James Sealy	348,000

Summary of principal alterations in the constitution of the Circuit Court
Increase to nine circuits by the division, with effect from 1 Jan. 1938, of the Northern into the North-Eastern and North-Western Circuits: Circuit Court (New Circuits) Order): S.I. No. 309 of 1937, and 1936, No. 48, s. 13; creation of the office of President of the Circuit Court: 1947, No. 20, ss 9, 10; power to alter the composition of circuits, ibid., s. 13; power to return to eight circuits, and to nine judges, 1953 No. 32, ss. 16, 17 applied with effect from 11April 1960 by S.I. No. 70 of 1960. Circuit Court (New Circuits) Order, 1960; reduction to eight (transitionally nine) ordinary judges: 1961, No. 39, s.16; increase to nine ordinary judges, and power to rename and regroup circuits: 1964, No. 11, s. 3 (1), with orders made thereunder, as follows: S.I. 206 of 1964, effective on 15 Sept. 1964, Sligo transferred from the Northern to the Midland Circuit; and Laois from the Midland Circuit to the South-Eastern; S.I. No. 201 of 1969, effective on 1 Jan. 1970, Wexford transferred from the Eastern to the South-Eastern Circuit; S.I. No. 327 of 1978, effective on 1 Jan. 1979, Laois transferred from the South-Eastern Circuit to the Midland Circuit.

Increase in the number of judges
Two additional judges: 1928 No. 15, s. 9; power to appoint temporary judges: 1936 No. 48, ss. 14-16; exceptional appointment of one additional judge: 1947 No. 20, s. 14; increase to 11 judges (4 in Dublin): 1977 No. 11, ss 1, 2; to 12 judges (5 in Dublin): 1981 No. 11, s. 30; to 15 judges (6 in Dublin): 1985 No. 23, s. 2; to 17 ordinary judges (8 in Dublin and 2 in Cork): 1991 No. 20, s. 18; to 24 ordinary judges plus the President of the District Court *ex officio* (10 judges permanently in Dublin and 3 in Cork): 1995 No. 31, s. 10; to 27 ordinary judges: 1996 No. 26, s. 1; to 30 ordinary judges: 2002 No. 15, s. 26; to 33 ordinary judges: 2004, No. 31, s. 56.

Bench of the Circuit Court on 1 January 1938 [S.I. No. 309 of 1937]

Cahir Davitt *Dublin Circuit*
William G. Shannon *Dublin.Circuit*
Joseph K. O'Connor *Cork Circuit*
Eugene Sheehy *North Eastern Circuit*
George A. Moonan *North Western Circuit*
Charles Stewart Power *Western Circuit*
William J. Gleeson *Midland Circuit*
Michael Comyn *Eastern Circuit*
Edward J. McElligott *South-Western Circuit*
James Sealy *South-Eastern Circuit*

The Bench on 11 April 1960 [S.I. No. 70 of 1960]

Barra Ó Brian *South Western Circuit* and President
John Charles Conroy *Dublin Circuit*
Michael Binchy *Dublin Circuit*
Thomas J. Neylon *Cork Circuit*
Kenneth E.L. Deale *Eastern Circuit*
Patrick Noel Ryan *Northern Circuit*
John James Durcan *Western Circuit*
John Sweeney *Midland Circuit*
Diarmaid Fawsitt *South Eastern Circuit*

7 South-Western

1924-41	Edward John McElligott
194-431	Thomas O'Donnell
1943-74	Barra Ó Briain
1974-77	Herbert Wellwood
1977-86	Timothy Desmond
1986-88	John Gleeson
1988-97	Kevin O'Higgins
1998-03	Seán O'Leary
2004-	Carroll Moran

8 Southern
(from 1938, **South-Eastern**)

1924-48	James Sealy
1948-57	Patrick J. Roe
1957-74	Seán MacDairmaid Fawsitt
1974-80	Herbert Wellwood (sharing in 1979-80 with Sheridan)
1979-96	Diarmuid Sheridan
1996-97	Seán O'Leary
1997	*Olive Buttimer*

Permanent unassigned Judges

1947	Martin J. Connolly		1999-	John O'Hagan
1964-6	Conor P.J. Maguire		1999-	Bryan McMahon [Solr.]
1966-73	Herbert Wellwood		2001-03	Seán O'Donovan
1973-5	Stephen Declan Barrett		2001-	Desmond Hogan
1975-7	Gerard Clarke		2001-	Michael O'Shea
1977-8	John W. O'Connor		2002-02	*Katherine Delahunt* [Solr.]
1978-80	Gerard Buchanan		2002-	Alan Mahon
1986-88	Kevin Chris. O'Higgins		2002-	Mary Faherty
1992 5	Esmond Smyth		2002-	Gerald Keys
1992-8	Cyril Kelly		2002-	*Patricia Ryan*
1995-6	*Catherine McGuinness*		2002-	*Miriam Reynolds-Buckley*
1996-9	Raymond Groarke		2002-	James O'Donoghue [Solr.]
1996-8	Frank O'Donnell [Solr.]		2004-	*Alice Doyle*
1996-	Michael White [Solr.]		2004-	*Doirbhile Flanagan*
1996-03-	Patrick McCartan [Solr.]		2004-	Donagh McDonagh
1996-03	Joseph Matthews		2004-	Con Murphy [Solr.]
1998-01	*Jacqueline Linnane*		2004-	Terence O'Sullivan
1998-04	Carroll Moran			

Temporary Assistant Circuit Judges
(for 3 years and 9 months from 12 April 1924:Courts Act, 1924, s. 46; Courts Act, 1927)
1925-28 John H. Pigot (attached to Dublin Circuit)
1925-31 Bernard Roche (attached to Midland Circuit)

Additional Judges of the Circuit Court
(Courts of Justice Act, 1928, s. 9)
1928-31 Bernard Roche
(attached to the Midland Circuit)
1928-37 William G. Shannon
1932-37 George A. Moonan

Temporary Additional Circuit Judges
(Courts of Justice Act, 1929)

1930-1 William J. Gleeson
1931-2 George A. Moonan
1933-6 William Black
c. 1942 Patrick McEnery

1972-4 Peter O'Malley
1974-5 David Sheehy

1974-5 Gerard Clarke
1975-6 Frank Martin
1975-7 James D'Arcy
1976-7- Kieran O'Connor
1978-80 John Gleeson

Presidents of the Circuit Court
(Courts Act 1947 [No. 20], ss 9, 10)

1947-59 George William Shannon
1959-73 Barra Ó Briain
1973-5 Charles Conroy
1975-7 John James Durcan
1977-86 Thomas Joseph Neylon
1986-90 Thomas Francis Roe
1990-91 Peter O'Malley
1991-7 Francis Robert Spain
1998-8 Diarmuid Sheridan
1998-05 Esmond Smyth
2005- Matthew Deery
[sworn, 16 June 2005]

President of the District Court
(ex officio: 1995 [No. 31], s. 33)
1995-05 Peter Swithwick [Solr.]
2005- *Miriam Malone*
[sworn, 15 June 2005]

King's Inns-educated Judges and Law Officers in Northern Ireland and England

Lord Chief Justice of Northern Ireland
Sir Denis Henry, *Bart.* (appt. 15 Aug. 1921; d. 1 Oct. 1925)
Sir William Murphy Moore, *Bart.* (appt. 2 Nov. 1925; ret. 30 Nov. 1937)
Sir James Andrews, *Bart.* (appt. 1 Dec. 1937; d. 18 Feb. 1951)
John Clarke MacDermott, Baron MacDermott (appt. 6 April 1951; ret. 31 July 1971)

Lord Justices of Appeal
William Murphy Moore (appt. 17 Oct. 1921; ret. 1 Nov. 1925 [prom. L.C.J.])
James Andrews (appt. 17 Oct. 1921; ret. 30 Nov. 1937 [prom. L.C.J.])
Richard Best (appt. 5 Nov. 1925; ret. 23 Feb. 1939)
Anthony Brutus Babington (appt. 2 Dec. 1937; res. 26 Feb. 1949)
Edward Sullivan Murphy (appt. 13 April 1939; d. 3 Dec. 1945)
Samuel Clarke Porter (appt. 15 March 1946; d. 10 July 1956)
Arthur Black (appt. 3 March 1949; ret. 31 Aug. 1964)
Lancelot Ernest Curran (appt. 1 Oct. 1956; ret. 31 Aug. 1975)

Judges of the Chancery Division
Daniel Martin Wilson (appt. 17 Oct. 1921; d. 5 Jan. 1932)
Robert Dick Megaw (appt. 12 Feb. 1932; res. 6 Nov. 1943)
Arthur Black (appt. 20 Nov. 1943; res. 2 March 1949)
Lancelot Ernest Curran (appt. 4 Nov. 1949; res. 27 Sept. 1956)

Judges of the King's Bench Division (other than the Lord Chief Justice)
William Murphy Moore (judge since 1917)
Thomas Watters Brown (appt. 8 Feb. 1922; d. 7 Oct. 1944)
John Clarke MacDermott (appt. 2 Nov. 1944; res. on appointment as Lord of Appeal in Ordinary, 23 April 1947)

William Lowry (appt. 5 June 1947; res. 11 Oct. 1949)

Judge of the Queen's Bench Division
Charles Leo Sheil (appt. 3 March 1949; died 5 Sept. 1968)

Judicial Commissioner, Land Purchase Commission
Robert Dick Megaw

Attorney-General (N.I.)
Brown, Thomas Watters (formerly Attorney-General for Ireland)
Best, Richard (Feb. 1922-Nov. 1925)
Babington, Anthony Brutus (appt. 24 Nov. 1925; res. 2 Dec. 1937)
Murphy, Edward Sullivan (appt. 3 Dec. 1937; ret. 13 April 1939) (M.P., 1929-39)
Black, Arthur (appt. April 1939; res. 20 Nov. 1943) (M.P., 1925-41)
MacDermott, John Clarke (appt. 1942; res. 2 Nov. 1944) (M.P., 1938-44)
Lowry, William (appt. 3 Nov. 1944; res. 5 June 1947) (M.P. 1939-47)
Curran, Lancelot Ernest (appt. 6 June 1947; res. 1 Oct. 1956) (M.P., 1945-49)
Warnock, John Edmond (appt. 9 Nov. 1949; res. 10 April 1956) (M.P., 1938-69)
Maginnis, William Brian (appt. 14 April 1956; res. 20 March 1964) (1901-1967) (M.P., 1938-64)

Judges in England

Lord Carson of Duncairn, Attorney-General [for England and Wales], 1915-16, and Lord of Appeal in Ordinary, 24 May 1921 - October 1929

Lord MacDermott of Belmont, Lord of Appeal in Ordinary, 23 April 1947 - April 1951

Sir James Comyn, Judge of the High Court, 1977-85.

Peerages and Baronetcies
conferred on judges and law officers

Two hereditary peerages (Shandon and Glenavy), two life peerages (Carson and MacDermott), and eight* baronetcies were the lot of those called to the Irish Bar after 1868. Scions of the families of Irish judicial peers of earlier generations (e.g. O'Grady, Gibson and Hemphill) also appear in these pages.**

* The total of eight includes Sir Ignatius O'Brien and Sir James Campbell, who were created baronets before they became peers as Shandon and Glenavy respectively. The other six were Barton, Ross and Molony from the Dublin Bench, and Henry, Moore and Andrews, successive Lords Chief Justice in Belfast.

** The 9th Viscount Midleton, leader of the Southern Unionists, a descendant of the first of the peers noted below, was prominent in public life in the early twentieth century, though not a barrister.

Judicial knighthoods

Knighthoods awarded for colonial judicial service were numerous. At home the honour was bestowed on two Recorders of Dublin [Sir Frederick Falkiner and Sir Thomas O'Shaughnessy], and on one other Recorder [Sir John Chute Neligan]: but there appear to be just two instances (Sir Edmund Thomas Bewley and Sir James O'Connor, after their retirement, in 1898 and 1925 respectively) of knighthoods conferred on judges of the higher courts.

These meagre statistics illustrate a principle. In Ireland knighthood was not, as it was and remains in England, the automatic expectation of a High Court judge.† The custom in Ireland – and a practice preferred by the Irish judiciary when consulted about the question in 1892 – was to dignify High Court judges by swearing them of the Privy Council, a rank which allowed them to be styled 'Right Honourable'. See *I.L.T. & S.J.*, xxv (1891), 99, 'The custom of knighting judges'; and *ibid.*, xxvii (1893), 148, 'Points of difference between the English and the Irish Bench and Bar': but for a theory linked to the precedence of judges' wives, see also *ibid.*, xxxvi (1906), 146-7.

† The knighting of the High Court judges in Northern Ireland, which began in 1988 when Lord Mayhew was Attorney-General, was novel, and represents the introduction to Northern Ireland of the English practice.

Judicial peerages and baronetcies since the eighteenth century
Titles which are extant are identified in bold type

Alan Brodrick, Baron Brodrick of Midleton, 13 Apr. 1715; Viscount **Midleton**, 15 Aug. 1717.

Thomas Wyndham, Baron Wyndham of Finglass, 18 Sept. 1731. Extinct on his death, 24 Nov. 1745.

Robert Jocelyn [H 1718], Baron Newport, 29 Nov. 1743; Viscount Jocelyn, 6 Dec. 1755. [The 2nd Viscount became Earl of **Roden**, 1 Dec. 1771].

John Bowes [M 1725], Baron Bowes of Clonlyon, Co. Meath, 1758. Extinct on his death, July 1767.

John Gore [M 1742], Baron Annaly of Tenelick, 17 Jan. 1766. Extinct on his death, 26 Nov. 1747.

James Dennis [M 1746], Baron Tracton of Tracton Abbey, Co. Cork, 1781. Barony extinct on his death, 1782.

James Hewitt, Baron Lifford, 9 Jan. 1768; Viscount **Lifford**, 8 Jan. 1781.

John Scott [E 1765], Baron Earlsfort, 10 May 1784; Viscount Clonmell, 18 Aug. 1789; Earl, 20 Dec. 1793. Extinct on the death of the 8th Earl, 16 Jan. 1935.

Hugh Carleton [T 1764], Baron Carleton of Anner, Co. Tipperary, 1789; Viscount Carleton of Clare, 1797. Extinct on his death, 25 Feb. 1826.

John Fitzgibbon [T 1772], Baron
Clare, 16 June 1789; Viscount
Fitzgibbon of Limerick, 20 Dec.
1793; and Earl of Clare, 10 June
1795. Extinct on the death of the 3rd
Earl, 10 Jan. 1864, the latter's only
son having died in the Charge of the
Light Brigade at Balaklava, 25 Oct.
1854.

Barry Yelverton [T 1764], Baron
Avonmore, 1795 [Viscount 1800].
Extinct or dormant on death of the
6th Viscount, 3 Sept. 1910.

Arthur Wolfe [M 1766], Baron
Kilwarden of Newlands, 1798;
Viscount Kilwarden, 1802. Extinct
on death of the 2nd Viscount, 16
May 1830.

John Toler [M 1770], Baron Norbury,
27 Dec. 1800; Viscount Glandine
and Earl of Norbury, 23 June 1827.

John Mitford, Baron Redesdale, 1802

Thomas Manners-Sutton, Baron
Manners, of Foston, Co. Lincoln,
20 April 1807.

William Conyngham Plunket [H
1787], Baron Plunket, of Newton,
Co. Cork, 1 May 1827.

Standish O'Grady [E 1787], Baron
O'Grady and Viscount Guillamore,
28 Jan. 1831. Extinct on death of the
9th Viscount, Oct. 1955.

John Campbell, Baron Campbell of
St. Andrews, 30 June 1841
[continues under the style
Stratheden and Campbell].

Thomas O'Hagan [H 1836], Baron
O'Hagan of Tullahogue, Co.
Tyrone, 14 June 1870.

Edward Gibson [H 1860], Baron
Ashbourne, 4 July 1885.

Sir Michael Morris [T 1849], Baron
Morris (life peerage, 1889) and
Killanin (hereditary) 15 June 1900.

David Robert Plunket [H 1862], Baron
Rathmore of Shanganagh, 14 Nov.
1895. Extinct on his death
unmarried, 22 Aug. 1919.

Sir Peter O'Brien, Baron O'Brien of
Kilfenora, 1900. Extinct on his
death, 7 Sept. 1914.

Charles Hare Hemphill [M 1845],
Baron Hemphill of Rathkenny and
of Cashel, 12 Jan. 1906.

Sir Ignatius John O'Brien, Baron
Shandon, 1918. Extinct on his death,
1930.

Sir James Henry Mussen Campbell,
Baron Glenavy, of Milltown, Co.
Dublin, 1921. Extinct on death of 4th
Baron, 1984.

Baronetcies

Sir Standish Hartstonge of Bruff,
1681. Baronetcy extinct in 1797;
female descent through the family of
Pery, Earls of Limerick.

Sir Richard Levinge, 26 Oct. 1704.

Sir Gilbert Dolben [T 1701], 1 April
1704. Extinct on death of 4th
Baronet, 27 Sept. 1837.

Sir Richard Cox [M 1674], of
Dunmanway, 21 Nov. 1706. Extinct
on death of 12th Baronet in 1873.

Sir Michael Smith [H 1769], 1799.
The 2nd Baronet died in 1866
leaving a grandson as heir
presumptive to the baronetcy.

Sir William MacMahon [T 1799], 6
May 1814. Extinct on death of the
4th Baronet in 1926.

Sir Michael O'Loghlen [M 1811], of
Drumconora, Ennis, 16 July 1838.

Sir Joseph Napier [E 1831], of
Merrion Square, 9 April 1867.

Sir Maziere Brady [M 1819], of
Hazlebrook, Co. Dublin, 1869.
Extinct on death of the 4th Baronet,
1927.

Sir Edward Sullivan [M 1844], of
Garryduff, Co. Cork, Dec. 1881.
Extinct with the 3rd Baronet, 1937.

Sir Michael Morris [T 1849], 14 Sept.
1885. Continues with the barony of
Killanin.

Sir Peter O'Brien [M 1860], 1891.
Subsequently a peer, 1900.
Baronetcy and peerage extinct with
his death, 1914.

Sir Andrew Marshall Porter [T 1860]
of Merrion Square, City and County
of Dublin, 22 July 1902. The
baronetcy continues under the style
Horsbrugh-Porter.

Sir Samuel Walker [E 1855], of
Pembroke House, City of Dublin, 12
July 1906.

Sir William Moore Johnson [M 1853],
1909. Extinct on his death, 1918.

Sir Walter Boyd [E 1856], of Howth
House, Howth, Co. Dublin, 29 June
1916.

Sir Ignatius John O'Brien [E 1881], 1916. Subsequently a peer. Peerage and baronetcy extinct on his death, 1930.

Sir James Henry Mussen Campbell [E 1878], 1916. Subsequently a peer, 1921. Peerage and baronetcy extinct on death of 4th Baron Glenavy, 1984.

Sir Dunbar Plunket Barton [H 1880], 1918. Extinct on his death, 1937.

Sir John Ross [M 1879], of Dumoyle, Parish of Errigal, Keerogue, Co. Tyrone, 1919. Extinct with the death of the 2nd Baronet, 1958.

Sir Thomas Francis **Molony** [M 1877], of the City of Dublin, 21 Jan. 1925.

Sir Denis **Henry** [E 1885], of Cahore, Co. Londonderry, 26 Feb. 1923.

Sir William **Moore** [M 1887], of Moore Lodge, Co. Antrim, 20 June 1932.

Sir James Andrews [M 1900], of Comber, Co. Down, 1942. Extinct on his death, 1951.

**Life peerages conferred on
Lords of Appeal in Ordinary**

John David Fitzgerald, Baron Fitzgerald [E 1838], 1882-1889.

Sir Michael Morris [T 1849], Baron Morris (life peerage, 1889-1901) and Killanin (hereditary).

John Atkinson [M 1865], Baron Atkinson, 1905-1932.

Sir Edward Carson [knighted, 1900], Baron Carson of Duncairn, 1921-1935.

John Clarke MacDermott, Baron MacDermott of Belmont, 1947-1979.

The most recent edition of *Burke's Peerage** indicates that the Irish judicial honours are continued in twenty families by persons bearing the following titles:

The 12th Viscount Midleton of Midleton
The 10th Earl of Roden, of High Roding, Co. Tipperary
The 9th Viscount Lifford
The 7th Earl of Norbury, Viscount Glandine, of Glandine, King's County
The 6th Baron Redesdale of Redesdale, Northumberland
The 5th Baron Manners of Foston, Co. Lincoln
The 8th Baron Plunket of Newton, Co. Cork
The 6th Baron Stratheden of Cupar and Campbell of St. Andrews
The 4th Baron O'Hagan of Tullahogue, Co. Tyrone
The 4th Baron Ashbourne of Ashbourne, Co. Meath
The 5th Baron Hemphill of Rathkenny and Cashel, Co. Tipperary
The 4th Baron Killanin of Galway, Co. Galway
Sir Richard Levinge, 12th Bart., of High Park, Co. Westmeath
Sir Charles Joseph Napier, 6th Bart., of Merrion Square, Dublin
Sir John Simon Horsbrugh-Porter, 4th Bart., of Merrion Square, City and
    County of Dublin
Sir Hugh Ronald Walker, 4th Bart., of Pembroke House, Dublin
Sir Alexander Walter Boyd, 3rd Bart., of Howth House, Howth, Co. Dublin
Sir Patrick Denis Henry, 3rd Bart., of Cahore, Co. Londonderry
(Sir) (Thomas) Desmond Molony, 3rd Bart. [who does not use the title]
Sir William Moore, 3rd Bart., of Moore Lodge, Co. Antrim

*	Charles Mosley (ed.), *Burke's Peerage Baronetage & Knightage Clan Chiefs Scottish Feudal Barons*, 107th ed. (3 vols., 2003).
	See also: Sir Bernard Burke, *A Genealogical History of the Dormant, Abeyant, Forfeited and Extinct Peerages in the British Empire* (New edition, 1883); and John Burke and John Bernard Burke, *A Genealogical History of the Extinct and Dormant Baronetcies of England Ireland and Scotland* (2nd edition, 1841).

'The Levee of the Right Hon. the Lord High Chancellor of Ireland. Easter Sittings, 1900'

The photograph (p. 442) which bears this printed title is a Lafayette production of which there are three framed copies in King's Inns. The event responsible for bringing together a group of seventeen judges attired in their robes occurred on the morning of Wednesday 18th April 1900; and the likelihood is that the photograph was taken in the garden of 12 Merrion Square, the residence of Lord Ashbourne, the Lord Chancellor. The stone wall is probably the western boundary, and the roofs in the background those of the houses on Merrion Square North. No. 12 Merrion Square, a large and important house, is described in the *Georgian Society Records*, iv, 72-3.

The occasion of the photograph is fixed by reference to this report in *I.L.T. & S.J.*, xxxiv, 21 April 1900, p. 170:

> The Lord Chancellor's Levee on last Wednesday was largely attended. Almost all the judges were present. Lord Morris was also present. After the Levee a photograph was taken of a group of the Judges.
>
> After the Levee the Judges proceeded in State to the Four Courts, where the usual reception was held in the Hall, where many of the general public and a large number of ladies were present.

One Queen's Bench judge, the elderly Mr. Justice James Murphy (1823-1901), was absent when the picture was taken. Lord Morris, a former Chief Justice and current Law Lord, though noted as being present at the levee, was not one of those photographed. His omission was doubtless a proper decision, for he was no longer a member of the *Irish* judiciary.

In 1900 the establishment of the Irish Supreme Court was eighteen, eleven red-robed, and seven black-robed. Entitled to be attired in black were the Chancellor, Vice-Chancellor,[1] Master of the Rolls, two ordinary Lord Justices of Appeal, one additional Lord Justice,[2] and one puisne Chancery judge [the Land Judge, whose juridicdiction dervived from the Landed Estates Court]. On the common law side were a Lord Chief Justice and eight puisne judges, with an additional judge as head of the Land Commission.

Mr. Justice Meredith, who is attired as a Queen's Bench judge, was head of the Land Commission, to which he had been appointed in

---

[1] The office of Vice-Chancellor, created for Hedges Eyre Chatterton in 1867, was left vacant on his retirement in 1904.

[2] Lord Justice Walker, a former Liberal Lord Chancellor (1892-5), was serving as an additional Lord Justice of Appeal. He served again as Chancellor, 1905-11.

1898. A curiosity of Ball's *Judges* is the failure to accord due biographical treatment to the holders of the Land Commission office, and a reader of his book (*cf.* ii, 382) could be pardoned for thinking that Meredith joined the bench only in 1906, when he was Master of the Rolls. Although Ball concedes (ii, 324) that the heads of the Land Commission had since 1881 been members of the High Court (and in one sentence lists the six men who reached the High Court bench by that route), the scheme of his book is misleading on this point, because it implies that the Land Commission appointment did not carry the status of the ancient judicial offices. The photograph, by its inclusion of Meredith, demonstrates that he was there as an equal. A technicality to be noted is that the *Land Commisison* judge was, as the Land Law (Ireland) Act of 1881 envisaged, a judge of the common law, while the *Land Judge* [Ross] was a Chancery judge in black.

Although the photograph is monochrome, it is easy to imagine how it might have appeared in colour. The group of 17 includes ten red [Queen's Bench] and seven black [Chancery] judges, and shows evidence of being suitably composed. The red judges can be identified from the ermine lining of their robes, which shows up as white. The black judges can be found from the elaborate ornamentation of braid on their robes, and from their long lace bands.

To be noted are the Lord Chancellor's purse [on the ground at his foot], and the 'collars of SS' worn by the Lord Chief Justice and the Chief Baron.[1] It may be surmised that Lady Ashbourne has put her dining chairs at the disposal of her guests, having first spread a couple of carpet rugs to keep them out of contact with the earth.

[1] 'The judicial chain of the Chief Justice', in *I.L.T. & S.J.*, 10 May 1919, p. 114; V.T.H. Delany, 'The Gold Collar of SS in Ireland', in *Law Quarterly Review*, lxxxi (1961), pp 169-72.

THE LEVEE OF THE RIGHT HON. THE LORD HIGH CHANCELLOR OF IRELAND.
EASTER SITTINGS, 1900

Lafayette [photograph No. 5260]

[back row, left to right] The Hon. Mr. Justice Meredith, the Hon. Mr. Justice Boyd, the Right Hon. Lord Justice FitzGibbon, the Right Hon. the Master of the Rolls [Porter], the Right Hon. Lord Justice Holmes, the Right Hon. Mr. Justice Gibson, The Hon. Mr. Justice Ross, The Right Hon. Mr. Justice Johnson, The Hon. Mr. Justice Barton.

[front row, left to right] The Hon. Mr. Justice Kenny, The Right Hon. the Vice-Chancellor [Chatterton], the Right Hon. the Lord Chief Justice [Peter O'Brien], the Right Hon. the Lord High Chancellor of Ireland [Lord Ashbourne], the Right Hon. the Lord Chief Baron [Palles], the Right Hon. Lord Justice Walker, the Right Hon. Mr. Justice Andrews, the Right Hon. Mr. Justice Madden.

Twelve of the seventeen (designated by the title 'Right Honourable') were members of the Privy Council. In 1900 still only five of the judges [Gibson, Ross, Kenny, Meredith and Barton] were post-1868 men.

Auditors of the
Law Students' Debating Society of Ireland
1860-2004 *

1830-60   No Auditors elected

1860-61	Richard Carmichael Belton	1899-00	Samuel Moore
1861-62	Richard Paul Carton	1900-01	William Black
1862-63	John Monroe	1901-02	St. Lawrence E.J. Devitt
1863-64	William H. O'Brien	1902-03	Cornelius Lehane
1864-65	Hugh Holmes	1903-04	Walter E.E. Callan
1865-66	John Butler Yeats	1904-05	Vincent Rice
1865-66	Frederick John O'Carroll	1905-06	James A. Rearden
1866-67	Charles Hamilton Teeling	1906-07	J.J. Treacy
1868-69	John Dockrill	1907-08	Denis F. Condon
1869-70	John B. Falconer	1908-09	Michael Smithwick
1870-71	John Russell Stritch	1909-10	Eugene Sheehy
1871-72	Denis Baylor Sullivan	1910-11	Joseph B. Lee
1872-73	John Francis Barry	1911-12	Martin Cyril Maguire
	Richard Adams	1912-13	Thomas P. Bodkin
1873-74	Luke Plunkett Dillon	1913-14	Francis S. Sheridan
1874-75	James Gordon McCullagh	1914-15	Bernard J. Fox
1875-76	John G. Swift MacNeill	1915-16	James P. Coghlan
1876-77	Richard D. Crotty	1916-17	John R. MacMahon
1877-78	Richard E. Meredith	1917-18	J.A. McCarthy
1878-79	Seymour C. Bushe	1918-19	Edward J. Murphy
1879-80	Dunbar Plunket Barton	1919-20	John J. Hearne
1880-81	William F. Kenny	1920-21	Charles H. Shiel
1881-82	J.D. Mayne Colles	1921-22	M.J.B. Daly
1882-83	Daniel Francis Browne	1922-23	F.J. Cawley
1883-84	Robert William Lucas	1923-24	Daniel P. Forde
	James W. Bird	1924-25	Richard McGonigal
1884-85	Henry Hunt	1925-26	S.F. Stapleton
1885-86	Joseph Maguire	1926-27	J. Barry Tynan O'Mahony
1886-87	Edward H. Ennis	1927-28	Robert St. Claire Adamson
1887-88	J.H. Gallagher	1928-29	Domhnall Ó Grianna
1888-89	Richard W.W. Littledale	1929-30	Eoin S. O'Mahony
1889-90	J.D.A. Johnson	1930-31	James Matthew Dillon
1890-91	Thomas J. Smyth	1931-32	William P. Fay
1891-92	Andrew F. Russell Stritch	1932-33	Kenneth E.L. Deale
1892-93	C. O'Kane Donegan	1933-34	Noel K. Macdonald
1893-94	Alfred A. Dickie	1934-35	D.B.W. Good
1894-95	John Sandes	1935-36	John J. Durcan
1895-96	William McGrath	1936-37	Henry A. McDevitt
1896-97	Richard Healy	1937-38	J. Noel L. Peart
1897-98	John O'Mahony	1938-39	Austen Bradfield-England
1898-99	A.H. Houston	1939-40	Frank G. Igoe

* compiled by Camilla McAleese

1940-41	Brian Walsh	1972-73	Kevin T. Feeney
1941-42	William D. Finlay	1973-74	*Mary MacKenzie*
1942-43	—	1974-75	Patrick Hanratty
1943-44	Patrick O'Donoghue	1975-76	Eamon Ó Briain
1944-45	Conor J.P. Maguire	1976-77	Julian Deale
1945-46	Patrick C. Holland	1977-78	Gerry Danaher
1946-47	Liam Proud	1978-79	F. Rory Brady
1947-48	William C. Toomey	1979-80	Richard T. Keane
1948-49	John H.G. Lovatt-Dolan	1980-81	John L. O'Donnell
1949-50	B.J. O'Quigley	1981-82	Patrick J. McCarthy
1950-51	J.G. Coleman	1982-83	Feíchín McDonagh
1951-52	Oliver G.V. Adye-Curran	1983-84	Thomas Finn
1952-53	James de Valera Mansfield	1984-85	Hugh I. Mohan
1953-54	Denis G. Moloney	1985-86	*Dympna Cusack*
1954-55	W.J.L. [Liam] Hamilton	1986-87	David Sutton
1955-56	Robert P. Barr	1987-88	*Suzanne Egan*
1956-47	Denis Corboy	1988-89	Maurice Collins
1957-58	Garrett Cooney	1989-90	Garnet Orange
1958-59	Rory O'Connor	1990-91	Patrick Treacy
1959-60	John E. Kerry Keane	1991-92	Desmond Dockery
1960-61	Thomas S. McCann	1992-93	John McCoy
1961-62	Charles E. Lysaght	1993-94	*Aisling O'Kelly*
1962-63	Maurice Hearne	1994-95	Frederick Oluwole
1963-64	Peter E. O'Connor	1995-96	Maurice Coffey
1964-65	Henry Nash	1996-97	Seán Guerin
1965-66	John J.M. Collins	1997-98	Mark Dunne
1966-67	Ian G. Brennan	1998-99	Terence Walsh
1967-68	John A. Doherty	1990-00	Wesley Farrell
1968-69	Eoin McGonigal	2000-01	William Abrahamson
	Brian R. Mathews	2001-02	Michael Block
1969-70	Sean T. Moylan	2002-03	*Karen Nolan*
1970-71	Conor J. Maguire	2003-04	Eunan O'Donnell
1971-72	Seán Kelleher	2004-05	Gareth Robinson

ERRATA

in

King's Inns Admission Papers 1607-1867

p. 55   For BROWE read BROWNE, ALEXANDER

p. 188   GIBBON, WILLIAM MONCK   For. b 17 March 1824 read 1804

p. 442   For SEAGRAVE, PATRICK read SEGRAVE

p. 450   After SINGLETON, HENRY, barrister, Prime Serjeant, insert:
'SINGLETON, SYDENHAM: see *supra*, p. 175, FOWKE, SYDENHAM'

p. 479   THORP, ROBERT, s. of Robet: read s. of Robert

p. 496   WALTACE, ROBERT SMYTH: read WALLACE